DESIGN OF CONCRETE STRUCTURES

McGRAW-HILL CIVIL ENGINEERING SERIES

Harmer E. Davis, *Consulting Editor*

Babbitt · Engineering in Public Health
Benjamin · Statically Indeterminate Structures
Chow · Open-channel Hydraulics
Davis, Troxell, and Wiskocil · The Testing and Inspection of Engineering Materials
Dunham · Advanced Reinforced Concrete
Dunham · Foundations of Structures
Dunham · The Theory and Practice of Reinforced Concrete
Dunham and Young · Contracts, Specifications, and Law for Engineers
Gaylord and Gaylord · Structural Design
Hallert · Photogrammetry
Hennes and Ekse · Fundamentals of Transportation Engineering
Krynine and Judd · Principles of Engineering Geology and Geotechnics
Leonards · Foundation Engineering
Linsley and Franzini · Elements of Hydraulic Engineering
Linsley, Kohler, and Paulhus · Applied Hydrology
Linsley, Kohler, and Paulhus · Hydrology for Engineers
Lueder · Aerial Photographic Interpretation
Matson, Smith, and Hurd · Traffic Engineering
Mead, Mead, and Akerman · Contracts, Specifications, and Engineering Relations
Norris, Hansen, Holley, Biggs, Namyet, and Minami · Structural Design for Dynamic Loads
Peurifoy · Construction Planning, Equipment, and Methods
Peurifoy · Estimating Construction Costs
Troxell and Davis · Composition and Properties of Concrete
Tschebotarioff · Soil Mechanics, Foundations, and Earth Structures
Wang and Eckel · Elementary Theory of Structures
Winter, Urquhart, O'Rourke, and Nilson · Design of Concrete Structures

DESIGN OF CONCRETE STRUCTURES

George Winter

Professor of Engineering
Head, Department of Structural Engineering

L. C. Urquhart

Late Professor of Structural Engineering
Colonel, U.S. Army Engineers, Ret.

C. E. O'Rourke

Late Professor of Structural Engineering

Arthur H. Nilson

Associate Professor of Structural Engineering

All of Cornell University

Seventh Edition

McGraw-Hill Book Company

New York San Francisco Toronto London

Design of Concrete Structures

Library of Congress Catalog Card Number 63-23261

71118

II

PREFACE

In recent years, developments have been rapid and sweeping both in reinforced-concrete construction and in engineering education. The present edition has been largely rewritten and reorganized to do justice to these developments. The fast pace of technological change is no longer served by young engineers primarily trained in special skills and techniques, such as specific, codified design methods which undergo frequent modification and obsolesce as new research leads to new developments. As preparation for such continuing changes, an understanding is required of the basic performance of concrete and steel as structural materials and of the mechanics and behavior, elastic and inelastic, of reinforced-concrete members and structures. On the other hand, the final goal of the structural engineer is to design structures, safely, economically, and efficiently. Understanding fundamental behavior and keeping abreast of current research are not aims in themselves; they are tools which help the structural engineer to perform effectively his technological and economic function, the designing of structures.

The present edition has been aimed at this double orientation: to lay the foundation of a thorough understanding of the basic mechanics and performance of reinforced- and prestressed-concrete structures as developed by modern research and, at the same time, to present ample material on design practices and details, for more conventional structures as well as for newer forms.

The first two chapters, entirely new, present the structurally relevant *properties and modes of behavior of steel and concrete* and the *basic mechanics and performance of reinforced-concrete members.* These two chapters are written without any reference to codes or specifications. Through use of the fundamentals of materials performance, the mechanics and behavior in compression, tension, bending, eccentric compression, shear, and bond and the fundamentals of prestressing are developed in a systematic manner through all loading stages, from small loads to failure. This presentation is not encumbered by details of design practices which are derived from, but are not identical with, this basic information.

The following four chapters (*beams, slabs, columns, footings*), also very largely new, present the design methods for reinforced-concrete members, in close conformity with the 1963 edition of the building code of the American Concrete Institute. This code edition constitutes a departure from its predecessors and, in many respects, represents a new document. It adopts ultimate-strength design as the basic philosophy, even though it continues to permit the conventional working-stress design as an alternative. It makes provision for the safe utilization of high-strength materials, particularly the new high-strength reinforcing steels, includes prestressed-concrete and composite construction, and reflects other innovations too numerous to mention. All these are fully discussed and illustrated with detailed examples in these four chapters and elsewhere in the text. At the same time, this book does not attempt to represent a complete commentary on all details of the latest code edition. Such a commentary is being published by the American Concrete Institute, and the reader is referred to it for minor details, mostly of a transitory nature. Apart from practical design methods, these four chapters also contain a sizable amount of fundamental information not included in the first two. For instance, modern approaches to ensuring structural safety are briefly discussed, as is the behavior of slabs under semielastic conditions, as well as at failure, by means of yield-line theory; a treatment of slabs on ground is included; the presentation of the effects of slenderness on the strength of columns and frames is far broader than a mere discussion of code provisions.

The last five chapters, as in previous editions, cover the major design aspects of various types of structures. The chapter on *continuous beams and frames* has been streamlined, and material has been added on inelastic moment redistribution and limit design. The chapter on *reinforced-concrete buildings* retains a distinctive feature of this book in presenting reasonably complete design examples for various types of framing, brought up to date and chiefly carried out by ultimate-strength design. The chapter on *arches* has been broadened to include a first introduction into the behavior of *cylindrical shells, folded plates, hyperbolic paraboloids,* and *spherical domes.* The chapter on *prestressed concrete* has been greatly expanded. A complete treatment of design fundamentals will permit the engineer to attack ordinary problems with confidence. The last chapter, on *bridges,* has not only been updated in regard to applicable AAHSO specifications, but also includes a new section on *composite construction.* Here, too, complete design examples are presented.

In regard to *torsion,* no definite design method is accepted in American practice. Yet, proper consideration of torsion becomes increasingly important. Appendix C contains a method of analysis and design for torsion which the authors consider adequate for use until such time as a subsequent edition of the ACI Code, based on research now in progress, will make appropriate provisions.

These features, plus updated appendixes which contain a variety of practical design aids, tables, and graphs, should continue to make this book a valuable *desk aid for the practicing engineer.*

To the teacher it may be important that the text is designed to accommodate itself to a variety of course organizations. A thorough first course in reinforced-concrete design, of at least four semester hours, would consist of the first five or six chapters of the book, supplemented by as much material on prestressed concrete as time permits. At the other extreme, there are engineering schools which no longer find time for design instruction. For such curricula the first two chapters, which aim to present the engineering science fundamentals of reinforced concrete, would constitute the main content of an abbreviated course. Any course organization between these two extremes can be accommodated. The material is so arranged that, if desired, chapters can be broken up rather than being taken in sequence. Thus, the fundamentals of flexure in Chapter 2 can be followed by presentation of the pertinent design methods given in Chapter 3. Without break in continuity, one can then return to Chapter 2 for a discussion of behavior and research information on shear and bond, this again to be followed by pertinent material on shear and bond design in Chapter 3, and so on. The authors hope that, by arranging the book in this manner, they have made it adaptable to the wide range of experimentation in engineering education which is now in progress.

Both authors of the original editions have passed away; the present edition has been prepared by the undersigned. They wish to thank Cornell University for essential secretarial and other assistance, numerous graduate students for detecting errors and making valuable suggestions, and Mr. Craig Miller, also a graduate student, for calculating many examples and for other help.

George Winter *Arthur H. Nilson*

CONTENTS

chapter 1

CONCRETE AND REINFORCING STEEL

1.1 Introduction: Concrete, Reinforced Concrete, Prestressed Concrete *Concrete* is a stonelike material obtained by permitting a carefully proportioned mixture of cement, sand and gravel or other aggregate, and water to harden in forms of the shape and dimensions of the desired structure. The bulk of the material consists of fine and coarse aggregate. Cement and water interact chemically to bind the aggregate particles into a solid mass. Additional water, over and above that needed for this chemical reaction, is necessary to give the mixture the workability that enables it to fill the forms and surround the embedded reinforcing steel prior to hardening. Concretes in a wide range of strength properties can be obtained by appropriate adjustment of the proportions of the constituent materials. Special cements (such as high-early-strength cements), special aggregates (such as various lightweight or heavyweight aggregates), and special curing methods (such as steam-curing) permit an even wider variety of properties to be obtained.

These properties depend to a very substantial degree on the proportions of the mix, on the thoroughness with which the various constituents are intermixed, and on the conditions of humidity and temperature in which the mix is maintained from the moment it is placed in the forms until it is fully hardened. The process of controlling these conditions is known as *curing.* To protect against the unintentional production of substandard concrete, a high degree of skillful control and supervision is necessary throughout the process, from the proportioning by weight of the individual components, through mixing and placing, until the completion of curing.

The factors which make concrete a universal building material are so pronounced that it has been used, in more primitive kinds and ways than at present, for thousands of years, probably beginning in Egyptian antiquity. The facility with which, while plastic, it can be deposited and made to fill forms or moulds of almost any practical shape is one of these factors. Its high fire and weather resistance are evident advantages. Most of the constituent materials, with the possible exception of cement, are usually available at low cost locally or at small distances from the construction site. Its compressive strength, as that of natural stones, is high, which makes it suitable for members primarily subject to compression, such as columns and arches. On the other hand, again as in natural stones, it is a relatively brittle material whose tensile strength is small compared to its compressive strength. This prevents its economical use in structural members which are subject to tension either entirely (such as tie rods) or over part of their cross sections (such as beams or other flexural members).

To offset this limitation, it has been found possible, in the second half of the nineteenth century, to use steel with its high tensile strength to reinforce concrete, chiefly in those places where its small tensile strength would limit the carrying capacity of the member. The reinforcement, usually round steel rods with appropriate surface deformations to provide interlocking, is placed in the forms in advance of the concrete. When completely surrounded by the hardened concrete mass, it forms an integral part of the member. The resulting combination of two materials, known as *reinforced concrete,* combines many of the advantages of each: the relatively low cost, good weather and fire resistance, good compressive strength, and excellent formability of concrete and the high tensile strength and much greater ductility and toughness of steel. It is this combination which allows the almost unlimited range of uses and possibilities of reinforced concrete in the construction of buildings, bridges, dams, tanks, reservoirs, and a host of other structures.

In more recent times it has been found possible to produce steels, at relatively low cost, whose yield strength is of the order of 4 times and more that of ordinary reinforcing steel. Likewise, it is possible to produce concrete 2 and 3 times as strong in compression as the more ordinary concretes. There are limits to the strengths of the constituent materials beyond which they can no longer be combined effectively in one member. To be sure, the strength of such a member would increase roughly in proportion to those of the constituent materials. However, the high strains which result from such high stresses, particularly in the steel, would make for large deformations and deflections of such members under load. Equally, if not more important, the large strains in such high-strength reinforcing steel would induce large cracks in the surrounding low-tensile-strength concrete, cracks which would not only be unsightly, but which would expose the steel reinforcement to corrosion by moisture and other chemical action. This limits the useful yield strength of reinforcing steel to about 80 ksi, about twice that of conventional reinforcing steels.

A special way has been found, however, to use steels and concretes of very high strength in combination. This type of construction is known as *prestressed concrete*. The steel, mostly in the shape of wires or strands, but sometimes as bars, is embedded in the concrete under high tension which is held in equilibrium by compression stresses in the surrounding concrete after hardening. Because of this precompression, the concrete in a flexural member will crack on the tension side at a much larger load than when not so precompressed. This reduces radically both the deflections and the tensile cracks at service loads in such structures and thereby enables these high-strength materials to be used effectively. Prestressed concrete is particularly suited to prefabrication on a mass-production basis, although it is being used as well without such prefabrication. Its introduction has extended, to a very significant degree, the range of structural uses of the combination of these two materials.

Figure 1.1 shows simplified sketches of some of the *principal structural forms* of reinforced concrete; pertinent design methods for many of them are discussed later in this volume. A slab, beam, and girder floor, as it is used in many multistory buildings, is shown in (*a*), and a ribbed floor which permits savings of concrete and reuse of standardized metal forms in (*b*). The flat-slab floor of (*c*), distinct in the absence of beams and girders, is frequently used for more heavily loaded buildings, such as warehouses. The rigid-frame structure of (*d*) can be made to span large openings for auditoria, gymnasia, or industrial buildings. Figure 1.1*e* and *f* show a cylindrical shell roof and a folded-plate roof, respectively, forms which, like the other shell roofs in (*h*), (*l*), and (*m*), have been developed in recent years and permit the use of extremely thin surfaces, often thinner, relatively, than an eggshell. Two of the many bridge forms are shown in (*g*) and (*j*), the former a multiarch bridge for large spans, the latter a rigid-frame bridge typical of highway overpasses. The tank or reservoir of (i) combines a cylindrical and a spherical shell, the former frequently prestressed. Representative of the extensive use of reinforced concrete in foundation work is the counterfort retaining wall of (k).

The forms of Fig. 1.1 do not comprise a complete range, but are merely

Fig. **1.1** Principal structural forms in reinforced concrete: (a) beam-and-girder floor, (b) ribbed floor, (c) flat-slab floor, (d) rigid-frame building, (e) cylindrical-shell roof, (f) folded-plate roof, (g) multiple-arch bridge.

typical of shapes appropriate to the properties and possibilities of concrete structures. They illustrate the adaptability of the material to a great variety of one-dimensional (beams, girders, columns), two-dimensional (slabs, arches, rigid frames), and three-dimensional (shells) structures and structural components. This variability allows the shape of the structure to be adapted to its function in an economical manner and furnishes the architect with a wide range of possibilities for esthetically satisfying structural solutions.

1.2 Cement A cementing material is one which has the adhesive and cohesive properties necessary to bond inert aggregates into a solid mass of adequate strength and durability. This technologically important cate-

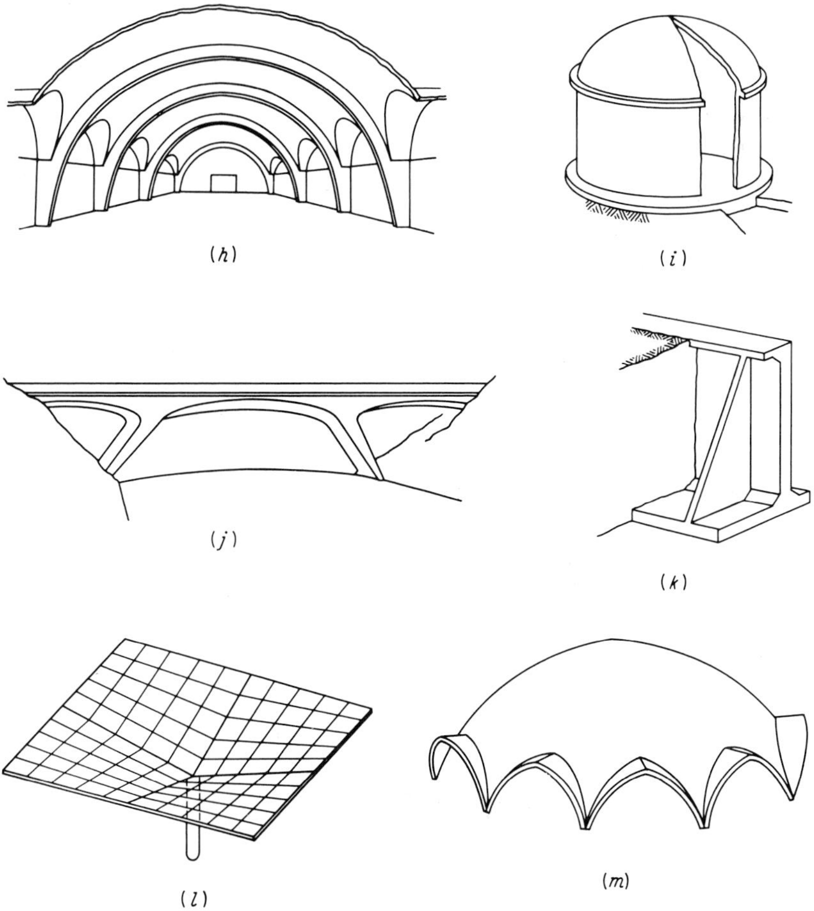

***Fig.* 1.1 (Continued)** Principal structural forms in reinforced concrete: (*h*) shell roof, (*i*) storage tank, (*j*) rigid-frame bridge, (*k*) counterfort retaining wall, (*l*) hyperbolic-paraboloid umbrella shell, (*m*) point-supported dome roof.

gory of materials includes not only cements proper, but also limes, asphalts and tars as they are used in road building, and others. For making structural concrete, so-called *hydraulic* cements are used exclusively. Water is needed for the chemical process (hydration) in which the cement powder sets and hardens into one solid mass. Of the various hydraulic cements which have been developed, *portland cement*, which was first patented in England in 1824, is by far the most common.

Portland cement is a finely powdered, grayish material which consists chiefly of calcium and aluminum silicates. The common raw materials from which it is made are limestones, which provide CaO, and clays or shales, which furnish SiO_2 and Al_2O_3. These are ground, blended, fused to clinkers in a kiln, cooled, and ground to the required fineness. The material is shipped in bulk or in bags containing 94 lb of cement. Concretes made with portland cement generally need about two weeks to reach sufficient strength so that forms of beams and slabs can be removed and reasonable loads applied; they reach their design strength after 28 days and continue to gain strength thereafter at a decreasing rate. To speed construction when needed, *high-early-strength cements* have been developed; they are more costly than ordinary portland cement, but reach, within 1 to 3 days, the strength a portland cement would have after 28 days. They have the same basic composition as portland cements, but are more carefully blended and more finely ground, both before and after clinkering.

When cement is mixed with water to form a soft paste, it gradually stiffens until it becomes a solid. This process is known as *setting* and *hardening;* the cement is said to have set when it has gained sufficient rigidity to support an arbitrarily defined pressure, after which it continues for a long time to harden, i.e., to gain further strength. The water in the paste dissolves material at the surfaces of the cement grains and forms a gel which gradually increases in volume and stiffness. This leads to a rapid stiffening of the paste 2 to 4 hr after water has been added to the cement. *Hydration* continues to proceed deeper into the cement grains, at decreasing speed, with continued stiffening and hardening of the mass. In ordinary concrete the cement is probably never completely hydrated. The gel structure of the hardened paste seems to be the chief reason for the volume changes which are caused in concrete by variations in moisture, such as the *shrinkage* of concrete as it dries.

For complete hydration of a given amount of cement, according to H. Rüsch, an amount of water equal to about 25 per cent of that of cement, by weight, is needed chemically. An additional 10 to 15 per cent must be present, however, to provide mobility for the water in the cement paste during the hydration process so that it can reach the cement particles. This makes for a total minimum *water-cement ratio* of 0.35 to 0.40 by weight. This corresponds to 4 to 4.5 gal of water per sack of cement, the more customary way of expressing the water-cement ratio. Water-cement ratios in concretes are generally considerably larger than this minimum, to provide the necessary workability of the concrete mix. Any amount of water above the 25 per cent consumed in the chemical reaction produces pores in the cement paste. The strength of the hardened paste decreases in inverse proportion to the fraction of the total volume occupied by pores. Put differently, since only the solids, and not the voids, resist stress, strength increases directly as the fraction of the total volume occupied by the solids. This is why the strength of the cement paste depends primarily on, and decreases directly with, increasing water-cement ratio.

The chemical process involved in the setting and hardening liberates heat, known as *heat of hydration*. In large concrete masses, such as dams, this heat is dissipated very slowly and results in a temperature rise and volume expansion of the concrete during hydration, with subsequent cooling and contraction. To avoid the serious cracking and weakening which may result from this process, special measures must be taken for its control.

1.3 Aggregates In ordinary structural concretes the aggregates occupy about 70 to 75 per cent of the volume of the hardened mass. The remainder consists of hardened cement paste, uncombined water (i.e., water not involved in the hydration of the cement), and air voids. The latter two evidently do not contribute to the strength of the concrete. In general, the more densely the aggregate can be packed, the better are the strength, weather resistance, and economy of the concrete. For this reason the gradation of the particle sizes in the aggregate, to produce close packing, is of considerable importance. It is also important that the aggregate have good strength, durability, and weather resistance, that its surface be free from impurities such as loam, silt, and organic matter which may weaken the bond with the cement paste, and that no unfavorable chemical reaction take place between it and the cement.

Natural aggregates are generally classified as fine and coarse. *Fine aggregate* or *sand* is any material which will pass a No. 4 sieve, i.e., a sieve with four openings per linear inch. Material coarser than this is classified as *coarse aggregate* or *gravel*. When favorable gradation is desired, aggregates are separated by sieving into two or three size groups of sand and several size groups of coarse aggregate. These can then be combined according to grading charts to result in a densely packed aggregate. The *maximum size of coarse aggregate* in reinforced concrete is governed by the requirement that it shall easily fit into the forms and between the reinforcing bars. For this purpose it should not be larger than one-fifth of the narrowest dimension of the forms nor three-quarters of the minimum distance between reinforcing bars. Authoritative information on aggregate properties, their influence on concrete properties, and their determination, and on selection, preparation, and handling of aggregate is found in the report of ACI Committee 621 (Ref. 1.1).[1]

The *unit weight* of so-called *stone concrete,* i.e., concrete with natural stone aggregate, varies from about 145 to 152 pcf and can generally be assumed as 150 pcf. For special purposes, lightweight concretes on the one hand and heavy concretes on the other are being used with increasing frequency.

Lightweight concrete can be obtained by gas-forming admixtures. However, in American practice they are almost universally produced by using special lightweight aggregates. The use of such concretes, if of strength equal to that of corresponding stone concrete, evidently reduces the dead loads of the structure. Also, the insulating properties of lightweight concrete are generally better than those of stone concrete, so that concretes of extremely light weight, whose strength may no longer be adequate for load-carrying purposes, are often employed as insulating fills.

A variety of lightweight aggregates is available. Natural materials, such as pumice and tuff, or by-products such as cinders, find some use without prior processing except for crushing and grinding. The majority of such aggregates, however, are produced artificially in kilns. Among them are expanded clays (haydite), shales, and slag and sintered fly ash. Some are used primarily for insulating purposes or masonry units; the heavier aggregates, such as expanded clays and shales, are suitable for lightweight structural concrete. Unit weights of lightweight concretes range from 30 to 80 pcf for insulating concrete, 65 to 100 pcf for masonry units, and 65 to 115 pcf for structural concrete. In general, the lower the weight, the lower the strength. The proportioning and control of lightweight aggregate mixes are more delicate than those of stone concrete, and considerable care is needed to assure the desired properties (Refs. 1.2, 1.3).

Heavyweight concrete is frequently required for shielding against gamma and X radiation in nuclear-reactor and similar installations, for protective structures, and for special purposes, such as counterweights of lift bridges. Heavy aggregates are used for such concretes. These consist of heavy iron ores or barite (barium sulfate) rock crushed to suitable sizes. Steel in the form of scrap, punchings, or shot (as fines) is also used. Unit weights of heavyweight concretes with natural heavy rock aggregates range from about 200 to 230 pcf; if iron punchings are added to high-density ores, weights as high as 270 pcf are achieved. The weight may be as high as 330 pcf if ores are used for the fines only, and steel for the coarse aggregate.

[1] References are listed at the end of the chapter.

1.4 Proportioning and Mixing of Concrete The various components of a mix are proportioned so that the resulting concrete has adequate strength, proper workability for placing, and low cost. The latter calls for use of the minimum amount of cement (the most costly of the components) which will achieve adequate properties. The better the gradation of aggregates, i.e., the smaller the volume of voids, the less cement paste is needed to fill these voids. In addition to the water required for hydration (see Art. 1.2), water is needed for wetting the surface of the aggregate. As water is added, the plasticity and fluidity of the mix increases (i.e., its workability improves), but the strength decreases because of the larger volume of voids created by the free water. To reduce the free water while retaining the workability, cement must be added. Therefore, as for the cement paste, the *water-cement ratio* is the chief factor which controls the strength of the concrete. For a given water-cement ratio, one selects that minimum amount of cement, in sacks per cubic yard, which will secure the desired workability.

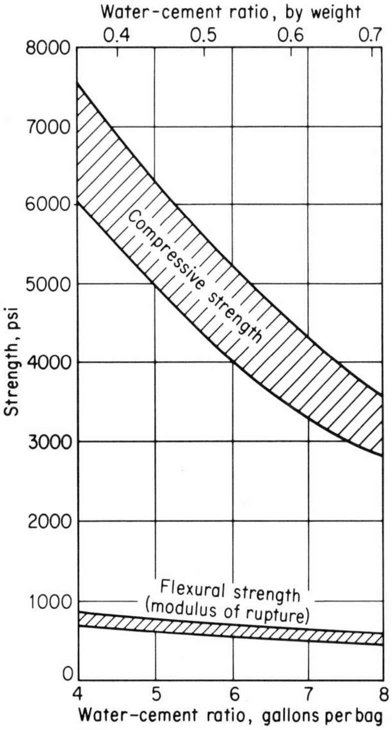

Fig. **1.2** Effect of water-cement ratio on 28-day compressive and flexural strength. (*Adapted from Ref.* 1.4.)

Figure 1.2, adapted from Ref. 1.4, shows the decisive influence of the water-cement ratio on the compressive strength of concrete. Its influence on the tensile strength, as measured by the nominal flexural strength or modulus of rupture, is seen to be pronounced, but much smaller than its effect on compression strength. This seems to be so because, in addition to the void ratio, the tensile strength depends strongly on the strength of bond between coarse aggregate and cement mortar (i.e., cement paste plus fine aggregate). According to tests at Cornell University, this bond strength is relatively slightly affected by the water-cement ratio (Ref. 1.4*a*).

It has been customary to define the *proportions* of a concrete mix by the ratio, by volume or weight, of cement to sand to gravel, for example, 1:2:4. This method refers to the solid components only and, unless the water-cement ratio is specified separately, is insufficient to define the properties of the resulting concrete either in its fresh state or when set and hardened. For a complete definition of proportions it is now customary to specify, per 94-lb bag of cement, the weight of water, sand, and coarse aggregate. Thus, a mix may be defined as containing (per 94-lb bag of cement) 45 lb of water, 320 lb of sand, and 500 lb of coarse aggregate.

Various methods of proportioning are used to obtain mixes of the desired properties from the cements and aggregates at hand. One is the so-called *trial-batch method.* Selecting a water-cement ratio from information such as that in Fig. 1.2, one produces several small trial batches with varying amounts of aggregate to obtain the required consistency and other properties with a minimum amount of paste. Concrete *consistency* is most frequently measured by the *slump test.* A metal mold in the shape of a truncated cone 12 in. high is filled with fresh concrete in a carefully specified manner. Immediately upon being filled, the mold is lifted off, and the slump of the concrete is measured as the difference in height between the mold and the pile of concrete. The slump is a good measure of the total water content in the mix and should be kept as low as is compatible with workability. Slumps for concretes in building construction generally range from 2 to 6 in. The so-called *ACI method of proportioning* makes use of the slump test in connection with a set of tables which permit one to select proportions which will result in the desired properties for a wide variety of conditions (types of structures, dimensions of members, degrees of exposure to weathering, etc.). Details of this and other methods are beyond the scope of this volume and are fully treated in Refs. 1.4 to 1.6.

In addition to the main components of concretes, *admixtures* are often used for special purposes. There are admixtures to improve workability, to accelerate or retard setting and hardening, to aid in curing, to improve durability, to add color, and to impart other properties. While the beneficial effects of some admixtures are well established, the claims of others should be viewed with caution. *Air-entraining agents* at present are the most important and most widely used admixtures. They cause the entrainment of air in the form of small, well-dispersed bubbles in the concrete. These improve workability and durability, chiefly resistance to freezing and thawing, and reduce segregation during placing. They decrease density because of the increased void ratio and thereby decrease strength; however, this decrease can be partially offset by reduction of mixing water without loss of workability. The chief use of air-entrained concretes is in pavements, but they are also used for structural work, particularly for outdoor structures.

On all but the smallest jobs, *batching* is carried out in special batching plants. Separate hoppers contain cement and the various fractions of aggregate. Proportions are controlled, by weight, by means of manually operated or automatic dial scales connected to the hoppers. The mixing water is batched either by measuring tanks or by water meters.

The principal purpose of *mixing* is to produce an intimate mixture of cement, water, fine and coarse aggregate, and possible admixtures of uniform consistency throughout each batch. This is achieved in machine mixers of the revolving-drum type. Minimum mixing time is 1 min for mixers of not more than 1 yd^3 capacity, with an additional 15 sec for each additional ½ yd^3. Mixing can be continued for a considerable time without adverse effect. This fact is particularly important in connection with ready-mixed concrete.

On large projects, particularly in the open country where ample space is available, movable mixing plants are installed and operated at the site. On the other hand, in construction under congested city conditions, on smaller jobs, and frequently in highway construction, *ready-mixed concrete* is used. Such concrete is batched in a stationary plant and then hauled to the site in trucks in one of three ways: (1) mixed completely at the stationary plant and hauled in a truck agitator, (2) transit-mixed, i.e., batched at the plant but mixed in a truck mixer, or (3) partially mixed at the plant with mixing completed in a truck mixer. Concrete should be discharged from the mixer or agitator within at most 1½ hr after the water is added to the batch.

1.5 Conveying, Placing, Compacting, Curing *Conveying* of most building concrete from the mixer or truck to the form is done in wheelbarrows or buggies on horizontal runways or by pumping through steel pipelines. The chief danger during conveying is that of *segregation*. The individual components of concrete tend to segregate because of their dissimilarity. In overly wet concrete standing in containers or forms, the heavier gravel components tend to settle, and the lighter materials, particularly water, to rise. Lateral movement, such as flow within the forms, tends to separate the coarse gravel from the finer components of the mix. The danger of segregation has caused the discarding of some previously common means of conveying, such as chutes and conveyor belts, in favor of methods which minimize this tendency.

Placing is the process of transferring the fresh concrete from the conveying device to its final place in the forms. Prior to placing, loose rust must be removed from reinforcement, forms must be cleaned, and hardened surfaces of previous concrete lifts must be cleaned and treated appropriately. Placing and compacting are critical in their effect on the final quality of the concrete. Proper placement must avoid segregation, displacement of forms or of reinforcement in the forms, and poor bond between successive layers of concrete. Immediately upon placing, the concrete should be *compacted* by means of hand tools or vibrators. Such compacting prevents honeycombing, assures close contact with forms and reinforcement, and serves as partial remedy to possible prior segregation. Compacting is achieved by hand tamping with a variety of special tools, but now more commonly and successfully with high-frequency, power-driven *vibrators*. These are of the *internal* type, immersed in the concrete, or of the *external* type, attached to the forms. The former are preferable, but must be supplemented by the latter where narrow forms or other obstacles make immersion imposible (Ref. 1.7).

Fresh concrete gains strength most rapidly during the first few days and weeks. Structural design is generally based on the *28-day strength*, about 70 per cent of which is reached at the end of the first week after placing. The final concrete strength depends greatly on the conditions of moisture and temperature during this initial period. The maintenance of proper conditions during this time is known as *curing*. Thirty per cent of the strength or more can be lost by premature drying out of the concrete; similar amounts may be lost by permitting the concrete temperature to drop to 40°F or lower during the first few days unless the concrete is maintained continuously moist for a long time thereafter. Freezing of fresh concrete may reduce its strength by as much as 50 per cent.

To prevent such damage, concrete should be protected from loss of moisture for at least 7 days and, in more sensitive work, up to 14 days. When high-early-strength cements are used, curing periods can be cut in half. Curing can be achieved by keeping exposed surfaces continually wet through sprinkling, ponding, covering with wet burlap, or the like. Recent methods include the use of sealing compounds which, when properly used, form evaporation-retarding membranes, and waterproof papers. In addition to improved strength, proper moist curing provides better shrinkage control. To protect the concrete against low temperature during cold weather, the mixing water and, occasionally, the aggregates are heated, temperature insulation is used where possible, and special admixtures, particularly calcium chloride, are employed. When air temperatures are very low, external heat may have to be supplied in addition to insulation.

1.6 Tests, Quality Control, Inspection The quality of mill-produced materials, such as structural or reinforcing steel, is guaranteed by the producer, who must exercise systematic quality controls, usually specified by pertinent ASTM (American Society for Testing and Materials) standards. Concrete, in contrast, is produced at or close to the site, and its final qualities are affected by a number of factors which have been briefly discussed. Thus, systematic quality control must be instituted at the construction site.

The main measure of the structural quality of concrete is its *compression strength*. Tests for this property are made on cylindrical specimens of height equal to twice the diameter, usually 6 × 12 in. Impervious molds of this shape are filled with concrete during the operation of placement as specified by ASTM C172, "Method of Sampling Fresh Concrete," and ASTM C31, "Method of Making and Curing Concrete Specimens in the Field." The cylinders are moist-cured at 70 ± 5°F, generally for 28 days, and then tested in the laboratory at a specified rate of loading. The compression strength obtained from such tests is known as the *cylinder strength* f'_c and is the main property specified for design purposes.

To provide structural safety, continuous control is necessary to ensure that the strength of the concrete as furnished is in satisfactory agreement with the value called for by the designer. The "Building Code Requirements for Reinforced Concrete" of the American Concrete Institute, ACI 318-63 (henceforth referred to as the *ACI Code*), specify that a pair of cylinders shall be tested for each 150 yd^3 of concrete. It provides two degrees of control: (1) the average of any five consecutive pairs shall be at least equal to the specified design strength, and not more than 20 per cent of the pairs of tests may have values smaller than specified, and (2) the average of any three consecutive pairs shall be at least equal to the specified design strength, and not more than 10 per cent of the pairs of tests may have values smaller than the specified strength. These requirements provide for adequate average strength as well as for satisfactory uniformity. At the same time they recognize that it is not economically possible to manufacture concrete, or any other material, for that matter, without occasionally producing small quantities of somewhat substandard quality (Ref. 1.15). The more advanced design methods known as *ultimate-strength design* may be used only when control conforms to the more rigorous requirements of (2), above, which also apply to prestressed concrete.

In spite of scientific advances, building in general, and concrete making in particular, retain some elements of an art; they depend on many skills and imponderables. It is the task of systematic *inspection* to ensure close correspondence between plans and specifications and the finished structure. Inspection during construction should be carried out by a competent engineer, preferably the one who produced the design or one who is responsible to the design engineer. The inspector's main functions in regard to materials quality control are sampling, examination, and field testing of materials, control of concrete proportioning, inspection of batching, mixing, conveying, placing, compacting, and curing, and supervision of preparation of specimens for laboratory tests. In addition, he must inspect foundations, formwork, placing of reinforcing steel, and other pertinent features of the general progress of work, keep records of all the inspected items, and prepare periodic reports. The importance of thorough inspection to the correctness and adequate quality of the finished structure cannot be emphasized too strongly.

This brief account of concrete technology represents the merest outline of an important subject. Anyone in practice who is actually responsible for any of the phases of producing and placing concrete must familiarize himself with the details in much greater depth. In addition to the literature quoted in the preceeding articles, Refs. 1.8 to 1.11 are relevant in this connection.

1.7 Strength and Deformation of Concrete in Compression

a. Short-time loading Performance of a structure under load depends to a large degree on the stress-strain relationship of the material from which it is made, under the type of stress to which the material is subjected in the structure. Since concrete is used mostly in compression (see Art. 1.1), its compressive stress-strain curve is of primary interest. Such a curve is obtained by appropriate strain measurements in cylinder tests (Art. 1.6) or on the compression side in beams. Figure 1.3 shows a typical set of such curves, obtained at normal, moderate testing speeds on concretes 28 days old, for various cylinder strengths f'_c.

All the curves have somewhat similar character. They consist of an initial relatively straight elastic portion in which stress and strain are closely proportional, then begin to curve to the horizontal, reaching the maximum stress, i.e., the compressive strength, at a strain of approximately 0.002 in. per in., and finally show a descending branch. It is also seen that concretes of lower strength are less brittle, i.e., fracture at a larger maximum strain, than high-strength concretes.

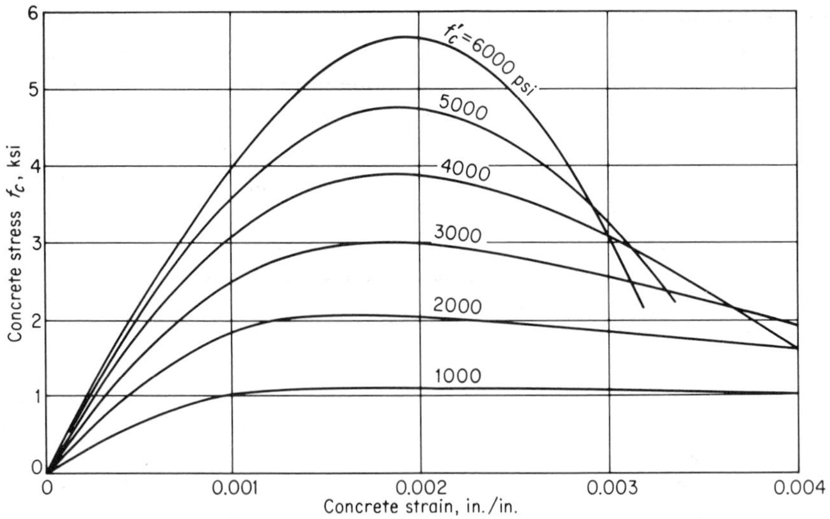

Fig. 1.3 Typical concrete stress-strain curves.

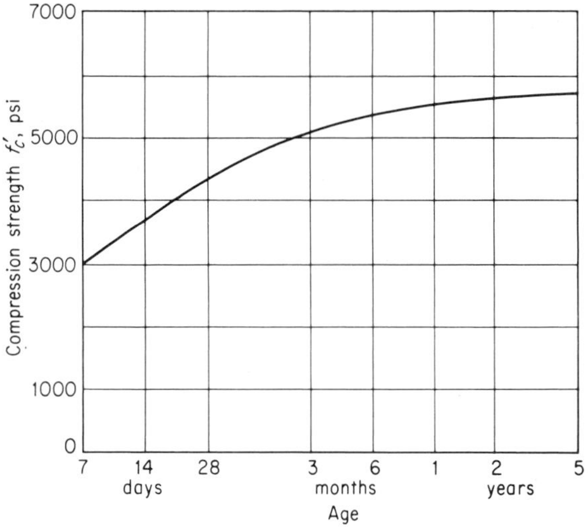

Fig. 1.4 Effect of age on compression strength f'_c. (*From Ref.* 1.4.)

The *modulus of elasticity* E_c (in psi units), that is, the slope of the initial straight portion of the stress-strain curve, is seen to be the larger the higher the strength of the concrete. It can be computed with reasonable accuracy from the empirical equation

$$E_c = 33w^{3/2}\sqrt{f'_c} \tag{1.1}$$

where w is the unit weight of the hardened concrete in pcf, and f'_c its cylinder strength in psi. Equation (1.1) has been obtained by testing structural concretes with values of w from 90 to 155 pcf. For normal sand-and-stone concretes, with $w = 145$ pcf, one obtains

$$E_c = 57{,}500\sqrt{f'_c} \tag{1.2}$$

w = 150 p.c.f.

Information on concrete strength properties such as those discussed is usually obtained through tests made 28 days after pouring. However, cement continues to hydrate, and consequently concrete continues to harden, long after this age, at a decreasing rate. Figure 1.4 shows a typical curve of the gain of concrete strength with age.

In present practice, 28-day cylinder strengths in the range of

$$f'_c = 2500 \text{ to } 5000 \text{ psi}$$

are usually specified for reinforced-concrete structures, with values between 3000 and 4000 being the most common. For prestressed concrete, higher strengths are designated, from about 4000 to 8000 psi, with $f'_c = 5000$ to 6000 psi being most customary.

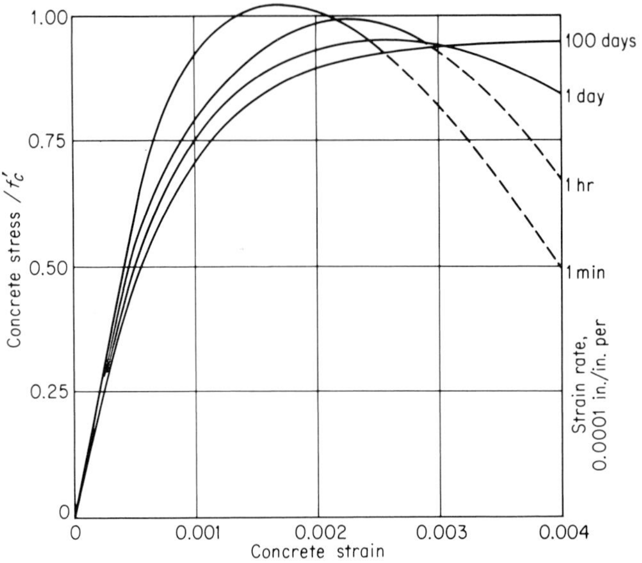

Fig. 1.5 Stress-strain curves at various strain rates, concentric compression. (*Adapted from Ref.* 1.13.)

It should be noted that the shape of the stress-strain curve for various concretes of the same cylinder strength, and even for the same concrete under various conditions of loading, varies considerably. An example of this is shown in Fig. 1.5, where different specimens of the same concrete are loaded at different rates of strain, from one corresponding to relatively fast loading (0.001 in. per in. per min) to one corresponding to an extremely slow application of load (0.001 in. per in. per 100 days). It is seen that the descending branch of the curve, probably indicative of internal disintegration of the material, is much more pronounced at fast than at slow rates of loading. It is also seen that the peaks of the curves, i.e., the maximum strength reached, is somewhat smaller at slower rates of strain.

When compressed in one direction, concrete, like other materials, expands in the direction transverse to that of the applied stress. The ratio of the transverse to the longitudinal strain is known as *Poisson's ratio* and depends on composition and other factors. At stresses lower than about $0.7f'_c$, Poisson's ratio for concrete falls within the limits of 0.15 and 0.20, with 0.17 being the most representative value.

b. Longtime loading In some engineering materials, such as steel, strength and the stress-strain relationship are independent of rate and duration of loading, at least within the usual ranges of rate of stress, temperature, and other variables. In contrast, Fig. 1.5 illustrates the fact that the influence of time, in this case of rate of loading, on the behavior of concrete under load is pronounced. The main reason for this is that concrete creeps under load, while steel does not exhibit creep under conditions prevailing in buildings, bridges, and similar structures.

Creep is the property of many materials by which they continue deforming over considerable lengths of time at constant stress or load. The nature of the creep process is shown schematically in Fig. 1.6. This particular concrete was loaded at age 28 days with resulting instantaneous strain ϵ_{inst}. The load was then maintained for 230 days, during which time creep is seen to have increased the total deformation to almost 3 times its instantaneous value. If the load were maintained, the deformation would follow the solid curve. If the load is removed, as shown by the dashed curve, the elastic instantaneous strain ϵ_{inst} is, of course, recovered, and some creep recovery is seen to occur. If the concrete is reloaded at some later date, instantaneous and creep deformations develop again as shown.

Creep deformations for a given concrete are practically proportional to the magnitude of the applied stress; at any given stress, high-strength concretes show less creep than lower-strength concretes. As seen in Fig. 1.6, with elapsing time creep proceeds at a decreasing rate and ceases after 2 to 5 years at a final value which, depending on concrete strength and other factors, attains 1.5 to 4 times the magnitude of the instantaneous strain. If, instead of being applied quickly and thereafter kept constant, the load is increased slowly and gradually, as is the case in many structures during and after construction, instantaneous and creep defor-

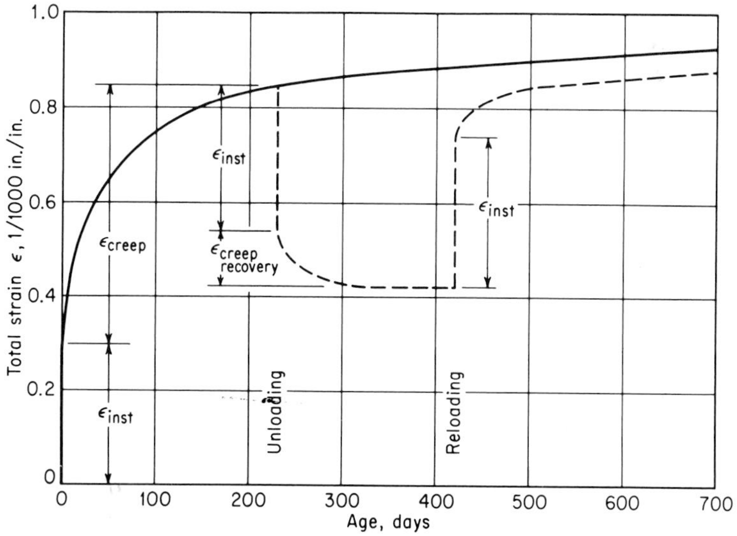

Fig. 1.6 Typical creep curve (concrete loaded to 600 psi at age 28 days).

mations proceed simultaneously. The effect is that shown in Fig. 1.5; that is, the previously discussed difference in the shape of the stress-strain curve for various rates of loading is chiefly the result of the creep deformations of concrete.

Sustained loads affect not only the deformation, but also the strength of concrete. The cylinder strength f'_c is determined at normal rates of test loading (about 35 psi per sec). Tests by Rüsch and others have shown that for concentrically loaded, unreinforced concrete prisms or cylinders the *strength under sustained load* is significantly smaller than f'_c, of the order of 75 per cent of f'_c for loads maintained for a year or more.

When concrete is subject to fluctuating rather than sustained loading, its *fatigue strength*, as for all other materials, is considerably smaller than its static strength. When plain concrete in compression is stressed cyclically from zero to maximum stress, its fatigue limit is from 50 to 60 per cent of the static compression strength, for 2,000,000 cycles. A reasonable estimate can be made for other stress ranges using the modified Goodman diagram. For other types of applied stress, such as flexural compression stress in reinforced-concrete beams or flexural tension stress in unreinforced beams or on the tension side of reinforced beams, the fatigue limit likewise appears to be about 55 per cent of the corresponding static strength (Ref. 1.14).

1.8 Tension Strength While concrete is best employed in a manner which utilizes its favorable compression strength, its tension strength is also of consequence in a variety of connections. Thus, the shear and torsion resistance of reinforced-concrete beams appears to depend primarily on the tension strength of the concrete. Also, the conditions under which cracks form and propagate on the tension side of reinforced-concrete flexural members depends strongly on the tension strength.

There are considerable experimental difficulties in determining true tensile strengths for concrete. In direct tension tests, minor misalignments and stress concentrations in the gripping devices are apt to mar the results. For many years, tension properties have been measured in terms of the *modulus of rupture*, i.e., that computed flexural tension stress Mc/I at which a test beam of plain concrete would fracture. Because this nominal stress is computed on the assumption that concrete is an elastic material, and because this bending stress is localized in the outermost fibers, it is apt to be larger than the strength of concrete in uniform axial tension. It is thus a measure of, but not identical with, the real axial tension strength.

In recent years the result of the so-called *split-cylinder* test has established itself as a measure of the tensile strength of concrete. A 6 × 12-in. concrete cylinder, the same type as is used for compression tests, is inserted in a compression-testing machine in the horizontal position, so that compression is applied uniformly along two opposite generatrices. Plywood pads are inserted between the compression platens of the machine and the cylinder in order to equalize and distribute the pressure. It can be shown that in an elastic cylinder so loaded, a nearly uniform tensile stress of magnitude $2P/\pi dL$ exists at right angles to the plane of load application. Correspondingly, such cylinders, when tested, split into two halves along that plane, at a stress which can be computed from the above expression. P is the applied compression load at failure, and d and L are the diameter and length of the cylinder. Because of local stress conditions at the load lines and the presence of stresses at right angles to the aforementioned tension stresses, the results of the split-cylinder tests likewise are not identical with (but are believed to be a good measure of) the true axial tensile strength. The results of all types of tensile tests show considerably more scatter than those of compression tests.

Tensile strength, whichever way determined, does not correlate well with the compression strength f'_c. It appears that for sand-and-gravel concrete the tensile strength depends primarily on the strength of bond between hardened cement paste and aggregate, whereas for lightweight concretes it depends largely on the tensile strength of the porous aggregate. The compression strength, on the other hand, is much less determined by these particular characteristics.

It appears that a reasonable estimate for the split-cylinder strength f'_{sp} is given by 6 to 7 times $\sqrt{f'_c}$ for sand-and-gravel concretes, and by 4 to 5 times $\sqrt{f'_c}$ for lightweight concretes.[1] The true tensile strength f'_t for the former appears to be of the order of 0.5 to 0.7 times f'_{sp}, and the flexural tension strength f_r (modulus of rupture) from 1.25 to 1.75 times f'_{sp}. The smaller of the foregoing factors apply to higher-strength concretes, and the larger to lower-strength concretes. These approximate expressions show that tension and compression strengths are by no means proportional and that any increase in compression strength, such as that achieved by lowering the water-cement ratio, is accompanied by a much smaller percentage increase in tensile strength (see also Fig. 1.2).

1.9 Strength under Combined Stress In many structural situations concrete is subjected simultaneously to various stresses acting in various directions. For instance, in beams much of the concrete is subject simultaneously to compression and shear stresses, in slabs and footings to compression in two perpendicular directions plus shear. By methods well known in the study of strengths of materials, any such state of combined stress, no matter how complex, can be reduced to three principal stresses

[1] In these expressions, f'_c is expressed in psi, and the resulting f'_{sp} is obtained in psi. For example, for $f'_c = 3600$ psi, $f'_{sp} = 6\sqrt{f'_c}$ to $7\sqrt{f'_c} = 6 \times 60$ to $7 \times 60 = 360$ to 420 psi.

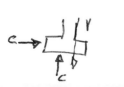

acting at right angles to each other on an appropriately oriented elementary cube in the material. Any or all the principal stresses can be either tension or compression. If one of them is zero, a state of *biaxial* stress is said to exist, if two of them are zero, the state of stress is *uniaxial*, either simple compression or simple tension. In most cases only the uniaxial strength properties of a material are known from simple tests, such as the cylinder strength f'_c and the tensile strength f'_t. For predicting the strengths of structures in which concrete is subject to biaxial or triaxial stress, it would be desirable to be able to calculate the strength of concrete in such states of stress, knowing from tests only either f'_c or f'_c and f'_t.

In spite of extensive and continuing research, no reliable theory of the strength of concrete under combined stress has yet emerged. Modifications of various strength theories, such as the maximum-tension-stress, the Mohr, and the octahedral-stress theories, all of which are discussed in strength-of-materials texts, have been adapted with varying partial success to concrete (Refs. 1.16 to 1.19). At this time none of them is free from internal contradictions or of sufficient reliability to be practically useful. One of the reasons for this lies in the highly nonhomogeneous nature of concrete and in the degree to which its behavior at high stresses and at fracture is influenced by microcracking and other discontinuity phenomena (Ref. 1.20).

invent a homogeneous concrete substance.

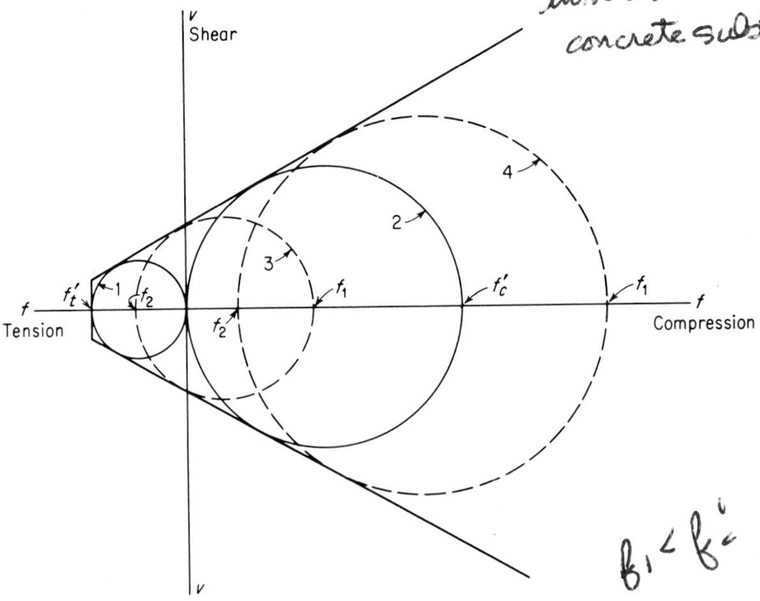

$f_1 < f'_c$

***Fig.* 1.7** Strength of concrete under combined stress. (*Schematically, according to Ref.* 1.17.)

Qualitatively, the effect of combined stress on strength is easily visualized from Fig. 1.7, which represents a modification of Mohr's strength theory (Ref. 1.16) proposed for concrete by Cowan (Ref. 1.17). In this presentation, circle 1 represents failure in simple tension at a stress f'_t, circle 2 failure in simple compression at a stress f'_c. The dashed circles show two states of combined stress. In circle 3 a principal tension stress f_2 acts at right angles to the principal compression stress f_1. It is seen that $f_1 < f'_c$; that is, when tension acts at right angles to compression, the compressive strength of concrete is reduced as compared to its strength f'_c in simple compression. In circle 4 a smaller principal compression stress f_2 acts at right angles to the larger principal compression stress f_1. It is seen that here $f_1 > f'_c$; that is, when compression acts at right angles to compression, the compressive strength of concrete is increased as compared to its strength f'_c in simple compression. Similar relations can be read off the figure for the strength of concrete in shear as it is affected by simultaneous compression or tension.

The fact that the strength of concrete under combined stress cannot yet be calculated rationally is one of the main reasons for continued reliance on tests. Because of this, the design of reinforced-concrete structures continues to be based on extensive experimental information rather than on consistent analytical theory, particularly in the many situations in which combined stresses occur.

1.10 Volume Changes: Shrinkage, Temperature The deformations discussed in Art. 1.7 were induced by stresses caused by external loads. Influences of a different nature cause concrete, even when free of any external loading, to undergo deformations and volume changes. The most important of these are shrinkage and the effects of temperature variations.

a. Shrinkage As was discussed in Arts. 1.2 and 1.4, any workable concrete mix contains more water than is needed for hydration. If the concrete is exposed to air, the larger part of this free water evaporates in time, the rate and completeness of drying depending on ambient temperature and humidity conditions. As the concrete dries, it shrinks in volume, probably due to the capillary tension which develops in the water remaining in the concrete. Conversely, if dry concrete is immersed in water, it expands, regaining much of the volume loss from prior shrinkage. Shrinkage, which continues at a decreasing rate for several months, depending on the configuration of the member, is a detrimental property of concrete in several respects. When not adequately controlled, it will cause unsightly and often deleterious cracks, particularly in slabs, walls, etc. In structures which are statically indeterminate (and most concrete structures are), it can cause large and harmful stresses. In prestressed concrete it leads to

what about water immersed concretes

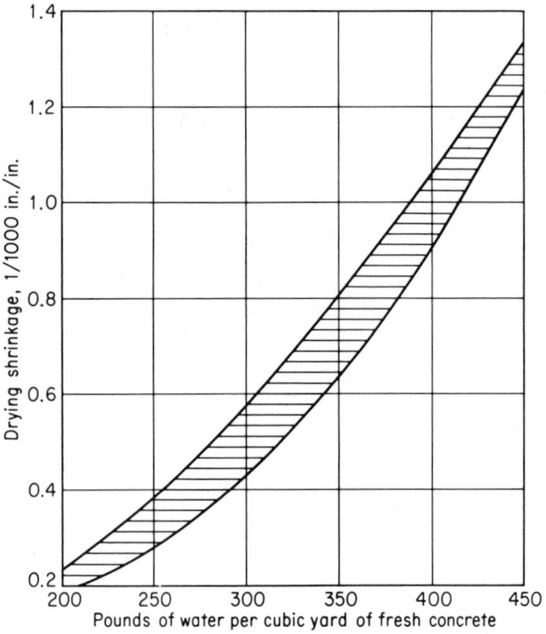

***Fig.* 1.8** Effect of water content on drying shrinkage. (*Adapted from Ref.* 1.4.)

partial loss of initial prestress. For these reasons it is essential that shrinkage be minimized and controlled.

As is clear from the nature of the process, the chief factor which determines the amount of final shrinkage is the unit water content of the fresh concrete. This is clearly illustrated in Fig. 1.8, which shows the amount of shrinkage in units of 0.001 in. per in. for varying amounts of mixing water. The same aggregates were used for all tests, but in addition to and independently of water content, the amount of cement was also varied, from 4 to 11 sacks per cubic yard of concrete. This very large variation of cement content had only very minor effects on the amount of shrinkage, as compared to the effect of water content; this is evident from the narrowness of the band which comprises the test results for the widely varying cement contents. It is evident from this that the chief means of reducing shrinkage is to reduce the water content of the fresh concrete to the minimum compatible with the required workability. In addition, prolonged and careful curing is beneficial for shrinkage control.

Values of final shrinkage for ordinary concretes are generally of the order of 0.0002 to 0.0007 in. per in., depending on initial water content, ambient temperature and humidity conditions, and the nature of the aggregate. Highly absorptive aggregates, such as some sandstones and slates, result in shrinkage values two and more times those obtained with less absorptive materials, such as granites and some limestones. Some lightweight aggregates, in view of their great porosity, easily result in much larger shrinkage values than ordinary concretes.

b. Temperature changes Like most other materials, concrete expands with increasing temperature and contracts with decreasing temperature. The effects of such volume changes are similar to those caused by shrinkage. That is, temperature contraction can lead to undue cracking, particularly when superposed on shrinkage; in indeterminate structures, deformations due to temperature changes can cause large and occasionally harmful stresses.

The coefficient of expansion varies somewhat, depending on type of aggregate and richness of mix. It is generally within the range of 0.000004 to 0.000006 in. per in. per °F. A value of 0.0000055 is generally accepted as satisfactory for calculating stresses and deformations caused by temperature changes.

1.11 Reinforcing Steels ***a. General*** As compared to concrete, steel is a high-strength material. The useful strength of ordinary reinforcing steels in tension as well as in compression, i.e., the yield strength, is of the order of 10 times the compression strength of common structural concrete, or of the order of 100 times its tensile strength. On the other hand, steel is a high-cost material as compared to concrete. It follows that the two materials are best used in combination if the concrete is made to resist the compression stresses, and the steel the tension stresses. Thus, in reinforced-concrete beams the concrete resists the compression force, longitudinal steel rods are located close to the tension face to resist the tension force, and frequently additional steel bars are so disposed that they resist the inclined tension stresses which are caused by the shear force in the webs of beams. However, reinforcement is also used for resisting compression forces, primarily where it is desired to reduce the cross-sectional dimensions of compression members, as in the lower-floor columns of multistory buildings. Even if no such necessity exists, a minimum amount of reinforcement is placed in all compression members to safeguard them against the effects of small accidental bending moments which might crack and even fail an unreinforced member.

For most effective reinforcing action, it is essential that steel and concrete deform together, i.e., that there be a sufficiently strong *bond* between the two materials so that no relative movements of the steel bars and the surrounding concrete occur. This bond is provided by the relatively large *chemical adhesion* which develops at the steel-concrete interface, by the *natural roughness* of the mill scale of hot-rolled reinforcing bars, and by the closely spaced rib-shaped *surface deformations* with which reinforcing bars are furnished in order to provide a high degree of interlocking of the two materials.

Additional features which make for the satisfactory joint performance of steel and concrete are the following: (1) The *thermal expansion coefficients* of the two materials, about 0.0000065 for steel vs. an average of 0.0000055 for concrete, are sufficiently close to forestall cracking and other undesirable effects of differential thermal deformations. (2) While the *corrosion resistance* of bare steel is poor, the concrete which surrounds the steel reinforcement provides excellent corrosion protection, minimizing corrosion problems and corresponding maintainance costs. (3) The *fire resistance* of unprotected steel is impaired by its high thermal conductivity and by the fact that its strength decreases sizably at high temperatures. Conversely, the thermal conductivity of concrete is relatively low. Thus, damage caused by even prolonged fire exposure, if any, is generally limited to the outer layer of concrete, and a moderate amount of concrete cover provides sufficient thermal insulation for the embedded reinforcement.

b. Types of reinforcement The most common type of reinforcing steel in reinforced (as distinct from prestressed) concrete is in the form of round bars. They are available in a large range of diameters, from about $\frac{1}{4}$ in. to about $1\frac{3}{8}$ in. for ordinary applications, and in two recently developed heavy bars of about $1\frac{3}{4}$ in. and $2\frac{1}{4}$ in. These bars, with the exception of the $\frac{1}{4}$-in. size, are furnished with surface deformations for the purpose of increasing the bond strength between steel and concrete. Minimum requirements for these deformations (spacing, projection, etc.) have been developed in lengthy experimental research and are specified in ASTM specification A305. Different bar producers use different patterns, all of which generally satisfy these requirements. Figure 1.9 shows a variety of current types of deformations (type 6 is no longer produced, since the spacing between its deformations exceeds the maximum specified value of 0.7 diam).

Bar sizes are designated by numbers, Nos. 2 through 11 being commonly used, and Nos. 14*S* and 18*S* representing the two special large-size bars previously mentioned. Designation by number, instead of by diameter, has been introduced because the surface deformations make it impossible to define a single easily measured value of the diameter. The numbers are so arranged that the unit in the number designation corresponds closely to $\frac{1}{8}$ in. of diameter size. That is, a No. 5 bar has a nominal diameter of $\frac{5}{8}$ in., and similarly for the other sizes. Table 1 of Appendix B gives areas, perimeters, and weights of standard bars. Tables 2 to 4 give similar information for groups of bars.

Apart from single reinforcing bars, two other types of reinforcement are in common use for reinforcing slabs and other surfaces, such as shells. One of these is *welded steel wire fabric.* This consists of a series of longitudinal and transverse cold-drawn steel wires at right angles to each other and welded together at all points of intersection. Size and spacing of wires may be the same in both directions or may be different, depending on

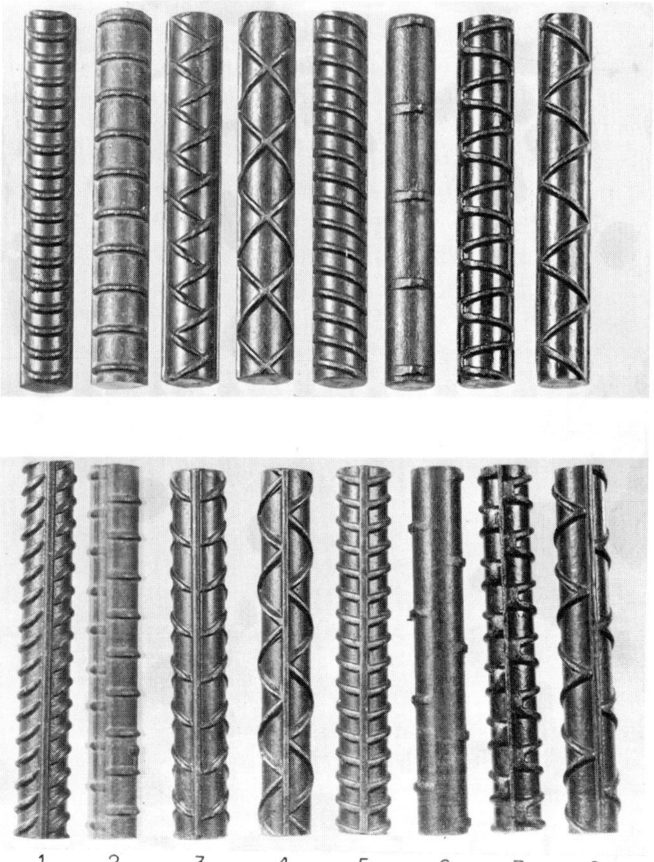

Fig. **1.9** Types of deformed bars.

the requirements of the design. Detailed data can be found in commercial catalogues. A somewhat similar type is known as *bar* or *rod mats*. In these, reinforcing bars or rods are used, instead of cold-drawn wire, to manufacture a grid of longitudinal and transverse bars, connected at their intersections either by welding or by clipping. For prestressed concrete, special forms and grades of reinforcement are used. The main types are *single prestressing wires*, with diameters ranging from 0.192 to 0.276 in., and *prestressing strands*. These are of the seven-wire type, having a center wire enclosed by six helically placed outer wires and ranging in nominal strand diameter from $\frac{1}{4}$ in. to $\frac{1}{2}$ in. More details on prestressing steels will be found in Chap. 11.

c. Grades and strengths Before the advent of prestressed concrete, almost the only grades of steel which were used for reinforcing bars were low-carbon steels with specified minimum yield points of 33 to 40 ksi and minimum tensile strengths of 55 to 70 ksi. Prestressing is most economical when reinforcement of very high strength is used; this brought into use the previously mentioned prestressing wires and strands, with yield strengths of 190 to 210 ksi and tensile strengths of 230 to 270 ksi. In very recent years, particularly with the advent of ultimate-strength design (see Chaps. 2 and 3), deformed reinforcing bars made of higher-strength carbon steels as well as of low-alloy steels have become available, with specified minimum yield points from 50 to 75 ksi and tensile strengths from 80 to 100 ksi.

***Table* 1.1 Standardized reinforcing steels**

Type	Grade	ASTM specification no.	Specified minimum	
			Yield point, ksi	Tensile strength, ksi
Billet or axle	Structural	A15 or A160	33	55
	Intermediate		40	70
	Hard		50	80
Rail	Regular	A16	50	80
	Hard		60	90
Billet	60-ksi yield	A432	60	90
Billet	High-strength	A431	75	100
Cold-drawn wire (e.g., for mesh)	. . . .	A82	64	80

At the time of writing of this edition, so-called *intermediate-grade* reinforcing steel with a specified yield point of 40 ksi is still the most prevalent, but it is being, and will increasingly be, displaced by reinforcing bars with 60 ksi yield point. The use of high-strength bars with 75 ksi yield point is so far limited by its higher cost and by the fact that, if used in flexural members, it requires special measures of deflection and concrete crack control; the latter is not yet completely understood and at this time is subject to intensive research relative to crack initiation and propagation. The higher-strength reinforcing bars are identified by the producers with rolled-in markings to prevent accidental substitution of the lower-strength intermediate-grade bars. Table 1.1 lists all presently available reinforcing steels (not including prestressing steels which are discussed in Chap. 11), their designations, the ASTM specifications which define their properties in detail, and their two main minimum specified strength values.

The large-size bars No. 14*S* and 18*S*, whose properties are specified in

ASTM A408, are available in the same three grades as the ASTM A15 steels.

d. Stress-strain curves The two chief numerical characteristics which determine the character of reinforcement are its yield point (generally identical in tension and in compression) and its *modulus of elasticity* E. The latter is practically the same for all reinforcing steels (but not for prestressing steels) and is taken as $E = 29{,}000{,}000$ psi.

In addition, however, the shape of the *stress-strain curve*, and particularly of its initial portion, has significant influence on the performance of reinforced-concrete members. Typical stress-strain curves of standardized American reinforcing steels are shown in Fig. 1.10. The curve for a low-alloy reinforcing steel with 90 ksi specified yield point, which at this writing is in the process of development, is also shown in that figure. The complete stress-strain curves are shown in the left part of the figure; the right part gives the initial portions of the curves magnified 10 times.

Low-carbon steels, typified by the 40-ksi curve, show an elastic portion followed by a "yield plateau," i.e., by a horizontal portion of the curve where strain continues to increase at constant stress. For such steels the yield point is that stress at which the yield plateau establishes itself. With further strain the stress begins to increase again, though at a slower rate, a process which is known as *strain-hardening*. The curve flattens out when the tensile strength is reached; it then turns down until fracture occurs. Higher-strength carbon steels, such as those with 60-ksi or 75-ksi yield points, either have a yield plateau of much shorter length or enter strain-hardening immediately without any continued yielding at constant stress. In the latter case the yield point is defined either by a residual strain of 0.2 per cent or by a total strain under load of 0.5 to 0.6 per cent,

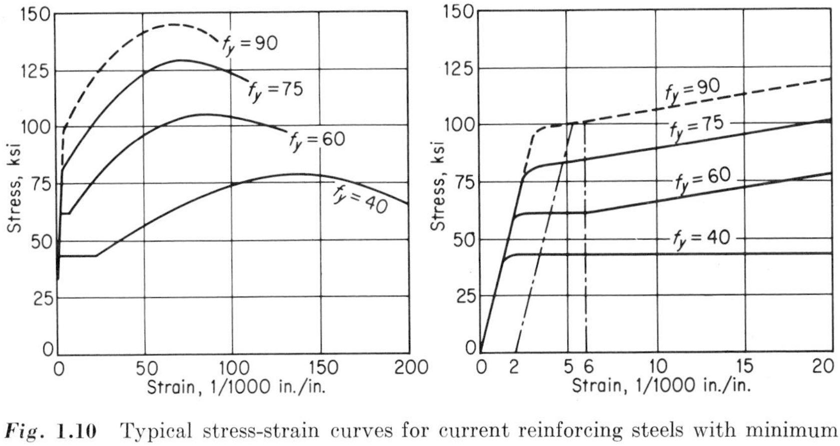

Fig. **1.10** Typical stress-strain curves for current reinforcing steels with minimum specified yield points f_y from 40 to 90 ksi.

as shown. Low-alloy, high-strength steels, such as the one with $f_y = 90$ ksi, rarely show any yield plateau and usually enter strain-hardening immediately upon beginning to yield.

REFERENCES

1.1 "Selection and Use of Aggregates for Concrete," reported by ACI Committee 621, *J. ACI*, vol. 58, p. 515, 1961.
1.2 G. W. Washa: Properties of Lightweight Aggregates and Concretes, *J. ACI*, vol. 53, p. 375, 1956.
1.3 R. W. Kluge: Structural Lightweight Aggregates and Concretes, *J. ACI*, vol. 53, p. 383, 1956.
1.4 G. E. Troxell and H. E. Davis: "Composition and Properties of Concrete," McGraw-Hill Book Company, Inc., New York, 1956.
1.4*a* T. C. Hsu and F. O. Slate: Tensile Bond Strength between Aggregate and Cement Paste or Mortar, *J. ACI*, vol. 60, p. 465, 1963.
1.5 "Selecting Proportions for Concrete," ACI standard 613.
1.6 "Selecting Proportions for Structural Lightweight Concrete," ACI standard 613A.
1.7 "Consolidation of Concrete," reported by ACI Committee 609, *J. ACI*, vol. 57, p. 985, 1961.
1.8 "Measuring, Mixing and Placing of Concrete," ACI standard 614.
1.9 "Winter Concreting," ACI standard 604.
1.10 "Hot Weather Concreting," ACI standard 605.
1.11 "Selection and Use of Aggregates for Concrete," reported by ACI Committee 621, *J. ACI*, vol. 58, p. 513, 1961.
1.12 E. Hognestad, N. W. Hansson, and D. McHenry: Concrete Stress Distribution in Ultimate Strength Design, *J. ACI*, vol. 55, p. 455, 1955.
1.13 Hubert Rüsch: Research toward a General Flexural Theory for Structural Concrete, *J. ACI*, vol. 57, p. 1, 1960.
1.14 G. M. Nordby: Fatigue of Concrete—a Review of Research, *J. ACI*, vol. 55, p. 191, 1958.
1.15 Evaluation of Compression Test Results of Field Concrete, reported by ACI Committee 214, *J. ACI*, vol. 53, p. 561, 1957.
1.16 S. Timoshenko: "Strength of Materials," part II, 3d ed., D. Van Nostrand Company, Inc., Princeton, N.J., 1956.
1.17 H. J. Cowan: The Strength of Plain, Reinforced and Prestressed Concrete under the Action of Combined Stresses, *Mag. Concrete Res.*, vol. 5, p. 75, 1953.
1.18 B. Bresler and K. S. Pister: Strength of Concrete under Combined Stress, *J. ACI*, vol. 55, p. 321, 1958.
1.19 D. McHenry and J. Karni: Strength of Concrete under Combined Tensile and Compressive Stress, *J. ACI*, vol. 54, p. 829, 1958.
1.20 T. C. Hsu, F. O. Slate, G. M. Sturman, and Geo. Winter: Microcracking of Plain Concrete and the Shape of the Stress-Strain Curve, *J. ACI*, vol. 60, p. 209, 1963.

chapter 2

MECHANICS AND BEHAVIOR OF REINFORCED CONCRETE

2.1 Fundamentals The chief task of the structural engineer is the design of structures. By *design* is meant the determination of the general shape and all specific dimensions of a particular structure so that it will perform the function for which it is created and will safely withstand the influences which will act on it throughout its useful life. These influences are primarily the loads and other forces to which it will be subjected, as well as other detrimental agents, such as temperature fluctuations, foundation settlements, and corrosive influences. *Structural mechanics* is one of the main tools in this process of design. As here understood, it is the body of scientific knowledge which permits one to predict with a good degree of certainty how a structure of given shape and dimensions will behave when acted upon by known forces or other mechanical influences. The chief items of behavior which are of practical interest are (1) the strength of the structure, i.e., that magnitude of loads of a given distribution which will cause the structure to fail, and (2) the deformations, such as deflections and extent of cracking, which the structure will undergo when loaded under service conditions.

In the present chapter, the structural mechanics of reinforced-concrete members will be developed in general terms. Specific methods of design and analysis, based on the information provided by structural mechanics but frequently simplified and conventionalized to various degrees, will be taken up in subsequent chapters.

The fundamental propositions on which the mechanics of reinforced concrete is based are the following:

1. The internal forces, such as bending moments, shear forces, and normal and shear stresses, at any section of a member are in equilibrium with the effects of the external loads at that section. This proposition is not an assumption but a fact, because any body or any portion thereof can be at rest only if all forces acting on it are in equilibrium.

2. The strain in an embedded reinforcing bar (unit extension or compression) is the same as that of the surrounding concrete. Expressed differently, it is assumed that perfect bonding exists between concrete and steel at the interface, so that no slip can occur between the two materials. Hence, as the one deforms, so must the other. With modern deformed bars (see Art. 1.10) a high degree of mechanical interlocking is provided in addition to the natural surface adhesion, so that this assumption is very close to correct.

3. Cross sections which were plane prior to loading continue to be plane in the member under load. Accurate measurements have shown that when a reinforced-concrete member is loaded close to failure, this assumption is not accurate. However, the deviations are usually minor, and the results of theory based on this assumption check well with extensive test information.

4. In view of the fact that the tensile strength of concrete is only a small fraction of its compressive strength (see Art. 1.8), the concrete in that part of a member which is in tension is usually cracked. While these cracks, in well-designed members, are generally so narrow as to be hardly visible (they are known as *hairline* cracks), they evidently render the cracked concrete incapable of resisting tension stress. Correspondingly, it is assumed that concrete is not capable of resisting any tension stress whatever. This assumption is evidently a simplification of the actual situation because, in fact, concrete prior to cracking, as well as the concrete located between cracks, does resist tension stresses of small magnitude. Also, in discussions of the resistance of reinforced-concrete beams to

shear, it will become apparent that under certain conditions this particular assumption is dispensed with and advantage is taken of the modest tension strength which concrete can develop.

5. The theory is based on the actual stress-strain relationships and strength properties of the two constituent materials (see Arts. 1.7 and 1.10) or some reasonable simplifications thereof, rather than on some assumptions of ideal material behavior. This last feature is a relatively new development. It supplants a method of analysis which was based on the assumption that both concrete and steel behave in an elastic manner at all stress levels relevant in calculations. This latter assumption, while leading to relatively simple computational methods, is very far from true (see Figs. 1.3, 1.5, and 1.10). Correspondingly, the newer methods of analysis which recognize the departure from elasticity at the higher stress levels are in much closer agreement with the actual behavior of structures and with very extensive experimental information. At the same time the facts that nonelastic behavior is reflected in modern theory, that concrete is assumed to be ineffective in tension, and that the joint action of the two materials is taken into consideration result in analytical methods which are considerably more complex, but also more challenging, than those which are adequate for members made of a single, substantially elastic material.

These five assumptions permit one to predict by calculation the performance of reinforced-concrete members only for some simple situations. Actually, the joint action of two materials as dissimilar and complicated as concrete and steel is so complex that it has not yet lent itself to purely analytical treatment. For this reason, methods of design and analysis, while utilizing these assumptions, are very largely based on the results of extensive and continuing experimental research. They are modified and improved as additional test evidence becomes available.

2.2 Axial Compression In members which sustain chiefly or exclusively axial compression loads, such as building columns, it is economical to make the concrete carry most of the load. Still, some steel reinforcement is always provided for various reasons. For one, very few members are truly axially loaded; steel is essential for resisting any bending that may exist. For another, if part of the total load is carried by steel with its much greater strength, the cross-sectional dimensions of the member can be reduced, the more so the larger the amount of reinforcement.

The two chief forms of reinforced-concrete columns are shown in Fig. 2.1. In the square column, the four longitudinal bars serve as main reinforcement. They are held in place by transverse small-diameter steel ties which prevent displacement of the main bars during construction operations and counteract any tendency of the compression-loaded bars to

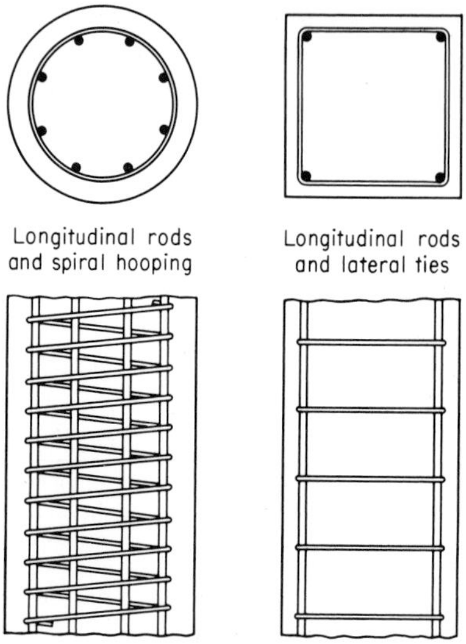

Fig. 2.1 Reinforced-concrete columns.

buckle out of the concrete by bursting the thin outer cover. On the left is shown a round column with eight main reinforcing bars. These are surrounded by a closely spaced spiral which serves the same purpose as the more widely spaced ties and acts to confine the concrete within it, thereby increasing its resistance to axial compression. The discussion which follows applies to tied columns.

When axial load is applied, the compression strain is the same over the entire cross section, and in view of the bonding between concrete and steel, is the same in the two materials (see propositions 2 and 3 of Art. 2.1). To illustrate the action of such a member as load is applied, Fig. 2.2 shows two typical stress-strain curves, one for a concrete with $f'_c = 3000$ psi (3 ksi) and the other for a steel with $f_s = 40{,}000$ psi (40 ksi). The curves for the two materials are drawn on the same graph using different vertical stress scales. Curve *b* has the shape which would be obtained in a concrete cylinder test. The rate of loading in most structures is considerably slower than that in a cylinder test, and this affects the shape of the curve (see Art. 1.7). Curve *c*, therefore, is drawn as being characteristic of the performance of concrete under slow or sustained loading. Under these conditions the maximum available compression strength of reinforced concrete is about $0.85f'_c$, as shown.

a. Elastic behavior (working stresses) At low stresses, up to about $f'_c/2$, the concrete is seen to behave nearly elastically, i.e., stresses and strains are quite closely proportional; the straight line *d* represents this range of behavior with little error for both rates of loading. For the given concrete the range extends to a strain of about 0.00045. The steel, on the other hand, is seen to be elastic nearly to its yield point of 40 ksi, or to the much greater strain of about 0.0013.

Because the compression strain in the concrete, at any given load, is equal to the compression strain in the steel,

$$\epsilon_c = \frac{f_c}{E_c} = \epsilon_s = \frac{f_s}{E_s}$$

from which the relation between the steel stress and the concrete stress is obtained as

$$f_s = \frac{E_s}{E_c} f_c = n f_c \tag{2.1}$$

where $n = E_s/E_c$ is known as the *modular ratio.*

Let A_c = net area of concrete, i.e., gross area minus area occupied by reinforcing bars
A_g = gross area
A_s = area of reinforcing bars
P = axial load

Then

$$P = f_c A_c + f_s A_s = f_c A_c + n f_c A_s$$

or

$$P = f_c(A_c + nA_s) \tag{2.2}$$

The term $(A_c + nA_s)$ can be interpreted as the area of a fictitious concrete cross section, the so-called *transformed area* which, when sub-

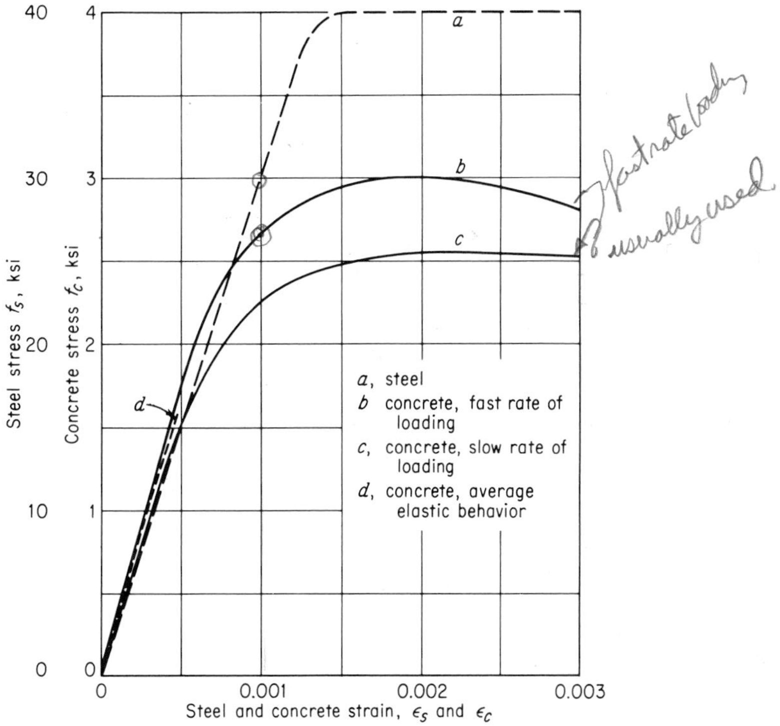

***Fig.* 2.2** Concrete and steel stress-strain curves.

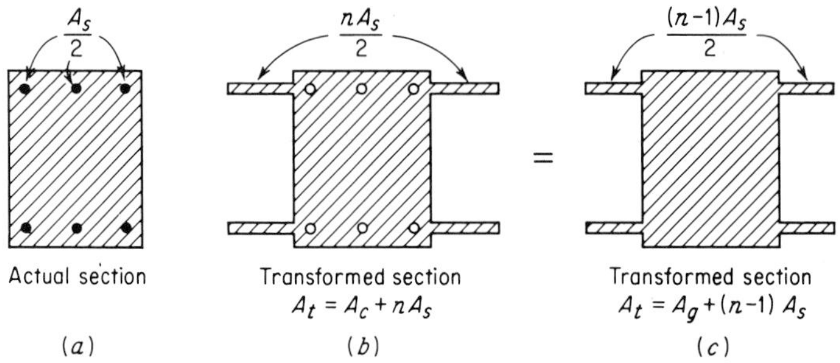

***Fig.* 2.3** Transformed section in axial compression.

jected to the particular concrete stress f_c, results in the same axial load P as the actual section composed of both steel and concrete. This transformed concrete area is seen to consist of the actual concrete area plus n times the area of the reinforcement. It can be visualized as shown in Fig. 2.3. That is, in Fig. 2.3*b* the three bars along each of the two faces are thought of as removed and replaced, at the same distance from the axis of the section, with added areas of fictitious concrete of total amount nA_s. Alternatively, as shown in Fig. 2.3*c*, one can think of the area of the steel bars as replaced with concrete, in which case one has to add to the gross concrete area A_g so obtained only $(n - 1)A_s$ in order to obtain the same total transformed area. Therefore, alternatively,

$$P = f_c[A_g + (n - 1)A_s] \tag{2.2a}$$

If load and cross-sectional dimensions are known, the concrete stress can be found by solving Eq. (2.2) or (2.2*a*) for f_c, and the steel stress can be calculated from Eq. (2.1). These relations hold in the range in which the concrete behaves nearly elastically, i.e., up to about 50 to 60 per cent of f'_c. For reasons of safety and serviceability, concrete stresses in structures under design loads are kept within this range. Therefore, these relations permit one to calculate *working stresses*, i.e., stresses which act in a member when it carries the working or design loading.

Example A column of the materials defined in Fig. 2.2 has a cross section of 16 × 20 in. and is reinforced by six No. 9 bars disposed as shown in Fig. 2.3. Determine the axial load which will stress the concrete to 1000 psi.

One finds $A_g = 16 \times 20 = 320$ in.^{2}, and, from Table 2 of Appendix B, $A_s = 6.00$ in. From Eq. (1.2), $E_c = 57{,}500\sqrt{3000} = 3{,}150{,}000$ psi, and $n = 29{,}000{,}000/3{,}150{,}000 = 9$. (In view of the scatter inherent in E_c, it is customary and satisfactory to round off the value of n to the nearest integer.) The load on the column, from Eq. (2.2*a*), is $P = 1000[320 + (9 - 1)6.00] = 368{,}000$ lb. Of this total load the concrete is seen to carry $P_c = f_cA_c = f_c(A_g - A_s) = 1000(320 - 6) = 314{,}000$ lb, and the steel $P_s = f_sA_s = (nf_c)A_s = 9000 \times 6 = 54{,}000$ lb, which is 14.7 per cent of the total axial load.

b. Inelastic range Inspection of Fig. 2.2 shows that the elastic relationships which have been utilized so far cannot be used beyond a strain of about 0.0005, for the given materials. To obtain information on the behavior of the member at larger strains and, correspondingly, at larger loads, it is therefore necessary to make direct use of the information of Fig. 2.2.

By way of example one may want to calculate the magnitude of the axial load which will produce a strain or unit shortening $\epsilon_c = \epsilon_s = 0.0010$ in the column of the previous example. At this strain the steel is seen to be still elastic, so that the steel stress $f_s = \epsilon_s E_s = 0.001 \times 29{,}000{,}000 = 29{,}000$ psi. The concrete is in the inelastic range, so that its stress cannot be directly calculated, but it can be read from the stress-strain curve for the given value of strain. (1) If the member has been loaded at a fast rate, curve *b* holds at the instant when the entire load is applied. The stress for $\epsilon = 0.001$ can be read as $f_c = 2660$ psi. Consequently, the total load can be obtained from

$$P = f_c A_c + f_s A_s \tag{2.3}$$

which evidently applies in the inelastic as well as in the elastic range. Hence, $P = 2660(320 - 6) + 29{,}000 \times 6 = 835{,}000 + 174{,}000 = 1{,}009{,}000$ lb. Of this total load, the steel is seen to carry 174,000 lb or 17.3 per cent. (2) For slowly applied or sustained loading, curve *c* represents the behavior of the concrete. Its stress at a strain of 0.001 can be read as $f_c = 2250$ psi. Then $P = 2250 \times 314 + 29{,}000 \times 6 = 707{,}000 + 174{,}000 = 881{,}000$ lb. Of this total load, the steel is seen to carry 19.7 per cent.

Comparison of the results for fast and slow loading show the following: Owing to creep of concrete, a given shortening of the column is produced by a smaller load when slowly applied or sustained over some length of time than when quickly applied. More important, the farther the stress is beyond the proportional limit of the concrete, and the more slowly the load is applied or the longer it is sustained, the smaller is the share of the total load carried by the concrete, and the larger that carried by the steel. In the sample column the steel was seen to carry 14.7 per cent of the load in the elastic range, 17.3 per cent for a strain of 0.001 under fast loading, and 19.7 per cent at the same strain under slow or sustained loading.

c. Ultimate strength The one quantity of chief interest to the structural designer is the *ultimate strength*, i.e., the maximum load which his structure or member will carry. Information on stresses, strains, and similar quantities serve chiefly as tools for determining carrying capacity. The performance of the column discussed so far indicates two things: First, in the range of large stresses and strains which precede attainment of ultimate strength and subsequent failure, elastic relationships cannot be utilized. Second, the member behaves differently under fast than under slow or sustained loading and shows less resistance to the latter than to the former. In usual construction, many types of loads, such as the weight of the structure and any permanent equipment housed therein, are sustained, and others are applied at slow rates. For this reason, to calculate a reliable magnitude of ultimate strength, curve *c* of Fig. 2.2 must be used as far as the concrete is concerned.

As for the steel, Fig. 1.10 shows that it reaches its ultimate strength (peak of the curve) at strains of the order of 0.10. However, as load is applied and increased, the compression strains in concrete and steel are the same at all times. Figure 2.2 shows that the maximum stress which the concrete can carry is reached at a strain of 0.002 to 0.003, much smaller than that strain which the steel could sustain by itself. Still larger strains cause the concrete to fail by crushing (cf., Fig. 1.3). Correspondingly, the largest strains to which the steel can be subjected prior to failure of the member are equal to those which the concrete can sustain before crushing, that is, 0.002 to 0.003. It is seen from Fig. 2.2 that the stress in the steel in this range of strains is its yield-point stress. For this reason the yield point is the maximum strength of reinforcement which can be utilized without prior failure of the concrete.

If the small transition curve just prior to yielding is disregarded, the steel strain at which the yield point is reached can be calculated from

$$\epsilon_y = \frac{f_y}{E_s} \tag{2.4}$$

where f_y is the yield point. In the example,

$$\epsilon_y = 40{,}000/29{,}000{,}000 = 0.0014$$

which can also be read from Fig. 2.2. At this strain, the stress in the concrete can be read from curve *c* as 2450 psi, and the load in the member is $P = 2450 \times 314 + 40{,}000 \times 6 = 1{,}010{,}000$ lb. However, curve *c* is seen to continue rising beyond this strain. Consequently, the load can be increased further until the ultimate strength of this concrete is reached at a strain of about 0.002. As was mentioned before, from many tests this maximum strength is assumed to be $0.85f'_c$, or $0.85 \times 3000 = 2550$ psi in the example. During this stage of loading, the steel merely yields at a constant stress, its yield stress, as can be seen from Fig. 2.2.

It is evident from this discussion that, if the yield strain [Eq. (2.4)] is smaller than the strain at which the concrete reaches its ultimate stress $0.85f'_c$, the steel will start yielding and will continue to do so until that strain is reached at which the concrete attains this stress and begins to fail. Correspondingly, the ultimate load[1] of the member is

$$P'_u = 0.85f'_cA_c + f_yA_s \tag{2.5}$$

[1] Throughout this book, quantities which refer to the ultimate strength of a member are primed and furnished with the subscript *u*, for example, P'_u. The prime is used

Numerous careful tests have shown the reliability of Eq. (2.5) in predicting the ultimate strength of a concentrically loaded reinforced-concrete column, provided its slenderness ratio is small so that buckling will not reduce its strength (Ref. 2.1).

For the particular numerical example, $P'_u = 2550 \times 314 + 40{,}000 \times 6 = 800{,}000 + 240{,}000 = 1{,}040{,}000$ lb. At this stage the steel carries as much as 23 per cent of the load.

Summary In the elastic range of low stresses the steel carries a relatively small portion of the total load of an axially compressed member. As the ultimate strength is approached, there occurs a redistribution of the relative shares of the load resisted, respectively, by concrete and steel, the latter taking an increasing amount. The ultimate load at which the member is on the point of failure consists of the contribution of the steel when it is stressed to the yield point plus that of the concrete when its stress has attained the ultimate strength of $0.85f'_c$, as reflected in Eq. (2.5).

PROBLEM

The same 16 × 20 in. column as in the preceding examples is made of the same concrete and reinforced with the same six No. 9 bars, except that a steel with yield strength $f_y = 60$ ksi is used. The stress-strain diagram of this reinforcing steel is that shown in Fig. 1.10 for $f_y = 60$ ksi. For this column determine: (*a*) the axial load which will stress the concrete to 1000 psi; (*b*) the ultimate strength; (*c*) the share of the total load carried by the reinforcement at these two stages of loading. Compare results with those calculated in the preceding examples for $f_y = 40$ ksi, keeping in mind, in regard to relative economy, that the price per pound for reinforcing steels with 40 ksi and with 60 ksi yield points is about the same.

2.3 Axial Tension It was pointed out in Art. 1.8 that the tension strength of concrete is only a small fraction of its compressive strength. It follows that reinforced concrete is not well suited for use in tension members because the concrete will contribute little, if anything, to their strength. Still, there are situations in which reinforced concrete is stressed in tension, chiefly in tie rods in structures such as arches. Such members consist of one or more bars embedded in concrete in a symmetrical arrangement similar to compression members (cf. Figs. 2.1 and 2.3).

When the tension force in the member is sufficiently small so that the

---

to distinguish these quantities from those which the ACI Code prescribes for use in design. These ultimate design strengths are designated in the code by the subscript u without prime, for example, P_u. In order to ensure structural safety, the codified design values such as P_u are smaller than the actual ultimate-strength values, such as P'_u, by percentages which are specified in the code and explained in Chaps. 3 and 5.

stress in the concrete is considerably below its tensile strength, both steel and concrete behave elastically. In this situation all the expressions derived for compression in Art. 2.2*a* are identically valid for tension. In particular, Eq. (2.2) becomes

$$P = f_{ct}(A_c + nA_s) \tag{2.6}$$

where f_{ct} is the tensile stress in the concrete.

However, when the load is further increased, the concrete reaches its tensile strength at a stress and strain of the order of one-tenth of what it could sustain in compression. At this stage the concrete cracks across the entire cross section. When this happens, it ceases to resist any part of the applied tension force, since, evidently, no force can be transmitted across the air gap in the crack. At any load larger than that which caused the concrete to crack, the steel is called upon to resist the entire tension force. Correspondingly, at this stage

$$P = f_sA_s \tag{2.7}$$

With further increased load, the tensile stress f_s in the steel reaches the yield point f_y. When this occurs, the tension members cease to exhibit small, elastic deformations but, instead, stretch a sizable and permanent amount at substantially constant load. This does not impair the strength of the member. Its elongation, however, becomes so large (of the order of 1 per cent or more of its length) as to render it useless. Therefore, the maximum useful strength P'_{ut} of a tension member is that force which will just cause the steel stress to reach the yield point. That is,

$$P'_{ut} = f_yA_s \tag{2.8}$$

To provide adequate safety, the force permitted in a tension member under normal service loads should be of the order of $\frac{1}{2}P'_{ut}$. Because the concrete has cracked at loads considerably smaller than this, it does not contribute to the carrying capacity of the member in service. It does serve, however, as a fire and corrosion proofing and often improves the appearance of the structure.

There are situations, though, in which reinforced concrete is used in axial tension under conditions in which the occurrence of tension cracks must be prevented. A case in point is a circular tank (see Fig. 1.1*i*). To provide watertightness, the hoop tension caused by the fluid pressure must be prevented from causing the concrete to crack. In this case, Eq. (2.6) can be used to determine a safe value for the axial tension force P by using, for the concrete tension stress f_{ct}, an appropriate fraction of the tensile strength of the concrete, i.e., of that stress which would cause the concrete to crack.

PROBLEM

A reinforced-concrete water pipe has an inside diameter of 5 ft 0 in. and a wall thickness of 3½ in. The circumferential hoop reinforcement consists of No. 4 bars at 3 in. distance, center to center; the bars are located midway between inside and outside surfaces. The concrete has a compression strength $f'_c = 5000$ psi and a split cylinder strength $f'_{sp} = 450$ psi, for the reinforcement $f_y = 40{,}000$ psi. Determine: (*a*) the allowable water pressure such that there is a safety factor of 1.5 against leakage caused by tension cracks; (*b*) for this allowable water pressure, determine the safety factor against failure of the pipe. *Hint:* To expedite calculations, analyze a 1-ft length of pipe and make use of Tables 2 or 4 of Appendix B. Regarding tension strength of concrete, see Art. 1.8.

2.4 Bending ***a. Bending of homogeneous beams*** Reinforced-concrete beams are nonhomogeneous in that they are made of two entirely different materials. The methods used in the analysis of reinforced-concrete beams are therefore different from those used in the design or investigation of beams composed entirely of steel, wood, or any other structural material. The fundamental principles involved are, however, essentially the same as those relating to homogeneous beams. Briefly, these principles are as follows:

At any cross section there exist internal forces which may be resolved into components normal and tangential to the section. Those components which are normal to the section are the *bending* stresses (tension on one side of the neutral axis and compression on the other). Their function is to resist the bending moment at the section. The tangential components are known as the *shear* stresses, and they resist the transverse or shear forces.

FUNDAMENTAL ASSUMPTIONS

1. A cross section which was plane before loading remains plane under load. This means that the unit strains in a beam, above and below the neutral axis, are proportional to the distance from that axis.

2. The bending stress f at any point depends on the strain at that point in a manner given by the stress-strain diagram of the material. If the beam is made of a homogeneous material whose stress-strain diagram in tension and compression is that of Fig. 2.4*a*, the following holds: If the maximum strain at the outer fibers is smaller than the strain ϵ_p up to which stress and strain are proportional for the given material, then the compression and tension stresses on either side of the axis are proportional to the distance from the axis, as shown in Fig. 2.4*b*. However, if the maximum strain at the outer fibers is larger than ϵ_p, this is no longer true. The situation which then obtains is shown in Fig. 2.4*c*; that is, in the outer portions of the beam, where $\epsilon > \epsilon_p$, stresses and strains are no longer proportional. In these regions the magnitude of stress at any level, such as f_2

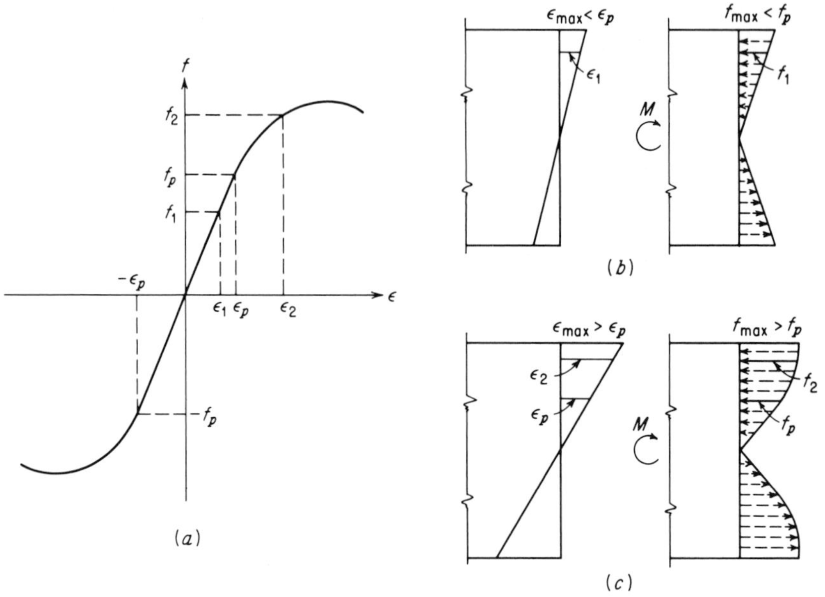

***Fig.* 2.4** Elastic and inelastic stress distributions in homogeneous beam.

in Fig. 2.4*c*, depends on the strain ϵ_2 at that level in the manner given by the stress-strain diagram of the material. In other words, for a given strain in the beam, the stress at a point is the same as that given by the stress-strain diagram.

3. The distribution of the shear stresses v over the depth of the section depends on the shape of the cross section and of the stress-strain diagram. These shear stresses are largest at the neutral axis and equal to zero at the outer fibers. The shear stresses on horizontal and vertical planes through any point are equal.

4. Owing to the combined action of shear stresses (horizontal and vertical) and flexure stresses, at any point in a beam there are inclined stresses of tension and compression, the largest of which form an angle of 90° with each other. The intensity of the inclined maximum or principal stress at any point is given by the equation

$$t = \frac{f}{2} \pm \sqrt{\frac{f^2}{4} + v^2} \tag{2.9}$$

where f = intensity of normal fiber stress
v = intensity of tangential shearing stress

The inclined stress makes an angle α with the horizontal such that $\tan 2\alpha = 2v/f$.

5. Since the horizontal and vertical shearing stresses are equal and

the flexural stresses are zero at the neutral plane, the inclined tensile and compressive stresses at any point in that plane form an angle of 45° with the horizontal, the intensity of each being equal to the unit shear at the point.

6. When the stresses in the outer fibers are smaller than the proportional limit f_p, the beam behaves *elastically* as shown in Fig. 2.4*b*. In this case the following obtains:

a. The neutral axis passes through the center of gravity of the cross section.

b. The intensity of bending stress normal to the section increases directly with the distance from the neutral axis and is a maximum at the extreme fibers. The stress at any given point in the cross section is represented by the equation

$$f = \frac{My}{I} \tag{2.10}$$

where f = bending stress at a distance y from neutral axis
M = external bending moment at section
I = moment of inertia of cross section about neutral axis

The maximum bending stress occurs at the outer fibers and is equal to

$$f_{\max} = \frac{Mc}{I} = \frac{M}{S} \tag{2.11}$$

where c = distance from neutral axis to outer fiber
$S = I/c$ = section modulus of cross section

c. The shear stress (longitudinal equals transverse) v at any point in the cross section is given by

$$v = \frac{VQ}{Ib} \tag{2.12}$$

where V = total shear at section
Q = statical moment about neutral axis of that portion of cross section lying between a line through point in question parallel to neutral axis and nearest face (upper or lower) of beam
I = moment of inertia of cross section about neutral axis
b = width of beam at given point

d. The intensity of shear along a vertical cross section in a rectangular beam varies as the ordinates of a parabola, the intensity being zero at the top and bottom of the beam and a maximum at the neutral axis. The maximum is $\frac{3}{2}V/ba$, since at the neutral axis $Q = ba^2/8$ and $I = ba^3/12$ in Eq. (2.12).

The remainder of this article deals only with bending stresses and their effects on reinforced-concrete beams. Shear stresses and their effects are discussed separately in Art. 2.5.

b. Reinforced-concrete beams: behavior under load Plain concrete beams are inefficient as flexural members because the tension strength in bending (modulus of rupture, see Art. 1.8 and Fig. 1.2) is a small fraction of the compression strength. In consequence, such beams fail on the tension side at low loads, long before the strength of the concrete on the compression side has been fully utilized. For this reason, steel reinforcing bars are placed on the tension side as close to the extreme tension fiber as is compatible with proper fire and corrosion protection of the steel. In such a reinforced-concrete beam the tension which is caused by the bending moments is chiefly resisted by the steel reinforcement, while the concrete alone is usually capable of resisting the corresponding compression. Such joint action of the two materials is assured if relative slip is prevented. This is achieved by using deformed bars with their high bond strength at the steel-concrete interface (see Art. 1.11) and, if necessary, by special anchorage of the ends of the bars. A simple example of such a beam, with the customary designations for the cross-sectional dimensions, is shown in Fig. 2.5. For the sake of simplicity the discussion which follows will deal with beams of rectangular cross section, even though members of other shapes are very common in most concrete structures.

When the load on such a beam is gradually increased from zero to that magnitude which will cause the beam to fail, several different stages of behavior can be clearly distinguished. At low loads, as long as the maximum tension stress in the concrete is smaller than the modulus of rupture, the entire concrete is effective in resisting stress, in compression on one side and in tension on the other side of the neutral axis. In addition, the reinforcement, deforming the same amount as the adjacent concrete, is also subject to tension stresses. At this stage all stresses in the concrete are of small magnitude and are proportional to strains. The distribution of strains and stresses in concrete and steel over the depth of the section is as shown in Fig. 2.5*c*.

When the load is further increased, the tension strength of the concrete is soon reached, and at this stage tension cracks develop. These propagate quickly upward to or close to the level of the neutral plane, which, in turn, shifts upward with progressive cracking. The general shape and distribution of these tension cracks is shown in Fig. 2.5*d*. In well-designed beams the width of these cracks is sufficiently small (hairline cracks) so that they are not objectionable either from the viewpoint of corrosion protection or from that of appearance. Their presence, however, affects profoundly the behavior of the beam under load. Evidently, in a cracked

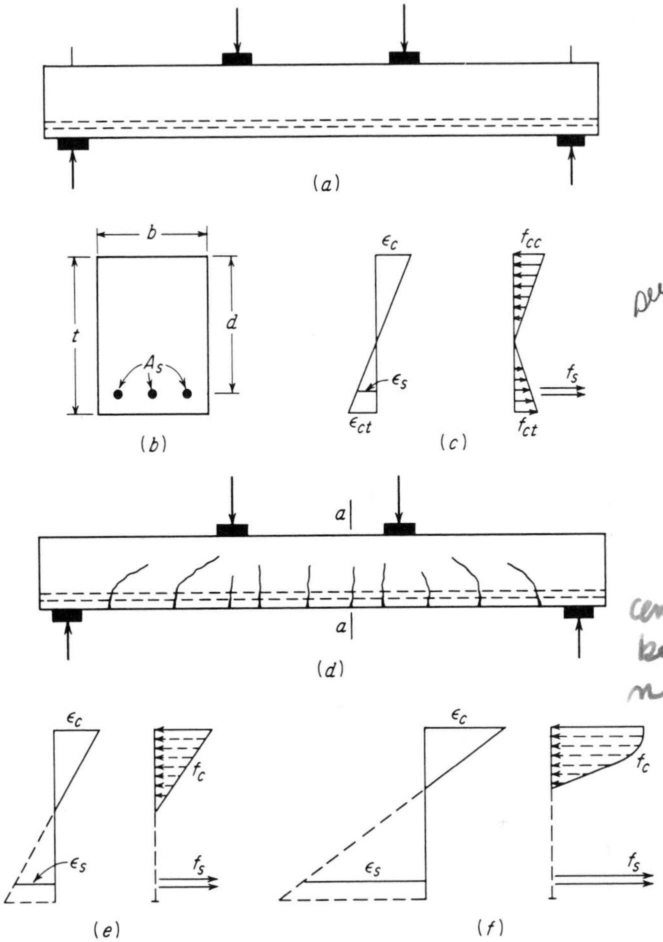

centroid must be same as n.a.

Fig. 2.5 Behavior of reinforced-concrete beam under increasing load.

section, i.e., in a cross section located at a crack such as *a-a* in Fig. 2.5*d*, the concrete does not transmit any tension stresses. Hence, just as in tension members (Art. 2.3), it is the steel which is called upon to resist the entire tension. At moderate loads, if the concrete stresses do not exceed approximately $f_c'/2$, stresses and strains continue to be closely proportional (see Fig. 2.2). The distribution of strains and stresses at or near a cracked section is then that shown in Fig. 2.5*e*. When the load is still further increased, stresses and strains rise correspondingly and are no longer proportional. The ensuing nonlinear relation between stresses and strains is that given by the concrete stress-strain curve. Therefore, just as in homogeneous beams (see Fig. 2.4), the distribution of concrete stresses on the compression side of the beam is of the same shape as the stress-strain curve. Figure 2.5*f* shows the distribution of strains and stresses close to the ultimate load.

Eventually, the carrying capacity of the beam is reached. Failure can be caused in one of two ways. When relatively moderate amounts of reinforcement are employed, at some value of the load the steel will reach its yield point. At that stress the reinforcement yields suddenly and stretches a large amount (see Fig. 1.10), and the tension cracks in the concrete widen visibly and propagate upward, with simultaneous significant deflection of the beam. When this happens, the strains in the remaining compression zone of the concrete increase to such a degree that crushing of the concrete, the so-called *secondary compression failure*, ensues at a load only slightly larger than that which caused the steel to yield. Effectively, therefore, attainment of the yield point in the steel determines the carrying capacity of moderately reinforced beams. Such yield failure is gradual and is preceded by visible signs of distress, such as the widening and lengthening of cracks and the marked increase in deflection.

On the other hand, if large amounts of reinforcement or normal amounts of steel of very high strength are employed, the compression strength of the concrete may be exhausted before the steel starts yielding. Concrete fails by crushing when strains become so large that they disrupt the integrity of the concrete. Exact criteria for this occurrence are not yet known, but it has been observed that rectangular beams fail in compression when the concrete strains reach values of about 0.003 to 0.004 for concretes with f'_c varying from 5000 to 2000 psi, respectively. Compression failure through crushing of the concrete is sudden, of an almost explosive nature, and occurs without warning. For this reason it is good practice to dimension beams in such a manner that, should they be overloaded, failure will be initiated by yielding of the steel rather than by crushing of the concrete.

The analysis of stresses and strength in the different stages just described will be discussed in the next several sections.

c. Stresses elastic, section uncracked As long as the tensile stress in the concrete is smaller than the modulus of rupture so that no tension cracks develop, the strain and stress distribution as shown in Fig. 2.5*c* is essentially the same as in an elastic, homogeneous beam (Fig. 2.4*b*).

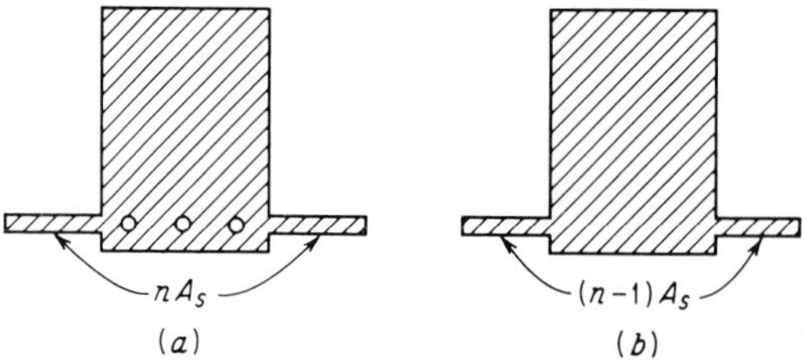

***Fig.* 2.6** Uncracked transformed section.

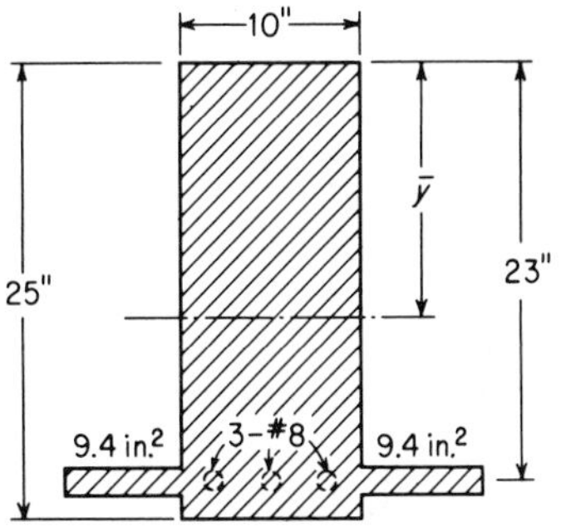

Fig. 2.7

The only difference is the presence of another material, the steel reinforcement. As was shown in Art. 2.2*a*, in the elastic range, for any given value of strain, the stress in the steel is n times that of the concrete [Eq. (2.1)]. In the same article it was shown that one can take account of this fact in calculations by replacing the actual steel-and-concrete cross section with a fictitious section thought of as consisting of concrete only. In this "transformed section" the actual area of the reinforcement is replaced with an equivalent concrete area equal to nA_s located at the level of the steel. The transformed, uncracked section pertaining to the beam of Fig. 2.5*b* is shown in Fig. 2.6.

Once the transformed section has been obtained, the usual methods of analysis of elastic homogeneous beams apply. That is, the section properties (location of neutral axis, moment of inertia, section modulus, etc.) are calculated in the usual manner, and, in particular, stresses are computed with Eqs. (2.10) to (2.12).

Example A rectangular beam has the dimensions (see Fig. 2.5*b*) $b = 10$ in., $t = 25$ in., and $d = 23$ in. and is reinforced with three No. 8 bars so that $A_s = 2.35$ in.² The concrete cylinder strength f'_c is 3000 psi, and the tensile strength in bending (modulus of rupture) is 450 psi. The yield point of the steel f_y is 40,000 psi, the stress-strain curves of the materials being those of Fig. 2.2. Determine the stresses caused by a bending moment $M = 40$ ft-kips.

With a value $n = E_s/E_c = 9$ (see the example of Art. 2.2*a*), one has to add to the rectangular outline an area $(n - 1)A_s = 8 \times 2.35 = 18.8$ in.², disposed as shown on Fig. 2.7, in order to obtain the uncracked, transformed section. Conventional calculations show that the location of the neutral axis of this section is given by $\bar{y} = 13.3$ in., and its moment of inertia about this axis is 15,030 in.⁴ For $M = 40$ ft-kips $= 480{,}000$ in-lb, the concrete compression stress at the top fiber is, from Eq. (2.11),

$$f_{cc} = 480{,}000 \times 13.3/15{,}030 = 425 \text{ psi}$$

and, similarly, the concrete tension stress at the bottom fiber is

$$f_{ct} = 480{,}000 \times 11.7/15{,}030 = 374 \text{ psi}$$

Since this value is substantially below the given tensile bending strength of the concrete, 450 psi, no tension cracks will form, and calculation by the uncracked, transformed section is justified. The stress in the steel, from Eqs. (2.1) and (2.10), is

$$f_s = n\frac{My}{I} = 9(480{,}000 \times 9.7/15{,}030) = 2890 \text{ psi}$$

By comparing f_{cc} and f_s with the cylinder strength and the yield point, respectively, it is seen that at this stage the actual stresses are quite small as compared to the available strengths of the two materials.

d. Stresses elastic, section cracked When the tension stress f_{ct} exceeds the modulus of rupture, cracks form as shown in Fig. 2.5*d*. If the concrete compression stress is less than approximately $\frac{1}{2}f'_c$ and the steel stress has not reached the yield point, both materials continue to behave elastically or very nearly so. This situation generally obtains in structures under normal service conditions and loads, since at these loads the stresses are generally of the order of magnitude just discussed. At this stage, for simplicity and with little if any error, it is assumed that tension cracks have progressed all the way to the neutral axis, and that sections plane before bending are plane in the bent member. The situation in regard to strain and stress distribution is then that shown in Fig. 2.5*e*.

To compute stresses, and strains if desired, the device of the transformed section can still be used. One need only take account of the fact that all the concrete which is stressed in tension is assumed cracked and, therefore, effectively absent. As shown in Fig. 2.8*a*, the transformed section then consists of the concrete in compression on one side of the axis, and n times the steel area on the other. The distance to the neutral axis, in this stage, is conventionally expressed as a fraction kd of the effective depth d. (Once the concrete is cracked, any material located below the steel is ineffective, which is why d is the effective depth of the beam.) To determine the location of the neutral axis, the moment of the tension area about the axis is set equal to the moment of the compression area, which gives

$$b\frac{(kd)^2}{2} - nA_s(d - kd) = 0 \qquad (2.13)$$

Having obtained kd by solving this quadratic equation, one can determine the moment of inertia and other properties of the transformed sec-

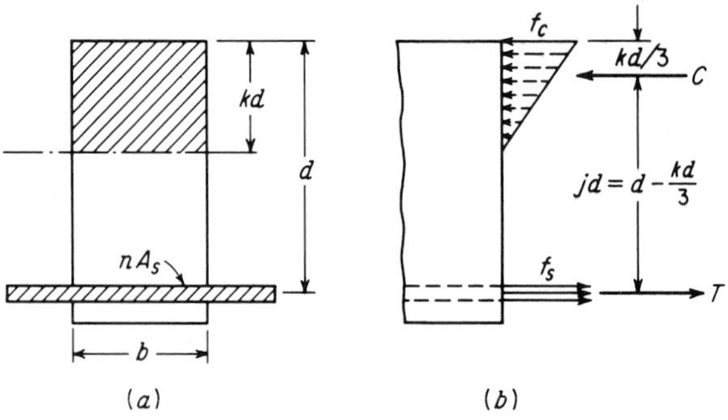

Fig. 2.8 Cracked transformed section.

tion as in the preceding case. Alternatively, one can proceed from basic principles by accounting directly for the forces which act in the cross section. These are shown in Fig. 2.8*b*. The concrete stress, with maximum value f_c at the outer edge, is distributed linearily as shown. The entire steel area A_s is subject to the stress f_s. Correspondingly, the total compression force C and the total tension force T are

$$C = \frac{bkd}{2} f_c \qquad \text{and} \qquad T = A_s f_s \tag{2.14}$$

The requirement that these two forces must be equal numerically has been taken care of by the manner in which the location of the neutral axis has been determined.

Equilibrium requires that the couple constituted by the two forces C and T be equal numerically to the external bending moment M. Hence, taking moments about C,

$$M = Tjd = A_s f_s jd \tag{2.15}$$

from which the steel stress is

$$f_s = \frac{M}{A_s jd} \tag{2.16}$$

Conversely, taking moments about T,

$$M = Cjd = \frac{bkd}{2} f_c jd = \frac{bd^2}{2} kjf_c \tag{2.17}$$

from which the concrete stress is

$$f_c = \frac{M}{\frac{1}{2}bd^2kj} \tag{2.18}$$

From Fig. 2.8*b* it is seen that $jd = d - kd/3$, or

$$j = 1 - \frac{k}{3} \tag{2.19}$$

Example The beam of the preceding example is subject to a bending moment $M = 80$ ft-kips (rather than 40 ft-kips as previously). Calculate the relevant properties and stresses.

If the section were to remain uncracked, the tension stress in the concrete would now be twice its previous value, that is, 748 ksi. Since this exceeds by far the modulus of rupture of the given concrete (450 psi), cracks will have formed, and the analysis must be adapted appropriately. Equation (2.13), with the known quantities b, n, and A_s inserted, gives the distance to the neutral axis kd = 7.97 in., or $k = 7.97/23 = 0.347$. From Eq. (2.19), $j = 1 - 0.347/3 = 0.885$.

With these values the steel stress is obtained from Eq. (2.16) as $f_s = 20{,}100$ psi, and the maximum concrete stress from Eq. (2.18) as $f_c = 1175$ psi.

Comparing the results with the pertinent values for the same beam when subject to one-half the moment, as previously calculated, one notices: (1) The neutral plane has migrated upward so that its distance from the top fiber has changed from 13.3 in. to 7.97 in.; (2) even though the bending moment has only been doubled, the steel stress has increased from 2890 psi to 20,100 psi, or about 7 times, and the concrete compression stress has increased from 425 psi to 1175 psi, or 2.7 times; (3) the moment of inertia of the cracked transformed section is easily computed to be 6730 in.^{4}, as compared to 15,030 in.^{4} for the uncracked section. This affects the magnitude of the deflection, as discussed in Art. 2.7. Thus it is seen how radical is the influence of the formation of tension cracks on the behavior of reinforced-concrete beams.

e. Ultimate strength, general analysis It is of interest in structural practice to calculate those stresses and deformations which occur in a structure in service under design load. For reinforced-concrete beams this can be done by the methods just presented, which assume elastic behavior of both materials. It is equally if not more important that the structural engineer be able to predict with satisfactory accuracy the ultimate strength of his structure or structural member. By making this strength larger by an appropriate amount than the largest loads which can be expected during the lifetime of the structure, an adequate margin of safety is assured. Until recent times, methods based on elastic analysis, such as those just presented or variations thereof, have been used for this purpose. It is clear, however, that at or near the ultimate load stresses are no longer proportional to strains. In regard to axial compression this has been discussed in detail in Art. 2.2, and in regard to bending it has been pointed out that at high loads, close to the ultimate, the distribution of stresses and strains is that of Fig. 2.5*f* rather than the elastic distribution of Fig. 2.5*e*. More realistic methods of analysis, based on actual inelastic rather than assumed elastic behavior of the materials and on results of extremely extensive experimental research, have been developed in recent years to predict the ultimate strength. They are used increasingly in structural-design practice.

If the distribution of concrete compression stresses at or near ultimate load (Fig. 2.5*f*) had a well-defined and invariable shape—parabolic, trapezoidal, or otherwise—it would be possible to derive a completely rational theory of ultimate bending strength, just as the theory of elastic bending with its known triangular shape of stress distribution (Figs. 2.4*b* and 2.5*c* and *e*) is straightforward and rational. Actually, inspection of Figs. 1.3 and 2.2, and of many more concrete stress-strain curves which have been published, shows that the geometrical shape of the stress distribution is quite varied and depends on a number of factors, such as the cylinder strength and the rate and duration of loading. For this and other reasons, a wholly rational flexural theory for reinforced concrete has not yet been developed (Refs. 2.2, 2.3). Present methods of analysis, therefore, are based in part on known laws of mechanics, supplemented, where needed, by extensive test information.

Let Fig. 2.9 represent the distribution of internal stresses and strains when the beam is about to fail. One desires a method to calculate that moment M'_u (ultimate moment) at which the beam will fail either by tension yielding of the steel or by crushing of the concrete in the outer compression fiber. For the first mode of failure the criterion is that the steel stress equal the yield point, $f_s = f_y$. It has been mentioned before that an exact criterion for concrete compression failure is not yet known, but that for rectangular beams strains of 0.003 to 0.004 in. per in. have been measured immediately preceding failure. If one assumes, slightly conservatively, that the concrete is about to crush when the maximum strain reaches 0.003, then comparison with a great many tests of beams and columns of a considerable variety of shapes and conditions of loading shows that a satisfactorily accurate and safe prediction of ultimate strength can be made (Ref. 2.4). In addition to these two criteria (yielding of the steel at a stress of f_y and crushing of the concrete at a strain of 0.003), it is not really necessary to know the exact shape of the concrete stress distribution in Fig. 2.9. What is necessary is to know, for a given distance c of the neutral axis, (1) the total resultant compression force C in the concrete and (2) its vertical location, i.e., its distance from the outer compression fiber.

In a rectangular beam the area which is in compression is bc, and the total compression force on this area can be expressed as $C = f_{av}bc$, where f_{av} is the average compression stress on the area bc. Evidently, the average compression stress which can be developed before failure occurs becomes larger the higher the cylinder strength f'_c of the particular con-

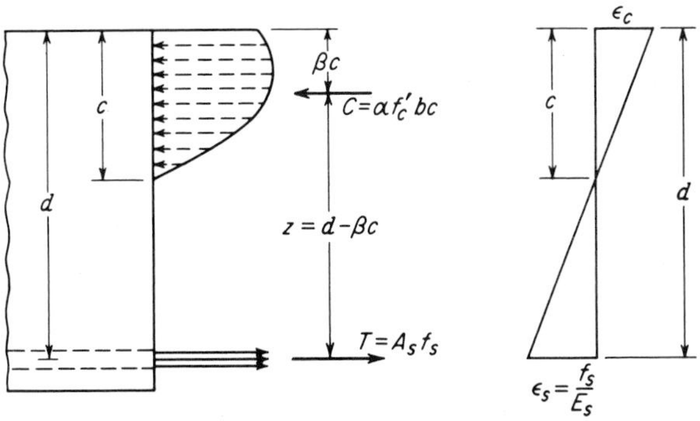

Fig. 2.9 Stress distribution at ultimate load.

crete. Let

$$\alpha = \frac{f_{av}}{f'_c} \tag{2.20}$$

Then

$$C = \alpha f'_c bc \tag{2.21}$$

For a given distance c to the neutral axis, the location of C can be defined as some fraction β of this distance. Thus, as indicated in Fig. 2.9, for a concrete of given strength it is only necessary to know α and β in order to define completely the effect of the concrete compression stresses.

Extensive direct measurements, as well as indirect evaluation of numerous beam tests, have shown that the following values for α and β are satisfactorily accurate (see Ref. 2.4, where α is designated as k_1k_3, and β as k_2):

α equals 0.72 for $f'_c \leq 4000$ psi and decreases by 0.04 for every 1000 psi above 4000.

β equals 0.425 for $f'_c \leq 4000$ psi, and decreases by 0.025 for every 1000 psi above 4000.

The decrease in α and β for high-strength concretes is related to the fact that such concretes are more brittle, i.e., show a more sharply curved stress-strain plot with a smaller near-horizontal portion (see Fig. 1.3). Figure 2.10 shows these simple relations.

If this experimental information is accepted, the ultimate strength can be calculated from the laws of equilibrium and from the assumption that plane cross sections remain plane. Equilibrium requires that

$$C = T \qquad \text{or} \qquad \alpha f'_c bc = A_s f_s \tag{2.22}$$

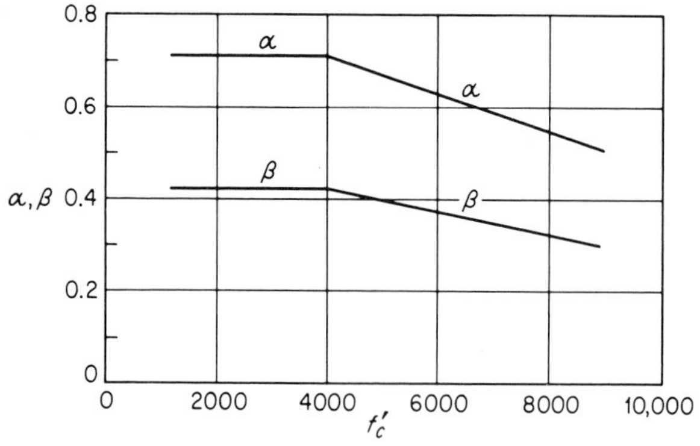

Fig. 2.10

Also, the bending moment, being the couple of the forces C and T, can be written as either

$$M = Tz = A_s f_s(d - \beta c) \tag{2.23}$$

or

$$M = Cz = \alpha f'_c bc(d - \beta c) \tag{2.24}$$

For *tension failure* by yielding of the steel, $f_s = f_y$. Substituting this value in Eq. (2.22), one obtains the distance to the neutral axis:

$$c = \frac{A_s f_y}{\alpha f'_c b} \tag{2.25}$$

It is often convenient to express the steel area nondimensionally as a fraction of the effective area of the section, the so-called *reinforcement ratio:*

$$p = \frac{A_s}{bd} \tag{2.26}$$

Using this quantity, one can also write

$$c = \frac{pf_y}{\alpha f'_c} d \tag{2.25a}$$

as the distance to the neutral axis when tension failure occurs. The ultimate moment M'_u is then obtained from Eq. (2.23), with the value for c just determined, and $f_s = f_y$; that is,

$$M'_u = A_s f_y d \left(1 - \frac{\beta f_y}{\alpha f'_c} p\right) \tag{2.27}$$

With the specific, experimentally obtained values for α and β given previously, this becomes

$$M'_u = A_s f_y d \left(1 - 0.59 \frac{f_y}{f'_c} p\right) \tag{2.27a}$$

On the other hand, for *compression failure* the criterion is that the compression strain in the concrete become $\epsilon_c = 0.003$, as previously discussed. The steel stress f_s, not having reached the yield point, is proportional to the steel strain ϵ_s; that is, according to Hooke's law,

$$\epsilon_s = \frac{f_s}{E_s}$$

From the strain distribution of Fig. 2.9, the distance to the neutral axis is obtained by evaluating the similar triangles and is

$$c = \frac{\epsilon_c}{\epsilon_s + \epsilon_c} d = \frac{0.003}{f_s/E_s + 0.003} d \tag{2.28}$$

The ultimate moment of a beam sufficiently heavily reinforced so that failure occurs by compression in the concrete can then be obtained by using the value of c from Eq. (2.28) in Eq. (2.24).

It was noted that compression failure occurs explosively and without warning. For this reason it is good practice to keep the amount of reinforcement sufficiently small so that, should the member be overstressed, it will give adequate warning before failing in a gradual manner by yielding of the steel, rather than by crushing of the concrete. This can be done by keeping the reinforcement ratio $p = A_s/bd$ below a certain limiting value. This value, the so-called *balanced steel ratio* p_b, represents that amount of reinforcement necessary to make the beam fail by crushing of the concrete at the same load which causes the steel to yield. But this means that the neutral axis must be so located that at the load at which the steel starts yielding the concrete reaches its assumed breaking strain of 0.003. Correspondingly, equating the right sides of Eqs. (2.25a) and (2.28) and solving for p, one obtains for the balanced steel ratio

$$p_b = \alpha \frac{0.003}{f_y/E_s + 0.003} \frac{f_c'}{f_y} \tag{2.29}$$

In a well-designed member the actual steel ratio $p = A_s/bd$ is kept well below the balanced ratio p_b.

Example Determine the ultimate moment M_u' at which the beam of the previous example will fail.

For this beam the steel ratio $p = A_s/bd = 2.35/10 \times 23 = 0.0102$. The balanced steel ratio [Eq. (2.29)] is found to be 0.0373. Since the amount of steel in the beam is less than that which would cause failure by crushing of the concrete, the beam will fail in tension by yielding of the steel. Its ultimate moment, from Eq. (2.27a), is found to be

$$\begin{aligned} M_u' &= 2.35 \times 40{,}000 \times 23[1 - 0.59(40{,}000/3000)0.0102] \\ &= 1.985{,}000 \text{ in.-lb} = 165 \text{ ft-kips} \end{aligned}$$

It is interesting to note that when the beam reaches its ultimate strength, the distance to its neutral axis, from Eq. (2.25a), is

$$c = \frac{0.0102 \times 40{,}000}{0.72 \times 3{,}000} 23 = 4.35 \text{ in.}$$

In previous calculations it was found that at low loads, when the concrete had not yet cracked in tension, the neutral axis was located at a distance of 13.3 in. from the compression edge; at higher loads, when the tension concrete was cracked but stresses were still sufficiently small to be elastic, this distance was 7.97 in. Immediately before the beam fails, as has just been shown, this distance has further decreased to 4.35 in. This migration of the neutral axis toward the compression edge as load is increased is a graphic illustration of the differences among the various stages of behavior through which a reinforced-concrete beam passes as its load is increased from zero to that value which causes it to fail.

f. Ultimate strength, equivalent rectangular stress distribution The preceding method of calculating the ultimate strength, derived from basic concepts of structural mechanics and pertinent experimental research information, also applies to situations other than the case of rectangular beams reinforced on the tension side. It can be used and gives valid answers for beams of other cross-sectional shapes, reinforced in other manners, and for members subject not only to simple bending, but also to the simultaneous action of bending and axial force (compression or tension). However, the pertinent equations for these more complex cases become increasingly cumbersome and lengthy. What is more important, it becomes increasingly difficult for the designer to visualize the physical basis for his design methods and formulas; this could lead to a blind reliance on formulas, with a resulting lack of actual understanding. This is not only undesirable on general grounds but, practically, is more likely to lead to numerical errors in design work than the situation in which the designer at all times has a clear picture of the physical situation in the member which he is dimensioning or analyzing. Fortunately it is possible, essentially by a conceptual trick, to formulate the ultimate-strength analysis of reinforced-concrete members in a different manner which gives the same answers as does the general analysis just developed, but which is much more easily visualized and much more easily applied to cases of greater complexity than that of the simple rectangular beam. Its consistency is shown below, and its application to more complex cases has been checked against the results of a vast number of tests on a great variety of types of members and conditions of loading (Ref. 2.4).

It was noted in the preceding section that the actual geometrical shape of the concrete compression-stress distribution varies considerably and that, in fact, one need not know this shape exactly, provided one does know two things: (1) the magnitude C of the resultant of the concrete compression stresses and (2) the location of this resultant. Information on these two quantities was obtained from the results of experimental research and expressed in the two parameters α and β.

Evidently, then, one can think of the actual complex stress distribution as replaced by a fictitious one of some simple geometrical shape, provided that this fictitious distribution results in the same total compression force C applied at the same location as in the actual member when it is on the point of failure. Historically, a number of simplified, fictitious equivalent stress distributions have been proposed by various investigators in various countries. The one which is finding general acceptance in this

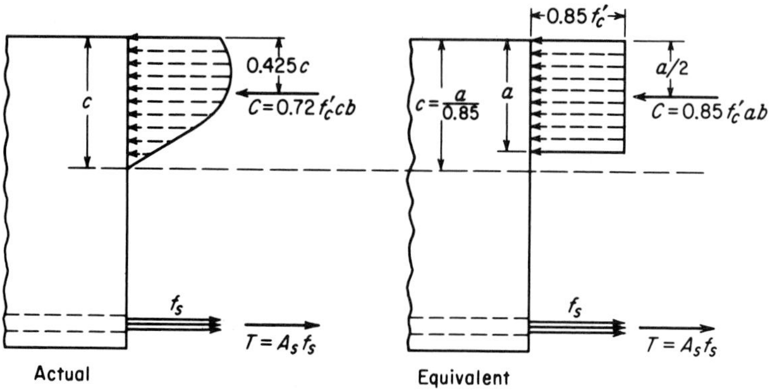

***Fig.* 2.11** Actual and equivalent rectangular stress distributions at ultimate load (for f_c' less than 4000 psi).

country was first proposed by C. S. Whitney and subsequently elaborated and checked experimentally by others (see, e.g., Ref. 2.4). For concrete with cylinder strength f_c' not exceeding 4000 psi, an actual stress distribution and the fictitious equivalent distribution are shown in Fig. 2.11.

It is seen that the actual distribution is replaced by a fictitious equivalent one of simple rectangular outline. The intensity of this uniform and constant equivalent compression stress is $0.85f_c'$, and it is thought of as acting over a part of the section of depth $a = 0.85c$, where c is the distance to the actual neutral axis. It is in no way maintained that the compression stresses are actually distributed in this most unlikely manner. It is maintained, however that this equivalent distribution gives the answers just derived for the actual situation. Of this one can easily convince oneself. In a rectangular beam of width b the equivalent uniform compression stress $0.85f_c'$ acts on an area ab, so that the total compression force is

$$C = 0.85f_c'ab \tag{2.30}$$

If one expresses the depth a of the rectangular stress block in terms of the distance c to the neutral axis as assumed, that is, $a = 0.85c$, one obtains for the compression force $C = 0.85f_c' \times 0.85c \times b = 0.72f_c'cb$, which is the same as Eq. (2.21) for $\alpha = 0.72$. Further, since the centroid of a rectangle is at middepth, the distance from the compression edge to C is evidently $a/2$. Again expressing a in terms of c as above, one obtains the distance to the compression resultant as $0.5 \times 0.85c = 0.425c$, which is the correct distance for $\beta = 0.425$.

Since the chosen equivalent rectangular stress distribution satisfies the stated requirements (1) and (2), it will give exactly the same answers as were derived previously. This is so for f_c' not exceeding 4000 psi because, in this range of concrete strengths, the parameters α and β are constants equal, respectively, to 0.72 and 0.425. For concretes of higher strength it has been stated that α and β decrease because of the greater brittleness of such concretes. In the equivalent rectangular stress distribution, this is reflected in the following stipulation:

$$a/c = k_1 = 0.85 \text{ for } f'_c \leq 4000 \text{ psi and decreases by 0.05 for every 1000 psi above 4000} \tag{2.31}$$

This equivalent rectangular stress distribution can be used for deriving the equations which have been developed in the previous section. The failure criteria, of course, are the same as before: yielding of the steel at $f_s = f_y$ or crushing of the concrete at $\epsilon_c = 0.003$. More important, however, because the rectangular stress block is easily visualized and its geometrical properties are extremely simple, many calculations are conveniently carried out directly without reference to formally derived equations.

Example Using the equivalent rectangular stress distribution, calculate directly the ultimate strength of the previously analyzed beam.

The distribution of stresses, internal forces, and strains is as shown in Fig. 2.12. The depth a of the equivalent stress block is found from the equilibrium condition $C = T$. Hence $ab \times 0.85f'_c = A_sf_y$, or $a \times 10 \times 2550 = 2.35 \times 40{,}000$, from which $a = 3.70$ in. The distance to the neutral axis, by the definition of the rectangular stress block, is $c = a/0.85 = 3.70/0.85 = 4.35$ in. One way of determining whether the strength of the beam is governed by yielding of the steel or by crushing of the concrete is to calculate whether the concrete strain in the top fiber is smaller or larger than 0.003 at the instant the steel starts yielding. At that point the strain in the steel is $\epsilon_s = f_y/E_s = 40{,}000/29{,}000{,}000 = 0.00138$. From the similar triangles of the strain distribution, $\epsilon_c = \epsilon_sc/(d - c) = 0.00138(4.35/18.65) = 0.00032$. This value is smaller than the assumed crushing strain of the concrete, and hence failure will be initiated

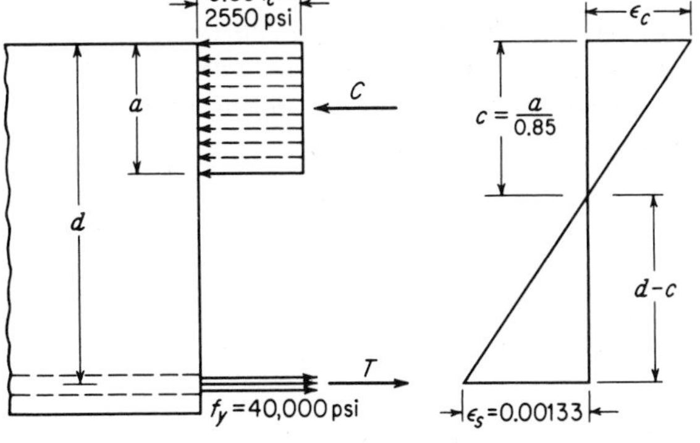

Fig. 2.12

by yielding of the steel. The ultimate moment, then, is $M'_u = T(d - a/2) = 2.35 \times 40{,}000(23.0 - 1.85) = 1.985{,}000$ in.-lb = 165 ft-kips.

If one wanted to determine the balanced steel ratio p_b for the given beam, one could proceed as follows: At simultaneous yielding of the steel and crushing of the concrete, it is known that the two pertinent strains are $\epsilon_s = 0.00138$ and $\epsilon_c = 0.003$. Hence, from the similar triangles of the strain distribution, $c/(d - c) = 0.003/0.00138$, from which $c = (3/4.38)d$, and $a = 0.85c = 0.85(3/4.38)23 = 13.4$ in. Hence the tensile force, equal to the compression force, is $T = C = 0.85f'_c ab = 2550 \times 13.4 \times 10 = 342{,}000$ lb. From this the balanced steel ratio is $p_b = A_s/bd = (T/f_y)/bd = 342{,}000/40{,}000 \times 10 \times 23 = 0.0371$. The results of this simple and direct numerical analysis, based on the equivalent rectangular stress distribution, are identical with those previously determined from the general ultimate-strength analysis of beams.

PROBLEM

A simple beam of 20-ft span has the cross section of the preceding examples, 10 × 25 in., and carries a uniform load of 1900 lb per ft in addition to its own weight. (*a*) Check whether this beam, if reinforced with three No. 8 bars as in the preceding examples, is adequate to carry this load with a minimum factor of safety against failure of 1.85. A different way of stating the same requirement is to stipulate that the ultimate strength of the beam shall be at least equal to 1.85 times the design load. If this requirement is not met, select a three-bar reinforcement of diameter adequate to provide this safety. (*b*) Determine the maximum stress in the steel and in the concrete under working load, i.e., when the beam carries its own weight and the specified uniform design load. (*c*) Will the beam show hairline cracks on the tension side under working load? As before, $f'_c = 3000$ psi, $f_y = 40{,}000$ psi. Use Table 2 of Appendix B for steel areas; assume a unit weight of 150 lb per ft³ for reinforced concrete.

(*Note:* Throughout the remainder of this chapter, additional problems frequently refer to this same beam and loading. To avoid repetitive calculations, the student is advised to retain his computation sheets until reaching the end of the chapter.)

2.5 Shear and Diagonal Tension *a. Homogeneous elastic beams*

The stresses acting in homogeneous beams were briefly reviewed in Art. 2.4*a*. It was pointed out that when the material is elastic (stresses proportional to strains), shear stresses

$$v = \frac{VQ}{Ib} \tag{2.12}$$

act in any section in addition to the bending stresses

$$f = \frac{My}{I} \tag{2.10}$$

except for those locations at which the shear force V happens to be zero.

The role of shear stresses is easily visualized by the performance under load of the laminated beam of Fig. 2.13; it consists of two rectangular pieces bonded together along their contact surface. If the adhesive is strong enough, the member will deform as one single beam, as shown in Fig. 2.13*a*. On the other hand, if the adhesive is weak, the two pieces will separate and slide relative to each other as shown in Fig. 2.13*b*. Evidently, then, when the adhesive is effective, there are forces or stresses acting in it which prevent this sliding or shearing. These horizontal shear stresses are shown in Fig. 2.13*c* as they act, separately, on the top and bottom pieces. The same stresses occur in horizontal planes in single-piece beams; they are different in intensity at different distances from the neutral axis.

Figure 2.13*d* shows a differential length of a single-piece rectangular beam acted upon by a shear force of magnitude V. Upward translation is prevented, i.e., vertical equilibrium is provided, by the vertical shear stresses v. Their average value is equal to the shear force divided by the cross-sectional area, $v_{avg} = V/ab$, but their intensity varies over the depth of the section. As is easily computed from Eq. (2.12), the shear stress is zero at the outer fibers and has a maximum of $1.5v_{avg}$ at the neutral axis, the variation being parabolic as shown. Other values and distributions are found for other shapes of the cross section, the shear stress always being zero at the outer fibers and of maximum value at the neutral axis.

If a small square element located at the neutral axis of such a beam

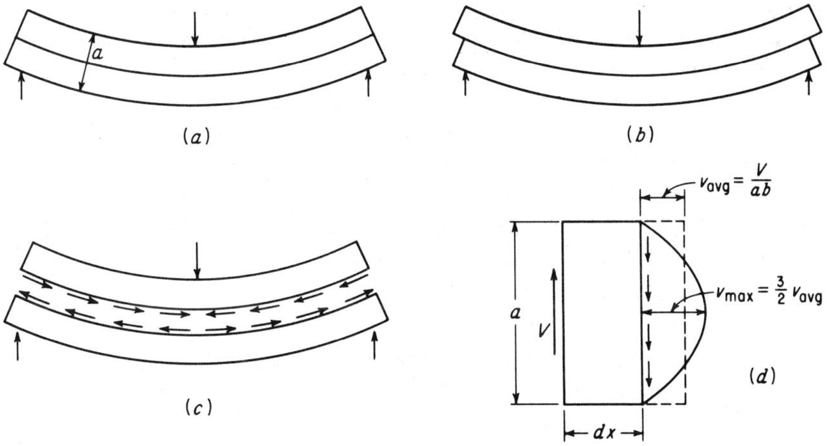

Fig. 2.13 Shear in homogeneous rectangular beam.

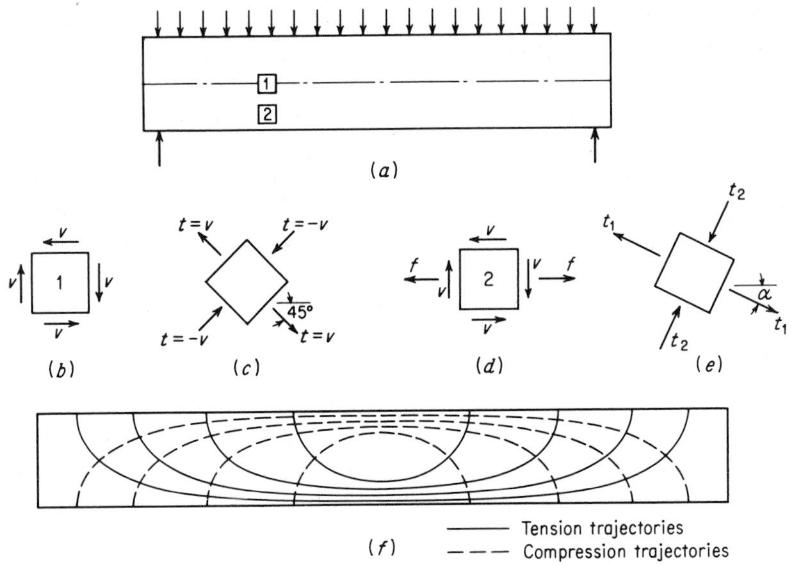

***Fig.* 2.14** Stress trajectories in homogeneous rectangular beam.

is isolated as in Fig. 2.14*b*, the vertical shear stresses on it, equal and opposite on the two faces for reasons of equilibrium, act as shown. However, if these were the only stresses present, the element would not be in equilibrium; it would spin. Therefore, on the two horizontal faces there exist equilibrating horizontal shear stresses of the same magnitude. That is, at any point in the beam the horizontal shear stresses of Fig. 2.14*b* are equal in magnitude to the vertical shear stresses of Fig. 2.13*d*.

It is proved in any strength-of-materials text that, on an element cut at 45°, these shear stresses combine in such a manner that their effect is as shown in Fig. 2.14*c*. That is, the action of the two pairs of shear stresses on the vertical and horizontal faces is the same as that of two pairs of normal stresses, one tension and one compression, acting on the 45° faces and of numerical value equal to that of the shear stresses. If an element of the beam is considered which is located neither at the neutral axis nor at the outer edges, then its vertical faces are subject not only to the shear stresses, but also to the familiar bending stresses whose magnitude is given by Eq. (2.10) (Fig. 2.14*d*). The six stresses which now act on the element can again be combined into a pair of inclined compression stresses and a pair of inclined tension stresses which act at right angles to each other. They are known as *principal* stresses (Fig. 2.14*e*). Their value, as was mentioned in Art. 2.4*a*, is given by

$$t = \frac{f}{2} \pm \sqrt{\frac{f^2}{4} + v^2} \tag{2.9}$$

and their inclination α by $\tan \alpha = 2v/f$.

Since the magnitudes of the shear stresses v and the bending stresses f change both along the beam and vertically with distance from the neutral axis, the inclinations as well as the magnitudes of the resulting principal stresses t also vary from one place to another. Figure 2.14*f* shows, for a rectangular beam uniformly loaded, the inclinations of these principal stresses. That is, these stress trajectories are lines which, at any point, are drawn in that direction in which the particular principal stress, tension or compression, acts at that point. Is is seen that the principal stresses which result from the shear and tension stresses in a beam are always inclined at 45° to the neutral axis. In the vicinity of the outer fibers they are horizontal near midspan.

An important point which follows from this discussion is the following: Tension stresses, which are of particular concern in view of the low tensile strength of the concrete, are not confined to the horizontal bending stresses f which are caused by bending alone. Tension stresses of various inclinations and magnitudes, resulting from shear alone (at the neutral axis) or from the combined action of shear and bending, exist in all parts of a beam and can impair its integrity if not adequately provided for. It is for this reason that the inclined tension stresses, known as *diagonal tension*, must be carefully considered in reinforced-concrete design.

b. Reinforced-concrete beams without shear reinforcement The discussion of shear in a homogeneous elastic beam applies very closely to a plain concrete beam without reinforcement. As the load is increased in such a beam, a tension crack will form where the tension stresses are largest and will immediately cause the beam to fail. Except for beams of very unusual proportions, the largest tension stresses are those caused at the outer fiber by bending alone, at the section of maximum bending moment. In this case, shear has little, if any, influence on the strength of a beam.

However, when tension reinforcement is provided, the situation is quite different. Even though tension cracks form in the concrete, the required flexural tension strength is furnished by the steel, and much higher loads can be carried. Shear stresses increase proportionally to the loads. In consequence, diagonal tension stresses of significant intensity are created in regions of high shear forces, chiefly close to the supports. The longitudinal tension reinforcement has been so calculated and placed that it is chiefly effective in resisting longitudinal tension near the tension

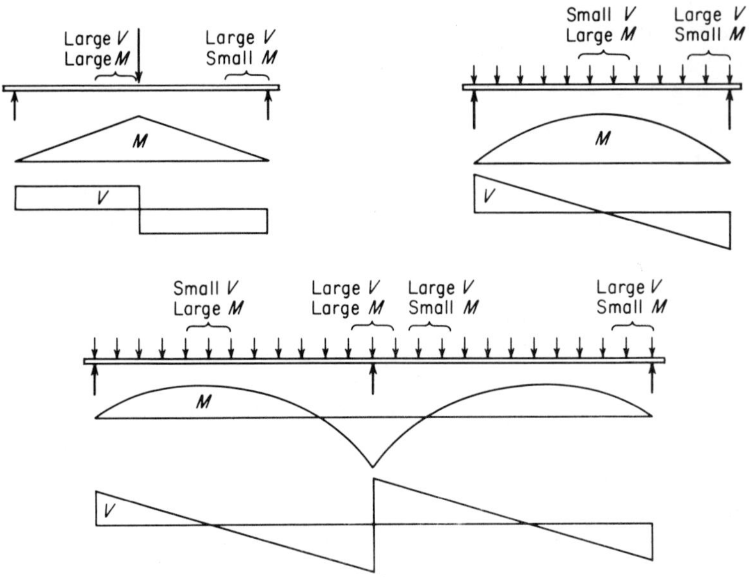

***Fig.* 2.15** Typical locations of critical combinations of shear and moment.

face. It does not reinforce the tensionally weak concrete against those diagonal tension stresses which occur elsewhere, caused by shear alone or by the combined effect of shear and flexure. Eventually these stresses attain magnitudes sufficient to open additional tension cracks in a direction perpendicular to the local tension stress. These are known as *diagonal* cracks, in distinction to the vertical flexural cracks. The latter occur in regions of large moments, the former in regions in which the shear forces are high. Both types of cracks are shown in Fig. 2.16. In beams in which no reinforcement is provided to counteract the formation of large diagonal tension cracks, their appearance has far-reaching and generally detrimental effects. For this reason methods of predicting the loads at which these cracks will form are desired.

CRITERIA FOR FORMATION OF DIAGONAL CRACKS. It is seen from Eq. (2.9) that the diagonal tension stresses t represent the combined effect of the shear stresses v and the bending stresses f. These, in turn, are, respectively, proportional to the shear force V and the bending moment M at the particular location in the beam [Eqs. (2.10) and (2.12)]. Depending on configuration, support conditions, and load distribution, at a given location in a beam one may find a large moment combining with a small shear force, or the reverse, or large or small values for both shear and moment. Evidently, the relative values of M and V will affect the magnitude as well as the direction of the diagonal tension stresses. Figure 2.15

shows a few typical beams and their moment and shear diagrams and draws attention to locations at which various combinations of high or low V and M occur.

At a location of large shear force V and small bending moment M there will be little flexural cracking, if any, prior to the development of a diagonal tension crack. Consequently, the average shear stress prior to crack formation is

$$v = \frac{V}{bd} \tag{2.32}$$

The exact distribution of these shear stresses over the depth of the cross section is not known. It cannot be computed from Eq. (2.12) because this equation does not account for the influence of the reinforcement, and because concrete is not an elastic homogeneous material. The value computed from Eq. (2.32) must, therefore, be regarded merely as a measure of the average intensity of shear stresses in the section. The maximum value, which occurs at the neutral axis, will exceed this average by an unknown but moderate amount.

If flexural stresses are negligibly small at the particular location, the diagonal tension stresses, as in Fig. 2.14*b* and *c*, are inclined at about 45° and are numerically equal to the shear stresses, with a maximum at the neutral axis. Consequently, diagonal cracks form mostly at or near the neutral axis and propagate from that location as shown in Fig. 2.16*a*. In this situation a diagonal tension crack can be expected to form when the diagonal tension stress in the vicinity of the neutral axis becomes equal to the tension strength of the concrete. The former, as was indicated, is of the order of and somewhat larger than $v = V/bd$; the latter, as discussed in Art. 1.8, varies from about $3.5\sqrt{f'_c}$ to about $5\sqrt{f'_c}$. An evaluation of a very large number of beam tests is in fair agreement with this reasoning (Ref. 2.5). It was found that in regions with large shear and small moment, diagonal tension cracks form at an average or nominal shear stress v_{cr} of about

$$v_{cr} = \frac{V_{cr}}{bd} = 3.5\sqrt{f'_c} \tag{2.33a}$$

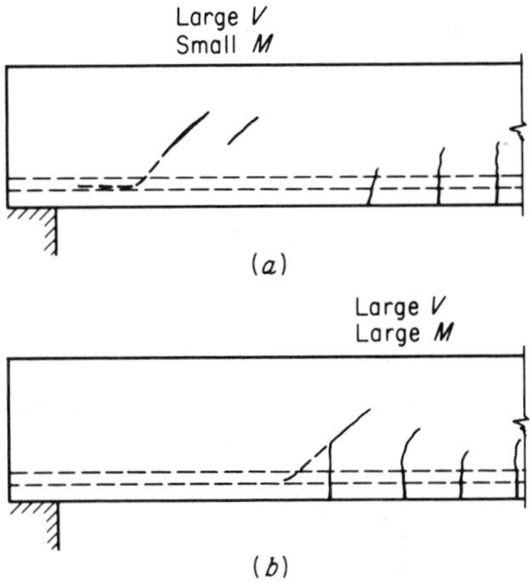

Fig. 2.16 Flexural and diagonal tension cracks.

where V_{cr} is that shear force at which the formation of the crack was observed.[1]

The situation is different where both the shear force and the bending moment have large values. At such locations, in a well-proportioned and reinforced beam, flexural tension cracks form first. Their width and length is well controlled and kept small by the presence of longitudinal reinforcement. However, when the diagonal tension stress at the upper end of one or more of these cracks exceeds the tensile strength of the concrete, the crack bends in a diagonal direction and continues to grow in length and width (see Fig. 2.16*b*).

It is evident that at the instant at which a diagonal tension crack of this type develops, the average shear stress is larger than that given by Eq. (2.32). This is so because the preexisting tension crack has reduced the area of uncracked concrete which is available to resist shear to a value smaller than that of the uncracked area bd used in Eq. (2.32). The amount of this reduction will vary, depending on the unpredictable length of the preexisting flexural tension crack. Furthermore, the simultaneous bending stress f combines with the shear stress v to further increase the diagonal tension stress t [see Eq. (2.9)]. No way has been found to calculate reliable values of the diagonal tension stress under these conditions, and recourse must be had to test results.

A large number of beam tests have been evaluated for this purpose (Ref. 2.5). They show that in the presence of large moments (for which adequate longitudinal reinforcement has been provided) the nominal shear stress at which diagonal tension cracks form and propagate is conservatively given by

$$v_{cr} = \frac{V_{cr}}{bd} = 1.9\sqrt{f'_c} \tag{2.33b}$$

Comparison with Eq. (2.33*a*) shows that large bending moments can reduce the shear force at which diagonal cracks form to roughly one-half the value at which they would form if the moment were zero or nearly so. This is in qualitative agreement with the discussion just given.

It is evident, then, that the shear at which diagonal cracks develop depends on the ratio of shear force to bending moment, V/M, or, in non-dimensional terms, on Vd/M. Equation (2.33*a*) gives the cracking shear for very large values of Vd/M, and Eq. (2.33*b*) for very small values.

[1] Actually, diagonal tension cracks form at places where a compression stress acts in addition to and perpendicular to the diagonal tension stress, as shown in Fig. 2.14*c* and *e*. The crack, therefore, occurs at a location of biaxial stress, rather than uniaxial tension. However, the effect of this simultaneous compression stress on the cracking strength appears to be small.

Moderate values of Vd/M must be expected to result in magnitudes of v_{cr} intermediate between these extremes. Again, from evaluations of large numbers of tests (Ref. 2.5), it has been found that the nominal shear stress at which diagonal tension cracking develops is conservatively predicted by

$$v_{cr} = \frac{V_{cr}}{bd} = \left(1.9 + 2500 \frac{pVd}{M\sqrt{f'_c}}\right)\sqrt{f'_c} \leq 3.5\sqrt{f'_c} \tag{2.33}$$

where $p = A_s/bd$ as before, and 2500 is an empirical constant in psi units. A graph of this relation is given in Fig. 2.17.

Apart from this influence of Vd/M, it is seen from Eq. (2.33) that increasing amounts of tension reinforcement, i.e., increasing values of the steel ratio p, have a beneficial effect in that they increase the shear at which diagonal cracks develop. This is so because larger amounts of longitudinal steel result in smaller and narrower flexural tension cracks prior to the formation of diagonal cracking, leaving a larger area of uncracked concrete available to resist shear. [For more details on the development of Eq. (2.33), see Ref. 2.5.]

BEHAVIOR OF DIAGONALLY CRACKED BEAMS. In regard to flexural, as distinct from diagonal, tension, it was explained in Art. 2.4 that cracks on the tension side of a beam are permitted to occur and are in no way detrimental to the strength of the member. One might expect a similar situation in regard to diagonal cracking caused chiefly by shear. The analogy, however, is not that simple. Flexural tension cracks are harmless only because adequate longitudinal reinforcement has been provided to resist those flexural tension stresses which the cracked concrete is no longer able to transmit. In contrast, the beams now being discussed, while furnished with the usual longitudinal reinforcement, are not equipped with any other reinforcement to offset the effects of diagonal cracking. Such members, without shear or "web" reinforcement, are frequently used. The very fact, however, that no shear reinforcement is provided makes the diagonal cracks much more decisive in subsequent performance and strength of the beam than the flexural cracks.

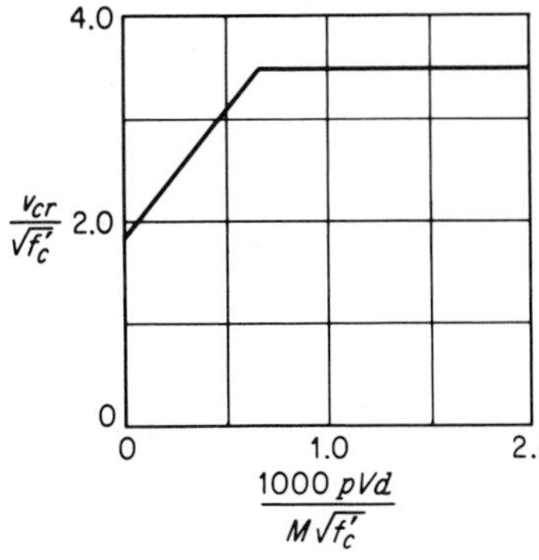

Fig. 2.17

Two types of behavior have been observed in the many tests on which present knowledge is based: (1) The diagonal crack, once formed, spreads either immediately or at only slightly higher load, traversing the entire

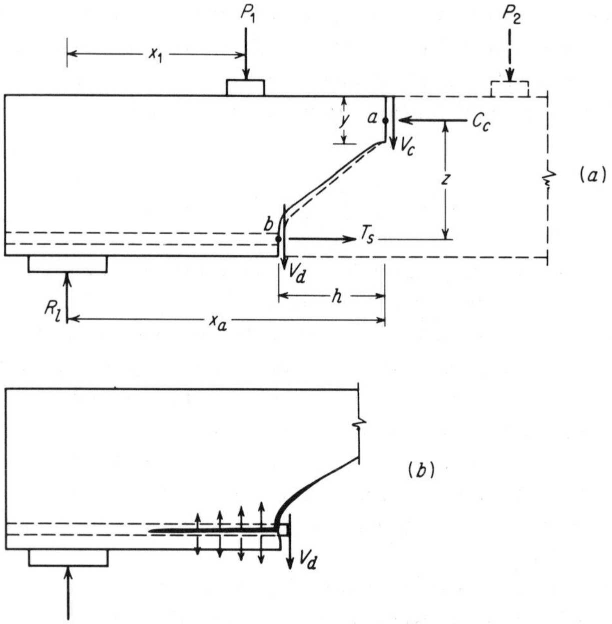

Fig. 2.18 Forces at diagonal crack in beam without web reinforcement.

beam from the tension reinforcement to the compression face, splitting it in two and failing the beam. This process is sudden and without warning and occurs chiefly in the shallower beams, i.e., beams with span-depth ratios of about 8 or more. (2) The diagonal crack, once formed, spreads toward and partially into the compression zone but stops short of penetrating to the compression face. In this case no sudden collapse occurs, and the failure load is usually significantly higher than that at which the diagonal crack first formed. This behavior is chiefly observed in the deeper beams with smaller span-depth ratios and will be analyzed now.

Figure 2.18 shows a portion of a beam, arbitrarily loaded, in which a diagonal tension crack has formed. Consider the part of the beam to the left of the crack, shown in solid lines. There is an external upward shear force V_{ext} acting on this portion, which, for the particular loading shown, happens to be

$$V_{ext} = R_l - P_1$$

The crack cannot transmit any forces, and so the only internal vertical forces are those acting in the uncracked portion of the concrete, V_c, and in or across the longitudinal steel, V_d. Thus, the internal shear force is

$$V_{int} = V_c + V_d$$

Equilibrium requires $V_{int} = V_{ext}$ so that the part of the shear resisted by the uncracked concrete is

$$V_c = V_{ext} - V_d \tag{2.34}$$

In a beam provided with longitudinal reinforcement only, the portion of the shear force resisted by the steel, in dowel action as it were, is usually quite small. In fact, the reinforcing rods on which the dowel force V_d acts are supported against vertical displacement chiefly by the thin concrete layer below. The bearing pressure caused by V_d creates, in this concrete, vertical tension stresses as shown in Fig. 2.18*b*. Because of these stresses, diagonal cracks often result in splitting of the concrete along the tension reinforcement, as shown. Correspondingly, it is likely that most of the shear is resisted by the uncracked portion of concrete at the head of the diagonal crack, or

$$V_c \cong V_{ext} \tag{2.34a}$$

Next, consider moments about point *a* at the intersection of V_c and C_c; the external moment for the loading shown happens to be

$$(M_{ext})_a = R_l x_a - P_1(x_a - x_1)$$

and the internal moment is

$$(M_{int})_a = (T_s)_b z + (V_d)_b h$$

Here *h* is the horizontal projection of the diagonal crack, and the designations $(T_s)_b$ and $(V_d)_b$ are meant to emphasize that these two forces in the steel act at point *b* rather than vertically below point *a*. Again, equilibrium requires that $(M_{int})_a = (M_{ext})_a$, so that the longitudinal tension in the reinforcement at *b* is

$$(T_s)_b = \frac{(M_{ext})_a}{z} - \frac{(V_d)_b h}{z} \tag{2.35}$$

Neglecting the dowel force V_d as being only a small fraction of the tension force T_s, one has, with very little error,

$$(T_s)_b \cong \frac{(M_{ext})_a}{z} \tag{2.35a}$$

The formation of the diagonal crack, then, is seen to produce the following redistribution of internal forces and stresses:

1. In the vertical section through *a* the average shear stress before crack formation was V_{ext}/bd [see Eq. (2.32)]. After crack formation, that same shear force is almost entirely resisted by the much smaller area *by*

of the remaining uncracked concrete [see Eq. (2.34*a*) and Fig. 2.18*a*]. Hence, the average shear stress in the concrete has now increased to V_{ext}/by.

2. The diagonal crack, as was described previously, usually rises above the neutral axis and traverses some part of the compression zone before it is arrested by the compression stresses. Consequently, the compression force C_c also acts on an area by smaller than that on which it acted before the crack was formed. Correspondingly, formation of the crack has increased the compression stresses in the remaining uncracked concrete.

3. Prior to diagonal cracking, the tension force in the steel at point b was caused by and was proportional to the bending moment in a vertical section through the same point b. As a consequence of the diagonal crack, however, Eq. (2.35*a*) shows that the tension in the steel at b is now caused by and is proportional to the bending moment at a. Since the moment at a is evidently larger than that at b, formation of the crack has caused a sudden increase in the steel stress at b.

4. The previously described dowel action causes bearing and tension stresses which contribute to the tendency of the concrete to split along the bar toward the nearby support.

If the two materials are capable of resisting these increased stresses, equilibrium will establish itself after internal redistribution, and further load can be applied before failure occurs. Such failure can then develop in various ways. For one, if only enough steel has been provided at b to resist the moment at that section, then the increase of the steel force, in (3) above, will cause the steel to yield because of the larger moment at a, thus failing the beam. If the beam is properly designed to prevent this occurrence, it is usually the concrete at the head of the crack which will eventually crush. This concrete is subject simultaneously to large compression and shear stresses, and this biaxial stress combination is conducive to earlier failure than would take place if either of these stresses were acting alone (Ref. 2.6). Finally, if there is splitting along the reinforcement, it will cause the bond between steel and concrete to weaken to such a degree that the reinforcement may pull loose. This may either be the cause of failure of the beam or, more frequently, may occur simultaneously with crushing of the remaining uncracked concrete.

It was noted earlier that relatively deep beams will usually show continued and increasing resistance after formation of a critical diagonal tension crack, but relatively shallow beams will fail almost immediately upon formation of the crack. The amount of reserve strength, if any, was found to be erratic. In fact, in several test series in which two specimens as identical as one can make them were tested, one failed immediately upon formation of a diagonal crack, while the other reached equilibrium under the described redistribution and failed at a higher load.

For this reason, in modern procedures for designing beams in which no special shear reinforcement is provided, this reserve strength is discounted. Design is based on that shear force V_{cr} or shear stress v_{cr} at which the formation of a diagonal crack must be expected. Thus, Eq. (2.33) has become the criterion for the usable shear strength of such a beam.

PROBLEM

In the problem at the end of Art. 2.4 it was found that a rectangular beam with $b = 10$ in., $t = 25$ in., $d = 23$ in., three No. 9 bars, $f'_c = 3000$ psi, $f_y = 40{,}000$ psi will carry a uniform design load of 1900 lb per ft, plus its own weight with a safety factor slightly larger than the value 1.85 stipulated in that problem. Check whether this beam has a safety factor of at least 2.0 against the formation of diagonal cracks at the indicated load. Decide whether or not shear reinforcement is required. *Explanatory comments:* (*a*) It has been explained that if a beam without web reinforcement fails in shear, collapse is likely to be sudden and complete. On the other hand, if a beam were to be overloaded and to fail in bending, collapse will be gradual and preceded by excessive cracking and deflections which serve as warning of distress. For this reason a larger safety margin is desirable against shear than against flexural failure, as is here stipulated. The detailed manner in which these differential margins are provided in the ACI Code is explained in Chap. 3. (*b*) Tests have shown that diagonal cracks rarely form at a distance from the nearby support smaller than the depth d of the beam, because of the local stress conditions in the immediate vicinity of a support (see also Art. 3.14). For this reason it is now accepted practice that the maximum shear force for which the adequacy of a member must be checked is that acting at a distance d from the face of the support, rather than the larger shear force directly at that face.

c. Reinforced-concrete beams with web reinforcement Economy of design demands, in most cases, that a flexural member be capable of developing its full moment capacity rather than having its strength limited by premature shear failure. This is also desirable in that structures, if overloaded, should not fail in the sudden and explosive manner characteristic of many shear failures, but should show adequate ductility and warning of impending distress. The latter, as was pointed out, obtains for flexural failure caused by yielding of the longitudinal steel, which is preceded by gradual, excessive deflections and noticeable enlargement of cracks. If, then, the available shear strength as given by Eq. (2.33) is not adequate, special shear reinforcement, known as *web reinforcement*, is used to increase this strength.

Web reinforcement may be in either of the two forms shown in Fig. 2.19, or a combination of the two. Figure 2.19*a* shows web reinforcement consisting of vertical stirrups; Fig. 2.19*b* shows inclined bars. The latter

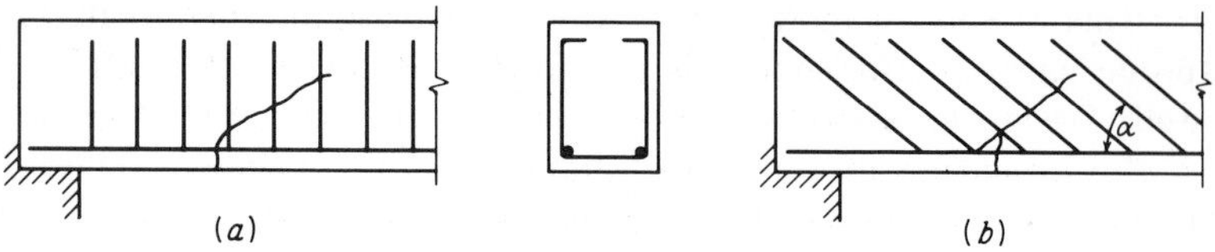

Fig. 2.19

can consist of individual stirrups placed at an angle or part of the longitudinal flexural reinforcement bent up where it is no longer needed to furnish moment resistance. A diagonal crack is shown traversed by a number of web bars.

Web reinforcement has no noticeable effect prior to the formation of diagonal cracks. In fact, measurements show that the web steel is practically free of stress prior to crack formation. After diagonal cracks have developed, web reinforcement augments the shear resistance of a beam in three separate ways: (1) Part of the shear force is resisted by the bars which traverse a particular crack. The mechanism of this added resistance is discussed below. (2) The presence of these same bars restricts the growth of diagonal cracks and reduces their penetration into the compression zone. This leaves more uncracked concrete available at the head of the crack for resisting the combined action of shear and compression, already discussed. (3) As seen in the cross section of Fig. 2.19, the stirrups are so arranged that they tie the longitudinal reinforcement into the main bulk of the concrete. This provides some measure of restraint against the splitting of concrete along the longitudinal reinforcement, shown in Fig. 2.18*b*, and increases the share of the shear force resisted in dowel action.

It will be realized from this description that the behavior, once a crack is formed, is quite complex and dependent in its details on the particulars of crack configuration (length, inclination, and location of the main or critical crack). The latter, in turn, is quite erratic and has, so far, defied purely analytical prediction. For this reason, the concepts which underlie present design practice are not wholly rational. They are based partly on rational analysis, partly on test evidence, and partly on successful long-time experience with structures in which certain procedures for designing web reinforcement have resulted in satisfactory performance. Research in this field, both on plain and web-reinforced members, performed mostly between 1945 and 1960, has furnished important experimental data for recent improvements in shear design and analysis It has not yet resulted in a completely consistent rational analysis of shear behavior.

BEAMS WITH VERTICAL STIRRUPS. The web reinforcement being ineffective in the uncracked beam, the magnitude of the shear force or stress which causes cracking to occur is the same as in a beam without web reinforcement and is given by Eq. (2.33). Most frequently, web reinforcement consists of *vertical stirrups;* the forces acting on the portion of such a beam between the crack and the nearby support are shown on Fig. 2.20. They are the same as those of Fig. 2.18, except that each stirrup traversing the crack exerts a force $A_v f_v$ on the given portion of the beam. Here A_v is the cross-sectional area of the stirrup (in the case of the U-shaped stirrup of Fig. 2.19, it is twice the area of one bar), and f_v is the tension stress in the stirrup. Equilibrium in the vertical direction requires

$$V_c + \sum_n A_v f_v + V_d = V_{ext}$$

where n is the number of stirrups traversing the crack. If s is the stirrup spacing, and h the horizontal projection of the crack, as shown, then

$$n = \frac{h}{s}$$

Prior to failure, part of the load, as before, is carried by the uncracked section at the head of the crack. The dowel force V_d will be disregarded, since it is of uncertain and probably minor value. Further opening of the crack is counteracted by the stirrups until the stress in them has reached the yield point f_y. The large stirrup extensions which occur at that stage permit the crack to open and extend, causing the remaining concrete to fail. Consequently, the stirrup stress being f_y when failure occurs, the ultimate shear force V_u' is

$$V_u' = V_c + nA_v f_y$$

While the share of the total shear carried by the stirrups is known, the shear V_c carried by the uncracked concrete at the head of the crack has yet to be defined. It is assumed in present-day methods that this shear, at failure, is the same as that which caused the diagonal crack to form; i.e.,

$$V_c = V_{cr}$$

[V_{cr} is given by Eq. (2.33).] This assumption seems reasonable and conservative. In fact, it has been pointed out that beams without web reinforcement generally fail at loads above that which causes the crack to form, the difference often being insignificant, but under certain conditions sizable. Also, since the presence of stirrups restricts crack growth, the shear resistance of the larger uncracked concrete area in web-reinforced beams should, if anything, exceed that of identical beams without

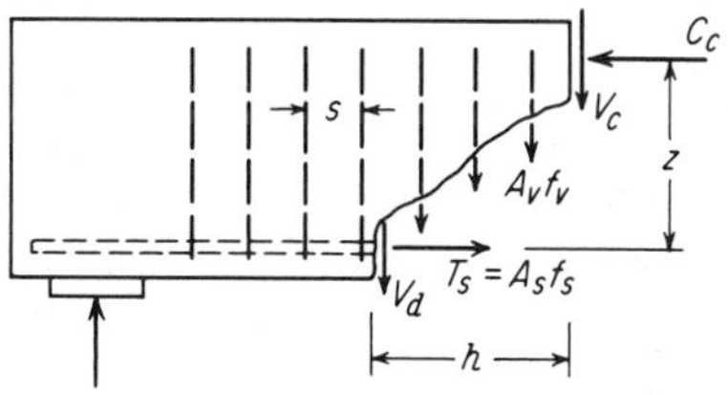

Fig. 2.20 Forces at diagonal crack in beam with vertical stirrups.

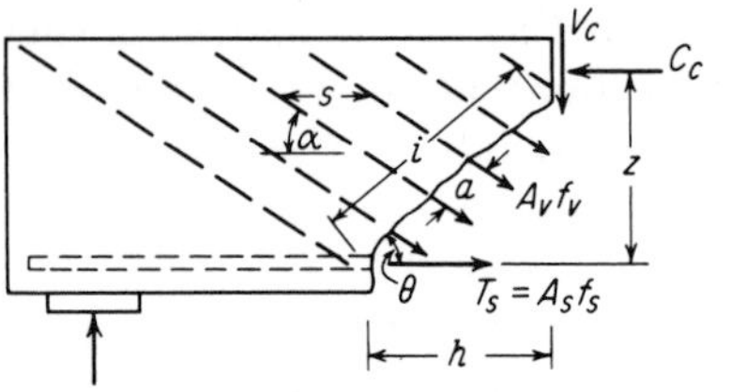

Fig. 2.21 Forces at diagonal crack in beam with inclined web reinforcement.

such reinforcement. In addition, as has been pointed out, the dowel force V_d is likely to be larger in web-reinforced than in plain-web beams. All this points to the fact that in a web-reinforced beam the part of the shear which is not resisted by the stirrups should be at least equal to, and is most likely larger than, the shear force which will cause an identical plain-web beam to crack.

The number of stirrups n spaced a distance s apart was seen to depend on the length h of the horizontal projection of the diagonal crack. If this length is assumed equal to the effective depth of the beam ($h = d$), implying a crack somewhat flatter than 45°, then the above equation for the ultimate shear force V'_u becomes

$$V'_u = V_{cr} + \frac{A_v f_y d}{s} \tag{2.36}$$

Dividing both sides by bd, one obtains the same relation expressed in terms of the nominal ultimate shear stress:

$$v'_u = \frac{V'_u}{bd} = v_{cr} + \frac{A_v f_y}{bs} \tag{2.36a}$$

In Ref. 2.5 the results of 166 beam tests are compared with Eq. (2.36*a*). It is shown that the equation predicts the actual shear strength quite conservatively, the observed strength being on the average 45 per cent larger than predicted; a very few of the individual test beams developed strength just slightly below that of Eq. (2.36*a*). At the same time the very considerable scatter, even though almost entirely on the conservative side, indicates that a deeper and more precise understanding of shear strength has yet to be developed.

BEAMS WITH INCLINED BARS. The function of *inclined web reinforcement*, Fig. 2.19*b*, can be discussed in very similar terms. Figure 2.21 again indicates the forces which act on the portion of the beam to one side of that diagonal crack which results in eventual failure. The dowel force V_d has been omitted for clarity. The crack with horizontal projection h and inclined length $i = h/\cos\theta$ is crossed by inclined bars horizontally spaced a distance s apart. The inclination of the bars is α, and that of the crack θ as shown. The distance between bars measured parallel to the direction of the crack is seen from the irregular triangle to be

$$a = \frac{s}{\sin\theta\,(\cot\theta + \cot\alpha)}$$

The number of bars crossing the crack, $n = i/a$, after some transformation, is obtained as

$$n = \frac{h}{s}(1 + \cot\alpha \tan\theta)$$

The vertical component of the force in one bar or stirrup is $A_v f_v \sin\alpha$, so that the total vertical component of the forces in all bars which cross the crack is

$$V_s = nA_v f_v \sin\alpha = A_v f_v \frac{h}{s}(\sin\alpha + \cos\alpha\tan\theta)$$

As in the case of vertical stirrups, shear failure occurs when the stress in the web reinforcement reaches the yield point. Also, the same assumptions are made as in the case of stirrups, namely that the horizontal projection of the diagonal crack is equal to the effective depth d, and that the concrete, at failure, resists the same force V_{cr} which caused the formation of the diagonal crack. Lastly, the inclination θ of the diagonal crack, which varies somewhat depending on various influences, is generally assumed to be 45°. On this basis, the ultimate strength when failure is caused by shear is obtained as

$$V'_u = V_{cr} + \frac{A_v f_y d(\sin\alpha + \cos\alpha)}{s} \tag{2.37}$$

or, dividing both sides by bd,

$$v'_u = v_{cr} + \frac{A_v f_y(\sin\alpha + \cos\alpha)}{bs} \tag{2.37a}$$

It is seen that Eqs. (2.36) and (2.36*a*), developed for vertical stirrups, are only special cases, for $\alpha = 90°$, of the more general expressions (2.37) and (2.37*a*).

It should be noted that Eqs. (2.36) and (2.37) apply only if web reinforcement is so spaced that any conceivable diagonal crack is traversed by at least one stirrup or inclined bar. Otherwise web reinforcement would not contribute to the shear strength of the beam, because diagonal cracks which could form between widely spaced web reinforcement would fail the beam at the load at which it would fail if no web reinforcement were present. This imposes upper limits on the permissible spacing s to ensure that the web reinforcement is actually effective as calculated.

The inconsistencies in the preceding derivations are fairly evident. For instance, in the case of inclined bars, the assumptions that $h = d$ and $\theta = 45°$ actually mean, by simple geometry, that the diagonal crack has spread all the way to the compression face of the beam. If this were so, no uncracked compression zone would remain available to resist the share V_{cr} of the total shear force. However, this assumption, which is evidently on the unconservative side, appears to be compensated for by other conservative approximations. For one, the share of the shear which is resisted by dowel action has been neglected; for another, as has been pointed out, the share which the uncracked concrete is able to carry has probably been underestimated.

One must conclude that at this time the nature and mechanism of diagonal tension failure are rather clearly understood qualitatively, that some of the quantitative assumptions which have been made cannot be justified by rational analysis, that the calculated results are in acceptable and generally conservative agreement with a very large body of empirical data, and that structures designed on this basis have proved satisfactory.

PROBLEM

The beam discussed in the problem at the end of Art. 2.5*b* (b = 10 in., t = 25 in., d = 23 in., f'_c = 3000 psi, span = 20 ft) has been more heavily reinforced with three No. 10 bars, f_y = 60 ksi, in order to enable it to carry in flexure a uniform design load of 3300 lb per ft in addition to its own weight, with a minimum safety factor of 1.85. For the section of the beam at a distance d from the support, determine whether web reinforcement is required if a safety factor of at least 2.0 is stipulated against failure by diagonal tension. If so, use vertical U-shaped stirrups as shown on Fig. 2.19*a*, made of No. 2 bars with f_y = 40 ksi, and determine the required spacing s at two locations: (1) a distance equal to d = 23 in. and (2) a distance of 36 in. from the support.

2.6 Bond and Anchorage In a short piece of a beam of length dx, shown in Fig. 2.22, the moment at one end will generally differ from that at the other end by a small amount dM. If this piece is isolated, and if one assumes that after cracking the concrete does not resist any tension stresses, then the internal forces are those shown in Fig. 2.22*b*. The change

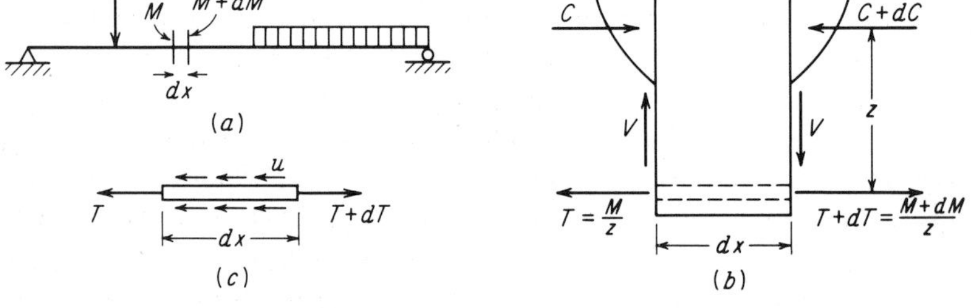

Fig. 2.22

in bending moment dM produces a change in the bar force

$$dT = \frac{dM}{z}$$

Since the bar or bars must be in equilibrium, this change in bar force is resisted at the contact surface between steel and concrete by an equal and opposite force produced by the bond between steel and concrete. If U is the magnitude of this bond force per unit length of bar,

$$U\,dx = (T + dT) - T = dT \qquad (a)$$

from which

$$U = \frac{dT}{dx} = \frac{1}{z}\frac{dM}{dx} = \frac{V}{z} \qquad (b)$$

Assuming that this bond force per unit length is the resultant of shear-type bond stresses u (see Fig. 2.22*c*) uniformly distributed over the contact area, the nominal bond stress is $u = U/\Sigma_0$ or

$$u = \frac{V}{\Sigma_0 z} \qquad (2.38)$$

where Σ_0 is the sum of the perimeters of all the bars. [It is customary to take for the lever arm z the value jd obtained from elastic analysis, Eq. (2.19), so that

$$u = \frac{V}{\Sigma_0 jd} \qquad (2.38a)$$

is the more customary form of this equation.] This bond stress is caused by the change dM in bending moment and, for this reason, is known as *flexural bond.*

When plain bars without surface deformations were used, initial bond strength was provided only by the relatively weak chemical adhesion and mechanical friction between steel and concrete. Once adhesion and static friction were overcome at larger loads, small amounts of slip led to interlocking of the natural roughness of the bar with the concrete. However, this natural bond strength is so low that in beams reinforced with plain bars the bond between steel and concrete is frequently broken. Such a beam will collapse as the bar is pulled through the concrete. To prevent this occurrence, end anchorage is provided, chiefly in the form of hooks as in Fig. 2.23. If the anchorage is adequate, such a beam will not collapse even if the bond is broken over the entire length between anchorages.

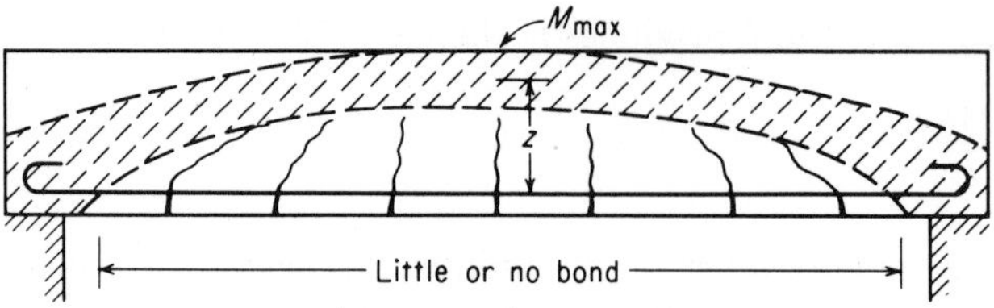

Fig. 2.23 Tied-arch action in beam with little or no bond.

This is so because the member acts as a tied arch, as shown in Fig. 2.23, the uncracked concrete representing the arch (shaded), and the anchored bars the tie rod. In this case, over the length in which the bond is broken, $u = 0$, and, therefore, $dT = 0$. This means that over the entire unbonded length the force in the steel is constant and equal to $T = M_{max}/z$. In consequence, the total steel elongation in such beams is larger than in those in which bond is preserved, resulting in larger deflections and larger widths of cracks.

To improve this situation, deformed bars are now universally used in the United States (see Art. 1.11). With such bars, the shoulders of the projecting ribs bear on the surrounding concrete and result in greatly increased bond strength. It is then possible in most cases to dispense with special anchorage devices such as hooks and anchor plates. In addition, crack widths, as well as deflections, are reduced.

The actual distribution of bond stresses along deformed reinforcing bars is more complex than that represented by Eq. (2.38). In actuality, concrete fails to resist any tension stresses only where a crack is located. Between cracks, the concrete does resist moderate amounts of tension stress; this reduces the tension force T in the steel, as shown in Fig. 2.24 for a beam portion in pure bending. Since, from Eq. (*b*),

$$u = \frac{dT/dx}{\Sigma_0}$$

local bond stresses, being proportional to the rate of change of the bar force, act in the immediate vicinity of tension cracks and are distributed as shown in Fig. 2.24. Very high values of such bond stresses adjacent to cracks have been measured at Cornell University (Ref. 2.7). They

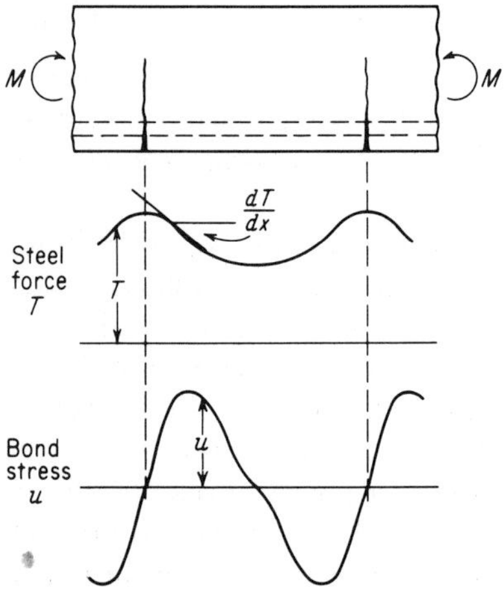

Fig. 2.24 Variation of steel force and bond stress at flexural cracks.

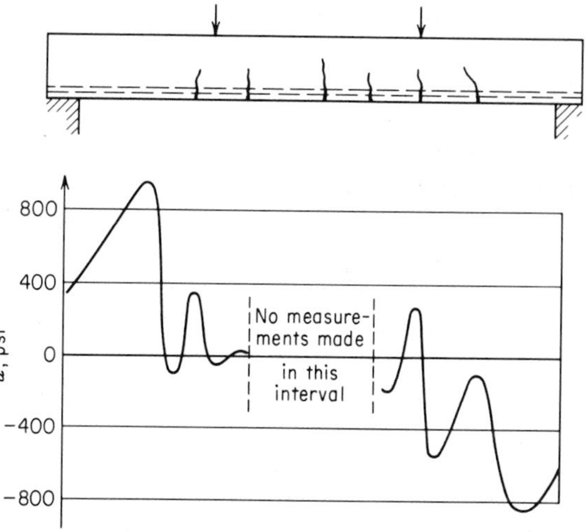

***Fig.* 2.25** Measured bond-stress distribution. (*From Ref.* 2.7.)

are so high, particularly when high-strength steels are used, that a certain amount of localized slip between steel and concrete occurs at each crack.

If bond stresses become excessive, bond failure ensues. Equation (2.38) shows that this will generally occur where shear forces are large, i.e., in the vicinity of supports. In these regions, bond failure starts at cracks, because there the described localized bond stresses superpose on the flexural bond. Thus, bond stresses at loads close to those which cause bond failure have been measured to be distributed in the general manner shown in Fig. 2.25 (Ref. 2.7).

When bond failure ensues, it results generally in splitting of the concrete along the bars, either in vertical planes as in Fig. 2.26*a*, or in horizontal planes as in Fig. 2.26*b*. Such splitting comes largely from wedging action when the ribs of the deformed bars bear against the concrete. The horizontal type of splitting of Fig. 2.26*b* frequently begins at a diagonal

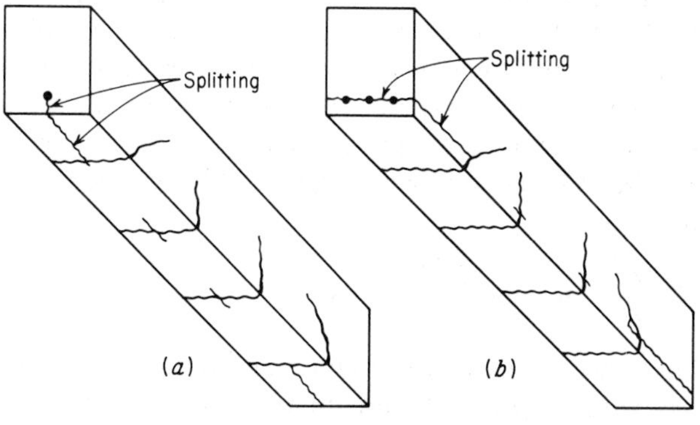

***Fig.* 2.26** Splitting along reinforcement (schematic).

crack. In this case, as discussed in connection with Fig. 2.18*b*, the dowel action increases the tendency toward splitting. This indicates that shear and bond failures are often intricately interrelated.

When splitting has spread all the way to the end of an unanchored bar, complete bond failure occurs. That is, sliding of the steel relative to the concrete leads to immediate collapse of the beam.

It is seen that the mechanism of bond failure in beams with modern deformed bars is more complex than in those with plain bars. In the latter the bond depends directly on the surface area which is in contact with the concrete and for which adhesion, friction, and surface roughness provide the bond strength. The ultimate bond strength u'_u per unit area, at which complete slip of plain bars occurs without any splitting, is of the order of 300 psi for concretes with cylinder strengths of about 3000 to 3500 psi.

In contrast, for modern deformed bars, recent tests at the University of Texas and at the United States Bureau of Standards (Refs. 2.8, 2.9) seem to indicate that splitting occurs when the total bond force U per inch of length of bar, which is transmitted from steel to concrete, reaches a critical value. This ultimate bond force, in pounds per linear inch of bar, is largely independent of bar size or perimeter. The concept of a wedging action is in reasonable conformity with this finding, since the effects of a wedge of given shape depend more on the force with which it is driven than on its size.

It was found that the ultimate average bond force per inch of length of bar is approximately

$$U'_u = 30\sqrt{f'_c} \quad \text{to} \quad 35\sqrt{f'_c} \tag{2.39}$$

Bond forces of this magnitude were observed to result in failure by splitting, in large and excessive slip, or in other prohibitive deformations. These tests were made mostly on beams of the type in Fig. 2.26*a*, with a single bar causing vertical splitting. They do not give adequate information on the influence of such factors as bar spacing in the more realistic situation of Fig. 2.26*b*, nor on the evidently favorable influence which substantial stirrup reinforcement must have on resistance to splitting.

This information can be expressed in terms of the conventional nominal average bond stress per square inch of contact area by dividing U'_u by $\Sigma_0 = \pi D$, D being the bar diameter. This gives, for the ultimate bond stress,

$$u'_u = 9.5\frac{\sqrt{f'_c}}{D} \quad \text{to} \quad 11\frac{\sqrt{f'_c}}{D} \qquad \text{psi} \tag{2.40}$$

The fact that bond resistance was found to correlate better with $\sqrt{f'_c}$ than with f'_c agrees with the concept that the resistance of concrete to splitting depends chiefly on its tensile, rather than compressive, strength.

If one considers the large local variations of bond stress caused by flexural and diagonal cracks (see Figs. 2.24 and 2.25), it becomes clear that local bond failures immediately adjacent to cracks will often occur at loads considerably below the failure load of the beam. These result in small local slips and some widening of cracks and increase of deflections, but will be harmless as long as failure does not propagate all along the bar with resultant total slip. In fact, as was discussed in connection with Fig. 2.23, in those cases in which end anchorage is reliable, bond can be severed along the entire length of bar, excluding the anchorages, without endangering the carrying capacity of the beam.

In the beam of Fig. 2.27, the moment, and therefore the steel stress, is evidently zero at the supports and maximal at point a (neglecting the weight of the beam). If one designates the steel stress at a as f_s, the total tension force at that point in a bar of area A_s is $T_s = A_s f_s$, while at the end of the bar it is zero. Evidently, this force has been transferred from the concrete into the bar over the length L by bond stresses on the surface. Therefore, the average bond force over the length L is

$$U = \frac{A_s f_s}{L}$$

If this bond force per unit length is smaller than the ultimate value U'_u of Eq. (2.39), no splitting or other complete failure will occur over the length L.

To put it differently, the minimum length which is necessary to develop, by bond, a given bar force $A_s f_s$ is

$$L_d = \frac{A_s f_s}{U'_u} \tag{2.41}$$

where the ultimate bond force per unit length U'_u is given by Eq. (2.39). This length L_d is known as the *development length* of the bar. In particular, in order to ensure that a bar is securely anchored by bond to develop its maximum usable strength (the yield stress), this development length

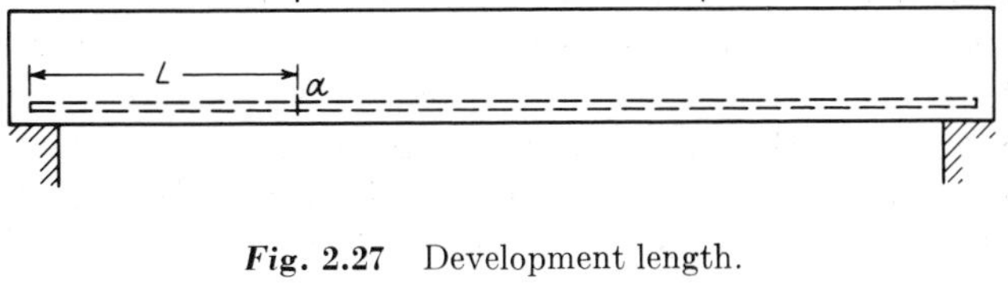

Fig. 2.27 Development length.

must be

$$L_{du} = \frac{A_s f_y}{U'_u} \tag{2.41a}$$

Therefore, if, in the beam of Fig. 2.27, the actual length L is equal to or larger than the development length L_{du}, no premature bond failure will occur. That is, the beam will fail by yielding of the steel, rather than by bond failure. This will be so even if, in the immediate vicinity of cracks, local slips may have occurred over small regions along the beam.

From this discussion it is seen that the main requirement for safety against bond failure is this: The length of the bar, from any point of given steel stress (f_s or, at most, f_y) to its nearby free end must be at least equal to its development length as given by Eq. (2.41) or (2.41*a*). If this requirement is satisfied, the magnitude of the nominal flexural bond stress along the beam, as given by Eq. (2.38), is of only secondary importance, since the integrity of the members is assured even in the face of possible minor local bond failures. Conversely, if the actual available length is inadequate for full development, special anchorage, such as by hooks, must be provided to ensure adequate strength.

The development length for a given steel stress f_s, or for the yield strength f_y, can also be written in terms of the conventional nominal bond stress u'_u:

$$L_d = \frac{A_s f_s}{u'_u \Sigma_0} \qquad \text{or} \qquad L_{du} = \frac{A_s f_y}{u'_u \Sigma_0} \tag{2.41b}$$

where u'_u is given by Eq. (2.40).

It should be noted that the actual local intensity of the bond stress along the embedded length of a bar is not constant. It varies, depending on the crack pattern, on the distance from the section of maximum steel stress, and on other factors. This was illustrated by Figs. 2.24 and 2.25. The ultimate values of Eqs. (2.39) and (2.40) were obtained, from tests with a variety of embedded lengths L, by dividing the bar force by the development length or development surface; that is, $U'_u = A_s f_s / L$ or $u'_u = A_s f_s / L\Sigma_0$. These quantities, therefore, are merely the average values over the embedded length at bond failure, regardless of local variations.

It is seen that U'_u is largely independent of the diameter of the bar. This means that the bond force per inch is substantially the same for large as for small bars. On the other hand, for a given steel stress f_s, the bar force $A_s f_s = f_s \pi D^2/4$ is proportional to the square of the diameter. If this is substituted in Eq. (2.41), the result is $L_d = f_s \pi D^2 / 4U'_u$; the necessary development length increases with the square of the bar diameter.

Therefore, a beam reinforced with a larger number of small bars requires a smaller development length than a beam reinforced with a small number of large bars of the same total area. This demonstrates the superiority of small bars in developing bond strength.

PROBLEM

Verify whether the beam discussed at the end of Art. 2.5 is adequately designed to provide a safety factor of at least 2.0 against failure in bond. *Notes:* (*a*) For the present purpose it is sufficiently accurate to use the approximate value $j = 7/8$ for determining the internal lever arm $z = jd$. (*b*) Bond should be checked both at the support where the flexural bond stress is largest and in reference to the development length. (*c*) For identifying the development length, assume that the beam has a clear span of 20 ft and that the reinforcement is carried 6 in. beyond the face of the support, as shown schematically in Fig. 2.27. (*d*) The maximum steel stress evidently occurs at the point of maximum moment, and development length must be checked for that point. However, in a uniformly loaded beam the bending moment, and thereby the steel stress, at first decrease quite slowly with increasing distance from midspan. For this reason, adequacy of development length should also be checked at one or more additional locations, closer to the supports; it is suggested that this be done for the quarter-points of the span. (*e*) For bar diameters and perimeters see Tables 1 and 3 of Appendix B.

2.7 Deflections at Service Loads In order to serve its intended purpose, a structure must be (1) safe and (2) serviceable. A structure is safe if it is able to resist, without distress and with some margin to spare, all forces which foreseeably will act on it during its lifetime. Serviceability implies, among other things, that deflections and other distortions under load shall be unobjectionably small. For example, excessive beam and slab deflections can lead to objectionable cracking of partitions, ill-fitting doors and windows, poor drainage, misalignment of sensitive machinery or other equipment, excessive vibrations, etc. It becomes important, therefore, to be able to predict deflections with reasonable accuracy, so that members can be dimensioned to ensure both adequate strength and appropriately small deflections.

The deflections of interest are those which occur under normal service conditions. In service, a structure sustains the full dead load plus some fraction or all of the maximum design live load. The usual safety factors provide that under service loading the steel and concrete are not stressed beyond their respective elastic ranges. For this reason the deflections which occur immediately upon application of the load, the so-called *instantaneous deflections*, can be calculated by methods based on the elastic behavior of flexural members as analyzed in Art. 2.4*c* and *d*.

It was pointed out in Arts. 1.7 and 1.9 that, in addition to those concrete deformations which occur immediately upon load application, there are other deformations and volume changes which take place gradually and over long intervals of time. These are chiefly creep deformations and shrinkage. In consequence, deflections of reinforced-concrete members continue to increase for some time after load application, at a decreasing rate, and the *longtime deflections* may exceed the instantaneous deflections by a large amount. For this reason, methods for estimating both the instantaneous and the longtime deflections are essential.

a. Instantaneous deflections Elastic deflections can be expressed in the general form

$$\delta = \frac{F \text{ (loads, spans)}}{EI}$$

where EI is the flexural rigidity, and F (loads, spans) is a function of the particular load-and-span arrangement. For instance, the deflection of a uniformly loaded simple beam is $5wL^4/384EI$, so that $F = 5wL^4/384$. Similar deflection equations have been tabulated, or can easily be computed, for many other loadings and span arrangements, simple, fixed, or continuous, and the corresponding functions F may be determined. The particular problem in reinforced-concrete structures is, therefore, the determination of the appropriate flexural rigidity EI for a member consisting of two materials with properties and behavior as widely different as steel and concrete.

If the maximum moment in a flexural member is sufficiently small so that the tension stress in the concrete does not exceed the flexural tensile strength (modulus of rupture, which can be taken as about $7.5\sqrt{f'_c}$), and if the shear stresses are less than v_{cr} [see Eq. (2.33)], neither flexural nor diagonal tension cracks will occur. The full, uncracked section is then available for resisting stress and providing rigidity. This stage of loading has been analyzed in Art. 2.4*c*. In agreement with this analysis, the effective moment of inertia for this range of low loads is that of the uncracked, transformed section, I_{ut}, and E is the modulus of concrete E_c as given in Art. 1.7. Correspondingly, for this load range,

$$\delta_1 = \frac{F}{E_c I_{ut}} \qquad (2.42)$$

At higher loads flexural tension cracks are formed; in addition, if shear stresses are sizable, and web reinforcement is employed to resist them, diagonal tension cracks can exist at service loads. In the region of flexural cracks the position of the neutral axis varies: directly at each crack it is located at the level calculated for the cracked, transformed section (see Art. 2.4*d*); midway between cracks it dips to a location closer to that calculated for the uncracked, transformed section (Art. 2.4*c*). It does not reach the latter location because, even between cracks, the concrete stress cannot exceed the flexural tensile strength. Correspondingly, flexural tension cracking causes the effective moment of inertia to be that of the cracked, transformed section in the immediate neighborhood of flexural tension cracks, and closer to but smaller than that of the uncracked, transformed section midway between cracks, with a gradual transition between these extremes. Diagonal cracks sometimes extend beyond the calculated location of the neutral axis, reducing the effective rigidity. Also, some redistribution of steel stresses is caused by diagonal cracking (see Art. 2.5) and by localized slip between steel and concrete adjacent to cracks (see Art. 2.6). This is accompanied by an increase in deflections. These effects add to that of flexural tension cracks in further reducing the effective moment of inertia.

It is seen from this brief discussion that, once cracking has started, the effective moment of inertia is close to that of the cracked, transformed section, its actual value depending on the details of crack development. These, in turn, vary with distribution of moments and shears along the beam, magnitude of tensile stresses at service loads depending on the grade of steel used, etc. Tests have shown that in this range, i.e., for loads between the cracking load and the service load, the deflections can be computed from

$$\delta_2 = \frac{F}{E_c k I_{ct}} \tag{2.43}$$

where I_{ct} is the moment of inertia of the cracked, transformed section, and k is a coefficient which varies from about 0.75 to 0.90, depending on severity of cracking. That is, high steel stresses and high shear stresses will result in a lower value of k, and vice versa.

By way of example, it may be recalled that in the particular beam discussed in the example of Art. 2.4, for the uncracked section $I_{ut} = 15{,}030\text{ in.}^4$, and for the cracked section $I_{ct} = 7630\text{ in.}^4$ It is seen that in this case, once cracks have developed, the rate of deflection is more than twice that observed at low loads for the uncracked beam.

The situation is shown schematically in Fig. 2.28. A reasonable and simple estimate of instantaneous deflections can often be made as follows: If the service load does not (significantly) exceed the cracking load, as is frequently the case in lightly reinforced slabs, the moment of inertia of the uncracked section I_{ut} can be used. Conversely, investigations at Cornell University have shown that, if the service load exceeds the cracking load sizably, instead of calculating separately δ_1 and δ_2 and adding, one may

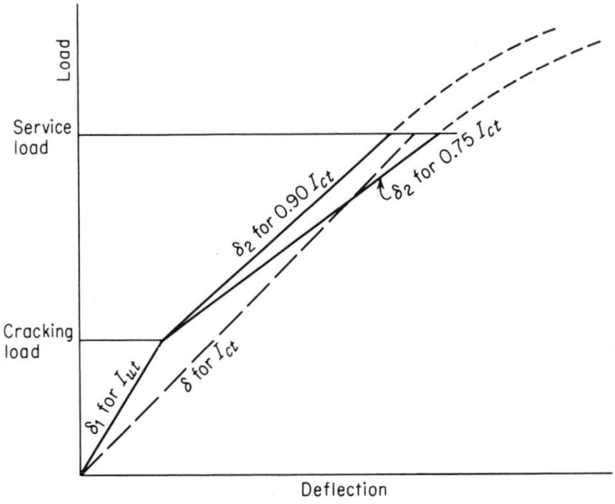

Fig. 2.28 Deflections of reinforced-concrete beams (schematic).

estimate the entire deflection δ by using the moment of inertia I_{ct} of the cracked, transformed section (Refs. 2.10, 2.11). This, likewise, is shown schematically in Fig. 2.28.

b. Longtime deflections Longtime deflections are caused by shrinkage and by creep (chiefly the latter). It was pointed out in Art. 1.7 that creep deformations of concrete are directly proportional to the compression stress. They increase asymptotically with time and, for the same stress, are larger for low- than for high-strength concretes. Correspondingly longtime deflections caused by sustained loads can be estimated by replacing E_c with an equivalent sustained modulus. This modulus must also be used in determining n when calculating I_{ut} or I_{ct}. One such method, including data on the magnitude of this equivalent sustained modulus, is given in Ref. 2.10.

In this same investigation at Cornell University (Ref. 2.10), it was shown from many tests that the following simplified method leads to an adequate estimate of longtime deflections, including the effect of normal shrinkage: (1) Calculate the instantaneous deflection due to the sustained load. (2) Multiply this short-time deflection by a coefficient A; the resulting value is the additional longtime deflection caused by creep and normal shrinkage. That is, (*additional longtime deflection*) $= A \times$ (*instantaneous deflection*).

The coefficient A depends on the duration of the sustained load. It also depends on whether the flexural member carries only reinforcement of amount A_s on the tension side, or whether additional longitudinal reinforcement A_s' is provided on the compression side. In the latter case,

***Table* 2.1 Multiplier A for additional longtime deflections (Ref. 2.10)**

Duration of loading	A_s only	$A'_s = A_s/2$	$A'_s = A_s$
1 month	0.6	0.4	0.3
6 months	1.2	1.0	0.7
1 year	1.4	1.1	0.8
5 years and more	2.0	1.2	0.8

the longtime deflections are much reduced. This is so because, when no compression reinforcement is provided, the compression concrete is subject to unrestrained creep and shrinkage. On the other hand, since steel is not subject to creep, if additional bars are located close to the compression face, they will resist, and thereby reduce, the amount of creep and shrinkage and the corresponding deflection. The appropriate coefficient can be read from Table 2.1.

It will be realized from this discussion that the magnitude of the deflections in reinforced-concrete structures depends on so many influences that no precise calculation is possible. On the other hand, great precision is not necessary practically. From extensive experimental information it can be said that the methods presented here permit deflections to be estimated with an accuracy of about ± 20 per cent, which is adequate for purposes of design.

PROBLEM

For the beam analyzed in the problem at the end of Art. 2.4, estimate the longtime deflection at full service load. Assume that in the particular structure that part of the total service load which acts continually and constitutes the longtime loading consists of the weight of the beam plus 1200 lb per ft. This longtime loading consists of the weight of the floor structure and of other permanent portions of the building supported by the given beam, plus that part of the live load which acts more or less continuously, such as furniture, equipment, the time average of the weight of occupants, etc. The remaining 700 lb per ft are short-duration peak loads, such as the brief peak loading of corridors in an office building at the end of the working day. *Note:* to avoid repetitive calculations, utilize those cross-sectional properties which have been calculated in connection with the problem in Art. 2.4.

2.8 Compression plus Bending The behavior and strength of members which are axially, i.e., concentrically, compressed, have been discussed in Art. 2.2. Such members occur rarely, if ever, in buildings and other structures. Components such as columns and arches chiefly carry loads in compression, but simultaneous bending is almost always present.

Bending moments are caused by continuity, i.e., by the fact that building columns are parts of monolithic frames in which the support moments of the girders are partly resisted by the abutting columns, by transverse loads such as wind forces, by loads carried eccentrically on column brackets, or in arches when the arch axis does not coincide with the pressure line. Even when design calculations show a member to be loaded purely axially, inevitable imperfections of construction will introduce eccentricities and consequent bending in the member as built. For this reason members which must be designed for simultaneous compression and bending are very frequent in almost all types of concrete structures. Their behavior is easily understood by combining the information and principles of Arts. 2.2 and 2.4.

a. Elastic behavior Up to loads of the order of one-half the ultimate, eccentrically compressed members behave substantially elastically in the manner, and for the reasons, discussed for axially compressed members and for beams. In elastic members made of materials with substantial tension strength, the stresses can be calculated by a simple addition of those caused by axial compression and those caused by bending. A similar situation prevails in eccentrically compressed reinforced-concrete members, provided that no tension cracking has occurred to reduce the effective concrete section. This will be the case if the eccentricity is small enough so that tension stresses in the concrete will not exist or, if present, will be smaller than the bending tension strength f_r (modulus of rupture). This case of small eccentricity will be analyzed first.

(1) SMALL ECCENTRICITY, SECTION UNCRACKED. Figure 2.29*a* shows the cross section of a rectangular eccentrically loaded column, (*b*) its transformed section, and (*c*) the load P acting at a distance (eccentricity) e measured from the centroid of the transformed section. If $A_s' = A_s$, as is most frequently the case and as is assumed here for simplicity of presentation, then the eccentricity is measured from the center line of the column. The eccentric force P can be replaced with an axial force of equal magnitude and a moment $M = Pe$, as shown.

The axial force causes uniform concrete compression stresses

$$f_a = \frac{P}{A_t}$$

and the moment causes maximum concrete bending stresses

$$f_b = \pm \frac{Mc}{I_t} = \pm \frac{Mt/2}{I_t}$$

the first of the two expressions for f_b being general, and the second applying when $A_s' = A_s$. Here A_t and I_t are, respectively, the area and moment

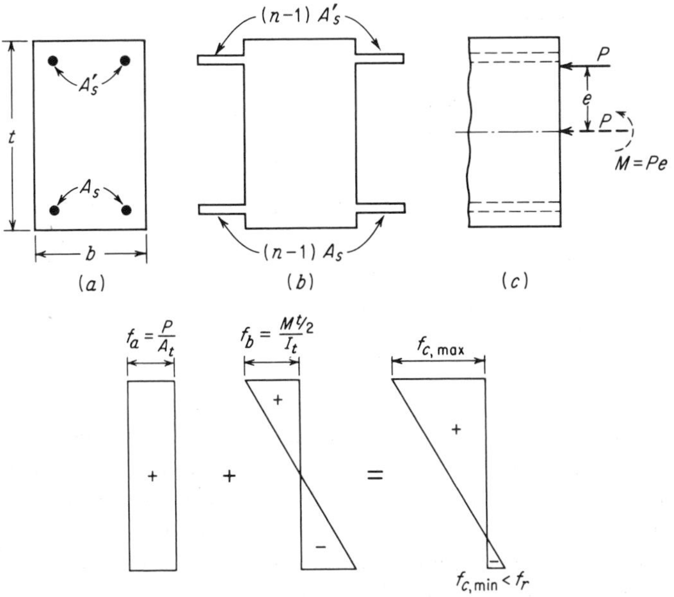

(d)

Fig. 2.29

of inertia of the transformed section. Substituting $Pe = M$, the outer fiber stresses in the concrete, by superposition, become

$$f_{c,\substack{\max\\ \min}} = \frac{P}{A_t} \pm \frac{Mc}{I_t} = \frac{P}{A_t} \pm \frac{Mt/2}{I_t} \tag{2.44}$$

and are shown in Fig. 2.29*d*. Depending on the relative magnitudes of the two terms, $f_{\min}$ can be either positive (compression), in which case the entire cross section is under compression of varying intensity, or negative, in which case a portion of the section is in tension. In the latter case, which is shown in Fig. 2.29*d*, it is assumed that the section remains uncracked as long as the numerically largest tension stress $f_{c,\min}$ does not exceed the modulus of rupture f_r. Then the transformed section of Fig. 2.29*b* continues to be correct, and the above analysis applies. Otherwise, if $f_{c,\min}$ exceeds f_r in absolute value, tension cracks develop, and the transformed section must be modified accordingly.

It is evident from Eq. (2.44) that, for a given cross section and a given load P, there is a limiting value for the eccentricity e beyond which $f_{\min}$ will numerically exceed f_r, causing tension cracks to appear. This limiting eccentricity can be calculated from Eq. (2.44) by substituting $-f_r$ for $f_{\min}$, Pe for M, and solving for e.

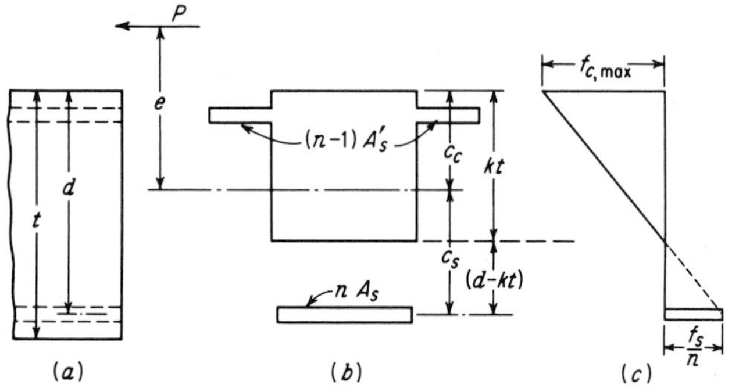

Fig. 2.30

(2) LARGE ECCENTRICITY, SECTION CRACKED. If the eccentricity exceeds the value just defined, tension cracks will make part of the concrete area ineffective. Then it is usually assumed, just as in the case of beams, that the concrete is not capable of resisting any tension whatever. The shape of the transformed cracked section is then that shown in Fig. 2.30*b*, and the elastic stresses are distributed as in (*c*).

In this case the depth kt of that part of the section which is in compression becomes an additional unknown. It can be found from the equilibrium requirement that the moment of all internal forces about the action line of the external force P must be zero. The internal forces are the stresses shown in Fig. 2.30*c* acting on the transformed area of (*b*). The mentioned condition

$$M_P = 0$$

results in a cubic equation for kt which can be solved either explicitly or by successive approximation. Once kt is known, the stresses are calculated from the first (general) form of Eq. (2.44). Thus, the maximum concrete stress becomes

$$f_{c,\max} = \frac{P}{A_t} + \frac{Pec_c}{I_t} \qquad (2.44a)$$

and the stress in the tension steel

$$f_s = n\left[\frac{P}{A_t} - \frac{Pec_s}{I_t}\right] \qquad (2.44b)$$

Here A_t and I_t refer, of course, to the transformed cracked section. The eccentricity e and the fiber distances c_c and c_s for concrete and steel, respectively, are measured from the centroidal axis of the transformed section; compression is designated as positive, tension negative.

b. Ultimate strength In eccentrically compressed members, at loads approaching the ultimate, a nonelastic redistribution of stresses takes place which is similar to that discussed for axially compressed members in Art. 2.2 and for flexural members in Art. 2.4. In compression members, even more than in beams and girders, the designer is chiefly interested in the carrying capacity, i.e., the ultimate strength. Stresses and rigidity at service loads, which govern deflections of flexural members (see Art. 2.7), are of little interest for compression members, whose deflections or other service behavior need rarely be computed. In earlier days, the elastic stresses under service loads, calculated as just described, were taken as a measure of carrying capacity by limiting them to appropriate fractions of f'_c or f_y. Experimental evidence showed, however, that satisfactory correlation of actual strength with elastically computed stresses could not be obtained. This is not surprising if one considers that, as loads become sufficiently large to cause inelastic behavior, not only the magnitude, but also the manner of distribution of the stresses over the cross section, changes decisively. In attempts to account for these discrepancies without upsetting established methods of elastic stress calculation, various arbitrary corrections and adjustments were gradually introduced in these elastic methods. Such methods continue to be used in this and other countries. However, ways of calculating ultimate strength on the basis of inelastic behavior have now been developed for eccentrically compressed members as for other members. Their results are in satisfactory agreement with extensive test evidence. Increasingly, in engineering practice, they are replacing these older and internally inconsistent methods.

If a rectangular column with cross section as in Fig. 2.31*a* is compressed by an eccentric load P applied as shown, the steel and concrete stresses just prior to failure, i.e., at ultimate load, are distributed in the manner of Fig. 2.31*b*. That is, with plane sections assumed to remain

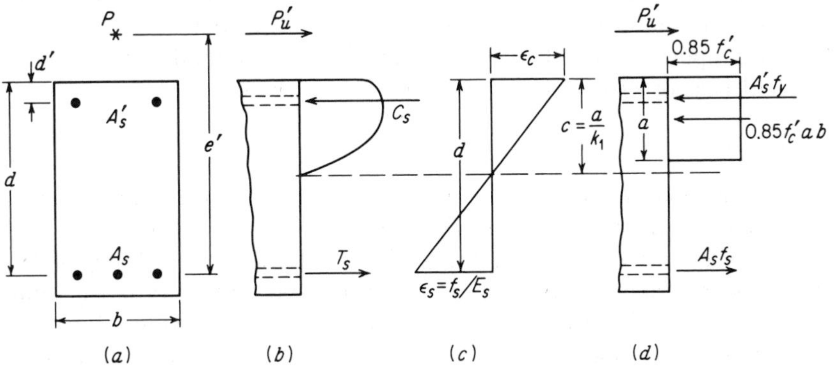

Fig. 2.31 Eccentric compression, ultimate strength.

plane, the strains are those shown in Fig. 2.31*c*, which, for the reasons discussed in connection with Fig. 2.9, result in the shown stress distribution. Just as for simple bending, this actual distribution can be replaced, for purposes of calculation, with the equivalent rectangular stress distribution (Fig. 2.31*d*) discussed in Art. 2.4*f* and shown in Fig. 2.11. A large number of tests on columns of a variety of shapes have shown that the ultimate strengths computed on this basis are in satisfactory agreement with test results (Ref. 2.4).

It is assumed in Fig. 2.31*d* that at ultimate load, when the concrete fails in compression, i.e., when $\epsilon_c = \epsilon_u = 0.003$, the compression steel is yielding, so that $f'_s = f'_y$ as shown. For ordinary conditions this is usually the case; it can easily be checked, as will be demonstrated in a numerical example.

Equilibrium between external and internal axial forces requires that

$$P'_u = 0.85f'_c ab + A'_s f'_y - A_s f_s \tag{2.45}$$

Also, the moment about the centroid of the tension steel A_s of the internal stresses must be equal and opposite to the moment of the external force P'_u, so that

$$P'_u e' = 0.85f'_c ab\left(d - \frac{a}{2}\right) + A'_s f'_y (d - d') \tag{2.46}$$

These are the two basic equilibrium relations for rectangular, eccentrically compressed members. The fact that the presence of the compression reinforcement A'_s has displaced a corresponding amount of concrete, of area A'_s, is neglected in Eqs. (2.45) and (2.46). If necessary, particularly for large steel ratios, one can account for this very simply. Evidently, in the above equations a nonexistent concrete compression force of amount $A'_s(0.85f'_c)$ has been included as acting in the displaced concrete at the level of the compression steel. This excess force can be removed in both equations by multiplying A'_s by $(f'_y - 0.85f'_c)$ rather than by f'_y.

For simplicity, the following presentation will be limited to the most frequent case of *symmetrical cross section*, i.e., where

$$A'_s = A_s \qquad \text{and} \qquad f'_y = f_y \tag{2.47}$$

Other conditions, dealt with by the same type of analysis, merely result in lengthier expressions and calculations.

For large eccentricities, failure will be initiated by yielding of the tension steel, followed by a shift of the neutral axis toward the compression side until crushing of the concrete causes a secondary compression failure. Conversely, for small eccentricities, the concrete may crush while the tension steel may be far from yielding. For any cross section of given dimensions and material strength values, there is one specific eccentricity e' such that a force applied at that distance will cause failure by simultaneous yielding of the tension steel and crushing of the concrete. For this so-called *balanced condition*, let the particular eccentricity be e'_b, and the corresponding ultimate load P_b.

For the *balanced condition*, the concrete strain is $\epsilon_c = \epsilon_u = 0.003$, and simultaneously the strain in the tension steel at the instant at which yielding commences is $\epsilon_s = \epsilon_y = f_y/E_s$. With these values, from the geometry of Fig. 2.31*c*, the distance to the neutral axis is

$$c_b = \frac{\epsilon_u}{\epsilon_y + \epsilon_u} d = \frac{0.003}{f_y/E_s + 0.003} d \tag{2.48}$$

On the other hand, with Eq. (2.47) for symmetrical sections, the depth of the rectangular stress block, from Eq. (2.45), becomes

$$a = \frac{P'_u}{0.85 f'_c b} \tag{2.49}$$

Also, by definition of the rectangular stress block [see Eq. (2.31)],

$$a_b = k_1 c_b \tag{2.50}$$

Equating the right sides of Eqs. (2.49) and (2.50), and using c_b from Eq. (2.48), one has, for the ultimate load under balanced conditions,

$$P'_b = 0.85 k_1 f'_c bd \frac{0.003}{f_y/E_s + 0.003} \tag{2.51}$$

In particular, for concretes with f'_c not exceeding 4000 psi, from Eq. (2.31), $k_1 = 0.85$, so that in this case

$$P'_b = 0.72 f'_c bd \frac{0.003}{f_y/E_s + 0.003} \tag{2.51a}$$

The eccentricity e'_b which results in balanced conditions can then be obtained from Eq. (2.46) by substituting P'_b for P'_u and a_b for a and solving for e'. Loads with eccentricities smaller than e'_b result in primary compression failures at ultimate values larger than P_b; loads with eccentricities larger than e'_b result in primary tension failures at loads smaller than P_b.

(1) FAILURE BY YIELDING OF TENSION STEEL. When $e' > e'_b$, failure is initiated by yielding of the tension steel, followed by lengthening of cracks, shift of the neutral axis, and secondary compression failure by crushing of the concrete. In this case, $f_s = f_y$ and, for a symmetrical section, from Eq. (2.47),

$$A_s f_y = A'_s f'_y$$

Therefore, Eqs. (2.45) and (2.46) become

$$P'_u = 0.85f'_c ab \tag{2.45a}$$

$$P'_u e' = P'_u\left(d - \frac{a}{2}\right) + A'_s f'_y(d - d') \tag{2.46a}$$

Solving Eq. (2.45*a*) for the depth of the rectangular stress block, one has

$$a = \frac{P'_u}{0.85f'_c b} \tag{2.52}$$

If this value is substituted in Eq. (2.46*a*), one obtains the following quadratic equation:

$$\frac{P'^2_u}{2 \times 0.85f'_c b} + (e' - d)P'_u - A'_s f_y(d - d') = 0$$

Dividing through by d and solving, one obtains the ultimate load for large eccentricities:

$$P'_u = 0.85f'_c bd\left[-\left(\frac{e'}{d} - 1\right) + \sqrt{\left(\frac{e'}{d} - 1\right)^2 + 2pm\left(1 - \frac{d'}{d}\right)}\right] \tag{2.53}$$

where the parameter

$$m = \frac{f_y}{0.85f'_c} \tag{2.54}$$

is the ratio of the effective strengths of the two materials in connection with the rectangular stress distribution and is useful in this and other connections.

(2) FAILURE BY COMPRESSION OF CONCRETE. When $e' < e'_b$, failure is initiated by crushing of the concrete. That is, when the concrete reaches its ultimate strain $\epsilon_u = 0.003$, the tension steel has not yet reached its yield point, so that $f_s < f_y$. From the geometry of the strain distribution of Fig. 2.31*c* with $\epsilon_c = \epsilon_u$, the depth to the neutral axis is

$$c = \frac{\epsilon_u}{f_s/E_s + \epsilon_u}\, d \tag{2.55}$$

from which the tension steel stress becomes

$$f_s = E_s\epsilon_u \frac{d - c}{c} = E_s\epsilon_u \frac{d - a/k_1}{a/k_1} \tag{2.55a}$$

If f_s is substituted in Eq. (2.45), and the depth of the stress block a is eliminated between Eqs. (2.45) and (2.46), one obtains a cubic equation in P'_u. From this, the ultimate load for small eccentricities can be determined

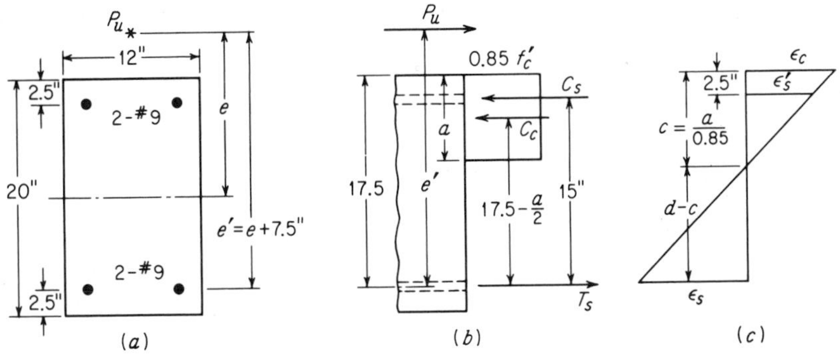

Fig. 2.32

by solving for P'_u either explicitly or, often more quickly, by successive approximation.

Examples The following two examples (in one of which tension governs, and in the other compression) are directly solved numerically, without reference to the previously derived equations. The simplicity of the equivalent rectangular stress block enables such direct numerical analyses, without reference to elaborate formulas, to be carried out for most situations.

The cross section of the column is shown in Fig. 2.32*a*. Four No. 9 bars are used, of 1.0 in.² area each. The cylinder strength is $f'_c = 3000$ psi, and the yield point is $f_y = 40{,}000$ psi.

(1) ECCENTRICITY $e = 15$ IN. FROM CENTERLINE OF COLUMN. The compression force is applied outside the boundaries of the cross section; it is therefore sensible to assume that failure will be initiated by yielding of the tension steel. Assuming the compression steel to yield as well (to be checked later), the three internal forces of Fig. 2.32*b* are:

$$T_s = -2.0 \times 40{,}000 = -80{,}000 \text{ lb}$$
$$C_s = 2.0 \times 40{,}000 = 80{,}000 \text{ lb}$$
$$C_c = 0.85 \times 3000 \times 12a = 30{,}600a$$

As T_s and C_s are equal and opposite, the total internal force being equal and opposite to the external load, P'_u is

$$P'_u = C_c = 30{,}600a$$

from which the depth of the rectangular stress block is

$$a = \frac{P'_u}{30{,}600}$$

Taking moments about the tension steel,

$$P'_u \times 22.5 - 80{,}000 \times 15 - C_c\left(17.5 - \frac{a}{2}\right) = 0$$

Substituting P'_u for C_c and $P'_u/30{,}600$ for a, as previously calculated, one obtains the quadratic equation

$$\frac{P'^2_u}{61{,}200} + 5P'_u - 1{,}200{,}000 = 0$$

whose solution gives the ultimate load

$$P'_u = 159{,}000 \text{ lb}$$

It was assumed that the compression steel yields when, after failure is initiated by yielding of the tension steel, the concrete reaches its crushing strain $\epsilon_u = 0.003$. For this to be true, the strain of the compression steel, ϵ'_s of Fig. 2.32*c*, must be at least equal to that strain at which yielding starts, that is, $\epsilon_y = f'_y/E_s = 40{,}000/29{,}000{,}000 = 0.00138$. To check this, use is made of the strain distribution of Fig. 2.32*c*.

The depth of the rectangular stress block is

$$a = \frac{P'_u}{30{,}600} = \frac{159{,}000}{30{,}600} = 5.2 \text{ in.}$$

and the depth to the neutral axis is

$$c = \frac{a}{k_1} = \frac{5.2}{0.85} = 6.12 \text{ in.}$$

From similar triangles it is seen that

$$\epsilon'_s = \epsilon_c \frac{c - d'}{c} = 0.003 \frac{6.12 - 2.5}{6.12} = 0.00177 > 0.00138$$

Hence, at the instant at which the ultimate concrete strain is reached, the compression steel strain exceeds the yield strain, verifying the assumption that at ultimate load the compression steel is, in fact, yielding.

(2) ECCENTRICITY $e = 6$ IN. FROM CENTER LINE OF COLUMN. For this small eccentricity it is sensible to assume that failure will be initiated by crushing of the concrete. Proceeding by successive approximations, assume that for this small eccentricity the major part of the cross section is in compression. Thus, try

$$a = 11.0 \text{ in.}$$

Hence

$$c = \frac{a}{k_1} = \frac{11}{0.85} = 12.95 \text{ in.}$$

From the similar triangles of the strain distribution of Fig. 2.32*c*,

$$\epsilon_s = \frac{f_s}{E_s} = \epsilon_c \frac{d - c}{c}$$

from which the steel stress in the tension reinforcement is

$$f_s = 0.003 \times 29{,}000{,}000 \frac{17.5 - 12.95}{12.95} = 30{,}600 \text{ psi}$$

Taking moments about the centroid of the tension steel,

$$P'_u \times 13.5 = 0.85 \times 3000 \times 11 \times 12(17.5 - 5.5) + 80{,}000 \times 15$$

from which, as a first approximation,

$$P'_u = 388{,}000 \text{ lb}$$

Taking the sum of the axial forces,

$$388{,}000 = 0.85 \times 3000 \times 12a + 2.0 \times 40{,}000 - 2.0 \times 30{,}600$$

from which

$$a = 12.1 \text{ in.}$$

which differs from the assumed value of $a = 11.0$ in.

If this simple calculation is repeated assuming $a = 12.0$ in., one obtains $P'_u = 402{,}500$ lb and $a = 11.9$ in. The latter being satisfactorily close to the assumed value for a, the second approximation,

$$P'_u = 402{,}500 \text{ lb}$$

is taken as the final answer.

Finally, if one computes the ultimate load for balanced conditions from Eq. (2.51*a*), one finds $P'_b = 314{,}000$ lb. For case 1, $P'_u = 159{,}000 \text{ lb} < P'_b$, indicating that failure is, in fact, initiated by yielding of the tension steel; for case 2, $P'_u = 402{,}500 \text{ lb} > P'_b$, indicating that failure is, in fact, caused by crushing of the concrete, as was assumed.

PROBLEM

If the column of the preceding examples is made of high-strength concrete with $f'_c = 5000$ psi and reinforced with high-strength steel with $f_y = 75{,}000$ psi, calculate the ultimate loads. Check whether the substitution of high-strength materials has led to the same percentage increase in carrying capacity for the two conditions of loading. If not, why not? *Note:* As is seen from Table 1.1, steel with $f_y = 75$ ksi is the highest-strength reinforcing steel available at this time under ASTM standards. The stress-strain curve for such steels frequently has the shape shown in Fig. 1.10. For simplicity of calculation, in the given problem assume that the shape of the curve is similar to that for the lower-strength steels, i.e., that it exhibits a horizontal yield plateau before entering the strain-hardening range.

2.9 Prestressed Concrete ***a. Prestressing*** The successful combination of two materials as unlike in almost every respect as are concrete and steel enables reinforced concrete to occupy an important place in modern construction. Yet there are weaknesses inherent in this combination. They result mainly from the presence of tension cracks which, wherever substantial flexure or shear is present, affect the value of the ultimate load; cracks also occur under service conditions, i.e., at design loads. This has the following disadvantages:

1. In bending, all the concrete on the tension side of the neutral axis, two-thirds or more in flexural members, is lost as a means of resisting stress; its chief structural function is merely to hold the reinforcing bars in place and protect them from corrosion.

2. In shear, as was discussed, the formation of diagonal tension cracks is decisive in limiting the available strength.

3. Deflections being inversely proportional to the moment of inertia of the transformed section, cracked or uncracked as the case may be, beams in which tension cracks have formed show deflections sizably larger than would be the case if cracking could have been prevented.

4. High-strength steels with yield points in excess of 200,000 psi and ultimate strengths of the order of 250,000 psi, 3 to 5 times the strength of ordinary reinforcing steels, are available for use in concrete structures. However, the amount of cracking (width and number of cracks) is roughly proportional to the steel strain, i.e., to the steel stress. Therefore, the high stresses which these steels could sustain cannot be utilized with conventional reinforcement because they would cause an amount of cracking prohibitive with respect to both appearance and corrosion protection and would result in large and frequently prohibitive deflections.

These limitations have been largely overcome by the development of *prestressed concrete*. The essence of prestressing consists in intentionally applying to a structure or structural member forces in a manner which will counteract the effects of the subsequent loads. Specifically, forces are introduced in advance of loading in such a way that they cause internal stresses opposite in sign and distribution to those subsequently produced by the external loads. The resulting total stresses being the sums of those caused by prestressing and those caused by useful load, the performance of the member is improved.

Prestressing steel, in American practice, consists chiefly of seven-wire strands with tension strengths f'_s of 250,000 psi or more and 0.2 per cent offset yield strengths f_y of 200,000 psi or more. Heat-treated, cold-worked alloy-steel bars with tensile strengths of 145,000 psi or more and 0.2 per cent offset yield strengths of about 90 per cent of this value are also utilized. The modulus of elasticity for both types is about 27,000,000 psi.

Suppose a beam is fabricated in the following manner: First, high-strength steel strands are placed in the form and passed through holes in two anchor plates, one at each end. The strands are then pretensioned by applying the *initial prestress force* P_i by a suitable means, such as jacks bearing against abutments (Fig. 2.33*a*). Then the concrete, poured so that the anchor plates bear against the ends of the beam, is allowed to harden. Next the steel strands are secured to the anchor plates, and the jacks

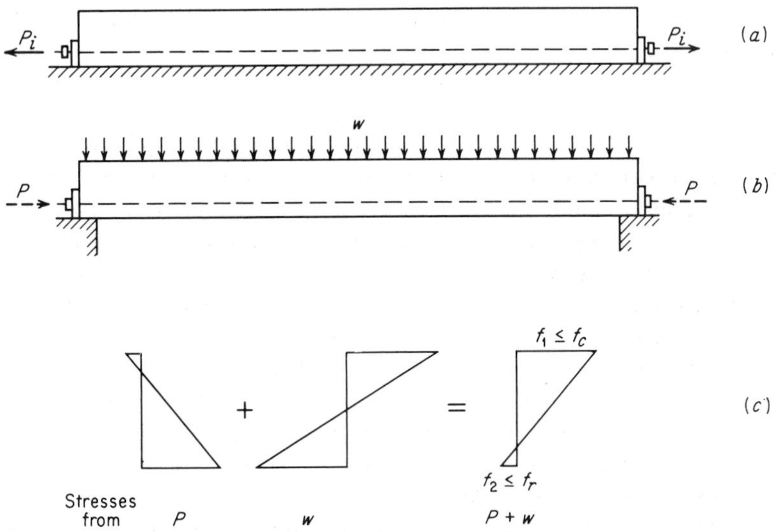

Fig. 2.33 Principle of prestressing.

released. The steel, tending to contract to its original length, is prevented from doing so by the concrete interposed between the anchor plates. Hence, it remains under tension, and this tension is equilibrated by a corresponding compression in the concrete. The effect of the prestressing force, then, is the same as that of an external compression force P applied to the concrete as shown in Fig. 2.33*b*. This stage is known as "transfer"; i.e., the force which equilibrates the steel tension has been transferred from the jacks to the concrete.

After some time has elapsed, the initial prestress P_i will have decreased somewhat, for various reasons which include the elastic compression of the concrete when stressed by the prestressing force, concrete creep and shrinkage, and possible creep of the steel. With current prestressing methods, these losses amount to about 12 to 20 per cent, so that the *final stress* P is smaller by this amount than the initial prestress P_i.

b. Elastic behavior at service loads The principal advantage of a prestressed member is its behavior at service loads. At such loads, stresses in both steel and concrete are kept within the elastic range. The magnitude and location of the prestressing force generally are so arranged that tension cracks will not occur under working loading, dead plus live. In most cases, tension cracking is also prevented, or at least minimized, under temporary conditions such as when a girder, having been fabricated in a prestressing yard, is transported to the site and placed in position, during which time the only load it carries is its own weight. Cracking is prevented by limiting the elastically computed tension stress in the concrete to some fraction of the modulus of rupture f_r. The latter is of the order of $8\sqrt{f'_c}$. When a crackfree member is desired, but the accidental formation of occasional small cracks would be of no consequence, an allowable maximum tension stress of $6\sqrt{f'_c}$ is considered adequate.

Corrosion protection is of more critical importance in prestressed than in reinforced concrete. This is so for two reasons: (1) Other things being equal, smaller amounts of high-strength prestressing tendons than of ordinary reinforcing rods are employed to carry the same loads. If corrosion were to penetrate to a certain depth in the reinforcement and, thereby, to remove a certain cross-sectional area of the steel, this area would constitute a larger percentage of the light prestressing steel than of the heavier conventional reinforcement; it would, therefore, constitute a greater danger to the integrity of the member. (2) More important, steel under permanent high stress, as used in prestressing, is more easily subject to corrosion than steel under no or low stress. This phenomenon is known as *stress corrosion*. Mildly corrosive conditions which may be harmless to reinforced concrete (such as those connected with the usual hairline cracks) can be damaging to prestressing tendons. Thus, it has been observed that some antifreeze compounds and some high-alumina cements, used chiefly abroad as high-early-strength cements, have led to corrosion difficulties in prestressed concrete, but not in conventionally reinforced concrete. For reasons such as this, it is customary to permit no tensile stresses to occur under service conditions in outdoor structures or in other corrosive environments.

The following discussion of behavior, stresses, and strength of prestressed beams is limited to the situation in the midportions of simple beams, for the sake of simplicity.

In the cross section of a prestressed beam, the prestress force P (Fig 2.34*a*), applied with an eccentricity e below the centroidal axis, gives rise to the compression stess $-P/A_t$ and the bending stress $\pm Pec/I_t$ as shown. (In this discussion, compression stresses are designated as negative, tension as positive.) The bending stress produces a shortening of the bottom fibers and a lengthening of the top fibers, which results in an upward deflection of the beam. In other words, when the prestress force is transferred to the concrete (i.e., in the above described procedure, when the jacks are released), the beam lifts off its soffit, as shown in Fig. 2.34*b*. Then the weight of the girder w_g becomes an active load which, for a prismatic girder, results at midspan in the moment

$$M_g = \frac{w_g L^2}{8}$$

This moment causes additional bending stresses $\pm M_g c/I_t$ of sign opposite

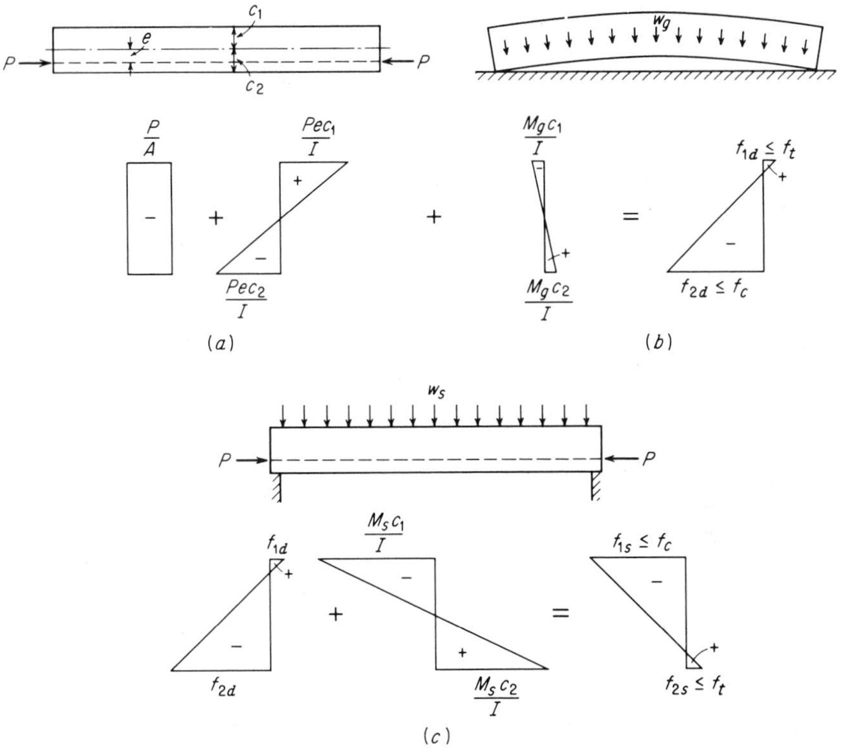

Fig. 2.34

those due to prestress, as shown. These three types of stresses are caused by prestressing and the consequent dead-load stresses resulting from upward deflection; their sums are designated here as f_{1d} and f_{2d} in top and bottom fibers, respectively. They are distributed as shown. In order to prevent cracking, the maximum concrete tension stress, which at this stage occurs at the top fiber, must not exceed the safe value f_t, stipulated as discussed before.

Hence, at this stage, the outer fiber stresses are:

$$f_{1d} = -\frac{P}{A_t} + \frac{Pec_1}{I_t} - \frac{M_g c_1}{I_t} \quad \text{and} \quad |f_{1d}| \le |f_t| \tag{2.56a}$$

$$f_{2d} = -\frac{P}{A_t} - \frac{Pec_2}{I_t} + \frac{M_g c_2}{I_t} \quad \text{and} \quad |f_{2d}| \le |f_c| \tag{2.56b}$$

In other words, the location and magnitude of the prestress force must be so arranged that at this stage the tension in the top fiber does not exceed the stipulated maximum f_t. Likewise, the compression at the bottom fiber must not exceed, in absolute value, the maximum compression stress f_c permitted to ensure safety against compression failure and substantially elastic behavior. This f_c is of the order of one-half the cylinder strength f'_c.

Next, when the girder is installed, it is subjected to the service load, which consists of additional dead load, such as a floor slab which may be supported on the girder, plus the design live load. This superimposed load w_s causes the additional moment M_s and the consequent bending stresses $M_s c/I$ as shown in Fig. 2.34*c*. These bending stresses superpose on those caused by prestress and girder weight. Hence, under design load, the outer fiber stresses are

$$f_{1s} = f_{1d} - \frac{M_s c_1}{I_t} \quad \text{and} \quad |f_{1s}| \leq |f_c| \tag{2.57a}$$

$$f_{2s} = f_{2d} + \frac{M_s c_2}{I_t} \quad \text{and} \quad |f_{2s}| \leq |f_t| \tag{2.57b}$$

In other words, the location and magnitude of the prestress force must also be arranged so that, at this stage, the maximum tension stress, which now acts in the bottom fiber, and the maximum compression stress, in the top fiber, do not exceed their respective stipulated limits.

Since tension cracking has been prevented in both stages, in these equations A_t and I_t are the area and moment of inertia of the uncracked transformed section, and c_1 and c_2 are the outer fiber distances of that section.

It will be observed that the stresses caused by prestressing, f_{1d} and f_{2d}, are of opposite sign to those caused by the design load. It is this arrangement which prevents cracking at design loads, so that the entire cross section of the concrete is available to resist stress. In combination with the fact that high-strength steel is used for reinforcement and that high-strength concrete can be used more effectively in prestressed than in reinforced concrete, this leads to sizable reductions in the required quantities of steel and concrete, to corresponding reductions of dead load, to smaller deflections (owing to the fact that the entire uncracked transformed section is available to provide flexural rigidity), and to improved durability and reduced maintenance because of the absence of hairline cracks.

c. Ultimate strength If the design load is significantly exceeded, the maximum tension stress in the concrete will eventually exceed the modulus of rupture. Tension cracks will form, and the beam will behave essentially like an ordinary cracked reinforced-concrete beam, except for the following: (1) In reinforced concrete, under zero load the strain in the reinforcement is, likewise, zero. In prestressed concrete, in contrast, the strain in the tendons at zero load is not zero, but corresponds to the effective prestress after losses; i.e.,

$$\epsilon_{se} = \frac{f_{se}}{E_s} = \frac{P}{A_s E_s}$$

where P and f_{se} are, respectively, the effective prestress force and corresponding stress. Any further steel strain caused by the applied loads adds to this preexisting strain. (2) The stress-strain characteristics of prestressing steel are quite different from those of reinforcing bars. Figure 2.35 shows typical stress-strain curves for prestressing wire and high-tensile bars. It is seen that in contrast to ordinary reinforcing bars (cf. Fig. 1.10) these steels do not show a definite yield plateau, i.e., continued yielding at constant stress. Yielding develops more gradually, and in the inelastic range the stress-strain curve continues to rise smoothly until the tensile strength is reached. Also, the spread between tensile strength f_s' and yield strength f_y is much smaller in prestressing steels than in reinforcing steels, and the total elongation at rupture ϵ_s' is much smaller.

For relatively small steel ratios, failure occurs by rupture of the steel when it has reached its tensile strength f_s'. In this case the beam is said to be *underreinforced*. The ultimate-strength theory, utilizing the equivalent rectangular stress block (Art. 2.4*f*), predicts such failure with ade-

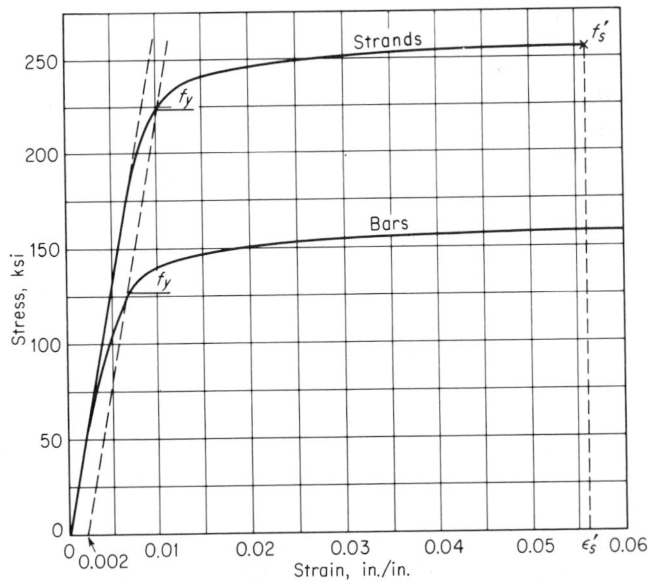

Fig. 2.35 Stress-strain curves for prestressing steels.

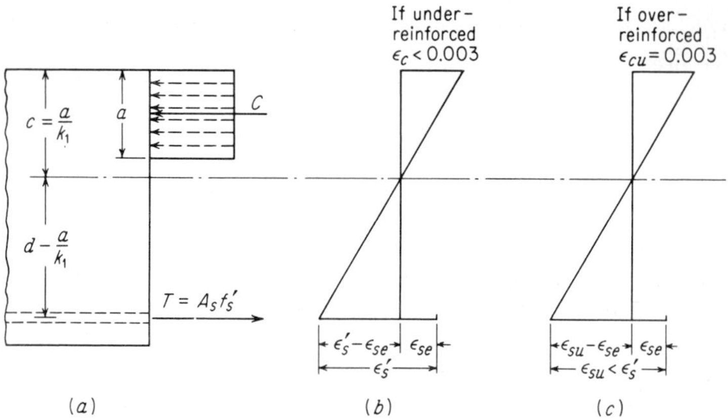

Fig. 2.36

quate accuracy. With reference to Fig. 2.36*a*, the tension force at failure, in this case, is

$$T = A_s f_s'$$

while, for a rectangular section, the compression force is

$$C = 0.85 f_c' ab$$

Equating the two, $T = C$, gives the depth of the rectangular stress block at failure:

$$a = \frac{A_s f_s'}{0.85 f_c' b} \tag{2.58}$$

The ultimate moment, then, is

$$M_u' = T\left(d - \frac{a}{2}\right) = A_s f_s'\left(d - \frac{A_s f_s'}{1.7 f_c' b}\right) \tag{2.59}$$

Introducing the steel ratio $p = A_s/bd$, this can be written in the alternative form

$$M_u' = A_s f_s' d\left(1 - 0.59p\frac{f_s'}{f_c'}\right) \tag{2.59a}$$

which is seen to be identical with Eq. (2.27*a*), except that the breaking strength of the strand f_s', rather than the yield point of the bars f_y, is seen to govern.

To determine whether the beam actually is underreinforced, one ascertains whether, at the instant of steel failure, i.e., when the steel has reached its ultimate breaking strain ϵ_s', the concrete strain ϵ_c is indeed smaller than the crushing strain, assumed to be equal to 0.003. Because the steel fractures in the inelastic range, the ultimate strain cannot be obtained by use of Young's modulus; it must be measured on the stress-strain diagram. For prestressing strands, ϵ_s' generally ranges from 0.045 to 0.060. From the strain distribution of Fig. 2.36*b* it is seen that

$$\epsilon_c = (\epsilon_s' - \epsilon_{se}) \frac{a/k_1}{d - a/k_1} \tag{2.60}$$

the depth a having been found from Eq. (2.58). If ϵ_c does not exceed the crushing strain, the beam is underreinforced, and Eqs. (2.59) and (2.59*a*) apply. If ϵ_c exceeds this value, the beam is *overreinforced*. That is, crushing of the concrete will occur before the steel has reached its tensile strength.

In the case of *overreinforced beams*, an explicit calculation of the ultimate moment is not possible for the following reason: The stress in the steel at the moment of concrete failure f_{su}', being smaller than f_s', is not known at the outset. Hence, the depth of the stress block cannot be computed [cf. Eq. (2.58)], making it impossible to calculate the moment of internal forces [cf. Eq. (2.59)]. In this case, successive approximation can be employed as follows: Assume a steel stress f_{su}', read the corresponding strain ϵ_{su} from the stress-strain diagram for the strand, and compute $T = A_s f_{su}'$. Then the depth of the stress block can be calculated from

$$a = \frac{A_s f_{su}'}{0.85 f_c' b} \tag{2.61}$$

and, from the strain relations of Fig. 2.36*c*, the steel strain is

$$\epsilon_{su} = 0.003 \frac{d - a/k_1}{a/k_1} + \epsilon_{se} \tag{2.62}$$

If this value differs from that which corresponds to the assumed steel stress f_{su}', the assumption was incorrect. A new value of ϵ_{su} is assumed on the basis of this first trial, the corresponding next approximation for f_{su}' read from the stress-strain curve, and the procedure repeated until adequate convergence is obtained, usually upon the second, or at most third, trial.

Once the steel stress f_{su}' and the corresponding depth of the stress block a are known, the ultimate moment is

$$M_u' = A_s f_{su}' \left(d - \frac{a}{2}\right) \tag{2.63}$$

The strain distributions of Fig. 2.36*b* and *c* and the calculations based on them neglect the small additional elastic compression strain caused in the concrete at the level of the steel by the prestressing force prior to load application. This strain is of the order of 5 per cent or less of the steel strain at failure, and neglecting it will cause no significant error in the analysis.

When a prestressed beam is underreinforced, failure is preceded by adequate warning, because the large inelastic steel strains cause visible cracking and sagging of the member. The failure of overreinforced beams can occur suddenly and without warning, for which reason this situation is generally avoided, except where special safeguards are used.

A particular, and undesirable, situation may obtain for beams with unusually small steel ratios. In this case, upon formation of tension cracks when the steel has to carry the entire tension, its total breaking strength $A_s f_s'$ may be insufficient to resist that moment at which the tension cracks form. Formation of the first tension crack is then followed by immediate rupture of the steel and sudden collapse of the beam. To guard against this eventuality, the cracking moment can be calculated from Eq. (2.57*b*), with the tension fiber stress f_{2d} taken as the modulus of rupture of the particular concrete. If this cracking moment exceeds the ultimate moment of the cracked section as calculated with Eq. (2.59), the described situation would obtain, and the beam should be redesigned.

These methods of analyzing the ultimate strengths of prestressed rectangular beams assume perfect bonding between steel and concrete. Only in this case is the steel strain equal to the strain in the immediately adjacent concrete so that the strain relationships of Fig. 2.36*b* and *c* hold. For so-called *bonded* members, i.e., where the concrete is poured around and in immediate contact with the strands, nearly perfect bond can be assumed. In some methods of prestressing, unbonded steel is employed. Corrections have been derived (Ref. 2.12) to account for possible slight bond deficiencies in bonded members and for the markedly reduced steel strain in unbonded members. Their design use is discussed in Chap. 11.

Example The beam of Fig. 2.37 is reinforced with prestressing strands whose stress-strain curve is that of Fig. 2.35, with $f_y = 224{,}000$ psi, $f_s' = 256{,}500$, $E_s = 27 \times 10^6$ psi; the concrete cylinder strength is $f_c' = 5000$ psi. The span is 36 ft. Determine (1) the available bending moment for superimposed (useful) loads M_s and (2) the ultimate strength of the beam. Permissible stresses at service load, to avoid cracking and inelastic deformations, are: $f_c = 0.45f_c' = 2250$ psi and $f_t = 6\sqrt{f_c'} = 425$ psi. Prestress after losses is $f_{se} = 140{,}000$ psi.

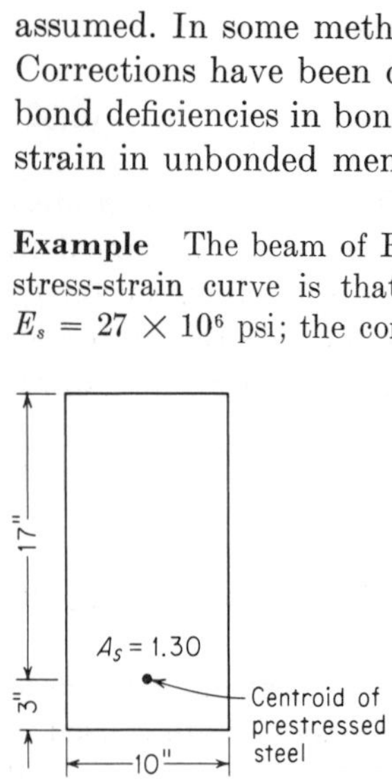

Fig. 2.37

The contribution of the small steel area to the properties of the transformed uncracked section being negligible, those of the gross section will be used. Then $I = 20^3 \times {}^{10}\!/_{12} = 6670$ in.^{4}; $A = 10 \times 20 = 200$ in.^{2} The prestressing force

$P = 140{,}000 \times 1.3 = 182{,}000$ lb. To calculate the maximum moment of the girder due to its own weight, one has weight per foot $= {}^{200}/_{144} \times 150 = 208$ lb per ft, and $M_g = (208 \times 36^2)/8 = 33{,}700$ ft-lb.

Checking the *outer fiber stresses after transfer* of prestress, the girder having deflected away from its soffit [cf. Eqs. (2.56)],

$$f_{\substack{1d\\2d}} = -\frac{182{,}000}{200} \pm \frac{182{,}000 \times 7 \times 10}{6670} \mp \frac{33{,}700 \times 12 \times 10}{6670} = \begin{matrix} 405 < 425 \text{ psi} \\ -2215 < -2250 \text{ psi} \end{matrix}$$

The moment M_s of the *superimposed loads* is limited to a value which will keep the maximum compression and tension stresses within the stipulated limits. Hence, two values of M_s are computed from Eqs. (2.57), one as governed by the tension stress f_t, and the other by the compression stress f_c. The smaller of the two, evidently, is the maximum admissible moment under design loading. Hence, equating f_{1d} to f_c in Eq. (2.57*a*),

$$-2250 - 405 = -\frac{M_{s1} \times 10}{6670} \qquad M_{s1} = 1{,}775{,}000 \text{ in.-lb}$$

Equating f_{2s} to f_t in Eq. (2.57*b*),

$$425 + 2215 = \frac{M_{s2} \times 10}{6670} \qquad M_{s2} = 1{,}760{,}000 \text{ in.-lb}$$

M_{s2}, being smaller than M_{s1}, is the limiting moment of the superimposed loads under service conditions; i.e.,

$$M_s = 1{,}760{,}000 \text{ in.-lb} = 146{,}700 \text{ ft-lb}$$

To calculate the *ultimate strength*, one must first check whether the beam is underreinforced. If so, it would fail by rupture of the strands at their tension strength of $f_s' = 256{,}500$ psi. Hence, the depth of the rectangular stress block [Eq. (2.58)] is

$$a = \frac{1.30 \times 256{,}500}{0.85 \times 5000 \times 10} = 7.85 \text{ in.}$$

For $f_c' = 5000$, from Eq. (2.31), $k_1 = 0.80$, so that the distance to the neutral axis is $a/k_1 = 7.85/0.80 = 9.8$ in. From Fig. 2.35 it is seen that the ultimate strain of the steel is $\epsilon_s' = 0.056$; the strain due to prestress after losses, $f_{se} = 140{,}000$ psi being in the elastic range of the steel (see Fig. 2.35), is $\epsilon_{se} = 140{,}000/27 \times 10^6 = 0.0052$. Then the maximum compression strain in the concrete [cf. Eq. (2.60)] would be

$$\epsilon_c = (0.056 - 0.0052)9.8/(17.0 - 9.8) = 0.069 > 0.003$$

This strain is seen to exceed by far the assumed ultimate strain of the concrete, which indicates that the concrete would crush before the steel ruptures. In this sense, then, the beam is overreinforced. Its ultimate strength will, therefore, be calculated by successive approximation.

The steel stress at the moment at which the concrete fails by crushing may be assumed to be $f'_{su} = 225{,}000$ psi; it is seen from Fig. 2.35 that this stress is in the nonlinear, i.e., inelastic, portion of the stress-strain curve. The corresponding steel strain is read from the curve to be $\epsilon_{su} = 0.010$. Then, from Eq. (2.61), $a = 6.9$ in., and, from Eq. (2.62), the corresponding steel strain is $\epsilon_{su} = 0.0081$. The strain read for the assumed f'_{su} from the stress-strain curve (0.010) and that calculated for the same f'_{su} from the strain relationships (0.081) differ by about 20 per cent. Hence, a second approximation is in order.

It will now be assumed that ϵ_{su} is about midway between the two values of the first trial, that is, $\epsilon_{su} = 0.0090$. The corresponding steel stress is read from Fig. 2.35 to be $f_{su} = 220{,}000$ psi. Repeating the steps of the previous calculations, one finds that for this stress $a = 6.75$ in. and, according to the assumed strain relations, $\epsilon_{su} = 0.0086$. It is seen that the two values of the steel strain for this approximation differ by less than 5 per cent. The accuracies of the various data and assumptions involved in this calculation being, at best, of the same order, no further approximation is indicated, and the steel stress at failure can be taken as $f'_{su} = 220{,}000$ psi.

Then, with $a = 6.75$ in., the ultimate moment is [Eq. (2.63)] $M'_u = 1.3 \times 220{,}000 \times 13.13 = 3{,}900{,}000$ in.-lb $= 325{,}000$ ft-lb. The service moment, consisting of that from the weight of the girder M_g and that from the superimposed loads M_s, is

$$M = 33{,}700 + 146{,}700 = 180{,}400 \text{ ft-lb}$$

The ultimate moment is $325/180.4 = 1.8$ times the design or service moment.

It is seen that this method of determining the ultimate strength of prestressed beams, which reflects the actual physical behavior of the member, presupposes a knowledge of the entire stress-strain curve of the particular steel. Even though minimum properties of prestressing steels are standardized in appropriate specifications, details of the shapes of stress-strain curves vary within limits. For this and other reasons, for routine design calculations, simpler approximate formulas have been developed on the basis of experimental information and calculations such as those just presented. These are discussed in Chap. 11.

REFERENCES

2.1 F. E. Richart and R. L. Brown: An Investigation of Reinforced Concrete Columns, *Univ. Illinois Eng. Exp. Sta. Bull.*, no. 267, 1934.

2.2 Hubert Rüsch: Researches toward a General Flexural Theory of Structural Concrete, *J. ACI*, vol. 57, p. 1, July, 1960.

2.3 L. B. Kriz: Ultimate Strength Criteria for Reinforced Concrete, *Proc. ASCE*, vol. 85, no. EM3, 1959; L. B. Kriz and S. L. Lee: Ultimate Strength of Overreinforced Beams, *Proc. ASCE*, vol. 86, no. EM3, 1960.

2.4 A. H. Mattock, L. B. Kriz, and E. Hognestad: Rectangular Concrete Stress Distribution in Ultimate Strength Design, *J. ACI*, vol. 57, p. 875, February, 1961.

2.5 Shear and Diagonal Tension, part 2, Report of ACI-ASCE Committee 326, *J. ACI*, vol. 59, p. 277, 1962 (with extensive bibliography).

2.6 S. A. Guralnick: Shear Strength of Reinforced Concrete Beams, *Trans. ASCE*, vol. 125, p. 603, 1960.

2.7 R. M. Mains: Measurement of the Distribution of Tensile and Bond Stresses along Reinforcing Bars, *J. ACI*, vol. 48, p. 225, 1951.

2.8 P. M. Ferguson and J. N. Thompson: Development Length of High Strength Reinforcing Bars, *J. ACI*, vol. 49, p. 887, 1962.

2.9 R. G. Mathey and David Watstein: Investigation of Bond in Beam and Pullout Specimens with High-yield-strength Deformed Bars, *J. ACI*, vol. 57, p. 1071, 1961.

2.10 W. W. Yu and G. Winter: Instantaneous and Long-time Deflections of Reinforced Concrete Beams under Working Loads, *J. ACI*, vol. 57, p. 29, 1960.

2.11 S. A. Guralnick: High-strength Deformed Steel Bars for Concrete Reinforcement, *J. ACI*, vol. 57, p. 241, 1960.

2.12 J. Warwaruk, M. S. Sozen, and C. P. Siess: Strength and Behavior in Flexure of Prestressed Concrete Beams, *Univ. Illinois Eng. Exp. Sta. Bull.*, no. 464, 1962.

chapter **3**

BEAMS

3-1, 3-2, 3-3, 3-4, 3-5, 3-6, 3-10, 3-11

GENERAL CONSIDERATIONS

3.1 Working-stress Design and Ultimate-strength Design It is evident from the discussion in Art. 2.4 that the design of reinforced-concrete structures can be performed by either of two alternative methods. The first of these directs attention to *stress conditions* within the structural member under *working loads* and is known as *working-stress design*. The second focuses on the *strength capacity* of the member at conditions corresponding to *failure* and is known as *ultimate-strength design*.

By working-stress methods, allowable stresses are established as some fraction of the stress capacities of the materials, i.e., the yield strength of the steel and the cylinder strength of the concrete. Members are proportioned so that these allowable stresses are not exceeded when working loads are applied. Working load is defined as the sum of the actual dead load of the structure and an estimate of the maximum live load which will be superimposed at some time during its life. In the concrete stress-strain curves of Fig. 2.2, it is seen that the concrete acts elastically as long as the maximum compressive stress is not more than about $\frac{1}{2}f'_c$. It follows directly that, as long as such stress levels are not exceeded in a reinforced-concrete flexural member, the stress variation in the concrete will be triangular, varying from zero at the neutral axis to a maximum at the extreme compression fiber (see Fig. 2.8*b*). Working-stress design is based on just such a stress distribution, on the grounds that elastic stress limits are not exceeded at working loads.

Ultimate-strength methods, on the other hand, base the design of members on conditions just before failure. Members are proportioned so that the full strength of the cross section is just utilized when the ultimate load is applied. The ultimate load is obtained by multiplying the actual dead load and the anticipated live load by separate overload factors greater than unity. The concrete compressive-stress distribution just before failure is quite different from the triangular distribution described above. At high stress levels, the nonlinearity of the upper part of the concrete stress-strain curve assumes great importance and results in a compressive-stress distribution in the beam such as that shown in Fig. 2.9. Ultimate-strength design is based on the nonlinear compressive-stress variation which is obtained before a member fails.

It may be evident, on further consideration, that working-stress design methods can give no information regarding the actual factor of safety against failure of a reinforced member. The two safety factors often inferred, i.e., (yield stress)/(working stress) in the steel, if steel controls, and (cylinder strength)/(working stress) in the concrete, if concrete controls, are not correct, because in the inelastic range stresses and loads are not proportional. However, elastic analysis does give a realistic representation of conditions in a member at working load and therefore is useful in predicting service-load behavior characteristics such as deflection and crack width. Ultimate-strength methods, on the other hand, permit an accurate appraisal of the strength capacities of members and so permit an evaluation of the actual factor of safety against failure. This is generally the matter of greatest concern to the structural engineer. However, strength procedures give little information about conditions at service load.

Reinforced-concrete structures must perform satisfactorily at working loads but must also be adequately safe against collapse. Consequently, if members are proportioned by working-stress methods, safeguards must be included to ensure that the actual factor of safety against failure is at least as large as implied. Conversely, ultimate-strength design methods must include adequate safeguards to ensure that conditions at working load, particularly crack widths and deflections, are satisfactory.

In the chapters which follow, the design of reinforced-concrete members will be treated first from the point of view of ultimate strength, then from the point of view of allowable stresses. While the methods are quite different in fundamental concept, many analogies will be apparent.

3.2 Historical Summary Historically, it is interesting to observe that early proposals for the design of reinforced-concrete members included both working-stress theories and ultimate-strength theories (Ref. 3.1). The theories advanced by Koenen (1886), Neumann (1890), and Coignet and Tedesco (1894) were elastic theories which assumed a linear variation of concrete stress with distance from the neutral axis. The theories of Thullie (1897) and Ritter (1899) were based on a prediction of the ultimate strengths of beams and assumed nonlinear stress distributions.

Because of its relative simplicity, the "straight-line" theory proposed by Coignet and Tedesco gained general acceptance about 1900. It was adopted by code-writing organizations such as the Joint Committee on Standard Specifications for Concrete and Reinforced Concrete (1909), which introduced the concepts of working loads and working stresses. While modifications were made over the ensuing years, the basic concepts of the straight-line theory became firmly established, to the extent that its limitations were generally overlooked.

In the 1930's, however, extensive testing of columns initiated by the American Concrete Institute indicated that measured steel stresses were considerably higher than those predicted by elastic theory. Work by Lyse, Slater, and Richart led to design formulas for columns which could only be described as ultimate-strength formulas in concept, although they were included in modified form in the working-stress design specifications of that time. A 1931 paper by Emperger generated intensive investigation into the ultimate strengths of beams, with significant work done in the United States by Jensen and Whitney.

In the early 1950's, a joint ASCE-ACI committee was organized in the United States to study current knowledge of ultimate-strength design methods and to coordinate research activities. In 1956 that committee published its "Report on Ultimate Strength Design," which contained specific design recommendations. Its proposed formulas were incorporated on an optional basis in the 1956 ACI Building Code (ACI 318-56),[1] and

[1] Throughout this text, repeated reference will be made to the American Concrete Institute and its recommendations. This organization of more than 10,000 members is dedicated to the advancement of concrete technology and of the analysis, design, and construction of reinforced-concrete buildings. As one part of its activity, the American Concrete Institute has published the widely recognized "Building Code Requirements for Reinforced Concrete" (ACI 318-63), which serves as a guide in the design and construction of reinforced-concrete buildings. The Code has no official status in itself. However, it is generally regarded as the most authoritative statement of current good

the present ACI Building Code (ACI 318-63) includes a greatly expanded treatment of ultimate-strength design (U.S.D.).

At the same time the present Code continues to include a full set of provisions for working-stress design (W.S.D.). The choice of using U.S.D. or W.S.D. is left to the designer. Over the last two decades, working-stress design has been subjected to a large number of more or less arbitrary adjustments. These were necessary where an analysis based strictly on assumed elastic behavior gave results which had no consistent relation to the actual usable carrying capacity of the member. These adjustments will be discussed in their proper places. Thus, while in earlier times working stresses were calculated on a rational elastic basis but showed no consistent relation to usable strength, the present working-stress design methods in the Code are a mixture of elastic calculations, ultimate-strength concepts, and arbitrary adjustments, all expressed in terms of allowable stresses under design load. In contrast, ultimate-strength design methods are based on a consistent approach which relates the design load that can be allowed on the structure to the actual ultimate strength of the members, as nearly as present knowledge permits this strength to be computed. Working-stress design is retained in the Code primarily because of the long habit of the profession of thinking in terms of elastic stresses. It seems reasonable to assume that the more realistic ultimate-strength methods, which are already widely used today, will become increasingly dominant.

SAFETY PROVISIONS IN REINFORCED-CONCRETE DESIGN

3.3 Safety and Serviceability To serve its purpose, a structure must be safe against collapse and serviceable in use. Serviceability requires that deflections be adequately small, that cracks, if any, be kept to tolerable limits, that vibrations be minimized, etc. Safety requires that the strength of the structure be adequate for all loads which may foreseeably act on it. If the strength of a structure, built as designed, could be predicted with precision, and if the loads and their internal effects (moments, shears, axial forces) were known with equal precision, then safety could be assured by providing a carrying capacity just barely in excess of the known loads. However, there are a number of sources of uncertainty in the analysis, design, and construction of reinforced-concrete structures.

---

practice in the field of reinforced concrete. As a result, it has been incorporated by law into countless municipal and regional building codes, which do have legal status. Its provisions thereby attain, in effect, legal significance. Most reinforced-concrete structures in the United States and in some other countries are designed in accordance with the current ACI Building Code.

These sources of uncertainty, which require a definite margin of safety, may be listed as follows:

1. Actual loads may differ from those assumed in the design.
2. Actual loads may be distributed in a manner different from that assumed in the design.
3. The assumptions and simplifications inherent in any analysis may result in calculated load effects—moments, shears, etc.—different from those which a more rigorous analysis would furnish.
4. The actual structural behavior may differ from that assumed, owing to imperfect knowledge (see Chap. 2).
5. Actual member dimensions may differ from those specified by the designer.
6. Reinforcement may not be in its proper position.
7. Actual material strength may be different from that specified by the designer.

In addition, in establishing a safety specification, consideration must be given to the consequences of failure. In some cases, a failure would merely be an inconvenience. In other cases, loss of life and significant loss of property may be involved. A further consideration should be the nature of the failure, should it occur. A gradual failure, with ample warning permitting remedial measures, is preferable to a sudden, unexpected collapse.

It is evident that the selection of an appropriate margin of safety is not a simple matter. While progress has been made toward rational safety provisions in design codes, the ideal safety specification has not yet been written.

3.4 Applied Loads The loads that act on structures can be divided into two broad categories: *dead load* and *live load*. Dead loads are those which are constant in magnitude and fixed in location. Usually the major part of the dead load is the weight of the structure itself. Live loads, on the other hand, may be either fully or partially in place, or not present at all. They may change in location. Live loads are usually established by local or regional building codes (see Art. 9.2) and include some margin of safety against overload and some allowance for dynamic effect.

If the actual magnitude of live load acting on a structure is plotted against the frequency of occurrence, it is reasonable to expect the results to fall along a curve known as a *normal distribution curve*, as shown in Fig. 3.1*a*. A certain mean value L_m would be observed. Most frequently, the applied load would be close to the mean, but, infrequently, loads considerably larger or smaller than the mean would be observed. A symmetrical distribution would be expected.

If the vertical ordinates were plotted as relative frequency rather than absolute frequency (dividing each ordinate value by the total number of

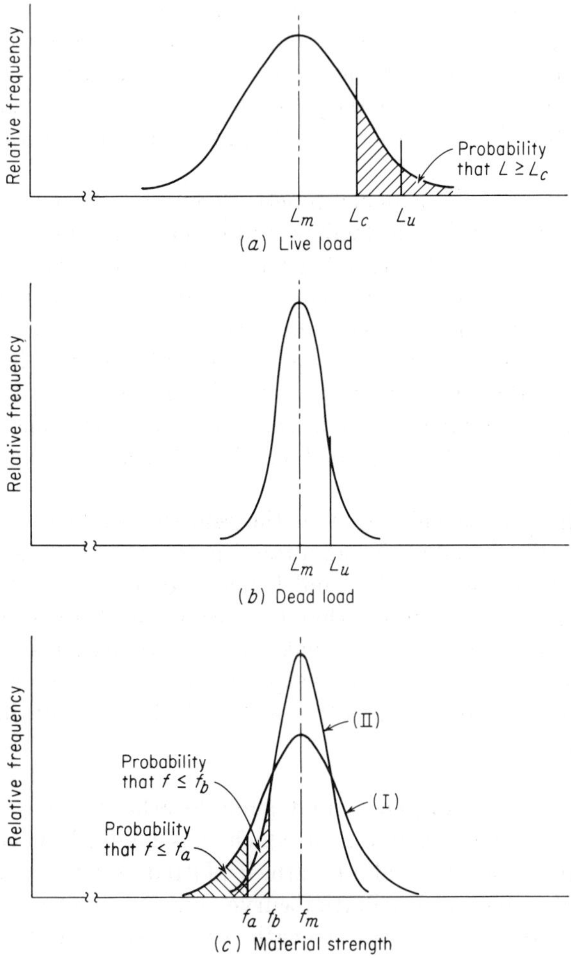

Fig. 3.1 Frequency distribution of loads and strength.

occurrences), then a graph would result which could be used to estimate the probability that the actual load would be greater than, or less than, a certain value. For example, 50 per cent of the area under the curve falls to the left of the mean value; hence there is a 50 per cent probability that a given applied load would be less than the mean value. The properties of normal distribution curves are mathematically defined and have been tabulated in terms of the variability of the given data. It is thus possible to establish the probability that a certain selected load would not be exceeded, knowing the variability of the data and the ratio between that load and the mean load (Ref. 3.2).

It is generally recognized that the value of live load legally specified by building codes L_c is considerably above the average value of load L_m that will act upon a structure. It has been estimated, for example, that legally specified loads would be exceeded in only about 10 per cent of the cases. Note that, as indicated by the shape of the curve, no matter how high the ratio of L_c/L_m, there is still a finite probability that L_c will be exceeded.

A similar relative-frequency function could be plotted for dead loads. The variability of the dead loads would be much smaller, however; dead loads can be predicted with a higher degree of accuracy than can live loads. The total area under the curve of relative frequency would still be 100 per cent, but most of the values would be very close to the mean. Figure 3.1*b* shows a relative-frequency distribution for dead loads, for comparison with Fig. 3.1*a*. With such information about live loads and dead loads, overload factors can be selected to obtain ultimate-load values L_u for design that will be exceeded only in an acceptably small percentage of cases.

An additional consideration in the selection of loads to be used in design is the likelihood of the simultaneous occurrence of various types of loads, e.g., occupancy loads, wind loads, and seismic loads. It appears highly unlikely, for example, that full occupancy load would be acting at the instant of a severe earthquake. Most specifications recognize this. The designer must allow in his design for the most unfavorable distribution and combination of loads that are likely to occur during the life of the structure.

3.5 Structural Strength Fundamental to the strength of a structure is the strength of the material of which it is made. It is convenient to assume that actual material strength, if plotted as a frequency function, would follow a normal distribution curve (Fig. 3.1*c*). The curve would be symmetrical about the mean strength, the mean strength would occur most frequently, and some, but relatively few, strengths far from the mean would occur.

It may be evident that the degree of "peakedness" of the material strength curve would be a function of the quality control of material production. A producer with only average quality control would obtain curve I, while a producer with a higher degree of control would obtain curve II. If a design strength is specified, and if it is stated that in only 1 case in 1000 may the actual strength be less than that specified, producer II could use material with a mean strength much closer to the specified strength than could producer I.

In addition to the strength of the material, structural strength will depend upon the care with which a structure is built, which in turn is a function of the quality of supervision and inspection. Member sizes may differ from specified dimensions, and reinforcement may be out of position. In this connection, it is observed that care in workmanship is most significant for thin members. If a construction tolerance of $\frac{1}{8}$ in. is accepted, for example, and if the thickness of a thin slab is smaller than its specified dimension by the full allowed amount, then this would represent a greater degree of understrength than would the same tolerance applied to a deep beam. The same can be said with regard to the placement of bar reinforcement, which is very critical for slabs as compared with deep beams. Ideally, the selection of safety margin should reflect this difference.

If the distributions of all the uncertainties listed in Art. 3.3 were statistically known in the manner described for loads and material strengths, then a safety margin could be selected as follows: Evidently one cannot design a structure that is 100 per cent safe against collapse, because small probabilities of considerable understrength or unusually high overloads can never be completely eliminated. One could, however, agree on a tolerably small probability of failure, say 1:100,000, and calculate, from the known distribution of uncertainties, that margin of safety which provides this small, specified probability (Ref. 3.2). Because the extensive statistical information necessary for this method exists only fragmentarily at present, today's safety provisions in design codes are a blend of rational approach, past experience, judgment, and compromise.

3.6 Safety Provisions of the ACI Building Code The ACI Code contains recommendations for the design of reinforced-concrete structures by two alternative methods, one based on stress conditions at working loads, and the other based on the ultimate-strength capacity of the structure. The working-stress provisions introduce the safety factor by means of allowable stresses, while the ultimate-strength provisions use separate overload and capacity-reduction factors.

Working-stress provisions The loads used in the design of members by working-stress methods are the computed dead loads and the live loads legally specified by the building code in force at the construction site. Working stresses, or allowable stresses, are established at approximately one-half the respective material strengths; they are not to be exceeded at full working loads. The provisions of the Code with respect to allowable stresses are reprinted in Table 3.1 (concrete) and Table 3.2 (steel). Because of the improbability of full occupancy load and full wind or earthquake load occurring at the same moment, members subject to wind or earthquake forces combined with other loads may be proportioned for stresses one-third greater than those specified in Tables 3.1 and 3.2, provided that the section required is not less than that required for the combination of dead and live load.

***Table* 3.1 Allowable stresses in concrete**

Description		Allowable stresses: For any strength of concrete	For strength of concrete shown below: $f'_c =$ 2500 psi	$f'_c =$ 3000 psi	$f'_c =$ 4000 psi	$f'_c =$ 5000 psi
Modulus of elasticity ratio n		$\frac{29{,}000{,}000}{w^{1.5}33\sqrt{f'_c}}$				
For concrete weighing 145 pcf	n		10	9	8	7
Flexure f_c:						
Extreme fiber stress in compression	f_c	$0.45f'_c$	1125	1350	1800	2250
Extreme fiber stress in tension in plain concrete footings and walls	f_c	$1.6\sqrt{f'_c}$	80	88	102	113
Shear v (as a measure of diagonal tension at a distance d from the face of the support):						
Beams with no web reinforcement*	v_c	$1.1\sqrt{f'_c}$	55*	60*	70*	78*
Joists with no web reinforcement	v_c	$1.2\sqrt{f'_c}$	61	66	77	86
Members with vertical or inclined web reinforcement or combined bent bars and stirrups	v	$5\sqrt{f'_c}$	250	274	316	354
Slabs and footings (peripheral shear)	v_c	$2\sqrt{f'_c}$	100*	110*	126*	141*
Bearing f_c:						
On full area		$0.25f'_c$	625	750	1000	1250
On one-third area or less†		$0.375f'_c$	938	1125	1500	1875

* Special provisions exist for lightweight aggregate concrete.

† This increase shall be permitted only when the least distance between the edges of the loaded and unloaded areas is a minimum of one-fourth the parallel side dimension of the loaded area. The allowable bearing stress on a reasonably concentric area greater than one-third but less than the full area shall be interpolated between the values given.

Table 3.2 Allowable stresses in steel

a. In tension	
For billet-steel or axle-steel concrete reinforcing bars of structural grade	18,000 psi
For main reinforcement, 3/8 in. or less in diameter, in one-way slabs of not more than 12-ft span, 50 per cent of the minimum yield strength specified by the American Society for Testing and Materials for the reinforcement used, but not to exceed	30,000 psi
For deformed bars with a yield strength of 60,000 psi or more and in sizes #11 and smaller	24,000 psi
For all other reinforcement	20,000 psi
b. In compression, vertical column reinforcement	
Spiral columns, 40 per cent of the minimum yield strength, but not to exceed	30,000 psi
Tied columns, 85 per cent of the value for spiral columns, but not to exceed	25,500 psi
Composite and combination columns:	
Structural-steel sections	
For ASTM A36 steel	18,000 psi
For ASTM A7 steel	16,000 psi
Cast-iron sections	10,000 psi
Steel pipe	special provisions
c. In compression, flexural members	special provisions
d. Spirals (yield-strength)	
Hot-rolled rods, intermediate grade	40,000 psi
Hot-rolled rods, hard grade	50,000 psi
Hot-rolled rods, ASTM A432 grade and cold-drawn wire	60,000 psi

Ultimate-strength provisions When designing by ultimate-strength methods, a separation is made between the possibilities of overload and understrength. The computed dead load and the legally specified live load are increased by overload factors to obtain the ultimate loads to be used for design. Overload factors are selected such that these ultimate loads have an acceptably small probability of ever being exceeded. In the selection of overload factors for *live load* L, recognition is given to the fact that legally specified loads themselves include an overload factor (see Fig. 3.1*a*). The recommended factor of increase for live load is 1.8.

Dead loads D have a much smaller variability than live loads. However, there is no prior overload factor included in computed dead loads, as there was for specified live loads. Consistent with these two facts, the overload factor recommended for dead loads is 1.5. The specific recommendation is made that, for structures in such locations and of such proportions that the effects of wind and earthquake may be neglected, the design capacity shall be:

$$U = 1.5D + 1.8L \qquad (A)$$

For structures in whose design *wind loading* W must be included, the design capacity shall be

$$U = 1.25(D + L + W) \tag{B}$$

or

$$U = 0.9D + 1.1W \tag{C}$$

whichever is greater, provided that no member shall have a capacity less than that required by Eq. (A). For structures in which *earthquake loading* E must be considered, E is substituted for W in Eqs. (B) and (C). The loads L, W, and E are the legally specified loads.

Regarding wind loads, requirement (C) governs in those cases in which the dead load tends to stabilize the structure and the wind load tends to produce failure. For instance, the wind load tends to overturn a free-standing smokestack, while its own weight counteracts this tendency. To provide safety, the smallest probable dead load must be combined with the largest probable wind load, which is the reason for requirement (C).

In predictions of the ultimate strength of the structure, the Code recognizes that the completed structure or member may be understrength because of understrength materials, inaccuracies in workmanship, manufacturing tolerances, and variations in the degree of supervision and control. Some recognition is given to the relative importance of the members in a structure, i.e., the consequences of failure, and to the state of knowledge of failure mechanisms. The Code provides that the following capacity-reduction factors be applied to the theoretical member strengths calculated for perfect materials and workmanship:

For flexure: $\phi = 0.90$
For diagonal tension, bond, and anchorage: $\phi = 0.85$
For spirally reinforced members with axial loads: $\phi = 0.75$
For tied members with axial load: $\phi = 0.70$

To provide safety, the theoretical ultimate strength, reduced by the coefficient ϕ, must be adequate to resist the ultimate loads specified by Eqs. (A) to (C).

FLEXURAL DESIGN

3.7 Singly Reinforced Rectangular Beams: Ultimate-strength Design It was shown in Chap. 2 that singly reinforced beams (i.e., beams reinforced with tensile steel only) can fail in two principal ways. If the steel ratio p is relatively low, then at some value of the load the steel will commence yielding. As it yields, the neutral axis migrates upward, the area available to resist compression is reduced, and a secondary

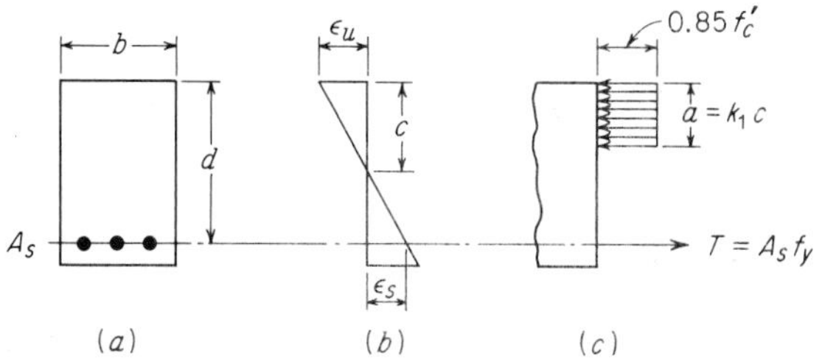

Fig. 3.2

compression failure occurs. If, on the other hand, the steel ratio is high, the concrete will reach its ultimate capacity before the steel yields. While failure due to yielding is a gradual one, with adequate warning of collapse, failure due to crushing of the concrete is sudden and without warning. The first type of failure is therefore preferred. It can be ensured by setting an upper limit on the ratio of tensile reinforcement.[1]

It was shown in the preceding chapter that the balanced steel ratio, such that the steel starts to yield and the concrete reaches its ultimate strain capacity at precisely the same load, is given by the expression

$$p_b = \alpha \frac{0.003}{f_y/E_s + 0.003} \frac{f'_c}{f_y} \tag{2.29}$$

Using the conventional designation $\alpha = 0.85k_1$ and substituting $E_s =$ 29,000,000 psi one obtains the ACI Code equation for balanced steel ratio:

$$p_b = 0.85k_1 \frac{f'_c}{f_y} \frac{87{,}000}{87{,}000 + f_y} \tag{3.1}$$

where $k_1 = 0.85$ for $f'_c \leq 4000$ psi and decreases by 0.05 for every 1000 psi above 4000 psi. The Code specifies that the steel ratio shall not exceed $0.75p_b$, in order that yielding-type failure be ensured. Thus:

$$p_{\max} = 0.75p_b \tag{3.2}$$

and, for all sections designed according to this specification, $f_s = f_y$ at failure. Based on the equivalent rectangular compressive-stress distribution described in Art. 2.4*f* and shown in Fig. 3.2, one obtains

$$a = \frac{A_s f_y}{0.85f'_c b} = \frac{p f_y d}{0.85f'_c} \tag{3.3}$$

[1] A third, undesirable, mode of failure may occur in very lightly reinforced beams. If the ultimate resisting moment of the cracked section is less than the moment which produces cracking of the transformed, uncracked section, then the beam will fail immediately upon formation of the crack. In order to avoid this type of failure, which would occur without warning of collapse, the ACI Code establishes a minimum tensile steel ratio equal to $200/f_y$.

and

$$M'_u = A_s f_y \left(d - \frac{a}{2}\right) \tag{3.4a}$$

By substituting the value of a obtained from Eq. (3.3), and substituting pbd for A_s, into Eq. (3.4*a*), one obtains the alternative expression

$$M'_u = pf_y bd^2 \left(1 - 0.59p \frac{f_y}{f'_c}\right) \tag{3.4b}$$

which is the same as Eq. (2.27*a*). In accordance with the safety provisions of the Code, this ultimate-moment capacity M'_u is reduced by the factor ϕ (equal to 0.90 for flexural members) to obtain the ultimate moment M_u to be used in design, so that

$$M_u = \phi A_s f_y \left(d - \frac{a}{2}\right) \tag{3.5a}$$

$$M_u = \phi p f_y bd^2 \left(1 - 0.59p \frac{f_y}{f'_c}\right) \tag{3.5b}$$

Rectangular beam, example 1: ultimate-moment capacity of a given section A rectangular beam has a width of 12 in. and an effective depth to the centroid of the reinforcing steel of 17.5 in. It is reinforced with four No. 9 bars[1] in one row. If $f_y = 60{,}000$ psi and $f'_c = 4000$ psi, what is the ultimate-moment capacity of the beam to be used in design?

The actual steel ratio, $p = 4.00/(12 \times 17.5) = 0.0190$, is found to be less than

$$p_{\max} = 0.75 \times 0.85k_1 \frac{f'_c}{f_y} \frac{87{,}000}{87{,}000 + f_y}$$

$$= 0.75 \times 0.85^2 \times 4/60 \times 87/147 = 0.0214$$

Consequently failure by yielding is assured. Then

$$a = \frac{A_s f_y}{0.85 f'_c b} = \frac{4.0 \times 60}{0.85 \times 4 \times 12} = 5.89 \text{ in.}$$

$$M_u = \phi A_s f_y \left(d - \frac{a}{2}\right) = 0.90 \times 4.0 \times 60(17.5 - 5.89/2) = 3140 \text{ in.-kips}$$

Rectangular beam, example 2: proportioning a section to resist a given moment Determine the cross section of concrete and area of steel required for a simply supported rectangular beam with a span of 15 ft which is to carry a computed dead load of 1.18 kips per ft and a working live load of 2.30 kips per ft. A 3000-psi concrete is to be used, and the specified steel yield stress is 40,000 psi.

[1] See Table 2, Appendix B, for bar areas.

Overload factors are first applied to the given working loads to obtain the ultimate load for which the beam is to be designed:

$$\text{Ultimate } w_t = 1.5 \times 1.18 + 1.8 \times 2.30 = 5.92 \text{ kips per ft}$$
$$M_u = \tfrac{1}{8} \times 5.92 \times 15^2 \times 12 = 2000 \text{ in.-kips}$$

The dimensions of the concrete will be directly influenced by the designer's choice of steel ratio. Selecting the maximum steel ratio $p = 0.75p_b$, which will result in the minimum concrete section,

$$p = 0.75 \times 0.85^2 \frac{f'_c}{f_y} \frac{87}{127} = 0.371 \frac{f'_c}{f_y}$$
$$M_u = \phi p f_y b d^2 \left(1 - 0.59p \frac{f_y}{f'_c}\right)$$
$$M_u = 0.90 \times 0.371 f'_c b d^2 (1 - 0.59 \times 0.371) = 0.260 f'_c b d^2$$
$$bd^2 = \frac{M_u}{0.260 f'_c} = \frac{2000}{0.260 \times 3} = 2560 \text{ in.}^3$$

A concrete section of 10 in. width and 16 in. effective depth will be used. For those dimensions,

$$A_s = pbd = 0.371 \times \tfrac{3}{40} \times 10 \times 16 = 4.44 \text{ in.}^2$$

Three No. 11 bars will be used, providing an area of 4.68 in.^{2}

A somewhat larger beam cross section using less steel may be more economical. In addition, the deflections associated with beams of minimum cross section may be undesirably large. The Code requires a check of deflections if a steel ratio larger than $p = 0.18 f'_c/f_y$ is used (see Art. 3.25).

As an alternative solution, the beam will be redesigned with $p = 0.18 f'_c/f_y$. In this case,

$$p = 0.18 \frac{f'_c}{f_y}$$
$$M_u = 0.90 \times 0.18 f'_c b d^2 (1 - 0.59 \times 0.18)$$
$$M_u = 0.145 f'_c b d^2$$
$$bd^2 = \frac{2000}{0.145 \times 3} = 4600 \text{ in.}^3$$

A beam 11.5 in. wide with an effective depth of 20 in. will be used. For this case,

$$A_s = 0.18 \times \tfrac{3}{40} \times 11.5 \times 20 = 3.11 \text{ in.}^2$$

Four No. 8 bars will be used, providing an area of 3.14 in.^{2}

It is apparent that an infinite number of solutions to the stated problem are possible, depending upon the steel ratio selected. That ratio may vary, according to the Code, from an upper limit of $0.75p_b$ to a lower limit of $200/f_y$.

Certain design aids suggest themselves. For example, it would be convenient in practice to graph the relation between the steel ratio p and the value $M_u/\phi bd^2$ for frequently used values of f'_c and f_y. A typical set of such design curves is given by Graph 1, Appendix B.[1] Other ultimate-strength design aids are given in Ref. 3.3.

Rectangular-beam problems can generally be classified as review problems and design problems. The first example illustrated a review problem, in which the section dimensions and material strength capacities were given and it was required to find the moment capacity. The second example illustrated a design problem, in which the design moment was known, as were the material strengths, and it was required to find the proportions of the cross section. There is a certain type of problem which falls into neither category, but which occurs frequently. In this case, the concrete dimensions are given and are known to be adequate to carry the specified moment. It is required only to find the necessary steel area. Typically, this situation obtains at critical design sections of continuous beams, in which the concrete dimensions are often kept constant although the steel reinforcement varies along the span. The concrete dimensions b and d are determined at the maximum moment section, usually at one of the supports. At other supports and at midspan locations, where moments are smaller, the concrete dimensions are known to be adequate, and only the tensile steel is to be found.

Rectangular beam, example 3: determination of steel area for a given moment Using the concrete dimensions of the preceding example ($b = 11.5$ in. and $d = 20$ in.) and the same specified stresses, find the steel area required to resist a design ultimate moment of 1600 in.-kips.

It is possible to obtain a direct solution to this problem by solving Eq. (3.5*b*) for p, which would appear in quadratic form. A somewhat quicker solution may usually be obtained by means of Eq. (3.5*a*). A reasonable value for a is assumed, and A_s is found. By use of Eq. (3.3), a revised estimate of a is obtained, and a modified A_s is obtained from Eq. (3.5*a*). This method can be made to converge

[1] To solve the preceding example by means of Graph 1, for $f_y = 40{,}000$ psi and $f'_c = 3000$ psi, one reads $p_{max} = 0.028$ (at the end of the given curve). The corresponding value of $M_u/\phi bd^2$, from the graph, is 870 psi. Then

$$bd^2 = M_u/(870 \times 0.9) = (2000 \times 1000)/785 = 2560 \text{ in.}^3$$

If $b = 10$ in. and $d = 16$ in. are selected as before, then

$$A_s = pbd = 0.028 \times 10 \times 16 = 4.48 \text{ in.}^2$$

The alternative solution used a steel ratio $p = 0.18f'_c/f_y = 0.18 + 3/40 = 0.0135$. From the graph, $M_u/\phi bd^2 = 483$, and $bd^2 = 2000 \times 1000/(483 \times 0.9) = 4600$ in.^{3} With $b = 11.5$ in. and $d = 20$ in., $A_s = pbd = 0.0135 \times 11.5 \times 20 = 3.11$ in.^{2}

very rapidly to the final answer. For example,

Assume $a = 4$ in.

$$A_s = \frac{M_u}{\phi f_y(d - a/2)} = \frac{1600}{0.90 \times 40(20 - 2)} = 2.47 \text{ in.}^2$$

Check:

$$a = \frac{A_s f_y}{0.85 f'_c b} = \frac{2.47 \times 40}{0.85 \times 3 \times 11.5} = 3.38 \text{ in.}$$

Assume $a = 3.30$ in.

$$A_s = \frac{1600}{0.90 \times 40 \times (20 - 1.65)} = 2.42 \text{ in.}^2$$

Check:

$$a = 3.38 \times 2.42/2.47 = 3.30 \text{ in.}$$

as assumed. Use $A_s = 2.42$ in.^{2} Four No. 7 bars will be provided.

Problems such as this can readily be solved using Graph 1. The required steel ratio p can be found for the known $M_u/\phi bd^2$. $A_s = pbd$ is then easily determined.

In the design of reinforced-concrete structures, the decision to use either a relatively high- or low-strength concrete or steel depends upon the economics of the particular case, the availability of materials, the importance of special requirements such as minimum member size, and concern for such factors as deflection and crack widths. In general, higher-strength concrete is attained by increasing the amount of cement in the mix. Since cement is the most expensive of the several ingredients, the cost of the concrete increases substantially with increasing strength. On the other hand, high-strength steels, produced either metallurgically or by cold-working lower-strength bars, are available at only slightly increased cost. It can be concluded that, while at the present time steel with a yield stress of 40 ksi is most widely used, in the near future bars of substantially higher strength will come into general use. Concrete strengths will probably remain at about present levels or increase somewhat with improved production methods. The reader may also wish to study Graph 1, Appendix B, with regard to the effect of changes in f_y and f'_c at various steel ratios.

PROBLEMS

U.S.D.: Singly reinforced rectangular beams:

1. A tensile-reinforced beam has a width of 10 in. and an effective depth of 20 in. to the centroid of the bars, which are placed all in one row. If steel with a yield stress of 60,000 psi is used with concrete having $f'_c = 4000$ psi, find the

ultimate resisting moment M_u for the following cases: (*a*) A_s = 2 No. 8 bars, (*b*) A_s = 2 No. 10 bars, (*c*) A_s = 3 No. 10 bars.

2. A singly reinforced rectangular beam is to be designed, with effective depth 1.5 times the width, to carry a working live load of 1500 plf, in addition to its own weight, on a 24-ft simple span. Using U.S.D. methods, with $f_y = 40{,}000$ psi and $f'_c = 4000$ psi, determine the required concrete dimensions and steel reinforcement (*a*) for $p = 0.18f'_c/f_y$ and (*b*) for $p = p_{max}$. Comment on your results, and include a sketch of each cross section drawn to scale.

3. A rectangular beam is to span 20 ft between simple supports and must carry a parallel partition weighing 800 plf of beam, in addition to a concentrated live load of 15,000 lb which acts at midspan. Design the beam, using $f_y = 50{,}000$ psi and $f'_c = 5000$ psi.

4. A four-span continuous beam of constant rectangular section is supported at *A*, *B*, *C*, *D*, and *E*. Ultimate moments resulting from analysis are:

At supports, ft-kips	*At midspan, ft-kips*
$M_a = 92$	$M_{ab} = 105$
$M_b = 147$	$M_{bc} = 92$
$M_c = 134$	$M_{cd} = 92$
$M_d = 147$	$M_{de} = 105$
$M_e = 92$	

Determine the required concrete dimensions for this beam, using $d = 1.75b$, and find the required reinforcement for all critical moment sections. Use a maximum steel ratio of $p = 0.50p_b$, $f_y = 60{,}000$ psi, and $f'_c = 5000$ psi.

3.8 Doubly Reinforced Rectangular Beams: Ultimate-strength Design

If a beam is limited in cross section, it may happen that the concrete cannot develop the compression force required to resist the given bending moment. In this case reinforcing is added in the compression zone, resulting in a so-called *doubly reinforced* beam, i.e., one with compression as well as tension reinforcement. Working-stress design indicates in an excessively restrictive manner that compression reinforcement is required for an economically designed beam whenever the steel ratio exceeds the value p_e [Eq. (3.24)]. In contrast, ultimate-strength design recognizes the much larger true compression capacity of the concrete. It calls for compression reinforcement only when the steel ratio exceeds the much larger value $0.75p_b$. In consequence, the use of compression reinforcement has decreased markedly with the introduction and wider use of ultimate-strength design methods. However, there are situations in which it is used for reasons other than strength. It has been found that the inclusion of some compression steel will reduce the long-term deflections of members (see Art. 2.7). In addition, in some cases, bars will be placed in the compression zone for minimum-moment loading (see Art. 8.9) or as stirrup support bars continuous throughout the beam span (see

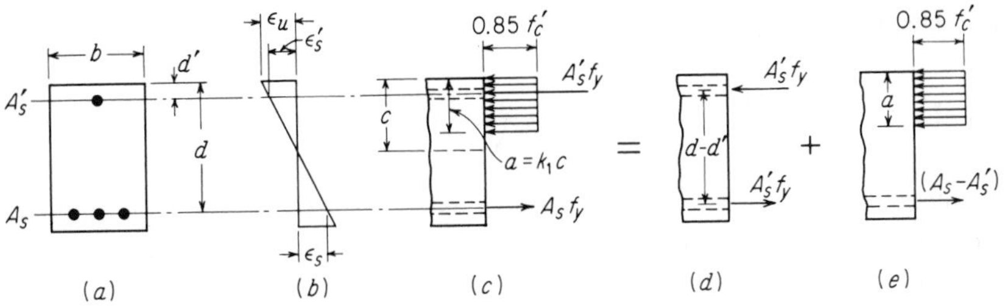

Fig. 3.3 Doubly reinforced rectangular beam.

Art. 3.19). It is often desirable to account for the presence of such reinforcement in flexural design.

If, in a doubly reinforced beam, the tensile-steel ratio p is equal to or less than $p_{max} = 0.75p_b$, the strength of the beam may be approximated within acceptable limits by disregarding the compression bars. The strength of such a beam will be controlled by tensile yielding, and the lever arm of the resisting moment will ordinarily be but little affected by the presence of the compression bars.

If the tensile steel ratio is larger than $0.75p_b$, a somewhat more elaborate analysis is indicated. In Fig. 3.3*a*, a rectangular beam cross section is shown with compression steel A_s' placed a distance d' from the compression face, and with tensile steel A_s at effective depth d. If it is assumed for the moment that both A_s' and A_s are stressed to f_y at failure, the total resisting moment can be thought of as the sum of two parts. The first part, M_1', is provided by the couple consisting of the force in the compression steel A_s' and the force in an equal area of tension steel:

$$M_1' = A_s'f_y(d - d') \tag{3.6}$$

as shown in Fig. 3.3*d*. The second part, M_2', is the contribution of the remaining tension steel $(A_s - A_s')$ acting with the compression concrete:

$$M_2' = (A_s - A_s')f_y\left(d - \frac{a}{2}\right) \tag{3.7}$$

where the depth of the stress block is

$$a = \frac{(A_s - A_s')f_y}{0.85f_c'b} \tag{3.8}$$

Defining $p = A_s/bd$ and $p' = A_s'/bd$, this can be written as

$$a = \frac{(p - p')f_yd}{0.85f_c'} \tag{3.8a}$$

The total resisting moment is then

$$M'_u = M'_2 + M'_1 = (A_s - A'_s)f_y\left(d - \frac{a}{2}\right) + A'_sf_y(d - d') \qquad (3.9)$$

In accordance with the safety provisions of the ACI Code, this ultimate-moment capacity is reduced by the factor ϕ to obtain the ultimate moment M_u to be used in design:

$$M_u = \phi M'_u = \phi\left[(A_s - A'_s)f_y\left(d - \frac{a}{2}\right) + A'_sf_y(d - d')\right] \qquad (3.10)$$

This development is predicated on the assumption that both the tension steel and the compression steel are at the yield stress when the beam fails. It is highly desirable, for reasons given earlier, that failure be precipitated by tensile yielding rather than by crushing of the concrete. This can be ensured by setting an upper limit on the tensile steel ratio. The balanced tensile steel ratio for a doubly reinforced beam is $p_b + p'$, where p_b is calculated according to Eq. (3.1). In order to ensure the same margin against brittle-concrete failure in a doubly reinforced beam as in a singly reinforced beam, one should have $p_{\max} = 0.75(p_b + p')$. The ACI Code specifies somewhat more liberally that $p_{\max} = 0.75p_b + p'$, or

$$(p - p')_{\max} = 0.75p_b$$

Whether or not the compression steel will have yielded at failure can be determined as follows: Referring to Fig. 3.3*b*, and taking as the limiting case $\epsilon'_s = \epsilon_y$, one obtains, from geometry,

$$\frac{c}{d'} = \frac{\epsilon_u}{\epsilon_u - \epsilon_y} \qquad \text{or} \qquad c = \frac{\epsilon_u}{\epsilon_u - \epsilon_y}d'$$

With the neutral axis so established, summing forces in the horizontal direction (see Fig. 3.3*c*) gives:

$$pf_ybd = 0.85k_1f'_cbc + p'f_ybd$$

$$(p - p') = 0.85k_1\frac{f'_c}{f_y}\frac{c}{d}$$

$$(p - p') = 0.85k_1\frac{f'_c}{f_y}\frac{d'}{d}\frac{\epsilon_u}{\epsilon_u - \epsilon_y} \qquad (3.11)$$

Taking $\epsilon_u = 0.003$ as usual and $\epsilon_y = f_y/E_s$, with $E_s = 29{,}000{,}000$ psi, one obtains the minimum value of $(p - p')$ which results in compressive yielding:

$$(p - p') \geq 0.85k_1\frac{f'_c}{f_y}\frac{d'}{d}\frac{87{,}000}{87{,}000 - f_y} \qquad (3.11a)$$

If $(p - p')$ is less than this limiting value, the compression steel stress at failure is less than the yield stress, and an analysis taking into account strains and actual stress in the compressive steel is necessary.[1]

If compression bars are used in a flexural member, precautions must be taken to ensure that these bars will not buckle outward under load, spalling off the outer concrete. The ACI Code requires that such bars be anchored by ties or stirrups, which shall not be less than ¼ in. in diameter, spaced not farther apart than 16 bar diameters or 48 tie diameters. At least one tie at each spacing should extend completely around all longitudinal bars, and such stirrups or ties should be used throughout the distance in which the compression reinforcement is required.

Compression-reinforced beam, example 1: ultimate-moment capacity of a given section A rectangular beam has a width of 12 in. and an effective depth to the centroid of the tension reinforcement of 18 in. The tension reinforcement consists of six No. 10 bars in two rows. Compression reinforcement consisting of two No. 9 bars is placed 2½ in. from the compression face of the beam. If $f_y = 50{,}000$ psi and $f'_c = 5000$ psi, what is the ultimate-moment capacity of the beam to be used in design?

$$A_s = 7.59 \qquad p = \frac{A_s}{bd} = \frac{7.59}{12 \times 18} = 0.0352$$

$$A'_s = 2.00 \qquad p' = \frac{A'_s}{bd} = \frac{2.00}{12 \times 18} = 0.0093$$

$$A_s - A'_s = 5.59 \qquad p - p' = \frac{A_s - A'_s}{bd} = \frac{5.59}{12 \times 18} = 0.0259$$

Check:

$$p_b = 0.85k_1 \frac{f'_c}{f_y} \frac{87{,}000}{87{,}000 + f_y}$$

$$= 0.85 \times 0.80 \frac{5}{50} \frac{87}{137} = 0.0432$$

$$p_{\max} = 0.75 \times 0.0432 = 0.0324$$

Since $p = 0.0352$ is larger than $p_{\max}$, the beam must be analyzed as doubly reinforced. Checking limits on $(p - p')$,

$$(p - p')_{\max} = 0.75p_b = 0.0324$$

$$(p - p')_{\min} = 0.85k_1 \frac{f'_c}{f_y} \frac{d'}{d} \frac{87{,}000}{87{,}000 - f_y}$$

$$= 0.85 \times 0.80 \frac{5}{50} \frac{2.5}{18} \frac{87}{37} = 0.0222$$

[1] As an alternative, the contribution of the compression steel could conservatively be neglected in the analysis.

Since the actual $(p - p') = 0.0259$ is between these limits, failure will be initiated by tensile yielding, and the compression steel will have yielded at failure. Then

$$M_1 = \phi A'_s f_y(d - d')$$
$$= 0.90 \times 2.00 \times 50(15.5) = 1400 \text{ in.-kips}$$
$$a = \frac{(A_s - A'_s)f_y}{0.85f'_c b} = \frac{5.59 \times 50}{0.85 \times 5 \times 12} = 5.48 \text{ in.}$$
$$M_2 = \phi(A_s - A'_s)f_y\left(d - \frac{a}{2}\right)$$
$$= 0.90(5.59)50 \times 15.26 = 3840 \text{ in.-kips}$$
$$M_u = M_1 + M_2 = 1400 + 3840 = 5240 \text{ in.-kips}$$

Compression-reinforced beam, example 2: determination of steel areas for a known moment. A rectangular beam which must carry a working live load of 2.33 kips per ft and a calculated dead load of 0.98 kips per ft on an 18-ft simple span is limited in cross section for architectural reasons to 10 in. width and 20 in. total depth. If $f_y = 40{,}000$ psi and $f'_c = 3000$ psi, what steel area(s) must be provided?

The working loads are first increased by U.S.D. overload factors to obtain the ultimate design load of $1.5 \times 0.98 + 1.8 \times 2.33 = 5.66$ kips per ft. Then $M_u = \frac{1}{8} \times 5.66 \times 18^2 = 229$ ft-kips $= 2750$ in.-kips. To satisfy spacing and cover requirements (see Art. 3.19), it will be assumed that the tension-steel centroid will be 4 in. above the bottom face of the beam, and that compression steel, if required, will be placed $2\frac{1}{2}$ in. below the beam's top surface. Then $d =$ 16 in., and $d' = 2\frac{1}{2}$ in.

First, checking the capacity of the section if singly reinforced, using $p = p_{\max}$,

$$p_b = 0.85^2 \times \frac{3}{40} \times \frac{87}{127} = 0.0371$$
$$p_{\max} = 0.0278$$
$$A_s = 0.0278 \times 10 \times 16 = 4.44 \text{ in.}^2$$
$$a = \frac{A_s f_y}{0.85f'_c b} = \frac{4.44 \times 40}{0.85 \times 3 \times 10} = 6.96 \text{ in.}$$
$$M_{\max} = \phi A_s f_y\left(d - \frac{a}{2}\right) = 0.90 \times 4.44 \times 40 \times 12.52 = 2000 \text{ in.-kips*}$$

Since the moment capacity of the singly reinforced beam, 2000 in.-kips, is less than the required capacity, 2750 in.-kips, compression steel is needed. Then

$$M_1 = 2750 - 2000 = 750 \text{ in.-kips}$$
$$A'_s = \frac{M_1}{\phi f_y(d - d')} = \frac{750}{0.90 \times 40 \times 13.5} = 1.54 \text{ in.}^2$$

* Alternatively, the quantity $M_{\max}$ may easily be found from Graph 1. For $f_y = 40{,}000$ psi and $f'_c = 3000$ psi, the graph gives $p_{\max} = 0.028$, and the corresponding value of $M_u/\phi bd^2$ is 870 psi. Then, for $b = 10$ in. and $d = 16$ in.,

$$M_u = M_{\max} = \frac{(0.9 \times 870 \times 10 \times 16^2)}{1000} = 2000 \text{ in.-kips}$$

giving the required compressive-steel area and one part of the tensile-steel area. Denoting the tensile-steel area, tensile-steel ratio, and maximum moment of the singly reinforced beam as $\bar{A}_s$, $\bar{p}_{max}$, and $\bar{M}_{max}$, respectively, the second part of the tensile-steel requirement in the doubly reinforced beam $(A_s - A_s')$ is equal to $\bar{A}_s$. [That is, $(p - p') = \bar{p}_{max}$, and $M_2 = \bar{M}_{max}$.]

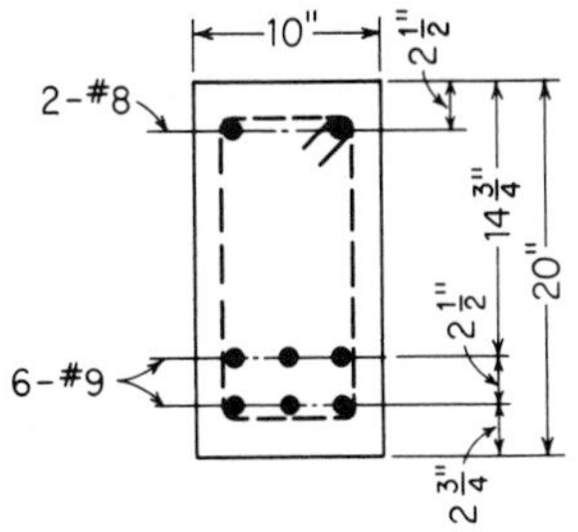

Fig. 3.4

$$(A_s - A_s') = 4.44 \text{ in.}^2$$
$$A_s = 4.44 + 1.54 = 5.98 \text{ in.}^2$$

Two No. 8 bars will be used for compression reinforcement, with six No. 9 bars providing the required tensile-steel area, as shown in Fig. 3.4. In order to place the tension bars within the 10 in. beam width, two rows of three bars each are used. Note that in design cases such as this, no check of $(p - p')$ is required, since this quantity is equal to the maximum value of 0.75 p_b.

PROBLEMS

U.S.D.: Doubly reinforced rectangular beams:

1. A rectangular concrete beam measures 12 in. in width and has an effective depth to the tensile-steel centroid of 18 in. Compression steel, consisting of two No. 8 bars, is located 2.5 in. from the compression face of the beam. If $f_c' =$ 4000 psi and f_y = 60,000 psi, what is the ultimate moment capacity of the beam, according to ACI Code, for the following alternative tensile-steel areas: (*a*) A_s = 3 No. 10 bars, (*b*) A_s = 4 No. 10 bars, (*c*) A_s = 6 No. 10 bars.

2. For architectural reasons, a certain rectangular beam of 16 ft span is limited in cross section to a width of 8 in. and a total depth of 16 in. (effective depth = 12 in.). It must carry a total working live load of 1.40 kips per ft, and a total dead load (including its own weight) of 1.10 kips per ft. If f_c' = 4000 psi and f_y = 40,000 psi, what reinforcement is required?

3.9 T Beams: Ultimate-strength Design With the exception of precast systems, reinforced-concrete floors are almost always monolithic. Forms are built for beam soffits and sides and for the underside of slabs, and the entire floor is poured at once, from the bottom of the deepest beam to the top of the slab (see Fig. 1.1*a* and *d*). Beam stirrups and bent bars extend up into the slab. It is evident, therefore, that a part of the slab will act with the upper part of the beam to resist longitudinal compression. The resulting beam cross section is T-shaped rather than rectangular. The slab forms the beam flange, while the part of the beam projecting below the slab forms what is called the *web* or *stem*. The upper part of such a T-beam is stressed laterally in compression as a part of the slab, but this does not reduce its capacity to carry longitudinal compression as a part of the beam.

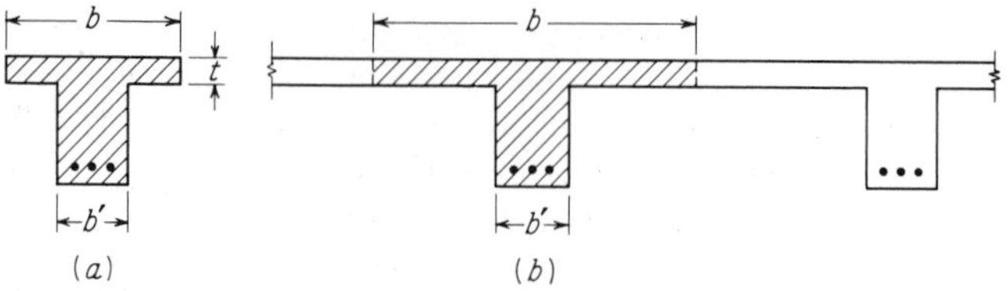

Fig. 3.5 Effective flange widths of T beams.

The first question to be resolved is that of effective width of flange. In Fig. 3.5*a* it is evident that, if the flange is but little wider than the stem width, the entire flange can be considered effective in resisting compression. For the floor system shown in Fig. 3.5*b*, however, it may be equally obvious that elements of the flange midway between the beam stems are less highly stressed in longitudinal compression than those elements directly over the stem. This is so because of shearing deformation of the flange, which relieves the more remote elements of some compressive stress.

While the actual longitudinal compression varies because of this effect, it is convenient in design to make use of an effective flange width which may be smaller than the actual flange width, but which is considered to be uniformly stressed. This effective width has been found to depend primarily on the beam span and on the relative thickness of the slab.

The recommendations for effective width given in the ACI Code are as follows:

1. The effective width b shall not exceed one-fourth the span length of the beam.

2. The overhanging width $(b - b')/2$ on either side of the beam web shall not exceed 8 times the thickness of the slab nor one-half the clear distance to the next beam.

For beams having a flange on one side only, it is recommended that the effective overhanging flange width shall not exceed one-twelfth the span length of the beam, nor 6 times the slab thickness, nor one-half the clear distance to the next beam.

The neutral axis of a T beam may be either in the flange or in the web, depending upon the proportions of the cross section, the amount of tensile steel, and the strengths of the materials. If the calculated depth to the neutral axis is less than or equal to the slab thickness t, the beam can be analyzed as if it were a rectangular beam of width equal to b, the effective flange width. The reason for this is illustrated in Fig. 3.6*a*, which shows a T beam with neutral axis in the flange. The compressive area is indicated by the shaded portion of the figure. If the additional concrete indicated by areas 1 and 2 had been added when the beam was poured, the physical cross section would have been rectangular in shape, with a width b. No

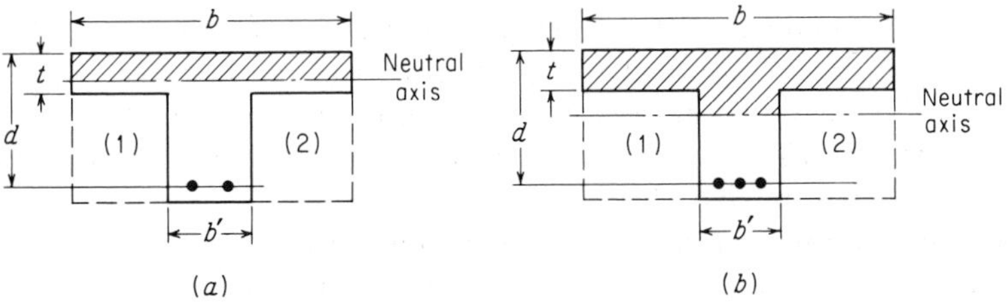

Fig. 3.6 Effective cross sections of T beams.

bending strength would have been added, because areas 1 and 2 are entirely in the tension zone, and tension concrete is disregarded in flexural calculations. The original T beam and the modified rectangular beam are equal in flexural strength, and rectangular beam analysis for flexure applies.

When the neutral axis is in the web, as in Fig. 3.6*b*, the above argument no longer is valid. In this case, methods must be developed which account for the actual T-shaped compressive zone.

Figure 3.7 shows a reinforced-concrete T beam with effective flange width b, web width b', effective depth to the steel centroid d, and flange thickness t. The first step is to locate the neutral axis. Assuming for trial purposes that it will fall in the flange,

$$k_1 c = a = \frac{A_s f_y}{0.85 f'_c b} = \frac{p f_y d}{0.85 f'_c} \tag{3.3}$$

where $p = A_s bd$. Then

$$c = \frac{p f_y d}{0.85 k_1 f'_c} \tag{3.12}$$

If c is equal to or less than the flange thickness t, the member acts as a rectangular beam of width b and depth d. If c is greater than t, then a T-beam analysis is required.

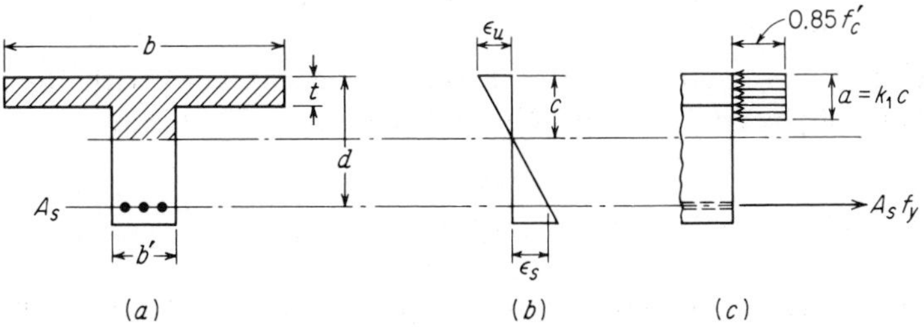

Fig. 3.7 Strain and equivalent stress distribution.

It will be assumed in the development that follows that the strength of the T beam is controlled by yielding of the tensile steel. This will usually be the case, because of the large compressive concrete area provided by the flange. In addition, an upper limit can be established for the steel ratio to ensure that this is so.

As a computational device, it is convenient to divide the total tensile steel into two parts. The first part, A_{sf}, represents the steel area which, when stressed to f_y, is required to balance the longitudinal compressive force in the overhanging portions of the flange. Thus

$$A_{sf} = \frac{0.85f'_c(b - b')t}{f_y} \tag{3.13}$$

The force $A_{sf}f_y$ and the equal and opposite force $0.85f'_c(b - b')t$ act with a lever arm $(d - t/2)$ to provide the resisting moment:

$$M'_1 = A_{sf}f_y\left(d - \frac{t}{2}\right) \tag{3.14}$$

The remaining steel area, $(A_s - A_{sf})$, at a stress f_y, is balanced by the compression in the rectangular portion of the beam. The depth of the equivalent rectangular stress block in this zone is found from horizontal equilibrium:

$$a = \frac{(A_s - A_{sf})f_y}{0.85f'_cb'} \tag{3.15}$$

An additional moment M'_2 is thus provided by the forces $(A_s - A_{sf})f_y$ and $0.85f'_cab'$, acting at the lever arm $(d - a/2)$,

$$M'_2 = (A_s - A_{sf})f_y\left(d - \frac{a}{2}\right) \tag{3.16}$$

and the total resisting moment is the sum of the moments M_1 and M_2:

$$M'_u = M'_1 + M'_2 = A_{sf}f_y\left(d - \frac{t}{2}\right) + (A_s - A_{sf})f_y\left(d - \frac{a}{2}\right) \tag{3.17}$$

This moment is reduced by the factor ϕ in accordance with the safety provisions of the ACI Code to obtain the design ultimate moment:

$$M_u = \phi M'_u = \phi\left[A_{sf}f_y\left(d - \frac{t}{2}\right) + (A_s - A_{sf})f_y\left(d - \frac{a}{2}\right)\right] \tag{3.18}$$

As for rectangular beams, it is desired to ensure that the tensile steel will yield prior to sudden crushing of the compression concrete, as assumed in the preceding development. Defining

$$p_w = \frac{A_s}{b'd} \tag{3.19}$$

and

$$p_f = \frac{A_{sf}}{b'd} \tag{3.20}$$

the balanced tensile-steel ratio is $p_b + p_f$, where p_b is calculated according to Eq. (3.1). Consistent with the treatment of singly reinforced beams, one should have $p_w \leq 0.75(p_b + p_f)$. According to the ACI Code, $p_w \leq (0.75p_b + p_f)$, or

$$(p_w - p_f) \leq 0.75p_b \tag{3.21}$$

It may be evident that the code provision does not really insure the desired ductility in heavily reinforced cases.

T beam, example 1: ultimate-moment capacity of a given section A floor slab 3 in. thick is supported by reinforced-concrete beams 5 ft on centers which act together with the slab as T beams. The beams are simply supported, and their span is 14 ft. They have a web width of 10 in., an effective depth of 16 in., and a total depth of 20 in. The tensile reinforcement consists of six No. 10 bars in two rows. If $f_y = 60{,}000$ psi and $f'_c = 4000$ psi, what is the ultimate-design-moment capacity of each beam?

The effective flange width cannot exceed

$16t + b' = 16 \times 3 + 10 = 58$ in.
Span/4 $= 14 \times {}^{12}\!/_4 = 42$ in.
Center-line beam spacing $= 60$ in.

The flange width is therefore taken equal to 42 in. For six No. 10 bars, $A_s = 7.59$ in.² First checking the location of the neutral axis on the assumption that rectangular-beam formulas may be applied,

$$p = \frac{A_s}{bd} = \frac{7.59}{42 \times 16} = 0.0113$$

$$c = \frac{pf_yd}{0.85k_1f'_c} = \frac{0.0113 \times 60 \times 16}{0.85 \times 0.85 \times 4} = 3.75 \text{ in.}$$

This exceeds the flange thickness, so a T-beam analysis is indicated.

$$A_{sf} = \frac{0.85f'_c(b - b')t}{f_y} = 0.85 \times \frac{4}{60} \times 32 \times 3 = 5.44 \text{ in.}^2$$

$$(A_s - A_{sf}) = 7.59 - 5.44 = 2.15 \text{ in.}^2$$

$$(p_w - p_f) = \frac{A_s - A_{sf}}{b'd} = \frac{2.15}{10 \times 16} = 0.0134$$

Check

$$(p_w - p_f)_{\max} = 0.75 \times 0.85k_1 \frac{f'_c}{f_y} \frac{87{,}000}{87{,}000 + f_y}$$

$$= 0.75 \times 0.85^2 \times \tfrac{4}{60} \times \tfrac{87}{147} = 0.0213$$

The actual $(p_w - p_f)$ is seen to be less than this limiting value, ensuring that the beam will fail by tensile yielding. Then

$$M_1 = \phi A_{sf} f_y \left(d - \frac{t}{2}\right) = 0.90 \times 5.44 \times 60 \times 14.50 = 4260 \text{ in.-kips}$$

$$a = \frac{(A_s - A_{sf})f_y}{0.85f'_c b'} = \frac{2.15 \times 60}{0.85 \times 4 \times 10} = 3.80 \text{ in.}$$

$$M_2 = \phi(A_s - A_{sf})f_y \left(d - \frac{a}{2}\right) = 0.90 \times 2.15 \times 60 \times 14.10 = 1640 \text{ in.-kips}$$

$$M_u = M_1 + M_2 = 4260 + 1640 = 5900 \text{ in.-kips}$$

The Code requires that a special check of deflections be made if $(p_w - p_f) > 0.18f'_c/f_y$ or if $f_y > 40{,}000$ psi. In this case,

$$0.18\frac{f'_c}{f_y} = 0.18 \times \frac{4}{60} = 0.0120$$

which is exceeded by the actual steel ratio $(p_w - p_f)$. A check of deflections is, therefore, required by each of these criteria.

In designing T beams, as contrasted to reviewing the capacity of a given section, normally the slab dimensions and beam spacing will have been established by transverse flexural requirements. Consequently, the only additional section proportions that must be determined from flexural considerations are the width and depth of the web and the tensile-steel area.

If the stem dimensions were selected, as for rectangular beams, on the basis of concrete stress capacity in compression, they would be very small because of the large compression flange width furnished by the presence of the slab. Such a design would not represent the optimum solution because of the large tensile-steel requirement resulting from the small effective depth, because of the excessive web reinforcement that would be required for shear, and because of large deflections associated with such a shallow member. It is better practice to select the proportions of the web (1) so as to keep an arbitrarily low web steel ratio $(p_w - p_f)$ or (2) so as to keep web shear stress at desirably low limits or (3) for continuous T beams, on the basis of the flexural requirements at the supports, where the effective cross section is rectangular and of width b'.

T beam, example 2: determination of steel area for a given moment A floor system consists of a 3-in. concrete slab supported by continuous T beams of 24-ft span, 47 in. on centers. Web dimensions, as determined by negative-moment requirements at the supports, are $b' = 11$ in. and $d = 20$ in. What tensile-steel area is required at midspan to resist an ultimate design moment of 6400 in.-kips if $f_y = 60{,}000$ psi and $f'_c = 3000$ psi?

First determining the effective flange width,

$16t + b' = 16 \times 3 + 11 = 59$ in.
Span/4 $= 24 \times {}^{12}\!/\!_4 = 72$ in.
Center-line beam spacing $= 47$ in.

The center-line T-beam spacing controls in this case, and $b = 47$ in. The concrete dimensions b' and d are known to be adequate in this case, as they have been selected for the larger negative support moment applied to the effective rectangular section $b'd$. The tensile steel at midspan is most conveniently found by trial. Assuming the stress-block depth equal to the flange thickness of 3 in.,

$$d - \frac{a}{2} = 20 - 1.50 = 18.50 \text{ in.}$$

Trial:

$$A_s = \frac{M_u}{\phi f_y(d - a/2)} = \frac{6400}{0.90 \times 60 \times 18.50} = 6.40 \text{ in.}^2$$

$$p = \frac{A_s}{bd} = \frac{6.40}{47 \times 20} = 0.00681$$

$$c = \frac{pf_yd}{0.85k_1f'_c} = \frac{0.00681 \times 60 \times 20}{0.85 \times 0.85 \times 3} = 3.77 \text{ in.}$$

Since c is greater than t, a T-beam analysis is indicated.

$$A_{sf} = \frac{0.85f'_c(b - b')t}{f_y} = \frac{0.85 \times 3 \times 36 \times 3}{60} = 4.58 \text{ in.}^2$$

$$M_1 = \phi A_{sf}f_y\left(d - \frac{t}{2}\right) = 0.90 \times 4.58 \times 60 \times 18.50 = 4570 \text{ in.-kips}$$

$$M_2 = M_u - M_1 = 6400 - 4570 = 1830 \text{ in.-kips}$$

Assume $a = 4.00$ in.

$$(A_s - A_{sf}) = \frac{M_2}{\phi f_y(d - a/2)} = \frac{1830}{0.90 \times 60 \times 18.00} = 1.88 \text{ in.}^2$$

Check:

$$a = \frac{(A_s - A_{sf})f_y}{0.85f'_cb'} = \frac{1.88 \times 60}{0.85 \times 3 \times 11} = 4.02 \text{ in.}$$

This is satisfactorily close to the assumed value of 4 in.* Then

$$A_s = A_{sf} + (A_s - A_{sf}) = 4.58 + 1.88 = 6.46 \text{ in.}^2$$

* Alternatively, from Graph 1, with

$$\frac{M_u}{\phi bd^2} = \frac{(1830 \times 1000)}{(11 \times 400 \times 0.9)} = 462$$

the steel ratio $(p_w - p_f)$ is found to be 0.0085. Then

$$(A_s - A_{sf}) = (p_w - p_f)b'd = 0.0086 \times 11 \times 20 = 1.88 \text{ in.}^2$$

Checking to ensure that tensile yielding will control the strength of the section,

$$(p_w - p_f) = \frac{A_s - A_{sf}}{b'd} = \frac{1.88}{11 \times 20} = 0.00855$$

$$(p_w - p_f)_{\max} = 0.75 \times 0.85k_1 \frac{f'_c}{f_y} \frac{87{,}000}{87{,}000 + f_y}$$

$$= 0.75 \times 0.85^2 \times 3/60 \times 87/147 = 0.0160 > 0.00855$$

The close agreement should be noted between the approximate tensile-steel area of 6.40 in.^{2} found by assuming the stress-block depth equal to the flange thickness and the more exact value of 6.46 in.^{2} found by T-beam analysis. The approximate solution would be satisfactory in many cases.

PROBLEMS

U.S.D.: T beams:

1. A tensile-reinforced T beam is to be designed to carry a uniformly distributed load on a 20-ft simple span. The total ultimate moment at midspan due to all loads is 6240 in.-kips. Concrete dimensions, as governed by web shear and clearance considerations, are $b = 20$ in., $b' = 10$ in., $t = 5$ in., and $d = 20$ in. If $f_y = 60{,}000$ psi and $f'_c = 4000$ psi, what tensile reinforcement is required at midspan?

2. A T beam has an effective flange width of 30 in., web width of 14 in., slab thickness 4 in., and effective depth to the steel centroid of 20 in. If steel having a yield stress of 60,000 psi is used with concrete of $f'_c = 2500$ psi, what is the ultimate-moment capacity of the beam for the following alternative tensile-steel areas: (*a*) A_s = 3 No. 11 bars and (*b*) A_s = 6 No. 11 bars?

3.10 Singly Reinforced Rectangular Beams: Working-stress Design The design of reinforced-concrete members can also be based on conditions at working load. Working-stress design methods are predicated on the assumption that, at working loads, the concrete stress is sufficiently low so that a linear relation exists between concrete stress and strain. With reference to Fig. 2.8*b*, the following relations have already been derived in Art. 2.4.

$$M = A_s f_s jd \qquad (2.15)$$

$$M = \frac{f_c}{2} kjbd^2 \qquad (2.17)$$

$$j = 1 - \frac{k}{3} \qquad (2.19)$$

If the dimensional properties of the cross section are given, the value of k, which locates the neutral axis, can be found by means of Eq. (2.13).

Substituting $p = A_s/bd$ in that equation, one obtains:

$$b\,\frac{(kd)^2}{2} - pnbd(d - kd) = 0$$

Dividing through by bd^2,

$$\frac{k^2}{2} - pn(1 - k) = 0$$

from which

$$k = \sqrt{2pn + (pn)^2} - pn \tag{3.22}$$

This expression for k is useful in reviewing the moment capacity of a given beam cross section for which the modular ratio and the steel ratio are known, or for calculating unit stresses in the steel and concrete when a known moment is applied.

If one is *designing* a cross section to resist a given moment, it is often convenient to express k in terms of the desired stresses in the concrete and steel. From the geometry of the strain diagram in Fig. 2.8c one obtains

balanced design

$$\frac{\epsilon_c}{\epsilon_s} = \frac{kd}{d - kd}$$

Substituting $\epsilon_c = f_c/E_c$ and $\epsilon_s = f_s/E_s$,

$$\frac{f_c}{E_c}\frac{E_s}{f_s} = \frac{k}{1 - k}$$

Introducing the modular ratio $n = E_s/E_c$ and the stress ratio $r = f_s/f_c$,

$$\frac{n}{r} = \frac{k}{1 - k}$$

and solving for k,

$$k = \frac{n}{n + r} \tag{3.23}$$

In this case, k is expressed in terms of the modular ratio and the ratio of simultaneous stresses (i.e., the stresses in the concrete and steel at any particular stage of loading). In the design, these stresses would normally be taken as the maximum allowable stresses in the two materials, and the value of k could then be calculated directly from Eq. (3.23).

It may be of interest in certain situations to know the value of p which should be used in designing a beam such that the steel and the concrete will reach their maximum allowable stresses for the same applied moment. This is known as *balanced-stress design*. Equating Eqs. (2.14*a*) and (2.14*b*) and substituting $p = A_s/bd$,

$$\frac{f_c}{2} bkd = pf_s bd$$

Dividing both sides by bd and solving for p, which is then designated as p_e,

$$p_e = \frac{k}{2}\frac{f_c}{f_s} = \frac{k}{2r}$$

With the desired simultaneous stress values known, Eq. (3.23) can be used to eliminate k, giving

$$p_e = \frac{n}{2r(n + r)} \tag{3.24}$$

The ratio p_e is called the *balanced-stress steel ratio*. If $p < p_e$, the steel will reach its allowable stresses at a lower load than the concrete, and the allowable moment will be determined by Eq. (2.15). If $p > p_e$, the concrete will reach its allowable stress first, and Eq. (2.17) will control.

The relation between beam behavior predicted by W.S.D. theory and that predicted by U.S.D. theory is illustrated by Graph 3.1, which plots resisting moment vs. steel ratio for a singly reinforced beam for $f_y =$ 40,000 psi and $f'_c = 3000$ psi. Values of M_u predicted by U.S.D. have been

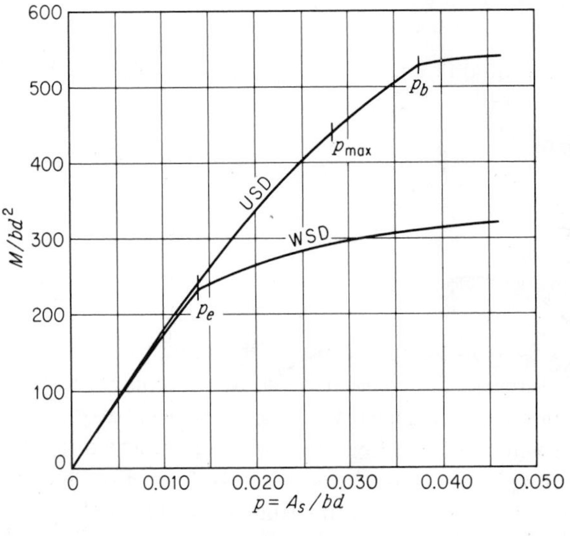

Graph 3.1

divided by a safety factor of 2 in order to permit direct comparison with W.S.D. results.

It is evident from the graph that U.S.D. theory does not differ significantly from elastic theory for values of p smaller than p_e. At that value, elastic theory assumes the resisting moments of steel and concrete to be equal. The bending moment corresponding to p_e can, by that theory, be increased by the addition of tension steel, but this is indicated to be uneconomical, since the steel would be stressed below its allowable value. Any amount of steel in excess of p_e, by elastic theory, provides half as much or less additional strength as does the same amount of steel added to an underreinforced beam with p less than p_e.

U.S.D. theory, confirmed by tests, shows that predictions of flexural capacity by W.S.D. for steel ratios larger than p_e are incorrect. The actual behavior is depicted by the upper curve of Graph 3.1. It shows that additional steel increases the strength of the beam at a practically constant rate until the much larger critical steel ratio p_b is reached. (The maximum steel ratio to be used, according to the ACI Code, is p_{max}, which is also shown on the graph).

The indication of W.S.D. theory that compression reinforcement is required in order to obtain economically moments larger than that corresponding to p_e is incorrect. It is at least partly in order to minimize this feature of W.S.D. that the ACI Code permits the use of compressive steel stress equal to twice the elastic value, thereby reducing the amount of compressive steel required.

Rectangular beam, example 1: allowable moment capacity of a given section A rectangular beam has a width of 12 in. and an effective depth to the centroid of the reinforcing steel of 17.5 in. It is reinforced with three No. 8 bars in one row. If 60,000-psi steel is used at a maximum allowable stress of f_s = 24,000 psi, and 4000-psi concrete is used at an allowable stress of $f_c = 0.45f'_c$ = 1800 psi, what is the maximum working moment that can be resisted?

The steel ratio is $p = A_s/bd = 2.35/(12 \times 17.5) = 0.0112$. With $n = 8$ (see Table 3.1), $pn = 0.0896$, and

$$k = \sqrt{2pn + (pn)^2} - pn = \sqrt{0.1792 + 0.0080} - 0.0896 = 0.343$$

$$j = 1 - \frac{k}{3} = 1 - \frac{0.343}{3} = 0.886$$

If steel stress controls, then from Eq. (2.15),

$$M = A_s f_s jd = 2.35 \times 24 \times 0.886 \times 17.5 = 875 \text{ in.-kips}$$

If concrete stress controls, then from Eq. (2.17),

$$M = \frac{f_c}{2} kjbd^2 = \frac{1.800}{2} 0.343 \times 0.886 \times 12 \times 17.5^2 = 1010 \text{ in.-kips}$$

The allowable moment capacity of the beam, controlled by allowable steel stress in this case, is 875 in.-kips. If desired, the actual concrete extreme-fiber stress at a moment of 875 in.-kips can be found as $1800 \times 875/1010 = 1560$ psi.

Alternatively, this problem could have been solved by calculating the balanced-stress steel ratio and comparing the actual steel ratio with that value. For example,

$$p_e = \frac{n}{2r(n + r)} = \frac{8}{2(24/1.80)(8 + 24/1.80)} = 0.0141$$

Since $p = 0.0112 < p_e$, the steel stress controls, and $M = 875$ in.-kips from Eq. (2.15) as before.[1]

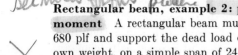

Rectangular beam, example 2: proportioning a beam to resist a known moment A rectangular beam must carry a uniformly distributed live load of 680 plf and support the dead load of a wall weighing 380 plf, in addition to its own weight, on a simple span of 24 ft. Design the beam for flexure, using intermediate-grade steel at a working stress of 20,000 psi and 3000-psi concrete at a working stress of 1350 psi.

The total load acting on the beam includes its own weight, which must be estimated. As a first trial a total depth equal to 1 in. per ft of span and a width of one-half that amount are assumed; the beam weight is estimated as $(12 \times 24/144)150 = 300$ plf. The total working load of $680 + 380 + 300 = 1360$ plf produces a maximum moment of

$$M = \tfrac{1}{8} \times 1.36 \times 24^2 = 98.2 \text{ ft-kips}$$

The choice of tensile steel ratio will directly influence the required dimensions of the concrete cross section. Unless circumstances dictate otherwise, the designer using W.S.D. methods would probably use $p = p_e$, such that steel and concrete reach their maximum allowable stresses for the same applied moment. For the given materials, with $p = p_e$,

$$k = \frac{n}{n + r} = \frac{9}{9 + 20/1.35} = 0.378$$

$$j = 1 - \frac{k}{3} = 1 - \frac{0.378}{3} = 0.874$$

Equating the concrete resisting moment to the total working moment of 98.2 ft-

[1] The reader should be aware of design aids included in Appendix B to facilitate the solution of W.S.D. problems. For the present example, with $p = 0.0112$ and $n = 8$, k and j are obtained directly from Table 6 as 0.343 and 0.886, respectively. Since p is less than p_e (obtained from Table 5), steel stress controls, and

$$M = A_s f_s jd = 875 \text{ in.-kips}$$

as before.

kips = 1180 in.-kips,

$$M = \frac{f_c}{2} kjbd^2$$

$$bd^2 = \frac{2M}{f_c kj} = \frac{2 \times 1180}{1.35 \times 0.378 \times 0.874} = 5290 \text{ in.}^3$$

The relative proportions of b and d may be influenced by architectural factors or by considerations of clearance. In this case, d will be selected equal to 20 in. Then

$$b = {}^{5290}/_{400} = 13.2 \text{ in.}$$

and

$$A_s = \frac{M}{f_s jd} = \frac{1180}{20} \times 0.874 \times 20 = 3.38 \text{ in.}^2$$

This area will be provided using two No. 10 bars and one No. 9 bar, all in one row. Concrete dimensions will be rounded off to $b = 13.5$ in. and $d = 20$ in., with a total depth of 22.5 in. As a check, the actual beam dead load is $(13.5 \times 22.5/144)$ $150 = 316$ plf, which is sufficiently close to the estimated dead load of 300 plf that no revision of moments is necessary.

It is apparent that, had a larger or smaller steel ratio been selected, different concrete dimensions would have resulted. The beam could also have been designed by selecting a steel ratio, finding k and j from Eqs. (3.22) and (2.19), respectively (or from Table 6, Appendix B), and then proceeding as above.

Frequently, in designing continuous beams, it will be required to find the steel area when the concrete dimensions are given and are known to be adequate, since they have been selected for a larger applied moment elsewhere in the span. For this situation, a trial-and-error approach, illustrated by the following example, is quickest.

Rectangular beam, example 3: determination of steel area for a known moment Using the concrete dimensions of the preceding example ($b = 13.5$ in. and $d = 20$ in.), find the steel area required to resist a working moment of 945 in.-kips.

As a first trial, assume that k will take the value for balanced-stress design found from Eq. (3.23). Then

$$k = \frac{n}{n + r} = \frac{9}{9 + 20/1.35} = 0.378$$

$$j = 1 - \frac{k}{3} = 1 - \frac{0.378}{3} = 0.874$$

$$A_s = \frac{M}{f_s jd} = \frac{945}{20 \times 0.874 \times 20} = 2.70 \text{ in.}^2$$

The values of k and j will now be revised to be consistent with this estimate of steel area, using Eqs. (3.22) and (2.19) (or Table 6, Appendix B):

$$p = \frac{A_s}{bd} = \frac{2.70}{13.5 \times 20} = 0.0100$$
$$k = \sqrt{2pn + (pn)^2} - pn = \sqrt{0.180 + 0.008} - 0.090 = 0.343$$
$$j = 1 - \frac{k}{3} = 1 - \frac{0.343}{3} = 0.886$$

A revised estimate of A_s is then obtained:

$$A_s = \frac{945}{20 \times 0.886 \times 20} = 2.66 \text{ in.}^2$$

The difference between the original and revised values of A_s is seen to be negligible.

This example shows that a sufficiently accurate calculation of A_s could be obtained simply by using the balanced-stress value of j. The variation of j with changing steel ratio is not great. In fact, it is likely that the difference between the required steel area and that actually provided will be larger, due to the necessity for using standard bar sizes, than the refinements in calculated values of A_s. In addition, the balanced-stress value of j will always give a conservative estimate of A_s for beams with steel ratios less than the balanced-stress value p_e.

PROBLEMS

W.S.D.: Singly reinforced rectangular beams:

1. A simply supported rectangular beam has a total cross section of 10 × 16 in. and a length of 20 ft. It is reinforced with four No. 5 bars in one row. The distance from the centers of the bars to the lower surface of the beam is 2½ in. With 2500-psi concrete and an allowable stress of 20,000 psi in the steel, what is the resisting moment of the beam?

2. If a concentrated load of 3500 lb were placed on the beam of Prob. 1 at a distance of 7 ft from the support, what would be the maximum unit stress in the concrete and the maximum unit stress in the steel?

3. A simply supported rectangular beam with a span of 18 ft supports a uniform live load of 975 plf and a concentrated load of 3000 lb at the middle of the span. With $f'_c = 3000$ psi and $f_s = 20{,}000$ psi, determine the required cross section and steel area.

4. A simply supported rectangular beam with a span of 17 ft supports a live load which varies uniformly in amount from zero at the left support to 1000 plf at the right support. A 2500-psi concrete and structural-grade reinforcing bars are to be used. Design the beam.

5. A rectangular beam, simply supported, has a width of 14 in. and an effective depth of 26 in. If $n = 9$, and if the allowable unit stresses are 1350 psi and 20,000 psi for the concrete and steel, respectively, what steel area must be used in order that the resisting moment with respect to the strength of the concrete may be the same as the resisting moment with respect to the steel?

6. What would be the resisting moment of the beam in Prob. 5 if the reinforcement consisted of four No. 7 bars?

3.11 Doubly Reinforced Rectangular Beams: Working-stress Design If both steel and concrete are completely elastic, the stress in the compression steel is n times the concrete stress at the same level, since the unit strains in the steel and the adjacent concrete are equal. This allows the compression steel stress to be computed. However, the stresses and strains in the concrete are proportional only at relatively low strains; at higher strains, the stresses no longer increase proportionately. Since the strains in the compression steel and the adjacent concrete remain equal, this means that at higher strain levels the unit stress in the steel, being proportional to the strain, will be larger than it would be if the concrete behaved elastically. This increase in the steel stress over that computed by assuming elastic behavior is accentuated by the fact that concrete, to a certain extent, compresses under constant load or stress (flow or creep). In contrast, steel, if stressed below the yield point, maintains its length essentially unchanged under constant stress. As a result, in a beam reinforced for compression, in the course of time the concrete, by minute flow, transfers part of its compression stress to the steel; the actual stress in the steel becomes higher than that computed on the basis of elastic behavior.

To approximate the effects of the nonlinear concrete stress-strain curve and of plastic flow of the concrete, the ACI Code specifies that the stress in compression reinforcement in beams and eccentric columns be taken as twice the value indicated by the straight-line relation between stress and strain and the appropriate modular ratio, but not of greater value than the allowable stress in tension. This provision is an attempt to compensate in part for the underestimate of the flexural compression strength inherent in working-stress design, as discussed previously.

In Fig. 3.8a, a rectangular-beam cross section is shown with com-

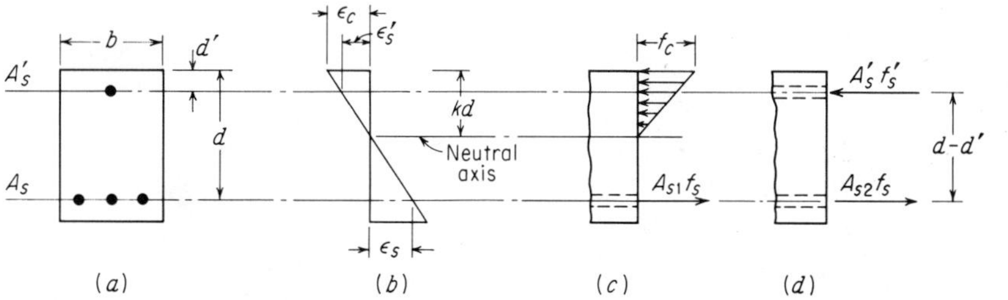

Fig. 3.8 Doubly reinforced rectangular beam.

BEER!

pression steel A_s' placed a distance d' from the compression face and with tensile steel A_s at an effective depth d. The stress in the tensile steel is f_s, while that in the compressive steel is f_s'. It is a design convenience to divide the total resisting moment into two parts. If M is the total resisting moment, and

M_1 = moment that can be developed by given cross section of concrete without compression reinforcement, working with a partial steel area A_{s1} to balance concrete compression

M_2 = moment in excess of M_1, developed by compression reinforcement, acting with additional tensile-steel area A_{s2}

Then

$$M = M_1 + M_2 \qquad \text{and} \qquad A_s = A_{s1} + A_{s2}$$

The moment M_1 depends on the concrete dimensions and allowable stresses and is

$$M_1 = \frac{f_c}{2} kjbd^2 \tag{3.25}$$

where k and j are computed from Eqs. (3.23) and (2.19). The area of tensile steel required for balanced-stress design of a singly reinforced beam having a resisting moment M_1 is

$$A_{s1} = \frac{M_1}{f_s jd} \tag{3.26}$$

A moment M_2 is provided by compressive steel and the remaining tensile steel $A_{s2} = A_s - A_{s1}$, acting with an internal lever arm $(d - d')$:

$$M_2 = A_{s2} f_s (d - d') = A_s' f_s' (d - d') \tag{3.27}$$

The additional moment M_2 may be governed by either the tensile or compressive steel, depending on the stresses in each and their relative areas. From the geometry of Fig. 3.8*b*,

$$\frac{\epsilon_s}{\epsilon_s'} = \frac{d - kd}{kd - d'} = \frac{f_s}{f_s'}$$

Then

$$f_s' = f_s \frac{kd - d'}{d - kd}$$

$$= f_s \frac{k - d'/d}{1 - k}$$

However, as was indicated, the ACI Code recommends that f_s' be taken equal to twice this value, but not greater than f_s. Thus,

$$f'_s = 2f_s \frac{k - d'/d}{1 - k} \leq f_s \qquad (3.28)$$

allowable.

The moment contribution M_2 can then easily be found from Eq. (3.27).

The above analysis is approximate in that it does not account for the shift in the neutral axis as the compression steel A'_s and the tensile steel A_{s2} are added. The error introduced is so small that it is safely neglected.

Compression-reinforced beam, example 1: allowable moment for a given section A rectangular beam has a width of 12 in. and an effective depth to the centroid of the tensile reinforcement of 18 in. The tension reinforcement consists of four No. 10 bars. Compressive reinforcement is provided by three No. 8 bars, the centroid of which is 2½ in. from the compression face of the beam. If 60,000-psi yield steel is used at a working stress $f_s = 24{,}000$ psi, and $f_c = 1800$ psi (4000-psi concrete), what is the allowable working moment that the beam can resist?

For the balanced-stress beam of 12 in. width and 18 in. effective depth,

$$k = \frac{n}{n + r} = \frac{8}{8 + 24/1.8} = 0.375$$

$$j = 1 - 0.375/3 = 0.875$$

The moment which could be resisted by the beam if singly reinforced with $p = p_e$ is

$$M_1 = \frac{f_c}{2} kjbd^2 = \frac{1.80}{2} 0.375 \times 0.875 \times 12 \times 18^2 = 1150 \text{ in.-kips}$$

and the corresponding steel area is

$$A_{s1} = \frac{M_1}{f_s jd} = \frac{1150}{24 \times 0.875 \times 18} = 3.05 \text{ in.}^2$$

Then $A_{s2} = A_s - A_{s1} = 5.06 - 3.05 = 2.01$ in.^{2}. The stress in the compressive steel is to be taken as twice the modular value, but not to exceed the tensile-steel stress. Thus,

$$f'_s = 2f_s \frac{k - d'/d}{1 - k} = 2 \times 24.0 \frac{0.375 - 2.5/18}{1 - 0.375} = 18.1 \text{ ksi}$$

Since this value is less than $f_s = 24.0$, the compressive steel is assumed to be stressed to 18.1 ksi. Then

$$A_{s2}f_s = 2.01 \times 24.0 = 48.2 \text{ kips}$$

$$A'_s f_s = 2.35 \times 18.1 = 42.5 \text{ kips}$$

The smaller of these two values controls, and

$$M_2 = A'_s f'_s(d - d') = 42.5 \times 15.5 = 660 \text{ in.-kips}$$

The total resisting moment is then the sum of M_1 and M_2:

$$M = 1150 + 660 = 1810 \text{ in.-kips}$$

Compression-reinforced beam, example 2: determination of steel areas to resist a known moment A rectangular beam is limited by architectural considerations to a width of 13 in. and a total depth of 24 in. It must resist a total working moment of 2530 in.-kips. If $f_s = 20{,}000$ psi and $f'_c = 4000$ psi, what reinforcement is required for flexural design?

Under the assumption that two layers of tensile steel will be required, 4 in. will be allowed from the bottom beam face to the tensile-steel centroid. Compressive steel, if required, will be located 3 in. from the compression beam face. For $p = p_e$, the maximum allowable resisting moment of the singly reinforced section is determined: with $f'_c = 4000$ psi, according to the ACI Code, $f_c = 1800$ psi and $n = 8$. Then,

$$k = \frac{n}{n + r} = \frac{8}{8 + 20.0/1.80} = 0.418$$

$$j = 1 - \frac{k}{3} = 1 - \frac{0.418}{3} = 0.861$$

$$M = \frac{f_c}{2} kjbd^2 = \frac{1.80}{2} 0.418 \times 0.861 \times 13 \times 20^2 = 1690 \text{ in.-kips}$$

This is substantially less than the design moment of 2530 in.-kips, indicating the necessity for compression steel. With $M_1 = 1690$,

$$A_{s1} = \frac{M_1}{f_s jd} = \frac{1690}{20.0 \times 0.861 \times 20} = 4.90 \text{ in.}^2$$

$$M_2 = M - M_1 = 2530 - 1690 = 840 \text{ in.-kips}$$

$$A_{s2} = \frac{M_2}{f_s(d - d')} = \frac{840}{20.0 \times 17} = 2.47 \text{ in.}^2$$

$$A_s = A_{s1} + A_{s2} = 4.90 \times 2.47 = 7.37 \text{ in.}^2$$

The stress in the compressive steel is then found:

$$f'_s = 2f_s \frac{k - (d'/d)}{1 - k} = 2 \times 20.0 \frac{0.418 - 3/20}{1 - 0.418} = 18.4 \text{ ksi}$$

but f'_s is not to exceed the stress in the tensile steel. In this case, $f'_s = 18.4$ ksi, and

$$A'_s = \frac{M_2}{f'_s(d - d')} = \frac{840}{18.4 \times 17} = 2.68 \text{ in.}^2$$

The required tensile-steel area of 7.37 in.² will be provided by six No. 10 bars placed in two layers. The compressive steel requirement is met by one No. 8 and two No. 9 bars in one row.

PROBLEMS

W.S.D.: Doubly reinforced beams:

1. A beam of 15 ft simple span carries a uniform live load of 600 plf and a concentrated load of 15,000 lb located 5 ft from the left support. It is limited in size to an overall cross section of 10 × 18 in. What reinforcement must be used if $f_s = 24{,}000$ psi, $f_c = 1800$ psi, and $n = 8$? Assume that the tension steel will be placed in one row, and that the distance from the center of each row to the nearest surface of the beam is 2.5 in.

2. A simply supported rectangular beam with a span of 20 ft has an overall cross section of 8 × 23 in. It is reinforced for compression with two No. 6 bars in one row, the center of which is 2.5 in. from the upper surface of the beam, and for tension with four No. 7 bars in two rows, 2 in. center to center, the center of the lower row being 2.5 in. above the lower surface of the beam. What is the resisting moment of the beam if $f_c = 1125$ psi and $f_s = 20{,}000$ psi, with $n = 10$?

3. If the beam in Prob. 2 supports a single concentrated load at the midspan, what is the maximum safe value of this load?

4. A simply supported beam 10 × 22.5 in. in cross section has a span of 19 ft and is reinforced for tension with six No. 6 bars in two rows, 2 in. center to center, the center of the lower row being 2.5 in. above the lower surface of the beam. The beam also has compression reinforcement consisting of two No. 5 bars with their centers 2 in. from the upper surface of the beam. If $f_s = 18{,}000$ psi and $f_c = 800$ psi, with $n = 15$, what uniform live load per foot can the beam sustain?

3.12 T Beams: Working-stress Design The general discussion of Art. 3.9, with respect to effective width of flange and position of the neutral axis, applies to T beams designed by working-stress methods as well as those designed by ultimate-strength methods. When designing by working-stress methods, however, it is necessary to account for the variable concrete stress in the compression concrete zone. Figure 3.9 shows a T-beam cross section. The compressive force in the web, represented by the area *qrst*, is usually small in comparison with that in the flange and is neglected in the derivation of equations for ordinary design.

On the basis of the geometry of the strain diagram and assumed perfect elasticity of both materials, Eq. (3.23), obtained for rectangular

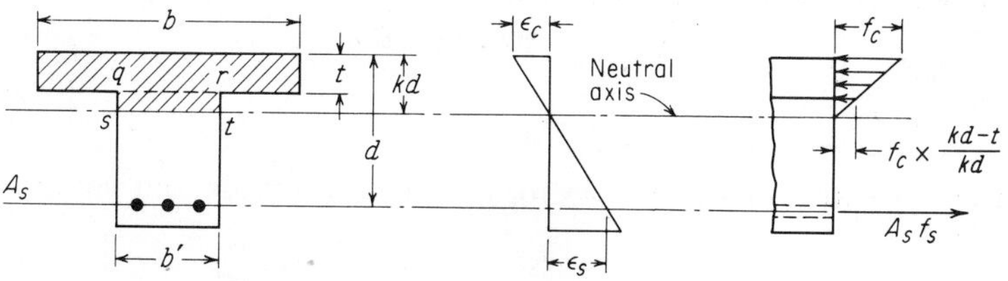

***Fig.* 3.9** T beam.

beams, applies here:

$$k = \frac{n}{n + r} \tag{3.23}$$

This permits the value of k to be calculated easily, provided both n and r are known. Unfortunately, for T beams, the actual $r = f_s/f_c$ is usually not known, even though the maximum allowable stresses are. In a T beam which is a part of a floor system, the compressive area provided by the slab is so large that the actual f_c will be some unknown fraction of its allowable value, and Eq. (3.23) cannot be used directly. In Fig. 3.9 the total tension force is A_sf_s, while the total compression force in the flange is

$$\frac{f_c + f_c(kd - t)/kd}{2} bt = f_c \frac{2kd - t}{2kd} bt$$

For horizontal equilibrium, the tension force must equal the compression force, and

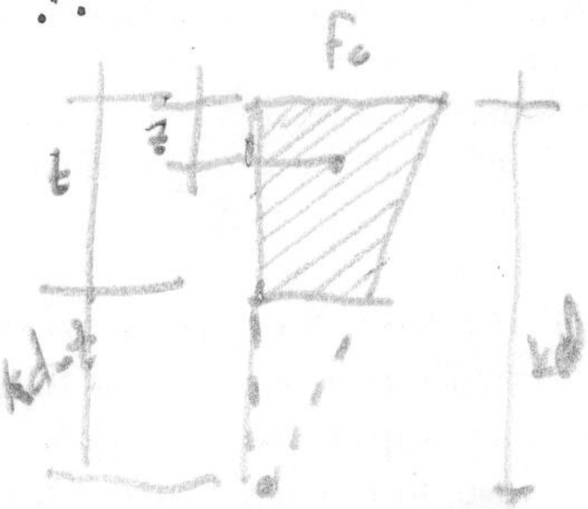

$$A_sf_s = pbdf_s = f_c \frac{2kd - t}{2kd} bt \tag{a}$$

From Eq. (3.23),

$$k = \frac{n}{n + r} = \frac{n}{n + f_s/f_c}$$

from which

$$f_c = f_s \frac{k}{n(1 - k)} \tag{b}$$

Substituting this expression for f_c into (a) to eliminate unit stresses,

$$k = \frac{np + \frac{1}{2}(t/d)^2}{np + t/d} \tag{3.29}$$

The distance to the center of compression (center of gravity of the trapezoid) from the upper face of the beam is

$$z = \frac{3kd - 2t}{2kd - t} \frac{t}{3} \tag{3.30}$$

and the lever arm of the couple formed by the tensile and compressive forces is

$$jd = d - z \tag{3.31}$$

From the above analysis,

$$j = \frac{6 - 6t/d + 2(t/d)^2 + (t/d)^3(1/2pn)}{6 - 3t/d} \tag{3.32}$$

The resisting moments of the steel and concrete are equal to the product of the lever arm jd of the internal stress couple and the total tension and compression, respectively; hence

$$M = A_s f_s jd \tag{3.33a}$$

or

$$M = f_c\left(1 - \frac{t}{2kd}\right) btjd \tag{3.33b}$$

Approximate equations for resisting moments can be developed as follows: Since the center of gravity of the compression-stress trapezoid is above the middle of the slab, the lever arm jd of the resisting couple is never less than $d - t/2$. The average unit compressive stress

$$f_c\left(1 - \frac{t}{2kd}\right)$$

is never as small as $f_c/2$, except when the neutral axis is at or above the bottom of the slab, in which case rectangular-beam equations apply. Equations (3.33) can be approximated by substituting these limiting values for jd and $f_c(1 - t/2kd)$. Then,

$$M = A_s f_s\left(d - \frac{t}{2}\right) \tag{3.34a}$$

or

$$M = \frac{f_c}{2} bt\left(d - \frac{t}{2}\right) \tag{3.34b}$$

The use of Eqs. (3.34) in *design* is justified for all practical purposes. They must not be used in *review* problems.

T beam, example 1: allowable-moment capacity of a given section A floor slab 4 in. thick is supported by reinforced-concrete beams 9 ft center to center which, together with the slab, act as T beams. The beams are simply supported, and their span is 19 ft. The cross section of each beam below the slab is 10 × 20 in.; the reinforcement consists of six No. 8 bars in two rows, 2 in. center to center vertically, the center of the lower row being 2½ in. above the lower surface of the beam. If a 2500-psi concrete and an allowable steel stress of 20,000 psi are used, what is the maximum allowable working moment of the beam?

For 2500-psi concrete, a working stress $f_c = 1125$ psi is specified by Code, with

$n = 10$. The effective width of the compression flange is not to exceed

$$16t + b' = 16 \times 4 + 10 = 74 \text{ in.}$$

$$\frac{\text{Span}}{4} = 19 \times \frac{12}{4} = 57 \text{ in.}$$

$$\text{Center-line beam spacing} = 108 \text{ in.}$$

The second criterion controls, and b is taken as 57 in. Then,

$$p = \frac{A_s}{bd} = \frac{4.71}{57 \times 20.5} = 0.00403$$

$$pn = 0.00403 \times 10 = 0.0403$$

$$\frac{t}{d} = \frac{4}{20.5} = 0.195$$

$$k = \frac{pn + 0.5(t/d)^2}{pn + t/d} = \frac{0.0403 + 0.5 \times 0.195^2}{0.0403 + 0.195} = 0.252^*$$

Checking the location of the neutral axis,

$$kd = 0.252 \times 20.5 = 5.16 \text{ in.} > 4.0 \text{ in.}$$

and the beam is, in effect, a T beam as assumed. Then,

$$j = \frac{6 - 6t/d + 2(t/d)^2 + (t/d)^3(1/2pn)}{6 - 3t/d}$$

$$= \frac{6 - 6 \times 0.195 \times 2 \times 0.195^2 + 0.195^3/(2 \times 0.0403)}{6 - 3 \times 0.195} = 0.923^*$$

If the allowable moment is governed by the steel stress, then

$$M = A_s f_s jd = 4.71 \times 20 \times 0.923 \times 20.5 = 1780 \text{ in.-kips}$$

Checking the concrete extreme fiber stress at that moment,

$$f_c = \frac{M}{(1 - t/2kd)btjd}$$

$$= \frac{1{,}780{,}000}{[1 - 4/(2 \times 0.252 \times 20.5)]57 \times 4 \times 0.923 \times 20.5} = 675 \text{ psi}$$

As this is well below the allowable concrete stress of 1125 psi, the working-load capacity of the beam is controlled by the steel as assumed, and the working moment is 1780 in.-kips.

T beam, example 2: determination of steel area for a given moment A floor system consists of a 3-in. concrete slab supported by continuous T beams of 24-ft span, 47 in. on centers. Web dimensions, as determined by negative flexural requirements at the supports, are $b' = 11$ in. and $d = 20$ in. What tensile-steel area is required at midspan to resist a working moment of 2500 in.-kips if $f_s = 20{,}000$ psi and $f'_c = 3000$ psi?

* Values of k and j for T beams may also be found using Graph 12, Appendix B, for known values of the parameters pn and t/d.

As in Example 2 of Art. 3.9, the effective flange width is determined by the 47-in. center-line spacing. For a 3000-psi concrete, the ACI Code specifies that $f_c = 1350$ psi and $n = 9$. The concrete dimensions are known to be adequate, having been selected for the larger negative bending moment at the supports, and only the tensile-steel area need be determined. A trial area is first found, using Eq. (3.34*a*):

$$A_s = \frac{M}{f_s(d - t/2)} = \frac{2500}{20(20 - 1.50)} = 6.76 \text{ in.}^2$$

If a further refinement is considered necessary, k and j can be found on the basis of this trial steel area, and the steel area refined as indicated:

$$p = \frac{A_s}{bd} = \frac{6.76}{47 \times 20} = 0.0072$$

$$pn = 0.0072 \times 9 = 0.0648$$

Then, with $t/d = 0.15$, from Eqs. (3.29) and (3.32), or from Graph 12, $k = 0.355$ and $j = 0.932$. The revised value of A_s is found from Eq. (3.33*a*):

$$A_s = \frac{M}{f_s jd} = \frac{2500}{20 \times 0.932 \times 20} = 6.72 \text{ in.}^2$$

The agreement between trial A_s and exact A_s will not always be as close as this, but the trial value will almost always be sufficiently accurate for design purposes. The maximum concrete stress should be checked from Eq. (3.33*b*):

$$f_c = \frac{M}{(1 - t/2kd)btjd}$$

$$= \frac{2,500,000}{[1 - 3/(2 \times 0.355 \times 20)]47 \times 3 \times 0.932 \times 20} = 1210 \text{ psi}$$

which is less than the allowed 1350 psi. In order to provide the required A_s of 6.72 in.^{2}, three No. 10 and three No. 9 bars will be used, in two layers.

PROBLEMS

W.S.D.: T beams:

1. A floor slab 4 in. thick is supported by reinforced-concrete beams, 9 ft center to center, which, together with the slab, act as T beams. The beams are simply supported, and their span is 19 ft. The slab supports a live load of 150 psf. The cross section of each beam below the slab is 10 × 20 in.; the reinforcement consists of six No. 7 bars in two rows, 2 in. center to center vertically, the center of the lower row being 2.5 in. above the lower surface of the beam. Determine f_s and f_c, assuming $n = 10$.

2. If each of the beams of Prob. 1 supports a concentrated load of 10,000 lb at midspan in addition to the load from the slab as specified in that problem, determine the revised cross section required and the area of the steel. Assume $f_c = 1350$ psi and $f_s = 20{,}000$ psi.

3. A particular T beam has an effective flange width of 50 in., web width of 11 in., and flange thickness of 4 in. The web depth below the flange is 23 in., and the reinforcement is three No. 11 bars in one row, the center of which is 3 in. above the bottom of the beam. Maximum allowable stresses in the materials are $f_c = 1125$ psi and $f_s = 24{,}000$ psi, with $n = 10$. If the span of the beam is 22 ft, and if it rests freely on brick walls at its ends, what is the maximum uniform load which can be superimposed?

DESIGN FOR SHEAR AND DIAGONAL TENSION

3.13 General Considerations In addition to meeting flexural requirements, beams must be safe against premature failure due to diagonal tension. This mechanism of failure was described in Art. 2.5. Beams may be designed with cross sections sufficiently large that the concrete can resist all the diagonal tension. However, a more economical design will usually result if a smaller cross section is employed, with steel reinforcement provided to carry the excess shear greater than that which can be carried by the concrete alone.

Reinforcement to resist diagonal tensile stresses in a beam may take several forms. A part of the longitudinal steel may be bent up where it is no longer needed to resist flexural tension, as shown in Fig. 3.10*a*. While the ACI Code requires only that the inclined part of any such bar make an angle of at least 30° with the longitudinal part, usually such bars are bent at a 45° angle. Only the center three-fourths of the inclined part of such a bar is to be considered effective as web reinforcement.

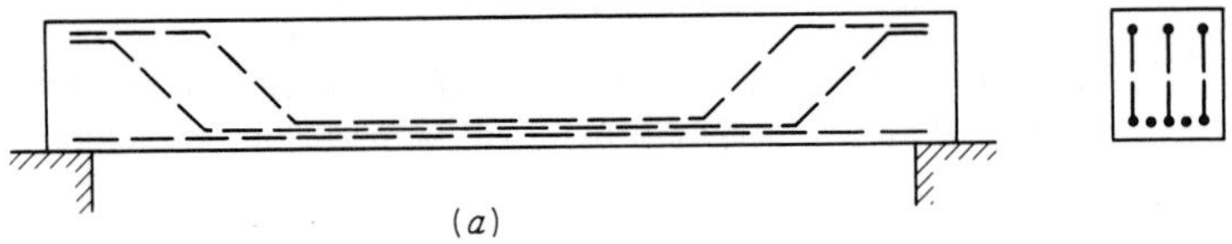

(*a*)

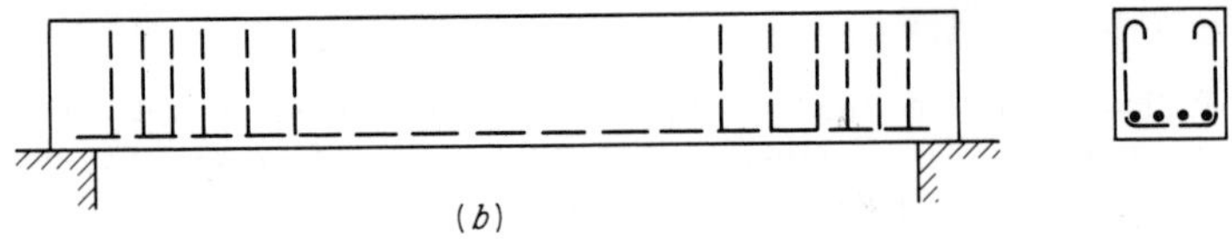

(*b*)

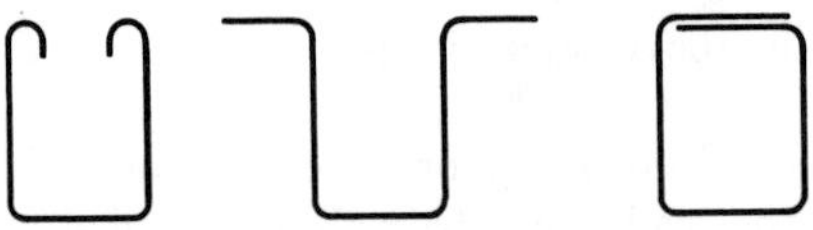

(*c*)

Fig. 3.10

Alternatively, separate web steel may be used, as shown in Fig. 3.10*b*. These separate bars, called *stirrups*, are usually placed perpendicular to the axis of the beam, although they may sometimes be inclined. Where inclined stirrups are used, the code requires that they make an angle of at least 45° with the longitudinal reinforcement and that they be securely anchored against slipping.

Because of the relatively short length of stirrup embedded in the compression zone of a beam, bond requirements (see Art. 3.16) usually dictate the use of special anchorage, obtained by hooking the end of the stirrup. Various forms of stirrups are shown in Fig. 3.10*c*. The 180° and 90° hooks shown in the first two sketches are most common. The closed stirrup shown in the third sketch is convenient when separate straight bars are used for negative flexural reinforcement. These bars can be wired directly to the upper part of the stirrups for temporary support while concrete is poured.

Longitudinal bars at the bottom of a continuous beam are often bent up to provide tensile reinforcement at the top of the beam over the supports. The inclined portions of such bars can be used to provide some or all of the required diagonal tension reinforcement, as previously described. However, because the requirements for longitudinal reinforcement often conflict with those for diagonal tension, and because the saving in steel is usually small, many designers prefer to include separate stirrups to carry all the excess shear, counting on the bent part of the longitudinal bars only to increase the overall safety against diagonal tension failure.

Where vertical stirrups are used, it is undesirable to space them closer than about 4 in.; the size of the stirrups should be chosen so as to avoid a closer spacing. When vertical stirrups are required over a comparatively short distance, it is good practice to space them uniformly over the entire distance, the spacing being calculated for the point of greatest shear (minimum spacing). If the web reinforcement is required over a long distance, and if the shear varies materially throughout this distance, it is more economical to compute the spacings required at several sections and to place the stirrups accordingly, in groups of varying spacing.

Where web reinforcement is needed, the code requires it to be spaced so that every 45° line, representing a potential diagonal crack and extending from the middepth $d/2$ of the member to the longitudinal tension bars, is crossed by at least one line of web reinforcement. When the total working shear stress v exceeds $3\sqrt{f'_c}$ (or when the total ultimate shear stress v_u exceeds $6\phi\sqrt{f'_c}$), every such line must be crossed by at least two lines of web reinforcement. These limitations are shown in Fig. 3.11 for both vertical stirrups and inclined bars, for situations in which the unit shear stress does not exceed the stated limits. For higher shear stresses, the distances s are one-half those shown. The maximum total shear stresses

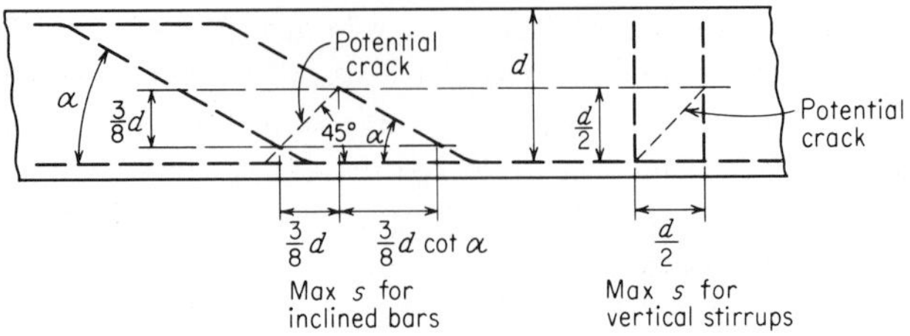

***Fig.* 3.11**

allowed by the ACI Code are a working value of $5\sqrt{f'_c}$ and an ultimate value of $10\phi\sqrt{f'_c}$.

The Code further requires that, where web reinforcement is needed, its area should not be less than $0.0015bs$, where b is the width of the beam, and s is the stirrup spacing. *For beams of* I *or* T *section, only the web width b' is considered effective in resisting diagonal tension, and b' is to be substituted for b in this and all other diagonal-tension formulas.* This minimum area provides a second criterion for maximum spacing:

$$s_{\max} = \frac{A_v}{0.0015b}$$

The maximum shear force V, and therefore the maximum calculated shear stress v, generally occur immediately adjacent to a support. Numerous tests have shown, however, that the first diagonal crack occurs not directly at the support, but at some distance from it, of the order of the depth of the beam. This is so because at and adjacent to the supports the additional local stresses caused by reactions counteract crack formation (see Art. 1.9 for strength of concrete under combined stress). *For this reason the ACI Code specifies that the maximum shear stress to be considered is that at a section a distance d from the face of the support, where d is the effective depth of the beam.* In order that each potential diagonal tension crack originating in the zone of excess shear be contained by web reinforcement, it is required that web reinforcement be provided for a distance d beyond that point at which it is no longer theoretically needed.

Special provisions are included in the Code for cases in which longitudinal stresses are superimposed.

In addition to shear stress resulting from transverse loads, shear stress results from torsional loading of members. Design for this type of shear is treated in Appendix C.

3.14 Ultimate-strength Design for Diagonal Tension

Beams with no web reinforcement Beams which are to be reinforced only for flexural tension must be designed so that shearing stresses throughout the critical portion of the beam are below the value that would result in diagonal tension cracking of the beam web. As discussed in Art. 2.5*b*, the shear stress causing diagonal cracking can be estimated with the expression

$$v_{cr} = \frac{V_{cr}}{bd} = \left(1.9 + 2500\,\frac{pVd}{M\sqrt{f'_c}}\right)\sqrt{f'_c} \leq 3.5\sqrt{f'_c} \qquad (2.33)$$

where p = longitudinal tensile-steel ratio
d = effective beam depth
V = external shear force at section under consideration
M = external bending moment at section under consideration (not less than Vd)

With V, d, and M in self-consistent units, and $\sqrt{f'_c}$ in psi units, v_{cr} is given in psi units. For reasons of safety, the useful shear capacity of the unreinforced beam web, $v_{uc} = V_{uc}/bd$, is taken as ϕ times the shear stress causing cracking. With a slight rearrangement of terms, one obtains, from Eq. (2.33),

$$v_{uc} = \frac{V_{uc}}{bd} = \phi\left(1.9\sqrt{f'_c} + 2500\,\frac{pVd}{M}\right) \leq 3.5\phi\sqrt{f'_c} \qquad (3.35)$$

The understrength factor ϕ is taken equal to 0.85 for diagonal-tension calculations. As an alternative to Eq. (3.35), the Code permits the use of the simpler, more conservative, but less accurate expression

$$v_{uc} = \frac{V_{uc}}{bd} = 2\phi\sqrt{f'_c} \qquad (3.36)$$

Example 1: beam without web reinforcement A rectangular beam is to be designed to carry an ultimate shear force of 40,000 lb. No web reinforcement is to be used, and f'_c is 4000 psi. What is the minimum beam cross section if controlled by shear?

If no web reinforcement is to be used, it is necessary that the cross-sectional dimensions be selected so that the ultimate shear stress V_u/bd is no larger than the value permitted on the unreinforced web. Adapting Eq. (3.36),

$$v_{uc} = 2\phi\sqrt{f'_c} = 2 \times 0.85\sqrt{4000} = 107 \text{ psi}$$

and

$$bd = \frac{V_u}{v_{uc}} = \frac{40{,}000}{107} = 374 \text{ in.}^2$$

A beam section with b = 16 in. and d = 23.5 in. will be satisfactory. [Note that Eq. (3.35) may not be used directly in problems of this type because v_{uc} as given by that expression depends upon the section chosen and upon the steel ratio p. Advantage could be taken of the higher permitted value given by Eq. (3.35) by a series of successive trials, however.]

Region in which web reinforcement is required When the unit shearing stress $v_u = V_u/bd$ anywhere in the critical region of a beam exceeds that value which can be resisted by the unreinforced beam web,

web reinforcement must be provided. For reasons given in Art. 2.5, the shear resistance of the concrete beam web after the first crack has formed can be taken conservatively equal to the shear which caused the first crack, and web reinforcement need be provided only for the excess above that value. For design purposes, the value of shear stress causing cracking is given by Eq. (3.35) or (3.36). The portion of any span through which web reinforcement is required can be found by drawing the shear diagram for the span and superimposing a plot of the value $V_{uc} = v_{uc}bd$.

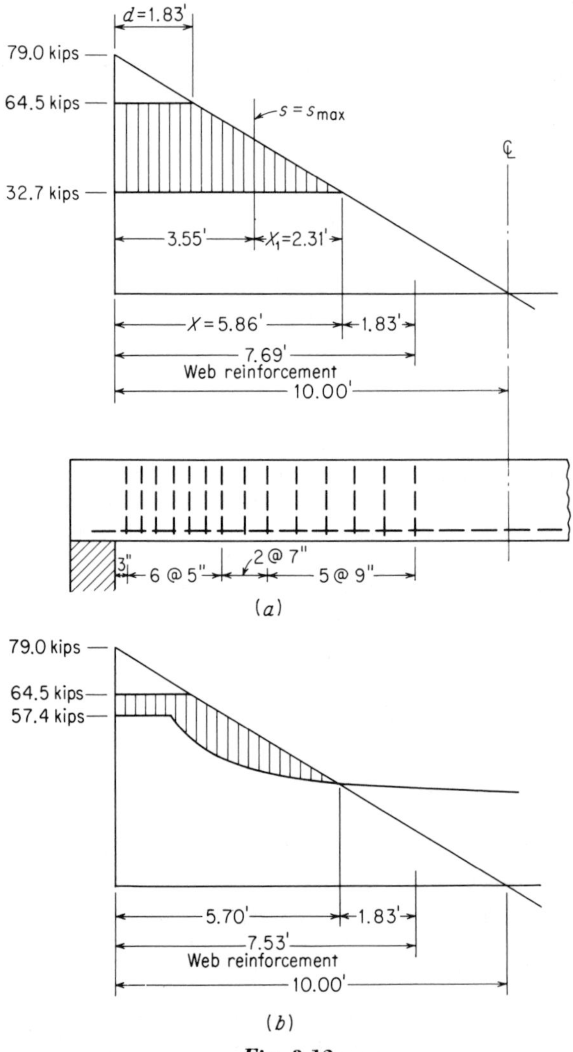

Fig. 3.12

Example 2: limits of web reinforcement A simply supported rectangular concrete beam 16 in. wide, having an effective depth of 22 in., carries a total ultimate load of 7.9 kips per foot on a 20-ft clear span. It is reinforced with 9.86 in.^{2} of tensile steel, which continues uninterrupted into the supports. If $f'_c = 3000$ psi, through what part of the beam is web reinforcement required?

The maximum external shear force occurs at the end of the span, where $V_u = 7.9 \times 20/2 = 79.0$ kips. At the critical section for shear, a distance d from the support, $V_u = 79.0 - 7.9 \times 1.83 = 64.5$ kips. The shear force varies linearly to zero at midspan, as shown in Fig. 3.12*a*. Adopting the simpler criterion of Eq. (3.36),

$$v_{uc} = 2\phi \sqrt{f'_c} = 2 \times 0.85 \sqrt{3000} = 93 \text{ psi}$$
$$V_{uc} = v_{uc}bd = 93 \times 16 \times 22 = 32{,}700 \text{ lb}$$

This value is superimposed on the shear diagram, and, from geometry, the point at which web reinforcement theoretically is no longer required is

$$x = 10\,\frac{79.0 - 32.7}{79.0} = 5.86 \text{ ft}$$

from the support face. In accordance with the Code, web reinforcement is carried a distance d beyond this point, and the total distance in which stirrups are provided is $5.86 + 1.83 = 7.69$ ft.

If the more complicated but more accurate Eq. (3.35) is used, the steel ratio, shear force, and bending moment must be known at several points along the span, and the curves of $V_{uc} = v_{uc}bd$ and V_u superimposed to determine the limits of web reinforcement. For the given beam, $p = 9.86/(16 \times 22) = 0.028$. The calculation of v_{uc} and V_{uc} is best done in tabular form as follows:

Distance from support, ft	M, ft-kips	V_u, kips	$v_{uc} = \phi\left(1.9\sqrt{f'_c} + 2500\frac{pVd}{M}\right) \le 3.5\phi\sqrt{f'_c}$, psi	$V_{uc} = v_{uc}bd$, kips
0	0	79.0	163	57.4
1	76	71.1	163	57.4
2	142	63.2	137	48.2
3	201	55.3	118	41.6
4	252	47.4	108	38.0
5	296	39.5	103	36.3
6	332	31.6	99	34.8
7	360	23.7	95	33.4
8	379	15.8	93	32.7
9	391	7.9	91	32.0
10	395	0	88	31.0

The ultimate V_u and the shear capacity of the concrete V_{uc} are plotted as functions of the span in Fig. 3.12*b*. Stirrups are required wherever $V_u > V_{uc}$. The point at which stirrups are no longer theoretically required is found, by scaling the diagram, to be 5.70 ft from the support. With the required distance d added to this, the total distance through which stirrups are used is $5.70 + 1.83 = 7.53$ ft.

Design of web reinforcement For beams in which the shear force through the critical region exceeds that which can be resisted by the unreinforced beam web, stirrups or bent bars must be provided to carry the excess. The following equations are developed in Art. 2.5:

For vertical stirrups: $$V_u = V_{cr} + \frac{A_v f_y d}{s} \tag{2.36}$$

For bars inclined at angle α:

$$V_u = V_{cr} + \frac{A_v f_y d(\sin\alpha + \cos\alpha)}{s} \tag{2.37}$$

where V_u = ultimate shear force
V_{cr} = shear force causing cracking of concrete web
A_v = cross-sectional area of web reinforcement
f_y = yield stress of web steel
d = effective beam depth
α = angle of inclination of web reinforcement measured from beam axis
s = spacing of web reinforcement

For design purposes, the predicted strength must be reduced by the understrength factor ϕ. With this modification, and with $V_{uc} = \phi V_{cr}$, Eqs. (2.36) and (2.37) are solved for the required spacing s:

For vertical stirrups: $$s = \frac{A_v f_y \phi d}{(V_u - V_{uc})} \tag{3.37}$$

For bars inclined at angle α: $$s = \frac{A_v f_y \phi d(\sin\alpha + \cos\alpha)}{(V_u - V_{uc})} \tag{3.38}$$

It may be convenient in some cases to express these relationships in terms of the unit shear stress rather than the total shear force. Since

$$(V_u - V_{uc}) = (v_u - v_{uc})bd$$

the last two expressions can be written alternatively as

For vertical stirrups: $$s = \frac{A_v f_y \phi}{(v_u - v_c)b} \tag{3.37a}$$

For bars inclined at angle α: $$s = \frac{A_v f_y \phi(\sin\alpha + \cos\alpha)}{(v_u - v_{uc})b} \tag{3.38a}$$

Example 3: design of web reinforcement Using vertical U stirrups, with $f_y = 40{,}000$ psi, design the web reinforcement for the beam of Example 2.

The solution will be based on the shear diagram in Fig. 3.12*a*. The stirrups must be designed to resist that part of the shear shown shaded. With No. 3

stirrups used for trial, the two maximum spacing criteria are first applied. For $v_u = 64{,}500/(16 \times 22) = 183$ psi, which is less than $6\phi \sqrt{f'_c}$, the spacing must not exceed $d/2 = {}^{22}\!/_2 = 11$ in. Also,

$$s_{\max} = \frac{A_v}{0.0015b} = \frac{0.22}{0.0015 \times 16} = 9.2 \text{ in.}$$

The second criterion controls in this case, and a maximum spacing of 9 in. is adopted. From the support to a distance d from the support, the excess shear $(V_u - V_{uc}) = 31.8$ kips. In this region, the required spacing is

$$s = \frac{A_v f_y \phi d}{(V_u - V_{uc})} = \frac{0.22 \times 40 \times 0.85 \times 22}{31.8} = 5.2 \text{ in.}$$

This is neither so small that placement problems would result, nor so large that maximum spacing criteria would control, and the choice of No. 3 stirrups is confirmed. Solving Eq. (3.37) for the excess shear at which the maximum spacing can be used,

$$(V_u = V_{uc}) = \frac{A_v f_y \phi d}{s} = \frac{0.22 \times 40 \times 0.85 \times 22}{9} = 18.3 \text{ kips}$$

With reference to Fig. 3.12*a*, this is attained at distance x_1 from the point of zero excess shear, where $x_1 = 5.86 \times 18.3/(79.0 - 32.7) = 2.31$ ft. This is $5.86 - 2.31 = 3.55$ ft from the support face. With this information, a satisfactory spacing pattern can be selected. The first stirrup is usually placed at distance $s/2$ from the support. The following spacing pattern is satisfactory:

1 space at 3 in. =	3 in.
6 spaces at 5 in. =	30 in.
2 spaces at 7 in. =	14 in.
5 spaces at 9 in. =	45 in.
Total	92 in.

As an alternative solution, it is possible to plot a curve showing required spacing as a function of distance from the support. Once the required spacing at some reference section, say at the support is determined,

$$s_0 = \frac{A_v f_y \phi d}{(V_u - V_{uc})} = \frac{0.22 \times 40 \times 0.85 \times 22}{46.3} = 3.55 \text{ in.}$$

it is easy to obtain the required spacing elsewhere by a single setting of the slide rule. In Eq. (3.37), only $(V_u - V_{uc})$ changes with distance from the support. For uniform load $(V_u = V_{uc})$ is a linear function of the distance from the point of zero excess shear, 5.86 ft from the support face. Hence, at 1-ft intervals,

$$s_1 = 3.55 \times 5.86/4.86 = 4.27 \text{ in.}$$
$$s_2 = 3.55 \times 5.86/3.86 = 5.39 \text{ in.}$$
$$s_3 = 3.55 \times 5.86/2.86 = 7.27 \text{ in.}$$
$$s_4 = 3.55 \times 5.86/1.86 = 11.18 \text{ in.}$$
$$s_5 = 3.55 \times 5.86/0.86 = 24.20 \text{ in.}$$

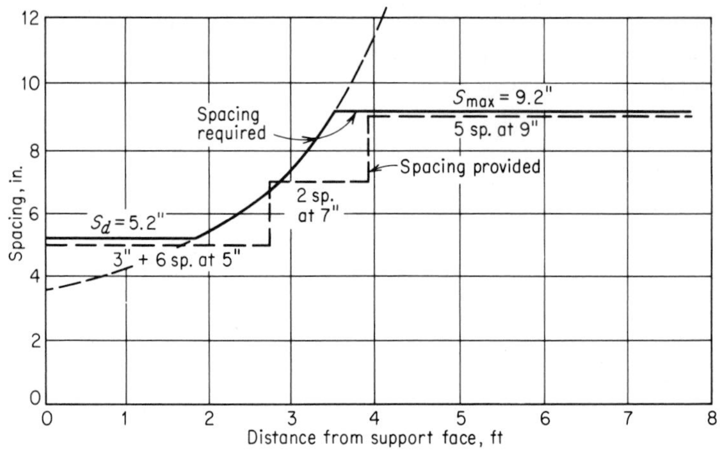

***Fig.* 3.13**

This is plotted in Fig. 3.13, together with the maximum spacing of 9.2 in., and a practical spacing pattern is selected. The spacing at a distance d from the support face is selected as the minimum requirement, in accordance with the ACI Code. The pattern of No. 3 U-shaped stirrups selected (shown on the graph) is identical with the previous solution. In many cases the experienced designer would find it unnecessary actually to plot the spacing diagram of Fig. 3.13 and would select a spacing pattern directly after calculating the required spacing at intervals along the beam.

If the web steel were to be designed on the basis of the excess-shear diagram of Fig. 3.12*b*, the second approach illustrated above would necessarily be selected, and spacings would be calculated at intervals along the span. In this particular case, the maximum permitted spacing of 9.2 in. is less than that required by excess shear anywhere between the point of zero excess shear and a distance d from the support. Consequently, the following spacing could be used:

1 space at 5 in.	=	5 in.
10 spaces at 9 in.	=	90 in.
Total		95 in.

Eleven No. 3 stirrups would be used, rather than the 14 previously calculated, in each half of the span. In designs for which the stress governs the stirrup spacing for both methods rather than the maximum spacing requirements, the saving obtained by the second solution would be even more significant.

PROBLEMS

U.S.D.: Shear and diagonal tension:

1. A beam is to be designed to carry a total ultimate shear of 67,600 lb, using a concrete with f'_c = 3000 psi. Proceeding on the basis that the beam cross section will be determined by diagonal tension requirements, select an appropriate width and effective depth (*a*) for a beam in which no web reinforcement is to be used and (*b*) for a beam in which stirrups are used to carry excess shear.

2. A beam of 12 in. width and effective depth 22 in. carries and ultimate uniformly distributed load of 6.0 kips per ft, including its own weight, and is simply supported on an 18-ft span. It is reinforced with three No. 11 bars continuing uninterrupted into the supports. If $f'_c = 4000$ psi, through what part of the beam is web reinforcement required (*a*) if $v_c = 2\phi \sqrt{f'_c}$ and (*b*) if $v_c = (1.9 \sqrt{f'_c} + 2500pVd/M)\phi \leq 3.5\phi \sqrt{f'_c}$.

3. In Prob. 2*a*, what effect would a clockwise moment of 200 ft-kips (ultimate) at the right support have on the placement of shear reinforcement previously determined?

4. Design the web reinforcement for the beam of Prob. 2*a* using (*a*) No. 2 stirrups with $f_y = 40{,}000$ psi and (*b*) No. 3 stirrups with $f_y = 40{,}000$ psi. Compare the total weight of web reinforcement for these two alternative designs. Use standard hooks (see Fig. 3.15) at the upper ends of the stirrups. What is your recommendation for the final design?

3.15 Working-stress Design for Diagonal Tension Beams which are to be reinforced only for flexural tension must be designed so that the shearing stresses through the critical portions of the span are below the allowable shearing unit stress permitted on the unreinforced web. This stress is given by

$$v_c = \left(\sqrt{f'_c} + 1300 \frac{pVd}{M}\right) \leq 1.75 \sqrt{f'_c} \tag{3.39}$$

Equation (3.39) will be recognized as being Eq. (3.35) divided by an appropriate safety factor. As an alternative to Eq. (3.39), the Code permits use of the simpler, more conservative, but less accurate

$$v_c = 1.1 \sqrt{f'_c} \tag{3.40}$$

When the unit shearing stress anywhere in the critical region of a beam exceeds that value which is allowed on the unreinforced web, as given by Eq. (3.39) or (3.40), web reinforcement must be provided. The shear resistance of the concrete beam web is taken equal to $V_c = v_c bd$, and web reinforcement is provided for the excess above that value.

Working-stress stirrups-spacing formulas, which establish the contribution of web reinforcement in resisting shear, result from a development which is analogous to that used in the derivation of similar ultimate-strength formulas and are:

$$\text{For vertical stirrups:} \quad V = V_c + \frac{A_v f_v d}{s} \tag{3.41}$$

$$\text{For bars inclined at angle } \alpha\text{:} \quad V = V_c + \frac{A_v f_v d(\sin \alpha + \cos \alpha)}{s} \tag{3.42}$$

These equations may be solved for the required spacing of web reinforcement:

For vertical stirrups: $$s = \frac{A_v f_v d}{(V - V_c)} \tag{3.43}$$

For bars inclined at angle α: $$s = \frac{A_v f_v d(\sin \alpha + \cos \alpha)}{(V - V_c)} \tag{3.44}$$

It may be convenient in some cases to express the spacing in terms of the unit shear stress rather than the total shear force. Since

$$(V - V_c) = (v - v_c)bd$$

the last two equations can be written

For vertical stirrups: $$s = \frac{A_v f_v}{(v - v_c)b} \tag{3.43a}$$

For bars inclined at angle α: $$s = \frac{A_v f_v(\sin \alpha + \cos \alpha)}{(v - v_c)bd} \tag{3.44a}$$

Example 4: design of web reinforcement A simply supported rectangular beam 16 in. wide, having an effective depth of 22 in., carries a total working load of 5.12 kips per foot on a 20-ft clear span. For $f'_c = 3000$ psi, using vertical U stirrups with $f_v = 20{,}000$ psi, design the web reinforcement.

The shear diagram is shown in Fig. 3.14. Maximum shear, at the support face, is 51.2 kips, and the shear reduces linearly to zero at midspan. At the critical section for shear, a distance d from the support face, the shear is 41.8 kips. Adopting the simpler criterion of Eq. (3.40),

$$v_c = 1.1\sqrt{f'_c} = 1.1\sqrt{3000} = 60 \text{ psi}$$
$$V_c = v_c bd = 60 \times 16 \times 22 = 21{,}200 \text{ lb}$$

The quantity V_c is plotted on the shear diagram of Fig. 3.14; from geometry, the

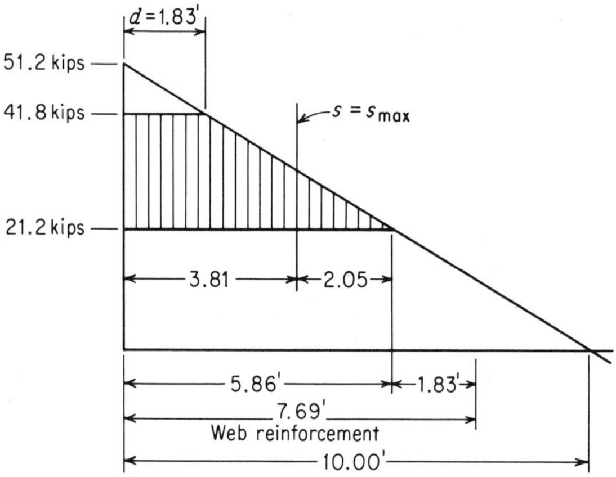

Fig. 3.14

point at which web reinforcement is no longer required is

$$x = 10\,\frac{51.2 - 21.2}{51.2} = 5.86 \text{ ft}$$

from the support face. In accordance with the Code, web reinforcement is carried a distance d beyond this point, for a total distance of 7.69 ft from the support. The stirrups must be designed to resist the shear shown shaded in the figure. With No. 3 stirrups used for trial, the two maximum-spacing criteria are applied as in Example 3 to obtain $s_{\max} = 9.2$ in. From the support to a distance d from the support, the required spacing is

$$s = \frac{A_v f_v d}{(V - V_c)} = \frac{0.22 \times 20 \times 22}{20.6} = 4.69 \text{ in.}$$

This is acceptable, and the choice of No. 3 stirrup is confirmed. Solving Eq. (3.43) for the excess shear at which the maximum spacing can be used,

$$(V - V_c) = \frac{A_v f_v d}{s} = \frac{0.22 \times 20 \times 22}{9.2} = 10.5 \text{ kips}$$

This is attained at a distance of 2.05 ft from the point of zero excess shear, or 3.81 ft from the support. With the first stirrup placed at distance $s/2$ from the support face, the following stirrups pattern is selected:

1 space at 2 in.	=	2 in.
6 spaces at 4½ in.	=	27 in.
3 spaces at 6 in.	=	18 in.
5 spaces at 9 in.	=	45 in.
Total		92 in.

BOND AND ANCHORAGE

3.16 General Considerations It was shown in Art. 2.6 that the intensity of the nominal flexural bond stress u on the interface between tensile reinforcement and concrete in a flexural member is

$$u = \frac{V}{\Sigma_0 jd} \qquad \text{or} \qquad V = u\Sigma_0 jd \tag{2.38a}$$

where V = external shear force
Σ_0 = sum of perimeters of all bars
jd = lever arm of the internal resisting moment

(jd is usually taken as obtained from elastic analysis and often simply as $\frac{7}{8}d$.) To provide for structural safety when designing by ultimate-strength methods, the capacity reduction factor ϕ is introduced. Then the design shear capacity of a beam, if controlled by bond stress, is

$$V_u = \phi u_u \Sigma_0 jd \tag{3.45a}$$

Conversely, if the designer wishes to calculate the bond stress for a given shear force V_u in the beam for comparison with ultimate bond-stress capacity,

$$u = \frac{V_u}{\phi \Sigma_0 jd} \tag{3.45b}$$

For purposes of bond calculation, the ACI Code specifies that ϕ be taken equal to 0.85.

The critical sections for flexural bond in a beam are at those places where the rate of change in moment is greatest and the total bar perimeter is least. These places are (1) at the face of support, (2) at each point at which tension bars terminate within a span, and (3) at points of inflection. Bent bars that are not more than $d/3$ from the level of the main longitudinal reinforcement may be included in calculating Σ_0, according to Code. While bond stresses exist at the surfaces of both compression and tension bars, those at the interface between compression bars and compression concrete are usually so low that they are not considered in design.

It is useful in many cases to treat the matter of bond in terms of the length of embedment necessary to develop a certain tensile or compressive stress in the bar (see Art. 2.6). This length is

$$L_d = \frac{A_s f_s}{u_u \Sigma_0} \tag{2.41b}$$

where A_s = bar cross-sectional area
f_s = stress to be developed in bar
u_u = ultimate bond-stress capacity
Σ_0 = bar perimeter

On the basis of test evidence [see Eq. (2.40)], the ACI Code specifies the values of flexural or development bond-stress capacity given in Table 3.3, in which f'_c is the specified concrete compressive strength, and D is the diameter of the reinforcing bar. For plain bars, the bond values are one-half those of Table 3.3, with a maximum ultimate value of 250 psi and a maximum working value of 160 psi.

Flexural bond stresses calculated by Eq. (3.45*b*) that are locally considerably higher than estimated bond capacity can be tolerated, provided adequate development length is provided for the reinforcement (see Fig. 2.21). Accordingly, the Code states that flexural bond need not be calculated for the tensile steel when the anchorage bond stress is as low as 0.8 times the limits given in Table 3.3.

Where tensile-steel area is provided using bars of different diameters, the flexural bond stress is different for the different bars. The change in steel stress df_s in a short length dx is essentially the same for all bars. The change of tension force in any bar of diameter D is $dT = df_s\, \pi D^2/4$. This

***Table* 3.3**

Type of bar	Ultimate bond stress, psi	Working bond stress, psi
Tension bars conforming to ASTM A305:		
Top bars*	$\frac{6.7\sqrt{f'_c}}{D} \leq 560$	$\frac{3.4\sqrt{f'_c}}{D} \leq 350$
All other bars	$\frac{9.5\sqrt{f'_c}}{D} \leq 800$	$\frac{4.8\sqrt{f'_c}}{D} \leq 500$
Tension bars conforming to ASTM A408:†		
Top bars*	$4.2\sqrt{f'_c}$	$2.1\sqrt{f'_c}$
All other bars	$6.0\sqrt{f'_c}$	$3\sqrt{f'_c}$
All deformed compression bars	$13\sqrt{f'_c} \leq 800$	$6.5\sqrt{f'_c} \leq 400$

* Top bars, in reference to bond, are horizontal bars so placed that more than 12 in. of concrete is cast in the member below the bar. The reason for lower values for top bars is that the wet concrete, as it is vibrated, may settle away from under the bar, causing a reduction in effective perimeter. In addition, overvibration may bring excess water to the top of a beam and into contact with the bars, reducing bond-stress capacity.

† These provisions apply to the special large bars No. 14*S* and No. 18*S*. Bond tests of such bars are as yet inconclusive but indicate that substantially lower bond-stress capacity can be expected for such bars than for bars of smaller diameter. In most cases special anchorage is required.

change in tension is balanced by the bond stress acting on the surface of the bar in the length dx, and $dT = u\pi D\,dx$. Equating the right sides of these two expressions,

$$u\pi D\,dx = df_s\pi\frac{D^2}{4}$$

$$u = \frac{df_s}{dx}\frac{D}{4}$$

The intensity of bond stress is seen to be directly proportional to bar diameter for a given stress (or moment) gradient, and the largest bond stress will be at the surface of the largest bar.

If mixed bar sizes are used, the bond stress on each bar can be calculated using Eq. (3.45*b*). If, for example, two sizes are present, the shear force V in that equation can be divided into two parts, V_1 and V_2, pertaining to the bars of diameter D_1 and D_2, respectively. Since

$$V = \frac{dM}{dx} = \frac{dT}{jd\,dx}$$

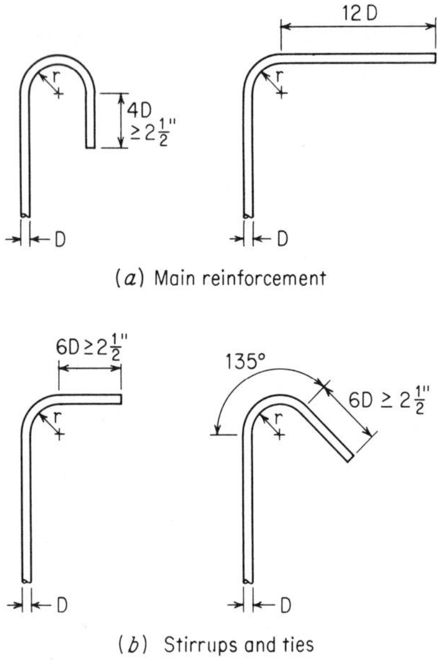

Fig. 3.15 Standard hooks.

it is apparent that the shears V_1 and V_2 will be proportional to the tensile forces in the bars of each size, which in turn are proportional to the steel areas provided by the bars of each size.

If A_s = total steel area
A_{s1} = area provided by n_1 bars of diameter D_1
A_{s2} = area provided by n_2 bars of diameter D_2

then

$$V_1 = V\frac{A_{s1}}{A_s} \qquad \text{and} \qquad V_2 = V\frac{A_{s2}}{A_s}$$

If Σ_{02} is the total perimeter of the larger bars, then the bond stress on these bars is

$$u = \frac{V_2}{\Sigma_{02}jd} = \frac{V(A_{s2}/A_s)}{\Sigma_{02}jd} = \frac{V}{(A_s/A_{s2})\Sigma_{02}jd}$$

But $(A_s/A_{s2})\Sigma_{02}$ is the perimeter that would be obtained if all the area A_s were provided by bars of the larger diameter D_2. Consequently, the bond stress on those bars can be found by Eq. (3.45*b*) using an equivalent perimeter,

$$\Sigma_0' = \frac{A_s}{n_2\pi D_2^2/4}n_2\pi D_2 = \frac{4A_s}{D_2}$$

rather than the actual total perimeter.

In the event that the desired stress in a bar cannot be developed by bond alone, it is necessary to provide mechanical anchorage at the end of the bar, usually by means of a 90° bend or a 180° hook. The dimensions and bend radii for hooks have been standardized by the ACI Code as follows (see Fig. 3.15):

1. A semicircular turn plus an extension of at least four bar diameters, but not less than 2½ in. at the free end of the bar, or
2. A 90° turn plus an extension of at least 12 bar diameters at the free end of the bar, or

3. For stirrup and tie anchorage only, either a 90° or 135° turn plus an extension of at least six bar diameters, but not less than 2½ in. at the free end of the bar

Table 3.4

Bar No.	*Minimum radius*
3, 4, or 5	2½ bar diameters
6, 7, or 8	3 bar diameters
9, 10, or 11	4 bar diameters
14*S* or 18*S*	5 bar diameters

The minimum radius of bend measured on the inside of the bar for standard hooks must not be less than the values of Table 3.4, except that, for sizes No. 6 through No. 11 inclusive in structural and intermediate grades of bars only, the minimum radius shall be 2½ bar diameters. Such standard hooks in tension may be considered as developing, in the bar, 10,000 psi working stress or 19,000 psi ultimate stress, or may be considered as simple extensions of the bars at the appropriate bond stresses. Hooks are not to be considered effective in adding to the compressive resistance of bars.

3.17 Example: ultimate-strength design for bond A continuous beam with bar details as shown in Fig. 3.16*a* is designed to carry a total uniformly dis-

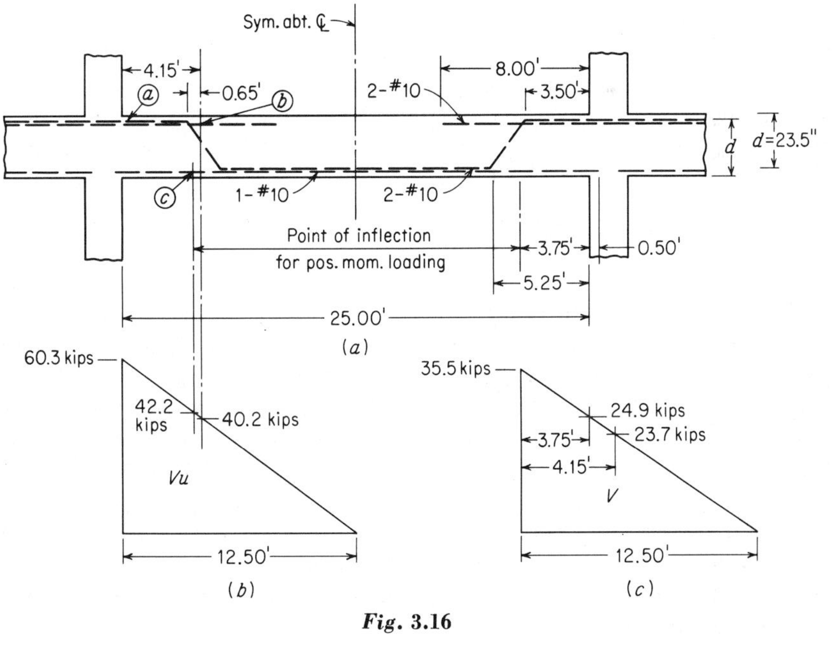

Fig. **3.16**

tributed ultimate load of 4.83 kips per ft. The resulting shear diagram at ultimate load is shown in Fig. 3.16*b*. If the material strengths f'_c and f_y are 3000 psi and 40,000 psi, respectively, and the point of inflection when the beam is loaded for maximum positive moment is 3.75 ft from the support face, check the intensity of bond stress at all critical points in the beam, and compare these with maximum specified values.

The maximum bond stress at the surface of a tension bar occurs where the shear is greatest and the bar perimeter is least. For simply supported beams, this is at the face of supports. For continuous beams, maximum shear and minimum perimeter do not ordinarily occur at the same location, and it is necessary to check all locations which may be critical. With reference to Fig. 3.16*a*, for negative bars, this will ordinarily be at the face of supports, where the shear is maximum, and at locations where tensile bars are bent downward. In the latter case, although the shear is not so large as at the support, the available perimeter is reduced. The ACI Code specifies that tensile bars within a distance $d/3$ of the main reinforcement may be included in calculating perimeter, so, if bars are bent at 45°, the critical location is a distance $d/3$ beyond the actual bend point. The critical location for positive bars is at the point of inflection. For the given beam,

$$\text{At } (a): \quad u = \frac{V}{\phi\Sigma_0 jd} = \frac{60{,}300}{0.85 \times 16.0 \times 0.875 \times 23.5} = 216 \text{ psi}$$

$$\text{At } (b): \quad u = \frac{40{,}200}{0.85 \times 8.0 \times 0.875 \times 23.5} = 286 \text{ psi}$$

$$\text{At } (c): \quad u = \frac{42{,}200}{0.85 \times 5.5 \times 0.875 \times 23.5} = 440 \text{ psi}$$

According to ACI specifications, for the top bars,

$$u_u = \frac{6.7\sqrt{f'_c}}{D} = \frac{6.7\sqrt{3000}}{1.27} = 289 \text{ psi}$$

and for the bottom bars,

$$u_u = \frac{9.5\sqrt{f'_c}}{D} = \frac{9.5\sqrt{3000}}{1.27} = 410 \text{ psi}$$

It is evident that the top bars at locations *a* and *b* are stressed below the specified maximum values, while the bond stress for the bottom bars at location *c* is somewhat above the maximum. According to the Code, however, flexural bond stresses which locally exceed maximum values need not be a concern, provided the development bond stress is not more than 80 per cent of the specified maximum value. For the given beam, to develop the full yield-strength capacity[1] of the

[1] In some cases it would not be necessary to develop the full yield-strength capacity of the bars. For example, if the bars were not bent at the maximum theoretical distance from the support, but were carried closer to the support before being bent, then the remaining straight bars would be stressed below f_y. In such a case it would be necessary only to develop the force $A_s f_s = M/z$.

two No. 7 bars at the point at which the other two bars are bent up,

$$u = \frac{A_s f_y}{\Sigma_0 L} = \frac{1.27 \times 40{,}000}{3.99 \times 5.75 \times 12} = 126 \text{ psi}$$

Since this is well below $0.80 \times 410 = 328$ psi, bond failure will not occur in spite of the locally high bond stress, and the beam is satisfactory.

PROBLEM

U.S.D.: Bond and anchorage:

A continuous beam of 24-ft clear span has an effective depth to both positive and negative bars of 24 in. and is 12 in. wide. All bars are 2.5 in. from the nearest beam face. The beam is reinforced for positive bending with three No. 10 bars, two of which are bent up at 45° 5 ft from the support faces to become continuous with negative reinforcement. Additional negative reinforcement consists of three No. 10 bars which are terminated 8 ft from the support faces. The beam carries a working live load of 4.0 kips per ft and a calculated dead load, including its own weight, of 2.0 kips per ft. When loaded for maximum positive moment, the working moments at the face of support are $M_d = 65$ ft-kips and $M_l = 145$ ft-kips. Determine the bond stresses on tension bars at all critical locations for this beam, and compare with the maximum values recommended by ACI Code. Concrete strength is $f'_c = 4000$ psi, and the steel has a yield stress of $f_y = 60{,}000$ psi.

3.18 Example: working-stress design for bond The design of the beam in the preceding example will now be checked for adequacy in bond at a working load of 2.84 kips per ft. Material strengths are as before, and an allowable working stress of 20,000 psi in the tensile steel is assumed.

The shear diagram under working load is shown in Fig. 3.16*c*. The critical locations for bond stress are at (*a*), (*b*), and (*c*) as before. Then

$$\text{At } (a)\text{:} \quad u = \frac{V}{\Sigma_0 jd} = \frac{35{,}500}{16.0 \times 0.875 \times 23.5} = 108 \text{ psi}$$

$$\text{At } (b)\text{:} \quad u = \frac{23{,}700}{8.0 \times 0.875 \times 23.5} = 144 \text{ psi}$$

$$\text{At } (c)\text{:} \quad u = \frac{24{,}900}{5.5 \times 0.875 \times 23.5} = 221 \text{ psi}$$

Allowable bond stress for the top bars is

$$u = \frac{3.4\sqrt{f'_c}}{D} = \frac{3.4\sqrt{3000}}{1.27} = 147 \text{ psi}$$

and for the bottom bars is

$$u = \frac{4.8\sqrt{f'_c}}{D} = \frac{4.8\sqrt{3000}}{1.27} = 207 \text{ psi}$$

It is seen that the bond stress for the top bars is below the allowable limit at both locations, while the bond stress for the bottom bars exceeds the allowable value. However, assuming that the No. 7 straight bars are fully stressed to f_s at the point at which the other two bars are bent up, the development bond stress is

$$u = \frac{A_s f_s}{\Sigma_0 L} = \frac{1.20 \times 20{,}000}{5.50 \times 5.75 \times 12} = 63 \text{ psi}$$

Since this is well below $0.80 \times 207 = 165$ psi, bond failure will not occur in spite of the locally high stress, and the beam is satisfactory with regard to bond.

DESIGN DETAILS

3.19 Selection of Bars and Bar Spacing The standard reinforcing-bar sizes and types available to the designer were described in Art. 1.10*b*. Common bars range in size from No. 2 to No. 11, with the bar number corresponding approximately to the number of eighth inches of bar diameter. The larger sizes, No. 14*S* (1¾-in. diameter) and No. 18*S* (2¼-in. diameter), are available on special order and are used primarily for column reinforcement. Table 1 of Appendix B gives areas, perimeters, and weights of standard bars; Tables 2 and 3 give information for groups of bars.

It is often desirable to mix bar sizes in order to meet steel-area requirements more closely. In general, mixed bars should be of comparable sizes; for example, it would be bad practice to use No. 11 bars in conjunction with No. 3 bars, while mixing No. 10 bars with No. 8 bars would be perfectly acceptable. There is some practical advantage to minimizing the number of different bar sizes used for a given structure.

Normally it is necessary to maintain a certain minimum distance between adjacent bars in order to ensure proper placement of concrete around them. Air pockets below the steel are to be avoided, and full surface contact between the bars and the concrete is desirable to optimize bond strength.[1] The ACI Code specifies that the minimum clear distance between adjacent bars shall not be less than the nominal diameter of the bars, or 1⅓ times the maximum size of the coarse aggregate, or 1 in. Where reinforcement is placed in two or more layers, the clear distance between layers must not be less than 1 in., and the bars in the upper layer should be placed directly above those in the bottom layer.

In order to provide the steel with adequate concrete protection against fire and corrosion, the designer must maintain a certain minimum thickness of concrete cover outside the outermost steel. The thickness

[1] In some cases bars are placed in direct contact with one another, i.e., "bundled," in order to save space. In such cases special attention must be given to effective perimeter for bond stress; in addition it is desirable that such bundled bars be fully enclosed with stirrups or ties.

Fig. 3.17

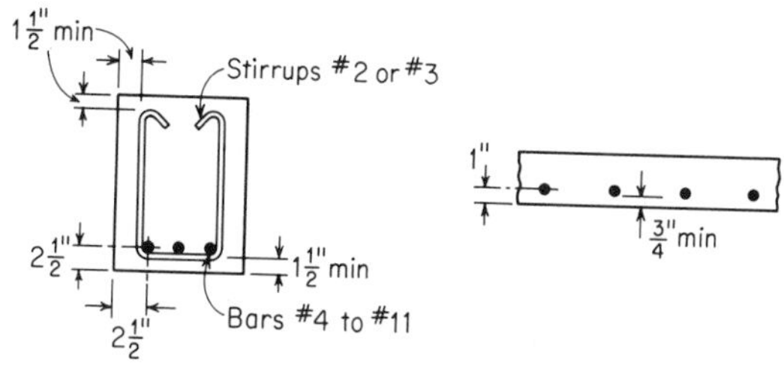

(*a*) Beam with stirrups (*b*) Slab

required will vary, depending upon the type of member and conditions of exposure. According to the ACI Code, concrete protection at surfaces not exposed directly to the ground or weather should not be less than ¾ in. for slabs and walls and 1½ in. for beams and girders. If the concrete surface is to be exposed to the weather or in contact with the ground, a protective covering of at least 2 in. is required (1½ in. for No. 5 bars and smaller), except that if the concrete is to be poured in direct contact with the ground, without the use of forms, a covering of at least 3 in. must be furnished.

In general, the centers of bars in beams should be placed at least 2½ in. from the bottom surface of the beam, in order to furnish at least 1½ in. of clear insulation below the bars and the stirrups (see Fig. 3.17). In slabs, 1 in. to the center of the bar is ordinarily sufficient to give the required ¾ in. insulation. Although the distances shown in Fig. 3.17 are not the exact distances required in all cases to furnish the clear insulation specified by the Code, they will almost always satisfy the minimum requirements, and they are sufficiently exact for all design purposes. Total depths of beams should be taken in multiples of not less than ½ in., and preferably 1 in.

3.20 Bar Cutoff and Bend Points Articles 3.7 to 3.12 have dealt with moments, stresses, concrete dimensions, and bar areas at the critical-moment sections of beams. The critical-moment sections are at the face of supports (negative bending) and near the middle of the span (positive bending). Occasionally, "haunched" members of variable depth or width are used so that the concrete flexural capacity will agree more closely with the variation in bending moment along a span or series of spans. Usually, however, prismatic members with constant concrete dimensions are used to simplify formwork and reduce cost.

The steel reinforcement, on the other hand, is easily varied in accordance with requirements for flexure, and it is common practice either to cut off bars where they are no longer required to resist stress, or, in the case of continuous beams, to bend up the bottom steel (usually at 45°)

so that it provides tensile reinforcement at the top of the beam over the supports.

As an illustration, in the uniformly loaded, simply supported beam shown in Fig. 3.18*a*, the tensile force to be resisted by the reinforcement at any cross section is

$$T = A_s f_s = \frac{M}{z}$$

where M is the value of bending moment at that section, and z is the internal lever arm of the resisting moment. The lever arm z varies only within narrow limits and is never less than the value obtained at the maximum-moment section. Consequently, the tensile force can be taken

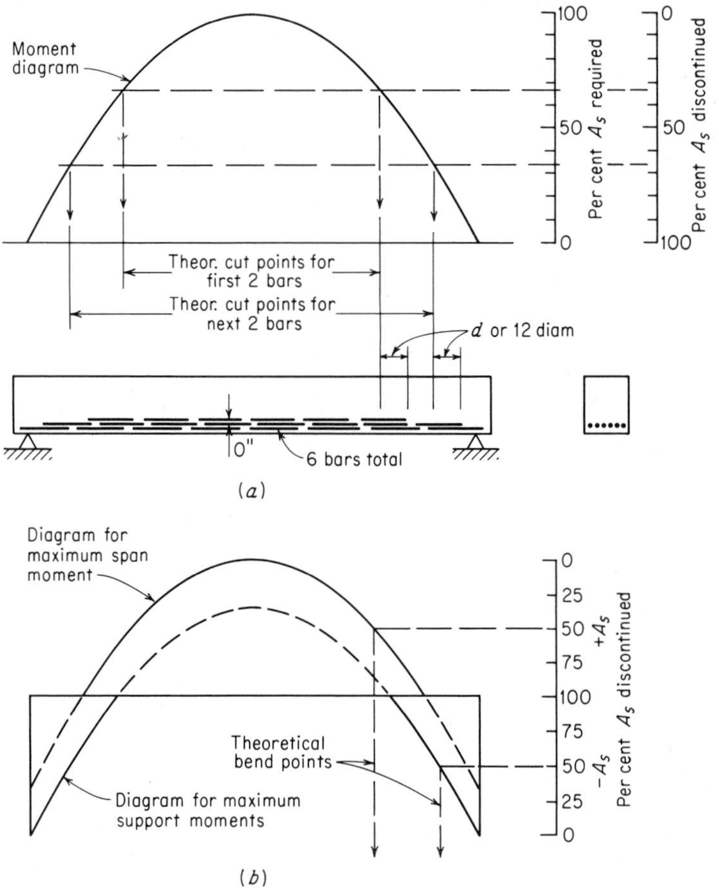

Fig. 3.18

with good accuracy as directly proportional to the bending moment. Since it is desirable to design so that the steel everywhere in the beam is as nearly fully stressed as possible, it follows that the required steel area is very nearly proportional to the bending moment.

The moment diagram of Fig. 3.18*a* can therefore be used as a steel-requirement diagram. At the maximum-moment section, 100 per cent of the tensile steel is required (zero per cent can be discontinued or bent), while at the supports, zero per cent of the steel is theoretically required (100 per cent can be discontinued or bent). The percentage of bars which could be bent elsewhere along the span is obtainable directly from the moment diagram, drawn to scale. To facilitate the determination of bend points for simple spans, Graph 10, Appendix B, has been prepared. It represents a half-moment diagram for a uniformly loaded simple span.

To determine bend points for continuous beams, the moment diagrams resulting from loading for maximum span moment and maximum support moment are drawn. A moment envelope results, which defines the range of values of moment at any section. Bend points can be found from the appropriate moment curve as for simple spans. Figure 3.18*b* illustrates, for example, a continuous beam with moment envelope resulting from alternate loadings to produce maximum span and maximum support moments. The locations of the points at which 50 per cent of the bottom and top steel may theoretically be bent are shown.

According to the ACI Code, uniformly loaded, continuous reinforced-concrete beams of fairly regular span may be designed using moment coefficients (see Table 8.1). These coefficients, analogous to the numerical constant in the expression $\frac{1}{8}wL^2$ for simple beam bending moment, give a conservative approximation of span and support moments for continuous beams. When such coefficients are used in design, bend points may conveniently be found from Graph 11, Appendix B. Moment curves corresponding to the various span- and support-moment coefficients are given at the top and bottom of the chart, respectively.

Actually, in no case should the tensile steel be discontinued exactly at the theoretically described points. It is necessary to develop at least part of the strength of the bar by bond stress before it can carry any tension. Also, as described in Art. 2.6*b* and shown in Fig. 2.18*b*, when diagonal tension cracks form, an internal redistribution of forces occurs in a beam. Prior to cracking, the steel tensile force at any point is proportional to the moment at a vertical section passing through that point. However, after the crack has formed, the tensile force in the steel at the crack is governed by the moment at a section nearer midspan, which may be much larger.

Recognizing these facts, the ACI Code specifies that every bar should be continued at least a distance equal to the effective depth of the beam

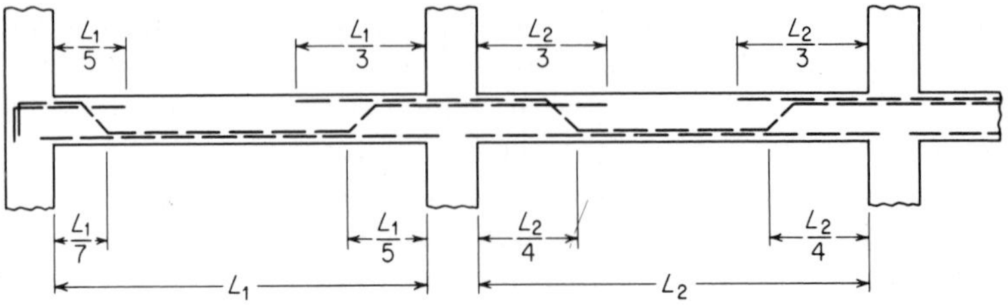

Fig. 3.19

or 12 bar diameters (whichever is larger) beyond the point at which it is theoretically no longer required to resist stress. In addition, it is specified that at least one-third of the bottom tensile steel (one-quarter in the case of continuous beams) must be continued uninterrupted along the same face of the beam a distance of at least 6 in. into the support. At least one-third of the total reinforcement provided for negative moment at the support must be extended beyond the extreme position of the point of inflection a distance not less than one-sixteenth of the clear span or the effective depth of the member, whichever is greater, according to Code.

When bars are cut off in a tension zone rather than bent so as to be continuous with steel on the other face of a beam, the Code requires special precautions. It is specified that no flexural bar shall be terminated in a tension zone unless *one* of the following conditions is satisfied:

1. The shear is not over one-half that normally permitted, including allowance for shear reinforcement, if any.

2. Stirrups in excess of those normally required are provided each way from the cutoff a distance equal to three-quarters of the depth of the, beam. The excess stirrups shall provide an area not less than $0.0015bs$ where b is the web width, and s the spacing of the stirrups. In addition, the stirrup spacing shall not exceed $d/8r_b$, where r_b is the ratio of the area of bars cut off to the total area of bars at the section.

3. The continuing bars provide twice the area required for flexure at that point or twice the perimeter required for flexural bond.

In some cases, particularly for relatively deep beams in which a large percentage of the total bottom steel is to be bent, it may be impossible to locate the bend-up point for bottom bars far enough from the support for the same bars to meet the requirements for top steel. The theoretical points of bend should be checked carefully for both bottom and top steel.

Since the determination of bend points may be a rather tedious matter, particularly for frames which have been analyzed by elastic methods rather than by moment coefficients, many designers specify that bars be bent at more or less arbitrarily defined points which experience has indicated are safe. For nearly equal spans, uniformly loaded, in which not more than about one-half the tensile steel is to be bent, the bend locations shown in Fig. 3.19 are satisfactory.

3.21 Integrated design example A floor system consists of single-span T beams 8 ft on centers, supported by 12-in. masonry walls spaced at 25 ft between inside faces. The general arrangement is shown in Fig. 3.20*a*. A 5-in. monolithic slab carries a uniformly distributed live load of 150 psf. The T beams, in addition to the slab load and their own weight, must carry two 15,000-lb equipment loads applied 3 ft from the span center line as shown. A complete design is to be provided for the T beams, using concrete of 4000 psi strength and bars with 60,000 psi yield stress.

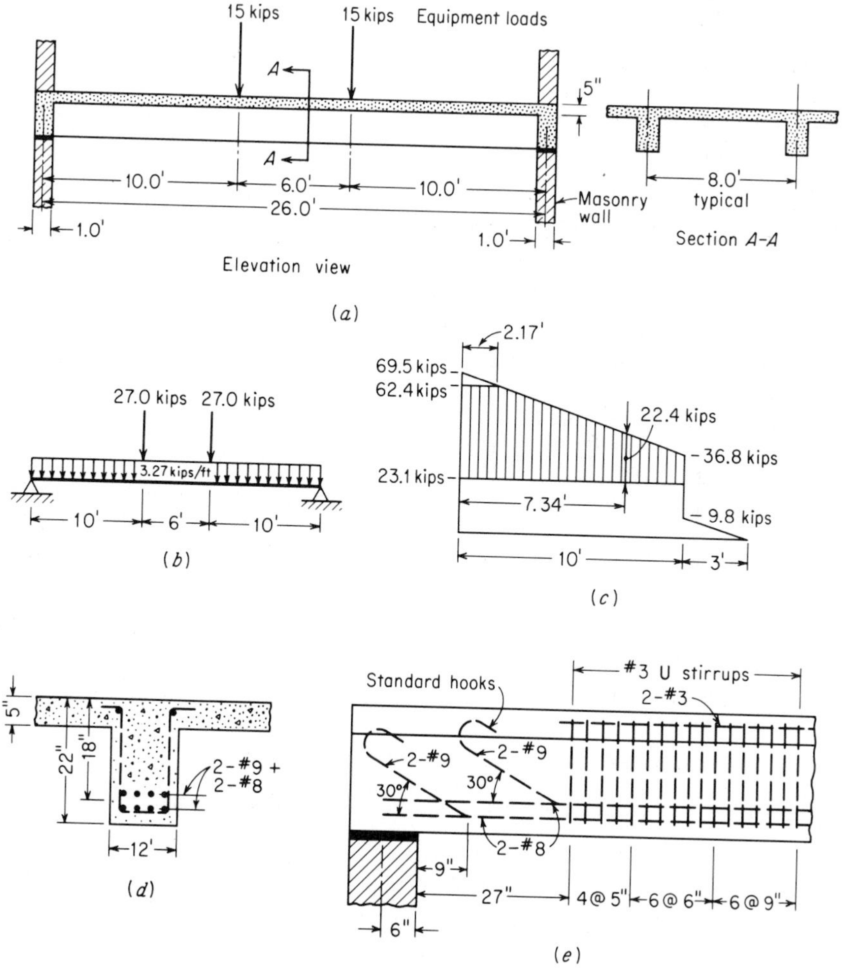

Fig. 3.20

According to Code, the span length is to be taken as the clear span plus the beam depth, but not less than the distance between centers of the supports. The latter provision controls in this case, and the effective span is 26 ft. Estimating the beam web dimensions to be 12 × 24 in., the working and ultimate dead loads are

$$\text{Slab: } \tfrac{5}{12} \times 150 \times 7 = 440 \text{ plf}$$
$$\text{Beam: } \frac{12 \times 24}{144} 150 = 300$$
$$w_{dw} = 740 \text{ plf}$$
$$w_{du} = 740 \times 1.5 = 1110 \text{ plf}$$

The uniformly distributed live load is

$$w_{lw} = 150 \times 8 = 1200 \text{ plf}$$
$$w_{lu} = 1200 \times 1.8 = 2160 \text{ plf}$$

Live-load overload factors are applied to the two concentrated loads to obtain $P_u = 15{,}000 \times 1.8 = 27{,}000$ lb. Ultimate loads are summarized in Fig. 3.20*b*.

In lieu of other controlling criteria, the beam web dimensions will be selected on the basis of shear. The left and right reactions under full ultimate load are $27.0 + 3.27 \times 13 = 69.5$ kips. With the effective beam depth estimated to be 20 in., the maximum shear which need be considered in design is $69.5 - 3.27(0.50 + 1.67) = 62.4$ kips. A maximum shear stress of $6\phi\sqrt{f'_c}$ will be selected (although the Code allows higher values of unit shear) in order to avoid heavy web reinforcement. In the present case, $v_{\max} = V/b'd = 6 \times 0.85\sqrt{4000} = 322$ psi, and the required web dimensions are $b'd = V/v_{\max} = 62{,}400/322 = 194$ in.^{2} Cross-sectional dimensions $b' = 12$ in. and $d = 18$ in. are selected, providing a total beam depth of 22 in. The assumed dead load of the beam need not be revised.

According to Code, the effective flange width b is the smallest of the three quantities

$$\frac{L}{4} = \frac{26 \times 12}{4} = 78 \text{ in.}$$
$$16t + b' = 80 + 12 = 92 \text{ in.}$$
$$\text{℄ spacing} = 96 \text{ in.}$$

The first controls in this case. The maximum moment is at midspan, where

$$M_{\max} = \tfrac{1}{8} \times 3.27 \times 26^2 + 27.0 \times 10 = 546 \text{ ft-kips}$$

Assuming for trial that the stress-block depth will equal the slab thickness,

$$A_s = \frac{M}{\phi f_y(d - a/2)} = \frac{546 \times 12}{0.90 \times 60 \times 15.5} = 7.82 \text{ in.}^2$$

Then

$$p = \frac{A_s}{bd} = \frac{7.82}{78 \times 18} = 0.0056$$

and

$$c = \frac{pf_yd}{0.85k_1f'_c} = \frac{0.0056 \times 60 \times 18}{0.85 \times 0.85 \times 4} = 2.10 \text{ in.}$$

The depth to the neutral axis is seen to be less than the slab depth. Since $a = k_1c = 0.85 \times 2.10 = 1.78$ in., a revised estimate of A_s is

$$A_s = \frac{546 \times 12}{0.90 \times 60 \times 17.11} = 7.10 \text{ in.}^2$$

Four No. 9 and four No. 8 bars will be used, providing a total area of 7.14 in.^{2} They will be arranged in two rows, as shown in Fig. 3.20*d*, with No. 9 bars at the outer end of each row.

Some of this steel can be bent up to assist in resisting diagonal tension stresses. While the Code permits as much as two-thirds of the steel to be bent in simple spans, in the present case only the No. 9 bars will be bent. The bond stress at the face of support on the remaining four No. 8 bars is

$$u = \frac{V_u}{\phi\Sigma_0 jd} = \frac{69{,}500 - (3270 \times 0.5)}{0.85 \times 12.6 \times 0.875 \times 18} = 402 \text{ psi}$$

This is close to, but satisfactorily below, the specified maximum of

$$u = \frac{9.5\sqrt{f'_c}}{D} = \frac{9.5\sqrt{4000}}{1.27} = 473 \text{ psi}$$

confirming that the four No. 9 bars may be bent. They will be bent upward in pairs, in order to maintain symmetry. The moment capacity of the section after two No. 9 bars have been bent up is

$$a = \frac{A_sf_y}{0.85f'_cb} = \frac{5.14 \times 60}{0.85 \times 4 \times 78} = 1.16 \text{ in.}$$

$$M_u = \phi A_sf_y\left(d - \frac{a}{2}\right) = 0.90 \times 5.14 \times 60(18.0 - 0.58)\tfrac{1}{12} = 403 \text{ ft-kips}$$

After two additional No. 9 bars have been bent, it is

$$M_u = 250 \text{ ft-kips}$$

For the present case, with a moment diagram resulting from combined distributed and concentrated loads, the point at which the applied moment is equal to these amounts must be calculated. (In the case of uniformly loaded beams, Graphs 10 and 11 of Appendix B are helpful.) If x_1 is the distance from the support center line to the point at which the moment is 403 ft-kips, then

$$69.5x_1 - 3.27\frac{x_1^2}{2} = 403$$

$$x_1 = 6.95 \text{ ft}$$

Similarly, x_2, the distance to the point of 250–ft-kip moment, is 3.95 ft. According to Code, the bent bars must be carried $d = 1.67$ ft or 12 diam $= 1.13$ ft beyond these theoretical points. Moment requirements will be satisfied if the first two bars are bent $6.95 - 1.67 = 5.28$ ft from the support center line, and the next two bars at 2.28 ft.

The shear diagram resulting from application of ultimate loads is shown in Fig. 3.20*c*. The shear resistance of the uncracked concrete is

$$V_{uc} = 2\phi \sqrt{f'_c}\, b'd = 2 \times 0.85 \sqrt{4000} \times 12 \times 18 = 23{,}100 \text{ lb}$$

Web reinforcement must be provided for that part of the shear diagram shown shaded in the diagram. For bars bent at 30°,

$$(\sin \alpha + \cos \alpha) = 0.500 + 0.866 = 1.37$$

Then, for the bent bars, within a distance d of the support face,

$$s = \frac{1.37 A_v f_y \phi d}{V_u - V_{uc}} = \frac{1.37 \times 2.00 \times 60 \times 0.85 \times 18}{39.3} = 64 \text{ in.}$$

However, governed by the requirement that each potential 45° crack should be crossed by one line of web steel (see Fig. 3.11), the maximum spacing is

$$s_{\max} = \tfrac{3}{8} d \left(1 + \frac{1}{\tan \alpha}\right) = \tfrac{3}{8} \times 18(1 + 1.73) = 18.4 \text{ in.}$$

say 18 in. Accordingly, two No. 9 bars will be bent up at a distance $s/2 = 9$ in. from the support face, and two No. 9 bars will be bent at 27 in. from the support face. The bars are anchored in the compression zone, using standard hooks as required by Code.

The first vertical stirrup will be placed at the bend point of the two upper No. 9 bars. At that point, 27 in. from the support center line, the total shear is 62,100 lb. Assuming No. 3 U stirrups,

$$s_{2.25} = \frac{A_v f_y \phi d}{V_u - V_{uc}} = \frac{0.22 \times 60 \times 0.85 \times 18}{62.1 - 23.1} = 5.18 \text{ in.}$$

For No. 3 stirrups, the maximum spacing is $d/2 = 9$ in. or $A_v/0.0015b = 12.2$ in. The first criterion controls. From Eq. (3.37), the maximum spacing of 9 in. can be adopted where the excess shear is no larger than 22.4 kips. This is attained at a distance of 7.34 ft from the support center line (see Fig. 3.20*c*). Stirrups will be provided a distance d beyond the concentrated load. The final spacing of vertical stirrups selected is

1 space at 27 in.	=	27 in.
4 spaces at 5 in.	=	20 in.
6 spaces at 6 in.	=	36 in.
6 spaces at 9 in.	=	54 in.
Total		137 in. = 11 ft 5 in.

As an alternative to the present design using bent bars, the longitudinal steel might have been continued straight along the bottom face of the beam and either cut off where no longer required or continued into the support.[1] Had this been done, only five extra vertical stirrups would have been required to carry the excess shear, the first 2 in. from the face of support, and the remainder at 5 in. spacing. In all probability, the extra cost of bar bending and the extra length of bars associated with the bent-bar design would more than offset the cost of the few stirrups saved, and the use of straight bars with vertical stirrups would be preferred. In continuous beams, in which both positive and negative moments must be provided for, bent bars can often be used advantageously as web reinforcement.

3.22 Splices In general, reinforcing bars are stocked by fabricators in lengths of 60 ft. For this reason, and because it is often more convenient to work with shorter bar lengths, it is frequently necessary to splice bars in the field. Splices in reinforcement at points of maximum stress in slabs, beams, and girders should be avoided wherever possible.

Splices are most often made simply by lapping the bars a sufficient distance to transfer stress by bond from one bar to the other. The lapped bars are usually placed in contact and lightly wired so that they stay in position as the concrete is poured. According to the ACI Code, lapped splices in tension bars must transfer the entire computed stress from bar to bar without exceeding three-fourths of the bond-stress values of Table 3.3. In addition, the minimum requirements of Table 3.5 apply. In determining lap lengths for compression splices, the values of Table 3.5 are to be used.

Alternatively, splicing may be accomplished by welding or by sleeves or mechanical devices which provide positive connection between the bars. An approved welded splice is described by the Code as one in which the bars are butted and welded so that the splice will develop in tension at least 125 per cent of the specified yield strength of the reinforcing bar. Approved connections for bars designed to carry critical tension or compression shall be equivalent in strength to an approved welded splice.

***Table* 3.5 Minimum lap distances* for splices**

Splices	f_y = 40 ksi	f_y = 50 ksi	f_y = 60 ksi	f_y = 75 ksi	But not less than
Tension..........	24 diam	30 diam	36 diam		12 in.
Compression†.....	20 diam	20 diam	24 diam	30 diam	12 in.

* Values shown are for bars meeting the requirements of ASTM A305 for deformations. For other bars, minimum lap distances are twice these values.

† If f'_c is less than 3000 psi, increase all values by one-third.

[1] The designer should note the very stringent Code restrictions in cases in which longitudinal steel is cut off in the tension zone of a beam.

When bar sizes exceed No. 11, welding or the use of positive mechanical connection devices is required by Code for tension bars and is recommended for compression bars as well.

If lapped tension splices are spaced laterally closer than 12 bar diameters or are located closer than 6 in. or 6 bar diameters to an outside edge, certain precautions are necessary in order to avoid failure by splitting of the concrete along the length of the bars. In such cases, the ACI Code requires that lap length shall be increased by 20 per cent, or that stirrups or closely spaced spirals shall enclose the splice for its full length. Such stirrups are to be excess of those otherwise required for web reinforcement and should have an area at least equal to $0.0015bs$, where b is the width of the beam, and s is the spacing of the stirrups. In addition, the maximum spacing is not to exceed $d/8r_b$, where d is the effective depth of the beam, and r_b is the ratio of the area of the bars spliced to the total bar area at the section. If more than half the area of tension bars is spliced within a length of 40 bar diameters, or if splices are made at points of maximum stress, special precautions must be taken.

In the case of compression splices, compressive stress may be transmitted by bearing of square-cut ends held in concentric contact by a suitably welded sleeve or mechanical device. If a lapped compression splice is used (see Fig. 3.21), and if the bars are offset at the splice, the slope of the inclined axis of the bar is not to exceed 1 in 6, and the portions of the bar above and below the offset are to be parallel to the axis of the column. Horizontal support at the offset bends, provided by ties, spirals, or parts of the floor construction, should be adequate to carry a horizontal thrust assumed equal to $1\frac{1}{2}$ times the horizontal component of the nominal stress in the inclined portion of the bar. In tied columns, the amount of reinforcement spliced by lapping shall not exceed a steel ratio of 0.04 in any 3-ft length of column, according to the Code.

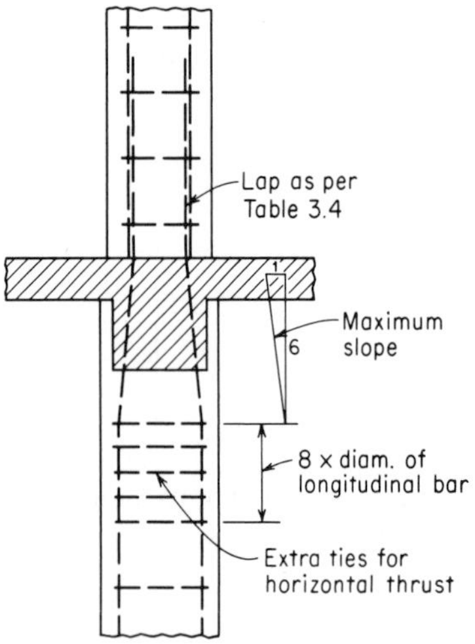

Fig. **3.21**

3.23 Control of Cracking

With the introduction and increasing use of steels with yield stresses above 40,000 psi, the question of cracking of the tensile portions of reinforced-concrete beams is receiving more attention than it has in the past. The primary concern is not the number of cracks which form, but rather the width of the cracks.

It is desirable to minimize the crack width (1) from the point of view of appearance and (2) because of the detrimental corrosion of the reinforcing steel that may occur if it is exposed by excessively wide cracks.

Extensive investigation of the cracking phenomenon in reinforced-concrete beams is in progress in the United States and abroad. In this country, no final conclusions have been drawn, but, in general, it has been observed (Ref. 3.5) that:

1. The widths of cracks due to loads are essentially proportional to reinforcing-steel stresses.

2. At any given steel stress, the widths of flexural cracks are minimized if the tensile bars are well distributed over the width of the cross section.

It has further been observed in testing at Cornell University that the widths of surface cracks at the level of the tensile steel are porportional to the amount of concrete cover provided for the bars. Placement of bars close to the surface of the beam will result in a larger number of concrete cracks of a smaller width than would be the case if a greater amount of concrete cover were used.

Quantitatively, little has been published to aid the designer in estimating the widths of cracks. The following empirical expression is suggested by Kaar and Mattock:

$$w_{\max} = 0.115 \sqrt[4]{A}\, f_s \times 10^{-6} \qquad \text{in.} \tag{3.46}$$

where f_s is the stress in the steel at the load for which the crack widths are to be determined, and A is the area of concrete surrounding one bar. The latter quantity is defined as the total effective concrete area divided by the number of bars, where the total effective concrete area is the area of concrete surrounding the reinforcing bars and having the same centroid as the total main reinforcement. Equation (3.46) fits observed experimental evidence reasonably well for values of A between 3 and 50 in.^{2}.

With regard to crack control, the ACI Code specifies that only deformed bars shall be used (except that plain bars may be used as temperature bars and column spirals, and No. 2 plain bars may be used as stirrups and column ties) and that tension reinforcement shall be well distributed in the zones of maximum concrete tension and in the flanges of T beams. It further specifies that the yield stress for the tension bars shall not exceed 60,000 psi unless it is shown by full-scale tests that the average crack width at service load at the concrete surface of the extreme tension edge does not exceed 0.015 in. for interior members and 0.010 in. for exterior members. The latter provisions give some guide also to current thinking with regard to acceptable crack widths in beams.

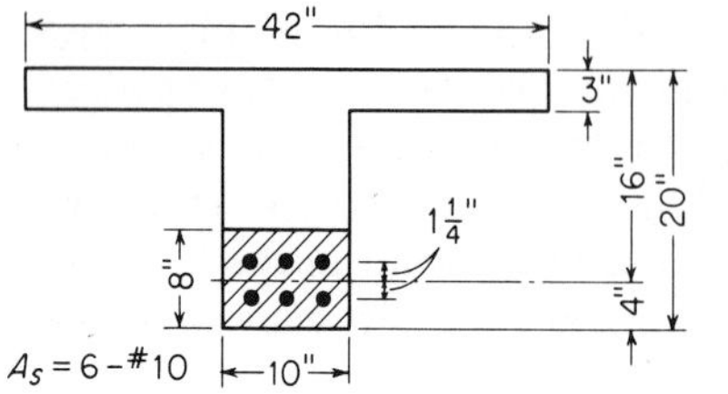

Fig. 3.22

3.24 Design example: control of cracking Estimate the maximum width of crack to be expected at the level of the tensile steel at a working load moment of 3480 in.-kips in the concrete tension zone of the T beam of Example 1, Art. 3.9.

The dimensions of the T beam of Example 1 are shown in Fig. 3.22. The total tensile-steel area provided by the six No. 10 bars is 7.59 in.² The steel stress at working load moment can be closely estimated by taking the internal lever arm equal to the distance $(d - t/2)$:

$$f_s = \frac{M_w}{A_s(d - t/2)} = \frac{3{,}480{,}000}{7.59 \times 14.50} = 31{,}600 \text{ psi}$$

The distance from the steel centroid to the tensile face of the beam is 4 in.; hence the total effective concrete area for purposes of cracking calculations is

$$A_c = 4 \times 2 \times 10 = 80 \text{ in.}^2$$

and the area of concrete surrounding one bar is

$$A = \frac{A_c}{\text{No. of bars}} = \frac{80}{6} = 13.30 \text{ in.}^2$$

The maximum width of crack is then estimated from Eq. (3.46) to be

$$\begin{aligned} w_{\max} &= 0.115 \sqrt[4]{A}\, f_s \times 10^{-6} \\ &= 0.115 \sqrt[4]{13.30} \times 31{,}600 \times 10^{-6} \\ &= 0.0069 \text{ in.} \end{aligned}$$

This value is well below the allowable values of crack width for either exterior or interior members. If the result had been otherwise, a redesign using a larger number of smaller-diameter bars, thus increasing the value of A, would have been indicated.

DEFLECTION OF REINFORCED - CONCRETE MEMBERS

3.25 General Considerations One of the significant results of the more widespread use of ultimate-strength design methods is that the members are often more slender than those designed by working-stress methods. Reasons for this include (1) the economical use of large steel ratios (above p_e) and (2) the economic utilization of high-strength steel and concrete. Recognizing that the deflection of slender members may in some cases exceed desirable limits, the ACI Code specifies that deflection should always be checked when the required net reinforcement ratio p,

$(p - p')$, or $(p_w - p_f)$ exceeds $0.18f'_c/f_y$* or when the specified yield strength exceeds 40,000 psi.

The designer may wish to calculate deflection of a member under one or several loading conditions. For example, it may be important to know the maximum instantaneous deflection under dead load plus full working live load. Or it may be that only the live-load deflection will be of interest. On the other hand, it may be of greatest significance to know the long-term deflection of a member under sustained load. Usually the total working live load will act only infrequently on a member, and the sustained-load deflection should be calculated for dead load plus some fraction of the working live load. The fractional part of the live load to be considered depends upon the type of occupancy. For example, in calculating long-term deflections for a beam carrying the floor of a residential apartment, the designer might reasonably consider about 20 per cent of the live load to be sustained. Longtime deflection for a storage warehouse, on the other hand, should probably be based on 100 per cent of design live load.

Methods for predicting instantaneous and longtime deflections were discussed in Art. 2.7. The usual methods for elastic deflections can be used, with E equal to the usual modulus of elasticity for concrete,

$$E_c = 33w^{1.5}\sqrt{f'_c}$$

and I equal to the moment of inertia of either the uncracked or cracked section, depending upon the condition of the beam under the load for which deflection is to be determined. If the extreme tensile fiber stress in the uncracked transformed section exceeds the modulus of rupture

$$f'_t = 7.5\sqrt{f'_c}$$

then the cracked transformed section should be used in calculating I. If the fiber stress is less than the modulus of rupture, calculations may be based on the moment of inertia of the uncracked transformed section. In lieu of this separate calculation, the ACI Code specifies that calculations be based on the uncracked section if pf_y is equal to or less than 500, and on the cracked section if pf_y is greater than that value. For continuous-beam deflections, it is sufficiently accurate in most cases to use a constant moment of inertia equal to the average of the values at the negative and positive bending regions.

The effects of longtime loads can be estimated using the multipliers of Table 2.1, which express additional longtime deflection as a function of duration of loading. The presence of compressive reinforcement is seen

* This value corresponds to the balanced stress ratio p_e for 40,000-psi yield steel used at a working stress of 20,000 psi, with $f_c = 0.45f'_c$.

to be of significance in reducing longtime deflection, and it may sometimes be included for this reason alone. For continuous beams, in which different values of A will ordinarily be obtained at positive and negative bending-moment regions, an average value may be used.

The ACI Code includes the following guide to what may be considered to be upper limits on permissible deflections:

1. Maximum limits for immediate deflection due to live load are:
a. For roofs which do not support plastered ceilings.................... $L/180$
b. For roofs which support plastered ceilings or for floors which do not support partitions.. $L/360$
2. For a floor or roof construction intended to support or to be attached to partitions or other construction likely to be damaged by large deflections of the floor, the allowable limit for the sum of the immediate deflection due to live load and the additional deflection due to shrinkage and creep under all sustained loads shall not exceed.......................... $L/360$

3.26 Example: deflection calculation The beam shown in Fig. 3.23*a* is a part of the floor system of an apartment house and is designed to carry a dead

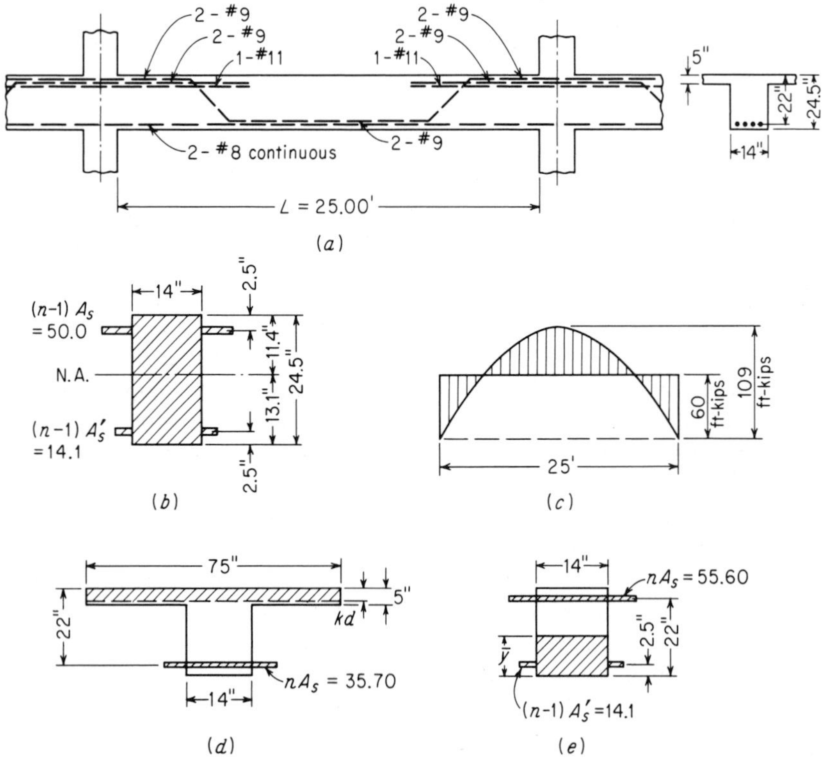

Fig. 3.23

load of 1.0 kip per ft and a working live load of 2.0 kips per ft. Materials of strength $f'_c = 2500$ psi and $f_y = 40{,}000$ psi have been used at working stresses of $f_c = 1125$ psi and $f_s = 20{,}000$ psi, with $n = 10$. Steel is placed $2\frac{1}{2}$ in. from the top and bottom beam faces, as shown in the sketches. It is desired to estimate the deflection of the beam after 5 years of sustained load consisting of full dead load and 20 per cent of the working live load. Under this condition of loading, negative moments are 60 ft-kips at each end of the span.

The beam will first be checked at the supports to determine if cracking occurs under full working load. The ACI moment coefficients (see Table 8.1) are assumed to be applicable, in which case

$$-M = \tfrac{1}{11}wL^2 = \tfrac{1}{11} \times 3.0 \times 25^2 = 171 \text{ ft-kips}$$

With reference to Fig. 3.23*b*, the location of the neutral axis at the support for the uncracked transformed section is found by taking moments about the bottom face of the beam:

$$\bar{y} = \frac{(14 \times 24.5 \times 12.2) + (50 \times 22) + (14.1 \times 2.5)}{(14 \times 24.5) + 50 + 14.1} = 13.1 \text{ in.}$$

Then

$$I_{ut} = (50 \times 8.9^2) + (14.10 \times 10.6^2) + \tfrac{1}{3} \times 14(11.4^3 + 13.1^3) = 22{,}910 \text{ in.}^4$$

and

$$f_{\text{top}} = \frac{My_t}{I_{ut}} = \frac{171 \times 12{,}000 \times 11.4}{22{,}910} = 1020 \text{ psi}$$

This substantially exceeds the modulus of rupture, which for this case is $f'_t = 7.5\sqrt{f'_c} = 7.5 \times \sqrt{2500} = 375$ psi, indicating that deflection calculations should be based on the cracked section. Alternatively, applying the ACI criterion,

$$pf_y = \frac{5.56}{14 \times 22} 40{,}000 = 720$$

which substantially exceeds the limiting value of 500 for uncracked analysis. The sustained-load moment diagram, with full dead load and 20 per cent of live load assumed to be acting, is shown in Fig. 3.23*c*. On the basis of this diagram, making use of the second moment-area principle (see Art. 8.3), the instantaneous deflection at midspan is

$$\Delta_i = \frac{1}{EI}[(\tfrac{2}{3} \times 109 \times 12.5 \times \tfrac{5}{8} \times 12.5) - (60 \times 12.5 \times 6.25)]$$
$$= \frac{2430}{EI} \quad \text{ft}$$

The modulus of elasticity is

$$E = E_c = 57{,}500\sqrt{f'_c} = 57{,}500\sqrt{2500} = 2{,}880{,}000 \text{ psi}$$

At midspan, the effective flange width of the T section is determined, in this case by the restriction that it should not exceed one-quarter of the span length, to be 75 in. In Fig. 3.23*d*, if the neutral axis is in the flange, then

$$p = \frac{3.57}{75 \times 22} = 0.0022$$
$$n = 10$$
$$k = \sqrt{2pn + (pn)^2} - pn = 0.188$$
$$kd = 0.188 \times 22 = 4.14 \text{ in.}$$

which confirms the location of the neutral axis above the bottom of the slab. Then

$$I_{ct} = (\tfrac{1}{3} \times 75 \times 4.14^3) + (35.70 \times 17.86^2) = 13{,}180 \text{ in.}^4$$

At the negative-moment section at the face of the supports, the effective cross section is rectangular and doubly reinforced, and the transformed section is shown in Fig. 3.23*e*. Taking moments about the bottom of the beam face to find the neutral axis,

$$\bar{y} = \frac{(55.60 \times 22) + (14.1 \times 2.5) + 14\bar{y}^2/2}{55.6 + 14.1 + 14\bar{y}} = 9.33 \text{ in.}$$

The moment of inertia is

$$I_{ct} = (55.60 \times 12.67^2) + (14.1 \times 6.83^2) + (\tfrac{1}{3} \times 14 \times 9.33^3) = 13{,}368 \text{ in.}^4$$

The average value of I_{ct} to be used for the calculation of deflection is

$$I_{ct,\text{avg}} = \frac{13{,}180 + 13{,}368}{2} = 13{,}274 \text{ in.}^4$$

To account for the sustained nature of the loads, the A factors of Table 2.1 will be used. At midspan, where no compression steel is present, $A = 2.0$. At the support sections, the ratio of compressive to tensile reinforcement is $A_s'/A_s = 1.57/5.56 = 0.283$. By interpolation from Table 2.1, A is found to be 1.5. It is satisfactory to adopt the average of $A = (2.0 + 1.5)/2 = 1.75$ for calculation of the longtime deflection. Then the total deflection due to full dead load and 20 per cent of the live load, after a five-year period of loading, is

$$\Delta_{℄} = \frac{2430}{E_c I_{ct,\text{avg}}}(1 + A) = \frac{2430 \times 1728(1 + 1.75)}{2880 \times 13{,}274} = 0.302 \text{ in.}$$

or slightly more than ¼ in. If $L/360$ is accepted as a reasonable maximum allowable deflection, then

$$\frac{L}{360} = \frac{25 \times 12}{360} = 0.833 \text{ in.}$$

and it is evident that the proposed construction is satisfactory.

REFERENCES

3.1 *Univ. Illinois Eng. Exp. Sta. Bull.*, no. 399, 1951.
3.2 A. M. Freudenthal: Safety and the Probability of Structural Failures, *Proc. ASCE*, vol. 121, pp. 1337–1397, 1956.
3.3 American Concrete Institute, "Ultimate Strength Design Handbook," 1964.
3.4 American Concrete Institute, "Working Stress Design Handbook," 1964.
3.5 P. H. Kaar and A. H. Mattock: High Strength Bars as Concrete Reinforcement, *Portland Cement Assoc. Res. Develop. Lab. Develop. Dept. Bull.*, January, 1963.

chapter 4

SLABS

4.1 Types of Slabs In reinforced-concrete buildings, slabs are used to provide flat, useful surfaces. A reinforced-concrete slab is a broad, flat plate, usually horizontal, with top and bottom surfaces parallel or nearly so. It may be supported by reinforced-concrete beams (and is usually poured monolithically with such beams), by masonry or reinforced-concrete walls, by structural-steel members, or directly by the ground.

Slabs may be supported on two opposite sides only, as in Fig. 4.1*a*, in which case the structural action of the slab is essentially one-way, the loads being carried by the slab in the direction perpendicular to the supporting beams. On the other hand, there may be beams on all four sides, as in Fig. 4.1*b*, so that two-way action is obtained. Intermediate beams, as shown in Fig. 4.1*c*, may be provided. If the ratio of length to width of one slab panel is larger than about 2, most of the load is carried in the short direction, and one-way action is obtained in effect, even though supports are provided on all sides.

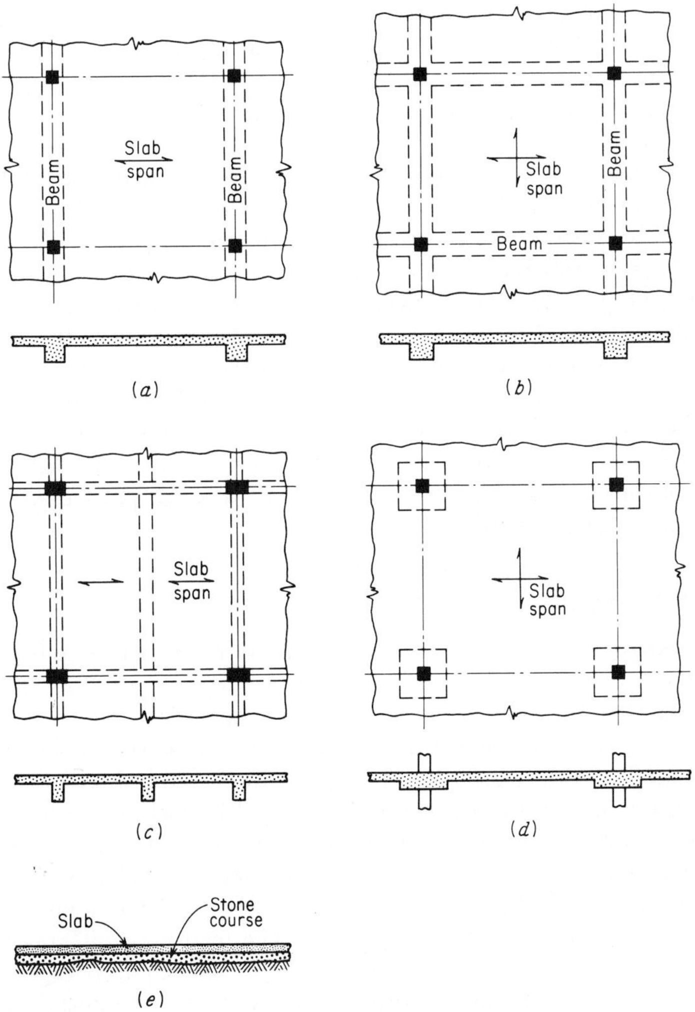

Fig. 4.1

Concrete slabs may in some cases be carried directly by the building columns, as in Fig. 4.1*d*, without the use of beams or girders. The term *flat-slab floor* is used to describe such systems, although in a strict sense all the types described above are flat slabs. In flat-slab floors, the slab may be thickened locally in the vicinity of the columns to reduce stresses due to shear and negative bending. Often the column tops are flared outward for the same reason.

Slabs resting directly on the ground, as in Fig. 4.1*e*, are commonly used in basement or ground floors, for sidewalks, and for highways. While such slabs are often designed by empirical methods, they can be analyzed by methods similar to those developed for beams on elastic foundations. A well-compacted layer of crushed stone or gravel is usually provided under such a slab to ensure uniform support and to provide for proper drainage.

Floor slabs in buildings are usually designed for a uniform live load covering the entire slab area. Concentrated loads on concrete slabs are supported by a width of slab greater than the contact width. Methods of computing the probable distribution of concentrated loads are explained in Art. 12.6. Very heavy, fixed, concentrated loads require supporting beams.

Reinforcing steel for slabs is placed primarily parallel to the surfaces. Straight bar reinforcement may be used, although in continuous slabs bottom bars are often bent up to provide for negative bending over the supports. Welded wire mesh is commonly used for reinforcement of slabs on ground (see Art. 1.10). Bar or rod mats are available for the heavier reinforcement of highway slabs. Slabs may also be prestressed, using high-tensile-strength wires or strands.

ONE - WAY SLABS

4.2 Flexural Analysis A one-way slab is essentially a rectangular beam of comparatively large ratio of width to depth. There are, however, certain factors entering into the design of such slabs which were not considered in the design of rectangular beams. A unit strip of slab cut out at right angles to the supporting beams (shaded area in Fig. 4.2) may be considered as a rectangular beam of unit width, with a depth equal to the thickness of the slab and a length equal to the distance between supports. This strip could be analyzed by the methods which were used in problems dealing with rectangular beams, the bending moment being computed for a unit width, for example. The load per unit area on the slab would then be the load per unit length on the imaginary beam. Since all the load on the slab must be transmitted to the two supporting beams, it follows that all the reinforcing steel should be placed at right angles to these beams, with the exception of any bars that may be placed in the other direction to carry shrinkage and temperature stresses. A one-way slab thus consists of a series of rectangular beams side by side. This simplified analysis, which assumes Poisson's ratio to be zero, is slightly conservative. Actually, longitudinal flexural compression will result in lateral expansion unless the compressed material is restrained. In a one-way slab, this lateral expansion is resisted by the adjacent beam strips, which tend to expand also. The net result is a slight strengthening in the longitudinal direction, but this effect is small and is almost always disregarded.

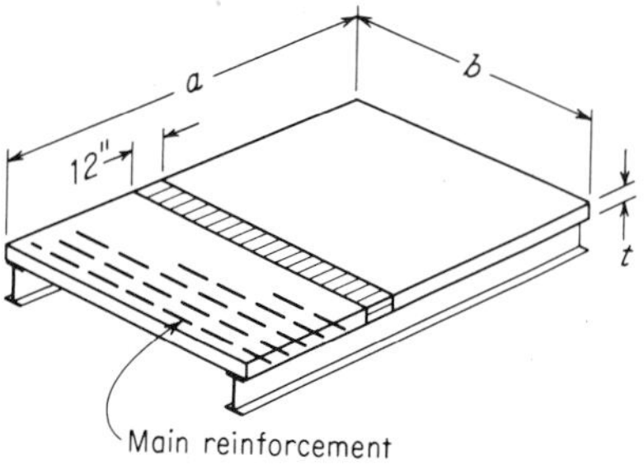

Fig. 4.2

The ratio of steel in a slab may be determined by dividing the sectional area of one bar by the area of concrete between two successive bars, the latter area being the product of the depth to the center of the bars and the distance between them, center to center. The ratio of steel may also be determined by dividing the average area of steel per foot of width by the effective area of concrete in a 1-ft strip. The average area of steel per foot of width is equal to the area of one bar times the average number of bars in a 1-ft strip (12 divided by the spacing in inches), and the effective area of concrete in a 1-ft (or 12-in.) strip is equal to 12 times the effective depth d.

To illustrate the latter method of obtaining the steel ratio p, assume a 5-in. slab with an effective depth of 4 in., with No. 4 bars spaced $4\frac{1}{2}$ in., center to center. The average number of bars in a 12-in. strip of slab is $12/4\frac{1}{2} = 2.7$ bars, and the average steel area in a 12-in. strip is $2.7 \times 0.20 = 0.54$ in.^{2} Hence $p = 0.54/(12 \times 4) = 0.0112$. By the other method, $p = 0.20/(4\frac{1}{2} \times 4) = 0.0112$.

The spacing of bars which is necessary to furnish a given area of steel per foot of width is obtained by dividing the number of bars required to furnish this area into 12. For example, to furnish an average area of 0.46 in.^{2} per ft, with No. 4 bars, requires $0.46/0.20 = 2.3$ bars per foot; the bars must be spaced not more than $12/2.3 = 5.2$ in., center to center.[1]

If the slab is of one span only, and if it rests freely on its supports, the maximum positive moment M, for a uniform load of w psf, is $M = \frac{1}{8}wl^2$. The span length l is taken as the center-to-center distance of supports, but it need not exceed the clear span plus the depth of the slab. If a single-span slab is built monolithically with the supporting beams, the positive and negative moments are computed either by elastic analysis or by moment coefficients (see Art. 8.1) as for continuous beams. Where the width of the support is not known, it may be assumed as 1 ft in obtaining the value of the clear span for use in computing the moments. Such an assumption is usually sufficiently accurate so that no revision is required when the exact width of the support becomes known.

Concrete compression will seldom control the flexural design of one-way slabs, particularly if ultimate-strength design methods are used. Flexural design will ordinarily consist in selecting a slab depth which will permit the use of an economically low steel ratio and which will not allow

[1] The determination of slab steel areas for various combinations of bars and spacing is greatly facilitated by Table 4, Appendix B.

Table 4.1 **Minimum slab thicknesses**

Simply supported	$L/25$
One end continuous	$L/30$
Both ends continuous	$L/35$
Cantilever	$L/12$

unsightly or damaging deflections. The ACI Code specifies the minimum thicknesses in Table 4.1 for all slabs of normal-weight concrete unless calculation of deflections proves that lesser thicknesses may be used without adverse effect. While diagonal tension and bond stresses will seldom influence the design of one-way slabs, these stresses should be checked, particularly for slabs of unusual proportions or loads.

The total slab thickness is usually rounded to the next higher ¼ in. for slabs up to 6 in. thickness, and to the next higher ½ in. for thicker slabs. The concrete protection below the reinforcement should follow the recommendations of the ACI Code (see Art. 3.20) unless conditions warrant some change. In the average slab, a depth of 1 in. below the center of the steel may be used. The lateral spacing of the bars, except those used only to prevent shrinkage and temperature cracks, should not exceed 3 times the thickness of the slab nor 18 in., according to Code. The minimum spacing is given in Art. 3.19.

4.3 Temperature and Shrinkage Reinforcement Concrete shrinks as the cement paste hardens, as was pointed out in Art. 1.9. It is advisable to minimize such shrinkage by using concretes with the smallest possible amounts of water and cement compatible with other requirements, such as strength and workability, and by thorough moist curing of sufficient duration. However, no matter what precautions are taken, a certain amount of shrinkage is usually unavoidable. If a slab of moderate dimensions rests freely on its supports, it can contract to accommodate the shortening of its length produced by shrinkage. Usually, however, slabs and other members are joined rigidly to other parts of the structure and cannot contract freely. This results in tension stresses which are known as *shrinkage stresses*. A decrease in temperature relative to that at which the slab was poured, particularly in outdoor structures such as bridges, may have an effect similar to shrinkage. That is, the slab tends to contract and, if restrained from doing so, becomes subject to tensile stresses.

Since concrete is weak in tension, these temperature and shrinkage stresses are likely to result in cracking. Cracks of this nature are not detrimental, provided their size is limited to what are known as *hairline* cracks. This can be achieved by placing reinforcement in the slab to counteract contraction and distribute the cracks uniformly. As the concrete tends to shrink, such reinforcement resists the contraction and, consequently, becomes subject to compression. The total shrinkage in a slab so reinforced is less than that in one without reinforcement; in addition, whatever cracks do occur will be of smaller width and more evenly distributed by virtue of the reinforcement.

In one-way slabs the reinforcement provided for resisting the bending moments has the desirable effect of reducing shrinkage and distributing cracks. However, as contraction takes place equally in all directions, it is necessary to provide special reinforcement for shrinkage and temperature contraction in the direction perpendicular to the main reinforcement. This added steel is known as *temperature* or *shrinkage reinforcement.*

Reinforcement for shrinkage and temperature stresses normal to the principal reinforcement should be provided in a structural slab in which the principal reinforcement extends in one direction only. The ACI Code specifies the following minimum ratios of reinforcement area to total concrete area, but in no case shall such reinforcement bars be placed farther apart than 5 times the slab thickness, nor more than 18 in.:

Slabs in which plain bars are used	0.0025
Slabs in which deformed bars with specified yield strengths less than 60,000 psi are used	0.0020
Slabs in which deformed bars with 60,000 psi specified yield strength or welded wire fabric having welded intersections not farther apart in the direction of the stress than 12 in. are used	0.0018

4.4 Example: one-way slab design A reinforced-concrete slab is built integrally with its supports and consists of two equal spans, each with a clear span of 15 ft. The working live load is 100 psf, and 4000-psi concrete is specified for use with steel of yield stress equal to 60,000 psi. Design the slab, using U.S.D. methods, following the provisions of the ACI Code.

The thickness of the slab is first estimated, based on the minimum thickness of Table 4.1: $L/35 = 15 \times {}^{12}\!/_{35} = 5.15$ in. A trial thickness of 5.25 in. will be used, for which the weight is $150 \times 5.25/12 = 66$ psf. The working live load and computed dead load are then multiplied by the ACI overload factors to obtain ultimate design loads:

Dead load:	$66 \times 1.5 =$	99 psf
Live load:	$100 \times 1.8 =$	180 psf
Total		279 psf

For this case, design moments at critical sections may be found using the ACI moment coefficients (see Table 8.1):

At interior support: $-M = \frac{1}{9} \times 0.279 \times 15^2 = 6.98$ ft-kips
At midspan: $+M = \frac{1}{14} \times 0.279 \times 15^2 = 4.48$ ft-kips
At exterior support: $-M = \frac{1}{24} \times 0.279 \times 15^2 = 2.62$ ft-kips

The maximum steel ratio premitted by Code is

$$0.75p_b = 0.75 \times 0.85k_1 \frac{f'_c}{f_y} \frac{87{,}000}{87{,}000 + f_y}$$
$$= 0.75 \times 0.85^2 \times 4/60 \times 87/147 = 0.021$$

The minimum required effective depth, as controlled by the negative moment at the interior support, is found from Eq. (3.5*b*) to be

$$d^2 = \frac{M_u}{\phi p f_y b(1 - 0.59 p f_y/f'_c)}$$
$$= \frac{6.98 \times 12}{0.90 \times 0.21 \times 60 \times 12(1 - 0.59 \times 0.021 \times 60/4)}$$
$$= 7.58 \text{ in.}^2$$
$$d = 2.75 \text{ in.}^*$$

This is less than the effective depth of 5.25 − 1.00 = 4.25 in. required by Code for deflection considerations, and the latter figure will be adopted. At the interior support, assuming the stress-block depth a = 1.00 in., the area of steel required per foot of width in the top of the slab is

$$A_s = \frac{M}{\phi f_y(d - a/2)} = \frac{6.98 \times 12}{0.90 \times 60 \times 3.75} = 0.41 \text{ in.}^2$$

Checking the assumed a,

$$a = \frac{A_s f_y}{0.85 f'_c b} = \frac{0.41 \times 60}{0.85 \times 4 \times 12} = 0.60 \text{ in.}$$

A second trial will be made with a = 0.50 in. Then

$$A_s = \frac{6.98 \times 12}{0.90 \times 60 \times 4.00} = 0.39 \text{ in.}$$

for which a = 0.60 × 0.39/0.41 = 0.57 in. No further revision is necessary. At other critical moment sections, it will be satisfactory to use the same lever arm, 4.25 − 0.50/2 = 4.00 in., to determine steel areas, and

$$\text{At midspan:} \quad A_s = \frac{4.48 \times 12}{0.90 \times 60 \times 4.00} = 0.25 \text{ in.}^2$$

$$\text{At exterior support:} \quad A_s = \frac{2.62 \times 12}{0.90 \times 60 \times 4.00} = 0.15 \text{ in.}^2$$

The maximum shear stress, at the face of the interior support, is

$$V_u = 1.15 \frac{279 \times 15}{2} = 2410 \text{ lb}$$

and

$$v_u = \frac{2410}{12 \times 4.25} = 47 \text{ psi}$$

* This depth is more easily found using Graph 1, Appendix B. For $p = p_{max}$, $M_u/\phi bd^2$ = 1050, from which d = 2.75 in.

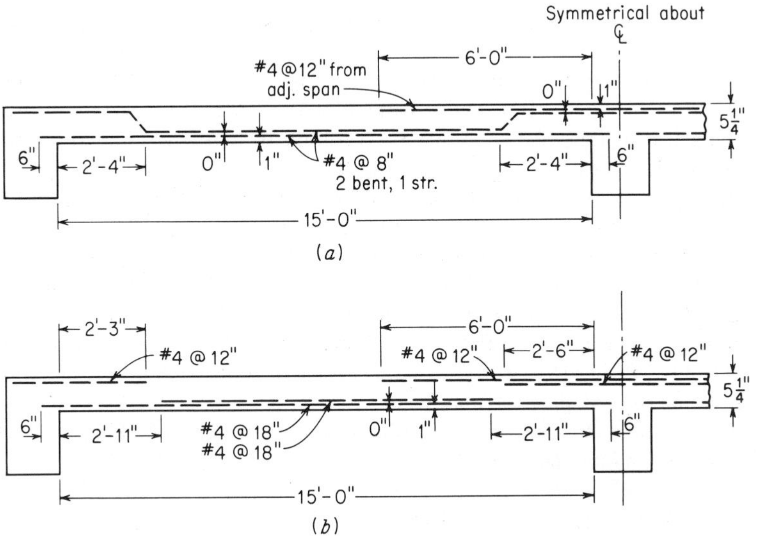

***Fig.* 4.3**

This is well below the permissible value of shear on the unreinforced concrete, which is $v_c = 2\phi\sqrt{f_c'} = 2 \times 0.85\sqrt{4000} = 107$ psi.

The required tensile-steel areas may be provided in a variety of ways, but, whatever the selection, due consideration must be given to actual placing of the steel during construction. The arrangement should be such that the steel may be placed rapidly with the minimum of labor costs even though excess steel is necessary to achieve this end.

Two possible arrangements are shown in Fig. 4.3. In Fig. 4.3*a* bent bars are used, while in Fig. 4.3*b* all bars are straight. The arrangement in (*a*) requires slightly more steel and the additional cost of bending but, on the other hand, requires fewer supporting chairs and permits easier placement, with less likelihood of bar omissions.

In the arrangement of Fig. 4.3*a*, No. 4 bars at 8 in. furnish 0.29 in.^{2} of steel at midspan, slightly more than required. If two-thirds of these bars are bent upward for negative reinforcement over the interior support, the average spacing of such bent bars at the interior support will be $(8 + 16)/2 = 12$ in. Since an identical pattern of bars is bent upward from the other side of the support, the effective spacing of the No. 4 bars over the interior support is 6 in. This pattern provides just the required steel area of 0.39 in.^{2} per ft width of slab over the support. The bars bent at the interior support will also be bent upward for negative reinforcement at the exterior support, providing reinforcement equivalent to No. 4 bars at 12 in., or 0.20 in.^{2} of steel, somewhat in excess of the required 0.15 in.^{2}

Note that it is not considered necessary to achieve uniform spacing of reinforcement in slabs, and that the steel provided can be calculated safely on the basis of average spacing as in the example. Care should be taken to satisfy requirements for both minimum and maximum spacing of principal reinforcement, however.

The locations of bend and cutoff points shown in Fig. 4.3*a* were obtained using Graph 11, Appendix B, as explained in Art. 3.20. A check of the development length provided against Table 8, Appendix B, makes evident the fact that flexural bond stress need not be considered.

The arrangement of Fig. 4.3*b* uses only straight bars. While apparently satisfactory according to the ACI Code, cutting off the shorter positive and negative bars as shown leads to an undesirable condition at the ends of those bars, where there will be concentrations of stress in the concrete. The design would be improved if the negative bars were cut off at 2 ft 11 in. from the face of supports, rather than 2 ft 3 in. and 2 ft 6 in. as shown, and if the positive steel were cut off at 2 ft 3 in., rather than at 2 ft 11 in. This would result in an overlap of approximately $2d$ of the cut positive and negative bars.

Reinforcement to control temperature and shrinkage cracking will be included in the amount of

$$A_s = 0.0018 \times 12 \times 5.25 = 0.11 \text{ in.}^2$$

per 12-in. strip. This requirement is met by using No. 3 bars, at 12 in. spacing, placed directly on top of the main reinforcement in the positive-moment region and directly underneath the main reinforcement in the negative-moment zone.

PROBLEMS

1. A small bridge consisting of a concrete slab supported by steel stringers is to carry a uniformly distributed load of 300 psf in addition to its own weight. The four stringers of the bridge, spanning in the long direction, are spaced 8 ft on centers. The concrete slab spans in the transverse direction and is continuous over the two interior stringers. Find the required thickness of the slab, and design and detail the bar reinforcement, using $f_s = 20{,}000$ psi and $f_c = 1350$ psi, with $n = 9$. Bent bars will be used in preference to all-straight-bar reinforcement. The ACI moment coefficients do not apply.

2. Redesign the bridge of Prob. 1, using ultimate-strength methods, with overload factors of 1.5 and 1.8 applied to dead and live loads, respectively. For the steel, $f_y = 40{,}000$ psi, and the concrete strength is $f'_c = 3000$ psi. Use a maximum steel ratio of $0.50p_b$.

TWO-WAY SLABS

4.5 Performance of Two-way Slabs

Most rectangular reinforced-concrete slabs are supported on all four sides by beams, girders, or walls. Figure 1.1*a* shows a typical example of a beam-and-girder floor in which each individual slab panel is so supported. If the proportions of the panel are not too far from square (side ratio up to about 2:1), the slab bends under load into a dished surface rather than into a cylindrical one, as would be the case for one-way slabs supported only at two opposite sides. This means that at any point the slab is curved in both principal directions, and since bending moments are proportional to curvatures, moments also exist in both directions. To resist these moments, the slab must be reinforced in both directions, by two mutually perpendicular layers of bars parallel, respectively, to the two pairs of edges, one layer resting directly on the other. The slab, then, transmits loads to all four supporting beams, the relative amounts depending on the proportions of the slab and the conditions of continuity at the four edges.

In order to visualize the flexural performance of such a slab, it is convenient to think of it as consisting of two sets of parallel strips, in each of the two directions, intersecting each other. Evidently, part of the load is carried by one set and transmitted to one pair of edge supports, and the remainder by the other. Figure 4.4 shows the two center strips of a rectangular plate with short span A and long span B. If the uniform load is w per ft^2 of slab, each of the two strips acts approximately like a simple beam uniformly loaded by its share of w. Because these imaginary strips actually are part of the same monolithic slab, their deflections at the intersection point must be the same. Equating the center deflections of the short and long strips,

$$\frac{5w_sA^4}{384EI} = \frac{5w_lB^4}{384EI}$$

where w_s = share of load w carried in short direction
w_l = share of load w carried in long direction

Consequently,

$$\frac{w_s}{w_l} = \frac{B^4}{A^4} \tag{4.1}$$

One sees that the larger share of the load is carried in the short direction, the ratio of the two portions of the total load being proportional to the fourth power of the ratio of the spans. This result is approximate because the actual behavior of a slab is more complex than that of the two intersecting strips, but it is a good approximation when the edge conditions are the same on all four sides (e.g., simply supported or rotationally fixed). The two pairs of edge beams can then be designed for the loads w_s and w_l transmitted to them by the slab.

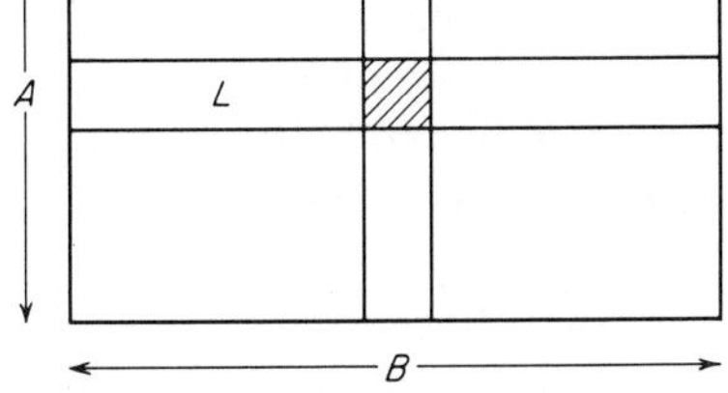

Fig. 4.4

An understanding of the flexural behavior of the slab itself can be

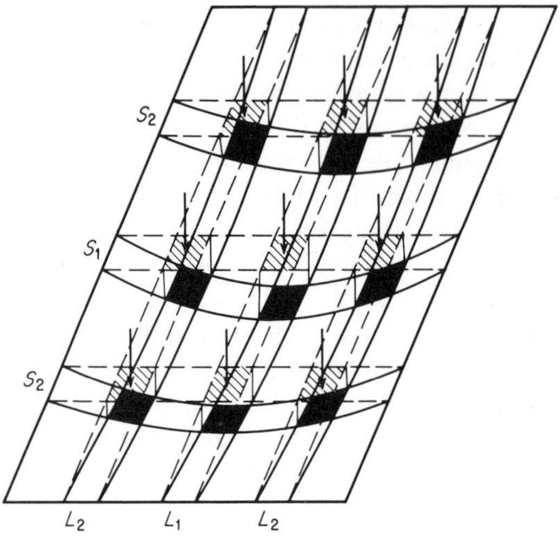

Fig. 4.5 Grid model of uniformly loaded, simply supported slab.

gained from Fig. 4.5, which shows a slab model consisting of two sets of three strips each. It is seen that the two central strips S_1 and L_1 bend in a manner similar to that of Fig. 4.4. The outer strips S_2 and L_2, however, are not only bent, but also twisted. Consider, for instance, one of the intersections of S_2 with L_2. It is seen that at the intersection the exterior edge of strip L_2 is at a higher elevation than the interior edge, while at the nearby end of strip L_2 both edges are at the same elevation; the strip is twisted. This twisting results in torsional stresses and torsional moments which are seen to be most pronounced near the corners. Consequently, the total load on the slab is carried not only by the bending moments in the two directions, but also by the twisting moments. For this reason bending moments in elastic slabs are smaller than would be computed for sets of unconnected strips loaded by w_s and w_l. For instance, for a simply supported square slab, $w_s = w_l = w/2$ [Eq. (4.1)]. If only bending were present, the maximum moment in each strip would be

$$(w/2)A^2/8 = 0.0625wA^2$$

The exact theory of bending of elastic plates shows that actually the maximum moment in such a square slab is only $0.048wA^2$, so that in this case the twisting moments relieve the bending moments by about 25 per cent.

The largest moment occurs where the curvature is sharpest. Figure 4.5 shows this to be the case at midspan of the short strip S_1. Suppose the load is increased until this location is overstressed, so that the steel at the middle of strip S_1 is yielding. If the strip were an isolated beam, it would now fail. Considering the slab as a whole, however, one sees that no immediate failure will occur. The neighboring strips (those parallel as well as those perpendicular to S_1), being actually monolithic with it, will take over that share of any additional load which strip S_1 can no longer carry, until they, in turn, start yielding. This inelastic redistribution will continue until, in a rather large area in the central portion of the slab, all the steel in both directions is yielding. Only then will the entire slab fail. From this reasoning, which is confirmed by tests, it follows that slabs need not be designed for the absolute maximum moment in each of the two directions (such as $0.048wA^2$ in the example of the preceding paragraph), but only for a smaller average moment in each of the two directions in the central portion of the slab. For instance, one of the several analytical methods provided in the ACI Code permits the above square slab to be designed for a moment of $0.036wA^2$. By comparison with the actual elastic maximum moment, $0.048wA^2$, it is seen that, owing to inelastic redistribution, a moment reduction of 25 per cent is provided.

The flexural behavior of a simply supported slab is summarized in the solid lines of Fig. 4.6. The largest moments occur in the center strips, along 1-1 and 2-2. The moment diagram in the short direction along 1-1 is given by Fig. 4.6*a* and shows a maximum $M_{A,\max}$ at midspan. From Fig. 4.5 it is seen that short strips located closer to the edges (such as S_2) deflect less, are less sharply curved, and consequently have smaller bending moments than the central strip. Therefore, the maximum moment

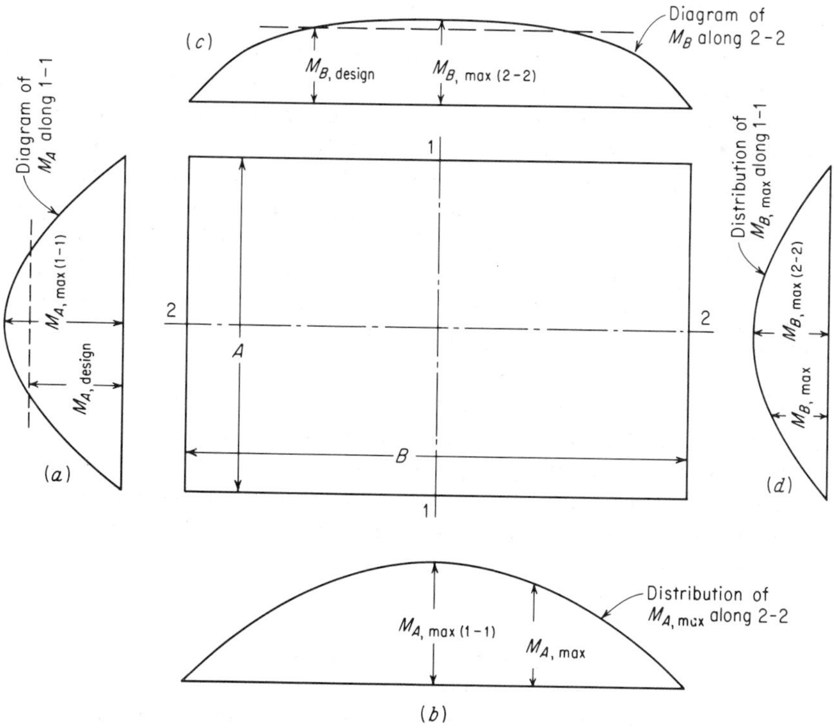

***Fig.* 4.6** Moments in uniformly loaded, simply supported slab.

$M_{A,\max}$ at the center of the short strips is distributed longitudinally, as in Fig. 4.6*b*; it is largest at the center and decreases toward zero at the edges. For a slab which departs significantly from square, the moment M_B in the center strip in the long direction is fairly constant in the middle half of the slab. This is seen from Fig. 4.6*c*, which gives the moment diagram along 2-2. Again, inspection of Fig. 4.5 shows that in long strips located closer to the edges (such as L_2) deflection, curvatures, and therefore bending moments are smaller than in the central strip L_1. The distribution of $M_{B,\max}$ as it varies in the short direction is shown in Fig. 4.6*d*. As explained before, in view of inelastic redistribution it is not necessary to design for the absolute maximum values of M_A and M_B. The manner in which this and other features are considered in design is discussed in the next article.

4.6 Design of Two-way Slabs by ACI Code The Code provides that slabs with side ratios no larger than 2:1 shall be designed as two-way slabs. From Eq. (4.1) it is seen that for a slab of this proportion the share of the load carried in the long direction is only of the order of one-sixteenth that in the short direction. Hence, such a slab acts almost as if it were spanning in the short direction only. In agreement with this, the Code provides that any slab more oblong than 2:1 shall be treated as a one-way slab.

The precise determination of moments in two-way slabs with various conditions of continuity at the edges is mathematically formidable and not suited to design practice. For this reason the Code provides simplified methods for determining moments, shears, and reactions of such slabs. In fact, the Code gives three different methods for this purpose. Of these, the authors hold method 3 to be the most rational and, generally, the most economical. The older methods 1 and 2, successfully applied over many years, also give reliable results but are not as clear and consistent in approach and assumptions. For reasons of clarity, and in view of space limitations, only method 3 is presented herein.

The Code provides tables of moment coefficients for a variety of conditions. These coefficients are based on elastic analysis but also account for inelastic redistribution. In consequence, the design moment in either direction is smaller by an appropriate amount than the elastic maximum moment in that direction. This is shown by dashed lines in Fig. 4.6*a* and *c*. The design moments in the two directions are computed from

$$M_A = C_A w A^2 \qquad M_B = C_B w B^2 \tag{4.2}$$

where C_A, C_B = tabulated moment coefficients
w = uniform load, per ft²
A, B = length of clear span in short and long directions, respectively

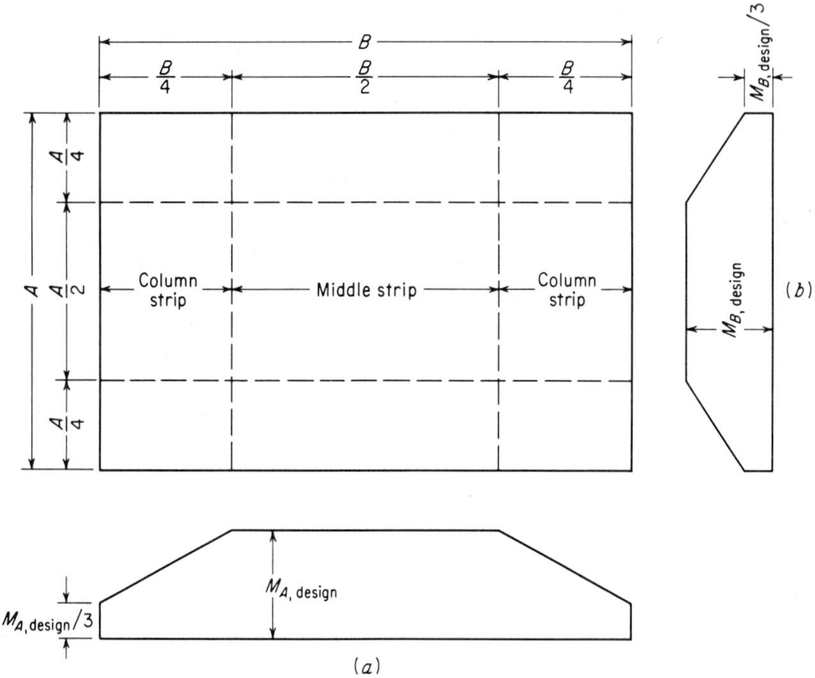

Fig. 4.7 Design moments, ACI method 3, for simply supported slab.

The Code provides that each panel be divided in both directions into a middle strip whose width is one-half that of the panel and two column strips of one-quarter of the panel width (see Fig. 4.7). As discussed before and shown in Fig. 4.6*b* and *d*, the moments in both directions are larger in the center portion of the slab than in regions close to the edges. Correspondingly, it is provided in method 3 that the entire middle strip be designed for the full, tabulated design moment. In the column strips this moment is assumed to decrease from its full value at the edge of the middle strip to one-third of this value at the edge of the panel. This distribution is shown in dashed lines in Fig. 4.7*a* and *b*.

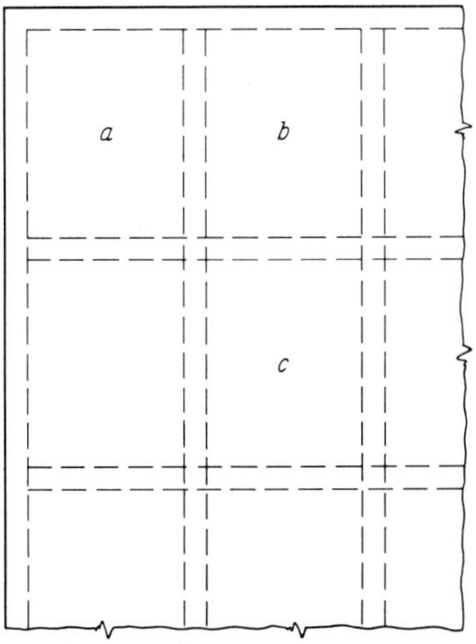

Fig. 4.8 Portion of typical two-way slab floor.

The discussion so far has been restricted to a single panel simply supported at all four edges. An actual situation is shown in Fig. 4.8, in

Table 4.2 **Coefficients for negative moments in slabs***

$$\left.\begin{array}{l} M_{A\,neg} = C_{A\,neg} \times w \times A^2 \\ M_{B\,neg} = C_{B\,neg} \times w \times B^2 \end{array}\right\} \text{ where } w = \text{total uniform dead plus live load}$$

Ratio $m = \frac{A}{B}$		Case 1	Case 2	Case 3	Case 4	Case 5	Case 6	Case 7	Case 8	Case 9
1.00	$C_{A\,neg}$		0.045		0.050	0.075	0.071		0.033	0.061
	$C_{B\,neg}$		0.045	0.076	0.050			0.071	0.061	0.033
0.95	$C_{A\,neg}$		0.050		0.055	0.079	0.075		0.038	0.065
	$C_{B\,neg}$		0.041	0.072	0.045			0.067	0.056	0.029
0.90	$C_{A\,neg}$		0.055		0.060	0.080	0.079		0.043	0.068
	$C_{B\,neg}$		0.037	0.070	0.040			0.062	0.052	0.025
0.85	$C_{A\,neg}$		0.060		0.066	0.082	0.083		0.049	0.072
	$C_{B\,neg}$		0.031	0.065	0.034			0.057	0.046	0.021
0.80	$C_{A\,neg}$		0.065		0.071	0.083	0.086		0.055	0.075
	$C_{B\,neg}$		0.027	0.061	0.029			0.051	0.041	0.017
0.75	$C_{A\,neg}$		0.069		0.076	0.085	0.088		0.061	0.078
	$C_{B\,neg}$		0.022	0.056	0.024			0.044	0.036	0.014
0.70	$C_{A\,neg}$		0.074		0.081	0.086	0.091		0.068	0.081
	$C_{B\,neg}$		0.017	0.050	0.019			0.038	0.029	0.011
0.65	$C_{A\,neg}$		0.077		0.085	0.087	0.093		0.074	0.083
	$C_{B\,neg}$		0.014	0.043	0.015			0.031	0.024	0.008
0.60	$C_{A\,neg}$		0.081		0.089	0.088	0.095		0.080	0.085
	$C_{B\,neg}$		0.010	0.035	0.011			0.024	0.018	0.006
0.55	$C_{A\,neg}$		0.084		0.092	0.089	0.096		0.085	0.086
	$C_{B\,neg}$		0.007	0.028	0.008			0.019	0.014	0.005
0.50	$C_{A\,neg}$		0.086		0.094	0.090	0.097		0.089	0.088
	$C_{B\,neg}$		0.006	0.022	0.006			0.014	0.010	0.003

*A cross-hatched edge indicates that the slab continues across or is fixed at the support; an unmarked edge indicates a support at which torsional resistance is negligible.

which a system of beams supports a two-way slab. It is seen that some panels, such as panel *a*, have two discontinuous exterior edges, while the other edges are continuous with their neighbors. Panel *b* has one discontinuous and three continuous edges, the interior panel *c* has all edges continuous, and so on. At a continuous edge in a slab, moments are negative, just as at interior supports of continuous beams. Also, the magnitude of the positive moments depends on the conditions of continuity at all four edges.

Correspondingly, Table 4.2, reproduced from the Code, gives moment coefficients C for *negative moments at continuous edges*. The details of the table are self-explanatory. Maximum negative edge moments obtain when both panels adjacent to the particular edge carry full dead and live load.

Table* 4.3 Coefficients for dead-load positive moments in slabs

$$\left.\begin{aligned} M_{A\ pos\ DL} &= C_{A\ DL} \times w \times A^2 \\ M_{B\ pos\ DL} &= C_{B\ DL} \times w \times B^2 \end{aligned}\right\} \text{ where } w = \text{total uniform dead load}$$

Ratio $m = \frac{A}{B}$		Case 1 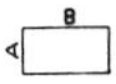	Case 2 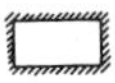	Case 3 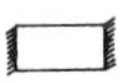	Case 4 	Case 5 	Case 6 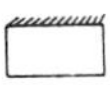	Case 7 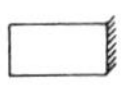	Case 8 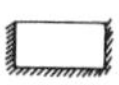	Case 9 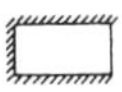
1.00	$C_{A\ DL}$	0.036	0.018	0.018	0.027	0.027	0.033	0.027	0.020	0.023
	$C_{B\ DL}$	0.036	0.018	0.027	0.027	0.018	0.027	0.033	0.023	0.020
0.95	$C_{A\ DL}$	0.040	0.020	0.021	0.030	0.028	0.036	0.031	0.022	0.024
	$C_{B\ DL}$	0.033	0.016	0.025	0.024	0.015	0.024	0.031	0.021	0.017
0.90	$C_{A\ DL}$	0.045	0.022	0.025	0.033	0.029	0.039	0.035	0.025	0.026
	$C_{B\ DL}$	0.029	0.014	0.024	0.022	0.013	0.021	0.028	0.019	0.015
0.85	$C_{A\ DL}$	0.050	0.024	0.029	0.036	0.031	0.042	0.040	0.029	0.028
	$C_{B\ DL}$	0.026	0.012	0.022	0.019	0.011	0.017	0.025	0.017	0.013
0.80	$C_{A\ DL}$	0.056	0.026	0.034	0.039	0.032	0.045	0.045	0.032	0.029
	$C_{B\ DL}$	0.023	0.011	0.020	0.016	0.009	0.015	0.022	0.015	0.010
0.75	$C_{A\ DL}$	0.061	0.028	0.040	0.043	0.033	0.048	0.051	0.036	0.031
	$C_{B\ DL}$	0.019	0.009	0.018	0.013	0.007	0.012	0.020	0.013	0.007
0.70	$C_{A\ DL}$	0.068	0.030	0.046	0.046	0.035	0.051	0.058	0.040	0.033
	$C_{B\ DL}$	0.016	0.007	0.016	0.011	0.005	0.009	0.017	0.011	0.006
0.65	$C_{A\ DL}$	0.074	0.032	0.054	0.050	0.036	0.054	0.065	0.044	0.034
	$C_{B\ DL}$	0.013	0.006	0.014	0.009	0.004	0.007	0.014	0.009	0.005
0.60	$C_{A\ DL}$	0.081	0.034	0.062	0.053	0.037	0.056	0.073	0.048	0.036
	$C_{B\ DL}$	0.010	0.004	0.011	0.007	0.003	0.006	0.012	0.007	0.004
0.55	$C_{A\ DL}$	0.088	0.035	0.071	0.056	0.038	0.058	0.081	0.052	0.037
	$C_{B\ DL}$	0.008	0.003	0.009	0.005	0.002	0.004	0.009	0.005	0.003
0.50	$C_{A\ DL}$	0.095	0.037	0.080	0.059	0.039	0.061	0.089	0.056	0.038
	$C_{B\ DL}$	0.006	0.002	0.007	0.004	0.001	0.003	0.007	0.004	0.002

*A cross-hatched edge indicates that the slab continues across or is fixed at the support; an unmarked edge indicates a support at which torsional resistance is negligible.

Table 4.4 **Coefficients for live-load positive moments in slabs***

$$\left.\begin{aligned} M_{A\ pos\ LL} &= C_{A\ LL} \times w \times A^2 \\ M_{B\ pos\ LL} &= C_{B\ LL} \times w \times B^2 \end{aligned}\right\} \text{ where } w = \text{total uniform live load}$$

Ratio $m = \frac{A}{B}$		Case 1	Case 2	Case 3	Case 4	Case 5	Case 6	Case 7	Case 8	Case 9
		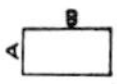		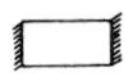				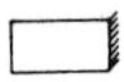	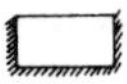	
1.00	$C_{A\ LL}$	0.036	0.027	0.027	0.032	0.032	0.035	0.032	0.028	0.030
	$C_{B\ LL}$	0.036	0.027	0.032	0.032	0.027	0.032	0.035	0.030	0.028
0.95	$C_{A\ LL}$	0.040	0.030	0.031	0.035	0.034	0.038	0.036	0.031	0.032
	$C_{B\ LL}$	0.033	0.025	0.029	0.029	0.024	0.029	0.032	0.027	0.025
0.90	$C_{A\ LL}$	0.045	0.034	0.035	0.039	0.037	0.042	0.040	0.035	0.036
	$C_{B\ LL}$	0.029	0.022	0.027	0.026	0.021	0.025	0.029	0.024	0.022
0.85	$C_{A\ LL}$	0.050	0.037	0.040	0.043	0.041	0.046	0.045	0.040	0.039
	$C_{B\ LL}$	0.026	0.019	0.024	0.023	0.019	0.022	0.026	0.022	0.020
0.80	$C_{A\ LL}$	0.056	0.041	0.045	0.048	0.044	0.051	0.051	0.044	0.042
	$C_{B\ LL}$	0.023	0.017	0.022	0.020	0.016	0.019	0.023	0.019	0.017
0.75	$C_{A\ LL}$	0.061	0.045	0.051	0.052	0.047	0.055	0.056	0.049	0.046
	$C_{B\ LL}$	0.019	0.014	0.019	0.016	0.013	0.016	0.020	0.016	0.013
0.70	$C_{A\ LL}$	0.068	0.049	0.057	0.057	0.051	0.060	0.063	0.054	0.050
	$C_{B\ LL}$	0.016	0.012	0.016	0.014	0.011	0.013	0.017	0.014	0.011
0.65	$C_{A\ LL}$	0.074	0.053	0.064	0.062	0.055	0.064	0.070	0.059	0.054
	$C_{B\ LL}$	0.013	0.010	0.014	0.011	0.009	0.010	0.014	0.011	0.009
0.60	$C_{A\ LL}$	0.081	0.058	0.071	0.067	0.059	0.068	0.077	0.065	0.059
	$C_{B\ LL}$	0.010	0.007	0.011	0.009	0.007	0.008	0.011	0.009	0.007
0.55	$C_{A\ LL}$	0.088	0.062	0.080	0.072	0.063	0.073	0.085	0.070	0.063
	$C_{B\ LL}$	0.008	0.006	0.009	0.007	0.005	0.006	0.009	0.007	0.006
0.50	$C_{A\ LL}$	0.095	0.066	0.088	0.077	0.067	0.078	0.092	0.076	0.067
	$C_{B\ LL}$	0.006	0.004	0.007	0.005	0.004	0.005	0.007	0.005	0.004

*A cross-hatched edge indicates that the slab continues across or is fixed at the support; an unmarked edge indicates a support at which torsional resistance is negligible.

Hence, the moment is computed for this total load. The Code provides that *negative moments at discontinuous edges* shall be assumed equal to one-third of the positive moments for the same direction. One must provide for such moments because some degree of restraint is provided discontinuous edges by the torsional rigidity of the edge beam or by the supporting wall.

As for *positive moments*, there will be little, if any, rotation at the continuous edges if *dead load* alone is acting, because the loads on both adjacent panels tend to produce opposite rotations which cancel, or nearly so. Hence, for this condition the continuous edges can be regarded as fixed, and the appropriate coefficients for the dead-load moments are given in Table 4.3. On the other hand, the maximum *live-load moments* are obtained when live load is placed only on the particular panel, and

Table* 4.5 Ratio of load w in A and B directions for shear in slab and load on supports

Ratio $m = \frac{A}{B}$		Case 1 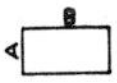	Case 2 	Case 3 	Case 4 	Case 5 	Case 6 	Case 7 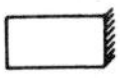	Case 8 	Case 9 
1.00	W_A	0.50	0.50	0.17	0.50	0.83	0.71	0.29	0.33	0.67
	W_B	0.50	0.50	0.83	0.50	0.17	0.29	0.71	0.67	0.33
0.95	W_A	0.55	0.55	0.20	0.55	0.86	0.75	0.33	0.38	0.71
	W_B	0.45	0.45	0.80	0.45	0.14	0.25	0.67	0.62	0.29
0.90	W_A	0.60	0.60	0.23	0.60	0.88	0.79	0.38	0.43	0.75
	W_B	0.40	0.40	0.77	0.40	0.12	0.21	0.62	0.57	0.25
0.85	W_A	0.66	0.66	0.28	0.66	0.90	0.83	0.43	0.49	0.79
	W_B	0.34	0.34	0.72	0.34	0.10	0.17	0.57	0.51	0.21
0.80	W_A	0.71	0.71	0.33	0.71	0.92	0.86	0.49	0.55	0.83
	W_B	0.29	0.29	0.67	0.29	0.08	0.14	0.51	0.45	0.17
0.75	W_A	0.76	0.76	0.39	0.76	0.94	0.88	0.56	0.61	0.86
	W_B	0.24	0.24	0.61	0.24	0.06	0.12	0.44	0.39	0.14
0.70	W_A	0.81	0.81	0.45	0.81	0.95	0.91	0.62	0.68	0.89
	W_B	0.19	0.19	0.55	0.19	0.05	0.09	0.38	0.32	0.11
0.65	W_A	0.85	0.85	0.53	0.85	0.96	0.93	0.69	0.74	0.92
	W_B	0.15	0.15	0.47	0.15	0.04	0.07	0.31	0.26	0.08
0.60	W_A	0.89	0.89	0.61	0.89	0.97	0.95	0.76	0.80	0.94
	W_B	0.11	0.11	0.39	0.11	0.03	0.05	0.24	0.20	0.06
0.55	W_A	0.92	0.92	0.69	0.92	0.98	0.96	0.81	0.85	0.95
	W_B	0.08	0.08	0.31	0.08	0.02	0.04	0.19	0.15	0.05
0.50	W_A	0.94	0.94	0.76	0.94	0.99	0.97	0.86	0.89	0.97
	W_B	0.06	0.06	0.24	0.06	0.01	0.03	0.14	0.11	0.03

*A cross-hatched edge indicates that the slab continues across or is fixed at the support; an unmarked edge indicates a support at which torsional resistance is negligible.

not on any of the adjacent panels. In this case some rotation will occur at all continuous edges. As an approximation, the Code assumes 50 per cent restraint for calculating these live-load moments. The corresponding coefficients are given in Table 4.4. Finally, for computing shear in the slab and loads on the supporting beams, Table 4.5 gives the fractions of the total load w which are transmitted in the two directions. It is easily checked that for cases 1 and 2 these fractions are in exact accord with Eq. 4.1. In the other cases they are different, depending on the particular edge conditions.

Since positive-moment steel is placed in two layers, the distance d for the upper layer is smaller than that for the lower layer by one bar diameter (when the same bar size is used for both layers.) Because the moments in the long direction are the smaller ones, it is economical to place the steel in that direction on top of the bars in the short direction. The twisting moments discussed in Art. 4.5 are usually of consequence only in exterior corners, where they tend to crack the slab along 45° lines of the corner panels. For this reason the Code provides that, in addition to the calculated reinforcement, special reinforcement shall be provided at exterior corners in both bottom and top of the slab, for a distance in each direction from the corner equal to one-fifth the long span. The reinforcement in the top of the slab shall be parallel to the diagonal from the corner. The reinforcement in the bottom of the slab shall be at right angles to the diagonal, or it may consist of bars in two directions parallel to the sides of the slab. The reinforcement in each band shall be of size and spacing equivalent to that required for the maximum positive moment in the slab.

The precise locations of inflection points in two-way slabs are not easily determined, since they depend on the side ratio, ratio of live to dead load, and continuity conditions at the edges. A reasonable rule is to assume that a line of inflection exists parallel to any continuous edge at a distance from it of one-sixth the span. The rule may be applied to both the long and the short directions. If bent bars are used, they are generally bent up at these inflection locations.

To limit deflections, the code provides that the minimum thickness of a two-way slab shall be 3.5 in. or the panel perimeter divided by 180, whichever is larger.

4.7 Design example Design a slab panel 20 ft 0 in. by 25 ft 0 in. to support a uniform live load of 125 psf. The panel is a corner panel of a group. A 3000-psi concrete and steel with $f_y = 60{,}000$ psi are used, in connection with ultimate-strength design.

The minimum thickness, by Code, of $^{90}/_{180} = \frac{1}{2}$ ft $= 6$ in. will be used. (For heavy loads, such as in warehouses, deeper slabs lead to steel savings which frequently prove more economical than minimum-thickness slabs.) Consequently, the dead load is $\frac{1}{2} \times 150 = 75$ psf, and the design loads for ultimate-strength design are

Live load:	$1.8 \times 125 =$	225 psf
Dead load:	$1.5 \times \ \ 75 =$	112.5 psf
Total		337.5 psf

MOMENT CALCULATIONS FOR MIDDLE STRIPS. $m = A/B = {}^{20}\!/_{25} = 0.80$. The negative moments at continuous edges, from Table 4.2, are

$$M_{A,neg} = 0.071 \times 337.5 \times 20^2 = 9580 \text{ ft-lb} = 115{,}000 \text{ in.-lb}$$
$$M_{B,neg} = 0.029 \times 337.5 \times 25^2 = 6110 \text{ ft-lb} = 73{,}400 \text{ in.-lb}$$

The positive moments, from Tables 4.3 and 4.4, are

Dead load: $M_{A,pos} = 0.039 \times 112.5 \times 20^2 = 1755 \text{ ft-lb} = 21{,}000 \text{ in.-lb}$
Live load: $M_{A,pos} = 0.048 \times 225 \times 20^2 = 4320 \text{ ft-lb} = 51{,}800 \text{ in.-lb}$
Total $M_{A,pos} = 72{,}800 \text{ in.-lb}$

Dead load: $M_{B,pos} = 0.016 \times 112.5 \times 25^2 = 1125 \text{ ft-lb} = 13{,}500 \text{ in.-lb}$
Live load: $M_{B,pos} = 0.020 \times 225 \times 25^2 = 2820 \text{ ft-lb} = 33{,}800 \text{ in.-lb}$
Total $M_{B,pos} = 47{,}300 \text{ in.-lb}$

The negative moments at discontinuous edges are

$$M_{A,neg} = \tfrac{1}{3}(72{,}800) = 24{,}300 \text{ in.-lb}$$
$$M_{B,neg} = \tfrac{1}{3}(47{,}300) = 15{,}800 \text{ in.-lb}$$

SELECTION OF REINFORCEMENT. From Graph 1, Appendix B:

1. Short direction

a. Span:

$$\frac{M_u}{\phi b d^2} = \frac{72{,}800}{0.9 \times 12 \times 52} = 270 \qquad p = 0.0048$$

A_s is equal to $0.0048 \times 12 \times 5 = 0.288$ in.^{2}/ft. From Table 4, Appendix B, No. 4 bars at 7 in. spacing are selected, giving $A_s = 0.34$ in.^{2}/ft.

b. Continuous edge:

$$\frac{M_u}{\phi b d^2} = \frac{115{,}000}{0.9 \times 12 \times 5^2} = 426; \ p = 0.0078$$

A_s is equal to $0.0078 \times 12 \times 5 = 0.468$ in.^{2}/ft. If two of every three positive-moment bars are bent up, and likewise for the adjacent panel, the negative-moment steel area furnished at the continuous edge will be four-thirds the positive-moment steel area in the span, or $A_s = \tfrac{4}{3} \times 0.34 = 0.453$ in.^{2}/ft. It is seen that this is 3.5 per cent less than the required amount of 0.468. On the other hand, the positive-moment steel furnished, 0.34, represents about 15 per cent more than the required amount. As is discussed in Art. 8.15, the Code permits a certain amount of inelastic moment redistribution, within strictly specified limits. In the case at hand the negative steel furnished suffices for only 96.5 per cent of the calculated moment, but the positive steel permits about 115 per cent of the calculated moment to be resisted. This more than satisfies the conditions for inelastic moment redistribution set by the Code. This situation illustrates how such moment redistribution can be utilized to obtain a simpler and more economical distribution of steel.

c. Discontinuous edge: The negative moment at the discontinuous edge is one-third the positive moment in the span; it would be adequate to bend up every third bar from the bottom to provide negative-moment steel at the discontinuous edge. However, this would make for a 21-in. spacing, which is larger than the maximum spacing of $3t = 18$ in. permitted by the Code. Hence, for the discontinuous edge, two of every three bars will be bent up from the bottom steel.

2. Long direction

a. Span:

$$\frac{M_u}{\phi bd^2} = \frac{47{,}300}{0.90 \times 12 \times 4.5^2} = 216 \qquad p = 0.0038$$

(The positive-moment steel in the long direction is placed on top of that for the short direction. This makes the depth d for the former one bar diameter smaller than for the latter. This is the reason for using $d =$ 4.5 in. for the positive-moment steel in the long direction, and $d = 5$ in. in all other locations.) A_s is equal to $0.0038 \times 12 \times 4.5 = 0.205$ in.²/ft. From Table 4, Appendix B, No. 3 bars at 6 in. spacing are selected, giving $A_s = 0.22$ in.²/ft.

b. Continuous edge:

$$\frac{M_u}{\phi bd^2} = \frac{73{,}400}{0.90 \times 12 \times 5^2} = 272; \; p = 0.0048$$

A_s is equal to $0.0048 \times 12 \times 5 = 0.288$ in.²/ft. Again, bending up two of every three bottom bars from both panels adjacent to the continuous edge, one has, at that edge, $A_s = \frac{4}{3} \times 0.22 = 0.29$ in.²/ft.

c. Discontinuous edge: For the reasons discussed in connection with the short direction, two out of every three bottom bars will, likewise, be bent up at this edge.

The steel selections above refer to the middle strips in both directions. For the *column strips*, as was pointed out, the moments are assumed to decrease linearly from the full calculated value at the inner edge of the column strip to one-third of this value at the edge of the supporting beam or wall. To simplify steel placement, a uniform spacing will be used in the column strips. The average moments in the column strips being two-thirds of the corresponding moments in the middle strips, adequate column strip steel will be furnished if the spacing of this steel is 1½ times that in the middle strip.

According to the recommendation of Art. 4.6, inflection points may be assumed a distance $L/6$ from the continuous edges, that is, 3 ft 4 in. in the short direction and 4 ft 2 in. in the long direction. Two of every three bars are bent up at approximately these locations. The bent-up bars are carried over the support and beyond the inflection point of the adjacent panel a distance not less than one-sixteenth of the span, or the depth of the member, or 12 bar diameters, whichever is greater. It is customary and slightly conservative, instead, to extend these bars to the quarter point of the adjacent span. This extension will also satisfy the bond requirements of these negative-moment bars at the continuous edges. At the discontinuous edges twice as much steel has been furnished as is needed for the design moments. Therefore, only one-half of the development length of Table 8, Appendix B, must be provided. For the No. 4 bars this length is $\frac{1}{2} \times 17 = 8.5$ in. Flexural bond need not be considered if anchorage bond is no larger than 80 per cent of the permissible value. This will be so if actual development length is no less than 1.25 times this minimum length, or $1.25 \times 8.5 = 10.6$ in. An 11-in. anchorage length will be used for both No. 4 and No. 3 bars.

The reactions of the slab constitute loads on the edge beams and are calculated from Table 4.5, which indicates that 71 per cent of the load is transmitted in the short direction, and 29 per cent in the long direction. The total load on the panel being $20 \times 25 \times 337.5 = 169{,}000$ lb, the load per foot on the long beam is $(0.71 \times 169{,}000)/(2 \times 25) = 2400$ lb per ft, and on the short beams $(0.29 \times 169{,}000)/(2 \times 20) = 1220$ lb per ft. However, the Code suggests that the short beams be designed for a uniform load not smaller than $wA/3$; in the present case $337.5 \times {}^{20}\!/_{3} = 2250$ lb per ft exceeds 1220 lb per ft and, therefore, governs. In addition, the edge beams evidently carry their own weight and, in the case of the beams along the continuous edges, the corresponding reactions from the adjacent panels.

PROBLEMS

1. A concrete slab roof is to be designed to cover a transformer vault. The outside dimensions of the vault are 17×20 ft, and walls are 8-in. brick. A design live load of 80 psf, uniformly distributed over the roof surface, will be assumed. Design the roof as a two-way slab, using U.S.D. methods, with $f'_c = 4000$ psi and $f_y = 50{,}000$ psi.

2. A concrete warehouse floor is framed by beams on column lines, which are 18 ft on centers in one direction and 24 ft on centers in the other. Beam webs may be assumed to be 12 in. wide. A working live load of 225 psf must be carried. Design a typical interior panel, using U.S.D. methods, with $f'_c = 5000$ psi and $f_y = 60{,}000$ psi.

3. Design a typical exterior and first-interior panel for the warehouse floor of the preceding problem. The 24-ft dimension of the exterior panel is parallel to the outside wall.

FLAT SLABS

4.8 Description of General Type

A flat-slab floor, as its name implies, is one consisting of a reinforced-concrete floor slab built monolithically with the columns and supported directly by the columns without the aid of beams and girders. The slab may be of uniform thickness

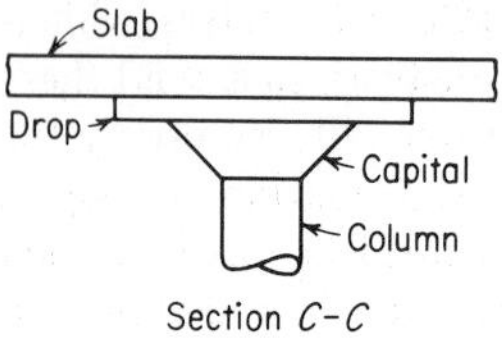

Fig. 4.9

throughout the entire floor area, or a part of it, symmetrical about the column, may be made somewhat thicker than the rest of the slab, the thickened portion of the slab thus formed constituting what is known as a *dropped panel*, or *drop* (see Figs. 4.9, 4.12, and 9.12).

Dropped panels are used to reduce the shearing stress in the slab within the area of the drop. The increase in effective slab thickness provided by the drop also decreases the compression stresses in the concrete and reduces the amount of steel which is required over the column heads. In general, the use of dropped panels is not economical for live loads less than 150 psf.

Dropped panels are square or rectangular. The ACI Code specifies [Art. 2104(*e*), Appendix A] that the side of a drop panel shall be at least 0.33 times the span and that the total thickness to be used in computing the negative steel area for the column strip shall be not more than $1.5t_2$, nor shall the thickness below the slab be more than one-fourth the distance from the edge of the drop panel to the edge of the column capital [Art. 2102(*c*)5, Appendix A]. This usually results in a drop panel with a thickness of one-quarter to one-half the thickness of the slab outside the drop. When drops are used over interior columns, they are normally used over the wall columns also. Such drops should have a width parallel to the wall equal to the corresponding width of the interior-panel drops; at right angles to the wall they should project beyond the center of the column a distance equal to one-half the corresponding total width of the interior drops.

The columns in practically all cases flare out toward the top, forming a capital of a shape somewhat similar to an inverted truncated cone. This capital gives a wider support for the floor slab, which results in a decrease in the bending moment which the slab is called upon the resist and a decrease in the shearing stresses around the perimeter of the column, and tends toward a more rigid structure. The effective diameter of the capital should be taken as the diameter of the circle at the point at which a 45° line from the base of the capital intersects the bottom of the slab or dropped panel. The 45° line must fall within the concrete of the cap at all points.

At the wall columns, a bracket is often used in place of a regular half-capital. The width of the bracket is equal to the width of the column parallel to the wall; the sloping side of the bracket forms an angle of 45° with the horizontal; the projection of the bracket beyond the face of the column is the same as, or somewhat less than, the projection of the interior-column capital.

4.9 Advantages of Flat-slab Floors Structurally, a flat-slab floor has many advantages over an ordinary beam-and-girder floor. The most important of these may be enumerated as follows:

1. For ordinary spans with heavy loads, under average conditions, the flat-slab floor is more economical than the beam-and-girder floor when designed to present Code provisions.

2. In a multistoried building, the same number of stories of a given clear height may be obtained with a smaller total building height, because of the smaller floor thickness.

3. The slab formwork is much simpler.

4. The flat-slab floor, owing to the lack of many sharp corners, is better able to resist continued exposure to fire than the beam-and-girder floor. It has been found by actual experience that the worst damage caused to reinforced concrete by severe fires has occurred at places where there may be spalling, i.e., at exposed edges and sharp corners.

5. Automatic-sprinkler protection may be made more complete under a flat-slab floor, since the nozzles may be placed well up near the under side of the slab without obstruction to the path of the spray.

6. More light may be admitted into the building if desired, by placing the wall beams above the floor level and thus allowing the windows to be extended to the under side of the slab. The absence of deep beams and girders also removes the obstruction to the passage of light within the building.

7. The opportunity for inspecting the position of the reinforcement is excellent, and the conditions attending deposition and placing of the concrete are favorable to securing uniformity and soundness in the concrete.

4.10 Bending Moments in Flat-slab Floors Figure 4.10 represents a portion of a flat-slab floor including four column supports, the load on the floor being uniformly distributed. The full circles represent the column heads underneath the slab. It is evident that the curvature of the slab along any radial line from the column center will be convex upward for a certain distance, then concave upward, then convex upward again. This implies that at some point along each radial line there is a point of inflection where the radial bending

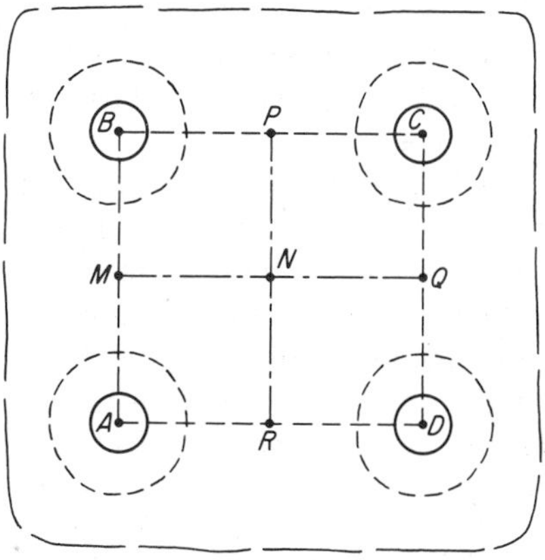

Fig. **4.10**

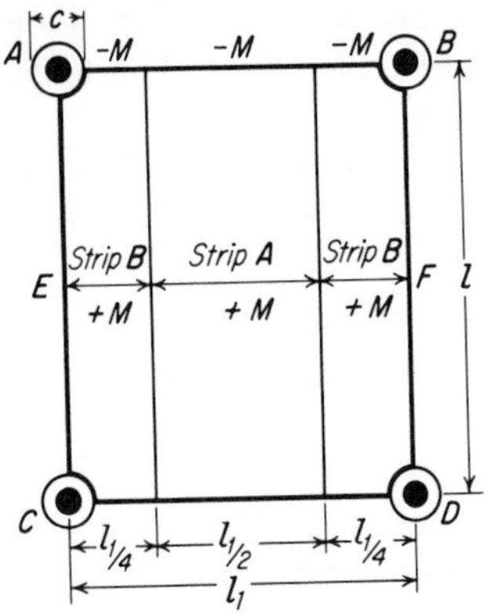

Fig. 4.11

moment changes from positive to negative. The locus of all these points may be represented by the dotted approximate circles centered about the column capitals.

As the slab is loaded, deflection occurs. The point N at the midpoint of the panel, being the farthest away from the support, will deflect more than a point M, P, Q, or R midway between any two adjacent columns. The points M, P, Q, and R will therefore be higher than point N but lower than the supports. This results in a negative moment along the line MQ at M, and a positive moment at N. The condition is similar along line PR.

The analysis of a flat-slab floor is a highly indeterminate problem, and the elastic and inelastic properties of the slab and the relative stiffness of its various parts must be considered in determining accurately the moments and shears in the slab. An arbitrary but satisfactory method of obtaining the theoretical bending moments is to divide each panel into rectangular strips, a middle strip A (Fig. 4.11) with a width equal to $l_1/2$ and two equal column strips B which occupy the outer portions of the panel. Similar strips A' and B' are assumed at right angles to those shown in Fig. 4.11. A system of imaginary beams is thus established, and the load on the panel is transferred to the columns by these beams.

Consider strip A and the two strips B to form one wide but shallow continuous beam, rigidly supported at the four corners by the columns, and partially supported between the columns along the lines AB and CD by the perpendicular strips B'. In this beam, negative moments exist along the lines AB and CD, and positive moments along the line EF. Strips B are obviously stiffer than strip A, and hence both the positive and negative moments in strips B (combined) will be greater than those in strip A.

It is a well-known fact that, in any continuous beam, the sum of the maximum positive moment in any span of the beam and the average of the negative moments at the adjacent supports is equal to the maximum moment in a corresponding simply supported beam. Nichols (Ref. 4.1) recommends that, in flat-slab analysis, the span of the corresponding simply supported beam be taken as $l - \frac{2}{3}c$, where l is the panel length center to center of columns, and c is the diameter of the capital. Thus, in Fig. 4.11,

$$M_{AB} + M_{EF} = \frac{1}{8} wl_1 \left(l - \frac{2}{3} c\right)^2 = \frac{1}{8} Wl \left(1 - \frac{2c}{3l}\right)^2 \tag{4.3}$$

where w = dead and live load on slab, per unit of area
W = total load on one panel
l = distance center to center of columns parallel to strips under consideration
l_1 = distance center to center of columns perpendicular to strips under consideration
c = diameter of column capital

The distribution of this total moment to the positive- and negative-moment sections EF and AB, respectively, must be determined, and then the total positive moment in the section EF and the negative moment in the section AB must be apportioned to the strips A and B. Westergaard and Slater presented a solution of this problem of distribution (Ref. 4.2). For a square interior panel with column capitals but without drop panels, they recommend the following average percentages of the total moment ($M_{AB} + M_{EF}$) for each of the various moment sections:

Column strips, negative moment	48 per cent
Column strips, positive moment	21 per cent
Middle strip, negative moment	17 per cent
Middle strip, positive moment	14 per cent
Total	100 per cent

The effect of a dropped panel is to stiffen the negative-moment portion of the column strip. This causes an increase in the negative moment in strip B and a corresponding decrease in the positive moment at the middle of the strip.

Equation (4.3) can be applied to the determination of moments in square panels and in rectangular panels in which the longer side of the panel is not more than 1.33 times the shorter side. In rectangular panels, separate moments must obviously be computed for the various sections of the two rectangular directions, using for l the length of the side of the panel in the direction parallel to the strip under consideration.[1]

[1] It is interesting to compare the behavior of flat slabs with that of two-way slabs (Art. 4.5). In flat-slab analysis, the full load is assumed to be carried by the slab in each of the two perpendicular directions. This is in apparent contrast to the analysis of two-way slabs, in which the load is divided, one part carried by the slab in the short direction, and the remainder carried by the slab in the long direction. However, in two-way slabs, while only a part of the load is carried by the slab in the short direction, the remainder is transmitted in the perpendicular direction to marginal beams, which then also span in the short direction. Similarly, with part of the load carried by the slab in the long direction, the remainder is transmitted by the slab in the short direction to marginal beams which span in the long direction. It is evident that in two-way slabs, as in flat slabs, conditions of equilibrium require that all the load be carried in each of the two principal directions.

4.11 Moments in Interior Panels Any theoretical analysis, such as that outlined above, gives only approximate results, because of the many assumptions which are necessary. Tests of full-sized panels show that the actual stresses in the steel are less than would be obtained from the usual rectangular-beam equations with moments as indicated in Art. 4.10. By comparing the stresses determined by a sound theoretical analysis with those obtained by actual tests, moment coefficients can be obtained which will give rational and safe results. This process has resulted in the development of flat-slab regulations which are part of practically all municipal building codes and technical society standards.

In addition to specifying moment coefficients, these codes usually give minimum requirements for slab thickness, cap and drop dimensions, and column sizes. They specify the arrangement of the reinforcement and outline the method of computing stresses due to shear and bending. The formulas and methods of one code may differ from those of another, but there is sufficient similarity so that the designer who is familiar with the application of the provisions of one code has little difficulty in following those of any other code.

The recommendations of the American Concrete Institute are given in Appendix A. These recommendations provide for two methods of design of flat-slab structures. One method applies to flat-slab floors in which (1) there are three or more panels in each direction, (2) the successive span lengths differ by not more than 20 per cent of the shorter span, and (3) the ratio of length to width of panel does not exceed 1:33. These conditions are usually met in practice. When they do not obtain, the second method is used. This method consists of recommendations governing the analysis of the structure as a series of rigid frames in the two directions of reinforcement (Refs. 4.3, 4.4). Only the former method will be considered in this chapter.

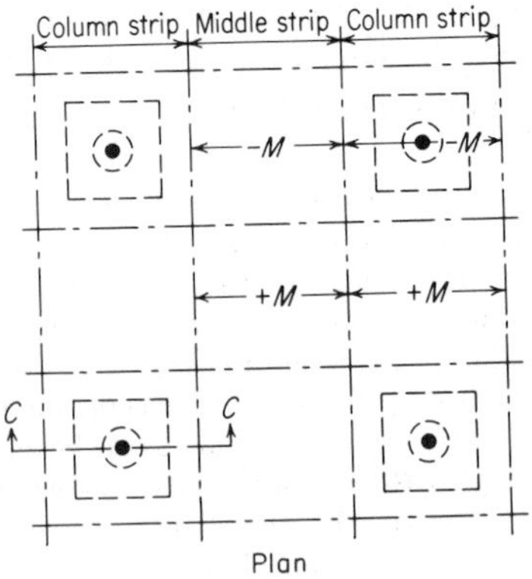

Fig. 4.12

In the ACI Code the total moment $M_{AB} + M_{EF}$ (Fig. 4.11) is specified as about 25 per cent less than the value given in Eq. (4.3), and the distribution varies slightly from the percentages tabulated in Art. 4.10. For convenience in specifying moment coefficients and to simplify the subsequent detailing of the reinforcement, it is desirable to consider two adjoining column strips in adjacent panels as one band. This band is centered about the column line and has a width equal to one-half the panel width. In all the following discussions, any reference to the "column strip" will imply the combined strips or band described above, as indicated in Fig. 4.12.

The moment distribution for interior panels, as given in the ACI Code, is as follows:

Let $M_0 = M_{AB} + M_{EF}$ (Fig. 4.11), ft-lb
W = total load on panel, including weight of drop, lb
L = span of strip under consideration, center to center of columns, ft
c = diameter of column capital, ft

Then

$$M_0 = 0.09WLF'\left(1 - \frac{2c}{3L}\right)^2 \tag{4.4}$$

where $F = 1.15 - c/L$, but not less than 1.

Moments in interior panels, ACI Code

Strip	Moments in slabs without drops		Moments in slabs with drops	
	Negative	Positive	Negative	Positive
Column strip	$-0.46M_0$	$+0.22M_0$	$-0.50M_0$	$+0.20M_0$
Middle strip	$-0.16M_0$	$+0.16M_0$	$-0.15M_0$	$+0.15M_0$

4.12 Moments in Exterior Panels In wall panels, the strips perpendicular to the wall are analogous to the end spans of a beam which is continuous over a number of supports. In such a beam, if the spans are all equal, the load is uniform, and the ends of the beam rest freely on the end supports, the maximum positive moment in the end spans is greater than in the intermediate spans; the negative moment at the first interior support is greater than the negative moment at any other interior support; the moment at the first support is equal to zero. If the ends of the beam are restrained instead of being freely supported, moments are induced at the end supports, and the maximum positive moments in the end spans as well as the negative moment at the first interior support are affected. The latter two values will normally be greater than the corresponding moments in a typical interior span.

In flat-slab construction, the restraint offered at the end supports may vary considerably. The wall panels may—but seldom do— rest freely on brick walls, they may be built monolithically with the wall columns and with marginal beams (wall beams) along the outer edge of the panels, capable of resisting torsional stresses, or they may be built monolithically with the columns but without the rigid marginal beams. Obviously, the moment coefficients for sections parallel to the wall (strips perpendicular to the wall) would differ materially for these various conditions. The ACI Code provides separate moment coefficients for different support conditions [Art. 2104(*f*), Appendix A].

Since brackets are normally used at exterior columns, and since the sloping face of these brackets usually projects beyond the columns a sufficient amount to make the distance from the center of the column to the extremity of the bracket equal to one-half the diameter of the interior-column capital, the values of c, and hence M_0, for the exterior-panel strips perpendicular to the wall are generally the same as for an interior panel. The moments at the various sections of these strips can therefore usually be obtained by multiplying the moments at the corresponding sections in the interior panel by the ratios of the appropriate moment coefficients given in Art. 2104(*f*), Appendix A.

The moments to be used in the design of the middle strip parallel to the wall in an exterior panel are the same as used for the corresponding sections in an interior panel. The moments to be used in the design of the half-column strip adjacent and parallel to the wall depend upon the relative size of the marginal or wall beam. If the depth of this beam is 1¼ times the thickness of the slab or less, the positive and negative moments are taken as 40 and 38 per cent, respectively, of the corresponding moments specified for a typical interior-panel column strip, and the marginal beam must be designed for 20 per cent of the panel load in addition to the superimposed load from the wall. If the depth of beam is 3 times the thickness of the slab or more, the positive and negative moments are taken as 25 and 26 per cent, respectively, of the corresponding moment specified for a typical interior-panel column strip, and the marginal beam must be designed for 40 per cent of the panel load in addition to the superimposed load from the wall [Table 2104(*f*), Appendix A].

4.13 Shearing Stresses There are two kinds of shearing stress that may be critical in the design of flat-slab structures. The first is the familiar beam-type shear leading to diagonal tension failure. In this case, the slab is considered to act as a wide beam, spanning essentially between supports provided by the perpendicular column strips, with a potential diagonal crack extending in a plane across the entire width of the slab. The critical section is taken a distance d from the face of the column or capital. As for beams, the nominal shear stress V/bd on the unreinforced concrete is not to exceed an allowable working value of

$$v_c = 1.1\sqrt{f'_c}$$

or an ultimate value of

$$v_c = 2\phi \sqrt{f'_c}$$

Alternatively, failure may occur by "punching shear," with the potential diagonal crack following the surface of a truncated cone or pyramid around the column capital or drop panel. In this case, the critical section for shear is taken perpendicular to the plane of the slab and a distance $d/2$ out from the periphery of the support. The nominal shear stress is V/b_0d, where b_0 is the perimeter along the critical section.

At such a critical section, in addition to the shearing stresses and horizontal compressive stresses due to negative bending over the support, vertical or somewhat inclined compressive stress is present, owing to the reaction of the column. The simultaneous presence of vertical and horizontal compression increases the shear resistance of the concrete. Tests have indicated that, when punching shear failure occurs, the shear stress computed on the perimeter of the critical section is larger than in beams or one-way slabs and is approximately equal to $4\sqrt{f'_c}$. Accordingly, the ACI Code specifies that, for punching shear, the nominal shear stress is not to exceed an allowable working value of

$$v_c = 2\sqrt{f'_c}$$

or an ultimate value of

$$v_{uc} = 4\phi \sqrt{f'_c}$$

unless shear reinforcement is provided, in which case an allowable value of $3\sqrt{f'_c}$ an an ultimate value of $6\phi\sqrt{f'_c}$ are permitted.

Shear reinforcement is sometimes used in flat-slab construction and is frequently desirable in flat-plate construction (see Art. 4.18). Such reinforcement may be in the form of bars, rods, or wire and may be designed by conventional methods, except that when such reinforcement is used the allowable stress and design yield strength are taken as one-half their usual values. Such shear reinforcement is not considered effective in members with a total thickness of less than 10 in.

4.14 Thickness of Slab In order to prevent undue deflection, certain limitations are placed on the minimum slab thickness that can be used in a given floor panel. Inasmuch as the actual deflection of a flat slab cannot be computed with any appreciable degree of accuracy, these limitations were developed from a study of the observed deflections in actual structures. The ACI Code specifies that the slab thickness, exclusive of the drop, shall not be less than $\frac{1}{40}$ of the longer dimension for slabs with drops, and not less than $\frac{1}{36}$ of the same dimension for slabs without drops.

It further specifies that for a slab with drops the thickness shall not be less than 4 in., nor less than

$$0.024L\left(1 - \frac{2c}{3L}\right)\sqrt{\frac{w'}{f'_c/2000}} + 1 \tag{4.5a}$$

and that for a slab without drops the thickness shall not be less than 5 in., nor less than

$$0.028L\left(1 - \frac{2c}{3L}\right)\sqrt{\frac{w'}{f'_c/2000}} + 1\tfrac{1}{2} \tag{4.5b}$$

Of course, the slab must also be thick enough so that allowable unit compressive and shear stresses will not be exceeded. In this connection, the Code requires that a reduced effective width be used in calculating flexural compression stress, in order to allow for the nonuniform variation of bending moment across the width of the critical sections. This reduced effective width is to be taken as three-fourths the width of the strip, except that on a section through a drop panel three-fourths the width of the drop panel is to be used.

4.15 Methods of Reinforcing Flat-slab Floors There are, in the main, four different methods or systems for reinforcing the slab in this type of floor: (1) two-way system, (2) four-way system, (3) three-way system, and (4) circumferential system.

Virtually all flat-slab floors built in this country at the present time have a two-way system of reinforcement. Originally all flat-slab systems were covered by patents. The basic patents have expired, and at present the two-way system is the one in general use. It has the advantage of being simple to design and construct and has proved thoroughly satisfactory. The other systems are chiefly of interest historically and to engineers working on renovations or additions to old buildings.

In the two-way system, bars are placed parallel to the lines of columns over the entire area of the floor at small intervals. The maximum allowable spacing varies in the different codes and specifications. The ACI Code permits a maximum bar spacing of 2 times the slab thickness.

The four-way system consists of two main bands of steel running parallel to the lines of columns, each band centered about the column lines, and two diagonal bands of sufficient width to fill up the floor area left uncovered by the direct bands. In some cases short bars are placed near the top of the slab at right angles to the direct bands over the middle portion of the band to resist the negative moment over that portion; they constitute what are known as the *across-direct* bands.

The three-way system involves a special arrangement of columns such that the lines connecting their center lines form a series of equilateral triangles. The reinforcement then follows the sides of these triangles, each band being centered about one of the panel sides.

In the circumferential system, radial steel emanating from the column head and circumferential steel in the form of concentric rings symmetrical about the column head are used. Concentric rings are also placed about the midpoint of the slab and about the midpoints of the four edges of each panel.

4.16 Factors to Be Considered in the Design of Flat-slab Buildings Flat-slab floors are ordinarily designed to carry only a uniform load over the entire surface, the assumption being that no breaks in the continuity occur. Where heavy concentrated loads are to be sustained in addition to the uniform load, beams should be introduced in such positions as will enable them to carry the weight of the concentrations. Where major openings in the slab occur, they should be framed by beams which will have the effect of restoring continuity to the slab. These beams should be designed to carry a portion of the floor load in addition to any concentrated loads that may rest upon them.

The columns should be designed to provide for bending stresses such as might be caused by unequally loaded panels. This is especially important in the exterior columns, where both the dead and live loads cause continual bending, and where the direct loads are relatively small. The interior roof columns are not likely to be subjected to such eccentric loading, and the ratio of the possible bending stress to the direct load stress decreases as the number of floors to be supported increases. Hence, bending in the interior columns is not so important as in the exterior columns. It should be investigated, however, especially in the upper stories. The amount of bending moment to be assumed is usually stated in the various regulations governing flat-slab design. The spacing of columns is governed by practically the same factors as in the case of beam-and-girder type floors.

To provide proper drainage, a slight pitch may be given to the roof slab without any change in the theoretical computations. Sudden changes in slope, or steps, on the other hand, require special attention.

4.17 Example: flat-slab floor A parking garage, to be designed as a flat-slab structure, is to carry a working live load of 200 psf. Drop panels 8 ft square will be used, and each column capital will consist of a 90° truncated cone with 4-ft diameter at the intersection of the capital with the bottom of the drop panel. Columns are spaced 22 ft on centers in each direction. Design the slab reinforcement, and determine concrete dimensions for a typical interior panel. Steel will be used at a working stress of 20,000 psi; concrete is of 3000 psi strength.

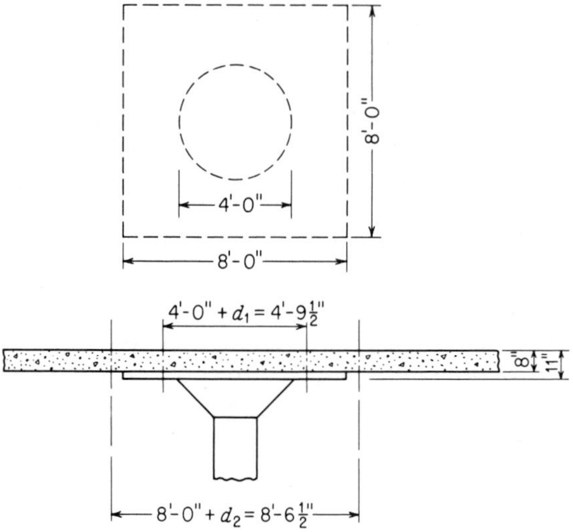

Fig. 4.13

The proposed structure falls within the limitations of the ACI empirical method of Art. 2104, Appendix A, and will be designed in accordance with that specification. The minimum thickness of the slab is established by the smallest of the criteria

$$\frac{L}{40} \quad \text{or} \quad 4 \text{ in.} \quad \text{or} \quad t_2 = 0.024L\left(1 - \frac{2c}{3L}\right)\sqrt{\frac{w'}{f'_c/2000}} + 1$$

With $c = 4$ ft, $L = 22$ ft, and the dead load of the slab estimated to be $150 \times 8/12 = 100$ psf,

$$\frac{L}{40} = \frac{22 \times 12}{40} = 6.6 \text{ in.}$$

$$t_2 = 0.024 \times 22(1 - 8/66)\sqrt{\frac{100 + 200}{3000/2000}} + 1 = 7.60 \text{ in.}$$

A slab thickness of 8 in. with 3-in. drop panels will be tentatively selected, as shown in Fig. 4.13.

Relative to punching shear, the critical section in the drop panel is at a distance $d_1/2$ from the edge of the column capital.[1] The diameter of the critical section is 4.79 ft. The floor area included within the critical section is $(\pi/4)4.79^2 = 18.0$ ft^2, and the shear force acting on the critical section is

$$V = (22 \times 22 - 18)300 = 140{,}000 \text{ lb}$$

[1] The effective depth is taken as the total depth less ¾ in. protection less 1½ times the diameter of an assumed No. 4 bar.

The nominal shear stress is

$$v = \frac{V}{b_0 d} = \frac{140{,}000}{3.14 \times 4.79 \times 12 \times 9.50} = 82 \text{ psi}$$

According to Code, the allowable shear stress on that section is

$$v_c = 2\sqrt{3000} = 110 \text{ psi} > 82 \text{ psi}$$

A second critical section for punching shear may occur at a distance $d_2/2$ from the edge of the drop panel. The side dimension of the critical section (see Fig. 4.13) is 8.54 ft, and the included area is $8.54^2 = 73$ ft². The shear force acting on this critical section is

$$V = (22 \times 22 - 73)300 = 123{,}000 \text{ lb}$$

and

$$v = \frac{V}{b_0 d} = \frac{123{,}000}{4 \times 8.54 \times 12 \times 6.50} = 47 \text{ psi}$$

well below the allowable value of 110 psi.

Beam shear is checked a distance d past the face of the support. Where round columns or capitals are used, the Code specifies that the face of the column be taken as the side of the square having the same area as the actual round support. In the present case, the equivalent square support has a side dimension of $\sqrt{\pi r^2} = 2.0\sqrt{3.14} = 3.54$ ft. At a distance d past that face, the shear force is

$$V = 300 \times 22 \times {}^{22}\!/_{2} - 300 \times 22 \times 2.31 = 57{,}300 \text{ lb*}$$

and the nominal shear stress is

$$v = \frac{V}{bd} = \frac{57{,}300}{22 \times 12 \times 6.50} = 33 \text{ psi}$$

The permitted shear on this section,

$$v_c = 1.1\sqrt{3000} = 60 \text{ psi}$$

is not exceeded.

The design moments are based on a value of

$$M_0 = 0.09WLF\left(1 - \frac{2c}{3L}\right)^2$$

in which

$$F = 1.15 - \frac{c}{L} \geqq 1$$

In the present case, $F = 1.15 - {}^4\!/_{22} = 0.97$, so that F is taken equal to unity. Then $W = 300 \times 22^2 = 145{,}000$ lb, and

$$M_0 = 0.09 \times 145{,}000 \times 22(1 - {}^8\!/_{66})^2 = 222{,}000 \text{ ft-lb}$$

* The presence of the drop panel over a part of the width of the critical section is neglected.

The maximum moment in the slab occurs in the column strip over the support and [see Table 2104(*f*), Appendix A] is $0.50M_0 = 111{,}000$ ft-lb. According to Code, only three-quarters of the width of the drop panel is to be considered effective in resisting flexural compression. The required depth for bending is therefore

$$d_1 = \sqrt{\frac{M}{Kb}} = \sqrt{\frac{111{,}000 \times 12}{223 \times 8 \times 12 \times 0.75}} = 9.11 \text{ in.}$$

The 9.5 in. effective depth provided by an 8-in. slab with 3-in. drop panels will be satisfactory. In the portion of the slab without drop panels, the maximum moment is $0.20M_0 = 44{,}400$ ft-lb. The required depth is

$$d_2 = \sqrt{\frac{44{,}400 \times 12}{223 \times 11 \times 12 \times 0.75}} = 4.92 \text{ in.}$$

The 8 in. total thickness required by other considerations will provide an effective depth of 6.50 in. in the positive-moment region of the column strips, more than satisfactory for flexure.

In flat-slab construction, a slab of any given total thickness will have different effective depths in the two perpendicular directions because of stacking of the bars. While actual depths may be used in the design of rectangular panels in which reinforcement will normally differ in the two directions, in the case of square panels it is convenient if the steel is identical in the two directions. This requires the use of the lesser effective depth in the determination of steel areas. This practice will be followed in the present design.

Using the moment coefficients of Table 2104(*f*), Appendix A, in the column strips, the negative moment is $0.50 \times 222{,}000 = 111{,}000$ ft-lb, and the required steel area is

$$A_s = \frac{M}{f_s jd} = \frac{111{,}000 \times 12}{20{,}000 \times 0.874 \times 9.5} = 8.02 \text{ in.}^2$$

Nineteen No. 6 bars will be used. The positive moment is $0.20 \times 222{,}000 = 44{,}400$ ft-lb, and the required steel is

$$A_s = \frac{44{,}400 \times 12}{20{,}000 \times 0.874 \times 6.50} = 4.70 \text{ in.}^2$$

Eleven No. 6 bars are selected.

In the middle strips, the negative and positive moments are identically $0.15 \times 222{,}000 = 33{,}400$ ft-lb, and the steel requirement is

$$A_s = \frac{33{,}400 \times 12}{20{,}000 \times 0.874 \times 6.50} = 3.53 \text{ in.}^2$$

which will be provided by twelve No. 5 bars. The maximum spacing of $2t = 16$ in. is not exceeded in either the column or middle strips.

Cutting off and bending of slab steel will follow the recommendations of Table 2104(*g*), Appendix A, and are shown in Fig. 4.14. In the column strips, the

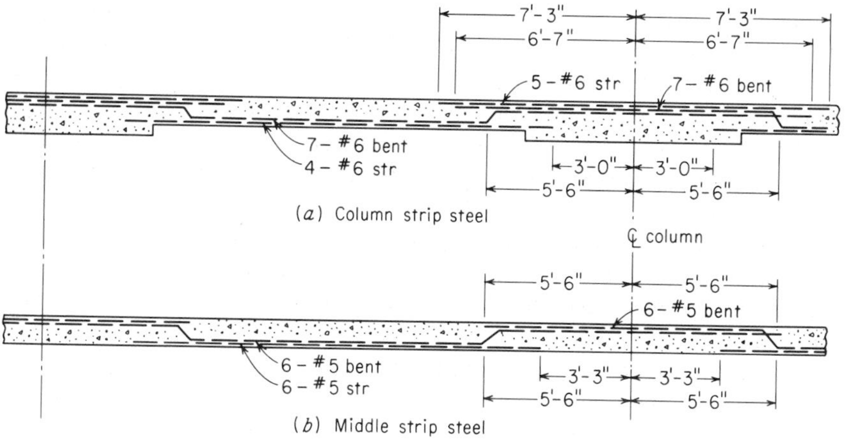

Fig. 4.14

four straight bottom bars are cut off 12 in. past the face of the drop panel, or 3 ft from the column line. The remaining seven bars are bent up at the quarter point of the span. The straight top bars added over the support are carried $0.33L$ past the column and cut off. The bent bars are terminated $0.30L$ past the column center line.

In the middle strips, half the bars are carried straight and cut off $0.15L$ from the support center line. The other half are bent up at the quarter point of the span. Bent-up bars are terminated $0.25L$ past the center line of the column.

From Table 8, Appendix B, it is evident that adequate development length is provided past the point of maximum stress for all bars.

4.18 Flat-plate Construction Flat-plate floors are a variation of flat-slab construction in which neither drop panels nor column capitals are used. The slab, of uniform thickness, is carried directly by columns of constant cross section. Where column spacing is not large, and where design loads are relatively light, a flat-plate design may be most economical. While material quantities may be somewhat greater than for conventional flat-slab or beam-and-girder floors, the savings which accrue from the simplified formwork and the reduction in construction depth often more than offset the increased cost of material. The resulting structural system presents a clean, unbroken appearance; in fact, in many cases, the under surface of the structural slab is used for the ceiling without further treatment. A typical flat-plate building is shown in Fig. 9.13.

The design procedure for flat plates is similar to that for ordinary flat-slab floors. They can be designed either by elastic methods of frame analysis (Art. 2103, Appendix A) or, provided dimensional limitations are met, by the empirical method of moment coefficients (Art. 2104,

Appendix A). Because of the lack of column capitals or drop panels, high shearing stresses may exist in flat-plate floors around the junction of column and slab, and often some type of steel shear reinforcement is employed in order to avoid an increase in slab thickness. With the inclusion of properly designed shear reinforcement, the ACI Code permits nominal shearing stresses of $3\sqrt{f'_c}$ (working value) and $6\phi\sqrt{f'_c}$ (ultimate value). Shear reinforcement consisting of bars, rods, or wires is not to be considered effective in slabs less than 10 in. thick, and in the design the working and yield stresses are reduced to one-half their usual values. In general, design methods follow those used in designing web reinforcement for beams.

Shear reinforcement for flat plates may take many forms. A few of the more common types are shown in Fig. 4.15. A number of early flat-plate buildings used the "shearhead" or "birdcage" type of reinforcement shown in (*a*). Hairpin-shaped stirrups of ⅜ in. or ½ in. diameter are welded to horizontal hoops near the top and bottom of the slab. The effectiveness of such reinforcement is questionable, in view of the short length of embedment of each stirrup. Although they are welded to the perpendicular hoops, it is difficult to obtain a reliable weld in such a case.

The bent-bar arrangement of Fig. 4.15*b* is preferred. Usually bent at 45°, such bars are placed over the top of the columns and are additional to the negative-moment reinforcement. They are extended a sufficient distance along the bottom face of the slab to develop their computed stress by bond (Ref. 4.5).

In cases in which a flat plate is supported by steel columns, a weldment fabricated of structural-steel channels may be used, as in Fig. 4.15*c*. Welded to the columns, such assemblies are embedded in the slab and act in the same sense as a column capital to reduce the shear force and increase the shear perimeter for which the slab is to be designed. The critical section for shear is probably about as indicated.

Many flat-plate buildings are constructed by the lift-slab method. A casting bed (often doubling as the ground-floor slab) is poured, steel columns are erected and braced, and at ground level successive slabs, which will later become the upper floors, are cast. A membrane or sprayed parting agent is laid down between successive pours, so that each slab can be lifted in its turn. Jacks placed atop the columns are connected to threaded rods extending down the faces of the columns and connecting, in turn, to lifting collars embedded in the slabs as shown in Fig. 4.15*d*. When a slab is in its final position, the collar is welded to the column. Lifting collars such as that shown, in addition to providing anchorage for the lifting rods, serve to increase the effective size of the support for the slab and consequently reduce the unit shear stress for which the slab must be designed.

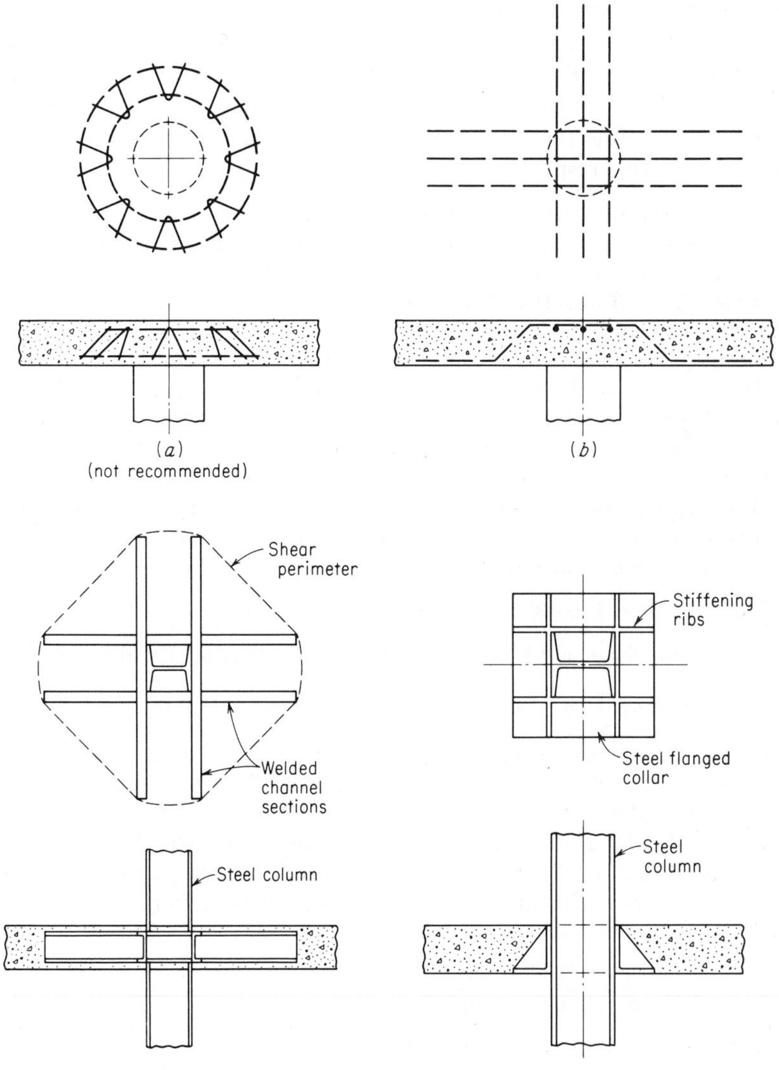

Fig. 4.15 Shear reinforcement for flat plates.

It should be noted that, according to ACI Code, the reinforcement of Fig. 4.15*a* and *b* can be used only in slabs 10 in. or more in thickness, while the devices shown in (*c*) and (*d*) permit a thinner slab to be used.

In flat-plate construction, with characteristically small support area, there is a tendency for the negative moment in the column strips to concentrate over the support. Whereas in ordinary flat-slab construction the

ACI Code recommends that a reduced effective width of 75 per cent of the actual width of the column strip be used to account for moment variation across the width of the section, there may be good reason to use a smaller effective width in computing flexural compression in flat plates. However, at the present time the Code does not differentiate between flat slabs and flat plates in this respect.

Example: design of flat-plate shear reinforcement A flat-plate floor slab 10¼ in. thick carries a uniformly distributed working load of 200 psf in addition to its own weight. It is supported by 14-in. square concrete columns located 20 ft on centers in each direction. Concrete of 4000 psi compressive strength is used with steel having a yield stress of 40,000 psi. Investigate the adequacy of the slab to resist diagonal tension, and design shear reinforcement if necessary.

The dead load of the slab is $150 \times 10.25/12 = 125$ psf, and the total uniform load is 325 psf. According to ACI Code, the critical section for diagonal tension in such slabs is a distance $d/2$ from the face of the column. With ¾-in. concrete protection, and with bar reinforcement of 1 in. diameter assumed, the effective depth in one direction will be 9 in., and in the perpendicular direction 8 in. An average value of $d = 8.5$ in. will be used. At a distance of 4.25 in. from the face of the column, the shear force is

$$V_{22.5} = (20^2 - 1.87^2)325 = 129{,}000 \text{ lb}$$

The maximum shear which can be carried at this section, according to Code, is

$$V = 3\sqrt{f'_c}\, b_0 d = 3\sqrt{4000}\,(4 \times 22.5 \times 8.5) = 145{,}000 \text{ lb} > 129{,}000 \text{ lb}$$

The concrete can resist a nominal stress $v_c = 2\sqrt{f'_c} = 2\sqrt{4000} = 126$ psi; hence $V_c = 126 \times 4 \times 22.5 \times 8.5 = 96{,}500 \text{ lb} < 129{,}000$ lb, indicating that reinforcement will be required to carry the excess shear. Bars of the type shown in Fig. 4.15*b*, bent at a 45° angle, will be used. According to Code, the allowable stress in such reinforcement is 50 per cent of the usual working value, which is 20,000 psi in the present case. With all bars bent at the same distance from the support, the required steel area is

$$A_v = \frac{V - V_c}{f_v \sin \alpha} = \frac{129{,}000 - 96{,}500}{10{,}000 \times 0.707} = 4.60 \text{ in.}^2$$

A total of six No. 8 bars, three in each direction, will provide an area of 4.71 in.^{2} The arrangement is shown in Fig. 4.16.

In recognition of the probable pattern of diagonal cracking and the Code requirement that only the center three-quarters of the inclined portion of the bars is to be considered effective as shear reinforcement, the next section to be investigated is a distance $3d/4$ beyond the previous critical section (see Fig. 4.16). The side dimension of this section is 35.30 in., or 2.94 ft. The shear force is

$$V_{35.30} = (20^2 - 2.94^2)325 = 127{,}000 \text{ lb}$$

The concrete can resist

$$V_c = 126 \times 4 \times 35.3 \times 8.5 = 151{,}000 \text{ lb} > 127{,}000 \text{ lb}$$

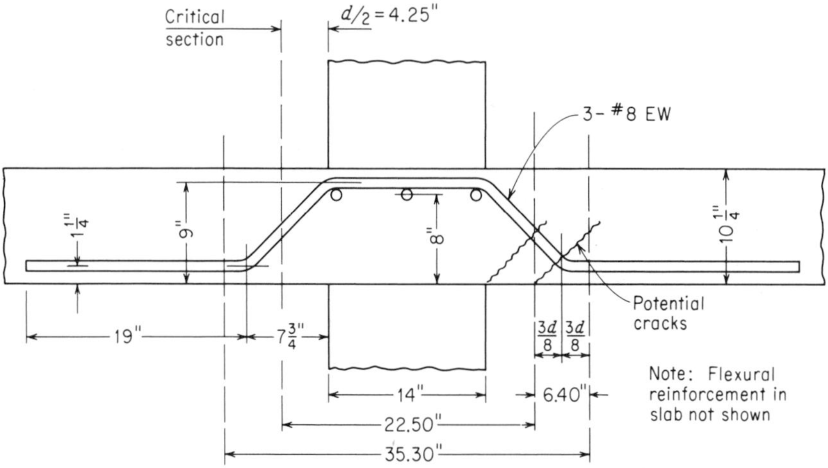

Fig. 4.16

indicating that no additional reinforcement is necessary. The six No. 8 bent bars will provide for all excess shear.

According to Code, bent bars are to be embedded on the compression side of the slab at a distance sufficient to develop by bond the stress for which the bar was designed, but in any case not less than 24 diam. With reference to Table 8, the length required to develop a stress of 10,000 psi is

$$L = 20.6 \times 10{,}000/20{,}000 = 10.3 \text{ in.}$$

The bars will therefore be embedded a distance of $24 \times 1 = 24$ in. in the compression concrete. With approximately 5 in. of length obtained in the sloping part of the bars, a horizontal extension along the bottom of the slab of 19 in. will be used, as shown in the sketch.

PROBLEM

The parking garage described in the example of Art. 4.17 consists of a floor area five bays wide and eight bays long, with all columns spaced 22 ft on centers in each direction. A perimeter beam of 24 in. total depth is used at the outside edge of each exterior panel. Using the ACI moment coefficients for flat slabs (Appendix A), determine the required slab thickness, and design and detail the reinforcement (*a*) for a typical exterior panel at the center of the long edge of the floor and (*b*) for the adjacent first interior panel. Allowable stresses are the same as for the example of Art. 4.17.

SLABS ON GROUND

4.19 General Considerations Concrete slabs are often poured directly on the ground; they receive more or less uniform support from the soil. Roadway and sidewalk slabs, basement floors, and warehouse

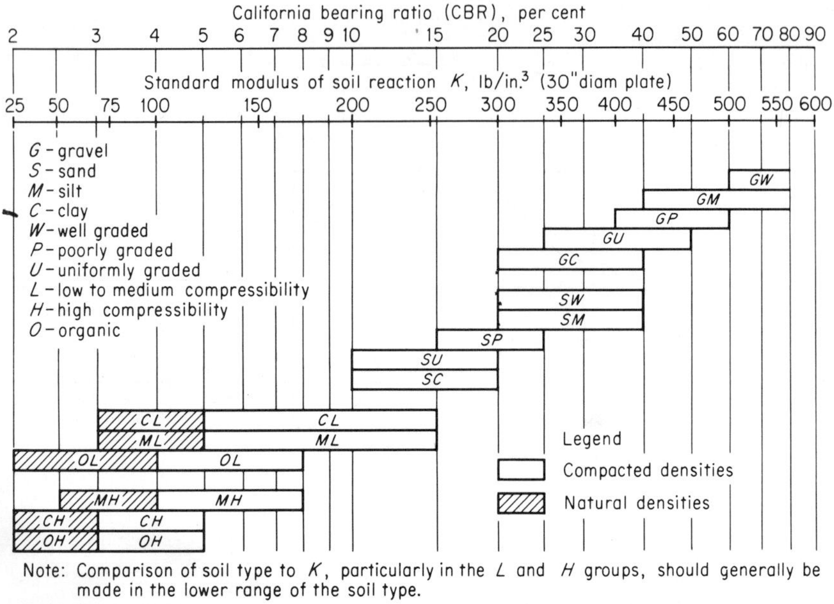

***Fig.* 4.17** Interrelationships of soil classifications and strength criteria.

floors are common examples of this type of construction. Ordinarily it is desirable to provide a base course of well-compacted crushed stone or gravel. The prepared subgrade, approximately 6 to 12 in. thick, serves (1) to provide more uniform support than if the slab were carried directly on the natural soil, and (2) to improve the drainage of water from beneath the slab. The latter is particularly important in outdoor locations subject to freezing temperatures.

Failures of concrete slabs on ground are not infrequent. Unequal settlement or overloading may cause cracking, as well as restrained shrinkage as volume changes occur. Passage of wheel loads over cracks or improperly made joints may lead to progressive failure by disintegration of the concrete. Failures are not spectacular and do not involve collapse in the usual sense. They may even pass unnoticed for a considerable period of time. Nevertheless, the function of the structure is often impaired, and repairs are both embarrassing and costly.

If the slab is loaded uniformly over its entire area and is supported by an absolutely uniform subgrade, stresses will be due solely to restrained volumetric changes. However, foundation materials are not uniform in their properties. In addition, most slabs are subjected to nonuniform loading. In warehouses, for example, the necessity for maintaining clear aisles for access to stored materials often results in a checkerboard-type load pattern. Wheel loads from trucks and other moving equipment may control the design.

Methods of analysis for such cases are similar to those developed for beams on elastic foundations. Usually the slab is assumed to be homogeneous, isotropic, and elastic; the reaction of the subgrade is assumed to be only vertical and proportional to the deflection. The stiffness of the soil is expressed in terms of the modulus of subgrade reaction k, usually in units of lb per in.^{2} per in., or, simply, lb per in.^{3} The numerical value of k varies widely for different soil types and degrees of consolidation and is generally based on experimental observations; typical values are given in Fig. 4.17. Shown for comparison are values of California bearing ratio, also widely used as a measure of soil consolidation under load.

4.20 Concentrated Loads on Slabs The analysis of slabs supporting concentrated loads is based largely on the work of Westergaard (Refs. 4.6, 4.7). Three separate cases, differentiated on the basis of the location of the load with respect to the edge of the slab, are considered.

Case 1; wheel load close to the corner of a large slab With a load applied at the corner of a slab, the critical stress in the concrete is tension at the top surface of the slab. An approximate solution, due to A. T. Goldbeck, assumes a point load acting at the corner of the slab (see Fig. 4.18). At small distances from the corner, the upward reaction of the soil has little effect, and the slab is considered to act as a cantilever. At a distance x from the corner, the bending moment is Px; it is assumed to be uniformly distributed across the width of the section of slab at right angles to the bisector of the corner angle. For a 90° corner, the width of this section is $2x$, and the bending moment per unit width of slab is

$$\frac{Px}{2x} = \frac{P}{2}$$

If h is the thickness of the slab, the tensile stress at the top surface is

$$f_t = \frac{M}{S} = \frac{P/2}{h^2/6} = \frac{3P}{h^2} \tag{4.6}$$

Equation (4.6) will give reasonably close results only in the immediate vicinity of the slab corner, and only if the load is applied over a small contact area.

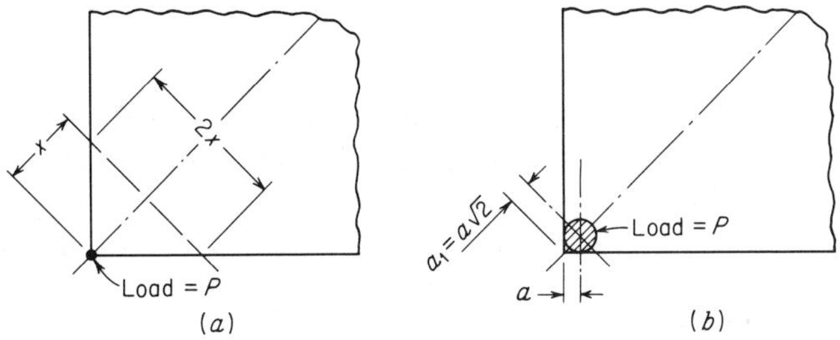

Fig. **4.18**

In an analysis which considers the reaction of the subgrade, and which considers the load to be applied over a contact area of radius a (see Fig. 4.18*b*), Westergaard derives the expression for critical tension at the top of the slab, occurring at a distance $2\sqrt{a_1 L}$ from the corner of the slab:

$$f_t = \frac{3P}{h^2}\left[1 - \left(\frac{a\sqrt{2}}{L}\right)^{0.6}\right] \tag{4.7}$$

in which L is the radius of relative stiffness, equal to

$$L = \sqrt[4]{\frac{Eh^3}{12(1-\mu^2)k}} \tag{4.8}$$

where E = elastic modulus of concrete, psi
μ = Poisson's ratio for concrete (approximately 0.15)
k = modulus of subgrade reaction, lb/in.^{3}

The value of L reflects the relative stiffness of the slab and the subgrade. It will be large for a stiff slab on a soft base and small for a flexible slab on a stiff base.

Case 2: wheel load a considerable distance from the edges of a slab With the load is applied some distance from the edges of the slab, the critical stress in the concrete will be tension at the bottom surface. This tension is greatest directly under the center of the loaded area and is given by the expression

$$f_b = 0.316\frac{P}{h^2}\left[\log h^3 - 4\log\left(\sqrt{1.6a^2+h^2} - 0.675h\right) - \log k + 6.48\right] \tag{4.9}$$

Case 3: wheel load at an edge of a slab, but removed a considerable distance from a corner When the load is applied at a point along an edge of the slab, the critical tensile stress is at the bottom of the concrete, directly under the load, and is equal to

$$f_b = 0.572\frac{P}{h^2}\left[\log h^3 - 4\log\left(\sqrt{1.6a^2+h^2} - 0.675h\right) - \log k + 5.77\right] \tag{4.10}$$

In the event that the tensile stress in the slab, as given by Eqs. (4.7), (4.9), and (4.10), exceeds the allowable tensile stress on the concrete, it is necessary either to increase the thickness of the slab or to provide reinforcement. Such reinforcement is usually designed to provide for all the tension indicated by the analysis of the assumed homogeneous, elastic slab. Its centroid should be no closer to the neutral axis than that of the tension concrete which it replaces.

Example: design of an unreinforced concrete slab on grade A warehouse floor, consisting of an unreinforced slab on ground, is to be designed to support a maximum wheel load of 6000 lb from fork-lift trucks, assumed to apply the load over a contact area of 4-in. radius. Concrete of 4000 psi compressive strength is to be used, with an allowable tensile stress of 200 psi. The slab will be poured in 30-ft-wide strips with construction joints at each edge, and contraction joints will be located every 30 ft in the long direction of the strip. It will be conservatively assumed that no shear transfer is possible across the joints. The wheel load can be applied anywhere within each 900-ft² panel. The soil is a clay-gravel with a subgrade modulus of 300 lb per in.³

It will be assumed initially that the critical load location is at the corner of the slab. With

$$E_c = 33w^{1.5}\sqrt{f'_c} = 33 \times 145^{1.5}\sqrt{4000} = 3{,}640{,}000 \text{ psi}$$

and assuming the slab thickness h to be 8 in., the radius of relative stiffness is

$$L = \sqrt[4]{\frac{Eh^3}{12(1-\mu^2)k}} = \sqrt[4]{\frac{3{,}640{,}000 \times 512}{12(1-0.15^2)300}} = 27 \text{ in.}$$

From Eq. (4.7),

$$h^2 = \frac{3P}{f_t}\left[1 - \left(\frac{a\sqrt{2}}{L}\right)^{0.6}\right]$$

$$= \frac{3 \times 6000}{200}\left[1 - \left(\frac{4\sqrt{2}}{27}\right)^{0.6}\right] = 54.7 \text{ in.}^2$$

$$h = 7.4 \text{ in.}$$

Tentatively a total depth of 7½ in. is selected. If the load is applied centrally within a panel, the tensile stress at the bottom of a 7½-in. slab is, from Eq. (4.9),

$$f_b = \frac{0.316 \times 6000}{56.2}(\log 421 - 4 \log 3.96 - \log 300 + 6.48)$$

$$= 144 \text{ psi} < 200 \text{ psi}$$

If the load is applied along the edge of a slab panel, the critical tension at the bottom of the concrete is, from Eq. (4.10),

$$f_b = \frac{0.572 \times 6000}{56.2}(\log 421 - 4 \log 3.96 - \log 300 + 5.77)$$

$$= 215 \text{ psi} > 200$$

Since this exceeds the allowable tension by a small amount, a total slab depth of 8 in. will be used.

4.21 Loads Distributed over Partial Areas

In addition to concentrated loads, it may be that uniform loads distributed over partial areas of slabs will produce the critical design condition. In warehouses, heavy loads are often stacked about columns, leaving clear aisles midway between the column lines for access, as shown in Fig. 4.19. For moderate column spacing, construction joints are located on column lines only.

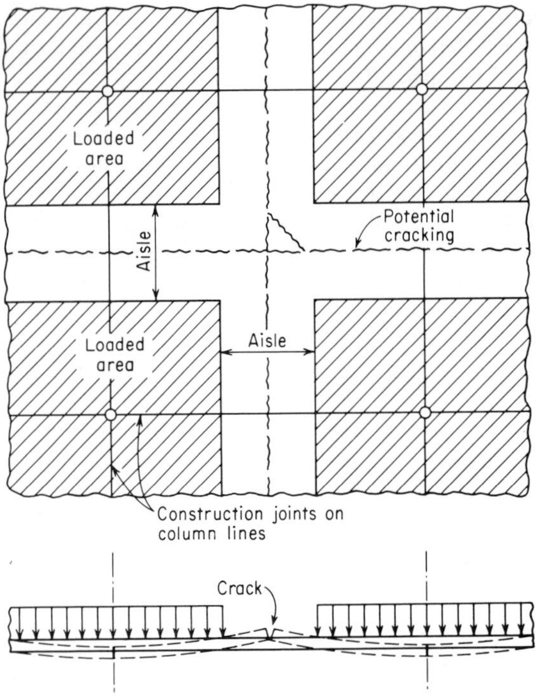

Fig. 4.19

With the loading pattern shown, cracking is likely to occur along the center line of the aisles. In addition, as wheel loads pass over the cracked slab, secondary corner cracks may occur, as shown in one panel.

In an analysis based on the loading and joint arrangement of Fig. 4.19, Rice (Ref. 4.8) derived an expression for the critical negative moment in the slab, which occurs at the center line of the aisle:

$$M_c = \frac{w}{2\lambda^2} e^{-\lambda a} \sin \lambda a \tag{4.11}$$

where M = slab moment, ft-lb per ft
$\lambda = \sqrt[4]{k/4EI}$, in.$^{-1}$
a = half-aisle width, in.
k = modulus of subgrade reaction, lb per in.^{3}
w = uniform load, psi
e = base of natural logarithms

Recognizing that the width of the aisle cannot always be predicted exactly, Rice suggests that a "critical aisle width" be used. This width is such as to maximize Eq. (4.11) for bending moment. Tables are available (Ref. 4.8) which give critical aisle width and corresponding bending moment for various slab thicknesses and various values of subgrade modulus.

YIELD - LINE THEORY OF SLAB ANALYSIS

4.22 General Considerations Presently the analysis for moments and shears of most reinforced-concrete slabs is based upon elastic theory, somewhat modified for inelastic redistribution. With idealized support conditions, and usually for only a uniformly distribution load, the critical forces and moments can be obtained for rectangular slabs.

While these methods of moment analysis are based essentially on elastic behavior, the actual proportioning of slabs, as for beams and other members, is increasingly being performed by ultimate-strength methods which recognize the inelastic nature of deformations before failure. Although there is a certain inconsistency in combining elastic-moment analysis with ultimate-strength design of sections, this procedure is known to be safe and conservative. It can be shown that a structure analyzed and designed in this way will not fail at a lower load than anticipated (although it may possess substantial reserve strength relative to final collapse; see Art. 8.15).

In recent years, methods have been advanced for moment analysis of reinforced-concrete structures which are based on inelastic considerations, and which direct attention to the conditions that obtain in the structure just prior to failure (see Art. 8.15). In the case of slabs, this failure theory of structural analysis is known as *yield-line theory* (Refs. 4.9, 4.10). It was first proposed by K. W. Johansen. A powerful tool in analysis, it permits the determination of failure moments in slabs of irregular as well as rectangular shapes for a variety of support conditions and loadings.

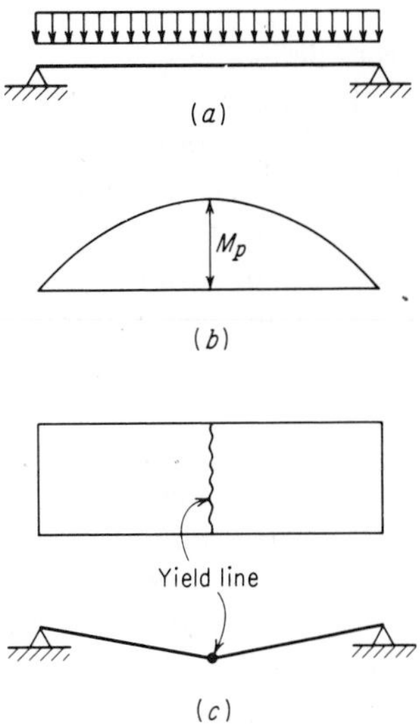

Fig. 4.20 Simply supported, uniformly loaded slab.

Figure 4.20*a* shows a simply supported, uniformly loaded, reinforced-concrete slab. For present purposes, it will be assumed to be underreinforced (as are most slabs), with $p < p_b$. The elastic distribution of moments is shown in Fig. 4.20*b*. As the load is gradually increased, and as the maximum applied moment becomes equal to the ultimate-moment capacity of the slab cross section, the tensile steel commences to yield along the transverse line of maximum moment.

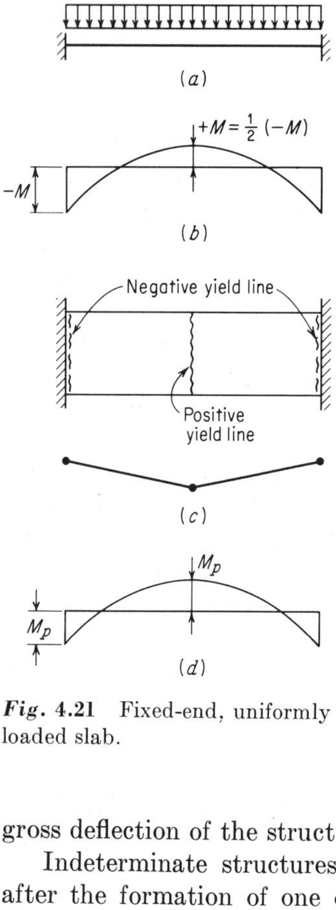

Fig. 4.21 Fixed-end, uniformly loaded slab.

Upon yielding, the curvature of the slab at the yielding section increases sharply, and deflection increases disproportionately. The elastic deformation of the slab is of a small order of magnitude compared with the change in shape of the deflected structure due to the plastic deformation at the yield line. It is acceptable to assume that the slab portions between yield line and supports remain rigid, with all the deformation taking place at the yield line as shown in Fig. 4.20*c*.

The "hinge" which forms at the yield line rotates at essentially a constant moment. (This moment-rotation relation is shown graphically in Fig. 8.22.) For all practical purposes, the restraining moment at the yielding hinge can be taken equal to the ultimate moment; that is, $M_p = M'_u$.

For a determinate slab such as that of Fig. 4.20, the formation of one yield line is tantamount to failure. A "mechanism" forms (the segments of the slab between the hinge and the supports are able to move without an increase in load), and gross deflection of the structure results.

Indeterminate structures, however, can maintain equilibrium even after the formation of one or more yield lines. The fixed-fixed slab of Fig. 4.21, for example, when loaded uniformly, will have an elastic distribution of moments as in (*b*). As the load is gradually increased (it is assumed for simplicity that the slab is equally reinforced for positive and negative moment), the more highly stressed sections at the supports commence yielding. Rotation of the end tangents occurs, but restraining moments of substantially constant amount M_p continue to act at the support lines. The load can be increased still further, until the moment at midspan becomes equal to the ultimate-moment capacity of the slab, and a third yield line forms as shown in (*c*). This converts the structure into a mechanism and results in collapse.

The moment diagram just before failure is shown in Fig. 4.21*d*. Note that the ratio of elastic positive to negative moments of 1:2 is no longer obtained. Owing to inelastic deformation, the ratio of these moments just before collapse is 1:1 for this particular structure. This is known as *inelastic redistribution of moments.*

Whether or not a concrete structure can sustain rotation and deformation such as to ensure full moment redistribution depends at least in part on the reinforcement ratio. Lightly reinforced members can generally undergo considerable rotation, while overreinforced members may fail by concrete crushing before much rotation occurs. For a more complete discussion of this important aspect of plastic or limit analysis of concrete structures, the reader is referred to Art. 8.15. It will be sufficient for the present to note that most slabs are relatively lightly reinforced, and that the required rotation capacity is normally available.

4.23 Location of Yield Lines The location and orientation of the yield line was evident in the case of the simple slab of Fig. 4.20. Similarly, for the one-way indeterminate slab of Fig. 4.21, the yield lines were easily established. For other cases it is helpful to have a set of guidelines for drawing yield lines and locating axes of rotation. When a slab is on the verge of collapse owing to the existence of a sufficient number of real or plastic hinges to form a mechanism, axes of rotation will be located along the lines of support or over point supports such as columns. The slab segments can be considered to rotate as rigid bodies in space about these axes of rotation. The yield line between any two adjacent slab segments is a straight line, being the intersection of two essentially plane surfaces. Since the yield line (as a line of intersection of two planes) contains all points common to these two planes, it must contain the point of intersection of the two axes of rotation, which is also common to the two planes. That is, the yield line (or yield line extended) must pass through the point of intersection of the axes of rotation of the two adjacent slab segments.

The terms *positive yield line* and *negative yield line* are used to distinguish between those associated with tension at the bottom and tension at the top of the slab, respectively.

Guidelines for establishing axes of rotation and yield lines are summarized as follows:

1. Yield lines are generally straight.

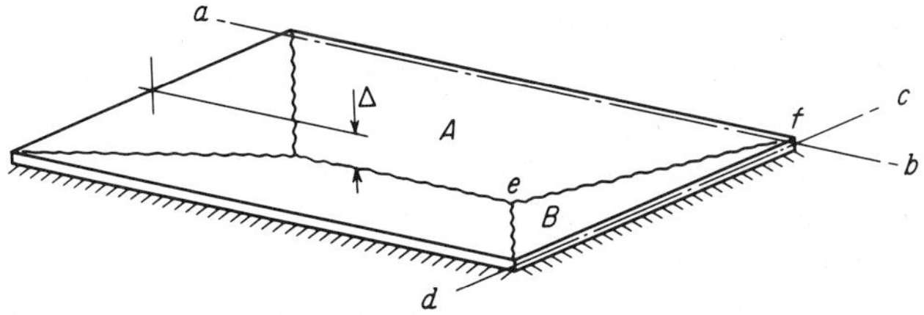

Fig. 4.22 Two-way slab on simple supports.

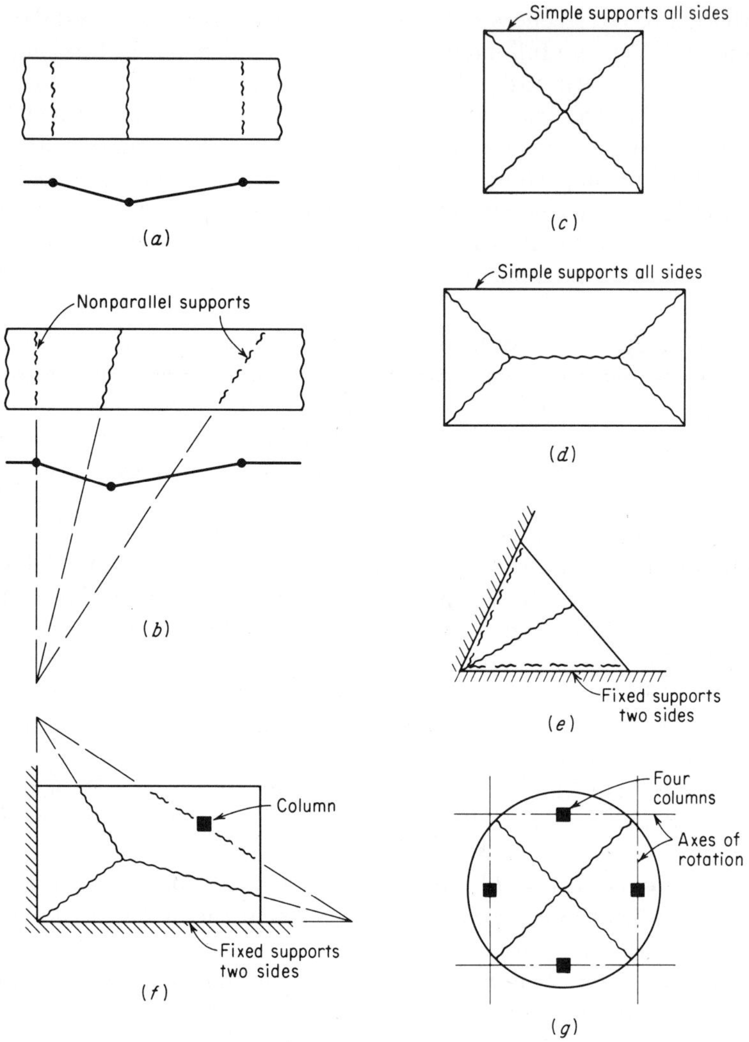

Fig. 4.23 Typical yield-line patterns.

2. Axes of rotation generally lie along lines of support (the support line may be a real hinge, or it may establish the location of a yield line which acts as a plastic hinge).

3. Axes of rotation pass over any columns.

4. A yield line passes through the intersection of the axes of rotation of adjacent slab segments.

In Fig. 4.22, which shows a slab simply supported along its four sides, rotation of slab segments *A* and *B* is about *ab* and *cd*, respectively. The yield line *ef* between these two segments is a straight line passing through *f*, the point of intersection of the axes of rotation.

Illustrations are given in Fig. 4.23 of the application of these guidelines to the establishment of yield-line locations and failure mechanisms for a number of slabs with various support conditions. Shown in (*a*) is a slab continuous over parallel supports. Axes of rotation are situated along the supports (negative yield lines) and near midspan, parallel to the supports (positive yield line). The particular location of the positive yield line in this case and the other cases of Fig. 4.23 depends upon the distribution of loading and the reinforcement of the slab. Methods for determining its location will be discussed later.

For the continuous slab on nonparallel supports, shown in (*b*), the midspan yield line (extended) must pass through the intersection of the axes of rotation over the supports. In (*c*) there are axes of rotation over all four simple supports. Positive yield lines form along the lines of intersection of the rotating segments of the slab. A rectangular two-way slab on simple supports is shown in (*d*). The diagonal yield lines must pass through the corners, while the central yield line is parallel to the two long sides (axes of rotation along opposite supports intersect at infinity in this case).

With this background, the reader should have no difficulty in applying the guidelines to the slabs of Fig. 4.23*e* through *g* to confirm the general pattern of yield lines shown.

4.24 Equilibrium Method of Analysis Once the general pattern of yielding and rotation has been established by applying the guidelines of Art. 4.23, the specific location and orientation of the axes of rotation and the failure load for the slab can be established by either of two methods. The first of these is based on the equilibrium of the various segments of the slab. The second, to be discussed in Art. 4.25, makes use of the principle of virtual work.

The correct locations of axes of rotation and the collapse load of a slab can be found by considerating the equilibrium of the slab segments. Each segment, studied as a free body, must be in equilibrium under the action of the applied loads, the moments along the yield lines, and the reactions or shear along the support lines. It is noted that, because the yield moments are principal moments, twisting moments are zero along the yield lines, and in most cases the shearing forces are also zero. Only the unit moment m generally is considered in writing equilibrium equations.

Example The application of the equilibrium method will be demonstrated first with respect to the one-way, uniformly loaded, continuous slab of Fig. 4.24*a*.

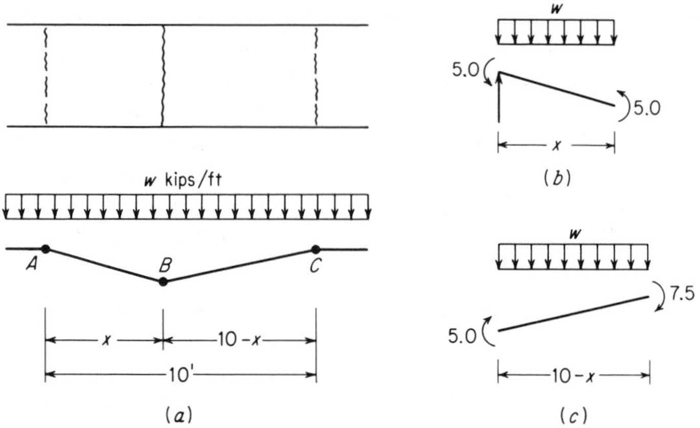

Fig. 4.24 Equilibrium method of analysis for one-way slab.

The slab has a 10-ft span and is reinforced so as to provide a resistance to positive bending of 5.0 ft-kips per ft through the span. In addition, negative steel over the supports provides moment capacities of 5.0 ft-kips per ft at A and 7.5 ft-kips per ft at C. Determine the ultimate load capacity of the slab.

The number of equilibrium equations required will depend upon the number of unknowns. One unknown is always the relation between the ultimate resisting moments of the slab and the load. Other unknowns are needed to define the locations of yield lines. In the present instance, one additional equation will suffice to define the distance of the yield line from the supports. Taking the left segment of the slab as a free body, and writing the equation for moment equilibrium about the left support line (see Fig. 4.24*b*),

$$\frac{wx^2}{2} - 10.0 = 0 \tag{a}$$

Similarly, for the right slab segment,

$$\frac{w}{2}(10 - x)^2 - 12.5 = 0 \tag{b}$$

Solving Eqs. (*a*) and (*b*) simultaneously for w and x results in

$$w = 0.89 \text{ kips per ft}^2 \qquad x = 4.75 \text{ ft}$$

If a slab is reinforced identically in orthogonal directions, the ultimate resisting moment is the same in these two directions, as it is along any other line, regardless of its direction. Such a slab is said to be *isotropically* reinforced. If, however, the ultimate strengths are different in two perpendicular directions, the slab is called *orthogonally anisotropic*, or simply *orthotropic*. Only isotropic slabs will be discussed in this section. Johansen has shown (Ref. 4.9) that orthotropic slabs can be reduced to equivalent isotropic cases, for purposes of analysis, by modifying the slab dimensions.

It is convenient in yield-line analysis to represent moments with vectors. The standard convention, in which the moment acts in a clockwise direction when viewed along the vector arrow, will be followed. Treatment of moments as vector quantities will be illustrated by the following example.

Example A square slab is simply supported along all sides and is to be isotropically reinforced. Determine the ultimate resisting moment m per linear foot required just to sustain a uniformly distributed load of w psf.

Conditions of symmetry indicate the yield-line pattern shown in Fig. 4-25*a*. Considering the moment equilibrium of any one of the identical slab segments about its support (see Fig. 4.25*b*), one obtains

$$\frac{wL^2}{4}\frac{L}{6} - 2\frac{mL}{\sqrt{2}}\frac{1}{\sqrt{2}} = 0$$

$$m = \frac{wL^2}{24}$$

4.25 Analysis by Virtual Work

Alternative to the method of Art. 4.24 is a method of analysis using the principle of virtual work. Since the moments and loads are in equilibrium when the yield-line pattern has formed, an infinitesimal increase in load will cause the structure to deflect further. The external work done by the loads to cause a small, arbitrary virtual deflection must equal the internal work done as the slab rotates at the yield lines to accomodate this deflection. The slab is therefore given a virtual displacement, and the corresponding rotations at the various yield lines may be calculated. By equating internal and external work, the relation between the applied loads and the ultimate resisting moments of the slab is obtained.

Example Determine the ultimate-load capacity of the one-way, uniformly loaded, continuous slab of Fig. 4.26, using the method of virtual work. The resisting moments of the slab are 5.0, 5.0, and 7.5 ft-kips per ft at A, B, and C, respectively.

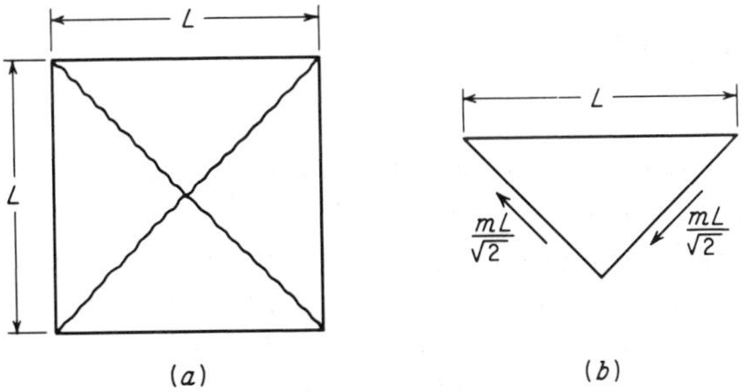

Fig. 4.25

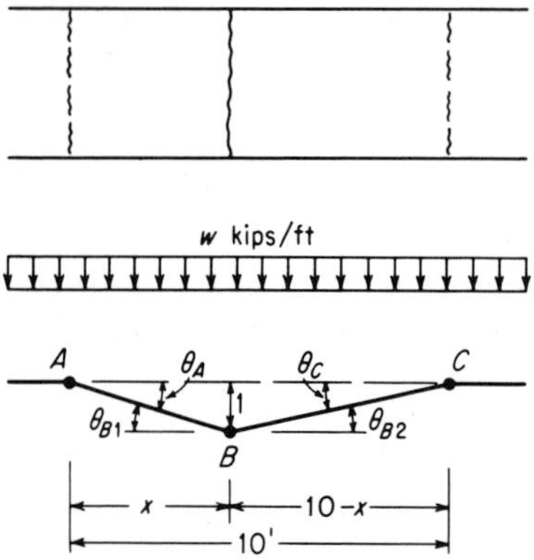

Fig. 4.26 Mechanism method of analysis for one-way slab.

A unit deflection is given to the slab at B (Fig. 4.26). Then the external work done by the load is the sum of the loads times their displacements and is equal to

$$\frac{wx}{2} + \frac{w}{2}(10 - x)$$

The rotations at the hinges are calculated in terms of the unit deflection (see Fig. 4.26) and are

$$\theta_a = \theta_{b1} = \frac{1}{x} \qquad \theta_{b2} = \theta_c = \frac{1}{10 - x}$$

The internal work is the sum of the moments times their corresponding rotation angles:

$$5\frac{1}{x}2 + 5\frac{1}{10 - x} + 7.5\frac{1}{10 - x}$$

Equating the external and internal work,

$$\frac{wx}{2} + 5w - \frac{wx}{2} = \frac{10}{x} + \frac{5}{10 - x} + \frac{7.5}{10 - x}$$

$$5w = \frac{10}{x} + \frac{25}{2(10 - x)}$$

$$w = \frac{2}{x} + \frac{5}{2(10 - x)}$$

To determine the minimum value of w, this expression is differentiated with respect to x and set equal to zero:

$$\frac{dw}{dx} = -\frac{2}{x^2} + \frac{5}{2(10 - x)^2} = 0$$

from which

$$x = 4.75 \text{ ft}$$

Substituting this value in the previous expression for w, one obtains

$$w = 0.89 \text{ kips per ft}^2$$

as before.

In many cases, particularly those with yield lines established by several unknown dimensions (such as Fig. 4.23*f*), direct solution by virtual work would become quite tedious. The ordinary derivatives in the above example would be replaced by several partial derivatives, producing a set of equations to be solved simultaneously. In such cases it is often more convenient to select an arbitrary succession of possible yield-line locations, solve the resulting mechanisms for the unknown load (or unknown moment), and determine the correct minimum load (or maximum moment) by trial.

Example The two-way slab of Fig. 4.27 is simply supported on all four sides and carries a uniformly distributed ultimate load of w psf. Determine the ultimate-moment resistance of the slab, which is to be isotropically reinforced.

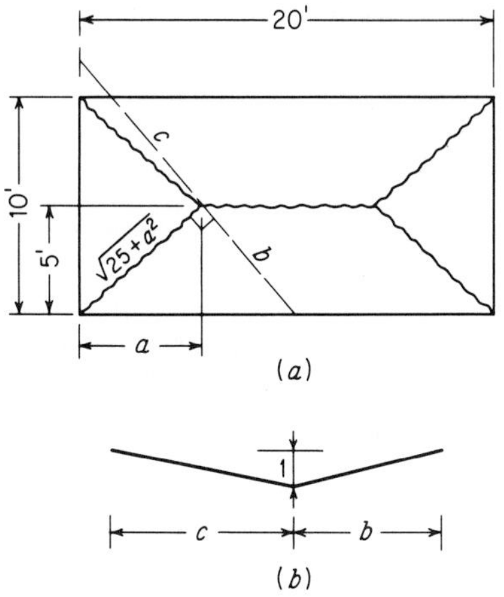

Fig. 4.27

Positive yield lines will form in the pattern shown in Fig. 4.27a, with the dimension a unknown. The correct dimension a will be such as to maximize the moment resistance required to support the load w. The values of a and m will be found by trial.

In Fig. 4.27a, the length of the diagonal yield is $\sqrt{25 + a^2}$. From similar triangles,

$$b = 5\frac{\sqrt{25 + a^2}}{a} \qquad c = a\frac{\sqrt{25 + a^2}}{5}$$

Then the rotation of the plastic hinge at the diagonal yield line corresponding to a unit deflection at the center of the slab (see Fig. 4.27b) is

$$\theta_1 = \frac{1}{b} + \frac{1}{c} = \frac{a}{5\sqrt{25 + a^2}} + \frac{5}{a\sqrt{25 + a^2}} = \frac{1}{\sqrt{25 + a^2}}\left(\frac{a}{5} + \frac{5}{a}\right)$$

The rotation of the yield line parallel to the long edges of the slab is

$$\theta_2 = \tfrac{1}{5} + \tfrac{1}{5} = 0.400$$

For a first trial, let $a = 6$ ft. Then the length of the diagonal yield line is

$$\sqrt{25 + 36} = 7.81 \text{ ft}$$

The rotation at the diagonal yield line is

$$\theta_1 = \frac{1}{7.81}\left(\tfrac{6}{5} + \tfrac{5}{6}\right) = 0.261$$

At the central yield line it is $\theta_2 = 0.400$. The internal work done as the incremental deflection is applied is

$$W_i = (m \times 7.81 \times 0.261 \times 4) + (m \times 8 \times 0.400) = 11.36m$$

The external work done during the same deflection is

$$W_e = (10 \times 6 \times \tfrac{1}{2}w \times \tfrac{1}{3} \times 2) + (8 + 5w \times \tfrac{1}{2} \times 2) + (12 \times 5 \times \tfrac{1}{2}w \times \tfrac{1}{3} \times 2) = 80w$$

Equating W_i and W_e, one obtains

$$m = \frac{80w}{11.36} = 7.05w$$

Successive trials for different values of a result in the following data:

a	W_i	W_e	m
6.0	11.36m	80.0w	7.05w
6.5	11.08m	78.4w	7.08w
7.0	10.87m	76.6w	7.04w
7.5	10.69m	75.0w	7.02w

It is evident that the yield-line pattern defined by $a = 6.5$ ft is critical. The required resisting moment for the given slab is 7.08w.

In common with the equilibrium method of analysis, the method of virtual work as applied to slabs is an "upper-bound" method in the sense that a yield pattern different from the one assumed may produce a lower failure load or, conversely, may require greater moment capacity to resist a given applied load. To illustrate, the rectangular slab of Fig. 4.28, supported along only three sides and free along the fourth, may fail by either of the two mechanisms shown. An analysis based on yield pattern *a* may indicate a minimum failure load higher than one based on pattern *b*. It is necessary to investigate all reasonable failure mechanisms in each case to establish that the correct solution has been found.

4.26 Corner Levers In the preceding discussion it has been assumed that yield lines enter the corners between the two intersecting sides. An alternative possibility is that the yield line forks before it reaches the corner, forming what is known as a *corner lever*, shown in Fig. 4.29*a*.

If the corner is not held down, the triangular element *abc* will pivot about the axis *ab* and lift off the supports. If the corner is held down, a similar situation obtains, except that the line *ab* becomes a yield line. If

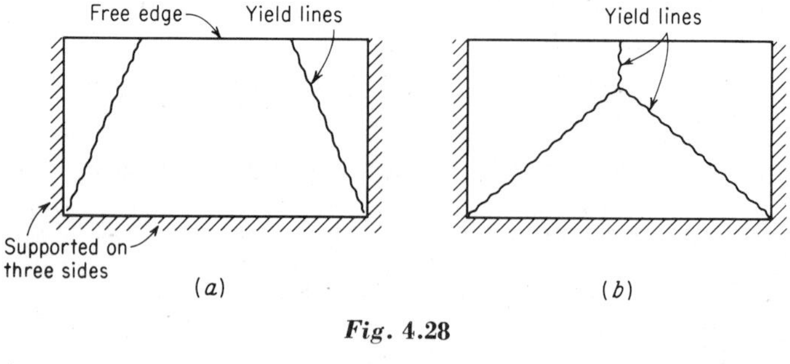

Fig. 4.28

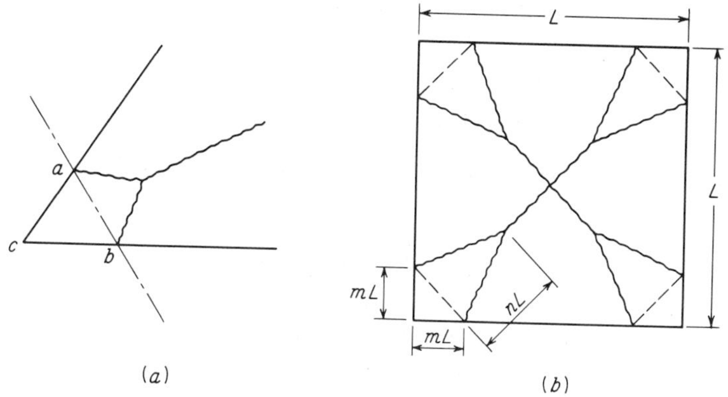

Fig. 4.29 Corner levers.

cracking at the corners of such a slab is to be controlled, top steel, more or less perpendicular to the line *ab*, must be provided. The direction taken by the positive yield lines near the corner indicates the desirability of supplementary bottom slab reinforcement at the corners, placed approximately parallel to the line *ab* (see Art. 4.6).

Although yield-line patterns with corner levers are generally more critical than those without, they are often neglected in yield-line analysis. The analysis becomes considerably more complicated if the possibility of corner levers is introduced, and the error made by neglecting them is usually small.

To illustrate, the uniformly loaded square slab of Art. 4.24, when analyzed for the assumed yield pattern of Fig. 4.25, required an ultimate-moment capacity of $wL^2/24$. The actual yield-line pattern at failure is probably as shown in Fig. 4.29*b*. Since two additional parameters m and n have necessarily been introduced to define the yield-line pattern, a total of three equations of equilibrium are now necessary. These are obtained by summing moments and vertical forces on the segments of the slab. Such an analysis results in a required moment of $wL^2/22$, an increase of about 9 per cent as compared with the results of an analysis neglecting corner levers.[1]

4.27 Limitations of Yield-line Theory The usefulness of yield-line theory is apparent from the preceding articles. In general, elastic solutions are available only for limited conditions, usually uniformly loaded rectangular plates. Even if available, they do not account for the effects of inelastic action. By means of yield-line analysis, a rational solution for the

[1] Analysis indicates (Ref. 4.10) that when the corner is acute the error due to neglect of corner levers may be significant.

failure load may be found for slabs of any shape, supported in a variety of ways, and for concentrated loads as well as distributed and partially distributed loads. It is thus seen to be a powerful analytical tool for the structural engineer.

In applying yield-line analysis to slabs, it must be remembered that the analysis is predicated upon available rotation capacity at the yield lines. If the slab reinforcement happens to correspond closely to the elastic distribution of moments in the slab, then little rotation is required. If, on the other hand, there is a marked difference, it may be that the required rotation will exceed the available rotation capacity, in which case the slab will fail prematurely. In general, slabs, being rather lightly reinforced, will have adequate rotation capacity to attain the ultimate loads predicted by yield-line analysis.

It should also be borne in mind that the yield-line analysis focuses attention on the moment capacity of the slab. It is presumed that earlier failure will not occur due to shear, bond, or other causes. In addition, yield-line theory gives no information on stresses, deflections, or severity of cracking under service load conditions.

In spite of these limitations, yield-line analysis provides answers to problems of slab design which cannot be handled by other means, and so will undoubtedly assume a position of increasing importance in engineering practice.

REFERENCES

4.1 J. R. Nichols: Statical Limitations upon the Steel Requirement in Reinforced Concrete Flat Slab Floors, *Trans. ASCE*, vol. 77, 1914.

4.2 H. M. Westergaard and W. A. Slater: Moments and Stresses in Slabs, *Proc. ACI*, vol. 17, 1921.

4.3 D. Peabody, Jr.: Continuous Frame Analysis of Flat Slabs, *J. Boston Soc. Civil Engrs.*, January, 1948.

4.4 "Flat Plate Floors Designed as Continuous Frames," Portland Cement Association Reprint from *R/C*, 1947.

4.5 R. C. Elstner and E. Hognestad: Shearing Strength of Reinforced Concrete Slabs, *J. ACI*, July, 1956.

4.6 H. M. Westergaard: Stresses in Concrete Pavements Computed by Theoretical Analysis, Public Roads, April, 1926.

4.7 H. M. Westergaard: Analytical Tools for Judging Results of Structural Tests of Concrete Pavements, *Public Roads*, December, 1933.

4.8 P. Rice: Design of Concrete Floors on Ground for Warehouse Loading, *J. ACI*, August, 1957.

4.9 E. Hognestad: Yield-line Theory for the Ultimate Flexural Strength of Reinforced Concrete Slabs, *J. ACI*, March, 1953.

4.10 L. L. Jones: "Ultimate Load Analysis of Reinforced and Prestressed Concrete Structures," John Wiley & Sons, Inc., New York, 1962.

chapter **5**

COLUMNS: AXIAL COMPRESSION PLUS BENDING

5.1 Types of Columns Concrete compression members whose unsupported length is more than 3 times the least dimension of the cross section are classified as columns. Such members should not be built without reinforcement of some type. In modern construction four types of reinforced-concrete columns are used, namely:

1. Columns reinforced with longitudinal steel and closely spaced spirals
2. Columns reinforced with longitudinal steel and lateral ties
3. Composite columns, in which a structural-steel or cast-iron member is thoroughly encased in a concrete column of type 1
4. Combination columns, in which a structural-steel member is wrapped with wire and encased in at least 2½ in. of concrete over all metal except rivet heads

Types 1 and 2 are more generally used, types 3 and 4 being economical with heavy construction loads or extremely heavy permanent loads. Pipe columns, in which a steel pipe is filled with concrete, are sometimes used.

Apart from building columns, there are other structural members that are subject to axial compression, mostly combined with some amount of bending. Among these are arches, variously inclined legs of rigid frames, and compression members in trusses. Even though, for brevity, the term *column* will mostly be used in this chapter, its content applies equally to these other compression members.

For columns of types 1 and 2, above, the ACI Code provides the following *limiting dimensions:* Columns constituting the principal supports of a floor or roof shall have a diameter of at least 10 in. or, for rectangular columns, a least dimension of at least 8 in. and a gross area not less than 96 in. More detailed provisions are given for a number of special cases. It is also provided that the reinforcement ratio of the longitudinal steel shall be not less than 0.01 nor more than 0.08, that at least six bars shall be used for spiral columns and at least four for tied columns, and that the minimum size for longitudinal bars shall be No. 5.

5.2 Columns Reinforced with Ties or Spirals Lateral reinforcement, in the form of individual relatively widely spaced ties or a continuous closely spaced spiral, serves several functions. For one, such reinforcement is needed to hold the longitudinal bars in position in the forms while the concrete is being placed. For this purpose, longitudinal and transverse steel are wired together to form cages, which are then moved into the forms and properly positioned prior to placing of the concrete. For another, transverse reinforcement is needed to prevent the highly stressed, slender longitudinal bars from buckling outward by bursting the thin concrete cover.

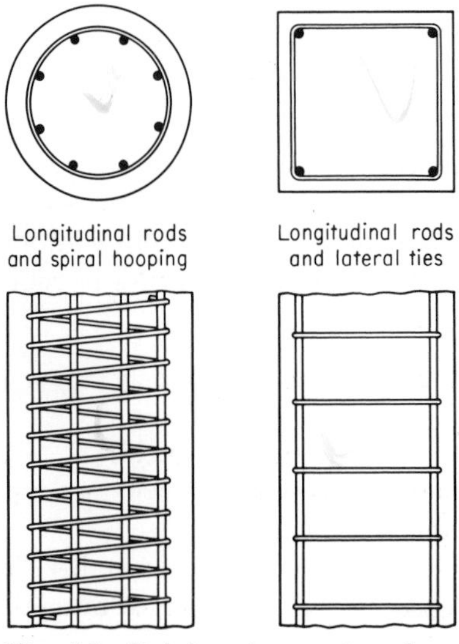

***Fig.* 5.1** Reinforced-concrete columns.

Closely spaced spirals evidently serve these two functions. Ties, which can be arranged and spaced in various ways, must be so designed that these two requirements are met. This means that the spacing must be sufficiently small to prevent buckling between ties and that, in any tie plane, a sufficient number of ties must be provided to position and hold all bars. On the

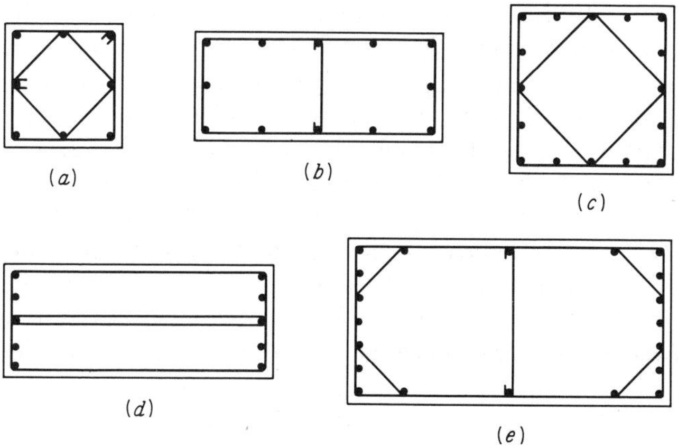

Fig. 5.2 Tie arrangements conforming to ACI Code.

other hand, in columns with many longitudinal bars, if the column section is crisscrossed by too many ties, they interfere with the placement of concrete in the forms. To achieve adequate tying, yet hold the number of ties to a minimum, the ACI Code gives the following rules for tie arrangement:

> All bars for tied columns shall be enclosed by lateral ties at least ¼ in. in diameter spaced apart not more than 16 bar diameters, 48 tie diameters, or the least dimension of the column. The ties shall be so arranged that every corner bar and alternate longitudinal bars shall have lateral support provided by the corner of a tie having an included angle of not more than 135°, and no bar shall be farther than 6 in. from such a laterally supported bar. Where the bars are located around the periphery of a circle, a complete circular tie may be used.

Fig. 5.2 shows some tie arrangements which satisfy these requirements.

Spirals, in contrast, are specified to be much more closely spaced than ties, no farther apart than 3 in. or one-sixth of the core diameter. The *core* is that part of the section located within the outer circumference of the spiral. In view of this close spacing, the presence of a spiral affects both the ultimate load and the type of failure as compared with an otherwise identical tied column.

The structural effect of a spiral is easily visualized by considering as a model a steel drum filled with sand (Fig. 5.3). When a load is placed on the sand, a lateral pressure is exerted by the sand on the drum, which causes hoop tension in the steel wall. The load on the sand can be increased until the hoop tension becomes large enough to burst the drum. The sand pile alone, if not confined in the drum, would have been able to support hardly any load. A cylindrical concrete column, to be sure, does have a definite strength without any lateral confinement. As it is being loaded, it shortens longitudinally and expands laterally, depending on Poisson's ratio. A closely spaced spiral confining the column counteracts the expansion, as did the steel drum in the model. This causes hoop tension in the spiral, while the carrying capacity of the confined concrete in the core is greatly increased. Failure occurs only when the spiral steel yields, which greatly reduces its confining effect, or when it fractures. It has been found that a given amount of steel per unit length of column, when in the form of a spiral, is at least twice as effective in adding to the carrying capacity as the same amount of steel used in the form of longitudinal bars.

A tied column fails at the load given by Eq. (2.5) as

$$P'_u = 0.85f'_cA_c + f_yA_s \tag{5.1}$$

At this load the concrete fails by crushing and shearing outward along inclined planes, and the longitudinal steel by buckling outward between ties (Fig. 5.4). In a spiral-reinforced column, when the same load is reached, the longitudinal steel and the concrete within the core are prevented from outward failing by the spiral. The concrete in the outer shell, however, not being so confined, does fail; i.e., the outer shell spalls off when the load P'_u is reached. It is at this stage that the confining action of the spiral takes effect, and, if sizable spiral steel is

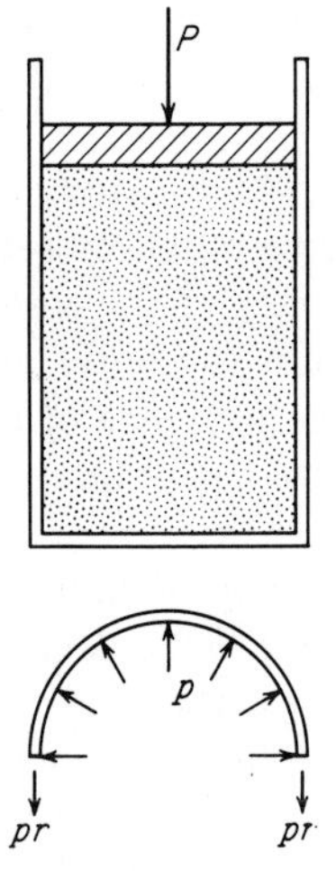

***Fig.* 5.3** Model for action of spiral.

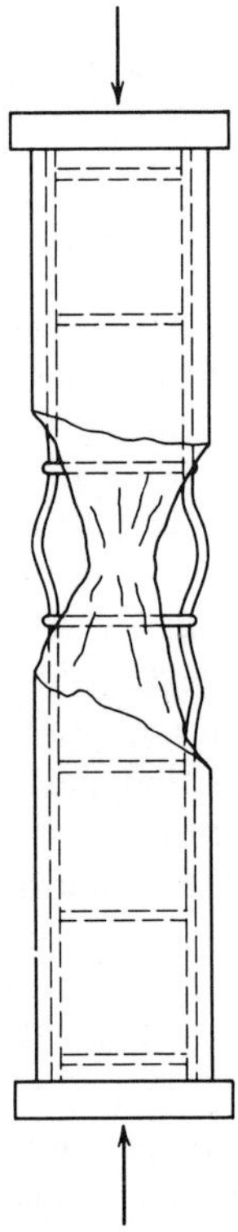

***Fig.* 5.4** Failure of tied column.

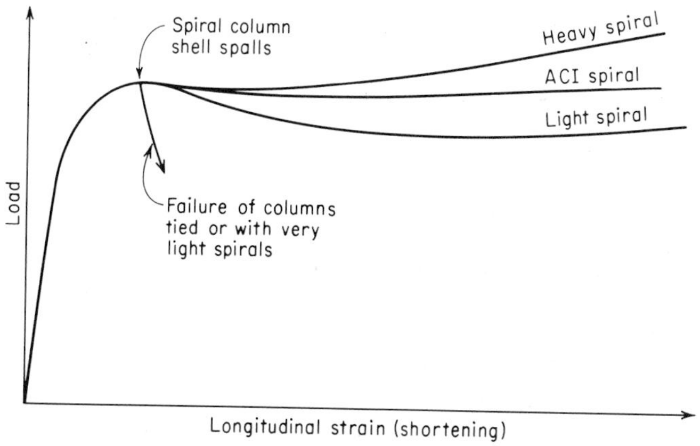

Fig. **5.5** Behavior of spiral and tied columns.

provided, the load which will ultimately fail the column by causing the spiral to yield or burst can be significantly larger than that at which the shell spalled off.

In contrast to the practice in some foreign countries, it is reasoned in American practice that any excess capacity beyond the spalling load of the shell is wasted because the member, although not actually failed, would no longer be considered serviceable. For this reason the Code provides a minimum spiral reinforcement of such amount that its contribution to the carrying capacity is just slightly larger than that of the concrete in the shell. The situation is best understood from Fig. 5.5, which compares the performance of a tied column with that of a spiral column whose spalling load is equal to the ultimate load of the tied column. The failure of the tied column is abrupt and complete. This is true, to almost the same degree, of a spiral column with a spiral so light that its strength contribution is considerably less than the strength lost in the spalled shell. With a heavy spiral the reverse is true, and, with considerable prior deformation, the spalled column would fail at a higher load. The "ACI spiral," its strength contribution about compensating for that lost in the spalled shell, hardly increases the ultimate load. However, by preventing instantaneous crushing of concrete and buckling of steel, it produces a more gradual and ductile failure, i.e., a tougher column.

To determine the right amount of spiral steel, one calculates:

$$\text{Strength contribution of shell} = 0.85f'_c(A_g - A_c) \qquad (a)$$

where A_g and A_c are, respectively, the gross and core concrete areas. On the other hand, since spiral steel is at least twice as effective as longitudinal steel, one has conservatively

$$\text{Strength contribution of spiral} = 2p_sA_cf_{sy} \qquad (b)$$

Here f_{sy} is the spiral yield strength, and p_s is the ratio of volume of spiral reinforcement to volume of core, per unit length of column. Equating (*a*) to (*b*) and solving for the spiral ratio,

$$p_s = 0.425 \frac{(A_g - A_c)f'_c}{A_c f_{sy}} \tag{c}$$

The ACI Code stipulates the minimum spiral ratio as

$$p_s = 0.45 \frac{(A_g/A_c - 1)f'_c}{f_{sy}} \tag{5.2}$$

spiral ratio

which is seen to be but slightly larger than (*c*).

It follows that, when designed to the Code, two concentrically loaded columns, one tied and one with spiral but otherwise identical, will fail at about the same load, the former in a sudden and brittle manner, the latter gradually with prior shell spalling and with more ductile behavior. This advantage of the spiral column is much less pronounced if the load is applied with significant eccentricity or when bending from other sources is present simultaneously with axial load. For this reason the Code permits somewhat larger loads on spiral than on tied columns when loaded concentrically or with small eccentricities but reduces this difference for large eccentricities.

ULTIMATE - STRENGTH DESIGN: COMPRESSION PLUS BENDING

5.3 Safety Provisions It was pointed out in Art. 3.7 that in ultimate-strength design adequate safety margins are established by applying overload factors to the design loads and strength-reduction factors to the theoretical ultimate strengths computed for members assumed to be perfect in workmanship and made of materials having exactly the specified strength. It was pointed out that the overload factors apply uniformly, while the strength-reduction factors are different for differently stressed members.

For columns in particular, i.e., for members subject to compression plus bending, the Code provides reduction factors

For tied members: $\phi = 0.70$
For spirally reinforced members: $\phi = 0.75$

The spread between these two values reflects the added safety furnished by the greater toughness of spirally reinforced columns.

There are various reasons why these coefficients are considerably lower than those for flexure or shear (0.90 and 0.85, respectively). For one, the strength of underreinforced flexural members is not much affected by variations in concrete strength, since it depends primarily on the yield strength of the steel, while the strength of axially loaded members depends strongly on the concrete compression strength [compare, e.g., Eqs. (2.5) and (2.27*a*)]. Because the cylinder strength of concrete under site conditions is less closely controlled than the yield strength of mill-produced steel, a larger occasional strength deficiency must be allowed for. This is particularly true for columns, in which concrete, being placed from the top down the long, narrow form, is more subject to segregation than in horizontally cast beams. Moreover, electrical and other conduits are frequently located in building columns; this reduces their effective cross sections, often unbeknown to the designer, even though this is poor practice and restricted by the Code. Finally, the consequences of a column failure, say in a lower story, would be more catastrophic than of that of a single beam in a floor system of the same building.

Correspondingly, then, the ultimate-strength values to be used for design are

$$P_u = \phi P'_u \tag{5.3a}$$
$$M_u = \phi M'_u \tag{5.3b}$$

where P'_u and M'_u are those simultaneous values of ultimate axial force and ultimate bending moment which are calculated to cause the "perfect" member to fail (see Art. 2.8*b*).

Additionally, the Code recognizes that no members are likely to be found which are purely axially loaded. Even if design calculations show a compression member to be free of any bending moments, imperfections of construction, such as slight beam eccentricities and deviations from straightness or verticality, will cause some unintentional bending moments. For this reason the Code specifies that the minimum load eccentricity for which a compression member must be designed is

For tied members: $e_{\min} = 0.10t$
For spirally reinforced members: $e_{\min} = 0.05t$

where t is the overall depth of a rectangular section or the outside diameter of a circular section, and $e = M/P$ is the eccentricity referred to the center line of the column. The difference between these values, again, represents a recognition of the greater toughness of spirally reinforced columns with zero or small eccentricities. Evidently, if structural analysis shows eccentricities e to be present which exceed the minimums, these larger design eccentricities must be used in dimensioning the member.

5.4 Rectangular Columns For a rectangular column reinforced by A_s and A'_s along the two faces parallel to the axis of bending, it was shown in Eqs. (2.45) and (2.46) that

$$P'_u = \frac{P_u}{\phi} = 0.85f'_c ab + A'_s f'_y - A_s f_s \tag{5.4}$$

$$P'_u e' = \frac{P_u e'}{\phi} = 0.85f'_c ab\left(d - \frac{a}{2}\right) + A'_s f'_y (d - d') \tag{5.5}$$

where the eccentricity e' in Eq. (5.5) is referred to the center of the tension steel. These equations hold for all but very small eccentricities; they assume that the steel A_s on the convex side will be in tension and that only part of the concrete section is in compression (see Fig. 2.31). For very small centroidal eccentricities e, the distance to the neutral axis $c = a/k_1$ may exceed the depth t of the section. Then the entire cross-sectional area will be in compression, so that the stress in the steel A_s will also be compressive, though of magnitude smaller than f'_y. The corresponding distribution of strains and stresses is shown in Fig. 5.6. The stress distribution of Fig. 5.6*b*, which corresponds to the strain distribution of Fig. 5.6*c*, is approximated for purposes of calculation by the rectangular stress distribution of Fig. 5.6*d*. Summing forces, as well as moments, about the steel A_s, it is seen that

$$P'_u = \frac{P_u}{\phi} = 0.85f'_c bt + A'_s f'_y + A_s f_s \tag{5.4a}$$

$$P'_u e' = \frac{P_u e'}{\phi} = 0.85f'_c bt\left(d - \frac{t}{2}\right) + A'_s f'_y (d - d') \tag{5.5a}$$

If, now, the centroidal eccentricity e is reduced to zero, i.e., the column is loaded in concentric compression, then the strains of concrete and steel

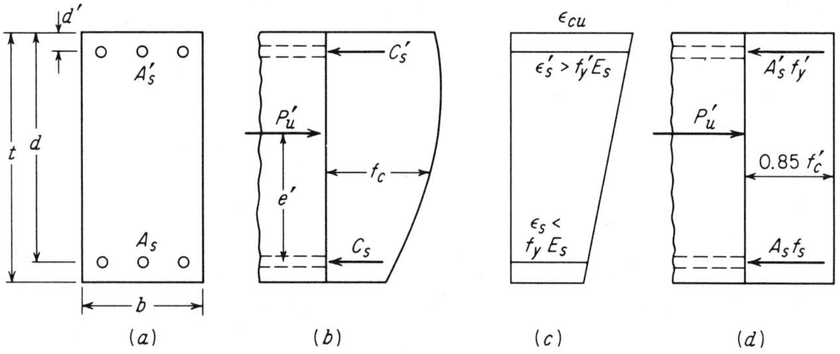

Fig. 5.6 Stresses and strains in eccentric column at failure.

are the same everywhere. Assuming that the yield point of all steel in the section is the same, Eq. (5.4*a*) becomes

$$P'_0 = 0.85f'_c bt + A'_s f'_y + A_s f_y = 0.85f'_c A_c + A_{st} f_y \quad (5.6)$$

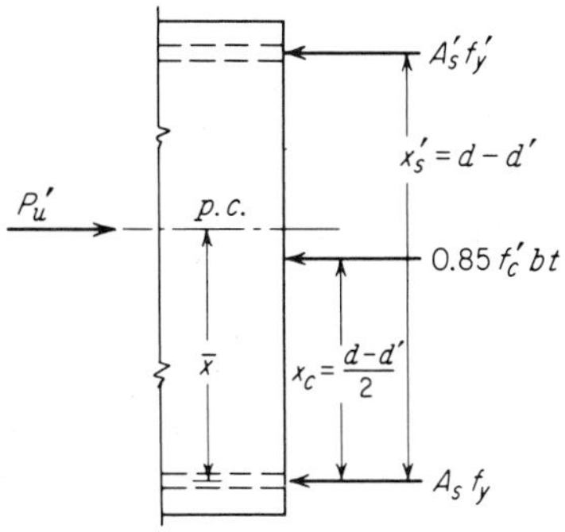

Fig. 5.7 Axis through plastic centroid.

Here A_{st} is the total steel area in the section. It is seen that the ultimate load for an axially loaded column (that is, $M = 0$), computed as the limiting case of an eccentrically loaded member, is identical with Eq. (2.5), which was derived for concentric compression and is supported by extensive tests on axially loaded members.

[It should be noted that a concentrically loaded member is one whose eccentricity e about the axis of the cross section is zero. This eccentricity is different from e', used in Eqs. (5.5) and elsewhere, which is measured from the center of the steel A_s. For symmetrically reinforced sections the member is concentrically loaded when the load passes through the center of the section. For an unsymmetrically reinforced section, with $A'_s \neq A_s$, to be concentrically loaded so that Eq. (5.6) is true, the load must pass through a point known as the *plastic centroid*. This point is the location of the resultant of the three internal forces that make up Eq. (5.6). Its distance from the steel A_s can be found from Fig. 5.7 as

$$\bar{x} = \frac{0.85f'_c btx_c + A'_s f'_y x'_s}{0.85f'_c bt + A'_s f'_y + A_s f_y}$$

Evidently, for reasons of equilibrium the external load P must act along the same line as the resultant of all internal forces, i.e., must pass through the plastic centroid. In a symmetrical section the center and the plastic centroid coincide.]

The other limiting case of a member in combined compression plus bending is the situation in which the compression force has become zero, so that bending alone is present. It can be shown, as for the other extreme, that in this case (that is, $P = 0$) the general equations for compression plus bending result in an ultimate bending moment M'_0 equal to that of a simple flexural member with tension reinforcement A_s and compression reinforcement A'_s (see Art. 3.9).

a. Interaction diagram for compression plus bending The information of Art. 2.8, supplemented by the above discussion, shows the considerable complexity of behavior and of corresponding strength calculations for eccentrically loaded members. This behavior ranges

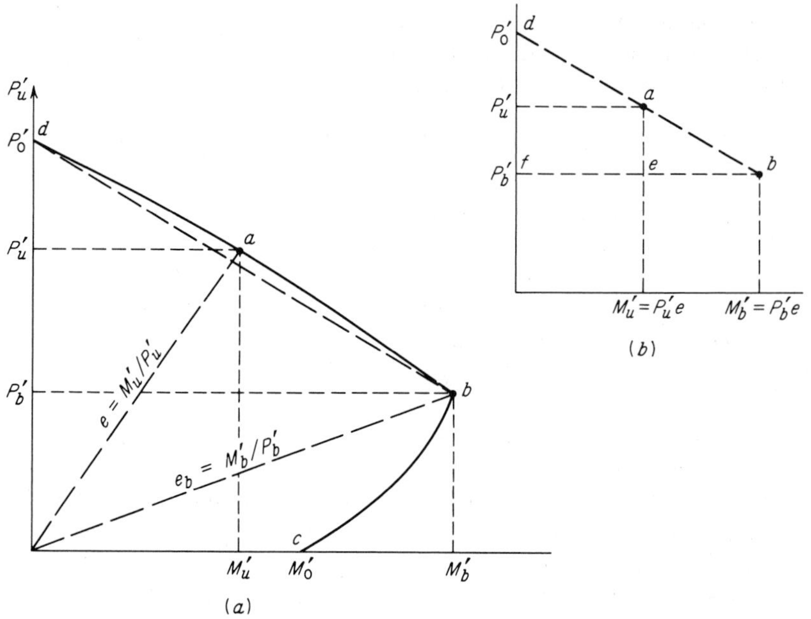

Fig. 5.8 Interaction diagram, compression plus bending, ultimate-strength P'_u and M'_u.

from concentric compression ($P = P'_0$, $M = 0$), over the interval in which failure occurs by crushing of the concrete, through the balanced condition and the interval in which failure occurs by yielding of the steel, to the other extreme of simple bending ($M = M'_0$, $P = 0$). The situation is more easily visualized if the results of the corresponding calculations are graphically depicted in a so-called *interaction diagram.*

For a given cross section and reinforcement, an interaction diagram has the general shape of Fig. 5.8*a*, plotted in terms of ultimate axial loads as ordinates and ultimate moments as abscissas. Moments and eccentricities are here referred to the plastic centroid (for symmetrical sections to the center line of the member), rather than to the center of the tension steel. Any point on the solid curve, such as point *a*, represents a pair of values P'_u and M'_u which, according to the ultimate-strength theory, will just fail the member.

For concentric compression ($M'_u = 0$) the curve starts at *d* with the strength P'_0 of a concentrically loaded member [Eq. (5.6)]. The portion *db* pertains to that range of small eccentricities in which failure is initiated by crushing of the concrete; the corresponding computations were discussed in Art. 2.8*b*. Point *b* represents the balanced condition; i.e., under the simultaneous action of the load P'_b [see Eq. (2.51)] and the corresponding moment M'_b, the concrete will reach its limiting strain (0.003) simultaneously with the tension steel reaching its yield stress f_y. The portion *bc* represents that range in which failure is initiated by yielding of the tension steel (see Art. 2.8*b*). Finally, the end point *c* refers to the moment capacity M'_0 in simple bending, i.e., when $P'_u = 0$. Any inclined line through the origin has a slope whose reciprocal represents the centroidal eccentricity corresponding to the particular combination of ultimate values P'_u and M'_u as shown; that is, $e = M'_u/P'_u$.

It will be observed that in the region *bd* of compression failure, the larger the axial load P'_u, the smaller is the moment M'_u which the section is able to sustain before failing. However, in the region *bc* of tension failures the reverse is true: the larger the axial load, the larger is the simultaneous moment capacity. This is easily understood. In region *bd* failure occurs through overstraining of the concrete. The larger the concrete compression strain caused by the axial load alone, the smaller is the margin of additional strain which can be utilized for the added compression caused by bending. On the other hand, in region *bc* yielding of the steel initiates failure. If a member is loaded in simple bending to the point at which yielding begins in the tension steel, and if an axial compression load is then added, the steel compression stresses caused by this load will superpose on the previous tension stresses. This reduces the total steel stress to a value below the yield strength. Consequently, an additional moment can now be sustained of such magnitude that the combination of the steel stress from the axial load and the increased moment again reaches the yield strength.

b. Design simplifications and Code requirements The lengthy trial-and-error procedures connected with explicit calculations of the strength of eccentrically compressed members call for simplified methods to expedite design. One of these is contained in the ACI Code directly. It consists in replacing the slightly curved line *bd* which covers the compression-failure range with the dashed straight line. This approximation is seen to be on the conservative side, the deviations being quite slight in all but very unusual cases.

In Fig. 5.8*b* this straight line is shown again. From the similarity of the triangles *abe* and *dbf*, the following relations are easily derived:

$$P'_u = \frac{P'_o}{1 + (P'_0/P'_b - 1)e/e_b} \tag{5.7}$$

or, alternatively,

$$P'_u = P'_0 - \frac{(P'_0 - P'_b)M'_u}{M'_b} \tag{5.8}$$

where P'_0 is given by Eq. (5.6), and, for symmetrical reinforcement, P'_b was derived in Eq. (2.51). A general expression for the balanced design

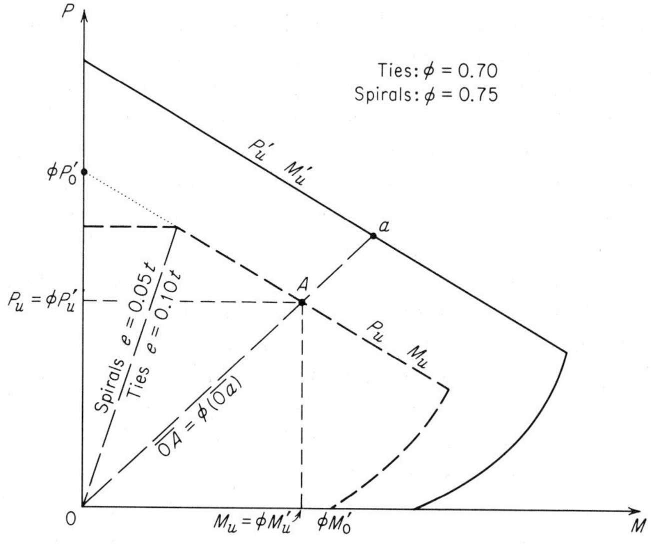

***Fig.* 5.9** Interaction diagram, design values P_u and M_u by ACI Code.

moment $M_b = \phi M'_b$ can be found as Eq. (19-3) in the Code. For the balanced eccentricity e_b, for symmetrically reinforced rectangular sections, J. G. MacGregor has derived the following approximate expression:

$$e_b = (0.20 + 0.77p_t m)t \tag{5.9}$$

where $p_t = (A_s + A'_s)/bt$
$m = f_y/0.85f'_c$

The *safety provisions of the Code*, as was mentioned in Art. 5.3, include the requirement that the design ultimate load and moment, P_u and M_u, respectively, be obtained by multiplying the calculated strength values P'_u and M'_u by the capacity reduction factor $\phi = 0.70$ [see Eqs. (5.3)]. They also provide that tied columns shall be designed for a minimum eccentricity $e_{\min} = 0.10t$. The effect of these provisions is shown in Fig. 5.9, where the solid line of Fig. 5.8 has been redrawn, indicating the calculated ultimate-strength relations and using the simplifying straight-line *bd*. The dashed curve, which indicates the design ultimate strength according to the Code, is obtained by reducing the length of any radial line Oa by $\phi = 0.70$ to obtain the corresponding length OA. The figure also indicates the stipulated minimum eccentricity $e_{\min} = 0.10t$. The Code, as was mentioned before, stipulates that tied columns with design eccentricities smaller than $e_{\min}$ be dimensioned for this minimum eccentricity.

c. *Design aids* In order to reduce the repetitive effort of dimensioning large numbers of columns, such as occur in any tier building frame, a number of design aids are available in the form of tables or graphs. They are available in handbooks or special pamphlets published by the American Concrete Institute, the Concrete Reinforcing Steel Institute, and the Portland Cement Association. They cover the most common practical cases, i.e., symmetrically reinforced, rectangular tied columns and spirally reinforced, circular and square columns. For other situations the methods of Art. 2.8 and this chapter furnish the necessary principles for direct analysis.

Graphs 2 through 5 of Appendix B represent a set of such design aids for symmetrically reinforced tied columns. They are somewhat approximate in that they have been calculated on the assumption that the compression reinforcement has yielded when ultimate strength is reached. As has been discussed in Art. 2.8, this is not always the case, but is easily verified by a separate calculation. The graphs are seen to consist of interaction diagrams of the type just described. However, instead of plots of P'_u versus M'_u, convenient nondimensional parameters have been selected (P'_u/btf'_c versus $M'_u/bt^2f'_c$) which, taken in conjunction with the radial lines for various e/t ratios and the interaction curves drawn for various values of p_tm, expedite the dimensioning or analysis of sections. The use of these graphs and associated calculations is illustrated in the following examples.

Example 1 A column is to be designed for 28 kips dead load, 36 kips live load, a moment from dead load of 43.7 ft-kips, and a moment from live load of 37.5 ft-kips; $f'_c = 3000$ psi, and $f_y = 40{,}000$ psi. Design the column.

According to the safety provisions of the ACI Code, the column must be designed for $P_u = 1.5 \times 28 + 1.8 \times 36 = 106.7$ kips and $M_u = 1.5 \times 43.7 + 1.8 \times 37.5 = 133.2$ ft-kips.

A cross section 12 × 20 in. will be tried, using the graphs for the design. According to the Code, the required ultimate load and moment are $P'_u = P_u/\phi = 106.7/0.70 = 152$ kips and $M'_u = M_u/\phi = 133.2/0.70 = 191.0$ ft-kips. For the selected column size, $e/t = (191.0 \times 12)/(152 \times 20) = 0.75$. To select the correct graph, with 2.5 in. from face to bar center for adequate cover over the stirrups, calculate $d/t = 17.5/20 = 0.875$; hence, it is necessary to interpolate between Graphs 3 and 4. To enter the graphs, calculate $K = 152{,}000/12 \times 20 \times 3000 = 0.21$, and $Ke/t = 0.21 \times 0.75 = 0.157$. Interpolating between the two graphs, one finds $p_tm = 0.23$. Since $p_t = A_s/bt$ and $m = f_y/0.85f'_c$, $A_s = 0.23 \times 12 \times 20(0.85 \times 3000/40{,}000) = 3.52$ in.². Four No. 9 bars with an area of 4 in.² are selected, one in each corner.

The column has now been designed for the maximum simultaneous values of axial load and moment caused by dead and live load. From the shape of the curves of Graphs 3 and 4, it is evident that if axial load on this column is reduced, its moment capacity will decrease. Consequently, it is generally necessary to check the adequacy for at least one more case of loading, namely that which combines a large moment with a small axial force. At the bottom section of an interior building column, simultaneous maximum moment and maximum load is generally obtained if all floors above that section are fully loaded by dead and live load and only one of the two abutting girders is under live load; this produces maximum joint moment. The other case to be checked is obtained by assuming dead load only on all overlying floors (giving minimal axial load) and again placing live load on one of the two abutting girders to obtain a maximum joint moment.

Example 2 The same column is made of concrete with $f'_c = 5000$ psi and reinforced with steel of $f_y = 75{,}000$ psi. If, as before, the eccentricity about the column axis is $e = 0.75t = 0.75 \times 20 = 15$ in., calculate the design load of the column. (The ACI Code stipulates that steel with yield point in excess of 60 ksi shall be used with a design yield stress equal to 85 per cent of the specified yield stress unless tests show that at the specified yield stress the strain does not exceed 0.003. This is required in order to assure that the concrete will not crush at a strain lower than that at which compression reinforcement begins to yield. It is here assumed that this test requirement has been met. The Code also stipulates safeguards against excessive cracking when high-strength tension reinforcement is used. This requirement is generally more critical for flexural members than for columns.)

To enter the graphs, calculate $p_t m = [4/(12 \times 20)](75{,}000/0.85 \times 5000) = 0.295$. With this value, and with $e/t = 0.75$, interpolating between Graphs 3 and 4, one finds $K = 0.245$. Therefore, the calculated ultimate load is $P'_u = 0.245 \times 12 \times 20 \times 5000 = 294{,}000$ lb, and the ultimate load to be used in design is $P_u = \phi P'_u = 0.70 \times 294{,}000 = 206{,}000$ lb.

From the graphs it is seen that the point representing $K = 0.245$ lies on the lower, curved portion of the $p_t m = 0.295$ curve. From the discussion of Fig. 5.8, it follows that, for the particular loading, failure of this column is initiated by yielding of the tension steel. As has been pointed out, Eq. (2.53), the more elaborate formulas of the Code, and Graphs 2 to 5 are all based on the assumption that in this case the compression steel too has yielded at failure. This should be verified, particularly when, as here, high-strength steel is used.

With reference to Fig. 2.32, which shows a column of the same cross section, if both compression and tension steel are yielding, $P'_u = A'_s f_y - A_s f_y + abf'_c = abf'_c$. From this, the depth of the rectangular stress block is found to be $a = P'_u/bf'_c = 294{,}000/12 \times 5000 = 4.9$ in., and the depth to the neutral axis $c = a/k_1$. For the high-strength concrete used, according to Eq. (2.31), $k_1 = 0.80$, so that $c = 4.9/0.80 = 6.1$ in. At failure the extreme fiber strain of the concrete is assumed to be 0.003, so that from Fig. 2.32*c* the strain in the compression steel is $\epsilon'_s = 0.003(c - 2.5)/c = 0.00167$. On the other hand, the yield strain of the given steel is $\epsilon_y = f_y/E = 75/29{,}000 = 0.00258$. This being larger than ϵ'_s, it is seen that at failure the compression steel is not stressed to the yield point, and the previous calculation is not strictly correct.

For a recalculation, assume by trial that $c = 6.4$ in. (The compression steel force being smaller than would be the case if the steel were yielding, the concrete has to supply a larger compression force than before; this is the reason for assuming a larger c than was found above.) Then $f'_s = 0.003(3.9/6.4)29{,}000{,}000 =$ 53,000 psi, and $P'_u = -A_s f_y + A'_s f_s + abf'_c$; with $a = 0.8 \times 6.4 = 5.12$, $P'_u =$ $-2.0 \times 75{,}000 + 2.0 \times 53{,}000 + 5.2 \times 12 \times 5000 = 268{,}000$ lb. If the assumed value for c is correct, then equilibrium requires that the moment of the external force P'_u about the tension steel must be equal to the moment of the internal forces. Hence $M_{ext} = 268{,}000(15.0 + 7.5) = 6{,}040{,}000$ in.-lb, and $M_{int} =$ $A'_s f'_s(d - d') + abf'_c(d - a/2) = 6{,}180{,}000$ in.-lb. It is seen that the difference between external and internal moments is 140,000 in.-lb or 2.3 per cent, an error sufficiently small to be neglected. Consequently, with $P'_u = 266{,}000$, the ultimate load to be used in design is $P_u = 0.7 \times 268{,}000 = 188{,}000$ lb. This compares with the value of 206,000 lb which was calculated from the graphs on the mistaken assumption that the compression steel has yielded at failure. For larger steel ratios than used in this column, errors would be correspondingly larger. This illustrates the special care which must be taken in design when high-strength steel is used for compression reinforcement.

In Example 1 the same column, with moderate-strength materials, was found to have a design ultimate load of 107,000 lb. Compare this with 188,000 lb when high-strength materials are used; the advantage of the latter in increasing carrying capacity, or in reducing member size for a given design load, is immediately evident.

d. Member with small axial load, tension reinforced The majority of columns are symmetrical and symmetrically reinforced. Unsymmetrical members do occur, however. For these, design aids are not usually available, but they can be handled without difficulty by using the basic premises of ultimate-strength design. By way of example, in single-story rigid frames, such as portal frames, large bending moments often combine with relatively small axial loads. In such cases unsymmetrical reinforcement frequently presents the most economical solution. For illustration such a member, reinforced for tension only, is analyzed herein.

For a member with tension reinforcement only, subject to a compression force with an eccentricity e' relative to the center of the tension steel, the ACI Code gives the equation

$$P_u = \phi P'_u = \phi 0.85 f'_c bd \left[-pm + 1 - \frac{e'}{d} + \sqrt{\left(1 - \frac{e'}{d}\right)^2 + \frac{e'pm}{d}} \right]$$

when failure is initiated by yielding of the tension steel. This formula can be derived from Eqs. (2.45) and (2.46) for the special case of $A'_s = 0$ in precisely the same way as Eq. (2.53) was derived for the special case of $A_s f_y = A'_s f'_y$. Whether to use the formula or direct analysis from general principles is a matter of individual preference.

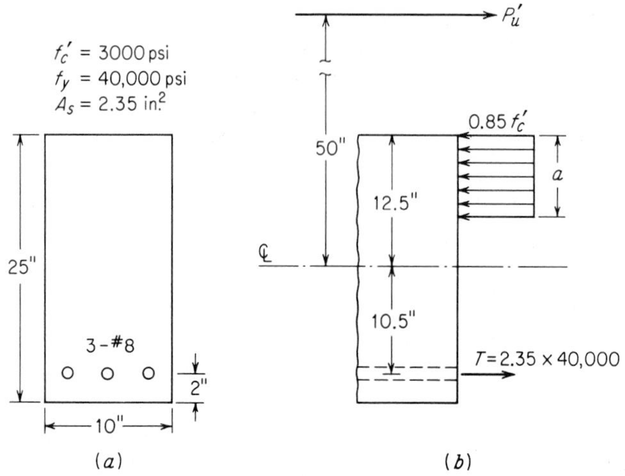

Fig. **5.10**

Example The member shown in Fig. 5.10 is subject to a compression force with eccentricity from the center line of $e = 50$ in. Determine the ultimate design load and moment.

With external and internal forces as shown, the two equilibrium equations are written as follows: Taking moments about the center of the steel,

$$P'_u(50 + 10.5) = a \times 10 \times 0.85 \times 3000 \left(23 - \frac{a}{2}\right)$$

and equating internal and external axial forces,

$$P'_u = a \times 10 \times 0.85 \times 3000 - 2.35 \times 40{,}000$$

These two simultaneous equations are solved either explicitly or by successive approximation (assuming a value of a and correcting). They give $a = 5.55$ in., $P'_u = 48{,}000$ lb, and, consequently, $M'_u = 50 \times 48{,}000 = 2{,}400{,}000$ in.-lb. According to the ACI Code, the ultimate values to be used in design are $P_u = 0.70 \times 48{,}000 = 33{,}600$ lb and $M_u = 0.70 \times 2{,}400{,}000 = 1{,}680{,}000$ in.-lb.

The same member, if subject to bending without axial force, would have an ultimate moment of $M'_u = 1{,}985{,}000$ in.-lb (see the example of Art. 2.8*f*). Comparison with $M'_u = 2{,}400{,}000$ in.-lb as calculated above illustrates the fact, discussed previously, that, for flexural members failing in tension, the presence of an axial compression force increases the moment capacity. On this flexural member without axial load, the ultimate moment to be used in design would be

$$M_u = 0.90 \times 1{,}985{,}000 = 1{,}785{,}000 \text{ in.-lb}$$

according to the Code. It is seen that the difference in ϕ values for members in bending and for members in bending plus axial load here leads to a lack of consistency; namely, the ultimate moment M_u to be used for design of the latter (that is, 1,680,000 in.-lb) is seen to be smaller than that for the former (that is, 1,785,000 in.-lb), in spite of the fact that the situation for the actual ultimate moments M_u' is exactly the reverse. *To avoid this inconsistency, the ACI Code permits, for members subject to bending plus small axial loads, the larger of the two moments* M_u *to be used, either the one calculated for simultaneous bending plus axial load, or the one calculated for flexure only* [see Art. 1901(*c*) of the Code]. For the case at hand, then, the design values are $P_u = 33{,}600$ lb and $M_u = 1{,}785{,}000$ in.-lb.

e. Contribution of intermediate bars When large bending moments are present, it is most economical to concentrate all or most of the steel along the two outer faces parallel to the axis of bending. Such arrangements are shown in Fig. 5.2*d* and *e*. On the other hand, when axial compression is prevalent and, particularly when a small cross section is desired, it is advantageous to place the steel more uniformly around the perimeter, as in Fig. 5.2*a* to *c*. In this case special attention must be paid to the intermediate bars, i.e., those which are not placed along the two most highly stressed faces. This is so because, when the ultimate-load condition is reached, the stresses in these intermediate bars are frequently below the yield point, even though the bars along either one or both extreme faces may be yielding. To analyze this situation, the distribution of strains over the cross section must be considered, as is illustrated below.

Example The column of Fig. 5.11*a* is loaded eccentrically, with $e = 17.0$ in.; $f_c' = 3.0$ ksi, and $f_y = 60.0$ ksi. Determine the magnitude of the ultimate load.

Trial calculation suggests that the neutral axis is located 13 to 15 in. from the compression edge. A value of $c = 14$ in. is tentatively selected. At the instant the concrete reaches its assumed failure strain of 0.003, the strain distribution is as shown in Fig. 5.11*b*. The strains at the locations of the individual bars are easily found from similar triangles and are shown on the figure.

The yield strain corresponding to the yield point of 60 ksi is $\epsilon_y = 60/29{,}000 = 0.00207$. By comparison of this value with the strains of the individual bar groups, it is seen that the exterior bar groups 1 and 4 have strains exceeding ϵ_y; that is, these bars will yield at failure. On the other hand, interior bar groups 2 and 3 show strains considerably less than ϵ_y. The stresses in these bars at ultimate load can be computed by multiplying their strains by E_s. Thus $f_{s2} = 0.0097 \times 29{,}000 = 28.2$ ksi, and $f_{s3} = 0.00054 \times 29{,}000 = 15.7$ ksi. From the assumed value of c, one finds $a = 0.85 \times 14.0 = 11.9$ in. From Fig. 5.11*c* it will be noted that bar groups 1 and 4, being stressed to the yield point, contribute equal and opposite forces which cancel. Hence

$$P_u' = 0.85f_c'ab + f_{s2}A_{s2} + f_{s3}A_{s3}$$
$$= 0.85 \times 3 \times 11.9 \times 12 + 28.2 \times 2.0 - 15.7 \times 2.0 = 389 \text{ kips}$$

The moment of all internal forces about the center line is

$$M_u' = 7.05(0.85f_c'ab) + 10.5f_yA_{s1} + 3.5f_{s2}A_{s2} + 3.5f_{s3}A_{s3} + 10.5f_yA_{s4}$$

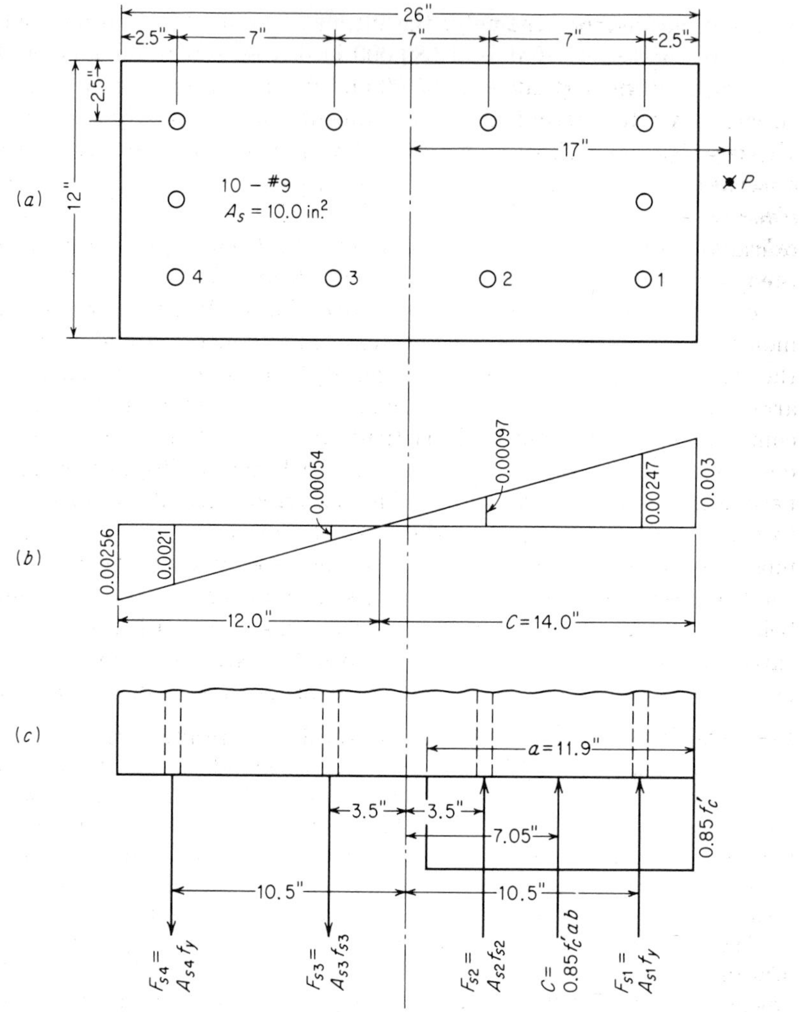

Fig. 5.11

which, upon substitution of the appropriate numbers, gives

$$M'_u = 6{,}650 \text{ in.-kips}$$

Consequently,

$$e = 6{,}650/389 = 17.1 \text{ in.}$$

This value of the eccentricity differs from the given value $e = 17.0$ in. by less than 1 per cent, indicating that the assumed value of $c = 14$ in. is satisfactory, and no further approximation is needed.

f. Rectangular columns in biaxial bending The methods discussed permit rectangular columns to be designed or analyzed if bending is present about only one of the two principal axes of the section. This situation obtains in the majority of structures. There are other situations, however, and they are by no means exceptional, in which axial compression is accompanied by simultaneous bending about both principal axes of the section. Such is the case, for instance, in corner columns of tier buildings, where beams and girders frame into the column in the directions of both walls and transfer their end moments into the column in two perpendicular planes. Similar situations can occur with respect to interior columns, particularly in irregular column layouts, and in a variety of other structures.

Figure 5.12 shows a rectangular section under the simultaneous action of a concentric load P and biaxial bending by the moments M_x and M_y. The resulting action is the same as when the load P is applied with eccentricities

$$e_x = \frac{M_x}{P} \qquad \text{and} \qquad e_y = \frac{M_y}{P}$$

about the centroidal x and y axes, respectively, as shown. It is possible to calculate the ultimate load of such a biaxially eccentric column on the basis of the general propositions of ultimate-strength design that have been utilized in all other situations (rectangular equivalent stress block of depth k_1c, ultimate concrete strain $e_u = 0.003$, etc.). The pertinent methods, which are developed in Ref. 5.1, are important as research tools but are cumbersome and not suited to design use.

An approximate design method has been developed by Boris Bresler (Ref. 5.2) and has been satisfactorily verified by comparison with a limited number of test results and with results of extensive computations similar to those in Ref. 5.1.

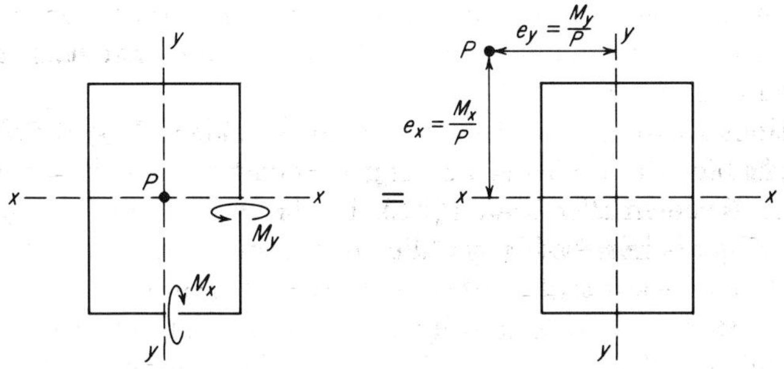

Fig. 5.12 Biaxial bending plus compression.

Bresler's equation can be written in the form of an interaction formula, namely,

$$\frac{P'_u}{P'_x} + \frac{P'_u}{P'_y} - \frac{P'_u}{P'_0} = 1 \qquad (5.10)$$

where P'_u = ultimate load for biaxial bending with eccentricities e_x and e_y
P'_x = ultimate load when only eccentricity e_x is present ($e_y = 0$)
P'_y = ultimate load when only eccentricity e_y is present ($e_x = 0$)
P'_0 = ultimate load for concentrically loaded column, Eq. (5.6) ($e_x = e_y = 0$)

The nature of this equation is easily illustrated. If, for instance, it were applied in the limit to a column bent only about the x axis, then e_y would equal zero; therefore P'_y would equal P'_0 by the definition of P'_y. If $P'_y = P'_0$ is substituted in Eq. (5.10), one finds $P'_u = P'_x$, as one should. That is, when bending is present in one direction only, the equation gives the correct answer to the effect that the ultimate load is that for uniaxial bending in the particular direction. For another example, assume that $P'_u/P'_0 = 0.20$. This means that the eccentricities are relatively large, so that the ultimate load is a small fraction of that for the concentric column. Assume further that $P'_u/P'_y = 0.40$. Substitution in Eq. (5.10) gives $P'_u/P'_x = 0.80$. That is, the simultaneous bending about the y axis has reduced the ultimate load of this column by 20 per cent as compared to what it would have been had bending been present about the x axis only.

For use in design, the equation can be written in the alternative form

$$\frac{1}{P'_u} = \frac{1}{P'_x} + \frac{1}{P'_y} - \frac{1}{P'_0} \qquad (5.10a)$$

which is used as follows:

Given the size and reinforcement of the column and the load eccentricities e_x and e_y, one computes, by the methods of the preceding sections, the ultimate loads P'_x and P'_y for uniaxial bending about the x and y axes, respectively, and the ultimate load P'_0 for concentric loading. Then Eq. (5.10*a*) permits one to compute $1/P'_u$ and, therefrom, the calculated ultimate load P'_u for biaxial bending. The design ultimate load, as usual, is obtained from $P_u = \phi P'_u$.

Equations (5.10) and (5.10*a*) are valid provided $P'_u \geq 0.10P'_0$. They are not reliable where biaxial bending is prevalent and is accompanied by an axial force smaller than $P'_0/10$. In the case of strongly prevalent bending, failure is initiated by yielding of the steel, and the situation corresponds to the lowest tenth of the interaction diagram of Fig. 5.8. In this range it is safe and satisfactorily accurate to neglect the axial force entirely and to calculate the section for biaxial bending only (see Art. 5.4*d*). This is so because, as was discussed before and as is evident from the shape of the interaction diagram, in the region of tension failure the addition of axial load increases the moment capacity, i.e., contributes to safety. If this contribution is neglected to simplify calculations, the result is on the conservative side.

Example Given the column of Example 2, Art. 5.4. In addition to the eccentricity about the x axis, $e_x = 0.75t_x = 0.75 \times 20 = 15$ in., there is an eccentricity about the y axis, $e_y = 3$ in. Calculate the design load for this column.

From Example 2, $f'_c = 5000$ psi, $f_y = 75{,}000$ psi, $p_t m = 0.295$, and $P'_x = 268$ kips. With $e_y/t_y = 3/12 = 0.295$, interpolation between Graphs 3 and 4 gives $K = 0.635$. Therefore $P'_y = 0.635 \times 12 \times 20 \times 5 = 562$ kips, $P'_0 = 0.85f'_c bt + A_{st}f_y = 0.85 \times 5 \times 12 \times 20 + 4 \times 75 = 1320$ kips, and, from Eq. (5.10*a*),

$$P'_u\left(\frac{1}{P'_x} + \frac{1}{P'_y} - \frac{1}{P'_c}\right) = 1$$

Substituting

$$P'_u(1/268 + 1/562 - 1/1320) = 1$$

gives

$$P'_u = 234 \text{ kips}$$

and the ultimate strength to be used in design, in connection with biaxial eccentricities of the stipulated amounts, is

$$P_u = \phi P'_u = 0.70 \times 234 = 164 \text{ kips}$$

This compares with $P_u = 188$ kips found in Example 2 for $e_y = 0$.

5.5 Circular Columns, Spiral Reinforced It was mentioned in Art. 5.2 that spiral-reinforced columns, when load eccentricities are small, show greater toughness, i.e., greater ductility, than tied columns, but that this difference fades out as the eccentricity is increased. For this reason, as was discussed in Art. 5.3, the Code provides a more favorable reduction factor $\phi = 0.75$ for spiral columns, as compared to $\phi = 0.70$ for tied columns. Also, the minimum stipulated design eccentricity for entirely or nearly axially loaded members is $e_{min} = 0.05t$ for spiral-reinforced members, as compared to twice this value for tied members. It follows that spirally reinforced columns permit a somewhat more economical utilization of the materials, particularly for calculated eccentricities smaller than $0.05t$. Further advantages lie in the facts that spirals are available prefabricated, which may save labor in assembling column cages, and that the circular shape is frequently desired by the architect.

Figure 5.13 shows the cross section of a spiral-reinforced column. From six to ten and more longitudinal bars of equal size are provided for longitudinal reinforcement, depending on column diameter. The strain

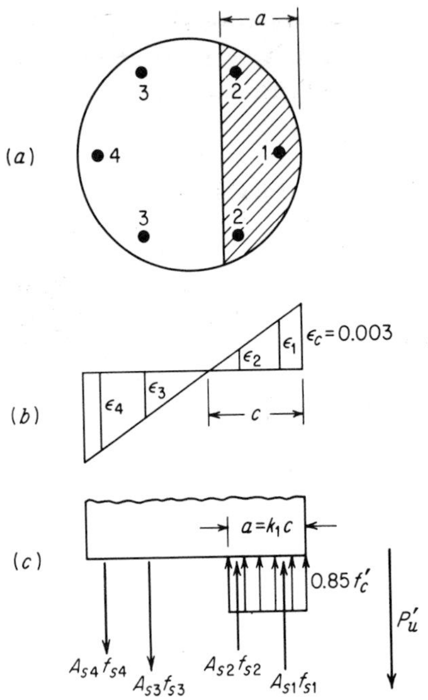

Fig. 5.13 Circular column, compression plus bending.

distribution at the instant at which the ultimate load is reached is shown in Fig. 5.13*b*. Bar groups 2 and 3 are seen to be strained to much smaller values than groups 1 and 4. The stresses in the four bar groups are easily found. For any of the bars with strains in excess of the yield strain $\epsilon_y = f_y/E_s$, the stress at failure is evidently the yield stress of the bar. For those bars with smaller strains, the stress is found from $f_s = \epsilon_s E_s$.

One then has the internal forces shown in Fig. 5.13*c*. They must be in force and moment equilibrium with the external load P'_u. It will be noted that the situation is exactly the same as that discussed, for rectangular columns, in Art. 5.4*f*. Calculations can be carried out exactly as in the example of that article, except that for circular columns the concrete compression zone subject to the equivalent rectangular stress distribution has the shape of a segment of a circle, shown shaded in Fig. 5.13*a*. Though this makes direct calculation awkward, no new principles are involved.

In practice, accurate calculations of this sort need rarely be carried out. The ACI Code gives the following approximate formulas: When tension controls,

$$P_u = \phi \left\{0.85 f'_c D^2 \left[\sqrt{\left(\frac{0.85e}{D} - 0.38\right)^2 + \frac{p_t m D_s}{2.5D}} - \left(\frac{0.85e}{D} - 0.38\right)\right]\right\} \tag{5.11}$$

When compression controls,

$$P_u = \phi \left[\frac{A_s f_y}{3e/D_s + 1} + \frac{A_g f'_c}{9.6De/(0.8D + 0.67D_s)^2 + 1.18}\right] \tag{5.12}$$

For determining the eccentricity for the balanced case, J. G. MacGregor gives the approximate expression

$$e_b = (0.24 + 0.39 p_t m) D \tag{5.13}$$

where D = overall diameter of circular section
D_s = diameter of circle through centers of longitudinal bars
A_g = gross area of section
e = eccentricity from plastic centroid
$p_t = A_s/A_g$

Proportioning or analysis is usually carried out by means of design aids, such as Graphs 6 to 9 in Appendix B, which have been computed from these formulas. Other more detailed tables and graphs are available, as mentioned in Art. 5.4*c*. These are generally more accurate than the above equations, since they have been calculated on digital computers from an accurate analysis of the situation indicated in Fig. 5.13.

It should be noted that these methods of design and analysis apply only if the steel ratio of the spiral is at least equal to that given by Eq. (5.2) of Art. 5.2, for reasons discussed in that article.

PROBLEMS

1. A column 18 in. square is reinforced with four No. 11 bars; $f'_c = 3$ ksi, and $f_y = 40$ ksi. If the column is axially loaded (design eccentricity $e = 0$), find P_u.

2. The column of Prob. 1 carries a load with an eccentricity $e = 3.5$ in. Find P_u and M_u.

3. If the eccentricity of the column of Prob. 1 is $e = 11.0$ in., find P_u and M_u.

4. A column carries, axially, a dead load of 90 kips and a live load of 70 kips. Using $f'_c = 4$ ksi and $f_y = 60$ ksi, design: (*a*) a square, tied column; (*b*) a circular, spiral column.

5. Redesign the columns of Prob. 4 if the live load is applied with an eccentricity $e = 6$ in.

6. Redesign the columns of Prob. 4 if the live load is applied with an eccentricity of 20 in.

7. For the situation of Prob. 6, design a rectangular, tied column with ratio of long to short side of the order of 2. Compare economy, i.e., compare quantity of concrete and steel, with Prob. 6.

WORKING-STRESS DESIGN OF COLUMNS

5.6 General Historically, the first departure from purely elastic methods in reinforced-concrete design occurred in the analysis of concentrically loaded columns. During the 1930's, elaborate experimental investigations at the University of Illinois under F. E. Richart and at Lehigh University under Inge Lyse showed that there was no recognizable relation between stresses calculated on an elastic basis for working loads [see Eqs. (2.2) and (2.2*a*)] and the actual carrying capacities of axially loaded columns. It was in these investigations that the basic so-called *addition law* [Eq. (2.5)] was established, to wit

$$P'_u = 0.85f'_cA_c + f_yA_{st} \qquad (5.14)$$

where A_{st} is the total area of longitudinal steel. Shortly thereafter the design of axially loaded columns, in the ACI and other codes, was changed to conform to this relationship rather than to presumed elastic behavior.

At the same time, flexural analysis continued to be based on elastic relations. Yet, simple bending on the one hand and simple concentric load on the other are only the two extremes of the general case of simultaneous compression plus bending. If one end point of this continuous range, axial compression, is treated on an ultimate-strength basis [Eq. (5.14)], and the other end point, simple bending, on a purely elastic basis [Eqs. (3.25) to (3.27), for example], it is clear that an inconsistent method must result for the general case of compression plus bending. In consequence, successive editions of the Code have presented ever-changing methods for this case, in repeated attempts to bridge the gap between the two methods by arbitrary adjustments of allowable stresses and other variables. The resulting provisions (by comparison of computed allowable loads with actual carrying capacity) gave safety factors which were mostly excessive, of the order of 3 to 4 and more, but which, for some combinations of eccentricities and steel ratios, were barely larger than 1.

The present (1963) ACI Code, in its ultimate-strength portion, contains a consistent treatment of the entire spectrum from simple bending to simple compression, with uniform and, on the whole, consistent safety provisions. This was discussed in Arts. 5.3 to 5.5. The Code continues to offer an alternative working-stress method of design, the choice between the two being left to the designer. In the 1963 edition the case of combined compression plus bending is once more treated by a method entirely different from those of previous versions. In this method, there is no pretense of calculating actual stresses under working loads by elastic means. The one aim is to obtain a reasonably uniform factor of safety when comparing the allowable working load with the actual carrying capacity as computed on an ultimate-strength basis. Therefore, although the method makes use of such devices of elastic computation as the transformed section (see Fig. 2.29), its chief aim is to make its results consistent with those of ultimate-strength design. A safety factor of 2.5 is aimed at, with actual values confined to the range of about 2.2 to 3.0. This is a considerable improvement over the excessive inconsistencies in previous editions. However, the method is admittedly merely a computational device, entirely usable but devoid of real physical meaning.

It can be assumed that in the foreseeable future ultimate-strength design methods will become prevalent, and methods such as those to be discussed below will eventually pass out of the picture.

5.7 Axially Loaded Columns For concentrically loaded, *spirally reinforced* columns the Code provides the following formula for the allowable load:

$$P = A_g(0.25f'_c + f_s p_g) \tag{5.15}$$

where A_g = gross area of column
$p_g = A_{st}/A_g$
f_s = allowable steel compression stress, equal to $0.40f_y$, but not to exceed 30,000 psi

If this equation is rewritten in the form

$$P = 0.25f'_c A_g + f_s A_{st} \tag{5.15a}$$

and compared with the basic ultimate-strength equation for axially loaded members [Eq. (5.14)], one notices the following: For the reinforcement, a safety factor $f_y/f_s = 2.5$ is employed. For the concrete, the safety factor is $0.85f'_c A_c/0.25f'_c A_g$. With steel ratios in columns limited to the range of 1.0 to 8.0 per cent, $A_c/A_g = 0.99$ to 0.92, so that the safety factor for the contribution of the concrete to the carrying capacity ranges from 3.1 to 3.4. It has been traditional, in working-stress design of columns based on the addition law, to apply such higher safety factors to the concrete contribution, on the assumption that concrete quality is less closely controlled than that of steel. Equation (5.15) holds provided the steel ratio of the spiral is at least that given by Eq. (5.2).

The Code recognizes the greater brittleness of *tied* columns, particularly when axially loaded, and stipulates that their allowable loads shall be 85 per cent of that given by Eq. (5.15); i.e.,

$$P = 0.85A_g(0.25f'_c + f_s p_g) \tag{5.16}$$

design of spirally reinforced col.

Example Design a circular, spiral-reinforced column for a concentric allowable working load of 480 kips, with $f'_c = 4.0$ ksi and $f_y = 60$ ksi for both longitudinal steel and spiral.

It is first necessary to select an approximate steel ratio. In general, lightly reinforced axially loaded columns are more economical than more heavily reinforced ones, except when small column sizes are desired in order to obtain maximum usable floor space. In the present case a moderate steel ratio of about $p_g = 0.02$ will be employed. The allowable steel stress is $f_s = 0.40 \times 60 = 24$ ksi. Thus

$$P = A_g(0.25 \times 4.0 + 24 \times 0.02)$$

or $480 = A_g \times 1.48$. Hence $A_g = 480/1.48 = 324$ in.^{2}

From Table 9, Appendix B, the area of a circular section with diameter $D = 20$ in. is $A_g = 314$ in.^{2} If this size is selected, a steel ratio larger than 0.02 must be provided, to make up for the difference between the furnished and calculated concrete areas.

The contribution of the concrete is then $P_c = 314 \times 0.25 \times 4.0 = 314$ kips, and the resistance to be supplied by the steel is $P_s = 480 - 314 = 166$ kips. With an allowable steel stress of 24 ksi, this requires a steel area $A_s = P_s/f_s = {}^{166}/_{24} = 6.9$ in.^{2} Seven No. 9 bars are selected from Table 2, with an area $A_s = 7.0$ in.^{2} The minimum steel ratio of the spiral is computed from Eq. (5.2). With a concrete cover over the spiral of 1.5 in., the core diameter is $D_c = 20 - 3 = 17$ in. Therefore, $A_g = 314$ in.^{2}, and from Table 9 for $D_c = 17$ in., $A_c = 227$ in.^{2} Then $p_s = 0.45(A_g/A_c - 1)f'_c/f_y = 0.45({}^{314}/_{227} - 1){}^{4}/_{60} = 0.0115$. If the pitch of the spiral is g, and the area of the wire a_s, the steel volume in one turn is $a_s\pi D_c$, and the volume of a slice of thickness g of the concrete core is $g\pi D_c^2/4$. (This neglects the small difference between the outside and center-line diameters of the spiral.) The steel ratio is the ratio of these two volumes:

$$p_s = \frac{4a_s}{gD_c}$$

As the ACI Code specifies that the pitch shall not exceed one-sixth of the core diameter, $g = 2.75$ in. is selected. Spirals are usually made of ¼-, ⅜-, ½-, or ⅝-in. wire. A ½ × 2¾ in. spiral, then, gives a steel ratio $p_s = 4 \times 0.20/2.75 \times 17 = 0.0017$. This is in excess of the required amount, but the next smaller size, ⅜ in., would fall short of the requirement.

5.8 Compression plus Bending It was mentioned in Art. 5.6 that the chief aims of the working-stress design methods for columns in the 1963 ACI Code are to define allowable design loads and moments which furnish a safety factor of about 2.5 when compared with ultimate loads and moments and to formulate the design procedures in terms of conventional elastic analysis. For this purpose, use is made of so-called *interaction equations.*

In an elastic member under compression and bending, but not subject to tension cracking, the maximum fiber stress is found from

$$\frac{P}{A} + \frac{M}{S} = f_{\max}$$

from which

$$\frac{P}{f_{\max}A} + \frac{M}{f_{\max}S} = 1$$

Now, that axial load P_a which, when acting alone without simultaneous bending, results in a given $f_{\max}$ is evidently $P_a = f_{\max}A$. Likewise, that flexural moment M_f which, when acting alone without simultaneous compression, results in $f_{\max}$ is evidently $M_f = f_{\max}S$. Hence, the last equation can be rewritten as

$$\frac{P}{P_a} + \frac{M}{M_f} = 1 \qquad (5.17)$$

A plot of this simple interaction equation is shown in Fig. 5.14. While the equation has been derived for elastic stresses, as long as compression governs it is also a good approximation for ultimate strength, as can be seen from the portion *bd* of Fig. 5.8. It relates the resistance to the combined action of P and M to the capacities in compression alone P_a and in flexure alone M_f. It holds only as long as the compression strength of the concrete governs. If cracking of the concrete and yielding of the steel determine failure, entirely different relationships obtain; this corresponds to the fact that in Fig. 5.8 for eccentricities larger than e_b, that is, when tension governs, a curve obtains which is entirely different from *dab* and from its straight-line approximation *db*.

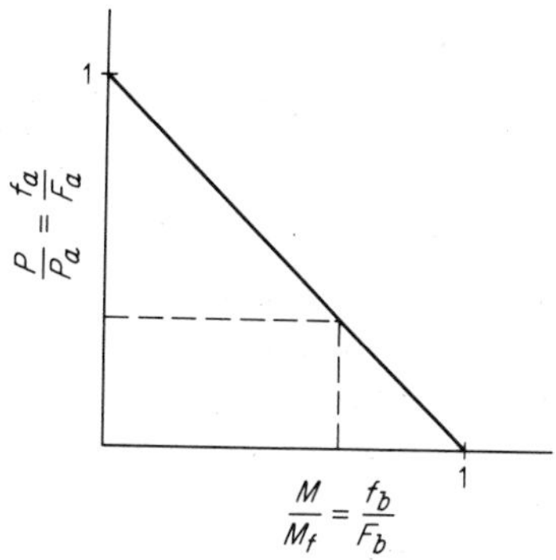

Fig. 5.14 Interaction diagram for elastic stresses, compression plus bending.

a. Concrete compression governs Equation 5.17 is utilized in the Code, for members in which compression governs, by taking $P_a = P'_u/2.5$ (2.5 being the safety factor) and $M_f = 0.45f'_cS_{ut}$. In the latter expression $0.45f'_c$ is the allowable stress in simple bending (see Art. 3.7), and S_{ut} is the section modulus of the uncracked, transformed section (see Fig. 2.3). It is specified that in computing S_{ut} the compression and tension steel areas shall be multiplied by $2n$ rather than by n, as a partial recognition of inelastic action.

If numerator and denominator of the first term in Eq. (5.17) are divided by the gross concrete area A_g, and those of the second term by S_{ut} as just defined, the equation can be written as

$$\frac{f_a}{F_a} + \frac{f_b}{F_b} \leqq 1 \tag{5.18}$$

where f_a = axial load divided by gross concrete area A_g

f_b = bending moment divided by section modulus of uncracked, transformed section, $2n$ being used for all longitudinal steel

$F_a = 0.34(1 + p_gm)f'_c$ (explained below)

F_b = allowable bending stress for bending alone, that is, $0.45f'_c$

and where $\leqq$ indicates that the section is adequate as long as the left side does not exceed 1.

As was explained, $F_a = P_a/A_g = P'_u/2.5A_g$. Now, Eq. (5.14) can be rewritten as $P'_u = 0.85f'_cA_g[1 + (f_y/0.85f'_c)(A_{st}/A_g)]$. If both sides are divided by A_g, and if the abbreviations $m = f_y/0.85f'_c$ and $p_g = A_{st}/A_g$ are used, one obtains $F_a = 0.34(1 + p_gm)f'_c$ as stated. Here A_{st} is the total area of all longitudinal steel; that is, $A_{st} = A_s + A'_s$. (As a minor simplifying approximation, the gross concrete area A_g instead of the net concrete area A_c is used in these Code provisions.)

Equation 5.18 is applicable in only a limited range of eccentricities $e = M/P$. On the one hand, an upper limit is set on P by Eqs. (5.15) and (5.16), which define the maximum permissible working loads on concentrically compressed columns. If, for small eccentricities, Eq. (5.18) results in a permissible load $P = f_a A_g$ larger than that given by Eq. (5.15) or (5.16), one of the latter governs.

On the other hand, Eq. (5.18) was devised for the situation in which compression of the concrete governs and in which tension cracking, if any, is of minor influence. The Code provides the following upper limits of eccentricity beyond which Eq. (5.18) no longer applies because tension would govern:

For symmetrical tied columns: $$e_b = (0.67p_g m + 0.17)d \qquad (5.19a)$$

For unsymmetrical tied columns: $$e_b = \frac{p'm(d - d') + 0.1d}{(p' - p)m + 0.6} \qquad (5.19b)$$

For spiral columns: $$e_b = 0.43p_g m D_s + 0.14t \qquad (5.19c)$$

(It should be noted that these eccentricity values e_b for working-stress design do not have the same significance as and are different in value from the balanced eccentricities e_b in ultimate-strength design, as discussed in Arts. 5.4 and 5.5.)

b. Steel tension governs For a given cross section, knowing e_b from Eqs. (5.19), one can use Eq. (5.18) to calculate the axial force P_b and the corresponding moment $M_b = e_b P_b$ which define the lower end point of the range of validity of Eq. (5.18). For eccentricities larger than e_b, tension begins to govern. At the other extreme, when the axial load P is zero, the section is in simple bending. Consistent with the previous assumptions, the allowable moment for this extreme is defined as 40 per cent of the ultimate moment M'_u in simple bending; i.e., a safety factor of 2.5 is again utilized. These moments M_0 are

For symmetrical tied columns: $$M_0 = 0.40A_s f_y(d - d') \qquad (5.20a)$$

For unsymmetrical tied columns: $$M_0 = 0.40A_s f_y jd \qquad (5.20b)$$

For spiral columns: $$M_0 = 0.12A_{st} f_y D_s \qquad (5.20c)$$

where A_s is the steel on the tension side, and A_{st} the total longitudinal steel. The first of these expressions is simply 40 per cent of M'_u for a compression-reinforced beam with equal tension and compression reinforcement, $A_s = A'_s$ (see Art. 3.9). The other two equations are close approximations to the ultimate moments for the respective cases, also divided by 2.5.

The Code provides that the allowable bending moment M on columns controlled by tension shall be considered to vary linearly with axial load, from M_0 when the section is in simple flexure to M_b when the axial load is equal to N_b. This can be expressed in the nondimensional equation

$$\frac{P}{P_b} = \frac{M - M_0}{M_b - M_0} \tag{5.21}$$

which is easily verified from the geometry of Fig. 5.15 and can be solved for either P or M, as needed.

c. *Summary and examples* The working-stress design procedure for members in compression plus bending is summarized in Fig. 5.15. The following are shown:

1. For zero or small eccentricities (interval ea), the allowable load is that for concentric compression [Eqs. (5.15) and (5.16)].

2. For moderate eccentricities, when compression governs in the interval ab, the interaction equation (5.18) applies. It is represented by the straight line connecting P_a (when $M = 0$) and M_f (when $P = 0$). In that range one determines P and M from Eq. (5.18) and compares P with P_{max} as calculated from Eq. (5.15) or (5.16). The smaller of the two is the allowable load.

3. Point b determines the boundary between members governed by compression and those governed by tension. It is found by calculating e_b from Eqs. (5.19), and then P_b from Eq. (5.18).

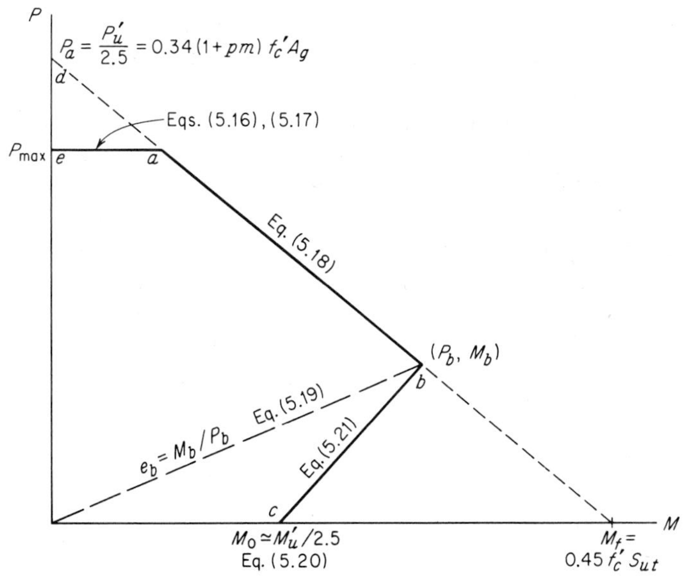

***Fig.* 5.15** Working-stress design, compression plus bending.

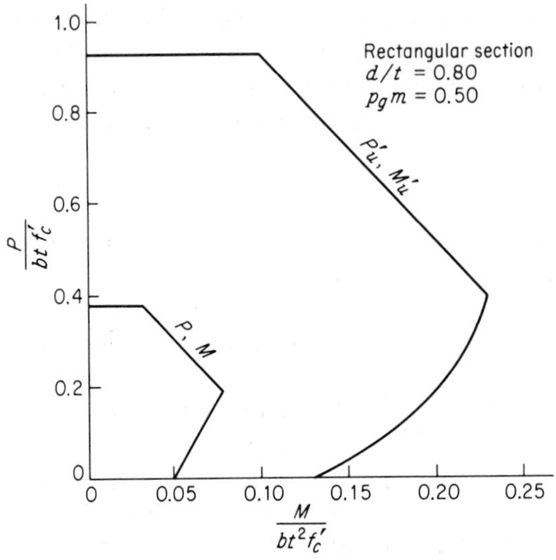

Fig. 5.16 Ultimate-strength P'_u and M'_u and allowable values P and M by working-stress design.

4. For large eccentricities, when tension governs, a linear variation is assumed between the moment M_b at the balance point b and M_0 for simple flexure, shown by the straight line bc. Equation (5.21) is used in this range for determining P if M is given, or vice versa.

The general shape of the figure *eabc*, it will be noted, is quite similar to that of the dashed curve in Fig. 5.9. The latter gives the ultimate design values P_u and M_u, and the similarity of the figures comes from the fact that the working-stress design method is devised to give a reasonably constant safety factor of about 2.5 when compared with ultimate values P'_u and M'_u. By way of example, this situation is specifically illustrated in Fig. 5.16, which applies to rectangular sections having the particular values $d/t = 0.80$ and $p_g m = 0.5$. The figure shows, in nondimensional form, the allowable values P and M as specified for working-stress design, as well as the ultimate capacities P'_u and M'_u. While the two figures are not strictly geometrically similar, in view of simplifications used in the working-stress method, it is easily verified that a satisfactorily uniform safety factor of about 2.5 is maintained throughout.

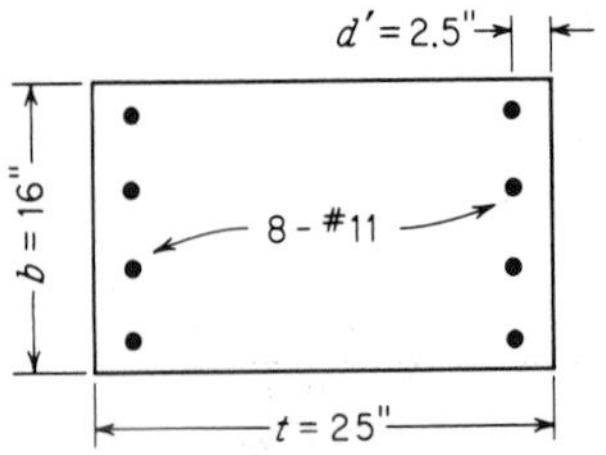

Fig. 5.17

Example 1 A column with the cross section shown in Fig. 5.17, with $f'_c = 4$ ksi and $f_y = 50$ ksi, is loaded concentrically. Calculate the allowable axial load.

With $A_g = 16 \times 25 = 400$ in.² and $A_{st} = 12.5$ in.², the steel ratio is $p_g = 12.5/400 = 0.0313$. The allowable steel stress is $f_s = 0.40 \times 50 = 20$ ksi.

Then, from Eq. (5.16),

$$P = 0.85 \times 400(0.25 \times 4 + 20 \times 0.313) = 553 \text{ kips}$$

Example 2 If the same column carries a compression load $P = 360$ kips, what is the allowable simultaneous moment?

For this column $m = 50/(0.85 \times 4) = 14.7$, $p_g m = 0.0313 \times 14.7 = 0.460$, and $n = 8$. Assume that compression governs. The section modulus of the transformed, uncracked section is $S_{ut} = I_{ut}/c = (1/c)[bt^3/12 + 2(2n - 1) A_s(t/2 - d')^2] = (1/12.5)[16 \times 25^3/12 + 2 \times 15 \times 12.5/2 \times (12.5 - 2.5)^2] = 3160$ in.³ (here $A_s = A_{st}/2$). The allowable average compression stress is $F_a = 0.34(1 + p_g m)f'_c = 0.34(1 + 0.460)4 = 1.98$ ksi, and the allowable bending stress is $F_b = 0.45f'_c = 0.45 \times 4 = 1.80$ ksi. The actual compression stress is $f_a = P/A_g = {}^{360}\!/_{400} = 0.90$ ksi, and the actual bending stress is $f_b = M/S_{ut} = M/3160$. Substituting these values in Eq. (5.18),

$$\frac{f_a}{F_a} + \frac{f_b}{F_b} = \frac{0.90}{1.98} + \frac{M}{3160 \times 1.80} = 1$$

Solving for the allowable moment, one has $M = 3110$ in.-kips.

To check whether compression governs as assumed, one has, from Eq. (5.19*a*), $e_b = (0.67 \times 0.460 + 0.17)22.5 = 10.75$ in. The actual eccentricity $e = M/P = {}^{3110}\!/_{360} = 8.63$ in. is smaller than e_b, so that compression does, in fact, govern.

Example 3 For the same column, what is the allowable moment if the simultaneous axial load is 100 kips?

Assuming that tension will govern, one first determines P_b and M_b for use in Eq. (5.21). This can be done using Eq. (5.18), which holds for eccentricities up to and including e_b. Hence, with $e_b = 10.75$ in. from Example 2, $P_b/(400 \times 1.98) + 10.75P_b/(3160 \times 1.80) = 1$ gives $P_b = 318$ kips, and $M_b = 10.75 \times 318 = 3420$ in.-kips. Because P is smaller than P_b, tension does, in fact, govern. From Eq. (5.20*a*), $M_0 = 0.40 \times 6.25 \times 50 \times 20 = 2500$ in.-kips. Solving Eq. (5.21) for M, one has

$$M = M_0 + \frac{P}{P_b}(M_b - M_0) = 2500 + {}^{100}\!/_{318}(3420 - 2500) = 2789 \text{ in.-kips}$$

Note that the allowable moment on the column, $M = 2789$ in.-kips, acting simultaneously with $P = 100$ kips, is now smaller than in Example 2, where the allowable moment was $M = 3110$ in.-kips when the axial load was $P = 360$ kips. As is seen from Figs. 5.15 and 5.16, this is characteristic of columns when tension governs. Consequently, in column design it is necessary to check the adequacy of the selected sections for two arrangements of live load: one which results in simultaneously large axial forces and large moments and one which results in large moments accompanied by small axial loads (see Example 1, Art. 5.4).

Example 4 Design a spiral-reinforced, circular column for $P = 300$ kips, with an eccentricity $e = 6.0$ in., using concrete with $f'_c = 3$ ksi and steel with $f_y = 40$ ksi. Here $n = 9$, $m = 40/(0.85 \times 3) = 15.7$, and $f_s = 0.40 \times 40 = 16$ ksi.

In order to arrive at an estimate of the required dimensions, the cross section of a column loaded concentrically by $P = 300$ kips will first be determined.

From Eq. (5.15), with the minimum reinforcement ratio of $p = 0.01$, $A_g = P/(0.25f'_c + f_s p_g) = 300/(0.25 \times 3 + 16 \times 0.01) = 330$ in.² Hence, a column of diameter $t = 21$ in. (having $A_g = 346$ in.²), reinforced with six No. 7 bars ($A_s = 3.61$ in.²), would be adequate for axial load alone.

With the stipulated eccentricity, a larger section evidently will be required to accomodate the additional moment eP. A few trial calculations indicate a column with $t = 24$ in., reinforced with ten No. 11 bars with $A_{st} = 15.62$ in.² From Table 9, Appendix B, $A_g = 452$ in.², so that $p = 15.62/452 = 0.0347$. The section modulus is calculated with the aid of Table 9. The moment of inertia of the uncracked concrete section is 16,280 in.⁴ The table shows for a 24-in. column with $p_g = 0.01$ the moment of inertia of the steel to be 204 in.⁴ Hence, for the given column the steel contributes an amount $100p_g(2n - 1)204 = 3.47(2 \times 9 - 1)204 = 12{,}000$ in.⁴ to the moment of inertia. The section modulus is $S_{ut} = I_{ut}/(t/2) = (16{,}280 + 12{,}000)/12 = 2360$ in.³ Further, $F_a = 0.34(1 + 0.0347 \times 15.7)3 = 1.58$ ksi, and $F_b = 0.45 \times 3 = 1.34$ ksi. Hence, according to Eq. (5.18),

$$\frac{300}{452 \times 1.58} + \frac{6.0 \times 300}{2360 \times 1.35} = 0.985 < 1.0$$

It follows that the selected section is adequate.

PROBLEMS

Solve the problems following Art. 5.5 by working-stress design.

d. Rectangular columns in biaxial bending For columns in biaxial bending, when *compression governs*, the Code provides the following expanded form of Eq. (5.18):

$$\frac{f_a}{F_a} + \frac{f_{bx}}{F_b} + \frac{f_{by}}{F_b} \leqq 1 \tag{5.22}$$

where f_a, F_a, and F_b are as defined in Art. 5.8*a*, and f_{bx} and f_{by} are the bending moments about the x and y principal axes, divided, respectively, by the section moduli S_{utx} and S_{uty} about the same axes. If a load P is applied at an eccentricity e from the centroid of the section, and if this eccentricity subtends an angle θ with the x axis (Fig. 5.18), then

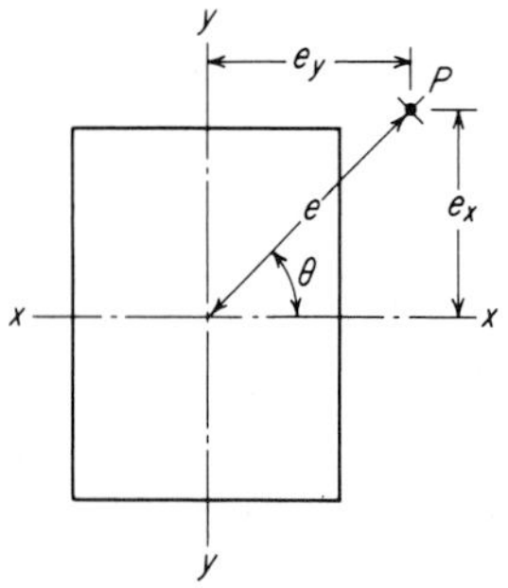

Fig. 5.18 Biaxial bending plus compression.

$$M_x = Pe_x = Pe \sin\theta \tag{5.22a}$$
$$M_y = Pe_y = Pe \cos\theta \tag{5.22b}$$

and f_{bx} and f_{by} are determined for these moments. As in uniaxial bending, the section moduli are calculated for the uncracked, transformed section, $2n$ being used for the longitudinal steel.

A column is considered to be governed by compression if neither e_x nor e_y exceeds the pertinent balanced eccentricity e_{bx} or e_{by} as calculated from Eq. (5.19*a*) or (5.19*b*).

When *tension governs*, a linear variation between the balanced condition and the condition of simple flexure is specified, analogous to that described in Art. 5.8*c* for uniaxial bending. For this linear interpolation, it is first necessary to determine, for biaxial bending, the balanced-condition P_b and M_b on the one hand, and the permissible inclined bending moment M_0 in simple flexure without axial load on the other.

Given the inclination θ of Fig. 5.18, the balanced eccentricity e_b in the direction of e of that figure is taken as either

$$e_b = \frac{e_{bx}}{\sin\theta} \tag{5.23}$$

or

$$e_b = \frac{e_{by}}{\cos\theta} \tag{5.24}$$

whichever is smaller. Here e_{bx} and e_{by} are calculated from Eq. (5.19*a*) or (5.19*b*) for the two principal directions. Then, with Eqs. (5.22) to (5.24) in mind, the balanced load P_b is determined from

$$\frac{P_b}{A_g F_a} + \frac{P_b e_b \sin\theta}{S_{utx} F_b} + \frac{P_b e_b \cos\theta}{S_{uty} F_b} = 1 \tag{5.25}$$

and the corresponding balanced moment is

$$M_b = P_b e_b \tag{5.26}$$

On the other hand, the Code stipulates that the inclined simple flexural moment M_0 in the absence of axial load be determined from

$$\frac{M_0 \sin\theta}{M_{0xx}} + \frac{M_0 \cos\theta}{M_{0yy}} = 1 \tag{5.27}$$

where M_{0xx} = value of M_0 from Eqs. (5.20) for bending about x axis alone
M_{0yy} = value of M_0 from Eqs. (5.20) for bending about y axis alone

Once P_b, M_b, and M_0 are determined, Eq. (5.21) is used as in uniaxial bending to calculate, for biaxial bending, either P or M, as needed.

The authors observe that this Code method will be found quite cumbersome and excessively conservative, resulting in safety factors of 3 and more. They suggest that Bresler's equation (5.10*a*), though not a part of the ACI Code, can be used with equal ease for working-stress and for ultimate-strength design. For the former the equation would take the form

$$\frac{1}{P} = \frac{1}{P_x} + \frac{1}{P_y} - \frac{1}{P_a} \tag{5.28}$$

where P = allowable load in biaxial bending
P_x = allowable load when only eccentricity e_x is present ($e_y = 0$)
P_y = allowable load when only eccentricity e_y is present ($e_x = 0$)
$P_a = 0.34(1 + p_g m)f'_c A_g$, as previously defined

with the proviso that P shall not exceed the value given by Eq. (5.16) as an upper limit. In this manner, P_x and P_y are first calculated for uniaxial bending, as summarized in Art. 5.8*c* and illustrated in the examples; the permissible load in biaxial bending is then obtained from the interaction expression of Eq. (5.28) in the manner illustrated for ultimate-strength design in the example of Art. 5.4*f*.

SLENDER COLUMNS

5.9 General A column is said to be *slender* if its cross-sectional dimensions are small as compared to its length. The degree of slenderness is generally expressed in terms of the *slenderness ratio* h/r, where h is the length of the member, and r the radius of gyration ($r = \sqrt{I/A}$) of its cross section. For square or circular members the value of r is the same about any cross-sectional axis; for other shapes r is smallest about the minor principal axis, and it is generally this value which must be used in determining the slenderness ratio.

It has long been known that a member of great slenderness will collapse under a smaller compression load than a stocky member of the same cross-sectional dimensions. This is so for the following reason: A stocky member, say with $h/r = 10$ (e.g., a square column of length equal to about 3 times its thickness t), when loaded in axial compression, will fail at the load given by Eq. (5.1), because at that load both concrete and steel are stressed to their maximum carrying capacity and give way, respectively, by crushing and by yielding. If a member with the same cross section has a slenderness ratio $h/t = 100$ (e.g., a square column hinged at both ends and of length equal to about 30 times its thickness), it may fail under an axial load of one-half or less of that given by Eq. (5.1). In this case collapse is caused by buckling, i.e., by lateral bending of the member with consequent overstressing of steel and concrete by the bending stresses which superpose on the axial compression stresses.

Until recently, reinforced-concrete columns were rarely so slender that their strengths were significantly affected by buckling. In design, account was taken of the slenderness effect in a very approximate manner by an equation of the form

$$P_{\text{slender}} = RP_{\text{stocky}} \tag{5.29}$$

where P_{slender} = carrying capacity under axial load with or without simultaneous bending of member of given slenderness

P_{stocky} = carrying capacity of stocky member of same cross section as slender member

$R = f(h/r) \leqq 1$, a reduction factor smaller than 1 which depends on slenderness and is equal to 1 when h/r is so small that no strength reduction occurs

For instance, in past ACI Codes no capacity reduction was prescribed (that is, R was equal to 1) for members with h/t up to 10 (approximately h/r up to 35). For columns with $h/t = 20$ (approximately $h/r = 70$), R became 0.70, and, generally, columns with h/t exceeding 20 were not permitted.

With the introduction of high-strength steels and concretes, and with more accurate design methods (such as ultimate-strength design), it is now possible, for a given amount of axial load with or without simultaneous bending, to design a much smaller cross section than heretofore. This, evidently, makes for more slender members, and it is chiefly because of this that reliable and rational design procedures for slender columns have now become important. In this regard the present ACI Code, while considerably improved, is not entirely satisfactory. It retains provisions of the form of Eq. (5.29), though with more refinements than previously, which lead to more realistic designs. Actually, however, Eq. (5.29) is not the most rational way of accounting for the effects of slenderness. These effects, particularly for an inelastic material such as reinforced concrete, which is also subject to tension cracking in eccentrically compressed members, are of unusual complexity. When more adequate research information is available, a more rational method for designing slender columns will undoubtedly be developed.

5.10 Slenderness Effects ***a. Concentrically loaded columns*** The basic information on the behavior of straight, concentrically loaded, slender columns was developed by Euler more than 200 years ago (Ref. 5.3). In generalized form it states that such a member will fail by buckling at the critical load

$$P_{cr} = \frac{\pi^2 E_t I}{h'^2} \tag{5.30}$$

which, when both sides are divided by the cross-sectional area, gives the

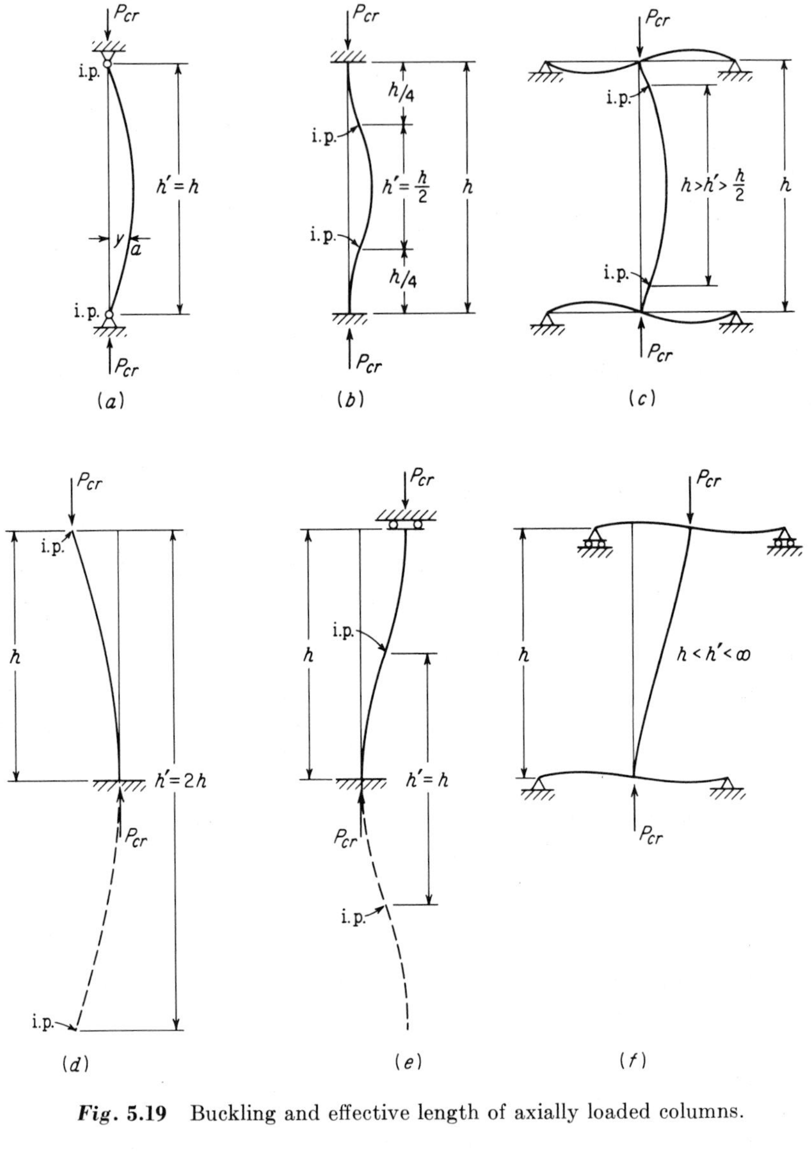

Fig. 5.19 Buckling and effective length of axially loaded columns.

compression stress at which buckling occurs as

$$\left(\frac{P}{A}\right)_{cr} = \frac{\pi^2 E_t}{(h'/r)^2} \tag{5.31}$$

For the simplest case of a column hinged at both ends and constructed of elastic material, E_t becomes simply Young's modulus, and h' is equal to the actual length h of the column. At the load or stress given by Eq. (5.30) or (5.31) the originally straight member buckles into a half sine wave as in Fig. 5.19*a*. In this bent configuration, bending moments Py act at any section such as a; y is the deflection at that section. These deflections continue to increase until the bending stress caused by the increasing moment, together with the original compression stress, overstresses and fails the member.

If the stress-strain curve of a short piece of the given member is of the shape of Fig. 5.20*a*, as it would be for reinforced-concrete columns, E_t is equal to Young's modulus, provided the buckling stress $(P/A)_{cr}$ is below the proportional limit f_p. If it is larger than f_p, buckling occurs in the inelastic range. In this case, in Eqs. (5.30) and (5.31) E_t is the tangent modulus, i.e., the slope of the tangent to the stress-strain curve. As the stress increases, E_t decreases. A plot of the buckling stress versus the slenderness ratio, a so-called *column curve*, therefore has the shape given in Fig. 5.20*b*, which shows the reduction in buckling strength with increasing slenderness. For very stocky columns one finds that the value of the buckling load or stress, calculated from Eq. (5.30) or (5.31), exceeds the direct crushing strength of the stocky column, given by Eq. (5.1). This is also shown in Fig. 5.20*b*. Correspondingly, there is a limiting slenderness ratio $(h'/r)_{\text{lim}}$. For values smaller than this, failure occurs by simple crushing, regardless of h'/r; for values larger than $(h'/r)_{\text{lim}}$, failure occurs by buckling, the buckling load or stress decreasing for greater slenderness.

If the member of Fig. 5.19*a* is fixed against rotation at both ends, it buckles in the shape of Fig. 5.19*b*, with inflection points i.p. as shown. The portion between inflection points is in precisely the same situation as the hinge-ended column of Fig. 5.19*a*, and thus the *effective length* h' of

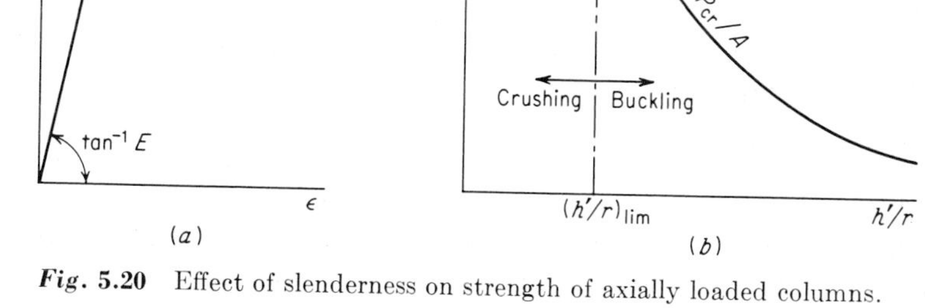

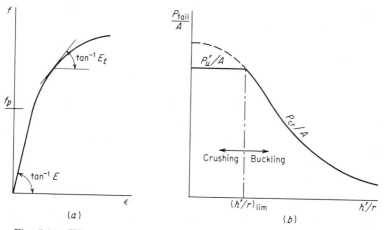

Fig. 5.20 Effect of slenderness on strength of axially loaded columns.

the fixed-fixed column, i.e., the distance between inflection points, is seen to be $h' = h/2$. Equation 5.30 shows that an elastic column, when fixed at both ends, will carry 4 times as much load as when hinged.

Columns in real structures are rarely either hinged or fixed, but rather have ends partially restrained against rotation by abutting members. This is schematically shown in Fig. 5.19*c*, from which it is seen that for such members the effective length h', that is, the distance between inflection points, has a value between h and $h/2$. The precise value depends on the degree of end restraint, i.e., on the ratio r' of the rigidity EI/h of the column to the sum of rigidities EI/l of the restraining members at both ends. In the columns of Fig. 5.19*a* to *c* it was assumed that one end was prevented from moving laterally relative to the other end, by horizontal bracing or otherwise. In this case it is seen that the effective length h' is always smaller than, or at most equal to, the real length h.

If a column is fixed at one end and entirely free at the other (cantilever column or flagpole), it buckles as shown in Fig. 5.19*d*. That is, the upper end moves laterally with respect to the lower, a kind of deformation which is known as *sidesway*. It buckles into a quarter of a sine wave and, therefore, is analogous to the upper half of the hinged column of Fig. 5.19*a*. The inflection points, one at the end of the actual column and the other at the imaginary extension of the sine wave, are seen to be a distance $2h$ apart, so that the effective length is $h' = 2h$.

If the column is rotationally fixed at both ends, but one end can move laterally with respect to the other, it buckles as shown in Fig. 5.19*e*, with an effective length $h' = h$. If one compares this column, fixed at both ends but free to sidesway, with a fixed-fixed column which is braced against sidesway (Fig. 5.19*b*), one sees that the effective length of the former is twice that of the latter. By Eq. (5.30), this means that the buckling strength of an elastic fixed-fixed column which is free to sidesway is only one-quarter that of the same column when braced against sidesway. This is an illustration of the general fact that *compression members free to buckle in a sidesway mode are always considerably weaker than when braced against sidesway.*

Again, the ends of columns in actual structures are rarely either hinged, fixed, or entirely free, but are usually restrained by abutting members. If sidesway is not prevented, buckling occurs as in Fig. 5.19*f*, and the effective length, as before, depends on the degree of restraint r'. If the cross beams are very rigid as compared with the column (giving r' close to zero), the case of Fig. 5.19*e* is approached, and h' is only slightly larger than h. On the other hand, if the restraining members are extremely flexible, a hinged condition is approached at both ends. Evidently, a column hinged at both ends and free to sidesway is unstable. It will simply topple, being unable to carry any load whatever.

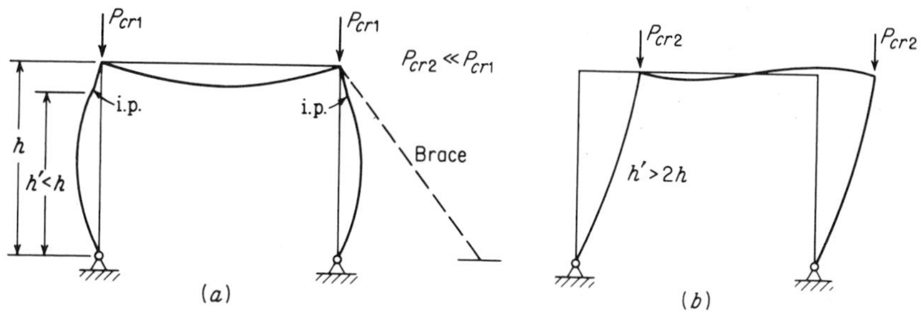

Fig. 5.21 Rigid frame buckling: (*a*) laterally braced; (*b*) unbraced.

In reinforced-concrete structures one is rarely concerned with single members, but rather with rigid frames of various configurations. The manner in which the described relationships affect the buckling behavior of frames is illustrated by the simple portal frame of Fig. 5.21, with loads applied concentrically to the columns. If sidesway is prevented, as indicated schematically by the brace of Fig. 5.21*a*, the buckling configuration will be as shown. The buckled shape of the column corresponds to that of Fig. 5.19*c*, except that the lower end is hinged. It is seen that the effective length h' is smaller than h. On the other hand, if no sidesway bracing is provided to an otherwise identical frame, buckling occurs as in Fig. 5.21*b*. The column is in a situation similar to that of Fig. 5.19*d*, upside down, except that the upper end is not fixed, but only partially restrained by the girder. It is seen that the effective length h' exceeds $2h$ by an amount depending on the degree of restraint. The buckling strength depends on h'/r in the manner shown in Fig. 5.20*b*. In consequence, even though they are dimensionally identical, the unbraced frame will buckle at a radically smaller load than the braced frame.

In summary, the following can be noted:

The strength of concentrically loaded columns decreases with increasing slenderness ratio h'/r.

In columns which are *braced against sidesway* or which are parts of frames braced against sidesway, the effective length h', that is, the distance between inflection points, falls between $h/2$ and h, depending on degree of end restraint.

The effective lengths of columns which are *not braced against sidesway* or which are parts of frames not so braced, are always larger than h, the more so the smaller the end restraint. In consequence, the buckling load of a frame not braced against sidesway is always substantially smaller than that of the same frame when braced.

b. Compression plus bending Most reinforced-concrete compression members are subject to simultaneous flexure, caused by transverse loads or by end moments due to continuity. The behavior of mem-

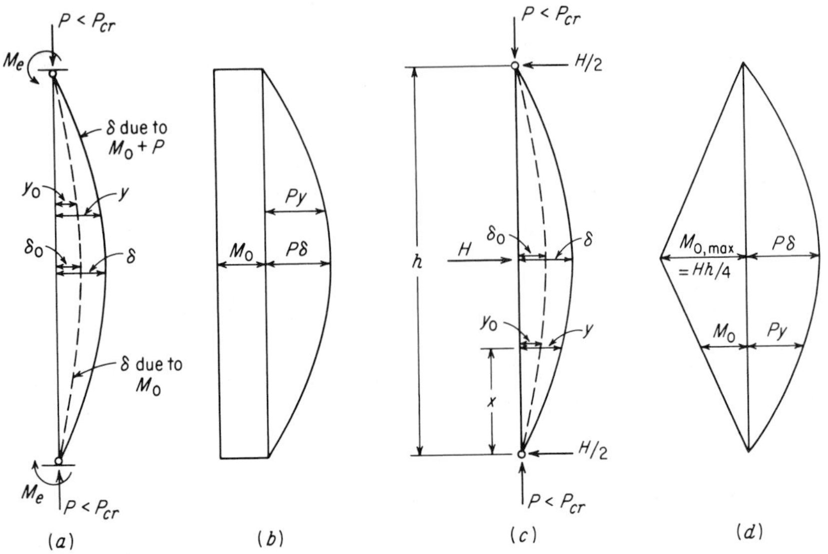

Fig. 5.22 Moments in slender members, compression plus bending, single curvature.

bers subject to such combined loading also depends greatly on their slenderness.

Figure 5.22*a* shows such a member, often known as a *beam-column*, axially loaded by P and bent by equal end moments M_e. If no axial load were present, the moment M_0 in the member would be constant throughout and equal to the end moments M_e. This is shown in Fig. 5.22*b*. In this situation, i.e., in simple bending without axial compression, the member deflects as shown by the dashed curve of Fig. 5.22*a*, where y_0 represents the deflection at any point caused by bending only. When P is applied, the moment at any point increases by an amount equal to P times its lever arm. The increased moments cause additional deflections, so that the deflection curve under the simultaneous action of P and M_0 is the solid curve of Fig. 5.22*a*. At any point, then, the total moment is now

$$M = M_0 + Py \tag{5.32}$$

that is, the total moment consists of the moment M_0 which acts in the absence of P and the additional moment caused by P, equal to P times the deflection.

A similar situation is shown in Fig. 5.22*c*, where bending is caused by the transverse load H. When P is absent, the moment at any point x is $M_0 = Hx/2$, with a maximum at midspan equal to $Hh/4$. The corresponding M_0 diagram is shown in Fig. 5.22*d*. When P is applied, additional moments Py are caused again, distributed as shown, and the total moment at any point in the beam-column consists of the same two parts as in Eq. (5.32).

The deflections y of elastic beam-columns of the type shown in Fig. 5.22 can be calculated from the deflections y_0 (i.e., from the deflections of the corresponding beam without axial load), using the following expression (see, e.g., Ref. 5.3):

$$y = y_0 \frac{1}{1 - P/P_{cr}} \tag{5.33}$$

If P and P_{cr} in Eq. (5.33) are divided by the area A, and $(P/A)_{cr}$ is replaced with the expression given in Eq. (5.31), then Eq. (5.33) can be rewritten in the form

$$y = y_0 \frac{1}{1 - P(h'/r)^2/A\pi^2E} \tag{5.34}$$

Given the external loading, that is, P and M_0, it is seen from Eqs. (5.32) and (5.34) that the moment M in the member increases with increasing slenderness ratio h'/r. The situation is shown schematically in Fig. 5.23. It indicates that for a given transverse loading, i.e., a given value of M_0, an axial force P causes a larger additional moment in a slender member than in a stocky member.

In the two members in Fig. 5.22, the largest moment caused by P, namely $P\delta$, adds directly to the maximum value of M_0, for example, $M_0 = Hh/4$ in Fig. 5.22*d*. As P increases, the maximum moment at midspan increases at a rate faster than that of P in the manner given by Eqs. (5.32) and (5.34) and shown in Fig. 5.24. The member will fail when the simultaneous values of P and M become equal to P'_u and M'_u, the ultimate strength of the cross section at the location of maximum moment.

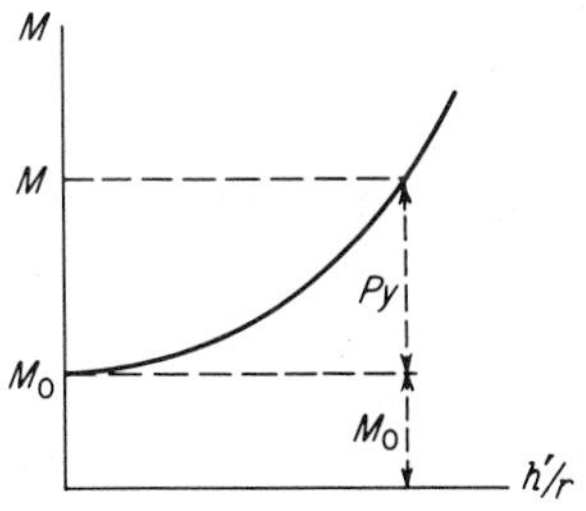

***Fig.* 5.23** Effect of slenderness on column moments.

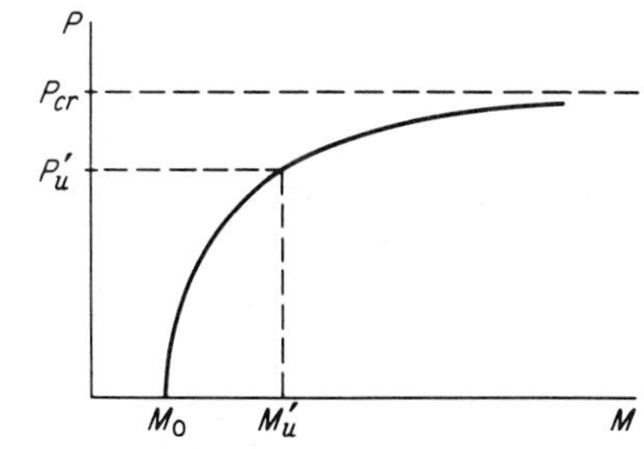

***Fig.* 5.24** Effect of axial load on column moments.

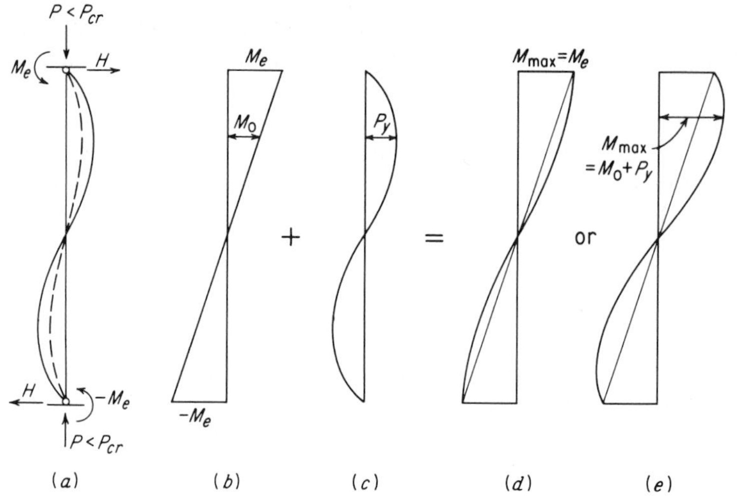

Fig. 5.25 Moments in slender members, compression plus bending, double curvature.

This direct addition of the maximum moment caused by P to the maximum moment caused by transverse load, clearly the most unfavorable situation, does not obtain for all types of deformations. For instance, the member of Fig. 5.25*a*, with equal and opposite end moments, has the M_0 diagram of Fig. 5.25*b*. The deflections caused by M_0 alone are again magnified when an axial load P is applied. In this case, these deflections under simultaneous bending and compression can be approximated by (Ref. 5.3)

$$y = y_0 \frac{1}{1 - P/4P_{cr}} \tag{5.35}$$

By comparison with Eq. (5.33), it is seen that the deflection magnification here is much smaller.

The additional moments Py caused by axial load are distributed as shown in Fig. 5.25*c*. While the M_0 moments are largest at the ends, the Py moments are seen to be largest some distance from the ends. Depending on their relative magnitudes, the total moments $M = M_0 + Py$ are distributed as in either Fig. 5.25*d* or *e*. In the former case, the maximum moment continues to act at the end and to be equal to M_e; the presence of the axial force, then, does not result in any increase in the maximum moment. Alternatively, in the case of Fig. 5.25*e*, the maximum moment is located some distance from the end; at that location M_0 is significantly smaller than its maximum value M_e, and for this reason the added moment Py increases the maximum moment to a value only moderately greater than M_e.

One can generalize as follows by comparing the situation of Fig. 5.22 with that of Fig. 5.25: If the applied moments M_0 alone, without axial force P, cause the member to deflect in single curvature, the addition of an axial force P will greatly magnify the maximum bending moment in the member, the more so the larger the slenderness ratio. On the other hand, if the moments M_0 cause the member to bend in double curvature, with an inflection point somewhere along the member (not necessarily in the middle), the added deflections caused by P are smaller, and the maximum moment either may not be magnified at all by the axial force P (Fig. 5.25*d*) or may be magnified to a generally less significant degree (Fig. 5.25*e*).

What has been said so far refers to *members braced against sidesway*. This includes the frequent case of columns which are parts of structures in which sidesway is prevented in one of various ways: by walls or partitions sufficiently strong and rigid in their own planes effectively to prevent horizontal displacement, by special bracing in vertical planes, such as wind-bracing, in tier buildings by designing the utility core to resist horizontal loads and furnish bracing to the frames, or by bracing the frame against some other essentially immovable support.

If no such bracing is provided, *sidesway can occur only for the entire frame simultaneously*, not for individual columns in the frame. If this is the case, the combined effect of bending and axial load is somewhat different from that in braced columns. For illustration, consider the simple portal frame of Fig. 5.26*a* subject to a horizontal load H, such as a wind load, and compression forces P, such as from gravity loads. The moments M_0 caused by H alone, in the absence of P, are shown in Fig. 5.26*b*; the corresponding deformation of the frame is given in dashed curves. When P is added, additional moments are caused which result in the magnified deformations shown in solid curves and in the moment diagram of Fig. 5.26*c*. It is seen that the maximum values of M_0, both positive and nega-

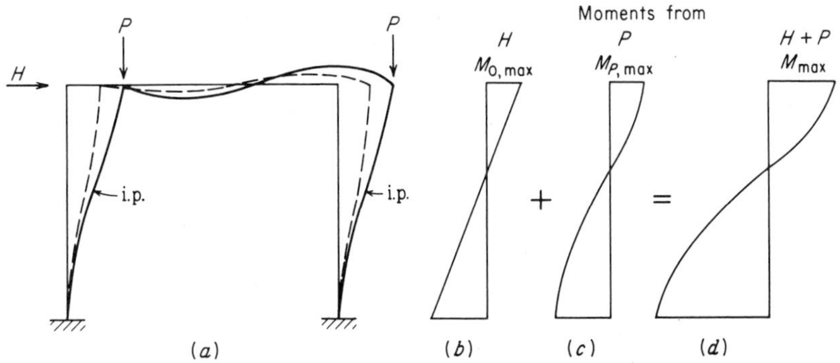

Fig. 5.26 Fixed portal frame, laterally unbraced.

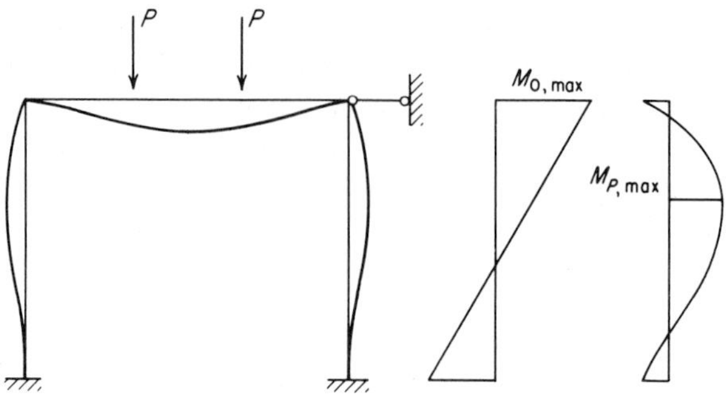

Fig. **5.27** Fixed portal frame, laterally braced.

tive, and the maximum values of the additional moments M_P of the same sign occur at the same locations, namely at the ends of the columns. They are, therefore, fully additive, leading to a large moment magnification. In contrast, if the frame of Fig. 5.26 is laterally braced and vertically loaded, Fig. 5.27 shows that the maximum values of the two different moments occur in different locations; the moment magnification, if any, is therefore much smaller. For the portal hinged at the bottom, as in Fig. 5.28, the discussion of Fig. 5.26 holds: the maximum moments of both kinds are fully additive at the column tops. The difference between the cases of Figs. 5.26 and 5.28, therefore, lies not in the presence or absence of an inflection point, but only in the greater stiffness of the columns fixed at the bottom. This results in the fact that their effective length h' is smaller than that in the hinged situation.

It should be noted that the moments which cause a frame to sidesway need not be caused by horizontal loads as in Figs. 5.26 and 5.28. Asymmetries, either of frame configuration or vertical loading or both, also result in sidesway displacements, as is discussed in Art. 8.6. In this case the presence of axial column loads results in the same deflection and moment magnification as before.

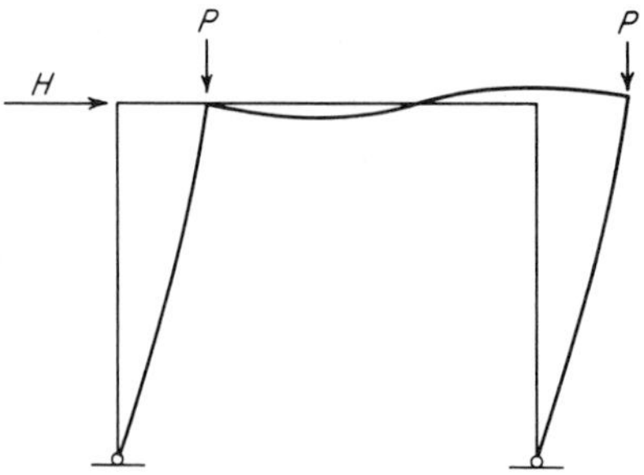

Fig. **5.28** Hinged portal frame, laterally unbraced.

In summary, the following can be stated:

In flexural members the presence of axial compression causes additional deflections and additional moments Py. Other things being equal, the additional moments increase with increasing slenderness ratio h'/r.

In *members braced against sidesway* and bent in single curvature, the maxima of both types of moments, M_0 and Py, occur at the same or at nearby locations and are fully additive; this leads to large moment magnifications. If the M_0 moments result in double curvature (i.e., in the occurrence of an inflection point), the opposite is true, and less or no moment magnification occurs.

In *members of frames not braced against sidesway*, the maximum moments of both kinds, M_0 and Py, almost always occur at the same locations, the ends of the column; they are fully additive, regardless of the presence or absence of an inflection point. Here, too, other things being equal, the additional deflections and the corresponding moments increase with increasing h'/r.

This discussion is merely a simplified presentation of a very complex subject. In particular, Eqs. (5.33) through (5.35) hold only for elastic members. They need modification in detail when applied to inelastic materials, even though the essential behavior, as presented in Figs. 5.23 and 5.29, is the same in both situations. For a material as complex as reinforced concrete, inelastic at relatively low stresses and subject to cracking on the tension side in bent members, an exact analysis of the described situations is not yet possible in most cases. Even if it were, it would be so complex as to need simplification for design purposes. Such a design method, quite possibly oversimplified, is that stipulated in the ACI Code for dealing with slender columns.

5.11 Slender-column Design by ACI Code ***a. General*** Figure 5.20*b* shows that the load capacity, i.e., the buckling load P_{cr}, of an axially compressed slender column is smaller than the ultimate strength P'_u of an axially loaded stocky column, provided the slenderness $h'/r > (h'/r)_{\text{lim}}$. This can be written as

$$P_{cr} = C_P P'_u$$

where $C_P = f_1(h'/r) \leqq 1$ is a *load-reduction factor* which expresses the effect of slenderness.

On the other hand, for compression plus bending, the combined information of Figs. 5.23 and 5.24 shows that the maximum bending moment M_0 which can be applied to a slender member by transverse forces or moments is smaller than that moment M'_u which, simultaneously with an axial load P'_u, would fail a stocky member. (A stocky member, in this context, is one for which the moment magnification is so small as to be negligible.) This can be written as

$$M_0 = C_M M'_u$$

where $C_M = f_2(h'/r) \leqq 1$ is a *moment-reduction factor* which expresses the effect of slenderness. Both C_P and C_M depend on the slenderness ratio, but the discussion of the preceding article makes clear that they represent different effects.

For simplicity, and partly for reasons of tradition, the *ACI Code applies to both the moment and the axial load the same reduction factor* $R = f(h'/r) \angle 1$. Explicitly, the Code stipulates that

$$P_{\text{slender}} = RP_{\text{stocky}} \tag{5.36}$$
$$M_{\text{slender}} = RM_{\text{stocky}} \tag{5.37}$$

where $P_{\text{slender}}, M_{\text{slender}}$ = carrying capacity in simultaneous axial compression and bending of member with slenderness ratio h'/r

$P_{\text{stocky}}, M_{\text{stocky}}$ = carrying capacity in simultaneous axial compression and bending of stocky member of same cross section as slender member

$R = f(h'/r) \angle 1$ = slenderness factor depending on h'/r and defined in more detail below

In design, these relations are used as follows: Let P and M be the axial load and the maximum moment caused in a given member by dead, live, wind, and other loads. P and M are obtained by any of the usual methods of structural analysis, without regard to moment magnification or other slenderness effects. If the slenderness of the member is large enough to reduce the carrying capacity, this reduction is taken care of by designing the member not for P and M, but for the larger quantities P/R and M/R. The member is designed for these increased forces and moments by the methods of ultimate-strength design discussed in Arts. 5.3 to 5.5 or by those of working-stress design as given in Arts. 5.7 and 5.8.

The Code provides that the radius of gyration r is sufficiently accurately given by

For rectangular sections: $r = 0.30t$
For circular sections: $r = 0.25D$

where t is the overall depth in the direction of bending, and D is the diameter of the cross section. For cross sections of other shapes, r may be computed for the gross concrete section, disregarding the reinforcement.

Example A structure is analyzed for the effects of dead and live load in the usual manner, and it is found that a particular member is subject to an axial load $P = 200$ kips and a maximum moment $M = 100$ ft-kips. Preliminary design has furnished approximate cross-sectional dimensions, from which the slenderness ratio h'/r was computed. For this particular slenderness ratio the applicable Code provisions (discussed below) indicate a reduction factor $R = 0.70$. Then the cross section of the member must be dimensioned for an axial load $P/R = 200/0.70 = 286$ kips and a simultaneous moment $M/R = 100/0.70 = 143$ ft-kips.

In agreement with the information given in Art. 5.10, the Code distinguishes between two types of members or, more accurately, between members in two types of structures. On the one hand, there are those structures in which sidesway of one floor or level with respect to the adjacent floor or level is prevented by the presence of adequate bracing. This corresponds to the situation of Figs. 5.21*a* and 5.27. In columns of such frames, *relative lateral displacement of the ends is prevented, and sidesway is not possible.* On the other hand, there are those structures which depend for their lateral stability chiefly or exclusively on the rigidity of the columns, rather than on some other means of bracing. Such frames behave under axial load as shown in Fig. 5.21*b*, or under lateral and axial load as in Figs. 5.26 and 5.28. In columns of such frames, *relative lateral displacement of the ends is not prevented, and sidesway is possible.*

In structures of the first category, bracing can be provided in various ways: by the rigidity of walls and partitions in their own planes, by special shear walls, by rigid utility cores, by special wind bracing, etc. The Code gives no criteria to define adequate bracing. In most practical cases this is not difficult to decide. Sidesway caused by axial forces alone (Fig. 5.21*b*) can be prevented by relatively light bracing. It has been shown by several investigators, including one of the authors (Ref. 5.4), that bracing capable of resisting a transverse force equal to about 2 per cent or less of the axial force will prevent such sidesway. On the other hand, to prevent sidesway caused by lateral forces alone, such as wind loads, evidently the bracing system by itself must be able to resist these lateral forces. Therefore, the following can be used as a general guide: *To effectively brace a frame against sidesway under the combined action of lateral and vertical forces, the bracing system by itself must be able to resist all the applied lateral loads plus at least 2 per cent of the total vertical load acting at and above the level of the column being designed.*

The discussion which follows deals with columns in which *compression governs* the design of the section, i.e., in which the eccentricity is smaller than e_b. A modification for the case in which tension governs is presented separately later.

b. Sidesway prevented It was shown in Art. 5.10*a* that the effective length h' of a column braced against sidesway ranges from $h/2$ for fixed-fixed conditions to h for hinged-hinged conditions. (Here, as elsewhere, h is defined in the Code as the *clear distance* between the floor at the bottom of the column and the underside of the beam, slab, capital, or drop panel at the top.) The Code ignores this variation of h' in the interest of simplicity and some conservatism. It specifies that *for laterally braced members the entire length h* shall be used for computing the slenderness ratio h'/r.

The values of the reduction factors R in the Code were obtained from a simplification and generalization of an elaborate experimental and analytical investigation of the inelastic behavior and strength of slender reinforced-concrete columns (Ref. 5.5).

For *members bent in single curvature* by the applied transverse forces or moments, the Code specifies

$$R = 1.07 - 0.008\frac{h}{r} \leqq 1 \tag{5.38}$$

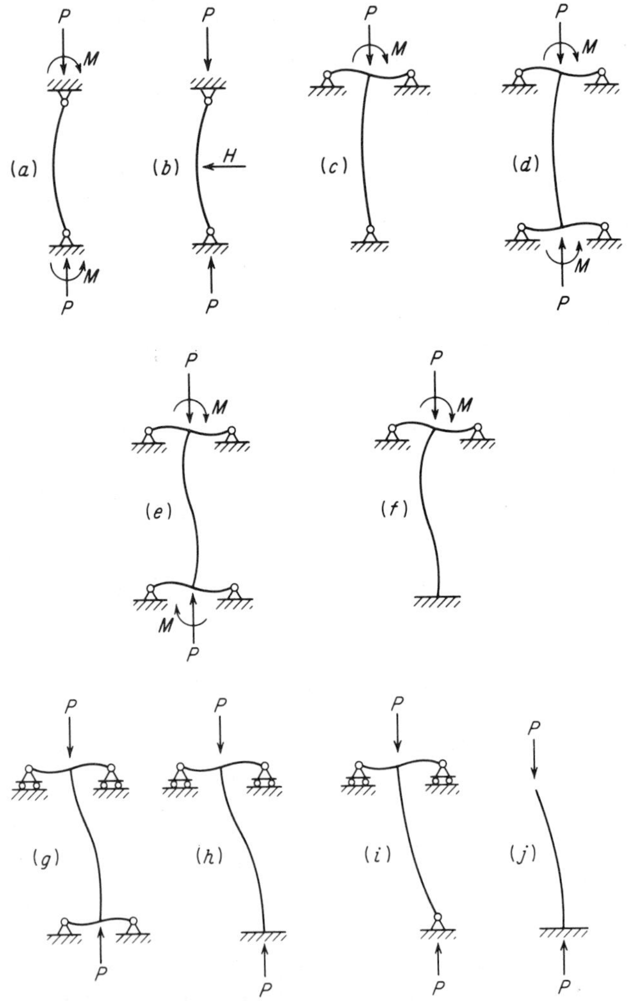

***Fig.* 5.29** Typical column situations, by ACI Code classification. Equation (5.38) holds for (*a*) to (*d*); Eq. (5.39) holds for (*e*) and (*f*); Eq: (5.42) holds for (*g*) to (*j*).

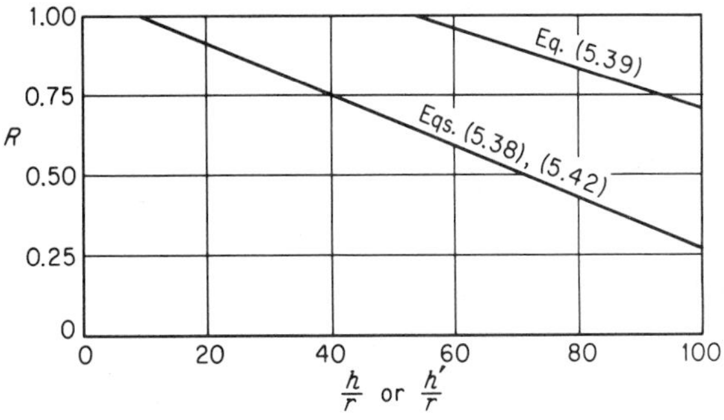

Fig. 5.30 ACI Code slenderness factors.

It was shown in Art. 5.10*b* that it is for this case that the moment magnification is particularly consequential. Hence, the reduction factor R decreases rapidly with increasing slenderness. Specifically, Eq. (5.38) applies to the four situations of Fig. 5.29*a* to *d*.

For *members bent in double curvature* by the applied forces or moments, the Code specifies

$$R = 1.32 - 0.006\frac{h}{r} \leqq 1 \tag{5.39}$$

It was shown in Art. 5.10*b* that for this case the moment magnification, if any, is much smaller than that for single curvature. Correspondingly, for any given slenderness ratio the reduction by Eq. (5.39) is much smaller than that by Eq. (5.38). Specifically, Eq. (5.39) applies to the situations of Fig. 5.29*e* and *f*.

The graphs of the two equations are shown in Fig. 5.30. It is seen that the limiting slenderness ratio, up to which no reduction is needed, is $(h/r)_{\text{lim}} = 8.75$ for Eq. (5.38) and $(h/r)_{\text{lim}} = 53$ for Eq. (5.39). It also shows the much smaller reductions which the Code applies to members bent in double curvature. The authors believe that, while it holds for some cases, this large difference may turn out to be exaggerated for others. Future refinements based on additional research are likely to reflect a more complete spectrum of behavior than is given by these two provisions.

c. Sidesway not prevented It was shown in Art. 5.10*a* that the effective length of a column not braced against sidesway ranges from the actual length h for rotationally fixed ends upward to very large values for the case in which little rotational restraint is provided. In the interest of safety it is, therefore, essential that account be taken of this variation of the effective length.

Based on suitable simplifications of more detailed information (Ref.

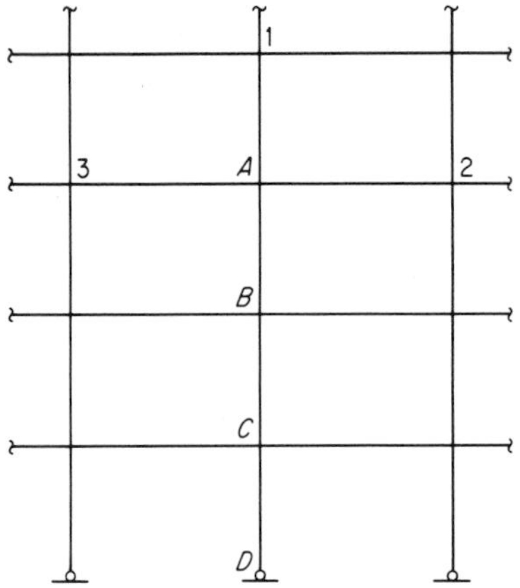

Fig. 5.31 Portion of typical building frame.

5.6), the Code provides the following method for determining the effective length of such a column:

It is first necessary to define and calculate the degree of end restraint at both ends of the column being designed. The rigidity of a structural member, i.e., its resistance to deflection or end rotation, is $K = EI/l$ (see Chap. 8). Consider the part of a building frame shown in Fig. 5.31. The column AB is restrained at its top by the girders $A2$ and $A3$. However, these same girders also provide restraint to the column above, $A1$. Consequently, the two members which tend to buckle, AB and $A1$, are restrained jointly at A by the two girders $A2$ and $A3$. The more rigid the girders in relation to the rigidities of the columns, the larger the degree of restraint against rotation of the columns at A. Therefore, the degree of restraint is $\Sigma K_{\text{girders}}/\Sigma K_{\text{columns}}$, the sums extending over all members in one plane meeting at the joint. In the Code equations, the reciprocal of this degree of restraint is used because it gives simpler expressions. This reciprocal is

$$r' = \frac{\Sigma K \text{ of columns}}{\Sigma K \text{ of girders or other floor members}}$$

the girders or floor members being located in one plane at one end of a column, such as end A of column AB. The magnitude of the end restraint being defined in this manner, the Code gives the effective length h' for *columns restrained against rotation at both ends* as

$$h' = h(0.78 + 0.22r') \geqq h \tag{5.40}$$

In this case, r' is defined as the average of the values at both ends of the given column (AB). It is seen that if r' is equal to or smaller than 1, then $h' = h$. This corresponds to the situation of Fig. 5.19*e*; i.e., the column in this case is regarded as effectively rotationally fixed at both ends. Specifically, Eq. (5.40) applies to the columns of Fig. 5.29*g* and *h*.

Equation (5.40) loses its meaning if one end is hinged, because in this case, at the hinged end, $r' = \infty$. The Code defines a hinged end as one either actually hinged or one in which the restraining members are so flexible that r' exceeds 25. For *columns restrained at one end and hinged at the other* (such as CD in Fig. 5.31), the effective length is given as

$$h' = 2h(0.78 + 0.22r') \geqq 2h \tag{5.41}$$

in which case r' is the value at the restrained end (end C of CD). Again, if r' is equal to or smaller than 1, this corresponds to the situation of Fig. 5.19*d* upside down; i.e., the column is regarded effectively fixed at one end and free to rotate at the other, resulting in an effective length $h' = 2h$. Specifically, Eq. (5.41) applies to the columns of Fig. 5.29*i* and *j*, the latter giving $h' = 2h$.

It was shown in Art. 5.10*b* that for columns not braced against sidesway the maximum moments of both kinds generally occur at the ends and that, consequently, full moment magnification takes place. For this reason, regardless of whether the column is bent into single or double curvature, the Code specifies the *reduction factor R for such unbraced columns* as

$$R = 1.07 - 0.008\frac{h'}{r} \leqq 1 \tag{5.42}$$

the same as is specified for braced columns bent in single curvature [Eq. (5.38)]. The difference is that for the latter the effective length is $h' = h$, whereas for the former h' will in general exceed the actual length h. This results in smaller values of R, that is, in a greater capacity reduction caused by slenderness. It agrees with the information presented in Art. 5.10 that the strength-reducing effects of slenderness are much larger in frames not braced against sidesway than in frames so braced. Specifically, Eq. (5.42) applies to the columns of Fig. 5.29*g* through *j*.

In laterally unbraced frames, the column moments which govern design are often caused by wind loading or, in seismic zones, by earthquake loads. These are loads of short duration as compared not only with dead load, but also with live loads caused by the usual types of occupancy. Deflections from such sustained loads are in part caused by creep (see Art. 2.7). In contrast, the described short-time loads are of such small duration that they do not cause creep deflections. Hence, the total magnitudes of these deflections, and of the moments Py caused by the deflections, are smaller than they would be under the more sustained regime of gravity loads. For this reason, when the *design is governed by lateral loads of short duration*, the Code permits the use of a 10 per cent more favorable reduction factor,

$$R = 1.18 - 0.009\frac{h'}{r} \leqq 1 \tag{5.43}$$

d. Columns governed by tension It is seen from Eq. (5.34) that the additional moment caused by P, that is, the moment magnification, depends not only on the slenderness ratio h'/r, but also on the magnitude of the compression force P. In particular, in the case of a simple, transversely loaded beam without axial force ($P = 0$), the additional moment and the moment magnification vanish, as they should.

On the other hand, the Code expressions for the reduction factor R which have just been presented have been developed for members with relatively large axial loads. For this reason they need modification for application to those members in which bending moments are relatively large and axial forces relatively small. In such a member the capacity of the cross section is governed by tension, i.e., by yielding of the steel. In the limit, for a simple beam with $P = 0$, the reduction factor must be $R = 1$. Correspondingly, the Code stipulates:

> When tension governs the design of the section, the factor R shall be considered to vary linearly from its full value at the balanced condition to a value of 1.0 when the axial load is zero.

Correspondingly, in this range in which the *eccentricity* e *exceeds the balanced value* e_b, the reduction factor can be obtained from

$$R' = 1 - (1 - R)\frac{e_b}{e} \geqq R \tag{5.44}$$

where R' = reduction factor for slender columns failing in tension
R = reduction factor according to applicable equation [Eq. (5.38), (5.39), (5.42), or (5.43)]
e = design eccentricity M/P
e_b = balanced eccentricity [see Eqs. (5.9), (5.13), (5.19)]

It is seen that for the balanced condition, $e = e_b$, Eq. (5.44) gives $R' = R$, the value prescribed for all columns whose strength is governed by compression. At the other extreme, for the case of purely flexural members, when $P = 0$, $e = M/P = \infty$, and Eq. (5.44) gives $R' = 1$. Within this range, R' is seen to increase gradually from R to 1.0, depending on the eccentricity e.

e. Concentrically loaded columns It appears clear from the preceding discussion that the R factors in the ACI Code are chiefly intended to reflect the moment-reduction factors (designated by C_M in Art. 5.11*a*) rather than the load-reduction factors C_P. Most axially compressed members are, in fact, subject to simultaneous bending and should be designed for the combined effect. However, cases do occur in which columns are subject to concentric compression loads without moments. An example is an interior column in a building frame braced against sidesway, with full live load on the floors above and below the column in question. If symmetry prevails, such a column may be entirely free from calculated moments. In other cases, moments may not be computed by the designer because, by inspection, they are known to be so small as to be negligible.

In such cases one cannot decide whether the column is bent in single or double curvature, because no external bending moments act to produce such curvature; consequently, the criterion for applying either Eq. (5.38) or (5.39) does not seem to hold. However, *when sidesway is prevented*, a column will buckle in single curvature (Fig. 5.19*a*) only if it is hinged at both ends. If it is fixed or significantly restrained, inflection points exist between the ends (Fig. 5.19*b* and *c*). Correspondingly, the authors suggest that, for concentrically loaded columns, Eq. (5.38) be used when little or no end restraint is present at either end, and that Eq. (5.39) be used when substantial rotational end restraint is present. One may assume substantial restraint to be present if the average values of r' at both ends are not larger than about 2.0. It is clear from the Code as well as from the preceding discussion of sidesway behavior that Eq. (5.42) applies *when sidesway is not prevented.*

Example In Example 2 of Art. 5.4*c* it was found that a 12×20 in. cross section with four No. 9 bars, for which $f'_c = 5000$ psi, $f_y = 75{,}000$ psi, and $p_t m = 0.295$, with an eccentricity $e = 0.75t$, has an ultimate design load $P_u = 188{,}000$ lb. The simultaneous moment is $M_u = 0.75 \times 20 \times 188{,}000 \text{ lb} = 2{,}820{,}000$ in.-lb. It was also found that tension governed the strength. Suppose that this cross section applies to the exterior column AB of the industrial building frame of Fig. 5.32. Gravity loading produces axial forces and moments such that $e/t = 0.75$, as in the quoted example. Determine the load and moment capacity of the column by ultimate-strength design (*a*) when the frame is laterally braced and (*b*) when it is not braced.

a. The radius of gyration of the columns is $r = 0.30 \times 20 = 6.0$ in., and the slenderness ratio in the braced condition, with $h' = h$, is $h/r = 240/6 = 40$. Gravity loads on girders AC and BD cause clockwise moments to act on joints A and B which bend column AB in double curvature. Consequently, when the frame is braced against sidesway, the slenderness reduction factor is found from Eq. (5.39) to be

$$R = 1.32 - 0.0006 \times 40 = 1.08 > 1.0$$

It is seen that no strength reduction is called for on account of slenderness, and the ultimate values to be used in design are equal to the full design strength of the cross section; that is, $P_u = 188{,}000$ lb, and $M_u = 2{,}820{,}000$ in.-lb.

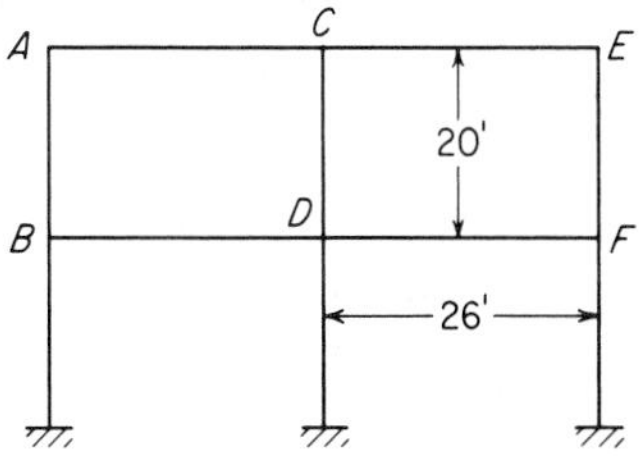

Exterior columns 12 x 20"
Girders 12 x 22"
Distances shown are clear lengths of members

Fig. 5.32

b. When the frame is not laterally braced, it is first necessary to determine the effective length h', depending on the amount of restraint at the ends. For the columns, the moment of inertia of the cross section is $I_c = (12 \times 20^3)/12 = 8000$, and the relative rigidity is $K_c = I_c/h = 8000/(20 \times 12) = 33.3$. The corresponding values for the girders are $I_g = 10{,}900$ and $K_g = 35.0$. (To simplify the example, clear lengths of members have been used to calculate K. In actual design it is customary and more accurate to use center-line distances for determining rigidities.) Hence the restraint factor r' for column AB is

At the top of the column: $r' = 33.3/35.0 = 0.95$
At the bottom of the column: $r' = 2 \times 33.3/35.0 = 1.91$
Average: $r' = (0.95 + 1.91)/2 = 1.43$

Then the effective length, by Eq. (5.42), is

$$h' = 240(0.78 + 0.22 \times 1.43) = 262 \text{ in.}$$

and the slenderness ratio is $h'/r = {}^{265}\!/_{6} = 43.8$. With this value, the reduction factor is obtained from Eq. (5.42) as

$$R = 1.07 - 0.008 \times 43.8 = 0.72$$

Hence, if compression governed the strength of the section, the slenderness effects would result in a 28 per cent reduction of the carrying capacity. However, for $e/t = 0.75$ it was found that tension governs. To calculate the corresponding reduction factor R' from Eq. (5.44), the balanced eccentricity e_b is needed. Using Eq. (5.9), with $p_t m = 0.295$,

$$e_b = (0.20 + 0.77 \times 0.295)t = 0.43t$$

and

$$R' = 1 - 0.28\frac{0.43t}{0.75t} = 0.84$$

It is seen that the capacity reduction caused by slenderness is 16 per cent, and the values to be used in design are

$$\text{Ultimate axial load} = 0.84 \times 188{,}000 = 158{,}000 \text{ lb}$$
$$\text{Ultimate bending moment} = 0.84 \times 2{,}820{,}000 = 2{,}370{,}000 \text{ in.-lb}$$

PROBLEMS

For the frame of the example above (Art. 5.11*e*), design the interior column *CD*. Maximum moments occur when live load is placed on spans *BD* and *CE*; these bend the column in single curvature. Under this loading the axial load from dead load is 70 kips, from live load 50 kips. Because of symmetry, dead load does not cause any moments. Maximum live-load moment in the column at *D* is 150 ft-kips. Steel and concrete are of the same strengths as in the example.

1. Design column *CD* by (*a*) ultimate-strength design and (*b*) working-stress design for this load-and-moment combination when the frame is (1) braced and (2) not braced against sidesway.

2. When full live load is placed on the girders on both sides of the column, gravity loads do not cause any moments. However, the axial load is increased by the additional live load which is now placed on girder *AC*. For this loading condition the axial load from dead load is 70 kips, from live load 100 kips, and the moment is zero. Check the columns designed in Prob. 1 for this condition of loading.

REFERENCES

5.1 A. H. Mattock, L. B. Kriz, and Eivind Hognestad: Rectangular Concrete Stress Distribution in Ultimate Strength Design, *J. ACI*, vol. 57, p. 875, 1961.
5.2 Boris Bresler: Design Criteria for Reinforced Concrete Columns under Axial Load and Biaxial Bending, *J. ACI*, vol. 57, p. 481, 1960; discussion, p. 1612.
5.3 S. P. Timoshenko and J. M. Gere: "Theory of Elastic Stability," 2d ed., McGraw-Hill Book Company, Inc., New York, 1961.
5.4 George Winter: Lateral Bracing of Columns and Beams, *Trans. ASCE*, vol. 125, p. 807, 1960.
5.5 Bengt Broms and I. M. Viest: Long Reinforced Concrete Columns, *Trans. ASCE*, vol. 126, part II, p. 309, 1961.
5.6 "Guide to Design Criteria for Metal Compression Members," Column Research Council, Ann Arbor, Mich., 1960.

chapter 6

FOOTINGS

6.1 Types and Function of Substructures The substructure, or foundation, is that part of a structure which is usually placed below the surface of the ground and which transmits the load to the underlying soil or rock. All soils compress noticeably when loaded and cause the supported structure to settle. The two essential requirements in the design of foundations are that the total settlement of the structure shall be limited to a tolerably small amount and that differential settlement of the various parts of the structure shall be eliminated as nearly as possible. With respect to possible structural damage, the elimination of differential settlement, i.e., different amounts of settlement within the same structure, is even more important than limitations on uniform overall settlement.

To limit settlements as indicated, it is necessary (1) to transmit the load of the structure to a soil stratum of sufficient strength and (2) to spread the load over a sufficiently large area of that stratum to minimize bearing pressure. If adequate soil is not found immediately below the structure, it becomes necessary to use deep foundations such as piles or caissons to transmit the load to deeper, firmer layers. If satisfactory soil directly underlies the structure, it is merely necessary to spread the load, by footings or other means. Such substructures are known as *spread* foundations, and it is mainly this type which will be discussed. Information on the more special types of deep foundations can be found in texts on foundation engineering.

6.2 Types of Spread Foundations Footings generally can be classified as wall and column footings. The horizontal outlines of the most common types are given in Fig. 6.1. A wall footing is simply a strip of reinforced concrete, wider than the wall, which distributes its pressure. Single-column footings are usually square, sometimes rectangular, and represent the simplest and most economical type. Their use under exterior columns meets with difficulties if property rights prevent the use of footings projecting beyond the exterior walls. In this case combined footings or strap footings are used which enable one to design a footing which will not project beyond the wall column. Combined footings under two or more columns are also used under closely spaced, heavily loaded interior columns where single footings, if they were provided, would completely or nearly merge.

Such individual or combined column footings are the most frequently used types of spread foundations on soils of reasonable bearing capacity. If the soil is weak and/or column loads are great, the required footing areas become so large as to be uneconomical. In this case, unless a deep foundation is called for by soil conditions, a mat or raft foundation is resorted to. This consists of a solid reinforced-concrete slab which extends under the entire building and which, consequently, distributes the load of the structure over the maximum available area. Such a foundation, in view of its own rigidity, also minimizes differential settlement. It consists, in its simplest form, of a concrete slab reinforced in both directions. A form which provides more rigidity and, at the same time, is often more economical consists of an inverted beam-and-girder floor. Girders are located in the column lines in one direction, with beams in the other, mostly at closer intervals. If the columns are arranged in a square pattern, girders are equally

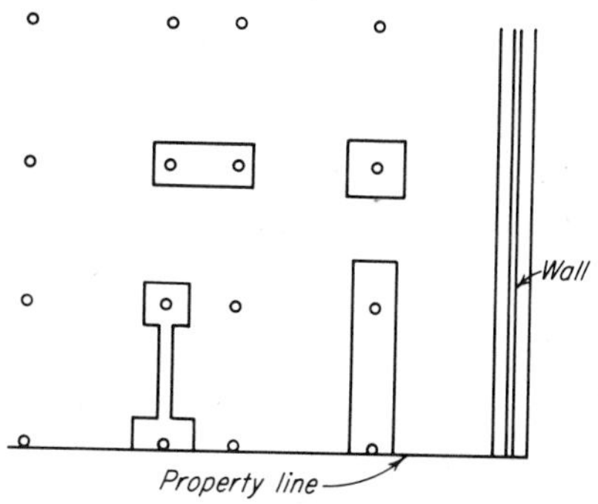

Fig. 6.1 Types of footings.

spaced in both directions, and the slab is provided with two-way reinforcement. Inverted flat slabs, with capitals at the bottoms of the columns, are also used for mat foundations.

6.3 Factors Affecting the Design of Concrete Footings In ordinary constructions the load on a wall or column is transmitted vertically to the footing, which, in turn, is supported by the upward pressure of the soil on which it rests. If the load is symmetrical with respect to the bearing area, the bearing pressure is assumed to be uniformly distributed. It is known that this is only approximately true. Under footings resting on coarse-grained soils the pressure is larger at the center of the footing and decreases toward the perimeter. This is so because the individual grains in such soils are somewhat mobile, so that the soil located close to the perimeter can shift very slightly outward in the direction of lower soil stresses. In contrast, in clay soils pressures are higher near the edge than at the center of the footing, since in such soils the load produces a shear resistance around the perimeter which adds to the upward pressure. It is customary to disregard these nonuniformities (1) because their numerical amount is uncertain and highly variable, depending on type of soil, and (2) because the influence of these irregularities on the magnitudes of bending moments and shearing forces in the footing is relatively small.

In order to avoid tilting of footings, the pressures under them should be symmetrically distributed, which implies that columns should be placed at the centers of single footings. For the same reason, for combined footings, the resultant of the column loads should strike at the center of the footing area. If this is not done, uneven pressure distribution will result in uneven settlement, with a corresponding tilting of the footing toward the side of higher soil pressure and possible damage to the superstructure. Only on quite incompressible soils (rock, highly compacted gravels) may exceptions be made to this rule.

The accurate determination of stresses, particularly in single-column footings, is not practical, since they represent relatively massive blocks which cantilever from the column in all four directions. Under uniform upward pressure they deform in a bowl shape, a fact which would greatly complicate an accurate stress analysis. For this reason present procedures for the design of such footings are based almost entirely on the results of two extensive experimental investigations, both carried out at the University of Illinois (Refs. 6.1, 6.2). These tests have recently been reevaluated, particularly in the light of newer concepts of strength in shear and diagonal tension (Refs. 6.2 to 6.4).

6.4 Reinforced-concrete Wall Footings The simple principles of beam action apply to wall footing with only minor modifications. Figure

6.2 shows a wall footing with the forces acting on it. If bending moments were computed from these forces, the maximum moment would be found to occur at the middle of the width. Actually, the very large rigidity of the wall modifies this situation, and the tests cited in Art. 6.3 show that for footings under concrete walls it is satisfactory to compute the moment at the face of the wall (section 1-1). Tension cracks in these tests formed at the locations shown in Fig. 6.2, i.e., under the face of the wall rather than in the middle. For footings supporting masonry walls, the maximum moment is computed midway between the middle and the face of the wall, since masonry is generally less rigid than concrete. The maximum bending moment in footings under concrete walls is, therefore, given by

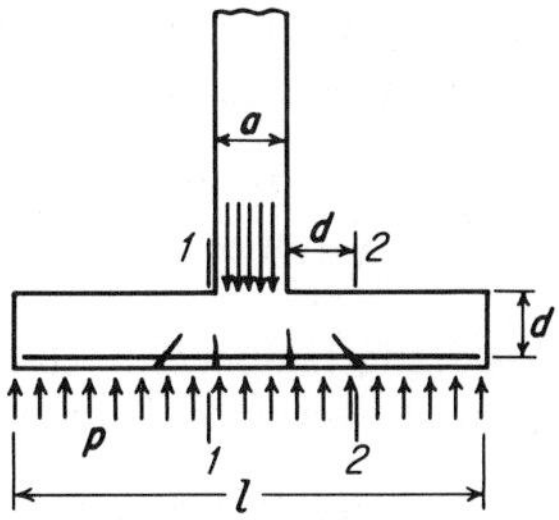

Fig. 6.2 Wall footing.

$$M = \tfrac{1}{8}p(l - a)^2 \tag{6.1}$$

The calculation of bond stresses is based on the shear for the same section, i.e.,

$$V_b = \tfrac{1}{2}p(l - a) \tag{6.2}$$

and the design provisions for bond are the same as for beams and one-way slabs.

For determining shear stresses, the vertical shear force is computed on section 2-2, located, as in beams, at a distance d from the face of the wall. Thus,

$$V_s = p\left(\frac{l - a}{2} - d\right) \tag{6.3}$$

It is generally not economical to use web reinforcement in footings.

Example: design of a wall footing A 16-in. concrete wall supports a total load of 23,100 lb per ft. The allowable bearing pressure of the soil is 2 tons per ft^2. Design a footing for this wall, using 2500-psi concrete and steel of $f_y = 40{,}000$ psi. Use working-stress design.

Assume the weight of the footing to be 900 lb per ft; the required width is then $24{,}000/4000 = 6$ ft. The net upward pressure caused by the wall load alone (see Art. 6.5 for explanation) is $23{,}100/6 = 3850$ lb per ft. This results in a moment at the critical sections 1-1 of

$$M = \tfrac{1}{8} \times 3850(6 - 1.33)^2 12 = 126{,}000 \text{ in.-lb per ft}$$

For the given grades of material, $K = 178$ and $j = 0.866$. The effective depth required for bending is

$$d = \sqrt{\frac{126{,}000}{178 \times 12}} = 7.7 \text{ in.}$$

Assuming temporarily that $d = 8.0$ in., the shear force to be used in computing shear stresses at a distance d from the wall is

$$V_s = 3850[\tfrac{1}{2}(6 - 1.33) - 8.0/12] = 6440 \text{ lb per ft}$$

and the effective depth required for shear is

$$d = \frac{6440}{12 \times \tfrac{7}{8} \times 55} = 11.2 \text{ in.}$$

It is seen that shear governs in this case. A depth of $d = 11.5$ in. is selected. *The ACI Code calls for a 3-in. clear insulation for footing bars,* which results in a total depth of 15 in.

The required area of transverse reinforcement is

$$A_s = \frac{126{,}000}{20{,}000 \times 0.866 \times 11.5} = 0.633 \text{ in.}^2 \text{ per ft}$$

Number 6 bars, 8 in. on centers, furnish $A_s = 0.66$ in.^{2} per ft. The area of one bar is 0.44 in.^{2}, its perimeter is 2.36 in., and its diameter is 0.75 in. With an allowable bond stress

$$u = \frac{4.8\sqrt{2500}}{0.750} = 320 \text{ psi}$$

the minimum development length required to develop the full allowable tension stress of 20,000 psi is

$$L_d = \frac{0.44 \times 20{,}000}{320 \times 2.36} = 11.6 \text{ in.}$$

The length of the bars, if end cover is 3 in., is $72 - 6 = 66$ in., and the actual development length from the section of maximum moment to the nearby end is

$$\tfrac{1}{2}(66 - 16) = 25 \text{ in.}$$

This being more than twice the required development length, flexural bond need not be checked.

The required longitudinal shrinkage reinforcement is

$$0.002 \times 12 \times 11.5 = 0.28 \text{ in.}^2 \text{ per ft of width of footing}$$

Number 5 bars spaced 12 in. on centers provide 0.31 in.^{2} per ft and have the added function of spacing the main reinforcement while the concrete is being poured. In addition, they help the footing to bridge accidental weak spots in the soil. For this reason it is good practice to select these bars somewhat in excess of the minimum requirements for shrinkage reinforcement.

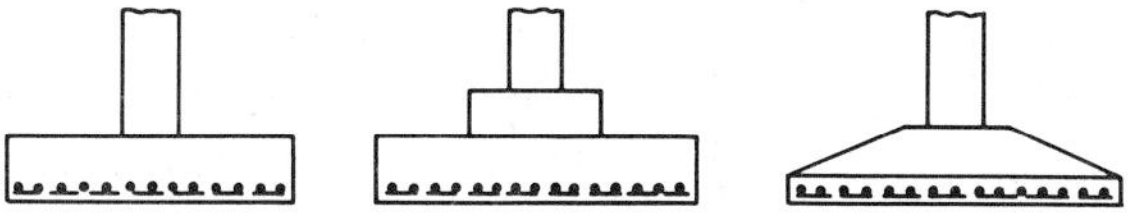

Fig. **6.3** Types of single-column footings.

6.5 Single-column Footings: General Information In plan, single-column footings are usually square. Rectangular footings are used if space restrictions dictate this choice, or if the supported columns are of strongly elongated rectangular cross section. In the simplest form, they consist of a single slab (Fig. 6.3*a*). Another type is that of Fig. 6.3*b*, where a pedestal or cap is interposed between the column and the footing slab; the pedestal provides for a more favorable transfer of load and in many cases is required in order to provide the necessary length for dowels. This form is also known as a *stepped* footing. All parts of a stepped footing must be poured in a single pour, in order to provide monolithic action. Sometimes sloped footings such as those in Fig. 6.3*c* are used. They require less concrete than stepped footings, but the additional labor necessary to produce the sloping surfaces (formwork, etc.) usually makes stepped footings more economical.

Single-column footings represent, as it were, cantilevers projecting out from the column in both directions and loaded upward by the soil pressure. Corresponding tension stresses are caused in both these directions at the bottom surface. Such footings are therefore reinforced by two layers of steel, perpendicular to each other and parallel to the edges.

The required bearing area is obtained by dividing the total load, including the weight of the footing, by the selected bearing pressure. Weights of footings, at this stage, must be estimated and amount usually to 4 to 8 per cent of the column load, the former value applying to the stronger types of soils.

In computing bending moments and shears, only that part of the upward pressure which is caused by the column load is considered. The weight of the footing proper does not cause moments or shears, just as, obviously, no moments or shears are present in a book lying flat on a table.

6.6 Design of Single Footings ***a. Bending moments, reinforcement, and bond*** If a vertical section is passed through a footing, the bending moment which is caused in the section by the net upward soil pressure (i.e., column load divided by bearing area) is obtained from simple statics. Figure 6.4 shows such a section *cd* located along the face of the column. The bending moment about *cd* is that caused by the

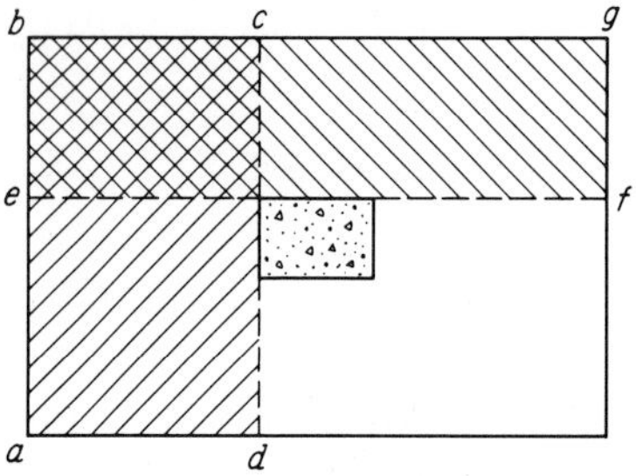

***Fig.* 6.4** Critical sections for bending and bond.

upward pressure on the area to one side of the section, i.e., the area *abcd*. The reinforcement perpendicular to that section, i.e., the bars running in the long direction, are calculated from this bending moment. Likewise, the moment about section *ef* is caused by the pressure on area *befg*, and the reinforcement in the short direction, i.e., perpendicular to *ef*, is calculated for this bending moment. In footings which support reinforced-concrete columns, these critical sections for bending are located at the faces of the column, as shown.

In footings supporting steel columns, the sections *ab* and *ef* are located, not at the edge of the steel base plate, but halfway between the edge of the column and that of the base plate.

In footings with *pedestals*, the width resisting compression in sections *cd* and *ef* is that of the pedestal; the corresponding depth is the sum of the thicknesses of pedestal and footing. Further sections parallel to *cd* and *ef* are passed at the edge of the pedestal, and the moments determined in the same manner, to check concrete and steel stresses at locations in which the depth is that of the footing only.

For footings with relatively small pedestals, the latter are often discounted in moment and shear computation, and bending is checked at the face of the column, with width and depth equal to that of the footing proper.

In *square footings*, the reinforcement is uniformly distributed over the width of the footing in each of the two layers, i.e., the spacing of the bars is constant. The moments for which the two layers are designed are the same. However, the effective depth d for the upper layer is less by 1 diam than that of the lower layer. Consequently, the required A_s is larger for the upper layer. Instead of using different spacings or different bar diameters in each of the two layers, it is customary to determine A_s for the upper layer and to use the same arrangement of reinforcement for the lower layer.

In *rectangular footings*, the reinforcement in the long direction is again uniformly distributed over the pertinent (shorter) width. In locating the bars in the short direction, one has to consider that the support provided to the footing by the column is concentrated near the middle. Consequently, the curvature of the footing is sharpest, i.e., the moment per foot largest, immediately under the column, and it decreases in the long direction with increasing distance from the column. For this reason a larger steel area per longitudinal foot is needed in the central portion than near the far ends of the footing. The ACI Code provides, therefore, that:

In the case of the reinforcement in the short direction that portion [of the reinforcement] determined by Eq. (6.4) shall be uniformly distributed across a band-width (B) centered with respect to the column and having a width equal to the length of the short side of the footing. The remainder of the reinforcement shall be uniformly distributed in the outer portion of the footing.

$$\frac{\text{Reinforcement in band-width } (B)}{\text{Total reinforcement in short direct}} = \frac{2}{(S+1)} \tag{6.4}$$

In Eq. (6.4), S is the ratio of the long side to the short side of the footing.

The critical sections for *bond* are the same as those for bending. Bond may also have to be checked at all vertical planes in which changes of section or of reinforcement occur, such as at the edges of pedestals or where part of the reinforcement may be terminated. The shear force to be used for calculating flexural bond is, again, the total upward pressure to one side of the critical section, e.g., the force on the area *abcd* when calculating flexural bond at section *cd*.

b. Shear A column supported by the slab of a simple footing (Fig. 6.5) tends to punch through that slab because of the shear stresses which act in the footing around the perimeter of the column. At the same time the concentrated compression stresses from the column spread out in the footing so that the footing concrete under and adjacent to the column is subject to vertical or somewhat inclined compression, in addition to shear. In consequence, if failure occurs, the fracture takes the shape of the truncated pyramid shown in Fig. 6.5 (or of a truncated cone for round columns), with sides sloping outward at approximately 45°. The average shear stress in the concrete which fails in this manner can

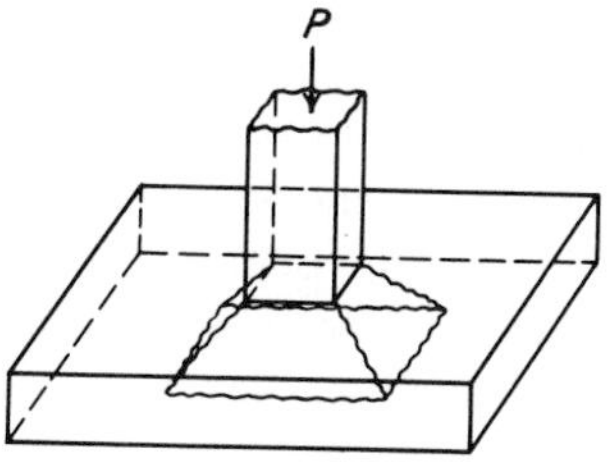

Fig. 6.5 Punching shear failure in single footing.

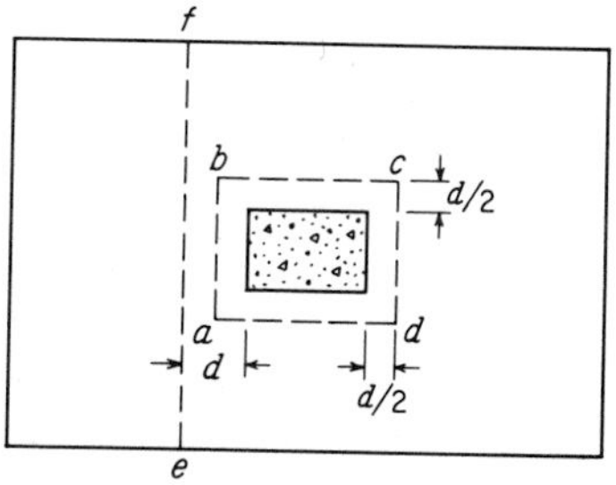

Fig. 6.6 Critical sections for shear.

be taken as that which acts on vertical planes laid through the footing at a perimeter a distance $d/2$ from the faces of the columns (vertical section through *abcd* in Fig. 6.6). Therefore, the nominal shear stress in the concrete in this critical perimeter section is

$$v = \frac{V}{b_0 d} \tag{6.5}$$

where b_0 = length of perimeter of critical section (*abcd* in Fig. 6.6)
V = shear force acting on that section, i.e., column load minus net upward soil pressure on area *abcd*

In addition to the described shear and vertical compression stresses, horizontal compression stresses caused by the bending moments act above the neutral plane on such a perimeter section. The simultaneous presence of vertical compression spreading out from the column and horizontal compression from bending increases the shear resistance of the concrete (see Art. 1.9). Tests of footings, as well as of flat slabs, have shown, correspondingly, that when a punching-type shear failure occurs the shear stress computed on this perimeter is larger than that in beams or one-way slabs and is approximately equal to $4\sqrt{f'_c}$ (Ref. 6.5). Therefore, the ACI Code stipulates that in ultimate-strength design

$$v_{uc} = \frac{V_u}{b_0 d} \leqq 4\phi\sqrt{f'_c} \tag{6.6a}$$

and in working-stress design

$$v_c = \frac{V}{b_0 d} \leqq 2\sqrt{f'_c} \tag{6.6b}$$

where V = shear force on perimeter section caused by sum of dead and live loads on column
V_u = sum of dead and live loads multiplied by respective load factors
$\phi = 0.85$

Shear failure can also occur at a section a distance d from the face of the column (such as section *ef* in Fig. 6.6), in the same manner as in beams or one-way slabs. For this reason the Code specifies additionally that shear in sections located at a distance d be checked in the same manner and for the same shear-stress values as in beams. (It will be noticed that these Code provisions for shear in footings are identical with those for slabs supported on columns, such as flat slabs or flat plates; see Art. 4.13.)

The preceding methods for locating the critical sections, both for bending and bond and for shear, are not directly applicable to *footings supporting round columns*, since, in this case, the "face of the column" needs special definition. The ACI Code specifies that for this purpose the face of the columns shall be taken as the side of the square having the same area as the column. The same holds for octagonal columns and for round or octagonal pedestals.

6.7 Transfer of Stress at Base of Column The compressive stress in the longitudinal reinforcement at the base of a reinforced-concrete column is transferred to the footing or pedestal by means of dowels. There should be at least one dowel for each column bar, and the total area of dowels must be at least equal to that of the column bars. The dowels must extend into the footing or pedestal the distance necessary to transfer to the concrete by bond their full working value, i.e., the area of the dowel times the full compression stress allowed on it. The dowels must extend up into the column a distance equal to that required for lapping of longitudinal columns bars; when f'_c is at least 3000 psi, this distance is 20, 24, or 30 diam for steel with specified yield strength of 50,000 psi or less, 60,000, or 75,000 psi, respectively.

When a column rests on a footing or pedestal, it transfers its load only to a part of the total area of the supporting member. The adjacent concrete, which is not under direct load, provides lateral support to the loaded part of the concrete, somewhat analogous to the function of spirals in columns. The permissible bearing stress on such partially loaded areas is, therefore, larger than that permitted in bearing over the full area. The ACI Code specifies the allowable bearing pressure on the full area (such as on the base area of a pedestal) as $0.25f'_c$, and on a partially loaded area (such as the top area of pedestal or footing) as $0.375f'_c$, if the loaded portion is one-third or less of the full area. The allowable stress on an area larger than one-third but less than the full area is obtained by linear interpolation between these two values. If the stress on the bottom surface of a pedestal is larger than $0.25f'_c$, the pedestal must be designed as a reinforced-concrete column. These values are for working-stress design. For ultimate-strength design, 1.9 times these values are to be taken.

6.8 Example: design of a square footing A column 18 in. square, with $f'_c = 4$ ksi, reinforced with eight No. 8 bars of $f_y = 50$ ksi, supports a dead load of 225 kips and a live load of 175 kips. The allowable soil pressure is 5 ksf. Design a square footing with $f'_c = 4$ ksi and $f_y = 50$ ksi. Use ultimate-strength design.

Assume the weight of the footing to be 6 per cent of the column load, or 24 kips; then the required bearing area is $^{424}\!/_5 = 84.8$ ft². A base 9 ft 3 in. square is selected, furnishing 85.5 ft². With the ultimate-strength load factors, the footing must be designed for a column load $P_u = 1.5 \times 225 + 1.8 \times 175 = 653$ kips. Then the net upward pressure for ultimate-strength design of the footing is $653/85.5 = 7.53$ ksf.

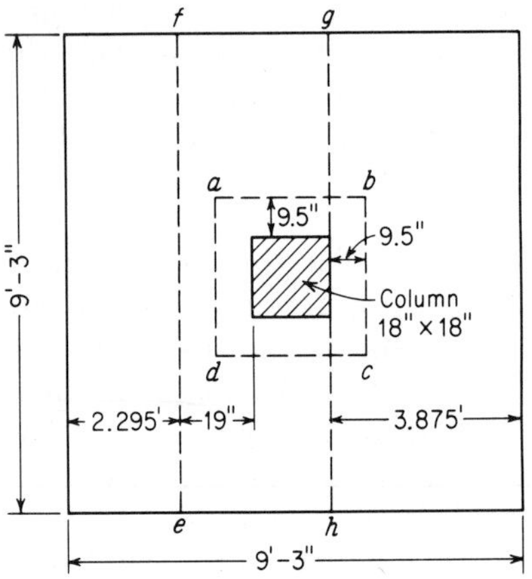

Fig. 6.7

The depth of such footings is usually governed by shear on the critical section *abcd* of Fig. 6.7. After one or two trials, a depth $d = 19$ in. is selected. From Eq. (6.6*a*), the shear stress on this section is not to exceed $4 \times 0.85 \sqrt{4000} = 215$ psi. The perimeter length of the critical sections is

$$b_0 = 4(18 + d) = 4(18 + 19) = 148 \text{ in.}$$

and the shear force on this perimeter is the column load minus the net upward pressure on the bearing area located within the perimeter; i.e.,

$$V_u = 653 = (^{37}\!/_{12})^2 7.53 = 581 \text{ kips}$$

Therefore, the nominal shear stress on the critical section *abcd* is

$$v_u = \frac{V_u}{b_0 d} = \frac{581{,}000}{148 \times 19} = 207 \text{ psi}$$

This being smaller than the maximum value of 215 psi, the section is adequate for resisting punching shear. It remains to check flexural shear on section *ef* of Fig. 6.7. The distance from that section to the edge is 2.295 ft, so that the nominal shear stress is

$$v_u = \frac{7530 \times 2.295 \times 9.25}{9.25 \times 19} = 76 \text{ psi}$$

The ultimate shear stress to be used in design is the same as in beams; i.e., taking the lower limit and neglecting the influence of moment [Eq. (3.36)],

$$v_c = 2 \times 0.85 \sqrt{4000} = 107 \text{ psi}$$

Since this is larger than 76 ksi, section *ef* is adequate in shear.

The moment on section *gh* of Fig. 6.7 is

$$M_u = 7.53 \times 9.25(3.875/2)^2 12 = 628 \text{ in.-kips}$$

The depth required for shear, $d = 19$ in., being greatly in excess of that required for bending, the steel ratio will be low, and the corresponding depth a of the equivalent rectangular stress block small. Assuming it to be $a = 2$ in., the steel area is

$$A_s = \frac{628}{0.9 \times 50(19 - 1)} = 7.75 \text{ in.}^2$$

Checking the depth of the rectangular stress block for this steel area,

$$a = \frac{7.75 \times 50}{0.85 \times 4 \times 9.25 \times 12} = 1.03 \text{ in.}$$

Hence, the lever arm is $c = 19 - 1.03/2 = 18.49$ in. rather than $19 - 1 = 18$ in. as assumed. The error is negligible and on the conservative side, and A_s need not be recomputed. Thirteen No. 7 bars, furnishing 7.82 in.², will be used in each direction.

The maximum design bond stress is $9.5\sqrt{f'_c}/D = 9.5\sqrt{4000}/0.875 = 685$ psi, and the required development length for No. 7 bars is

$$L_d = \frac{A_s f_y}{u\Sigma_0} = \frac{0.60 \times 50{,}000}{685 \times 2.75} = 15.9 \text{ in.}$$

The actual distance from section *gh* to the end of the bars, assuming 3 in. concrete cover at the ends, is $(3.875 \times 12) - 3 = 43.5$ in. This is greatly in excess of the required development length, and bond is adequate.

For concrete in contact with ground, a minimum cover of 3 in. is required for corrosion protection of the reinforcement. With $d = 19$ in. measured from the top face to the center of the upper layer of No. 7 bars, the total thickness of the footing, in order that 3 in. clear cover for the lower layer be provided, becomes

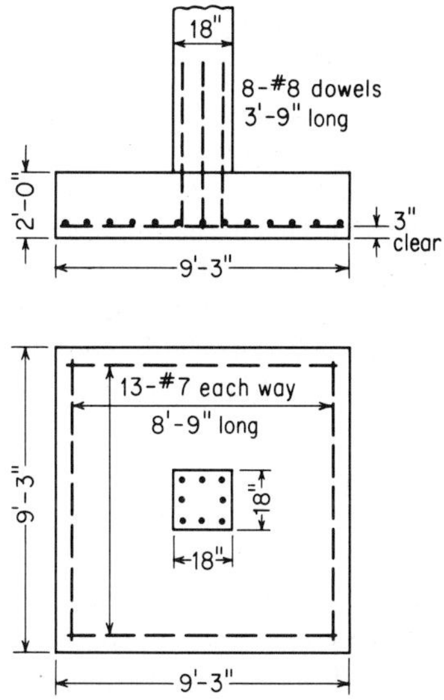

Fig. 6.8

$$t = 19 + 1.5 \times 0.875 + 3 = 23.2 \text{ in.}$$

say 24 in. The weight of the footing, $(9.25)^2 2 \times 150 = 25{,}600$ lb, is satisfactorily close to the assumed value of 24,000 lb.

For each of the No. 8 column bars there must be at least one dowel of equal size. With $f_y = 50$ ksi, the dowel must extend at least 24 diam or, for No. 8 bars, 24 in. upward into the column. It must reach downward into the footing at least the full development length. For No. 8 bars the maximum design bond stress is $9.5\sqrt{4000}/1.0 = 600$ psi, and the development length is

$$L_d = \frac{0.79 \times 50{,}000}{600 \times 3.14} = 21 \text{ in.}$$

This can just be accommodated in the 24 in. thickness with 3 in. cover. Had the required development length been greater than the available concrete thickness, a pedestal could have been used, or for each column bar two dowels of smaller diameter could have been provided.

The bearing stress at the interface of column and footing is $653/(18 \times 18) = 2.01$ ksi. This is less than the maximum permissible value of $1.9 \times 0.375 \times 4 = 2.85$ ksi. The footing is shown in Fig. 6.8.

6.9 Multiple-column Footings It is sometimes desirable and quite frequently necessary to support more than one column on the same footing. A multiple-column footing is necessary when two or more heavily loaded columns are so close to each other that there is not sufficient space for individual footings. They are also necessary when the face of an exterior column coincides with, or is close to, the property line so that a single footing centered under the column would project beyond that line. An eccentric single footing would result in unequal bearing-pressure distribution, with the possibility of tilting of the footing and consequent bending in the column. In such cases a combined footing, supporting the exterior and the adjacent interior column, can be so proportioned that the centroid of the footing area coincides with the resultant of the column loads, producing an even pressure distribution and uniform settlement without tilting.

A combined footing may be rectangular in plan or trapezoidal. The form is so chosen as to make the centroid and the resultant coincide. Hence, rectangular footings are suitable for interior columns, or for exterior columns when the exterior column has the lighter load and the footing may be extended beyond the interior column as far as necessary. The trapezoidal shape is required if column loads are unequal and if, for any reason, the footing cannot extend any appreciable distance beyond the heavier column.

Another expedient that is used if an independent footing cannot be centered under an exterior column is to place the exterior-column footing eccentrically and to connect it with the nearest interior-column footing by a beam or strap poured monolithically with both footings. This beam, which is counterweighted by the interior-column load, resists the tilting tendency of the eccentric exterior footing and equalizes the pressure under it. Such constructions are known as *strap*, *cantilever*, or *connected* footings.

6.10 Example: design of a combined footing supporting one exterior and one interior column An exterior 24 × 18 in. column with a total load of 200,000 lb and an interior 24 × 24 in. column with a total load of 300,000 lb are to be supported on a combined rectangular footing whose exterior cannot protrude beyond the outer face of the exterior column (see Fig. 6.1). The distance center to center of columns is 18 ft 0 in., and the allowable soil pressure is 4000 psf. Use working-stress design for a concrete with $f'_c = 3000$ psi and a steel with allowable stress $f_s = 20{,}000$ psi.

It is difficult to estimate the weights of footings of this type. The bearing area, as in single footings, depends only on the column loads and the bearing pressure. The depth, however, is often governed by the longitudinal bending moment, which increases rapidly with increasing distance between columns. Hence, for equal column loads and bearing pressures, larger column spacings result in heavier footings. As a crude rule, 6 to 15 per cent of the combined column loads can be taken as the approximate weight of such footings. In the present case, since the column spacing is relatively large and the bearing capacity rather low, the footing weight will be assumed as 12 per cent of the column loads, or 60,000 lb. The required bearing area is then $560{,}000/4000 = 140$ ft^2.

In order to secure uniform soil pressure, the centroid of the bearing area must coincide with the resultant of the column loads. The latter is located at a distance of $300{,}000 \times 18/500{,}000 = 10.8$ ft from the center of the exterior column. The length of the footing must be

$$2(10.8 + 0.75) = 23.1 \text{ ft}$$

A length of 23 ft 3 in. is selected. The required width is then

$$140/23.25 = 6.0 \text{ ft}$$

(see Fig. 6.10).

Longitudinally, the footing represents an upward-loaded beam spanning between columns and cantilevering beyond the interior column. Since this beam is considerably wider than the columns, the column loads are distributed crosswise by transverse beams, one under each column. In the present relatively narrow and long footing it will be found that the required minimum depth for the transverse beams is smaller than is required for the footing in the longitudinal direction. These "beams," therefore, are not really distinct members, but merely represent transverse strips in the main body of the footing, so reinforced that they are capable of resisting the transverse bending moments and the corresponding shears. It then becomes necessary to decide how large the effective width of this transverse beam can be assumed to be. Obviously, the strip directly under the column does not deflect independently and is strengthened by the adjacent parts of the footing. The effective width of the transverse beams is, therefore, evidently larger than that of the column, but cannot be taken as very much larger since the column load must be able to distribute itself reasonably uniformly over the entire width of the beam. In the absence of definite rules for this case, or research results on which to base such rules, the authors recommend that the effective width of such an integral, transverse beam be determined in the following manner: The effective width shall be equal to that of the column plus, on either side of the column, a strip of width equal to one-half that of the column or to one-half the depth of the footing, whichever is smaller. (This rule assumes that the load from the column will spread at an angle of about 30° with the vertical, a rather conservative assumption.)

Design in longitudinal direction The net upward pressure per longitudinal foot is $500{,}000/23.25 = 21{,}500$ lb per ft. The maximum negative moment between the columns occurs at the section of zero shear. Let x be the distance from the outer edge of the exterior column to this section. Then (see Fig. 6.9)

$$V = 21{,}500x - 200{,}000 = 0$$

results in $x = 9.32$ ft. The moment at this section is

$$M = [21{,}500 \times 9.32^2/2 - 200{,}000(9.32 - 0.75)]12 = -9{,}360{,}000 \text{ in.-lb}$$

The moment at the right edge of the interior column is

$$M = 21{,}500(3.5^2/2)12 = 1{,}575{,}000 \text{ in.-lb}$$

and the details of the moment diagram are as shown in Fig. 6.9.

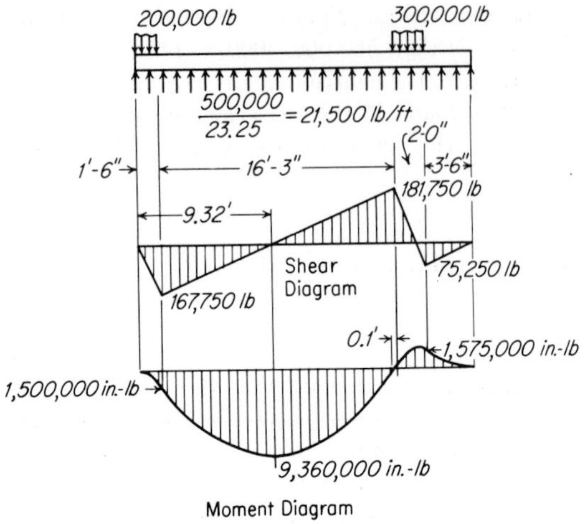

Fig. 6.9

The minimum depth of the footing is that necessary to accommodate the maximum moment without resort to compression reinforcement. With $K = 223$ (see Table 4, Appendix B),

$$d = \sqrt{\frac{9{,}360{,}000}{223 \times 72}} = 24.1 \text{ in.}$$

Trial calculations show that a larger depth is required for shear unless web reinforcement is employed. For footings it is usually more economical to increase d than to resort to web reinforcement. It is found that a depth $d = 28.5$ in. is adequate for that purpose.

From the shear diagram of Fig. 6.9 it is seen that the critical section for flexural shear is at a distance d to the left of the left face of the interior column. At that point, the shear force is

$$V = 181{,}750 - (28.5/12)21{,}500 = 129{,}600 \text{ lb}$$

and the shear stress is

$$v = \frac{129{,}600}{72 \times 28.5} = 63.2 \text{ psi}$$

The allowable shear stress (see Table 3.2) is $v_c = 60$ psi, unless use is made of the more liberal provision of Eq. (3.39). With the latter, the moment at the critical shear section is easily computed to be 450,000 ft-lb. Assuming $p_w = 0.01$ (to be checked later), Eq. (3.39) gives an allowable stress

$$v_c = \sqrt{3000} + 1300 \frac{0.01 \times 129{,}500(28.5/12)}{450{,}000} = 63.7 \text{ psi}$$

indicating that $d = 28.5$ is adequate.

Additionally, as in single footings, punching shear should be checked on a perimeter section a distance $d/2$ around the column, for which the allowable shear stress, from Eq. (6.6*b*), is $v_c = 2\sqrt{3000} = 109.5$ psi. Of the two columns, the exterior one with a three-sided perimeter a distance $d/2$ from the column is more critical in regard to this "punching shear." The perimeter is

$$b_0 = 2\left(1.5 + \frac{28.5/12}{2}\right) + (2.0 + 28.5/12) = 9.76 \text{ ft}$$

and the shear force, being the column load minus the soil pressure within the perimeter, is

$$V = 200{,}000 - 2.69 \times 4.38(21{,}500/6) = 157{,}700 \text{ lb}$$

Consequently, the shear stress on the perimeter section is

$$v = \frac{157{,}700}{9.76 \times 12 \times 28.5} = 47.2 \text{ psi}$$

considerably less than the allowable value.

With $d = 28.5$ in., and with 3.5-in. insulation from the center of the bars to the top surface of the footing, the total thickness is 32 in., and its weight is 55,700 lb, which agrees closely with the assumed value.

For the negative moment in the span between the columns, the required steel area is

$$A_s = \frac{9{,}360{,}000}{20{,}000 \times 7/8 \times 28.5} = 18.8 \text{ in.}^2$$

Fifteen No. 10 bars furnish $A_s = 20.25$ in.^{2} This represents a steel ratio $p = (20.25/72)28.5 = 0.0099$, very close to the value 0.01 assumed for calculating the allowable flexural shear stress from Eq. (3.39). The allowable bond stress for a No. 10 top bar is $3.4\sqrt{3000}/1.27 = 147$ psi, and the corresponding development length is

$$L_d = \frac{1.27 \times 20{,}000}{3.99 \times 147} = 43.5 \text{ in.} = 3.62 \text{ ft}$$

From Fig. 6.9, the distance from the point of maximum moment to the nearer left end of the bars is seen to be $9.32 - 3/12 = 9.07$ ft, much larger than the required minimum development length. The selected reinforcement is therefore adequate for both bending and bond.

For the portion of the longitudinal beam which cantilevers beyond the interior column,

$$A_s = \frac{1{,}575{,}000}{20{,}000 \times 7/8 \times 28.5} = 3.15 \text{ in.}^2$$

Eight No. 6 bars, with $A_s = 3.53$ in.^{2}, are selected, and their development length, computed as above but for bottom bars, is found adequate.

Design of transverse beam under interior column The width of the transverse beam under the interior column can now be established by the previously discussed rules to be $24 + 2 \times 12 = 48$ in. The net upward load per linear foot of the transverse beam is 300,000/6 = 50,000 lb per ft. The moment at the edge of the interior column is

$$M = 50{,}000(2^2/2)12 = 1{,}200{,}000 \text{ in.-lb}$$

Since the effective width of the transverse beam was determined as 48 in., the required depth is

$$d = \sqrt{\frac{1{,}200{,}000}{48 \times 223}} = 10.6 \text{ in.}$$

Since the transverse bars are placed on top of the longitudinal bars (see Fig. 6.10), the actual value of d furnished is, to the nearest quarter inch, 28.5 − 0.75 = 27.75 in. Then

$$A_s = \frac{1{,}200{,}000}{20{,}000 \times 0.9 \times 27.75} = 2.40 \text{ in.}^2$$

Seven No. 6 bars are selected and placed within the 48 in. effective width of the transverse beam, at a spacing of about 8 in. They are checked for bond, and it is found that their minimum development length L_d is considerably shorter than the distance from the edge of the column to the end of the bar.

Punching shear at the perimeter a distance $d/2$ from the column has been checked before. The critical section for regular flexural shear, at a distance d from the face of the column, lies beyond the edge of the footing, and, therefore, no further check on shear is needed.

The design of the transverse beam under the exterior column is the same as the design of that under the interior column, except that the effective width is 27 in. The details of the calculations are not shown. It will be easily checked that five No. 6 bars, placed within the 27 in. effective width, satisfy all requirements. Design details are shown in Fig. 6.10.

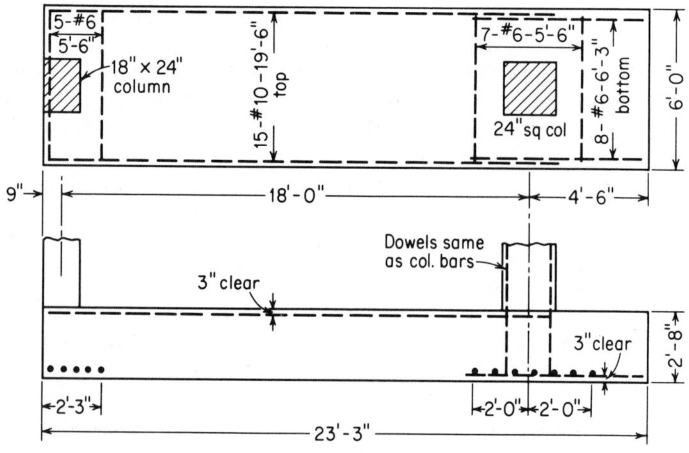

Fig. 6.10

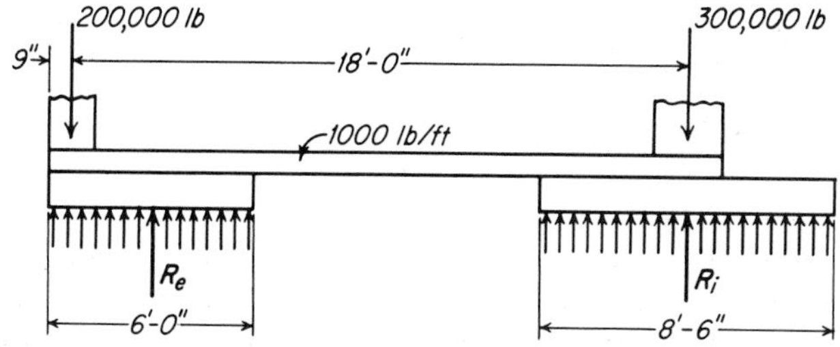

Fig. 6.11

6.11 Design of a Strap Footing In a strap or connected footing, the exterior footing is placed eccentrically under its column, in order that it does not project beyond the property line. Such a position would result in an uneven distribution of the bearing pressure and tipping of the footing. To counteract this tendency, the footing is connected by a beam or strap to the nearest interior footing.

The footing areas are so proportioned that the pressure under each of them is uniform and is the same under both footings. To achieve this, it is necessary, as in other combined footings, that the centroid of the combined area of the two footings coincide with the resultant of the column loads. The strap proper is generally constructed in such a manner that it will not bear directly on the soil.

To illustrate this design, the columns of Art. 6.10 will be so supported. Connected footings for larger column distances generally require less concrete than rectangular footings. Therefore the combined weight will be assumed to be $0.08(300{,}000 + 200{,}000) = 40{,}000$ lb. The total required bearing area is $540{,}000/4000 = 135$ ft^2.

In Art. 6.10 the resultant of the column loads was found to be located 10.8 ft from the center of the exterior column, or 11.55 ft from the exterior face of that column. To distribute the two footing areas so that their total will add up to the required 135 ft^2 and their centroid will be located at 11.55 ft from the outer edge requires several trial computations. The arrangement shown in Fig. 6.12 was determined by such trials and provides exactly 135 ft^2 of area. Its centroid is located at a distance $\bar{x} = (72 \times 18.75 + 63 \times 3.0)/135 = 11.40$ ft from the outer edge, which only insignificantly differs from 11.55 ft.

To compute the moments and shears in the various parts of the connected footings, it is first necessary to determine the intensity and location of all external forces and reactions. These are shown in Fig. 6.11. Since the footing areas are so arranged that the pressure on each of them is uniform, the resultants of these net pressures, R_e and R_i, act at the centers of the respective footings. Assuming the weight of the strap to be 1000 lb per ft, R_e is found by equating to zero the moments about the center line of the interior column; i.e.,

$$200{,}000 \times 18.0 + 1000 \times 18.75^2/2 - R_e \times 15.75 = 0$$

Hence $R_e = 240{,}000$ lb. The reaction R_i is then found by equating to zero the sum of all vertical forces; i.e.,

$$200{,}000 + 300{,}000 + 1000 \times 18.75 - 240{,}000 - R_i = 0$$

Hence $R_i = 278{,}750$ lb.

The design of the various parts of this strap footing is little different from that of other similar members. For this reason, the design features will merely be discussed in general terms, without showing the actual computations.

Design of strap The strap represents a single-span beam loaded upward by the loads transferred to it by the two footings and supported by downward reactions at the center lines of the two columns. Thus, the upward load in the portion from the exterior edge to a point 6 ft from that edge is simply $240{,}000/6 = 40{,}000$ lb per ft. A width of $b = 28$ in. is selected. For a column width of 24 in. this permits placing of beam and column bars where the two members intersect and allows the column forms to be supported on the top surface of the strap. With this width, the maximum moment determines the required depth of the strap. The location of maximum moment is determined by equating the shear force to zero and is found to be located 5.13 ft from the exterior edge. The moment decreases toward the interior column and is zero at the center line of that column. Hence, half the strap reinforcement is discontinued where no longer needed, and the other half is carried through the interior column.

In the portion of the strap immediately adjacent to the exterior column, the shear force is larger than that which can be resisted by the concrete alone. Web reinforcement is placed in this region; in view of the large width of the beam, it takes the form of double-looped stirrups (see Fig. 6.12).

Design of footings The *exterior footing* performs exactly like a wall footing of 6-ft length. Even though the column is located at its edge, the balancing action of the strap is such as to transmit the total reaction $R_e = 240{,}000$ lb uniformly over the 6-ft length, thus resulting in the desired uniform soil pressure. The design is carried out exactly as for a wall footing (see Art. 6.4).

The interior footing is loaded in a manner which makes it perform like a square single-column footing (see Arts. 6.6 and 6.8). The main difference is that, because of the presence of the strap, punching cannot occur along the truncated cone surfaces of Fig. 6.5. For this reason, punching shear [according to Eqs. (6.6)] should be checked along a perimeter section located at a distance $d/2$ outward from the longitudinal edges of the strap and from the free face of the column. Flexural shear, as usual, is checked at a distance d from the face of the column.

The weight of this strap footing is 44,700 lb, sufficiently close to the assumed value of 40,000 lb. It is interesting to compare this value with the weight of the combined footing designed in Art. 6.10 for the same situation. This weight was 55,700 lb, or about 25 per cent more than that of the strap footing. The actual saving in using the latter will be somewhat smaller than 25 per cent, since the steel ratio in the strap footing is larger than that in the combined footing, and somewhat more complex formwork is required for the former. Even so, the saving is substantial and would be even larger for greater distances between the two columns.

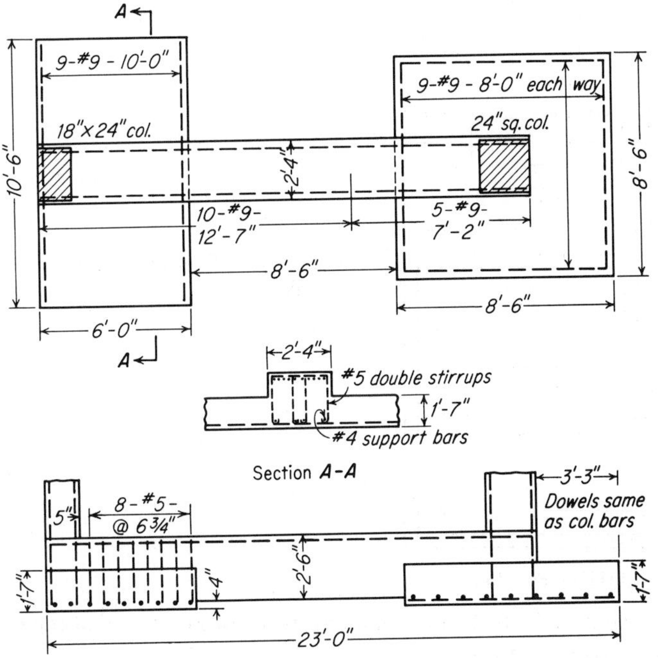

Fig. **6.12**

Complete details are shown in Fig. 6.12. The bottom of the strap has been located 4 in. above the bottom of the footings. This permits the bottom planks of the strap forms to be placed on wedges, so that they can be withdrawn after the concrete has hardened. This prevents direct bearing of the strap on soil. Depending on soil conditions, additional stirrups and longitudinal reinforcement at the bottom of the strap may be placed to guard against unforeseen shears and reverse moments due to possible uneven settlement.

6.12 Footings on Piles If soil conditions require the use of piles, these are usually driven in clusters, one to each column, and the load is transferred from the column to the piles by a footing. The design of such pile-supported footings is not much different from that of footings resting directly on soil, except for some special features.

The size of the footing is determined by the required number of piles and by the spacing between them, which usually, for friction piles, is not less than 3 ft for concrete piles or 2.5 ft for timber or H piles. End-bearing piles are sometimes driven at closer distances. The tops of the piles must be securely embedded in the footing. For this purpose the bottom of the footing is located not less than 6 in. below the top of the piles, and the distance from the center of outside piles to the edge of the footing is not

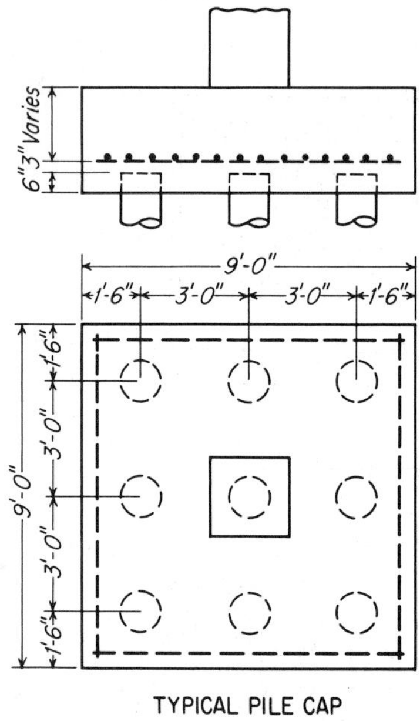

Fig. **6.13** Typical single-column footing on piles.

made less than 1.5 ft. Reinforcement is located at a distance of 3 in. above the tops of the piles.

Occasionally, individual piles are not driven to the design depth, with the result that their tops remain above the planned elevation. Under no circumstances should the footing reinforcement in such cases be bent around the protruding pile. If this were done, the smaller depth of concrete left above the top of such a pile and the complete absence of reinforcement above it would make it possible for the pile to punch through the footing. For this reason such piles must be cut to the required elevation before the footing is poured.

In designing the footing, the load from the column is assumed to be uniformly distributed to all piles in the cluster. For this purpose piles must be arranged symmetrically about the axis of the column. The net load per pile, i.e., the column load divided by the number of piles, is then assumed to act as an upward load on the footing, concentrated at the center of the pile.

The critical sections for moment and bond are the same as for footings resting on soil.

While for bending computations the pile reactions are assumed to be concentrated at the pile centers, in computing shear forces account is taken of the fact that these reactions are actually distributed over the bearing area of the pile. The fact that shear is usually the critical feature which determines the depth of a footing is the reason for the greater refinement in this determination. It is obviously unrealistic to assume that if the center of a pile is located 1 in. inside the critical section it will not produce any shear on that section, while, if it is located 1 in. outside, its full value will contribute to the shear. Correspondingly, the ACI Code stipulates:

> In computing the external shear, the entire reaction from any pile whose center is located 6 in. or more outside the section shall be assumed as producing shear on the section; the reaction from any pile whose center is located 6 in. or more inside the section shall be assumed as producing no shear on the section. For intermediate positions of the pile center, the portion of the pile reaction to be assumed as producing shear on the section shall be based on straight line interpolation between full value at 6 in. outside the section and zero value at 6 in. inside the section.

Actual pile positions frequently differ from assigned locations. On occasion this happens even with careful construction supervision and workmanship, particularly in irregular soils in which boulders and other obstructions may deflect piles during driving. Such off-location piles may produce moments and shears significantly in excess of the computed values. By the above-quoted rule, unfavorable pile displacements as small as 1 ft may change the shear on the section by an amount equal to the total pile reaction. Pile footings for soils in which such displacements are likely to occur should, therefore, be designed conservatively, that is, with unit stresses considerably below the stipulated values. By this means a strength reserve is created which is available in case actual moments and shears exceed the values computed for perfect pile location. Details of a typical footing on piles are shown in Fig. 6.13.

REFERENCES

6.1 A. N. Talbot: "Reinforced Concrete Wall Footings and Column Footings," *Univ. Illinois Eng. Exp. Sta. Bull.* 67, March, 1913.
6.2 F. E. Richart: Reinforced Concrete Wall and Column Footings, *J. ACI*, vol. 45, pp. 97, 237, 1948.
6.3 E. Hognestad: Shearing Strength of Reinforced Column Footings, *J. ACI*, vol. 50, p. 189, 1953.
6.4 J. Moe: Shearing Strength of Reinforced Concrete Slabs and Footings under Concentrated Loads, *Portland Cement Assoc. Res. Develop. Lab. Dep. Develop. Bull.* D47.
6.5 "Shear and Diagonal Tension," part 3, Slabs and Footings, Report of ACI-ASCE Committee 326, *J. ACI*, vol. 59, p. 353, 1962.

chapter 7
RETAINING WALLS

7.1 Function and Types of Retaining Walls Retaining walls are used to hold back masses of earth or other loose material where conditions make it impossible to let those masses assume their natural slopes. Such conditions occur when the width of an excavation, cut, or embankment is restricted by conditions of ownership, use of the structure, or economy. Thus, in railway or highway construction the width of the right of way is fixed, and the cut or embankment must be contained within that width. Similarly, the basement walls of buildings must be located within the property and must retain the soil surrounding the basement.

Free-standing retaining walls, as distinct from those which form parts of structures, such as basement walls, are of various types, the most common of which are shown in Fig. 7.1. The gravity wall (Fig. 7.1*a*) retains the earth entirely by its own weight. The reinforced-concrete cantilever wall (Fig. 7.1*b*) consists of the vertical arm which retains the earth and

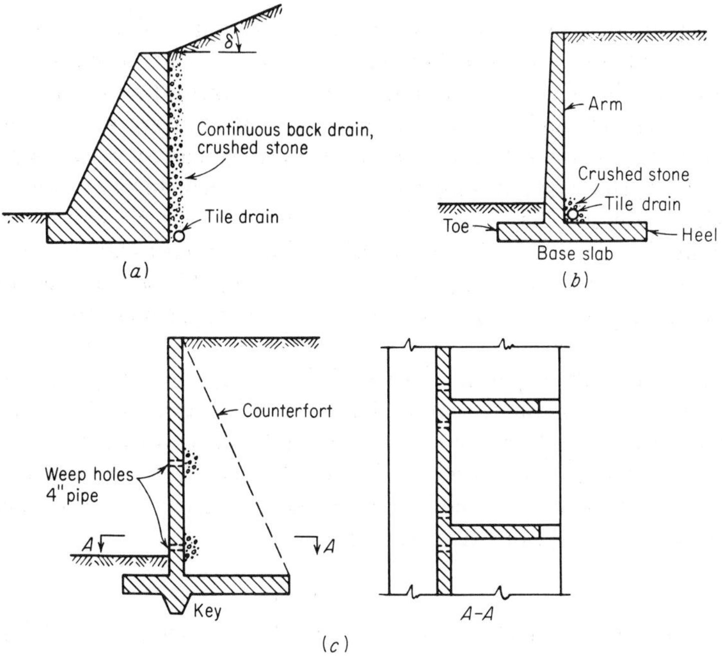

Fig. 7.1 Types of retaining walls and backdrains: (*a*) gravity wall; (*b*) cantilever wall; (*c*) counterfort wall.

is held in position by the footing or base slab. In this case the weight of the fill on top of the heel, in addition to the weight of the wall, contributes to the stability of the structure. Since the arm represents a vertical cantilever, its required thickness increases rapidly with increasing height. To reduce the bending moments in vertical walls of great height, counterforts are used spaced at distances from each other equal to or slightly larger than one-third of the height (Fig. 7.1*c*). Property rights or other restrictions sometimes make it necessary to place the wall at the forward edge of the base slab, i.e., to omit the toe. Wherever it is possible, toe extensions of one-third to one-fourth of the width of the base provide a more economical solution.

Which of the three types of walls is appropriate in a given case depends on a variety of conditions, such as local availability and price of construction materials and property rights. In general, gravity walls are economical only for relatively low walls, possibly up to about 15 ft. Cantilever walls are economical for heights from 10 to 20 ft, while counterforts are indicated for greater heights.

7.2 Earth Pressure In their physical behavior soils and other granular masses occupy a position intermediate between liquids and solids. If sand is poured from a dump truck, it flows, but, unlike a frictionless liquid, it will not assume a horizontal surface. It maintains itself in a stable heap with sides subtending with the horizontal an *angle of repose* whose tangent is roughly equal to the coefficient of intergranular friction. If a pit is dug in clay soil, its sides can usually be made vertical over considerable depths without support; i.e., the clay will behave like a solid and will retain the shape it is given. If, however, the pit is flooded, the sides will give way, and, in many cases, the saturated clay will be converted nearly into a true liquid. The clay is capable of maintaining its shape by means of its internal cohesion, but flooding reduces that cohesion greatly, often to zero.

If a wall is built in contact with a solid, such as a rock face, no pressure is exerted on it. If, on the other hand, a wall retains a liquid, as in a reservoir, it is subject at any level to the hydrostatic pressure $w_w h$, where w_w is the unit weight of water, and h the distance from the surface. If a vertical wall retains soil, the earth pressure similarly increases proportionally to the depth, but its magnitude is

$$p = Cwh \tag{7.1}$$

where w is the unit weight of the soil, and C is a constant which depends on the physical characteristics of the soil.

The pressure which soil exerts on an immovable wall, known as the *rest pressure,* has not been investigated thoroughly. The few measurements that have been made seem to indicate that in this case $C = 0.4$ to 0.5 for uncompacted, noncohesive soils, such as sands and gravels, while it may be as high as 0.8 for the same soils in a highly compacted state. For cohesive clay soils, C appears to be of the order of 0.7 to 1.0.

Usually, however, walls move slightly under the action of the earth pressure. Since walls are constructed of elastic material, they deflect under the action of the pressure, and since they generally rest on compressible soils, they tilt and shift away from the fill. For this reason, the wall is often constructed with a slight batter toward the fill on the exposed face, so that, if and when such tilting takes place, it does not appear evident to the observer. Even if this movement at the top of the wall is only of the order of a fraction of a per cent of the wall height ($\frac{1}{2}$ to $\frac{1}{10}$ per cent according to tests by C. Terzaghi), the rest pressure is materially decreased by it. The magnitude of this pressure against slightly yielding walls is much better explored and known than the rest pressure

If the wall moves away from the fill, a sliding plane ab (Fig. 7.2) forms in the soil mass, and the wedge abc, sliding along that plane, exerts pressure against the wall. Here the angle ϕ is known as the *angle of internal friction;* i.e., its tangent is equal to the coefficient of intergranular friction, which can be determined by appropriate laboratory tests. The corresponding pressure is known as the *active earth pressure*. If, on the other hand, the wall is pushed against the fill, a sliding plane ad is formed, and the wedge acd is pushed upward by the wall along that plane. The pressure which this larger wedge exerts against the wall is known as the *passive earth pressure*. (This latter case will occur, for example, at the left face of the gravity wall of Fig. 7.1 when this wall yields slightly to the left under the pressure of the fill.)

The magnitude of these pressures has been analyzed by Rankine, Coulomb, and others. If the soil surface subtends an angle δ with the horizontal (Fig. 7.1a), then, according to Rankine, the coefficient for active earth pressure is

$$C_a = \cos \delta \frac{\cos \delta - \sqrt{\cos^2 \delta - \cos^2 \phi}}{\cos \delta + \sqrt{\cos^2 \delta - \cos^2 \phi}} \tag{7.2}$$

and that for passive pressure is

$$C_p = \cos \delta \frac{\cos \delta + \sqrt{\cos^2 \delta - \cos^2 \phi}}{\cos \delta - \sqrt{\cos^2 \delta - \cos^2 \phi}} \tag{7.3}$$

For the frequent case of horizontal surface, that is, $\delta = 0$ (Fig. 7.2), for active pressure,

$$C_{ah} = \frac{1 - \sin \phi}{1 + \sin \phi} \tag{7.4}$$

and for passive pressure,

$$C_{ph} = \frac{1 + \sin \phi}{1 - \sin \phi} \tag{7.5}$$

Rankine's theory is valid only for noncohesive soils such as sand and gravel but, with corresponding adjustments, can also be used successfully for cohesive clay soils.

From Eqs. (7.1) to (7.5) it is seen that the earth pressure at a given depth h depends on the inclination of the surface δ, the unit weight w, and the angle of friction ϕ. The first two of these are easily determined, while little agreement has yet been reached as to the proper values of ϕ. For the ideal case of a dry, noncohesive fill, ϕ could be determined by

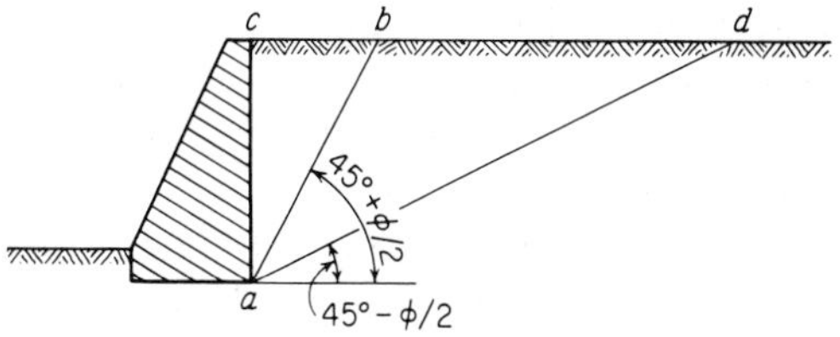

Fig. 7.2

laboratory test and then used in the formulas. This is impossible for clays, only part of whose resistance is furnished by intergranular friction while the rest is due to internal cohesion. For this reason their actual ϕ values are often increased by an arbitrary amount to account implicitly for the added cohesion. However, this is often unsafe since, as was shown by the example of the flooded pit, cohesion may vanish almost completely due to saturation and inundation.

In addition, fills behind retaining walls are rarely uniform, and, what is more important, they are rarely dry. Proper drainage of the fill is vitally important to reduce pressures (see Art. 7.5), but even in a well-drained fill the pressure will temporarily increase during heavy storms or sudden thaws. This is due to the fact that even though the drainage may successfully remove the water as fast as it appears, its movement through the fill toward the drains causes additional pressure (seepage pressure). In addition, frost action and other influences may temporarily increase its value over that of the theoretical active pressure. Many walls which were designed without regard to these factors have failed, been displaced, or cracked.

It is good practice, therefore, to select conservative values for ϕ, considerably smaller than the actual test values, in all cases except where extraordinary and usually expensive precautions are taken to keep the fill dry under all conditions. An example of recommended earth-pressure values, which are quite conservative though based on extensive research and practical experience, can be found in Ref. 7.1. Less conservative values are often used in practical designs, but these should be employed with caution in view of the fact that occasional trouble has been encountered with walls so designed.

Table 7.1 gives average values for w and two columns of values for ϕ. The first of these has been adapted by the authors from the information of Ref. 7.1; the second represents magnitudes which are frequently used in engineering practice and, at least for noncohesive soils, are closer to the actual laboratory test values. In contrast to the first, however, these take no account of probable additional pressures due to porewater, seepage, frost, etc. The table also contains values for the coefficient of friction f between concrete and various soils.

It is seen that the values of ϕ according to Ref. 7.1, particularly for soils 4 and 5, are considerably more conservative than the values of ϕ often used in engineering practice and reflect the fact that clays and silts, under suitable conditions of saturation, may become entirely liquid (that is, $\phi = 0$).

The low values of ϕ for soils 3 to 5 and the resulting high soil pressures indicate that soils of type 1 or 2 should be used for backfills of retaining walls wherever possible.

***Table* 7.1 Unit weights, effective angles of internal friction ϕ, and coefficients of friction with concrete, f**

Soil*	Unit weight, pcf	ϕ*	ϕ†	f
1. Sand or gravel without fine particles, highly permeable	110–120	35°	33–40°	0.5–0.6
2. Sand or gravel with silt mixture, low permeability	120–130	32°	25–35°	0.4–0.5
3. Silty sand, sand and gravel with high clay content	110–120	26°	23–30°	0.3–0.4
4. Medium or stiff clay	100–120	0‡	25–35°	0.25–0.4
5. Soft clay, silt	90–110	0°	20–25°	0.2–0.3

* Adapted from Ref. 7.1.
† Values often used.
‡ For this case the distance (h − 4 ft) should be used instead of h in Eq. (7.1).

7.3 Earth Pressure for Common Conditions of Loading In computing earth pressures on walls, three common conditions of loading are most often met: (1) horizontal surface of fill at the top of the wall, (2) inclined surface of fill sloping up and back from the top of the wall, and (3) horizontal surface of fill carrying a uniformly distributed additional load (surcharge) such as from goods in a storage yard or traffic on a road.

The increase in pressure caused by uniform surcharge s (case 3) is computed by converting its load into an equivalent, imaginary height of earth h' above the top of the wall such that

$$h' = \frac{s}{w} \tag{7.6}$$

and measuring the depth to a given point on the wall from this imaginary surface. This amounts to replacing h with $(h + h')$ in Eq. (7.1).

The distributions of pressure for cases 1 to 3 are shown in Fig. 7.3. The total earth thrust P per linear foot of wall is evidently equal to the area under the pressure-distribution figure, and its line of action passes through the centroid of the pressure. Figure 7.3 gives information, computed in this manner, on magnitude, point of action, and direction of P for these three cases.

Occasionally retaining walls must be built for conditions in which the ground-water level is above the base of the wall, either permanently or seasonally. In that case the pressure of the soil *above* ground water is determined as usual. The part of the wall *below* ground water is subject to the sum of the water pressure and the earth pressure. The former is equal to the full hydrostatic pressure $p_w = w_w h_w$, where w_w and h_w are, respectively, the unit weight of water and the distance from ground-

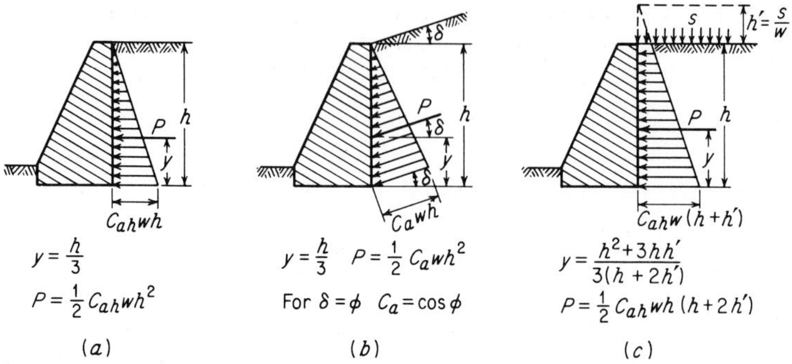

***Fig.* 7.3** Earth pressures for (*a*) horizontal surface; (*b*) sloping surface; (*c*) horizontal surface with surcharge *s*.

water level to the point on the wall. The additional pressure of the soil below ground-water level is computed from Eq. (7.1), where, however, for the portion of the soil below water, w is replaced with $w - w_w$, while h, as usual, is measured from the soil surface. That is, for submerged soil, buoyancy reduces the effective weight in the indicated manner. Pressures of this magnitude, which are considerably larger than those of drained soil, will also occur temporarily after heavy rainstorms or thaws in walls without provision for drainage, or if drains have become clogged.

The seeming simplicity of the determination of earth pressure as here indicated should not lull the designer into a false sense of security and certainty. No theory is more accurate than the assumptions on which it is based. Actual soil pressures are affected by irregularities of soil properties, porewater and drainage conditions, and climatic and other factors which cannot be expressed in formulas. This situation, on the one hand, indicates that involved refinements of theoretical earth-pressure determinations, as sometimes attempted, are of little practical value. On the other hand, the design of a retaining wall is seldom a routine procedure, since the local conditions that affect pressures and safety vary from one locality to another.

7.4 External Stability A wall may fail in two different ways: (1) its individual parts may not be strong enough to resist the acting forces, such as when a vertical cantilever wall is cracked by the earth pressure acting on it, and (2) the wall as a whole may be bodily displaced by the earth pressure, without breaking up internally. To design against the first possibility requires the determination of the necessary dimensions, thicknesses, reinforcements, etc., to resist the moments and shears; this procedure, then, is in no way different from that of determining required dimensions and reinforcements of other types of concrete structures. To safeguard the wall against bodily displacements, on the other hand, i.e., to ensure its external stability, requires special consideration.

A wall, such as that of Fig. 7.4, together with the soil mass *ijkl* which rests on the base slab, may be bodily displaced by the earth thrust P which acts on plane *ak* by *sliding* along the plane *ab*. Such sliding is resisted by the friction between soil and footing along the same plane. To forestall motion, the forces that resist sliding must exceed those that tend to produce sliding; a factor of safety of 1.5 is generally assumed satisfactory in this connection.

In Fig. 7.4, the force that tends to produce sliding is the horizontal component P_h of the total earth thrust P. The resisting friction force is fR_v, where f is the coefficient of friction between concrete and soil (see Table 7.1), and R_v is the vertical component of the total resultant R; that is, $R_v = W + P_v$. (W = weight of wall plus soil resting on the footing, P_v = vertical component of P.) Hence, to provide sufficient safety,

$$f(W + P_v) \geqq 1.5P_h \tag{7.7}$$

Actually, for the wall to slide to the left, it must push with it the earth *nmb*, which gives rise to the passive earth pressure indicated by the triangle *rmb*. This passive pressure represents a further resisting force which could be added to the left side of Eq. (7.7). However, this should be done only if the proper functioning of this added resistance is ensured. For

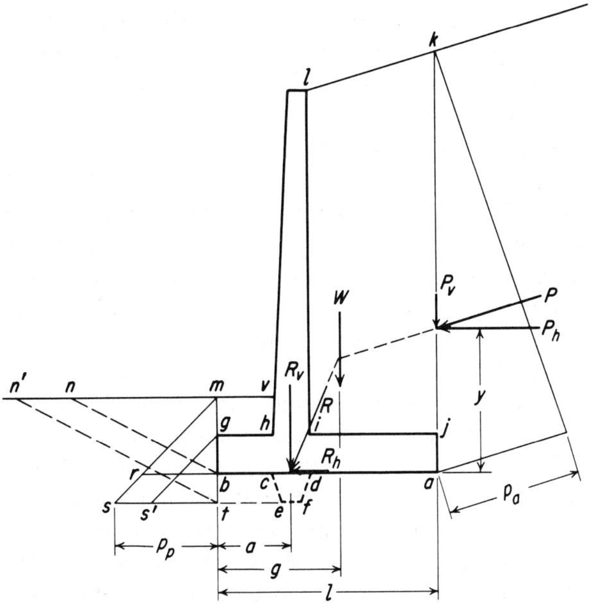

Fig. 7.4

that purpose the fill *ghmv* must be placed before the backfill *ijkl* is put in place and must be secure against later removal by scour or other means throughout the lifetime of the wall. If these conditions are not met, it is better not to count on the additional resistance of the passive pressure.

If the required sliding resistance cannot be developed by these means, a key wall *cdef* can be used to increase horizontal resistance. In this case sliding, if it occurs, takes place along the planes *ad* and *tf*. While along *ad* and *ef* the friction coefficient f applies, sliding along *te* occurs within the soil mass. The coefficient of friction that applies in this portion is consequently tan ϕ, where the value of ϕ may be taken from the next to last column in Table 7.1. In this situation sliding of the front soil occurs upward along *tn′* so that, if the front fill is secure, the corresponding resistance from passive soil pressure is represented by the pressure triangle *stm*. If doubt exists as to the reliability of the fill above the toe, the free surface should more conservatively be assumed at the top level of the footing, in which case the passive pressure is represented by the triangle *s′tg*.

Next, it is necessary to ensure that the pressure under the footing does not exceed the *permissible bearing pressure* for the particular soil. Let a (Fig. 7.4) be the distance from the front edge b to the intersection of the resultant with the base plane, and let R_v be the vertical component of R. (This intersection need not be located beneath the vertical arm, as shown, even though an economical wall generally results if it is so located.) Then the base plane *ab*, 1 ft wide longitudinally, is subject to a normal force R_v and to a moment about the centroid $(l/2 - a)R_v$. When these values are substituted in the usual formula for bending plus axial force

$$p_{1,2} = \frac{N}{A} \pm \frac{Mc}{I} \tag{7.8}$$

it will be found that if the resultant is located within the middle third ($a > l/3$), compression will act throughout the section, and the maximum and minimum pressures can be computed from the equations in Fig. 7.5*a*. If the resultant is located just at the edge of the middle third ($a = l/3$), the pressure distribution is as shown in Fig. 7.5*b*, and Eq. (7.8) results in the formula given there.

If the resultant were located outside the middle third ($a < l/3$), Eq. (7.8) would indicate tension at and near point a. Obviously, tension cannot be developed between soil and a concrete footing which merely rests on it. Hence, in this case the pressure distribution of Fig. 7.5*c* will develop, which implies a slight lifting off the soil of the rear part of the footing. Equilibrium requires that R_v pass through the centroid of the pressure-distribution triangle, from which the formula for p for this case can easily be derived.

It is good practice, in general, to have the resultant located within the middle third. This will not only reduce the magnitude of the maximum bearing pressure but will also prevent too large a nonuniformity of pressure. If the wall is founded on a highly compressible soil, such as certain clays, a pressure distribution as in Fig. 7.5*b* would result in a much larger settlement of the toe than of the heel, with a corresponding tilting of the wall. In a foundation on such a soil the resultant, therefore, should strike at or very near the center of the footing. If the foundation is on very incompressible soil, such as well-compacted gravel or rock, the resultant can be allowed to fall outside the middle third (Fig. 7.5*c*).

A third mode of failure is the possibility of the wall *overturning* bodily around the front edge *b*. For this to occur, the overturning moment yP_h about point *b* would have to be larger than the restoring moment $(Wg + P_v l)$ in Fig. 7.4, which is the same as saying that the resultant would have to strike outside the edge *b*. If, as is mostly the case, the resultant strikes within the middle third, adequate safety against overturning exists, and no special check need be made. If the resultant is located outside the middle third, a factor of safety of at least 1.5 should be maintained against overturning; i.e., the restoring moment should be at least 1.5 times the overturning moment.

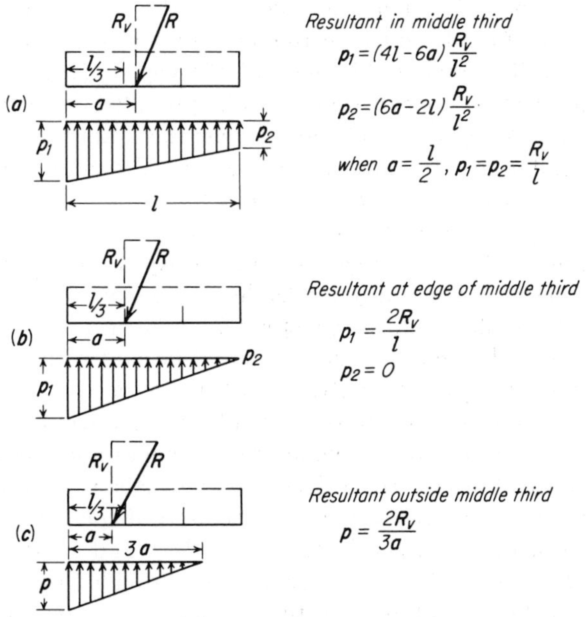

Fig. 7.5 Bearing pressures for different locations of resultant.

7.5 Drainage and Other Details Such failures or damage to retaining walls as have occasionally occurred were due, in most cases, to one of two causes: overstressing of the soil under the wall with consequent forward tipping or insufficient drainage of the backfill. In the latter case hydrostatic pressure from porewater accumulated during or after rainstorms increases greatly the thrust on the wall; in addition, in subfreezing weather ice pressure of considerable magnitude can develop in such poorly drained soils. The two causes are often interconnected, since large thrusts correspondingly increase the bearing pressure under the footing.

Allowable bearing pressures should be selected with great care. It is necessary, for this purpose, to investigate not only the type of soil immediately underlying the footing, but also the deeper layers. Unless reliable information is available at the site, subsurface borings should be made to a depth at least equal to the height of the wall. The foundation must be laid below *frost depth*, which amounts to 4 to 5 ft and more in the northern states, in order to ensure against heaving by the freezing of soils containing moisture.

Drainage can be provided in various ways. *Weep holes* consisting of 4-in. pipe embedded in the wall, as shown in Fig. 7.1*c*, are usually spaced horizontally at 5 to 10 ft. In addition to the bottom row, additional rows should be provided in walls of substantial height. To facilitate drainage and prevent clogging, 1 ft^3 or more of crushed stone is placed at the rear end of each weeper. Care must be taken that the outflow from the weep holes is carried off safely so as not to seep into and soften the soil underneath the wall. To prevent this, instead of weepers, *longitudinal drains* embedded in crushed stone or gravel can be provided along the rear face of the wall (Fig. 7.1*b*) at one or more levels; the drains discharge at the ends of the wall or at a few intermediate points. The most efficient drainage is provided by a *continuous back drain* consisting of a layer of gravel or crushed stone covering the entire rear face of the wall (Fig. 7.1*a*), with discharge at the ends. Such drainage is expensive, however, unless appropriate material is cheaply available at the site. Wherever possible the surface of the fill should be covered with a layer of low permeability and, in case of a horizontal surface, should be laid with a slight slope away from the wall toward a gutter or other drainage.

In long walls provision must be made against damage caused by *expansion or contraction* from temperature changes and shrinkage. The American Association of State Highway Officials recommends in its specifications that for gravity as well as reinforced-concrete walls expansion joints be made at intervals of 90 ft or less, and contraction joints at not more than 30 ft. The same specifications provide that in reinforced-concrete walls horizontal temperature reinforcement of not less than $\frac{1}{8}$ $in.^2$ per ft of depth be provided adjacent to the exposed surface.

7.6 Example: design of a gravity retaining wall A gravity wall is to retain a bank 11 ft 6 in. high whose horizontal surface is subject to a live-load surcharge of 400 psf. The soil is a sand-and-gravel mixture with a rather moderate amount of fine, silty particles. It can, therefore, be assumed to be in class 2 of Table 7.1, with the following characteristics: unit weight $w_s = 120$ pcf, $\phi = 30°$ (with adequate drainage to be provided), and base friction coefficient $f = 0.5$. With $\sin 30° = 0.5$, from Eqs. (7.4) and (7.5), the soil-pressure coefficients are $C_{ah} = 0.333$ and $C_{ph} = 3.0$. The allowable bearing pressure is assumed to be 4 tons per ft². This coarse-grained soil has little compressibility, so that the resultant can be allowed to strike near the outer-third point (see Art. 7.4). The weight of the concrete is $w_c = 150$ pcf.

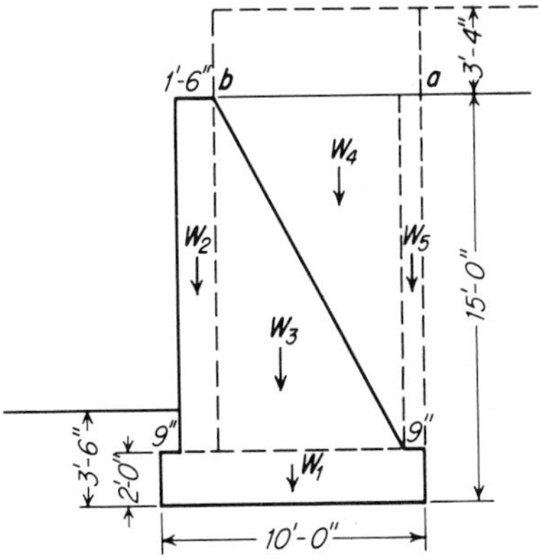

Fig. 7.6

The optimum design of any retaining wall is a matter of successive approximation. Reasonable dimensions are assumed by experience, and the various conditions of stability are checked for these dimensions. On the basis of a first trial, dimensions are readjusted, and one or two additional trials usually result in a favorable design. In the following, only the final design is analyzed in detail. The final dimensions are shown in Fig. 7.6.

The equivalent height of surcharge is $h' = 400/120 = 3.33$ ft. From Fig. 7.3c the total earth thrust is

$$P = \tfrac{1}{2} \times 0.333 \times 120 \times 15 \times 21.67 \doteq 6500 \text{ lb}$$

and its distance from the base is $y = (225 + 150)/(3 \times 21.67) = 5.77$ ft. Hence, the overturning moment $M_0 = 6500 \times 5.77 = 37{,}500$ ft-lb. To compute the weight W and its restoring moment M_r about the edge of the toe, individual weights are taken, as shown in Fig. 7.6. With x representing the distance of the line of action of each subweight from the front edge, the following computation obtains:

Component weights	W, lb	x, ft	$M_r = xW$, ft-lb
W_1: $10 \times 2 \times 150$	3000	5.0	15,000
W_2: $1.5 \times 13 \times 150$	2930	1.5	4,400
W_3: $7/2 \times 13 \times 150$	6830	4.58	31,300
W_4: $7/2 \times 13 \times 120$	5460	6.82	37,200
W_5: $0.75 \times 13 \times 120$	1170	9.62	11,250
Total	19,390		99,150

The distance of the resultant from the front edge is

$$a = (99{,}150 - 37{,}500)/19{,}390 = 3.18 \text{ ft}$$

which is just outside the middle third. The safety factor against overturning, 99,150/37,500 = 2.64, is ample. From Fig. 7.5*c* the maximum soil pressure is $p = (2 \times 19{,}390)/(3 \times 3.18) = 4070$ psf.

The above computations were made for the case in which the surcharge extends only to the rear edge of the wall, point *a* of Fig. 7.6. If the surcharge extends forward to point *b*, the following modification obtains:

$$W = 19{,}390 + 400 \times 7.75 = 22{,}490 \text{ lb}$$
$$M_r = 99{,}150 + 400 \times 7.75 \times 6.13 = 118{,}150 \text{ ft-lb}$$
$$a = (118{,}150 - 37{,}500)/22{,}490 = 3.58 \text{ ft}$$

This is inside the middle third, and, from Fig. 7.5*a*, the maximum bearing pressure is

$$p_1 = (40.0 - 21.5)\ 22{,}490/100 = 4170 \text{ lb per ft}^2$$

The situation most conducive to sliding obtains when the surcharge extends only to point *a*, since additional surcharge between *a* and *b* would increase the total weight and the corresponding resisting friction. The friction force is

$$F = 0.5 \times 19{,}390 = 9690 \text{ lb}$$

Additionally, sliding is resisted by the passive earth pressure on the front of the wall. Although the base plane is 3.5 ft below grade, the top layer of soil cannot be relied upon to furnish passive pressure, since it is frequently loosened by roots and the like, or it could be scoured out by cloudbursts. For this reason the top 1.5 ft will be discounted in computing the passive pressure, which then becomes

$$P_p = \tfrac{1}{2} w_s h^2 C_{ph} = \tfrac{1}{2} \times 120 \times 4 \times 3.0 = 720 \text{ lb}$$

The safety factor against sliding, $(9690 + 720)/6500 = 1.6$, is but slightly larger than the required value 1.5, indicating a favorable design.

7.7 Example: design of a cantilever retaining wall A cantilever is to be designed for the situation of the gravity wall in Art. 7.6. A concrete with $f'_c =$ 3000 psi and steel with $f_y = 40{,}000$ psi will be used.

To facilitate computation of weights for checking the stability of the wall, it is advantageous first to ascertain the *thickness of the arm and the footing*. For this purpose the thickness of the footing is roughly estimated, and then the required thickness of the arm is determined at its bottom section. With the bottom of the footing at 3.5 ft below grade and an estimated footing thickness of

1.5 ft, the free height of the arm is 13.5 ft. Hence, with respect to the bottom of the arm (see Fig. 7.3),

$$P = \tfrac{1}{2} \times 120 \times 13.5 \times 20.16 \times 0.333 = 5440 \text{ lb}$$

$$y = \frac{13.5^2 + 3 \times 13.5 \times 3.33}{3(13.5 + 6.66)} = 5.25 \text{ ft}$$

$$M = 5440 \times 5.25 \times 12 = 343{,}000 \text{ in.-lb}$$

For the given grades of concrete and steel, using working-stress design, $K = 223$, and hence the required thickness for bending is $d = \sqrt{343{,}000/(12 \times 223)} = 11.3$ in. A protective covering of 3 in. is required for reinforcement in concrete deposited against ground. Hence, the minimum required thickness of the arm at its base is 15 in. This will be increased to 18 in., since the cost of the excess concrete in such structures is usually more than balanced by the simultaneous saving in steel. The arm is checked for shear at a distance d above the base and is found to be more than adequate.

The thickness of the base is usually the same or slightly larger than that at the bottom of the arm. Hence, the estimated 1.5 ft need not be revised. Since the moment in the arm decreases with increasing distance from the base and is zero at the top, the arm thickness at the top will be made 8 in. It is now necessary to assume lengths of heel and toe slabs and to check the stability for these assumed dimensions. Intermediate trials are omitted here, and the final dimensions are shown in Fig. 7.7*a*. Trial computations have shown that safety against sliding can be achieved only by an excessively long heel or by a key. The latter, requiring the smaller concrete volume, has been adopted.

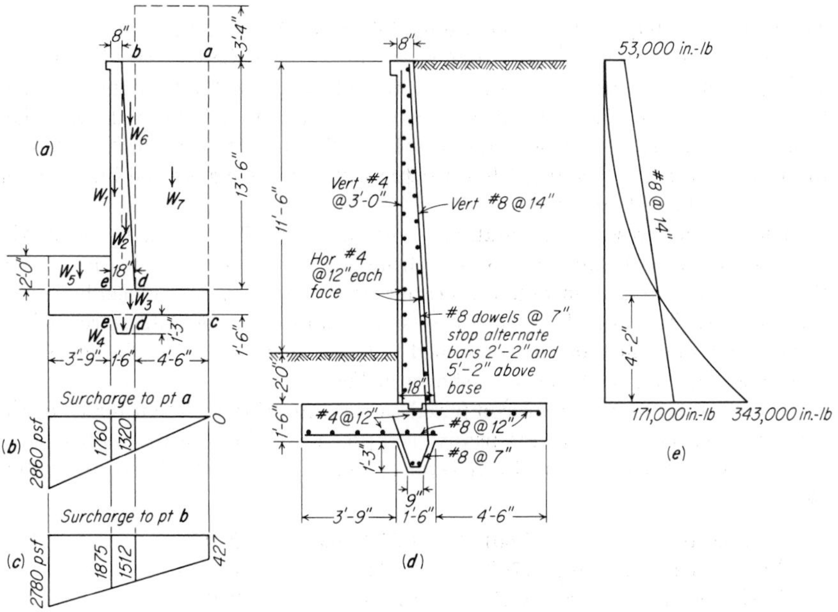

Fig. 7.7

Weights and moments about the front edge obtain as follows:

Component weights	W, lb	x, ft	M_r, ft-lb
W_1: 13.5 × 0.67 × 150	1,355	4.09	5,550
W_2: 13.5/2 × 0.83 × 150	840	4.70	3,950
W_3: 9.75 × 1.5 × 150	2,195	4.87	10,700
W_4: (1.25 + 0.67)/2 × 1.5 × 150	216	4.50	970
W_5: 3.75 × 2 × 120	900	1.87	1,680
W_6: 13.5/2 × 0.83 × 120	672	4.98	3,350
W_7: 13.5 × 4.5 × 120	7,280	7.50	54,550
Total	13,458		79,750

The total soil pressure on plane *ac* is the same as for the gravity wall of Art. 7.6, that is, $P = 6500$ lb, and the overturning moment is

$$M_0 = 37{,}500 \text{ ft-lb}$$

The distance of the resultant from the front edge is

$$a = (79{,}750 - 37{,}500)/13{,}458 = 3.14 \text{ ft}$$

which locates the resultant barely outside the middle third. The corresponding maximum soil pressure at the toe, from Fig. 7.5, is

$$p = 2 \times 13{,}458/3 \times 3.14 = 2860 \text{ psf}$$

The factor of safety against overturning, 79,750/37,500 = 2.12, is ample.

To check the safety against sliding, it will be remembered (Art. 7.4) that if sliding occurs it proceeds between concrete and soil along the heel and key (i.e., length $a - e$ in Fig. 7.4) but takes place within the soil in front of the key (i.e., along $t - e$ in Fig. 7.4). Consequently, the coefficient of friction that applies for the former length is $f = 0.5$, while for the latter it is equal to the internal soil friction, i.e., tan 30° = 0.577.

The bearing-pressure distribution is shown in Fig. 7.7*b*. Actually, since the resultant is at a distance $a = 3.14$ ft from the front, i.e., outside the middle third, formal computation would indicate that the last 4 in. of the heel have zero pressure (see Fig. 7.5). This length is so small that only a negligible error will be made if, for simplification, it is assumed that the bearing pressure becomes zero exactly at the edge of the heel, as shown in Fig. 7.7*b*.

The resisting force is then computed as the sum of the friction forces of the rear and front portion, plus the passive soil pressure in front of the wall. For the latter, as in Art. 7.6, the top 1.5-ft layer of soil will be discounted as unreliable. Hence,

Friction, toe:	$(2860 + 1760)/2 \times 3.75 \times 0.577$	= 4930 lb
Friction, heel and key:	$1760/2 \times 6.0 \times 0.5$	= 2640 lb
Passive earth pressure:	$3.25^2/2 \times 120 \times 3.0$	= 1900 lb
Total resistance to sliding		= 9470 lb

The factor of safety against sliding, 9470/6500 = 1.46, is less than 3 per cent below the recommended value of 1.5 and can be regarded as adequate.

These computations hold for the case in which the surcharge extends from the right to point *a* above the edge of the heel. The other case of load distribution, in which the surcharge is placed over the entire surface of the fill up to point *b*, evidently does not change the earth pressure on the plane *ac*. It does, however, add to the sum of the vertical forces and increase both the restoring moment M_r and the friction along the base. Consequently, the danger of sliding or overturning is greater when the surcharge extends only to *a*, for which situation these two cases have been checked and found adequate. In view of the added vertical load, however, the bearing pressure is largest when the surface is loaded to *b*. For this case,

$$W = 13{,}458 + 400 \times 5.33 = 15{,}590 \text{ lb}$$
$$M_r = 79{,}750 + 400 \times 5.33 \times 7.09 = 94{,}850 \text{ ft-lb}$$
$$a = (94{,}850 - 37{,}500)/15{,}590 = 3.68 \text{ ft}$$

which places the resultant inside the middle third. Hence, from Fig. 7.5,

$$p_1 = (4 \times 9.75 - 6 \times 3.68) \times 15{,}603/9.75^2 = 2780 \text{ psf}$$
$$p_2 = (6 \times 3.68 - 2 \times 9.75) \times 15{,}603/9.75^2 = 427 \text{ psf}$$

which is far below the allowable pressure of 4 tons per ft^2. The corresponding bearing-pressure distribution is shown in Fig. 7.7*c*.

The external stability of the wall has now been ascertained, and it remains to determine the required reinforcement and to check internal stresses.

Arm and key The moment at the bottom section of the arm has previously been determined as $M = 343{,}000$ in.-lb, and a thickness of 18 in. at the bottom and 8 in. at the top has been selected. With a concrete covering of 3 in. clear, $d = 18 - 3.5 = 14.5$ in. The required steel area at the bottom is

$$A_s = \frac{343{,}000}{\frac{7}{8} \times 14.5 \times 20{,}000} = 1.35 \text{ in.}^2 \text{ per ft}$$

The required area is provided by No. 8 bars at 7 in. center to center.

The bending moment in the arm decreases rapidly with increasing distance from the bottom. For this reason only part of the main reinforcement is needed at higher elevations, and alternate bars will be discontinued where no longer needed. To determine the cutoff point, the moment diagram for the arm has been drawn by computing bending moments at two intermediate levels, 10 ft and 5 ft from the top. These two moments, determined in the same manner as that at the base of the arm, were found to be 160,000 and 30,000 in.-lb, respectively. The resisting moment provided by alternate bars, i.e., by No. 8 bars at 14 in. center to center, at the bottom of the arm is

$$M = \tfrac{7}{8} \times 14.5 \times 0.675 \times 20{,}000 = 171{,}000 \text{ in.-lb}$$

At the top $d = 8.0 - 3.5 = 4.5$ in., and the resisting moment of the same bars is only $M = 171{,}000(4.5/14.5) = 53{,}000$ in.-lb. Hence, the straight line drawn in Fig. 7.7*e* indicates the resisting moment provided at any elevation by half the number of main bars. The intersection of this line with the moment diagram at a distance of 4 ft 2 in. from the bottom represents the point above which alternate bars are no longer needed. The ACI Code specifies that any bar shall be extended beyond the point at which it is no longer needed to carry flexural stress for a distance equal to d or 12 bar diameters, whichever is greater. In the arm, at a distance of 4 ft 2 in. from the bottom, $d = 11.5$ in., while 12 bar diameters for No. 8 bars are equal to 12 in. Hence, half the bars can be discontinued 12 in. above the point where no longer needed, or a distance of 5 ft 2 in. above the base.

In order to facilitate construction, the footing is poured first, and a construction joint is provided at the base of the arm, as shown in Fig. 7.7*d*. The main bars of the arm, therefore, end at the top of the base slab, and dowels are placed in the latter to be spliced with them. It will be realized that the integrity of the arm depends entirely on the integrity of the splicing of these tension bars. The ACI Code warns specifically against splicing all tension bars in one section by simple contact splices, since this situation can easily lead to splitting of the concrete owing to the stress concentrations at the ends of the spliced bars. One way to avoid this difficulty is to weld all splices; this will entail considerable extra cost.

In this particular wall, another way of placing the reinforcing offers a more economical solution. Because alternate bars in the arm can be discontinued at a distance of 5 ft 2 in. above the base, alternate dowels will be carried up from the top of the base to that distance. These need not be spliced at all, because above that level only alternate No. 8 bars, 14 in. on centers, are needed. These latter bars are placed full length over the entire height of the arm and are spliced at the bottom with alternate shorter dowels. By this means, only 50 per cent of the bars needed at the bottom of the arm are spliced; this is not objectionable.

For tension splices the ACI Code provides that the splice length shall be sufficient to transfer the entire steel stress at three-quarters of the permissible bond stresses, with a minimum of 24 diam for $f_y = 40{,}000$. The allowable bond stress for No. 8 bars is $u = 4.8\sqrt{3000}/1.0 = 263$ psi, and

$$\text{Required splice length} = \frac{0.79 \times 20{,}000}{0.75 \times 263 \times 3.14} = 25.5 \text{ in.}$$

The minimum of 24 diam = 24 in., for No. 8 bars, is less than this, so that 25.5 in. governs. Consequently, alternate dowels are carried a distance of 2 ft 2 in. above the base for splicing with the corresponding bars in the arm, while the intervening dowels are carried to 5 ft 2 in. above the base and terminated without splicing as being no longer needed to carry moments.

Since the dowels had to be extended at least partly into the key to produce the necessary length of embedment, they were bent as shown to provide reinforcement for the key. The exact force which the key must resist is difficult to determine, since probably the major part of the force acting on the portion of the soil in front of the key is transmitted to it through friction along the base of the footing. The relatively strong reinforcement of the key by means of the extended dowels is considered sufficient to prevent separation from the footing.

The sloping sides of the key were provided in order to facilitate excavation without loosening the adjacent soil. This is necessary in order to ensure proper functioning of the key.

Base slab Toe and heel are designed for moments and shears caused by the bearing pressure, acting upward and counteracted by the superimposed weight of fill and surcharge, including the weight of the footing proper. Since both the bearing pressure and the superimposed weights are different for the two cases of surcharge extending to a and to b, both these conditions must be checked. This has been done, and, for this particular wall, it was found that moments and shears were not much different for the two cases, but that slightly larger values were obtained for surcharge extending to b.

On the *heel*, the combined weights, including surcharge, are

$$13.5 \times 120 + 1.5 \times 150 + 400 = 2245 \text{ lb per ft}$$

The moment produced by this load is counteracted by that from the bearing pressure (Fig. 7.7c). Hence,

$$\begin{aligned} M_d &= 2245 \times 4.5^2/2 - 427 \times 4.5^2/2 - (1512 - 427)4.5^2/6 \\ &= 14{,}750 \text{ ft-lb} = 177{,}000 \text{ in.-lb} \end{aligned}$$

The 18-in. thickness is ample for concrete bending stresses, as can be seen without computation by comparison with the corresponding value at the base of the arm whose thickness, at that point, is equal to that of the footing. The required steel area,

$$A_s = \frac{177{,}000}{14.5 \times \frac{7}{8} \times 20{,}000} = 0.70 \text{ in.}^2 \text{ per ft}$$

is provided by No. 8 bars at 12 in. center to center, or 0.78 in.^{2} per ft.

The fill above the *toe* will be neglected as being subject to possible erosion. Hence, with only the weight of the footing,

$$1.5 \times 150 = 225 \text{ lb per ft}$$

acting downward,

$$\begin{aligned} M_e &= 1875 \times 3.75^2/2 + (2780 - 1875)3.75^2/3 - 225 \times 3.75^2/2 \\ &= 15{,}800 \text{ ft-lb} = 189{,}500 \text{ in.-lb} \end{aligned}$$

Comparison with the moment in the arm, 343,000 in.-lb, again shows the thickness to be ample for bending. The steel area,

$$A_s = \frac{189{,}500}{14.5 \times \frac{7}{8} \times 20{,}000} = 0.75 \text{ in.}^2 \text{ per ft}$$

will again be provided by No. 8 bars at 12 in. center to center, or 0.78 in.^{2} per ft. The required length of embedment beyond points e and d is provided as shown.

Shear has been checked in the arm at a distance d above the footing and in both parts of the footing at a distance d from the front and rear faces of the arm, and has been found to be more than adequate without shear reinforcement.

The No. 4 bars indicated in Fig. 7.7d furnish the shrinkage reinforcement and serve to space the main reinforcement. Drainage is to be secured by one of the methods shown in Fig. 7.1, depending on local conditions.

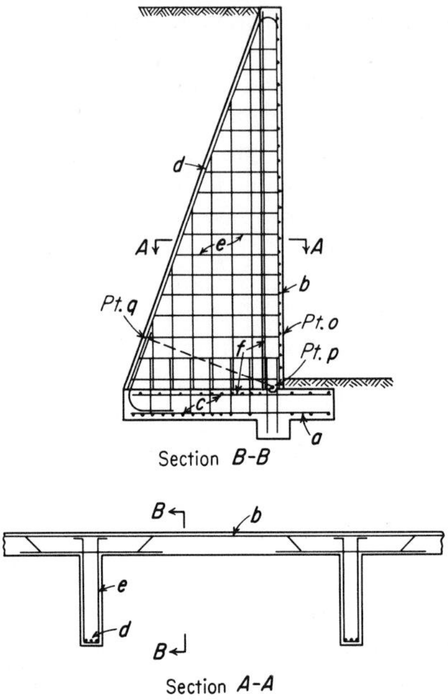

Fig. 7.8 Details of counterfort retaining wall.

7.8 Design of Counterfort Retaining Walls The *external stability* of a counterfort retaining wall is determined in the same manner as in the examples of Arts. 7.6 and 7.7. The *toe slab* represents a cantilever built in along the front face of the wall, loaded upward by the bearing pressure, exactly as in the cantilever wall of Art. 7.7. Reinforcement is provided by bars *a* in Fig. 7.8.

A panel of the *vertical wall* between two counterforts is a slab acted upon by the horizontal earth pressure and supported along three sides, i.e., at the two counterforts and the base slab, while the fourth side, the top edge, is not supported. The earth pressure, of course, increases linearly with distance from the free surface. The exact determination of moments and shears in such a slab supported on three sides and nonuniformly loaded is rather involved (Ref. 7.2). It is customary in the design of such walls to disregard the support of the vertical wall by the base slab and to design it as if it were a continuous slab spanning horizontally between counterforts. This procedure is conservative, because the moments obtained by this approximation are larger than those corresponding to the actual conditions of support, particularly in the lower part of the wall. Hence, for very large installations, significant savings may be achieved by a more accurate analysis.

Slab moments are determined for strips 1 ft wide vertically, usually for the strip at the bottom of the wall and for three or four equally spaced additional strips at higher elevations. The earth pressure on the different strips decreases with increasing elevation and is determined from Eq. (7.1). An elaborate moment analysis by moment distribution or some other method is not warranted in view of (1) the approximate assumptions of the design as just discussed and (2) the uncertain magnitude of the earth pressure, which depends, among other influences, on moisture content and may vary from one panel to the next. The authors consider it adequate to assume the positive moments midway between, and the negative moments at, the counterforts to be equal, and to use for these moments

$$M = \frac{pl^2}{12}$$

for the two lowermost strips and

$$M = \frac{pl^2}{10}$$

for the strips at higher elevations. The smaller moment value for the bottom strips accounts for the fact that the additional support provided by the base slab decreases the moments in the bottom portions of the slab as compared with those which would obtain if this support were absent. Horizontal bars *b* (Fig. 7.8) are provided as required by these moments, with increased spacing or decreased diameter at higher elevations, corresponding to the smaller moments. Alternate bars are bent up to provide for the negative moments at the counterforts, or additional straight bars are placed for them.

The *heel slab* is supported as is the wall slab, i.e., by the counterforts and at the wall. It is loaded downward by the weight of the fill resting on it, its own weight, and such surcharge as there may be. This load is counteracted by the bearing pressure. As in the vertical wall, a simplified analysis consists in neglecting the influence of the support along the third side and in determining moments and shears for strips parallel to the wall, each strip representing a continuous beam supported at the counterforts. With horizontal soil surface, the downward load is constant for the entire heel, whereas the upward load from the bearing pressure is usually smallest at the rear edge and increases frontward. For this reason the span moments are positive (compression on top) and the support moments negative in the rear portion of the heel. Near the wall the bearing pressure often exceeds the vertical weights, resulting in a net upward load. The signs of the moments are correspondingly reversed, and steel must be placed accordingly, i.e., near the top face in the span and near the bottom face at the supports. Bars *c* are provided for these moments.

The *counterforts* are wedge-shaped cantilevers built in at the bottom in the base slab. They support the wall slab and, therefore, are loaded by the total soil pressure over a length equal to the distance center to center between counterforts. They act as a T beam of which the wall slab is the flange and the counterfort the stem. For this reason concrete stresses are always low and need not be checked. The maximum bending moment is that of the total earth pressure, taken about the bottom of the wall slab. This moment is held in equilibrium by the force in the bars *d*, and hence the lever arm of internal forces *jd* is the perpendicular distance *pq* from the center of bars d to the center of the bottom section of the wall slab. Since the moment decreases rapidly in the upper parts of the counterfort, part of the bars d can be discontinued. To find the cutoff points, it is simplest to use the graphical method which was employed for the arm of the cantilever wall (Fig. 7.7*e*).

In regard to shear, the ACI Code specifies the critical section to be located a distance d from the support for prismatic members but does not provide any guidance for strongly sloping members, such as these counterforts. The authors suggest the horizontal section oq as a conservative location for checking adequacy in shear. Some modification of the customary shear-stress computation is required for wedge-shaped members. In general, such stresses, on a section parallel to the external load such as oq, are determined by the usual formula $v_c = V_1/bd$, where

$$V_1 = V \pm \frac{M}{d}(\tan\theta + \tan\phi) \tag{7.9}$$

V and M are the shear and moment at the section, and θ and ϕ are the angles which the longitudinal edges subtend with a line perpendicular to the section (Ref. 7.3). The minus sign is to be used when the depth increases with increasing bending moment, as is the case in counterforts. For the example of Fig. 7.8, one of the two angles, say θ, is zero for the front edge, while ϕ is the angle between the vertical and the rear edge. Usually concrete alone is sufficient to carry this shear, although bars e act as stirrups and can be used for resisting excess shear.

The main purpose of bars e is to counteract the pull of the wall slab, and they are thus designed for the full reaction of this slab.

The remaining bars of Fig. 7.8 serve as shrinkage reinforcement, except that bars f have an important additional function. It will be recalled that the wall and heel slabs are supported on three sides. Even though they were designed as if supported only by the counterforts, they develop moments where they join. The resulting tension in and near the reentrant corner is conducive to cracking, which is counteracted by bars f.

REFERENCES

7.1 Terzaghi and Peck: "Soil Mechanics in Engineering Practice," pp. 315–318, John Wiley & Sons, Inc., New York, 1948.

7.2 "Rectangular Concrete Tanks," *Concrete Information ST63*, Portland Cement Association, 1943.

7.3 "Recommended Practice and Standard Specifications for Concrete and Reinforced Concrete," Report of Joint Committee on Standard Specifications for Concrete and Reinforced Concrete, *Proc. ASCE*, part 2, pp. 55–56, June, 1940.

chapter 8

CONTINUOUS BEAMS AND FRAMES

8.1 Continuity of Reinforced-concrete Structures The individual members which compose a steel or timber structure are fabricated or cut separately and joined together by rivets, bolts, welds, or nails. Unless the joints are especially designed for rigidity, they are too flexible to transfer moments of significant magnitude from one member to another. In contrast, in reinforced-concrete structures as much of the concrete as is practical is poured in one single operation, and reinforcing steel is not terminated at the ends of a member but is carried over at the joints into adjacent members. At construction joints, special care is taken to bond the new concrete to the old by carefully cleaning the latter, carrying reinforcement across the joint, and other means. As a result, such structures represent monolithic or continuous units. Their behavior under load is shown in Fig. 8.1.

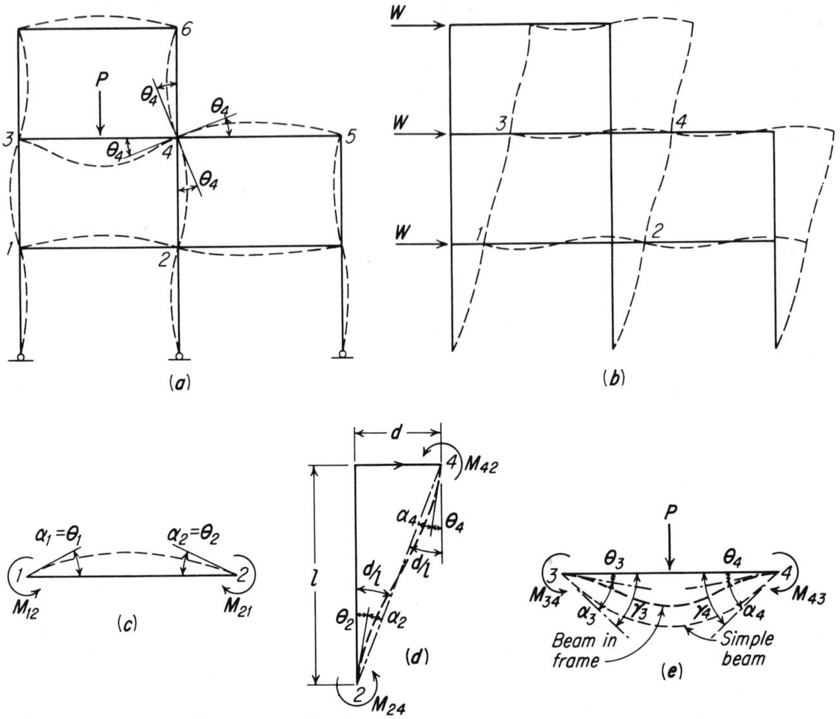

***Fig.* 8.1** Deflections and slopes of rigid frames.

With simple joints, as provided in steel construction by many types of riveted and bolted connections, only the beam 3-4 would bend in the frame of Fig. 8.1*a*, while all other members would remain essentially straight. With rigid joints, such as in a reinforced-concrete or welded steel frame, the distortion caused by a load on one single member is seen to spread to all other members of the frame, although the magnitude of deformation decreases with increasing distance from the loaded member. Consequently a beam, such as 1-2, even though free from load, bends because its ends are rotated by the amounts α_1 and α_2, as shown in Fig. 8.1*c*. Since curvature is proportional to bending moment ($1/r = M/EI$), this and all other members are subject to bending stresses, even though they are not loaded.

If horizontal forces, such as wind, act on the frame, it deforms as shown in Fig. 8.1*b*. Here, too, all members of the frame distort, even though the forces act only on the left side; the amount of distortion is seen to be about the same for all members, regardless of their distance from points of load, in contrast to the case of vertical loading. A member, such as 2-4, even though not directly loaded, will experience bending moments caused by the distortions imposed on it, which are shown in Fig. 8.1*d*. It is seen that, in addition to the rotations α_2 and α_4, one end is displaced horizontally with respect to the other by the amount d, resulting in an additional rotation d/l. If, too, a member carries transverse load, such as does beam 3-4, the end rotations γ caused by the load must be superposed on those due to the rotations α caused by the continuity at the joints (Fig. 8.1*e*). The final end slopes θ of each individual member are seen to be the sums of these individual contributions α, d/l, and γ.

In statically determinate structures, such as simple beams, the deflected shape and the moments and shears depend only on the type and magnitude of the loads and the dimensions of the member. In contrast, inspection of Fig. 8.1 shows that in statically indeterminate frames the deflection curve of any member, in addition to the loads, depends on the end slopes θ whose magnitudes, in turn, depend on the distortion of adjacent, rigidly connected members. In particular, for a rigid joint such as joint 4 (Fig. 8.1*a*), the slopes θ of all abutting members must be the same and equal to the rotation of the joint. For a correct design of such frames, it is evidently necessary to determine moments and shears with due consideration of the effect of continuity at the joints.

A number of methods have been developed for such determinations. Those that were available in the early days of concrete design were rather lengthy and tedious. To save time, it became customary to determine moments in continuous structures by using approximate coefficients such as are included in the present ACI Code. Such coefficients are satisfactory if used within their specified limitations. However, with the advent of more practical and efficient methods of analysis, it is now common practice to ascertain moments and shears in continuous structures with a high degree of accuracy and to use approximate moment coefficients only when a closer design would not result in significant economy.

In the following articles the practically useful methods of analysis are discussed as they apply to relatively simple and more or less standard structures. For the more intricate details of this important phase of design, the reader is referred to special texts on analysis of statically indeterminate structures.

8.2 Moments in Continuous Beams The calculation of moments, shears, and reactions for continuous beams may be based on the theorem of three moments. Considering all supports on the same level, the two fundamental equations are (see Fig. 8.2): For uniform loads,

$$M_1l_1 + 2M_2(l_1 + l_2) + M_3l_2 = -\tfrac{1}{4}w_1l_1^3 - \tfrac{1}{4}w_2l_2^3 \tag{8.1}$$

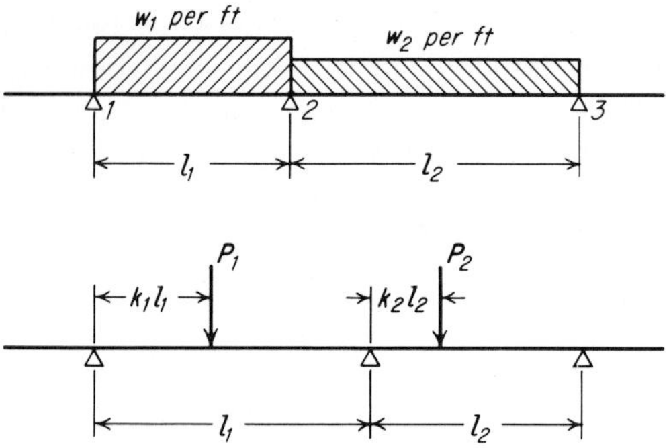

Fig. 8.2

For concentrated loads,

$$M_1l_1 + 2M_2(l_1 + l_2) + M_3l_2 = -\Sigma P_1l_1^2(k_1 - k_1^3) - \Sigma P_2l_2^2(2k_2 - 3k_2^2 + k_2^3) \quad (8.2)$$

In this simplest form the two equations apply to the most frequent case, that of uniform cross section.

By using a system of such equations, and solving simultaneously for the unknown moments, the bending moments at all the supports may be determined, the reactions computed, and, finally, the bending moment at any section of the beam obtained. From Eq. (8.2), influence lines may be plotted for the moment at any section of the beam, and the loading determined which will produce the maximum moment in that section. In the case of uniform load and equal spans, the exact coefficients of wl^2 for the theoretical maximum moments are given in Table 8.1.

***Table* 8.1 Moments in continuous, equal-span beams with uniformly distributed load**

Number of spans	Intermediate spans and supports				End spans and second support			
	At center, positive moment		At support, negative moment		At center, positive moment		At support, negative moment	
	Dead load	Live load	Dead load	Live load	Dead load	Live load	Dead load	Live load
2					0.070	0.095	0.125	0.125
3	0.025	0.075			0.080	0.100	0.100	0.117
4	0.036	0.081	0.071	0.107	0.071	0.098	0.107	0.120
5	0.046	0.086	0.079	0.111	0.072	0.099	0.105	0.120
6	0.043	0.084	0.086	0.116	0.072	0.099	0.106	0.120
7	0.044	0.084	0.085	0.114	0.072	0.099	0.106	0.120

These coefficients are derived for simple (knife-edge) supports and for the most unfavorable distribution of live loads.

Moment and shear coefficients are given in the ACI Code which are based on exact coefficients given above. They are reprinted in Table 8.2.

Table* 8.2 Moment and shear values using ACI coefficients

Positive moment:	
End spans:	
If discontinuous end is unrestrained	$\frac{1}{11}wl'^2$
If discontinuous end is integral with the support	$\frac{1}{14}wl'^2$
Interior spans	$\frac{1}{16}wl'^2$
Negative moment at exterior face of first interior support:	
Two spans	$\frac{1}{9}wl'^2$
More than two spans	$\frac{1}{10}wl'^2$
Negative moment at other faces of interior supports	$\frac{1}{11}wl'^2$
Negative moment at face of all supports for, (1) slabs with spans not exceeding 10 ft, and (2) beams and girders where ratio of sum of column stiffnesses to beam stiffness exceeds eight at each end of the span	$\frac{1}{12}wl'^2$
Negative moment at interior faces of exterior supports for members built integrally with their supports:	
Where the support is a spandrel beam or girder	$\frac{1}{24}wl'^2$
Where the support is a column	$\frac{1}{16}wl'^2$
Shear in end members at first interior support	$1.15\,\frac{wl'}{2}$
Shear at all other supports	$\frac{wl'}{2}$

* w = total load per unit length of beam or per unit area of slab.

l' = clear span for positive moment and shear and the average of the two adjacent clear spans for negative moment.

The ACI coefficients were derived with due consideration of the maximum allowable ratio of live to dead load (3:1), maximum allowable span difference (the larger of two adjacent spans not to exceed the shorter by more than 20 per cent), the fact that reinforced-concrete beams are never simply supported but either rest on supports of considerable width, such as walls, or are built monolithically with columns, and other factors. Since all these influences are considered, the ACI coefficients are necessarily quite conservative, so that actual, accurate moments in any particular design are likely to be considerably smaller than indicated. Hence, in many reinforced-concrete structures significant economy can be effected by making a precise analysis of the moments in beams and girders. This becomes mandatory for beams and slabs with spans differing by more than 20 per cent and/or sustaining unsymmetrical loads. Such analyses are more expeditiously carried out by the method of moment distribution (Art. 8.7) than by the use of Eqs. (8.1) and (8.2).

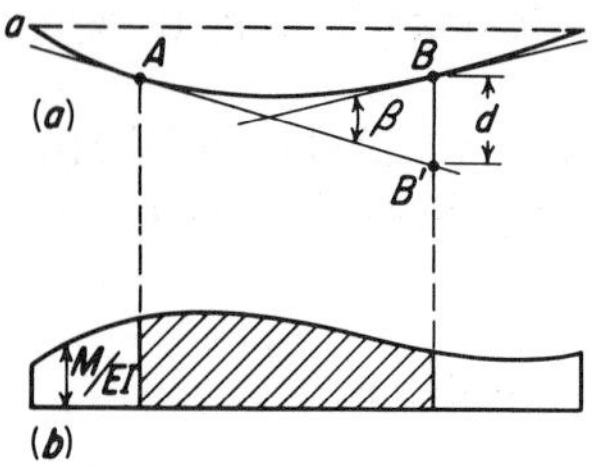

Fig. 8.3

8.3 Moment-area Principles It was indicated in Art. 8.1 that in continuous structures moments and shears caused by imposed deformations, such as the rotation α or the displacements d, superpose on those caused by the direct effect of the load acting on the particular member. To analyze this type of action, it is therefore necessary to establish the relations that exist between bending moments and the corresponding deformations. These are most easily expressed in the form of the two moment-area principles.

In Fig. 8.3*a* let the straight line *ab* represent the original, unloaded shape of an elastic member (beam, girder, column, or the like), and the curve *aABb* its deformed shape or elastic curve. In view of the relation $1/r = M/EI$, this distortion is connected with associated bending moments. Let Fig. 8.3*b* represent the corresponding M/EI diagram, i.e., the graph of the bending moments divided by the respective values of EI. If tangents are drawn to the elastic curve at two points A and B, the moment-area principles state:

1. *The change of slope β between the tangents to the elastic curve at two points A and B is equal to the area of the portion of the M/EI diagram between the two points.*

2. *The distance d of point B from the tangent at point A is equal to the moment about the perpendicular through B of the area of the portion of the M/EI diagram between the two points.*

The corresponding portion of the M/EI diagram is shaded in Fig. 8.3*b*. Note that the distance d is measured perpendicular to the original, undistorted position *ab* of the member (i.e., the line connecting its supports).

For a derivation of these two important principles the reader is referred to any text on the strength of materials.

8.4 Slope-deflection Method In computing moments and shears on isolated beams, the ends are usually considered as freely supported or as fixed. However, there is, even in isolated beams, often an intermediate condition. In frames in which the joints are rigid, such an intermediate condition is commonly encountered. No matter what the degree of restraint, once the end moments are known, moments and shears at any point of the member can be computed from the equations of statics. As is evident from Art. 8.1, the end slopes θ depend on (1) the rotation α of the end tangents to the elastic curve from the position they would have if the member were freely supported (see Fig. 8.1*c*); (2) the relative displacement d of the supports and the corresponding rotation d/l (see

Fig. 8.1*d*); (3) the rotations γ which the direct, transverse loads (if any) would cause if the members were freely supported (see Fig. 8.1*e*). The final end slopes θ are the sums of these individual rotations (see Fig. 8.1*d* and *e*).

In a freely supported beam, the end moments are zero, and the end slopes γ depend on the load and can be computed in the usual manner, e.g., by the moment-area principles (see Art. 8.3). In a fixed-end beam the end slopes are zero, and the end moments are known as the "fixed-end moments" M^f. If the beam is an intermediate condition (Fig. 8.1*e*), the end slopes θ obviously have intermediate values (between 0 and γ), and the end moments M have corresponding intermediate values between M^f and 0.

Once the end slopes θ are known, the end moments can be determined. Hence, the term "slope deflection" has been applied to this method of analysis, which was developed independently by A. Bendixen in Germany (1914) and G. A. Maney in the United States (1915).

In the discussion that follows, the relations between the end slopes and the end moments are first investigated separately for the three described types of rotations. Two subscripts are used for moments acting on one end of a member, the first indicating the "near" end, on which it acts, and the other indicating the "far" end. Thus (see Fig. 8.4) M_{12} indicates the moment acting on end 1 of beam 1-2.

In Fig. 8.4*a*, a member 1-2 has been isolated from the rest of a rigid frame by passing imaginary cuts around the joints at its two ends. The member then represents a freely supported simple beam. The effect of the adjacent frame members on this beam is to impose certain rotations and deflections on its ends, as can be seen from Fig. 8.1. These effects will be studied individually.

In Fig. 8.4*b* the left support, 1, of the beam has been rotated by the action of moments outside the span 1-2. This rotation causes bending in the beam and produces compression in the upper fiber at 1. In (*c*) the right support, 2, has also been rotated in the same direction by the action of moments outside the beam. This produces tension in the upper fiber at 2. Since

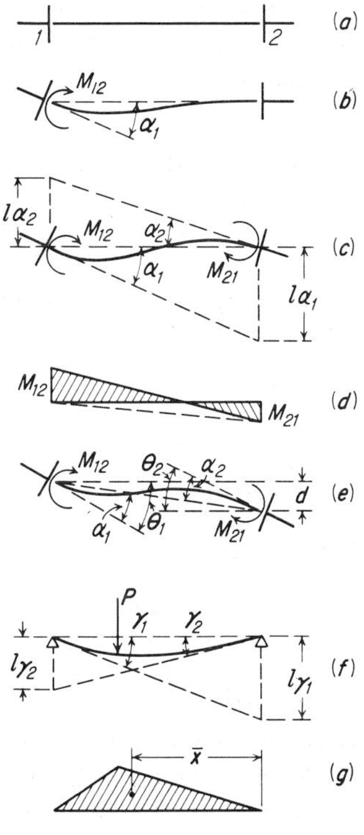

Fig. 8.4

the stresses in the upper fiber at 1 and 2 are of opposite sign, there is evidently a point of inflection in the beam, and the moment diagram for the beam is similar to that shown in (*d*).

Since the angles of rotation are small, the distance at 2 from a tangent to the axis of the beam at 1 is $l\alpha_1$, where l is the span 1-2. Then by the principle of moment areas, $l\alpha_1$ is equal to the moment of the M/EI diagram between 1 and 2 about 2. This moment is evidently equal to the algebraic sum of the moments of the shaded areas about 2, that is,

$$l\alpha_1 = \frac{1}{EI}\left(\frac{M_{12}l}{2}\frac{2l}{3} - \frac{M_{21}l}{2}\frac{l}{3}\right) \qquad \text{or} \qquad \alpha_1 = \frac{l}{6EI}(2M_{12} - M_{21})$$

Similarly,

$$\alpha_2 = \frac{l}{6EI}(2M_{21} - M_{12})$$

In Fig. 8.4*e* the joint 2 has been moved downward a vertical distance d from its original position, the horizontal distance between joints 1 and 2 remaining constant. This has increased the angles between the tangents to the member 1-2 at 1 and 2 and the horizontal by an amount $d/l = R$. If then $\theta_1 = \alpha_1 + R$ and $\theta_2 = \alpha_2 + R$,

$$\theta_1 = \frac{l}{6EI}(2M_{12} - M_{21}) + R \tag{8.3}$$

and

$$\theta_2 = \frac{l}{6EI}(2M_{21} - M_{12}) + R \tag{8.4}$$

from which

$$M_{12} = \frac{2EI}{l}(2\theta_1 + \theta_2 - 3R) \tag{8.5}$$

and

$$M_{21} = \frac{2EI}{l}(2\theta_2 + \theta_1 - 3R) \tag{8.6}$$

Equations (8.5) and (8.6) are the fundamental slope-deflection equations for the moments at the ends of a member sustaining no intermediate loads, in terms of the relative change in slope and displacement of its ends.

In the foregoing derivation the following sign convention has been used:

1. When the rotation of the end tangent is clockwise, the angle measuring this rotation is positive.
2. The deflection of one end with respect to the other is measured normal to the original position of the member and is positive when measured in the same direction as positive angles.
3. External end moments are positive when they tend to rotate the end of the member on which they act in a clockwise direction.

For illustration, in Fig. 8.4*a* to *e* the sense of all rotations, deflections, and moments is positive.

If a transverse load acts on a member, as shown in Fig. 8.4*f*, the corresponding rotations γ must be added to α and R to result in the final rotations θ. From 8.4*f* it is seen that for vertical load and by the sign convention just given, γ_1 is positive, while γ_2 is negative. If F is the area of the moment curve for the simple beam (Fig. 8.4*g*), and $\bar{x}$ the distance of its centroid from support 2, one obtains, from the second moment-area principle,

$$l_{\gamma_1} = \frac{F\bar{x}}{EI} \qquad \text{and} \qquad l_{\gamma_2} = -\frac{F(l - \bar{x})}{EI}$$

If these equations are divided by l and the resulting angles γ added to those of Eqs. (8.3) and (8.4), one obtains, for the case of members carrying transverse loads,

$$\theta_1 = \frac{l}{6EI}(2M_{12} - M_{21}) + R + \frac{F\bar{x}}{EIl} \tag{8.7}$$

and

$$\theta_2 = \frac{l}{6EI}(2M_{21} - M_{12}) + R - \frac{F}{EI}\left(\frac{l - \bar{x}}{l}\right) \tag{8.8}$$

from which

$$M_{12} = \frac{2EI}{l}(2\theta_1 + \theta_2 - 3R) - \frac{2F}{l^2}(3\bar{x} - l) \tag{8.9}$$

and

$$M_{21} = \frac{2EI}{l}(2\theta_2 + \theta_1 - 3R) + \frac{2F}{l^2}(2l - 3\bar{x}) \tag{8.10}$$

These are the complete equations of the slope-deflection method. By comparison with Eqs. (8.5) and (8.6) it is seen that the last terms of Eqs. (8.9) and (8.10) accounts for the influence of transverse loads on the member under consideration. Its physical significance is easily established in the following manner. If the member of Fig. 8.4 is fixed at its ends, then $\theta_1 = \theta_2 = R = 0$. In this case M_{12} and M_{21} would represent the fixed-end moments of the beam. Equating to zero the indicated terms, it is seen that these fixed-end moments are, respectively, equal to the last terms of Eqs. (8.9) and (8.10). These fixed-end moments will be designated by M^f.

If, in addition, the rigidity I/l of the member is designated by K, and subscripts n and f are used, respectively, for the "near" and "far" ends of the member, Eqs. (8.9) and (8.10) can be written in the following general form:

$$M_{nf} = 2EK(2\theta_n + \theta_f - 3R) + M_{nf}^f \tag{8.11}$$

The sign of M_{nf}^f is established from rule 3, given previously. For instance, the load of Fig. 8.4*f* produces fixed-end moments which tend to rotate the left end of the member counterclockwise and the right end clockwise. Hence, the former is negative, the latter positive, as is correctly reflected in Eqs. (8.9) and (8.10) In the general equation (8.11) they must be substituted with these same signs. (The reader will find that some texts on structural analysis use a sign convention for rotations, deflections, and moments other than that given in Rules 1 to 3. The choice of such a convention is entirely a matter of the designer's preference. One is as good as the other, provided it is consistent in itself and is used consistently.) The determination of the correct sign is greatly facilitated by the use of rough sketches of the deflected shape of the structure, such as Fig. 8.1. By means of such sketches the signs of the moments throughout the frame are easily determined even before an analysis is begun. In fact, the approximate shape of the final moment diagrams can be obtained directly from such sketches, which are of inestimable aid to the designer.

The slope-deflection equations enable one to compute the moments at both ends of all members of a rigid-joint structure by making use of the following requirements:

1. Condition of joint equilibrium: The sum of all moments acting on a joint is zero.

2. Condition of joint continuity: The rotations of the tangents of all members meeting at a joint are equal.

3. Condition of frame equilibrium: The external shears and reactions applied to the frame must be in equilibrium with the applied loads.

8.5 Restraint Conditions and Fixed-end Moments The general slope-deflection equations (8.7) to (8.11) were derived to hold for all conceivable situations, i.e., for any relative magnitudes of θ and M at

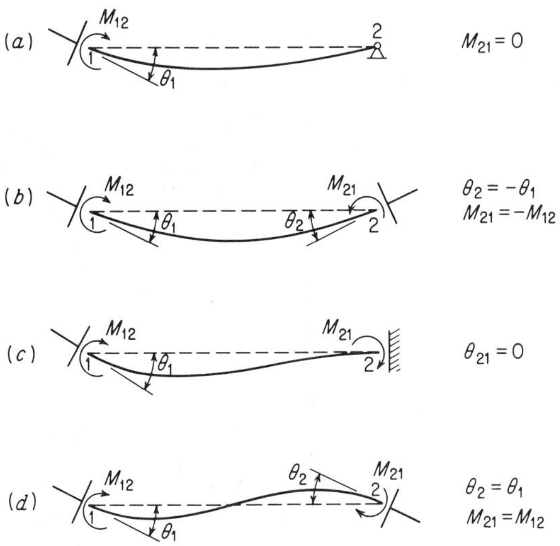

Fig. 8.5

both ends, and for any value of R. The values of θ and M in any particular case depend on the conditions of restraint at both ends, hinged, fixed, or partially restrained. In addition to the general case of partial, unequal restraint at both ends, for which the general equations were derived, there are four special conditions of restraint which are often met in structural analysis. These are shown in Fig. 8.5 and are (*a*) far end hinged, (*b*) symmetrical bending, (*c*) far end fixed, and (*d*) antisymmetrical bending. R equal to zero is assumed for these four simple cases, and the corresponding conditions are shown on the right of Fig. 8.5. By making use of these conditions, simplified equations are easily derived for these four frequent cases.

For instance, for case *a*, noting that $M_{21} = 0$ at the hinged end, Eqs. (8.9) and (8.10) become

$$\begin{aligned} M_{12} &= 2EK(2\theta_1 + \theta_2) + M_{12}{}^f \\ 0 &= 2EK(2\theta_2 + \theta_1) + M_{21}{}^f \end{aligned}$$

From the second equation,

$$\theta_2 = -\left(\frac{\theta_1}{2} + \frac{M_{21}{}^f}{4EK}\right)$$

If this value is substituted in the first equation, one obtains

$$M_{12} = 3EK\theta_1 - \left(M_{12}{}^f + \frac{M_{21}{}^f}{2}\right)$$

In particular, if no loads act on the member proper, so that bending is caused only by the end moments applied through the joints from

Table **8.3 Moments for different conditions of restraint**

Case (see Fig. 8.5)	Relation between θ angles, no load on span	Moment at near end in terms of θ_1, no load on span	Moment at far end in terms, of θ_1 and θ_2, no load on span	Moment at near end in terms of θ_1, intermediate loads on span	Moment at far end in terms of θ_1 and θ_2, intermediate loads on span
a. Far end hinged	$\theta_2 = -\frac{1}{2}\theta_1$	$M_{12} = 3EK\theta_1$	$M_{21} = 0$	$M_{12} = 3EK\theta_1 - (M_{12}^f + M_{21}^f/2)$	$M_{21} = 0$
b. Symmetrical bending	$\theta_2 = -\theta_1$	$M_{12} = 2EK\theta_1$	$M_{21} = -2EK\theta_1$ $M_{21} = 2EK\theta_2$	$M_{12} = 2EK\theta_1 - M_{12}^f$	$M_{21} = -2EK\theta_1 + M_{21}^f$ $M_{21} = 2EK\theta_2 + M_{21}^f$
c. Far end fixed	$\theta_2 = 0$	$M_{12} = 4EK\theta_1$	$M_{21} = 2EK\theta_1$	$M_{12} = 4EK\theta_1 - M_{12}^f$	$M_{21} = 2EK\theta_1 + M_{21}^f$
d. Antisymmetrical bending	$\theta_2 = \theta_1$	$M_{12} = 6EK\theta_1$	$M_{21} = 6EK\theta_1$ $M_{21} = 6EK\theta_2$	$M_{12} = 6EK\theta_1 - M_{12}^f$	$M_{21} = 6EK\theta_1 + M_{21}^f$ $M_{21} = 6EK\theta_2 + M_{21}^f$

adjacent members, $M_{12}{}^f = M_{21}{}^f = 0$. In this case the last equation indicates

$$M_{12} = 3EK\theta_1$$

while the next to last results in

$$\theta_2 = -\frac{\theta_1}{2}$$

In a similar manner, such special, simple relations are easily derived for the other three cases. The results are listed in Table 8.3.

If the far end of a member, say end 2, is hinged and subject to joint deflection, one has

$$\begin{aligned} M_{12} &= 2EK(2\theta_1 + \theta_2 - 3R) \\ 0 &= 2EK(2\theta_2 + \theta_1 - 3R) \end{aligned}$$

from which

$$M_{12} = 3EK\theta_1 - 3EKR$$

Consequently, *Table* 8.3 *can also be used if joint deflections are present*, by adding $-6EKR$ to the moments M_{12} and M_{21} for cases b to d, and $-3EKR$ to M_{12} of case a.

The use of these relations is easily seen from the following problem. Suppose it is required to find the moment at the fixed end of a beam whose other end is hinged and which carries transverse load. The condition that the left end is fixed while the right end is hinged requires that $\theta_1 = 0$ in case a of Table 8.3. Then M_{12} is the moment at the fixed end of that beam and is seen to be

$$M_{12} = -\left(M_{12}{}^f + \frac{M_{21}{}^f}{2}\right)$$

This equation indicates that the moment at the fixed end of a beam whose other end is hinged can be expressed in terms of the fixed-end moments of that beam, i.e., the end moments for both ends fixed.

The practical application of the slope-deflection equation obviously requires knowledge of the fixed-end moments $M_{nf}{}^f$ for the particular design loading. It was shown that these fixed-end moments are equal to the last terms of Eqs. (8.9) and (8.10), from which they can be computed for any type of loading. For the most frequent arrangements of load, values of $M_{12}{}^f$ and $M_{21}{}^f$ for the left and right end, respectively, are given in Table 8.4. The table also contains, for the same loadings, the moments at the fixed end if the other end is hinged, computed from Eq. (8.10).

***Table* 8.4 Fixed-end moments M^f and moments at fixed ends for beams with other end hinged, for various types of loading**

Type of loading	Left fixed-end moment M^f_{12}	Right fixed-end moment M^f_{21}	Moment at left fixed end; right end hinged $M^f_{12} + M^f_{21}/2$	Moment at right fixed end; left end hinged $M^f_{21} + M^f_{12}/2$
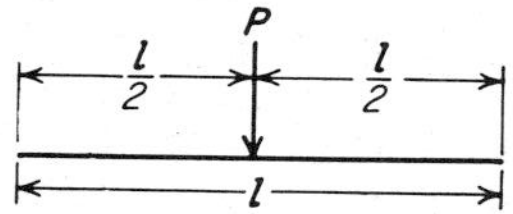	$\frac{1}{8}Pl$	$\frac{1}{8}Pl$	$\frac{3}{16}Pl$	$\frac{3}{16}Pl$
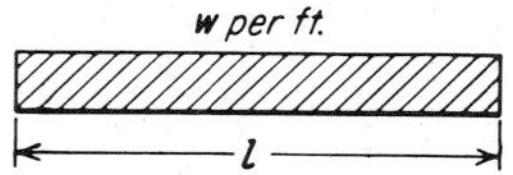	$\frac{1}{12}wl^2$	$\frac{1}{12}wl^2$	$\frac{1}{8}wl^2$	$\frac{1}{8}wl^2$
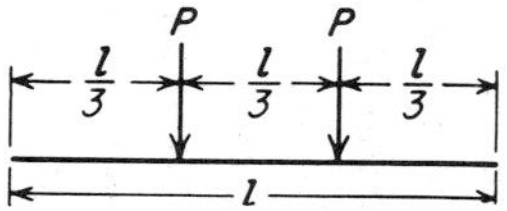	$\frac{2}{9}Pl$	$\frac{2}{9}Pl$	$\frac{1}{3}Pl$	$\frac{1}{3}Pl$
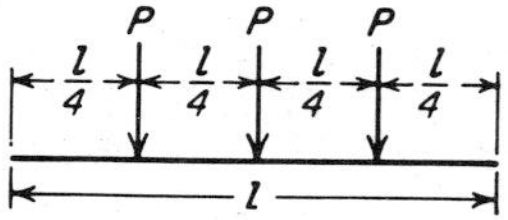	$\frac{5}{16}Pl$	$\frac{5}{16}Pl$	$\frac{15}{32}Pl$	$\frac{15}{32}Pl$
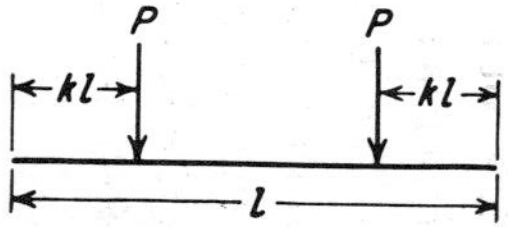	$Pkl(1-k)$	$Pkl(1-k)$	$\frac{3}{2}Pkl(1-k)$	$\frac{3}{2}Pkl(1-k)$

Table 8.4 Fixed-end moments M^f and moments at fixed ends for beams with other end hinged, for various types of loading (*Continued*)

Type of loading	Left fixed-end moment M^f_{12}	Right fixed-end moment M^f_{21}	Moment at left fixed end; right end hinged $M^f_{12} + M^f_{21}/2$	Moment at right fixed end; left end hinged $M^f_{21} + M^f_{12}/2$
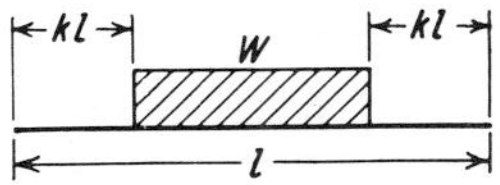	$\frac{Wl}{12}(1 + 2k - 2k^2)$	$\frac{Wl}{12}(1 + 2k - 2k^2)$	$\frac{Wl}{8}(1 + 2k - 2k^2)$	$\frac{Wl}{8}(1 + 2k - 2k^2)$
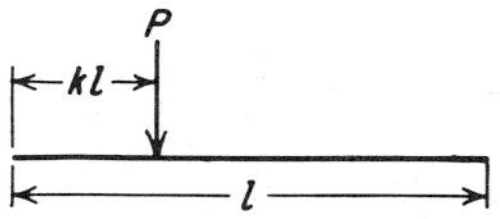	$Pk(1 - k)^2l$	$Pk^2(1 - k)l$	$\frac{1}{2}P(1 - k)(2 - k)kl$	$\frac{1}{2}P(1 - k^2)kl$
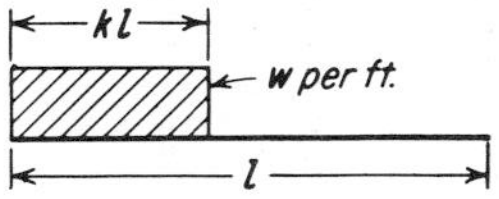	$\frac{wl^2k^2}{12}(3k^2 - 8k + 6)$	$\frac{wl^2k^3}{12}(4 - 3k)$	$\frac{1}{8}wl^2k^2(2 - k)^2$	$\frac{1}{8}wl^2k^2(2 - k^2)$
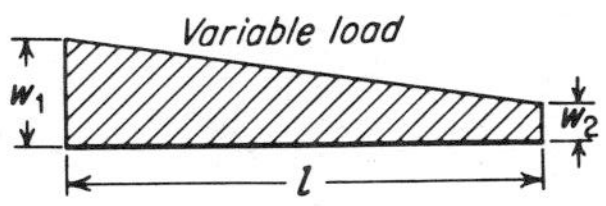	$\frac{l^2}{60}(3w_1 + 2w_2)$	$\frac{l^2}{60}(2w_1 + 3w_2)$	$\frac{l^2}{120}(8w_1 + 7w_2)$	$\frac{l^2}{120}(7w_1 + 8w_2)$
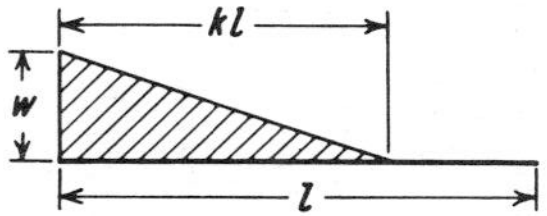	$\frac{wk^2l^2}{60}(10 - 10k + 3k^2)$	$\frac{wk^3l^2}{60}(5 - 3k)$	$\frac{wk^2l^2}{120}(20 - 15k + 3k^2)$	$\frac{wk^2l^2}{120}(10 - 3k^2)$

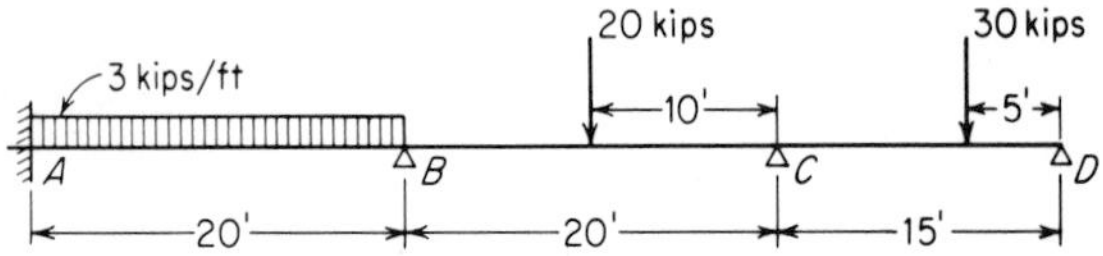

Fig. 8.6

8.6 Illustrative Examples Example 1 Determine the support moments in the three-span, continuous beam of Fig. 8.6. In this beam span, AB is fixed at A, corresponding to case c of table 8.3, while span CD is hinged at D, corresponding to case a. Span BC is partially restrained at both ends, so that for this span Eq. (8.11) must be used.

All moments of inertia are assumed equal. To simplify computations, it is convenient to express all values of K in terms of the K value for one of the members.[1] Thus

$$K_{AB} = \frac{I}{20} \qquad K_{BC} = \frac{I}{20} = K_{AB} \qquad K_{CD} = \frac{I}{15} = 1.33K_{AB}$$

Using the information of Tables 8.3 and 8.4, the fixed-end moments are

$$\begin{aligned} M_{AB}{}^f &= -M_{BA}{}^f = -100 \text{ ft-kips} \\ M_{BC}{}^f &= -M_{CB}{}^f = -50 \text{ ft-kips} \\ M_{CD}{}^f &= -66.7 \text{ ft-kips} \end{aligned}$$

and

$$\begin{aligned} M_{AB} &= 2K_{AB}\theta_B - 100 \\ M_{BA} &= 4K_{AB}\theta_B + 100 \\ M_{BC} &= 2K_{BC}(2\theta_B + \theta_C) - 50 = 4K_{AB}\theta_B + 2K_{AB}\theta_C - 50 \\ M_{CB} &= 2K_{BC}(2\theta_C + \theta_B) + 50 = 4K_{AB}\theta_C + 2K_{AB}\theta_B + 50 \\ M_{CD} &= 3K_{CD}\theta_C - 66.7 = 4K_{AB}\theta_C - 66.7 \end{aligned}$$

The condition that joints B and C be in equilibrium requires

$$M_{BA} + M_{BC} = 0 \qquad M_{CB} + M_{CD} = 0$$

that is,

$$8K_{AB}\theta_B + 2K_{AB}\theta_C + 50 = 0 \qquad 2K_{AB}\theta_B + 8K_{AB}\theta_C - 16.7 = 0$$

Solving these two simultaneous equations, one obtains

$$K_{AB}\theta_B = -7.23 \qquad K_{AB}\theta_C = +3.89$$

The end moments of the three spans are then obtained by substituting these values in the equations for M_{AB}, M_{BA}, etc.; for example,

$$M_{AB} = 2(-7.23) - 100 = -114.5 \text{ ft-kips}$$

Similarly $M_{BA} = +71.1$, $M_{BC} = -71.1$, $M_{CB} = +51.1$, and $M_{CD} = -51.1$ ft-kips.

[1] In problems other than those involving numerical values of support displacement, relative values of K may be used; thus the units of I and L need not agree. Similarly, the constant E does not affect relative stiffness K and can be omitted.

Example 2 The portal frame of Fig. 8.7*a* is subject to a wind load of 20 kips; determine the moments. As in Example 1 it is convenient to express the rigidities of all members as multiples of one value of K. Thus, for this frame, $K_1 = I_1/20$, $K_2 = 4I_1/40 = 2K_1$, $K_3 = K_1$.

Since changes of length of members due to tension or compression forces cause only negligible effects on the magnitudes of moments, it can be assumed that joints B and C displace the same amount d, as shown in Fig. 8.7*a*. Consequently, $R = d/20$ for both AB and CD. Since the frame is geometrically symmetrical and the top displacements of both legs are equal, both legs distort in precisely the same way and amount, causing the beam BC to deflect in an antisymmetrical shape. (This would not be true if, for example, $I_3 \neq I_1$, or if the lengths of both legs were not equal.) Hence, case d of Table 8.3 applies for member BC, while case c applies for AB and CD, since the bottom ends are fixed. The fixed-end moments are zero for all members, since no loads are applied between ends, but sidesway R is present in members AB and CD. With this information, the slope-deflection equations are

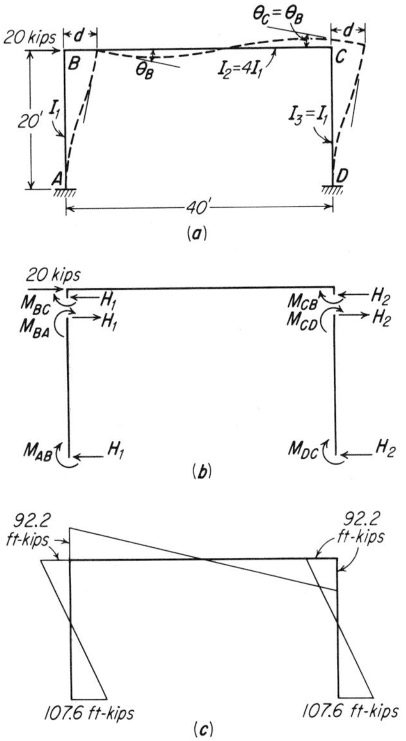

Fig. 8.7

$$
\begin{aligned}
M_{AB} &= M_{DC} = 2EK_1\theta_B - 6EK_1R \\
M_{BA} &= M_{CD} = 4EK_1\theta_B - 6EK_1R \\
M_{BC} &= M_{CB} = 6EK_2\theta_B = 12EK_1\theta_B
\end{aligned}
$$

The condition of joint equilibrium, $M_{BA} + M_{BC} = 0$, gives

$$16EK_1\theta_B - 6EK_1R = 0$$

To obtain a second equation for the unknown quantities θ_B and R, use is made of the condition of frame equilibrium, indicating that the sum of the horizontal reactions of both legs must be equal and opposite to the applied horizontal load. In Fig. 8.7*b* are shown the moments and horizontal forces on each leg. At this stage the moments and forces are not known, either in magnitude or direction. For this reason they are all shown in the positive sense, i.e., moments clockwise and forces resulting in positive deflections. In this manner one ensures that the moments and forces resulting from the analysis are obtained with correct sign.

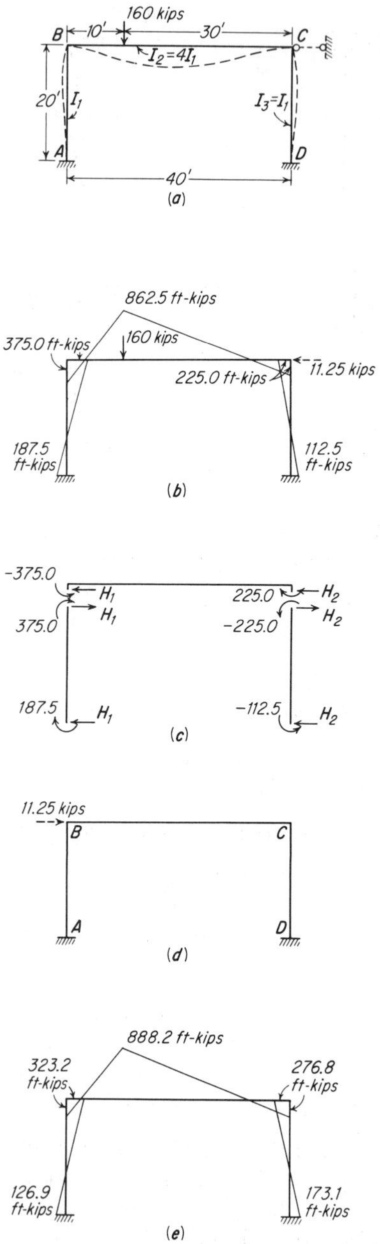

Fig. 8.8

Considering the equilibrium of each leg

$$H_1 = -\frac{M_{AB} + M_{BA}}{20}$$

$$H_2 = -\frac{M_{DC} + M_{CD}}{20}$$

The shears or reactions at the bottoms of the legs must be in equilibrium with the applied horizontal load, or

$$H_1 + H_2 - 20 = 0$$

This expression is often referred to as the *shear* or *bent* equation. Substitution of the values H_1 and H_2 results in

$$M_{AB} + M_{BA} + M_{CD} + M_{DC} + 400 = 0$$

If the values of the moments are substituted in this expression, one obtains a second equation in terms of θ_B and R, namely,

$$3EK_1\theta_B - 6EK_1R + 100 = 0$$

Simultaneous solution with

$$16EK_1\theta_B - 6EK_1R = 0$$

gives

$$EK_1\theta_B = 7.68 \qquad EK_1R = 20.5$$

If these values are substituted in the original moment equations, the following moments result:

$$M_{AB} = M_{DC} = -107.6 \text{ ft-kips}$$
$$M_{BA} = M_{CD} = -92.2 \text{ ft-kips}$$
$$M_{BC} = M_{CB} = 92.2 \text{ ft-kips}$$

The moment diagram is as shown in Fig. 8.7*c*.

Example 3 The frame of Example 2 is loaded as shown in Fig. 8.8*a*. From Table 8.4, with $k = \frac{1}{4}$, the absolute values of the fixed-end moments are $M_{BC}{}^f = 900$ ft-kips and $M_{CB}{}^f = 300$ ft-kips. With proper attention to signs, and noting that the bottoms of both legs are fixed, the slope-deflection equations are

$$M_{AB} = 2EK_1\theta_B$$
$$M_{BA} = 4EK_1\theta_B$$
$$M_{BC} = 8EK_1\theta_B + 4EK_1\theta_C - 900$$
$$M_{CB} = 8EK_1\theta_C + 4EK_1\theta_B + 300$$
$$M_{CD} = 4EK_1\theta_C$$
$$M_{DC} = 2EK_1\theta_C$$

Joint equilibrium requires

$$M_{BA} + M_{BC} = 0 \qquad \text{and} \qquad M_{CB} + M_{CD} = 0$$

which, upon substitution of the moment values, result in the two simultaneous equations

$$12EK_1\theta_B + 4EK_1\theta_C - 900 = 0$$
$$4EK_1\theta_B + 12EK_1\theta_C + 300 = 0$$

These give

$$EK_1\theta_B = 93.75 \qquad \text{and} \qquad EK_1\theta_C = -56.25$$

If these are substituted in the original moment equations, the following values result:

$$M_{AB} = 187.5 \qquad M_{CD} = -225.0$$
$$M_{CB} = 225.0 \qquad M_{BC} = -375.0$$
$$M_{BA} = 375.0 \qquad M_{DC} = -112.5$$

The corresponding moment diagram is shown in Fig. 8.8*b*.

Since no horizontal loads act on the frame, equilibrium requires that the sum of the horizontal reactions or shears at the bottoms of the legs be zero. In Fig. 8.8*c* are shown the moments acting at the ends of the legs. Since these moments are known from previous computations, they are shown in the correct sense, while the (as yet unknown) shears H are indicated as acting in the positive direction. Considering the equilibrium of both legs, it is seen that

$$H_1 + H_2 = -\frac{375.0 + 187.5}{20} + \frac{225.0 + 112.5}{20} = -11.25 \text{ kips} \neq 0$$

Consequently, the frame is not in equilibrium under the computed distribution of moments. It would be in equilibrium if an additional support were present at the level of the beam, as shown in broken lines in Fig. 8.8*a*, which would prevent horizontal displacement at that level. The reaction in that fictitious support must equilibrate the sum of the shears in the legs and is therefore as shown by the broken arrow in Fig. 8.8*b*. This condition is known as *sidesway prevented* or *no sidesway*. If such a support were physically present, as it sometimes is in bridge frames, the moment diagram of Fig. 8.8*b* would be correct.

In a free-standing frame, however, no such horizontal support exists. To realize the condition of zero horizontal load, it is necessary to apply to the frame a horizontal force equal and opposite to the fictitious horizontal reaction. This means that the correct moments in the free-standing frame are the sum of those computed for no sidesway (Fig. 8.8*b*) plus those resulting from a horizontal force equal to the sum of the horizontal leg reactions (Fig. 8.8*d*).

The latter loading is identical in character with that of Example 2, except that the load is now 11.25 kips instead of 20 kips. No new analysis is needed, since all moments are simply 11.25/20 times the moments of Example 2. Superposition of these sidesway moments on those previously obtained for no sidesway results in final moments as follows:

$$M_{AB} = 187.5 - 107.6 \times 11.25/20 = 126.9$$
$$M_{BA} = 375.0 - 92.2 \times 11.25/20 = 323.2$$
$$M_{BC} = -375.0 + 92.2 \times 11.25/20 = -323.2$$
$$M_{CB} = 225.0 + 92.2 \times 11.25/20 = 276.8$$
$$M_{CD} = -225.0 - 92.2 \times 11.25/20 = -276.8$$
$$M_{DC} = -112.5 - 107.6 \times 11.25/20 = -173.1$$

It can easily be checked that the frame is now in equilibrium, i.e., the sum of the moments at each joint is zero, and the sum of the horizontal reactions at the bottom is zero. These checks should always be made to guard against errors.

The final moment diagram is shown in Fig. 8.8*e*. Comparison with Fig. 8.8*b* shows the sizable difference which obtains between moments computed for no sidesway and those actually occurring in a free-standing frame, i.e., with free sidesway. A correct evaluation of the actual sidesway conditions is therefore a prerequisite for correct analysis. The influence of sidesway is more pronounced the more the frame or the distribution of loads, or both, departs from symmetry. Indeed, if the given portal frame were symmetrically loaded, sidesway would not occur, and the moments determined for no sidesway would be correct. It is the off-center location of the load of Fig. 8.8*a* which causes the frame to sidesway to the right. The direction of this sidesway is that corresponding to the horizontal force of Fig. 8.8*d*; this can also be realized from the fact that to prevent this sidesway it was found that a reaction acting to the left (Fig. 8.8*b*) would be required.

It is of some interest to determine the actual magnitude of such horizontal sidesway displacements. In Example 2 it was found that for a horizontal load of 20 kips, $EK_1R = 20.5$. Since $R = d/20$, one obtains, for the horizontal load of 11.25 kips of Fig. 8.8*e*, the sidesway displacement $d = 20(20.5/EK_1)(11.25/20)$ if all quantities are expressed in kips and feet. If a column section of 24 × 24 in. is required to resist the computed moments and loads, and if $E = 3 \times 10^6$ psi, one finds, with proper attention to units, that the sidesway is $d = 0.127$ in., that is, just over ⅛ in. It is seen that even such small sidesway displacements cause sizable changes in moments. Therefore the assumption of "no sidesway" is justified only if horizontal displacement of the actual structure is prevented by effective connection to a practically unyielding mass, such as solid rock, or to another structure which is very much more rigid than the frame proper.

PROBLEMS

For the following structures (*a*) compute the end moments, (*b*) draw complete moment and shear diagrams, and (*c*) sketch the deflected shape.

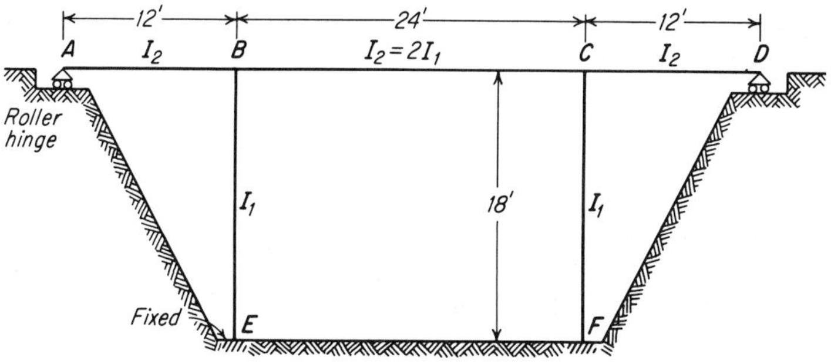

Fig. 8.9 Rigid-frame bridge.

1. The beam of Fig. 8.6, loaded as shown, but with the support C settled $\frac{1}{4}$ in. relative to the line ABD. Assume a cross section of 12 × 24 in.

2. The bridge frame of Fig. 8.9, subject to a uniform dead load of 1 kip per ft over the entire length. (*Hint:* the symmetry of the structure can be used to simplify computations.)

3. The bridge frame of Fig. 8.9, subject to a horizontal force of 1 kip, applied along the axis of the beam. (Such forces are caused by the inertia of vehicles when brakes are applied.)

4. The bridge frame of Fig. 8.9, subject to a uniform live load of 1 kip per ft on span AB.

8.7 Moment-distribution Method The slope-deflection method is a powerful and relatively simple tool for determining moments in continuous structures, as was illustrated in Art. 8.6. It was shown that this method results in as many simultaneous equations as there are unknown joint rotations and translations (not counting the rotations of hinged joints). If there are not more than three or four such unknowns, the method does not present any practical difficulties. However, in many structures, such as multistory, multibay frames, there may be anywhere from five to twenty or more joints, each with an unknown rotation and many with unknown translations. If the slope-deflection method were used to analyze such structures, the work and time involved in solving large numbers of simultaneous equations would be prohibitive. To overcome this difficulty, Hardy Cross developed and published the moment-distribution method in 1932. Because of the great saving of time it achieves, this method is now very widely used. It is different from most other types of analysis in that no equations are set up and solved unless sidesway is involved. Instead, the final moments are obtained by successive numerical approximations.

Suppose that the four members shown in Fig. 8.10*a* were part of a building frame. For the time being the ends B, C, D, and E will be considered fixed. A temporary fixation against rotation is now introduced at joint A, indicated symbolically in Fig. 8.10*b*. For this state all moments in the structure are known, since the moments at both ends of both girders are simply the fixed-end moments for the respective spans and can be obtained from Table 8.4, while the columns are not subject to any moments.

In general, $M_{AC}{}^f$ and $M_{AE}{}^f$ will not be equal and opposite, so that an *unbalanced moment* $M_A{}^u = M_{AC}{}^f + M_{AE}{}^f$ or in general

$$M_A{}^u = \Sigma_A M^f$$

acts on the joint. The right side of this equation stands for the sum of all fixed-end moments acting on the joint. This unbalanced moment is resisted by the temporary fictitious fixation.

If this fixation is now removed, i.e., the joint is released, it will rotate in the direction of $M_A{}^u$, as indicated in Fig. 8.10*c*, until equilibrium is established. Further rotation is then resisted by the bending rigidity of all members meeting at the joint, each of which exerts on the joint a moment that counteracts the rotation, as shown in Fig. 8.10*d*. For equilibrium to establish itself, the sum of these moments must be equal and opposite to the unbalanced moment, so that the sum of all moments

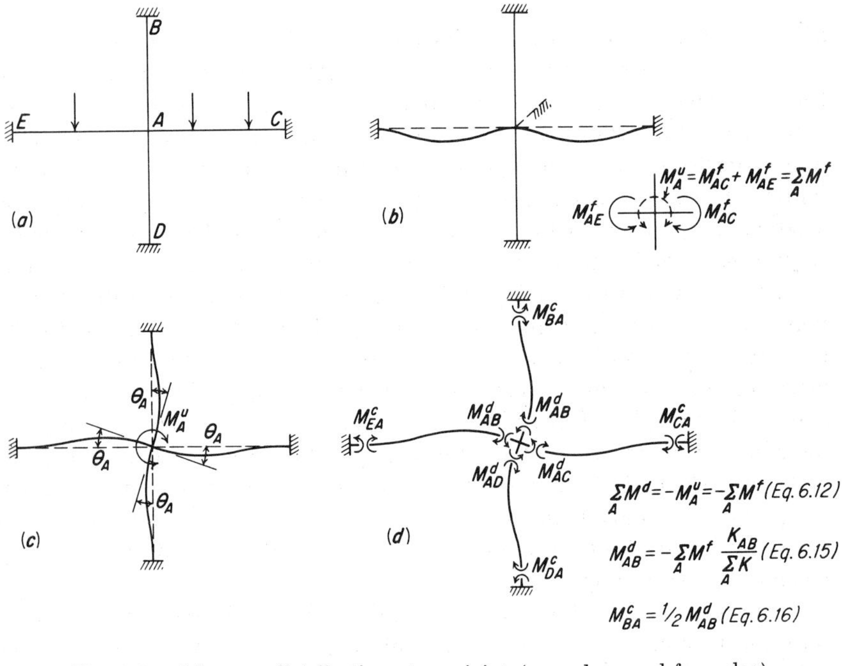

***Fig.* 8.10** Moment distribution at one joint (procedure and formulas).

at the joint is zero. Hence,

$$\Sigma_A M^d = M_{AB}{}^d + M_{AC}{}^d + M_{AD}{}^d + M_{AE}{}^d = -\Sigma_A M^f \tag{8.12}$$

These moments are known as the *distributed moments*, since they represent the fractions of the balancing moment, $-\Sigma_A M^f$, distributed to the respective abutting members.

In Fig. 8.10 all moments are shown in the direction in which they actually act in this particular example, regardless of sign. In connection with the moment-distribution method, *the same sign convention will be used as was established for the slope-deflection method in Art.* 8.4. In particular, the distributed moments in the free-body sketches of the members and joints of Fig. 8.10*d* are all seen to be positive in this case, since they act clockwise on their respective members, or counterclockwise on joint A.

Since joint A is rigid, the angles θ_A of all members (Fig. 8.10*c*) must be equal. From case *c* of Table 8.3, for a member whose far end is fixed, the angle at the near end is

$$\theta_1 = \frac{M_1}{4EK} \tag{8.13}$$

Hence, canceling $4E$, the condition that all end angles are equal can be written as

$$\frac{M_{AB}{}^d}{K_{AB}} = \frac{M_{AC}{}^d}{K_{AC}} = \frac{M_{AD}{}^d}{K_{AD}} = \frac{M_{AE}{}^d}{K_{AE}} \tag{8.14}$$

Using this relation to express all distributed moments in Eq. (8.12) in terms of $M_{AB}{}^d$, one obtains, if the first term is multiplied by (K_{AB}/K_{AB}),

$$M_{AB}{}^d \left(\frac{K_{AB}}{K_{AB}} + \frac{K_{AC}}{K_{AB}} + \frac{K_{AD}}{K_{AB}} + \frac{K_{AE}}{K_{AB}} \right) = -\Sigma_A M^f$$

from which

$$M_{AB}{}^d = (-\Sigma_A M^f) \frac{K_{AB}}{\Sigma_A K} \tag{8.15}$$

Similarly,

$$M_{AC}{}^d = (-\Sigma_A M^f) \frac{K_{AC}}{\Sigma_A K}, \quad \cdot \cdot \cdot$$

The quantities

$$\frac{K_{AB}}{\Sigma_A K}, \quad \cdot \cdot \cdot$$

are known as the *distribution factors,* since they indicate the fraction of the balancing moment, $-\Sigma_A M^f$, which is distributed to each individual member.

The distributed moments, acting at the near end of each member (at the joint), cause it to bend as shown in Fig. 8.10*d* and result in a moment at the fixed far end. By comparing M_{12} and M_{21} of case *c*, Table 8.3, one sees that the moment M_{21} at the fixed far end is one-half the moment M_{12} applied at the near end. Hence

$$M_{BA}{}^c = \tfrac{1}{2}M_{AB}{}^d \qquad M_{CA}{}^c = \tfrac{1}{2}M_{AC}{}^d \tag{8.16}$$

The moments $M_{AB}{}^c$, etc., are known as the *carry-over moments,* since they are carried over from the near to the far end, and the factor ½ is known as the *carry-over factor.* From the free-body sketches of Fig. 8.10*d* it is seen that the carry-over moments have the same sign as the distributed moments at the other end of the member. In the figure they are positive, since they act clockwise on their respective members, or counterclockwise on their joints *B* to *E*.

The *final moments* at either end of any member, then, are the sums of the original fixed-end moments (where they exist, as in the girders) and the distributed moments or the carry-over moments, as the case may be. Thus,

$$\begin{aligned}
M_{AC} &= M_{AC}{}^f + M_{AC}{}^d = M_{AC}{}^f - (\Sigma_A M^f)\frac{K_{AC}}{\Sigma_A K}\\
M_{AB} &= M_{AB}{}^d = -(\Sigma_A M^f)\frac{K_{AB}}{\Sigma_A K}\\
M_{EA} &= M_{EA}{}^f + M_{EA}{}^c = M_{EA}{}^f - \frac{1}{2}(\Sigma_A M^f)\frac{K_{AE}}{\Sigma_A K}\\
M_{DA} &= M_{EA}{}^c = -\frac{1}{2}(\Sigma_A M^f)\frac{K_{AD}}{\Sigma_A K}
\end{aligned} \tag{8.17}$$

and similarly for the other four end moments.

The above procedure may seem complicated in general terms. The following numerical example will indicate its actual simplicity. Since, in the moment-distribution method, all computations are carried out numerically rather than in the form of equations, it is important to organize the computing sheets in a systematic manner in order not to get lost in a maze of numbers. Various schemes may be used, at the computer's preference. The authors believe that the scheme employed in the following examples is simple and not conducive to errors.

The left upper sketch in Fig. 8.11 shows the dimensions and loads of the frame. The fixed-end moments (from Table 8.4) are computed as shown, and the stiffnesses *K* are determined. The moment distribution is carried out on a separate sketch, not necessarily drawn to scale, which

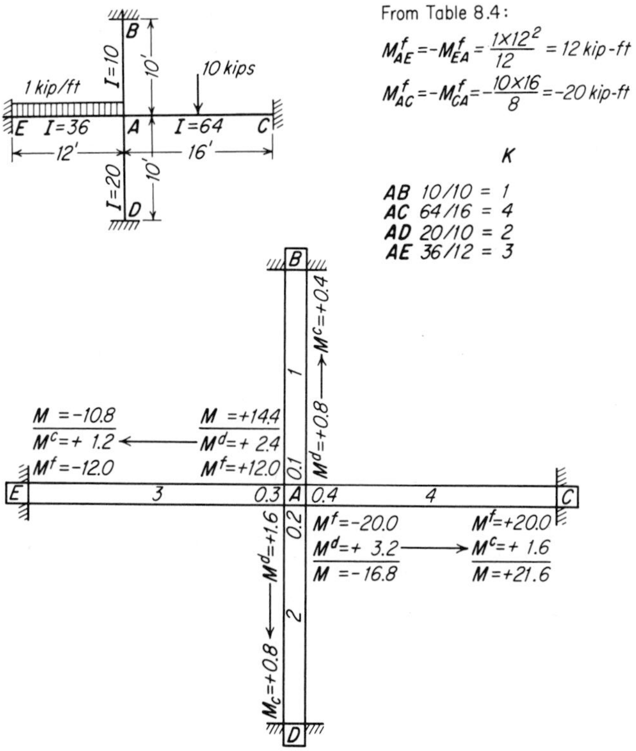

***Fig.* 8.11** Moment distribution at one joint (calculations).

includes the stiffness of each member (shown at midspan) and the distribution factor (shown near the joints). Fixed-end moments are shown at the sections at which they act. It is advantageous in cases such as this to write all moments in consecutive spans alternatingly on one and the other side of the member. This provides the necessary space to enter all subsequent moments. In the given frame no fixed-end moments act on AD and AB. The balancing moment (equal and opposite to the unbalanced moment at A) is now distributed to the abutting members according to Eq. (8.15); that is, $M_{AB}{}^d = 8.0 \times 0.1 = 0.8$, $M_{AC}{}^d = 8.0 \times 0.4 = 3.2$, etc. The carry-over moments at the far ends are one-half the distributed moments [Eq. (8.16)], the carry-over being indicated by arrows. The final moments at each end of all members are obtained by summing the individual entries. Once the distribution is completed, joint A is in equilibrium; i.e., the sum of the final moments is zero:

$$14.4 + 0.8 - 16.8 + 1.6 = 0$$

This check should always be made to guard against errors. At the ends of members AB and AD the respective M^d and M^c are the final moments, since no fixed-end moments are present.

It is seen that all eight end moments were determined without equations, by a very simple numerical process. With some practice the moment designations (M^f, M^c, etc.) as well as the carry-over arrows can be omitted on the computation sheets.

If the far end of a member is hinged rather than fixed (say end C in Fig. 8.10a), the moment it exerts on the locked joint (Fig. 8.10b) is the *moment at the fixed end of a beam hinged*, rather than fixed, *at the other end.* In this case the corresponding moments are those listed in the last two columns of Table 8.4. The rotation at the near end of a beam whose far end is hinged is obtained from case a of Table 8.3 and is

$$\theta_1 = \frac{M_1}{3EK} \tag{8.18}$$

Comparison with Eq. (8.13) shows that for such a beam the rotation for a given moment is four-thirds the rotation for the same moment M_1, but with the other end fixed. Put in different terms, it may be said that the stiffness of a beam with far end hinged is three-fourths that of the same beam with far end fixed. Hence, for computing distribution factors, the *modified stiffness of a member with far end hinged* is

$$K^m = \frac{3}{4}K = \frac{3}{4}\frac{I}{l} \tag{8.19}$$

rather than I/l for far end fixed. For such members, of course, *no moment is carried over to the hinged end,* since such a support is not capable of resisting a moment.

So far, the moment-distribution method has been discussed only for a structure with one single joint subject to rotation. If more than one such joint is present, each joint is unlocked, balanced, and relocked in turn. With reference to Fig. 8.12, the beam of Example 1, Art. 8.6, will be solved by moment distribution. Fixed-end moments, stiffnesses, and

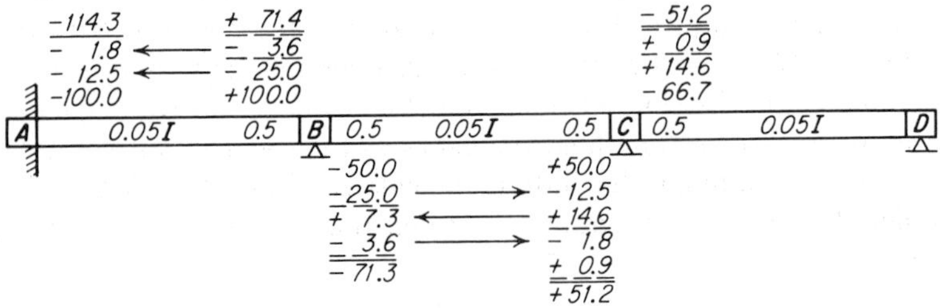

Fig. 8.12

distribution factors are computed and recorded on a separate sketch of the structure. In this particular case, it happens that all the stiffnesses are equal (note the use of modified stiffness for the span CD, with hinged end), so that the distribution factors at all interior joints equal 0.5.

The fixed-end moments are valid only if joints B and C are artificially restrained against rotation. Joint B is first released and permitted to rotate; the unbalanced moment is distributed to members AB and BC in accordance with their stiffnesses, and carry-over moments are recorded at joints A and C. Joint B is then relocked, and joint C is permitted to rotate. To the original unbalance at that joint is added the moment carried over from the rotation of joint B; the entire unbalanced moment is distributed at once, and again the carry-over moment is recorded. Joint C is then relocked, and the cycle is repeated, by returning to joint B, until the successive corrections become negligible. The sum of all moments entered in one column represents the final moment at that end of the member. It should be noted that the moments obtained from Fig. 8.12 differ by only a fraction of a per cent from those obtained by slope deflection in Art. 8.6, namely -114.5, $+71.1$, -71.1, $+51.1$, and -51.1.

It is seen in this example that the correction moments decrease very quickly. In this particular case two distribution cycles have resulted in more than adequate accuracy. In more complicated structures three or four cycles may be required. It is interesting to observe that, for this example, the three-moment method results in three simultaneous equations for M_a, M_b, and M_c, and the slope-deflection method in two simultaneous equations for θ_a and θ_b, while by the moment-distribution method the entire analysis is carried out numerically.

8.8 Moment Distribution for Frames with Joint Displacement (Sidesway) The method discussed in Art. 8.7 permits the determination of moments in structures whose joints, though rotated, are not linearly displaced (translated) under load. When such linear displacements occur, such as from horizontal wind loads or other sources, computations must be correspondingly modified to account for this influence. This process is exactly similar to that employed in Examples 2 and 3, Art. 8.6, except that now moments will be determined by distribution instead of by slope-deflection equations.

If a horizontal force acts on a frame, it will deflect an amount d, as indicated in Fig. 8.13. Even though, for any design, the horizontal force is usually known (say, the wind pressure) it is more convenient in connection with moment distribution to proceed in the reverse order.

The frame is given an arbitrary displacement d of convenient magnitude. Next, the moments due to this displacement and the magnitude

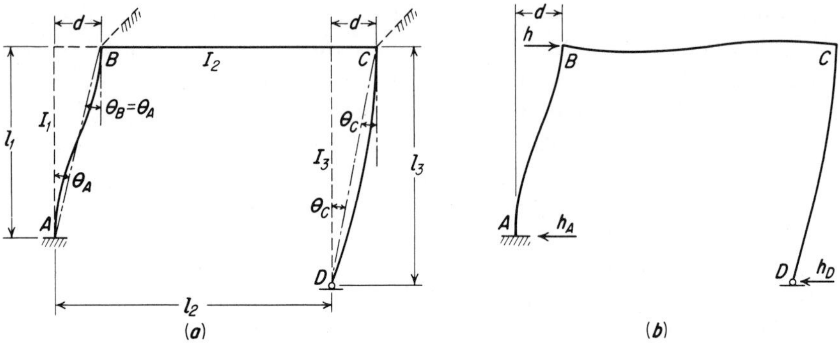

Fig. 8.13

of the force required to produce it are computed. Let the magnitude of this force be h, and the corresponding moments m, while the actual horizontal force is H. Then the actual moments are

$$M = m\frac{H}{h} \tag{8.20}$$

To compute m and h, the joints B and C (Fig. 8.13*a*) are first locked against rotation and then given an equal arbitrary displacement d. This causes moments m' to occur at A, B, and C (D being hinged in this particular example). Leg AB, with tangents at both ends parallel, bends antisymmetrically, as in Fig. 8.5*d*. Consequently for a given displacement the moments are obtained from case *d* of Table 8.3:

$$m'_{AB} = m'_{BA} = 6EK\theta_A = 6K\frac{Ed}{l_1} \tag{8.21}$$

which holds when *the bottom end of the column is fixed.* Column CD, being hinged at one end, corresponds to Fig. 8.5*a*. Consequently, *for a column with bottom end hinged*, the moment at the top is

$$m'_{CD} = 3EK\theta_C = 3K\frac{Ed}{l_3} \tag{8.22}$$

Next, the temporarily locked joints are released, and the moments m corresponding to the actual configuration of the frame (Fig. 8.13*b*) are computed by the usual procedure of distributing the moments m'. The horizontal reactions h_A and h_D are now determined by considering individually the equilibrium of each leg (see Fig. 8.7*b*). Hence,

$$h_A = \frac{m_{AB} + m_{BA}}{l_1} \tag{8.23}$$

and, since D is hinged, so that $m_{DC} = 0$,

$$h_D = \frac{m_{CD}}{l_3} \tag{8.24}$$

The horizontal force corresponding to the arbitrary displacement d is thus

$$h = h_A + h_D \tag{8.25}$$

Since the actual force that acts on the frame is H rather than the fictitious auxiliary force h, the actual moments are then computed from Eq. (8.20).

As was shown in Example 3, Art. 8.6, sidesway and corresponding moments are caused not only by actual horizontal loads, but also by asymmetry of vertical loads and/or of frame configuration.

The analysis of frames with sidesway is illustrated below.

Illustrative example To compute the moments in the frame of Fig. 8.14*a*, the stiffnesses $K = I/l$ are calculated for all members, except that for the hinged

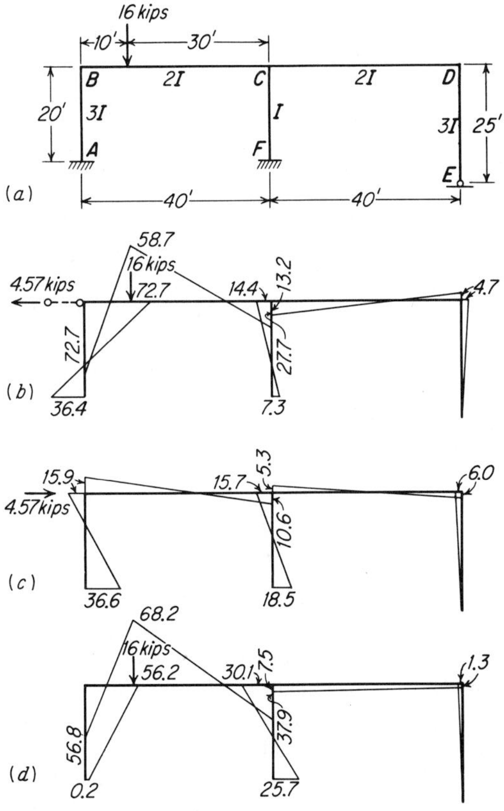

***Fig.* 8.14** Effect of sidesway on moments in rigid frame.

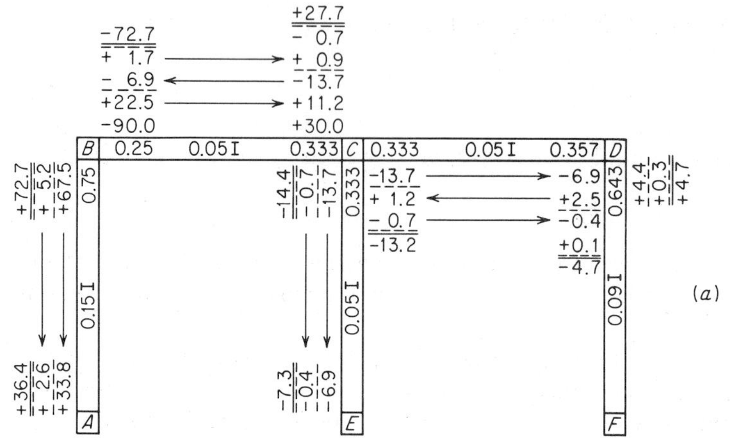

$$H = \frac{36.4 + 72.7}{20} - \frac{14.4 + 7.3}{20} + \frac{4.7}{25} = 4.57 \text{ kips}$$

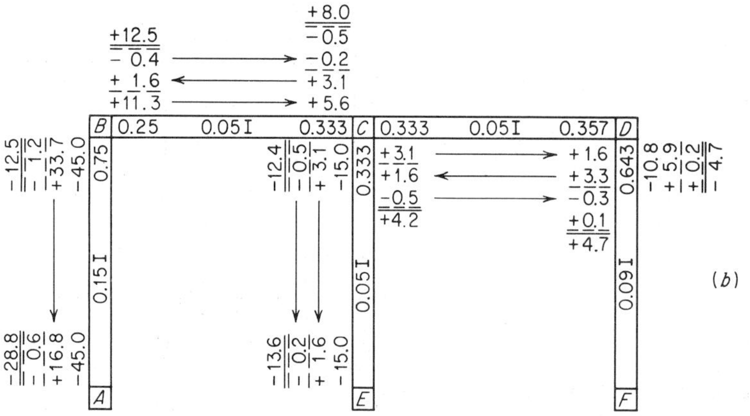

$$h = -\frac{28.8 + 12.5}{20} - \frac{13.6 + 12.4}{20} - \frac{4.7}{25} = -3.56 \text{ kips}$$

Fig. 8.15

member DE, $K^m = 0.75I/l$. Next, the distribution factors are computed for all members at joints B, C, and D and, together with the stiffnesses, are indicated on the computation sketch, Fig. 8.15*a*. The fixed-end moments for the loaded span BC may be obtained from Table 8.4.

1. With these data the moment distribution of Fig. 8.15*a* is carried out in the usual way for "no sidesway." The distribution was started by unlocking B and then, successively, C and D, then repeating the cycle. It is seen that the corrections produced by the second cycle amount to less than 10 per cent of those of the

first cycle. Since correction moments in successive cycles decrease in about the same proportion, a third cycle, if carried out, would contribute corrections of about 1 per cent or less of the final moments. These can be neglected, so that, in this example, a two-cycle distribution provides satisfactory accuracy.

After completion of the distribution computations, each joint is checked for equilibrium, that is, $\Sigma M = 0$. It is seen that joints B and D check exactly. At joint C there is a discrepancy in the third digit. Such discrepancies in the last digit result frequently from rounding off digits not shown in the computation. If computations are carried to three digits, as they usually are, slight discrepancies in the last digits are obviously negligible.

By computing the shears at the bottoms of the three legs, as shown in Fig. 8.15*a* [see Eqs. (8.23) and (8.24)], an unbalanced force of $H = 4.57$ kips is obtained. In other words, the frame would be in equilibrium under the moments of Fig. 8.15*a* only if an additional support were present to prevent sidesway and to supply a horizontal reaction of 4.57 kips. This fictitious state of loading and the corresponding moment diagram are shown in Fig. 8.14*b*.

2. It is now necessary to determine the "sidesway correction," i.e., to apply a force equal and opposite to H. This amounts to removing the fictitious support at D, which permits the natural sidesway to occur. The sidesway moments caused by H, if superposed on those of Fig. 8.14*b*, give the correct end moments.

To compute these moments, joints B, C, and D are locked and given an arbitrary horizontal displacement. This displacement is so chosen as to result in moments of convenient magnitude; here $Ed = 1000$ serves this purpose. The corresponding end moments for legs AB and CE are computed from Eq. (8.21), and for the hinged leg DF from Eq. (8.22); for $Ed = 1000$, they are -45.0, -15.0, and -10.8 ft-kips, respectively. These moments are applied and distributed in the usual manner, as shown in Fig. 8.15*b*. It is seen that a two-cycle distribution is again sufficient, since a third cycle would add corrections of less than 1 per cent. The horizontal shears are computed as in (1) [see Eqs. (8.23) and (8.24)], and the total horizontal force $h = -3.60$ kips, corresponding to the given deflection $Ed = 1000$, is calculated as indicated in Fig. 8.15*b* [see Eq. (8.25)]. Since the moments of Fig. 8.15*b* are caused by a force of 3.60 kips, while the force required to eliminate the reaction of Fig. 8.14*b* is 4.57 kips, the actual sidesway moments are 4.57/3.60 times those of Fig. 8.15*b* [see Eq. (8.20)]. The corresponding sidesway moment diagram is shown in Fig. 8.14*c*.

3. To obtain the final moments, the sidesway moments of Fig. 8.14*c* are added to those for no sidesway (Fig. 8.14*b*), resulting in the final moment diagram shown in Fig. 8.14*d*. Comparison of Fig. 8.14*b* and *d* shows the very large influence sidesway may have; not only are the magnitudes of the moments changed by 50 per cent and more, but even signs are reversed in some cases, such as at points A and D. Even though the relative influence of sidesway may be considerably smaller in many cases, the present example shows that it is unsafe to neglect sidesway in design except (1) if symmetry of the frame and loading forestall any sidesway tendency or (2) if the structure is so supported as to make sidesway physically impossible.

4. If a real horizontal force of, say, 10 kips, such as a wind load, acts on this frame, from left to right, the moments are 10/4.57 times those of Fig. 8.14*c* or,

which amounts to the same, 10/3.60 of those determined by the distribution of Fig. 8.15*b*.

PROBLEMS

Solve Probs. 2 to 4, Art. 8.6, by moment distribution.

8.9 Building Frames: Vertical Loads Rigid frames with a small number of spans, one or at most two stories high, occur frequently in industrial and commercial structures and in bridges. Since the number of joints in such frames is relatively small, their analysis presents no particular difficulty, as is illustrated by the examples of the preceding articles.

In contrast, the frames of multistory apartment or office buildings, warehouses, and the like have a multitude of members and joints, as is seen on the relatively small frame of Fig. 8.16. Such frames are known for short as *building frames* and are composed of columns and of girders or beams. These members must be designed for the largest moments, shears, and, in the case of columns, axial loads which can reasonably be expected to occur during the lifetime of the building. These moments, shears, and axial loads are brought about in part by the weight of the structure (dead load) and in part by live load. While the former is con-

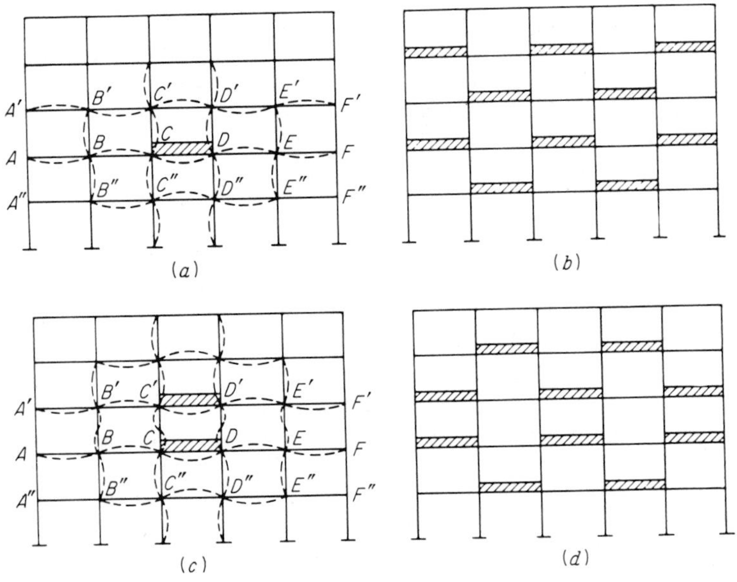

Fig. 8.16

stant, live loads, such as floor loads from human occupancy, can be placed in various ways, some of which will result in larger effects than others.

In Fig. 8.16*a*, only span *CD* is loaded by live load. The distortions of the various frame members are seen to be largest in and immediately adjacent to the loaded span and to decrease rapidly with increasing distance from the load. Since bending moments are proportional to curvatures, the moments in more remote members are correspondingly smaller than those in, or close to, the loaded span. However, the loading of Fig. 8.16*a* does not produce the maximum possible positive moment in *CD*. In fact, if additional live load were placed on span *AB*, this span would bend down, *BC* would bend up, and *CD* itself would bend down in the same manner, although to a lesser degree, as it is bent by its own load. Hence, the positive moment in *CD* is increased if *AB* and, by the same reasoning, *EF* are loaded simultaneously. By expanding the same reasoning to the other members of the frame, it is easily seen that the "checkerboard pattern" of live load of Fig. 8.16*b* produces the largest possible positive moments not only in *CD*, but in all loaded spans. Hence, two such checkerboard patterns are required to obtain the maximum positive moments in all spans.

In addition to maximum span moments, it is often necessary to investigate minimum span moments. Dead load, acting as it does on all spans, usually produces only positive span moments. However, live load, placed as in Fig. 8.16*a* and even more so in Fig. 8.16*b*, is seen to bend the unloaded spans upward, i.e., to produce negative moments in the span. If these negative live-load moments are larger than the generally positive dead-load moments, a given girder, depending on load position, may be subject at one time to positive span moments and at another to negative span moments. It must be designed to withstand both types of moments, i.e., it must be furnished with tensile steel at both top and bottom. Thus, the loading of Fig. 8.16*b*, in addition to giving maximum span moments in the loaded spans, gives minimum span moments in the unloaded spans.

Maximum negative moments at the supports of the girders are obtained, on the other hand, if loads are placed on the two spans adjacent to the particular support and in a corresponding pattern on the more remote girders. A separate loading scheme of this type is then required for each support for which maximum negative moments are to be computed.

In each column, the largest moments occur at the top or bottom, as can easily be seen from the examples of the preceding articles. While the loading of Fig. 8.16*c* results in large moments at the ends of columns *CC'* and *DD'*, the reader can easily convince himself with a simple moment distribution that these moments are further augmented if additional loads are placed as shown in Fig. 8.16*d*.

It is seen from this brief discussion that, in order to calculate the maximum possible moments at all critical points of a building frame, live load must be placed in a great variety of different schemes. If a complete moment distribution for the entire frame is carried out for each of these cases, the required amount of computation becomes prohibitive, even for frames with a limited number of spans and stories. The need is apparent, then, for simplified approximate methods which allow the determination of these moments with reasonable accuracy and yet limit the amount of computation. Although such abbreviated methods cannot result in the largest theoretically possible moments, the use of approximations is justified for a variety of reasons.

Thus, even though it is theoretically necessary to load span $B''C''$, among others, to obtain the maximum positive moment in $D'E'$ (Fig. 8.16*b*), the former is so far removed from the latter that its effect on this moment is negligibly small. Hence, the influence on any moments of loads on spans sufficiently far removed can generally be neglected. That such a procedure is legitimate is emphasized also by the fact that it is quite improbable for the exact loading schemes of Fig. 8.16*b* and *d* ever to occur during the lifetime of the structure. Considerations similar to these justify methods in which, to determine any particular moment, only the influence of the adjacent parts of the frame is considered.

In this connection it is also important to realize the difference in the importance of accurate moment determination for girders on the one hand and for columns on the other. In the former the required cross sections are dictated exclusively by moments and shears, and for this reason a relatively accurate determination of these quantities is called for. Columns, on the other hand, must resist the axial loads from overlying parts of the structure, in addition to the bending moments induced in them by the rigidly connected girders. An inaccuracy in determining these moments therefore affects only one of the two factors (loads and moments) which determine the required cross sections and, for this reason, has smaller overall effect than similar inaccuracies in determining girder moments. It should also be noted that the load distribution which results in maximum column moments does not at the same time result in maximum axial forces in the same columns. For instance, even though the loading of Fig. 8.16*d* results in maximum $M_{CC'}$, the axial load on that column would attain its maximum if all, instead of just a few, of the adjacent girder spans in the upper stories were loaded. While such full loading of overlying spans would result in maximum axial force, it would, conversely, cause a smaller moment $M_{CC'}$ than that resulting from Fig. 8.16*d*.

It is evident from this discussion that an approximate method of moment determination is reliable for design use if it permits the determination of girder moments with a relatively high degree of accuracy. For column moments, a cruder approximation is permissible, if such moments are used in conjunction with maximum axial loads (i.e., all overlying adjacent spans fully loaded, except for such decrease in live load with increasing number of stores as is permitted in most building codes).

Extensive investigation by means of numerous trial computations has shown that, for building frames with reasonably regular outline not involving unusual asymmetry of loading or shape, the influence of side-sway caused by vertical loads can be neglected.

In that case moments are determined with sufficient accuracy by breaking up the entire frame into simpler subframes. Each of these consists of one girder, plus the top and bottom columns framing into that particular girder. Placing the live loads on that girder in the most unfavorable manner permits sufficiently accurate determination of all girder moments and of the moments at the top ends of the bottom columns and at the bottom ends of the top columns. For this partial structure, the far ends of the columns are considered as fixed, except for such first-floor or basement columns where soil and foundation conditions more closely approach hinged ends. Consequently, the ACI Code specifies for floor members, including girders:

> (1) The live load may be considered to be applied only to the floor or roof under consideration, and the far ends of the columns may be assumed as fixed.
> (2) Consideration may be limited to combinations of dead loads on all spans with full live load on two adjacent spans (for negative support moments) and with full live load on alternate spans (for positive span moments).

When investigating the maximum negative moment at any joint, negligible error will result from considering the joints second removed in each direction to be completely fixed. Similarly, in determining maximum or minimum span moments, the joints at the far ends of the adjacent spans may be considered fixed. Thus, individual portions of a frame of many spans may be investigated separately.

In regard to columns, the Code indicates:

> Columns shall be designed to resist the axial forces from loads on all floors, plus the maximum bending due to loads on a single adjacent span of the floor under consideration. Account shall also be taken of the loading condition giving the maximum ratio of bending moment to axial load. In building frames, particular attention shall be given to the effect of unbalanced floor loads on both exterior and interior columns and of eccentric loading due to other causes. In computing moments in columns due to gravity loading, the far ends of columns which are monolithic with the structure may be considered fixed.

The following example illustrates the computation of moments in building frames.

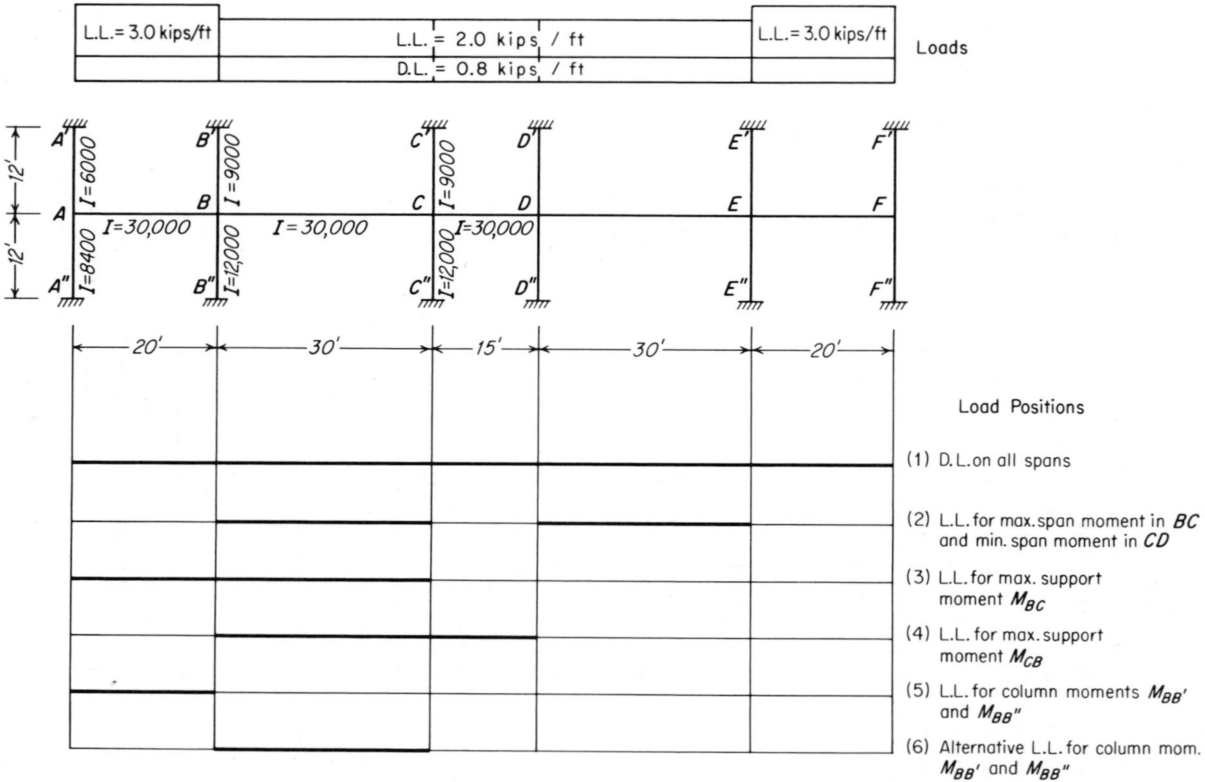

***Fig.* 8.17** Approximate determination of moments in building frames (vertical load).

Illustrative example The structure shown in Fig. 8.17 represents the second-story girder of the frame of Fig. 8.16, including the abutting top and bottom columns, isolated as just described. Dimensions and moments of inertia are shown in the main sketch, while the magnitude and character of loads are indicated at the top of the figure. Since span lengths differ by more than 20 per cent, and since the ratio of live to dead load, at least for some spans, exceeds 3:1, design by approximate moment coefficients such as those of Table 8.2 would be misleading and unsafe. Moment determination by more accurate frame analysis is, therefore, *mandatory* for this structure. Let it be required to compute all necessary moments for span BC, the minimum span moment for CD, and the column moments $M_{BB'}$ and $M_{BB''}$.

According to the preceding discussion, it is necessary, for this purpose, to determine moments from the six loading schemes shown at the bottom of Fig. 8.17. This would require six separate moment distributions. However, in this particular case considerable simplification can be achieved by noting that (1) all live and dead loads are uniformly distributed, though of varying magnitudes, and (2) the structure is symmetrical. To reduce computations, moments are determined separately for a uniform load of 1 kip per ft placed individually on spans AB, BC, and CD. The moments for all six loadings of Fig. 8.17 can then be computed by simple superposition of the moments obtained from these three distributions. Simplifications such as this depend on the shape of the structure and the type of loading and should always be used when possible.

The fixed-end moments $wl^2/12$ for $w = 1$ kip per ft are 33.3, 75.0, and 18.75 ft-kips for spans AB, BC, and CD, respectively. The stiffnesses and distribution factors are computed in the usual manner from the given lengths and moments of inertia.

For this particular type of moment computation in building frames, a special way of recording the calculations is often found convenient. This scheme is shown in detail in Fig. 8.18*a* and is self-explanatory. It has the advantage that all figures are written in one instead of two directions. Carry-overs along the girders can be indicated by arrows in the usual manner. This would not be possible for carry-overs along columns. However, these are not required, since only moments in the column end sections adjacent to the girder are determined in this special form of distribution. Moment $M_{B'B}$, for instance, would be found, not from this calculation, but from a similar analysis of girder $A'F'$ of Fig. 8.16, with its adjacent columns.

The three distributions for the unit loads on the three spans are given in Fig. 8.18*a* to *c*. In examining these calculations, the following features are noteworthy: (1) It is seen from Fig. 8.18*a* and *b* that moments decrease very rapidly with increasing distance from the loaded span, amounting here to less than 2 per cent of the loaded-span moments at those joints which are twice removed from the loaded span. This reduces very considerably the amount of calculation required for single-span loadings. (2) Two-cycle distribution at the near joints and a single cycle at the more remote joints is seen to result here in satisfactory accuracy, although in some cases more cycles may be required.

For Fig. 8.18*a* the order of joint release was A, B, C, D, A, B, while for Fig. 8.18*b* it was B, C, D, E, A, B, C, D, A, further distribution on each joint being

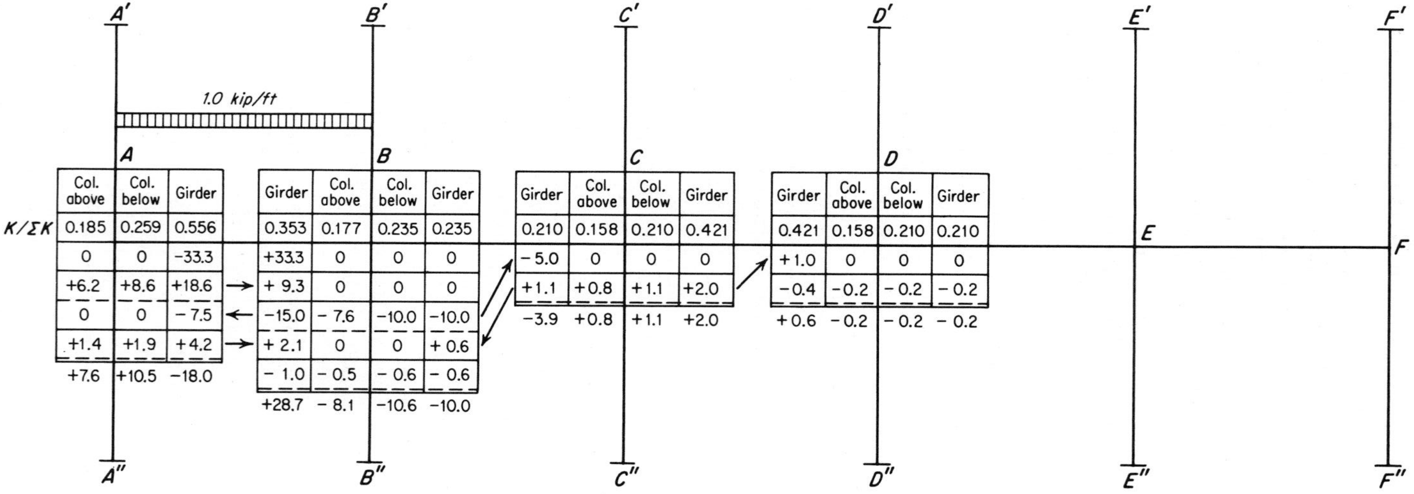
A′
B′
C′
D′
E′
F′
1.0 kip/ft
A
B
C
D
E
F
K/ΣK
Col. above | Col. below | Girder
0.185 | 0.259 | 0.556
0 | 0 | −33.3
+6.2 | +8.6 | +18.6
0 | 0 | − 7.5
+1.4 | +1.9 | +4.2
+7.6 | +10.5 | −18.0
Girder | Col. above | Col. below | Girder
0.353 | 0.177 | 0.235 | 0.235
+33.3 | 0 | 0 | 0
+ 9.3 | 0 | 0 | 0
−15.0 | − 7.6 | −10.0 | −10.0
+ 2.1 | 0 | 0 | + 0.6
− 1.0 | − 0.5 | − 0.6 | − 0.6
+28.7 | − 8.1 | −10.6 | −10.0
Girder | Col. above | Col. below | Girder
0.210 | 0.158 | 0.210 | 0.421
− 5.0 | 0 | 0 | 0
+1.1 | +0.8 | +1.1 | +2.0
−3.9 | +0.8 | +1.1 | +2.0
Girder | Col. above | Col. below | Girder
0.421 | 0.158 | 0.210 | 0.210
+1.0 | 0 | 0 | 0
−0.4 | −0.2 | − 0.2 | − 0.2
+0.6 | − 0.2 | − 0.2 | − 0.2
A″
B″
C″
D″
E″
F″

Fig. 8.18a

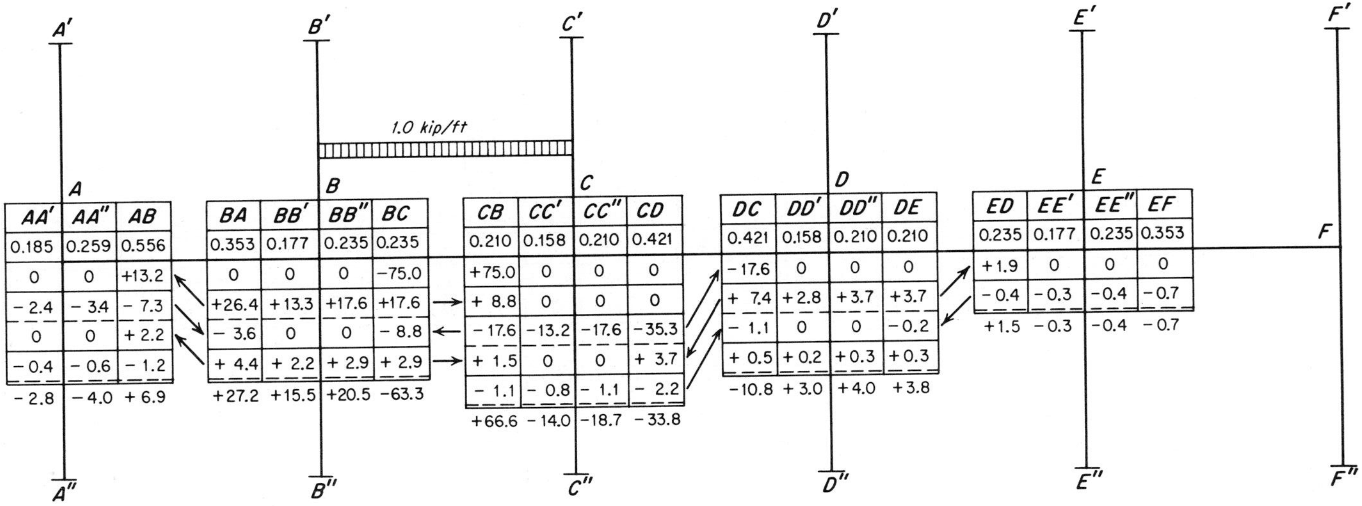
A′ B′ C′ D′ E′ F′
1.0 kip/ft
A B C D E F
AA′ AA″ AB
0.185 0.259 0.556
0 0 +13.2
− 2.4 − 3.4 − 7.3
0 0 + 2.2
− 0.4 − 0.6 − 1.2
− 2.8 − 4.0 + 6.9
BA BB′ BB″ BC
0.353 0.177 0.235 0.235
0 0 0 −75.0
+26.4 +13.3 +17.6 +17.6
− 3.6 0 0 − 8.8
+ 4.4 + 2.2 + 2.9 + 2.9
+27.2 +15.5 +20.5 −63.3
CB CC′ CC″ CD
0.210 0.158 0.210 0.421
+75.0 0 0 0
+ 8.8 0 0 0
− 17.6 −13.2 −17.6 −35.3
+ 1.5 0 0 + 3.7
− 1.1 − 0.8 − 1.1 − 2.2
+66.6 − 14.0 −18.7 − 33.8
DC DD′ DD″ DE
0.421 0.158 0.210 0.210
− 17.6 0 0 0
+ 7.4 + 2.8 + 3.7 + 3.7
− 1.1 0 0 − 0.2
+ 0.5 + 0.2 + 0.3 + 0.3
−10.8 + 3.0 + 4.0 + 3.8
ED EE′ EE″ EF
0.235 0.177 0.235 0.353
+ 1.9 0 0 0
− 0.4 − 0.3 − 0.4 − 0.7
+ 1.5 − 0.3 − 0.4 − 0.7
A″ B″ C″ D″ E″ F″

Fig. 8.18b

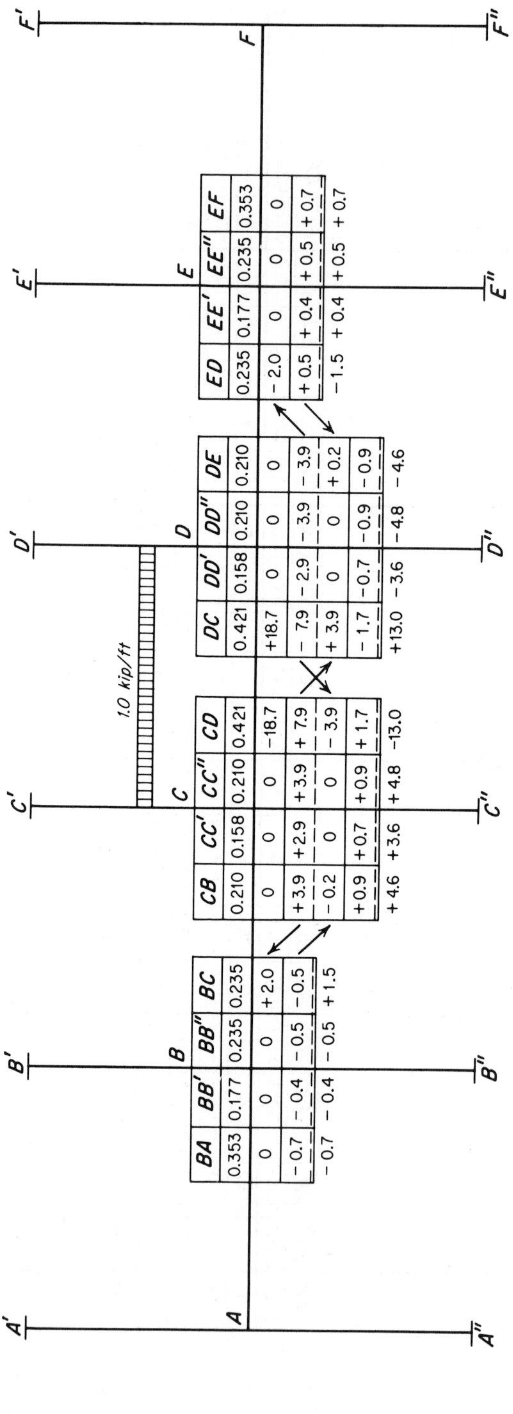
A' A A''
B' B B''
C' C C''
D' D D''
E' E E''
F' F F''
1.0 kip/ft
BA BB' BB'' BC
0.353 0.177 0.235 0.235
0 0 0 +2.0
−0.7 −0.4 −0.5 −0.5
−0.7 −0.4 −0.5 +1.5
CB CC' CC'' CD
0.210 0.158 0.210 0.421
0 0 0 −18.7
+3.9 +2.9 +3.9 +7.9
−0.2 0 0 −3.9
+0.9 +0.7 +0.9 +1.7
+4.6 +3.6 +4.8 −13.0
DC DD' DD'' DE
0.421 0.158 0.210 0.210
+18.7 0 0 0
−7.9 −2.9 −3.9 −3.9
+3.9 0 0 +0.2
−1.7 −0.7 −0.9 −0.9
+13.0 −3.6 −4.8 −4.6
ED EE' EE'' EF
0.235 0.177 0.235 0.353
−2.0 0 0 0
+0.5 +0.4 +0.5 +0.7
−1.5 +0.4 +0.5 +0.7
Fig. 8.18c

discontinued as soon as correction moments had decreased sufficiently. For the case of Fig. 8.18*c*, advantage was taken of symmetry by unlocking symmetrically located joints simultaneously in pairs. Thus *C* and *D* were simultaneously released first, next *B* and *E*, and finally *C* and *D*. It is seen that, if computed in this manner, all component moments on one side are equal and opposite those for the symmetrically located sections on the other side. With some experience such computations in cases of symmetry can be carried out showing only one set of figures. The resulting moments caused by unit loads on individual spans are given in the table below.

Unit load on span	Column moments						Girder moments				
	$M_{AA'}$	$M_{AA''}$	$M_{BB'}$	$M_{BB''}$	$M_{CC'}$	$M_{CC''}$	M_{AB}	M_{BA}	M_{BC}	M_{CB}	M_{CD}
AB	+7.6	+10.5	−8.1	−10.6	+0.8	+1.1	−18.0	+28.7	−10.0	−3.9	−0.6
BC	−2.8	−4.0	+15.5	+20.5	−14.0	−18.7	+6.9	+27.2	−63.3	+66.6	−33.8
CD			−0.4	−0.5	+3.6	+4.8		−0.7	+1.5	+4.6	−13.0
DE			+0.3	+0.4	−3.0	−4.0		+0.7	−1.5	−3.8	+10.8
EF					+0.2	+0.2				+0.2	+0.6
All spans	+4.8	+6.5	+7.3	+9.9	−12.4	−16.6	−11.1	+55.9	−73.3	+63.7	−36.0

The moments for span loads on *DE* and *EF* in the table above were obtained as being equal and opposite those for symmetrically located sections for span loads on *BC* and *AB*, respectively.

From these moments caused by the unit loads, the actual frame moments are easily computed as follows:

1. Maximum girder moments at supports:

M_{BC}:

D.L. all spans:	0.8 (−73.3)	=	−58.6
L.L. on *BC*:	2.0 (−63.3)	=	−126.6
L.L. on *AB*:	3.0 (−10.0)	=	−30.0
Maximum M_{BC}		=	−215.2 ft-kips

M_{CB}:

D.L. all spans:	0.8 (+63.7)	=	+51.0
L.L. on *BC*:	2.0 (+66.6)	=	+133.2
L.L. on *CD*:	2.0 (+4.6)	=	+9.2
Maximum M_{CB}		=	+193.4 ft-kips

2. Maximum midspan moment in *BC*:

M_{BC}:

D.L. as in (1)	=	−58.6
L.L. on *BC* as in (1)	=	−126.6
L.L. on *DE*: 2.0 (−1.5)	=	−3.0
M_{BC}	=	−188.2 ft-kips

M_{CB}:

D.L. as in (1)	=	+51.0
L.L. on BC as in (1)	=	+133.2
L.L. on DE: 2.0 (−3.8)	=	−7.6
M_{CB}	=	+176.6 ft-kips

Midspan moment:

$$M_{l/2} = 2.8\frac{30^2}{8} - \frac{188.2 + 176.6}{2} = 132.6 \text{ ft-kips}$$

(Since the two end moments differ somewhat, the maximum span moment does not occur at midspan, but at the point of zero shear. In most cases the difference is extremely small.)

3. Minimum midspan moment in CD:

$M_{CD} = -M_{DC}$:

D.L. all spans:	0.8 (−36.6)	=	−29.7
L.L. on BC:	2.0 (−33.8)	=	−67.6
L.L. on DE:	2.0 (+10.8)	=	+21.6
$M_{CD} = -M_{DC}$		=	−75.7 ft-kips

Midspan moment:

$$M_{l/2} = 0.8 \times 15^2/8 - 75.7 = -53.2 \text{ ft-kips}$$

(It is seen that the minimum midspan moment in CD is negative so that tension reinforcement is required near the top face of the girder.)

4. Column moments:

$M_{BB'}$:

D.L. all spans:	0.8 (+7.3)	=	+5.8
L.L. on BC:	2.0 (+15.5)	=	+31.0
$M_{BB'}$		=	+36.8 ft-kips

$M_{BB''}$:

D.L. all spans:	0.8 (+9.9)	=	+ 7.9
L.L. on BC:	2.0 (+20.5)	=	+41.0
$M_{BB''}$		=	+48.9 ft-kips

(Column moments of opposite sign are caused by live load on AB, instead of BC. It is quickly verified that the absolute values of the column moments at B are larger if live load is placed on BC, rather than on AB. In case of doubt, moments due to live load on either side of the column must be checked; the larger of them governs design.)

Moments at other sections of columns or girders can be computed in the same manner without additional distributions.

If dead and live loads are of different character so that they cannot be obtained as simple multiples of unit loads, and/or if the structure is not symmetrical, it may become necessary actually to carry out separate moment distributions for each case of loading, such as those illustrated in Fig. 8.17. In numerous practical cases, however, simplifications such as those illustrated in the example can be used to shorten computations.

8.10 Building Frames: Horizontal Loads Horizontal loads on building frames are caused primarily by wind pressure. Pressures per square foot of vertical wall surface are specified in building codes and, depending on locality, exposure, etc., vary from 10 to 50 psf. In addition, earthquake shocks produce horizontal sway, which results in inertia forces acting horizontally on the structure. It was found by extensive observation that these horizontal forces, rather than those induced by the simultaneous vertical motion of the ground, are chiefly responsible for structural earthquake damage. For this reason building codes in localities with high earthquake incidence require that structures be designed to resist corresponding horizontal forces. These are specified as stipulated percentages of the total load of the building above the given floor and are of the order of 10 per cent of that load.

In older buildings with massive bearing walls, wind forces are resisted by these walls acting as cantilever beams (loaded in the plane of the wall). In modern frame buildings, light curtain walls are usually employed which do not possess significant strength and stiffness, and horizontal loads must be resisted by the frame proper. With regard to earthquake forces, the older buildings were found to be easily damaged because the heavy and brittle bearing walls did not possess the necessary strength and flexibility to withstand the swaying motion. Correctly designed rigid-frame buildings, on the other hand, were found to stand up very well under such stress.

These horizontal forces, by means of walls and floors acting as rigid diaphragms in their own planes, are transmitted to the joints of the frame. For wind pressures, it is customary to compute the load on a joint from the area of exterior wall surface pertaining to it, i.e., from the rectangle outlined by vertical center lines between adjacent frames and by horizontal center lines between floor levels. Earthquake forces are distributed to individual joints in similar ways. These distributions are not very exact, particularly if the external forces do not act in the planes of the frames and if the outline of the structure is irregular in plan and/or elevation. More accurate ways of distributing the total forces to the individual frames are discussed in the references cited later in this chapter. The references also indicate that the actual distribution of wind forces, in particular, is frequently very different from the assumed uniform pressure on the surface of the windward walls.

For combinations of dead and live loads plus wind or earthquake loads, it must be recognized that the coincidence of full horizontal force with the most unfavorably distributed live load is extremely unlikely.

Also, the rarity and temporary nature of the maximum horizontal loads are likely to result in less damage than if those same forces were of great frequency and extended duration. Accordingly, the ACI Code treats wind and earthquake stresses as somewhat secondary effects, in comparison with the main effects of dead and live load. In working-stress design, an increase in allowable stress is permitted; in ultimate-strength design, reduced load factors are employed when the combined effect of dead, live, and wind load is considered.

Horizontal forces on building frames produce sidesway, and their effects can be accurately computed only by sidesway analysis, as discussed in previous articles. It will be realized that such an analysis, for frames with anywhere from 5 to 20 or more stories, requires very lengthy computations, even by the more rapid moment-distribution method. In most cases, however, such accurate determinations are neither required nor justified. It was pointed out that considerable uncertainty prevails regarding the magnitude as well as the distribution of wind and earthquake forces. It is useless, in analysis, to aim at an accuracy greater than that of the load data and other assumptions. In addition, the somewhat secondary effect of these rate and transitory forces justifies the use of more approximate analytical methods.

A considerable number of such approximate methods has been in use for many years. Although some of them result in slightly better theoretical accuracy than others, in view of the prevailing uncertainties these differences are usually not significant enough to cause the discard of the simpler methods in favor of the more accurate ones. For this reason only the simplest of those methods which are in reasonable agreement with accurate analysis will be discussed here, the approach which is known as the *portal method*.[1]

In simple frames, horizontal forces result in moments distributed as shown in Figs. 8.7*c* and 8.14*c*. It is seen that in all members moments vary linearly and, except in hinged members (*DE* in Fig. 8.14), have opposite signs at the ends (in the sense of the beam sign convention). It is further seen that in these members the points of zero moment (inflection points; see Fig. 8.7*a*) are located reasonably close to the midpoint of each member. In hinged members, of course, zero moment obtains only at the hinge. At the inflection points, only shear and axial forces act on the cross section. For symmetrical portals, such as that of Fig. 8.7, the shear forces are the same in both legs and are equal, each, to half the external horizontal load, as is easily checked from the information on

[1] For more information on other types of analyses, as well as on magnitude and distribution of horizontal forces, the reader is referred to "Wind Bracing in Steel Buildings," Final Report of Sub-committee 31, *Trans. ASCE*, vol. 105, p. 1713, 1940, and Ref. 8.4.

that figure. If one of the legs is more rigid than the other (larger value of K), it would require a larger horizontal force to displace it horizontally by the same amount as the more flexible leg. Consequently the portion of the total shear resisted by the stiffer column is larger than that of the more flexible column. This is easily checked by computing and comparing shears in AB and CF of Fig. 8.14*c*.

In building frames, moments and forces in the girders and columns of each individual story are distributed in substantially the same manner as just discussed for single-story frames. The portal method of computing approximate moments, shears, and axial forces from horizontal loads is, therefore, based on the following three simple propositions:

1. The total horizontal shear in all columns of a given story is equal and opposite to the sum of all horizontal loads acting above that story.
2. The horizontal shear is the same in both exterior columns; the horizontal shear in each interior column is twice that in an exterior column.
3. The inflection points of all members, columns and girders, are located midway between joints.

Although the last of these propositions is commonly applied to all columns, including those of the bottom floor, the authors prefer to deal with the latter separately, depending on conditions of foundation. If the actual conditions are such as practically to prevent rotation (foundation on rock, massive pile foundations, etc.), the inflection points of the bottom columns are above midpoint (see Figs. 8.7*c* and 8.14*c*) and may be assumed to be at a distance $2h/3$ from the bottom. If little resistance is offered to rotation, such as for relatively small footings on compressible soil, the inflection point is located closer to the bottom and may be assumed to be at a distance $h/3$ from the bottom or even lower. (In ideal hinges the inflection point is at the hinge, i.e., at the very bottom.) Since shears and corresponding moments are largest in the bottom story, a judicious evaluation of foundation conditions as they affect the location of inflection points is of considerable importance.

The first of the three cited propositions follows from the requirement that horizontal forces be in equilibrium at any level. The second takes account of the fact that in building frames interior columns are generally more rigid than exterior ones because (1) the larger axial loads require larger cross section and (2) exterior columns are restrained from joint rotation only by one abutting girder, while interior columns are so restrained by two such members. The third proposition is very nearly true because, except for the top and bottom columns and, to a minor degree, for the exterior girders, each member in a building frame is restrained about equally at both ends. For this reason it deflects under horizontal loads in an antisymmetrical manner, with the inflection point at midlength.

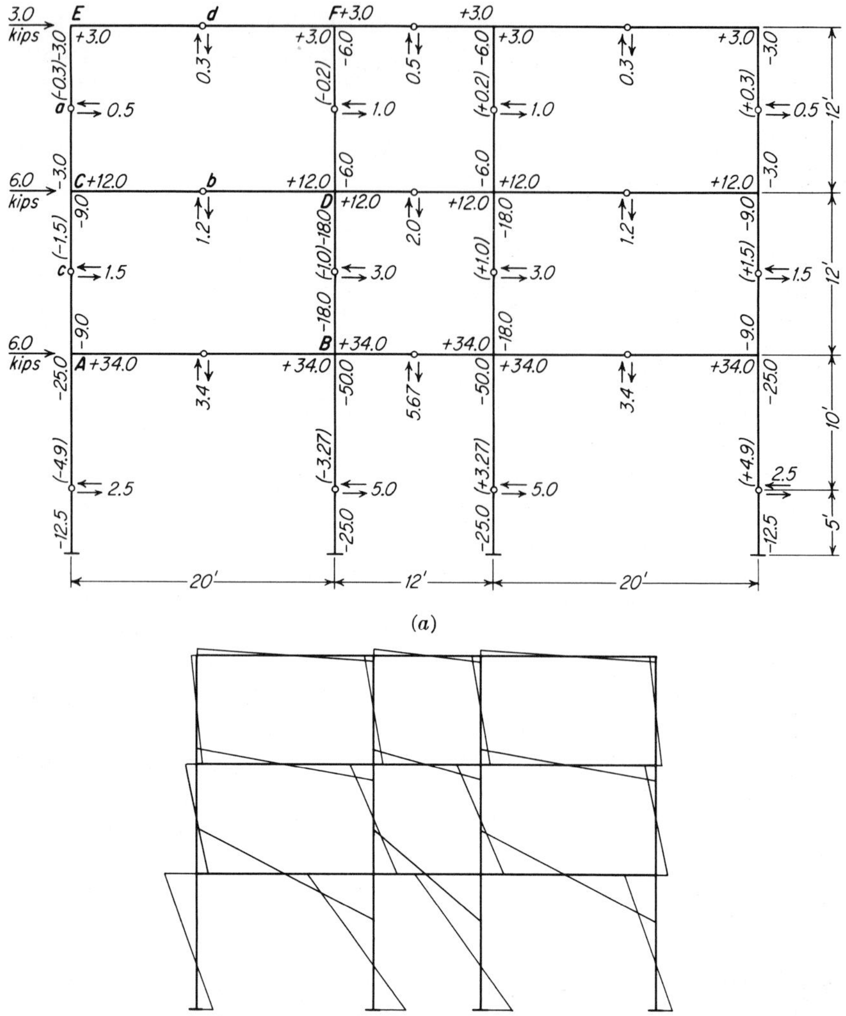

***Fig.* 8.19** Portal method for determining moments from wind load in building frame.

The actual computations in this method are extremely simple. At an inflection point, with $M = 0$, only shears and axial forces are transmitted from one half of the member to the other. An inflection point is, therefore, equivalent to a hinge, which also transmits only forces, but not moments. Once column shears are determined from propositions 1 and 2, and inflection points (hinges) located from proposition 3, all moments, shears, and forces are simply computed by statics. The process is illustrated in Fig. 8.19*a*.

Consider joints C and D. The total shear in the second story is $3 + 6 = 9$ kips. According to proposition 2, the shear in each exterior column is $9/6 = 1.5$ kips, and in each interior column $2 \times 1.5 = 3.0$ kips. The shears in the other floors, obtained in the same manner, act at the hinges as shown. Consider the equilibrium of the rigid structure between hinges a, b, and c; the column moments, 3.0 and 9.0, respectively, are obtained directly by multiplying the shears by their lever arms, 6 ft. The girder moment at C, to produce equilibrium, is equal and opposite to the sum of the column moments. The shear in the girder is obtained by recognizing that its moment (i.e., shear times half the girder span) must be equal to the girder moment at C. Hence this shear is $12.0/10 = 1.2$ kips. The moment at end D is equal to that at C, since the inflection point is at midspan. At D, column moments are computed in the same manner from the known column shears and lever arms. The sum of the two girder moments, to produce equilibrium, must be equal and opposite to the sum of the two column moments, from which the girder moment to the right of C is $18.0 + 6.0 - 12.0 = 12.0$. Axial forces in the columns also follow from statics. Thus, for the rigid body aEd, a vertical shear of 0.3 kip is seen to act upward at d. To equilibrate it, a tensile force of -0.3 kip is required in the column CE. In the rigid body abc an upward shear of 1.2 kips at b is added to the previous upward tension of 0.3 kip at a. To equilibrate these two forces, a tension force of -1.5 kips is required in column AC. If the equilibrium of all other partial structures between hinges is considered in a similar manner, all moments, forces, and shears are rapidly determined.

In the present case relatively flexible foundations were assumed, and the location of the lowermost inflection points was estimated to be at $h/3$ from the bottom. The general character of the resulting moment distribution is shown in Fig. 8.19*b*.

8.11 Effective Span Length In elastic frame analysis, a structure is usually represented by a simple line diagram, based dimensionally on the center-line distances between columns and between floor beams. Actually, the depths of beams and the widths of columns (in the plane of the frame) amount to sizable fractions of the respective lengths of these members; their clear lengths are therefore considerably smaller than their center-line distances between joints.

It is evident that the usual assumption in frame analysis that the members are prismatic, with constant moment of inertia between center lines, is not strictly correct. A beam intersecting a column may be prismatic up to the column face, but from that point to the column center line it has a greatly increased depth, with a moment of inertia which could be considered infinite compared with that of the remainder of the span. A similar variation in width and moment of inertia is obtained for the columns. Thus, to be strictly correct, fixed-end moments, stiffnesses, and carry-over factors which account for the actual variation in member depth should be used in the analysis. Qualitatively, this would increase beam support moments somewhat, and decrease span moments. In addition, it is apparent that the critical section for design for negative bending would be at the face of the support, and not at the center line, since for all practical purposes an unlimited effective depth is obtained in the beam across the width of the support.

It will be observed that, in the case of columns, the moment curve is not very steep, so that the difference between center-line moment and the moment at the top or bottom face of the beam is small and can in most cases be disregarded. However, the moment diagram for the beam is usually quite steep in the region of the support, and there will be a substantial difference between support center-line moment and face moment. If the former were used in proportioning the member, an unnecessarily large section would result. It is desirable, then, to reduce support moments found by elastic analysis to account for the finite width of the supports.

In Fig. 8.20, the change in moment between the support center line and the support face will be equal to the area under the shear diagram between those two points. For knife-edge supports, this shear area is seen to be very nearly equal to $VaL/2$. Actually, however, the reaction is distributed in some unknown way across the width of the support. This will have the effect of modifying the shear diagram as shown by the dashed line; it has been proposed that the reduced area be taken equal to $VaL/3$. The fact that the reaction is distributed will modify the moment diagram as well as the shear diagram, causing a slight rounding of the negative-moment peak, as shown in the figure, and the reduction of $VaL/3$ is properly applied to the moment diagram after the peak has been rounded. This will give nearly the same face moment as would be obtained by deducting the amount $VaL/2$ from the peak moment.

Another effect is present, however: the modification of the moment diagram due to the increased moment of inertia of the beam at the column. This effect is similar to that of a haunch, and it will mean slightly increased negative moment and slightly decreased positive moment. For ordinary values of the ratio a, this shift in the moment curve will be of the order of $VaL/6$.[1] Thus, it is convenient simply to deduct the amount $VaL/3$ from the unrounded peak moment obtained from elastic analysis. This allows for (1) the actual rounding of the shear diagram and the negative-moment peak due to the distributed reaction and (2) the down-

[1] Thor Germundsson, Effect of Column Width on Continuous Beam Moment, *J. ACI*, p. 1143, June, 1958.

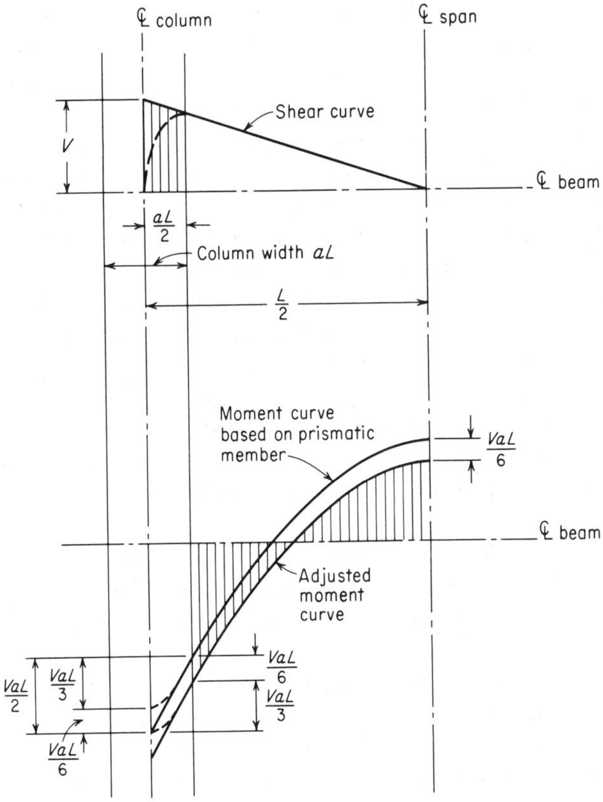

Fig. 8.20

ward shift of the moment curve due to the haunch effect at the supports. The consistent reduction in positive moment of $VaL/6$ is illustrated in Fig. 8.20. In connection with moment reductions, it should be noted that there are certain conditions of support for which no reduction in negative moment is justified. For example, when a continuous beam is carried by a girder of approximately the same depth, the negative moment in the beam at the center line of the girder should be used in designing the negative reinforcing steel.

8.12 Moments of Inertia The design of flexural members is based on the cracked section, i.e., on the supposition that the part of the concrete which is in tension is ineffective. Similarly, in calculating deflections (Art. 2.7) the flexural rigidity is based on the moment of inertia of the cracked, transformed section. It would seem, therefore, that moments of inertia to be used in computing stiffnesses K for frame analysis should be determined in the same manner.

It is evident from the preceding articles, however, that in most cases in frame analysis it is only the ratio of stiffnesses which influences the elastic analysis, and not the absolute values of the stiffnesses. Stiffness ratios are but little affected by different assumptions (e.g., use of cracked section vs. gross section) in computing moment of inertia, provided there is consistency for all members. In recognition of this fact, it is generally convenient and sufficiently accurate to base stiffness calculations for frame analysis on the full concrete cross section. The contribution of the reinforcement is usually neglected, which compensates to some extent for the neglect of the influence of cracks. There may be some justification for including the transformed area of the steel in computing moments of inertia of columns, because often the column stress will be entirely compressive, with no cracking to compensate for the neglect of the steel. In addition, steel percentages are considerably higher for columns than for beams. However, it is the usual practice to compute moments of inertia of columns just as for beams, considering only the cross section of the concrete.

For T beams, allowance should be made for the effect of the flange on member stiffness. It seems reasonable to assume the same effective width of flange for computing moment of inertia as is used in stress computations.

A problem arises in continuous T-beam construction, in that for flexural design the effective cross section is rectangular in the negative-moment regions. However, it is not unusual to provide compressive reinforcement in the negative-moment regions for such construction. This increases the stiffness over that of the plain rectangular concrete section. Consequently, there is some justification for the common practice of computing stiffnesses of such members on the basis of the gross cross section of the concrete, including flanges, and using this stiffness throught the entire span.

It is somewhat laborious to compute, in every case, the neutral axis of the effective T section and to find the moment of inertia, about that axis, of the unsymmetrical section. In the usual case it is satisfactory to estimate the moment of inertia of the unsymmetrical section under the assumption that it will be some multiple of that of the rectangular cross section of web width b' and total height h. For sections of usual proportions (flange width about 4 to 6 times web width, and flange thickness from 0.2 to 0.4 times total depth), this multiplier will be very close to 2.0.

8.13 Conditions of Support For purposes of analysis, many structures can be divided into a number of two-dimensional frames such as in the example of Art. 8.9. Even for such cases, however, there are situations in which it is impossible to predict with accuracy what the conditions of restraint might be at the ends of a span; yet moments are frequently affected to a considerable degree by the choice made. In many other cases, it is necessary to recognize that structures may be three-dimensional. The rotational restraint at a joint may be influenced or even governed by the characteristics of members framing into that joint at right angles. Adjacent members or frames parallel to the one under primary consideration may likewise influence its performance.

If floor beams are cast monolithically with reinforced-concrete walls (frequently the case when first-floor beams are carried on foundation walls), the moment of inertia of the wall about an axis parallel to its face may be so large that the beam end could be considered completely fixed for all practical purposes. If the wall is relatively thin, or the beam particularly massive, the stiffness of each should be calculated, that of the wall being equal to $I/L = bt^3/12h$, where t is the wall thickness, b the wall width tributary to one beam (i.e., center to center of adjacent panels), and h the wall height. Distribution factors can then be calculated in the usual manner.

If the outer ends of concrete beams rest on masonry walls, as is sometimes the case, an assumption of zero rotational restraint (i.e., hinged support) is probably closest to the actual.

For columns supported on relatively small footings, which in turn rest on compressible soil, a hinged end is generally assumed, since such soils offer but little resistance to rotation of the footing. If, on the other hand, the footings rest on solid rock, or if a cluster of piles is used with their upper portion encased by a concrete cap, the effect is to provide almost complete fixity for the supported column, and this should be assumed in the analysis. Columns supported by a continuous foundation mat should likewise be assumed fixed at their lower ends.

If members framing into a joint in a direction perpendicular to the plane of the frame under analysis have sufficient torsional stiffness, and if their far ends can be considered fixed or nearly so, their effect on joint rigidity should be included in the computations. The torsional stiffness of a member of length L is given by the expression GJ/L, where G is the shear modulus of elasticity of concrete (approximately equal to $E_c/2.2$), and J is the polar moment of inertia of the member. For beams of rectangular cross section, or of sections made up of rectangular elements, J can be taken equal to $(hb^3/3 - b^4/5)$, in which h and b are the cross-sectional dimensions of each rectangular element, b being the lesser dimension in each case. Torsional stiffness at a joint is treated in the same manner as flexural stiffness; the sum of the distribution factors must, as usual, equal unity. When the effect of torsional rigidity is included, it is important to observe that the absolute flexural stiffness $4EI/L$ must be used, rather than relative I/L values.

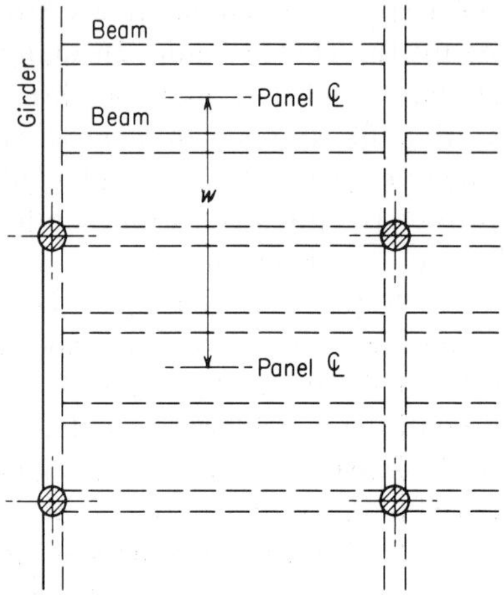

Fig. 8.21

A common situation in beam-and-girder floors and concrete-joist floors is illustrated by Fig. 8.21. The sketch shows a beam-and-girder floor system in which longitudinal beams are placed at the third points of each bay, supported by transverse girders, in addition to the longitudinal beams supported directly by the columns. If the transverse girders are quite stiff, it is apparent that the flexural stiffness of all beams in the width w should be balanced against the stiffness of one set of columns in the longitudinal bent. If, on the other hand, the girders have little torsional stiffness, there would be ample justification for making two separate longitudinal analyses, one for the beams supported directly by the columns, including the I/L values for those beams only, and a second for the beams framing into the girders, in which case simple supports would be assumed. Probably it would generally be sufficiently accurate to consider the girders very stiff torsionally and to add directly the I/L values of all beams tributary to a single column. This has the added advantage that all otherwise identical longitudinal beams will then have the same cross-sectional dimensions and the same reinforcing steel, which will greatly facilitate construction.

8.14 Preliminary Design In making an elastic analysis of a structural framework, it is necessary to know at the outset the cross-sectional dimensions of the members, so that moments of inertia, stiffnesses, and distribution factors can be calculated. Yet the determination of these same cross-sectional dimensions is the precise purpose of the elastic analysis. Obviously, a preliminary estimate of member sizes must be one of the first steps in the analysis. Subsequently, with the results of the analysis at hand, members are proportioned, and the resulting dimensions compared with those previously assumed. If necessary, the assumed section properties are modified, and the analysis is repeated. Since the procedure may become quite laborious, it is obviously advantageous to make the best possible original estimate of member sizes, in the hope of avoiding repetition of the analysis.

In this connection, it is worth repeating that in the ordinary frame analysis one is concerned with relative stiffnesses only, not the absolute stiffnesses. If, in the original estimate of member sizes, the sizes of all beams and columns are overestimated or underestimated by about the same amount, then correction of these estimated sizes after the first analysis will have little or no effect on the relative stiffnesses. Consequently no revision of the analysis would be required. If, on the other hand, a nonuniform error in estimation is made, and relative stiffnesses differ from assumed values by more than about 30 per cent, a new analysis should be made.

The experienced designer can estimate beam and column sizes with surprising accuracy. Those with little or no experience must rely on trial calculations or arbitrary rules, modified to suit particular situations. In building frames, beam sizes are usually governed by the negative moments and the shears at the supports, where their effective section is rectangular. Moments can be approximated by the fixed-end moments for the particular span, or by using the ACI moment coefficients. In most cases, shears will not differ greatly from simple beam shears. Alternatively, many designers prefer to estimate the depth of beams at about $\frac{3}{4}$ in. per ft of span, with the width about one-half the depth. Obviously, these dimensions are subject to modification, depending on the type and magnitude of the loads, method of design, and material strength.

Column sizes are governed primarily by axial loads, which can be estimated quickly, although the presence of moments in the columns is cause for some increase of the area as determined by axial loads. For interior columns, in which unbalanced moments will not be large, a 10 per cent increase may be sufficient, while for exterior columns, particularly for upper stories, an increase of 50 per cent in area may be appropriate. In deciding on these estimated increases, the following should be considered: Moments are larger in exterior than in interior columns, since, in the latter, dead-load moments from adjacent spans will largely balance, in contrast to the case in exterior columns. In addition, the influence of moments, as compared to that of axial loads, is larger in upper-floor than in lower-floor columns, because the moments are usually of about the same magnitude, while the axial loads are larger in the latter than in the former. Judicious consideration of factors such as these will enable a designer to produce a reasonably accurate preliminary design, which in most cases will permit a satisfactory analysis to be made on the first trial.

8.15 Inelastic Redistribution of Moments Since it is known that concrete does not respond elastically to loads of more than about one-half the ultimate, there is a certain inconsistency in designing reinforced cross sections by ultimate-strength methods (taking into account inelastic behavior) while the moments for which those sections are being designed have been found by elastic analysis. Although this presently accepted

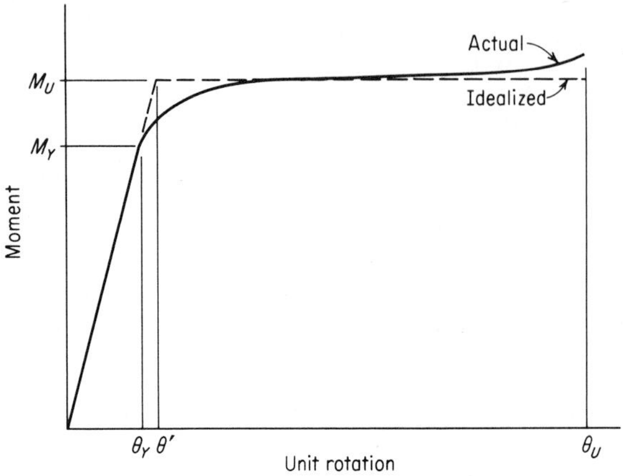

Fig. 8.22

procedure by which elastic analysis is coupled with inelastic design of sections is not consistent, it is safe and conservative. It can be shown that a frame so analyzed and designed will not fail at a lower load than anticipated; on the other hand, because of certain inelastic readjustments that may occur, it may be able to carry a somewhat higher load. The means for utilizing this excess strength is the subject of much current investigation.

If a short segment of a reinforced-concrete beam is subjected to a bending moment, curvature of the beam axis will result, and there will be a corresponding rotation of one face of the segment with respect to the other. It is convenient to express this in terms of an angular change θ per unit length of the member. A representative relation between applied moment M and resulting rotation for an underreinforced section is shown in Fig. 8.22. This relation can be idealized as shown by the dashed lines. As moment is applied, a linear relation between M and θ will be obtained up to that load which produces yielding of the reinforcing steel. A slight further increase in load produces large rotation with little or no increase in resisting moment. The elastic curve of the beam shows an abrupt change in slope at such a section. The beam behaves as if there were a hinge at that point. However, the hinge will not be "friction-free," but will have a fairly constant resistance to rotation, of amount M_u.

If such a plastic hinge forms in a determinate structure, as shown in Fig. 8.23, uncontrolled deflection takes place, and the structure will collapse. The resulting system is referred to as a *mechanism*, in analogy to linkage systems in mechanics. Generalizing, one can say that a

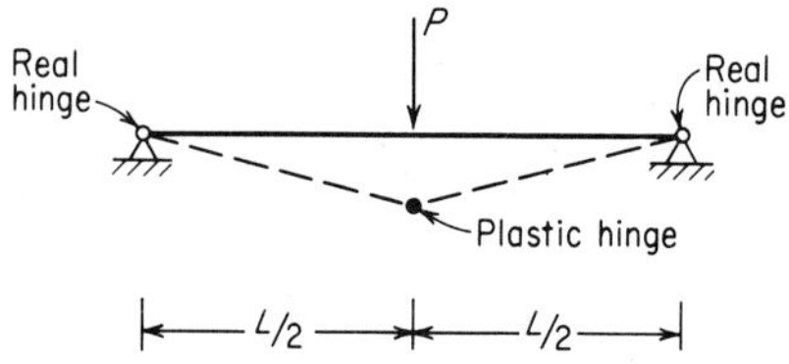

Fig. 8.23

statically determinate system requires the formation of only one plastic hinge in order to become a mechanism.

This is not so for indeterminate structures. In this case, stability may be maintained even though hinges have formed at several cross sections. The formation of such hinges in indeterminate structures permits a redistribution of moments within the beam or frame. It will be assumed for simplicity that the indeterminate beam of Fig. 8.24*a* is symmetrically reinforced, so that the negative bending capacity is the same as the positive. Let the load P be increased gradually until the elastic moment at the fixed support, $\frac{3}{16}PL$, is just equal to the plastic moment capacity of the section M_u. This load is

$$P = P_{el} = \frac{16}{3}\frac{M_u}{L} = 5.33\frac{M_u}{L} \qquad (a)$$

At this load, the positive moment under the load is $\frac{5}{32}PL$, as shown in Fig. 8.24*b*. The beam still responds elastically everywhere but at the left support. At that point, the actual fixed support can be replaced for purposes of analysis with a plastic hinge offering a known resisting moment M_u. Because a redundant reaction has been replaced by a known moment, the beam is now determinate.

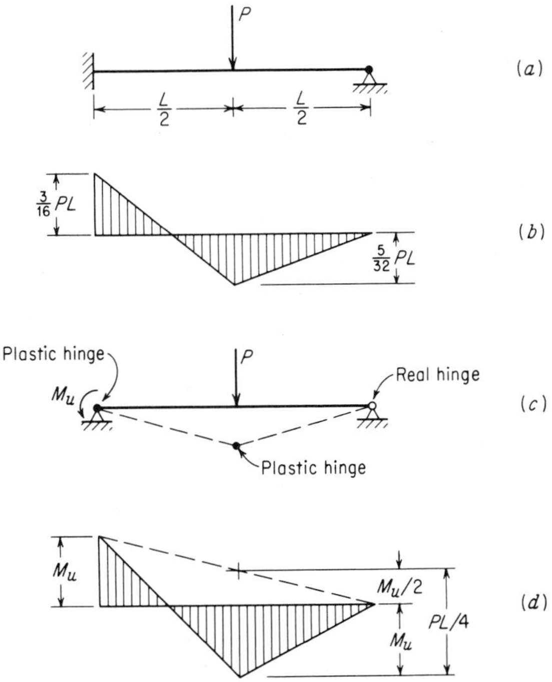

Fig. 8.24

The load can be increased further until the moment under the load also becomes equal to M_u, at which load the second hinge forms. The structure is converted into a mechanism, as shown in Fig. 8.24*c*, and collapse occurs. The moment diagram at collapse load is shown in Fig. 8.24*d*.

The magnitude of load causing collapse is easily calculated from the geometry of Fig. 8.24*d*:

$$M_u + \frac{M_u}{2} = \frac{PL}{4}$$

from which

$$P = P_u = \frac{6M_u}{L} \qquad (b)$$

By comparison of Eqs. (*b*) and (*a*), it is evident that an increase in P of 12.5 per cent is possible, beyond that load which caused the formation of the first plastic hinge, before the beam will actually collapse. Due to the formation of plastic hinges, a redistribution of moments has occurred such that, at failure, the ratio between positive moment and negative moment is equal to that assumed in reinforcing the structure.

It may be evident that there is a direct relation between the amount of redistribution desired and the rotation capacity required at the critical sections of a beam. In general, the greater the modification of the elastic moment ratio, the greater the required rotation capacity to accomplish that change. In the actual structure, the required rotation may or may not be attainable. To illustrate, a beam completely fixed at both ends might be designed and reinforced as a simply supported span, with no negative steel at the supports. Some redistribution would undoubtedly occur, but the large rotation required at the supports before the assumed moment ratio was realized would be accompanied by such severe cracking and spalling of the beam at the supports that its structural integrity would be destroyed, and premature failure would result.

Reinforced-concrete beams differ in their capacity to permit such rotation. Overreinforced beams, in which the strength is controlled by crushing of the concrete, permit only a small amount of rotation before failure. Underreinforced members, controlled by yielding of the tensile steel, permit considerably more rotation. Furthermore, underreinforced beams with low steel ratios permit more rotation than do those with high steel ratios.

"Limit analysis" in reinforced-concrete structures, based on the formation of plastic hinges and redistribution of moments, could proceed on the basis of full redistribution. *Full redistribution* is understood to mean the formation of a sufficient number of hinges to convert the structure into a mechanism. However, in this case it would have to be shown by special calculations that sufficient rotation capacity is available, at the locations at which the earlier hinges form, to permit all requisite hinges to develop. It would also have to be shown that the resulting structure, at service loads, would not exhibit an objectionable amount of cracking and excessive deflections. Methods for accomplishing this are not yet fully developed. This is in contrast to plastic design in steel structures, where the danger of cracking hardly exists, and where the much greater ductility of the material makes such special checks unnecessary.

On the other hand, in order to limit crack widths and deflections without elaborate proof, while still utilizing most of the advantages of moment redistribution, the designer may avail himself only of a stipulated, limited amount of such redistribution. This amount must be known to be safe in regard to available rotation capacity and crack development at service loads. Because, as was pointed out, rotation capacity increases with decreasing reinforcement ratio, safe conditions for limited redistribution are obtained if suitable limits are set for the steel ratio. This is the manner in which, at the present time, inelastic moment redistribution is now admitted in American and some foreign design codes.

For example, support moments may be reduced or increased 15 per cent from their elastic values, provided the positive moments in the corresponding spans are increased or reduced a statically consistent amount. This permits one to deviate from the moments calculated on the basis of elastic theory. Hence, one can place less steel at one section than is indicated by the elastic moment, if one places at another section more than is indicated to be necessary by elastic analysis. In such a case, when loaded, the beam will yield first where the lesser steel has been provided and will continue to yield until the moments adjust themselves to yield the steel at the second place, leaving the overall strength the same as if one had placed the steel strictly according to the elastic moments.

While most concrete beams have prismatic cross sections, they need not be reinforced equally at all sections. On the contrary, it is quite convenient to match the resisting capacity of the beam, as governed by the reinforcing steel, to the elastic-moment diagram. Accordingly, for the beam of Fig. 8.24*a*, the steel could have been detailed to resist a moment of $\frac{3}{16}PL$ at the support and $\frac{5}{32}PL$ under the load. Hinges would then have formed simultaneously at these two points. It would seem, then, that there would be little advantage in utilizing inelastic moment redistribution for concrete structures, aside from the possibility of thereby more fully utilizing the prismatic concrete section. On further consideration, however, important advantages are apparent. For example, in reinforced-concrete construction, the region in which beams and columns intersect is often very congested with reinforcement. Often beams frame into the joint from two directions, with substantial negative steel at the top, and some bottom steel as well. Large column bars must pass through the same zone. The result is a cage of steel so complex that not only is bar placement difficult, but often it is impossible to ensure proper deposition of concrete in this important zone. On the other hand, if a redistribution of moments is permissible, with negative design moments reduced and positive moments increased accordingly, an important reduction in this congestion of steel at the columns is possible.

A further and perhaps more significant advantage will be evident from study of Fig. 8.25. A three-span continuous beam is shown, with dead load of 1 kip per ft and live load of 2 kips per ft. In order to obtain maximum moments at all critical design sections, it is necessary to consider three alternative loadings. Case *a*, with live and dead load over exterior spans and dead load only over interior span, will produce maximum positive moment in the exterior spans. Case *b*, with dead load on exterior spans and dead and live load on the interior span, will produce the maximum positive moment in the interior span. The maximum negative moment over the interior support is obtained by placing dead and live load on the two adjacent spans and dead load only on the far exterior span, as shown in case *c*.

If it is assumed for purposes of demonstration that a 20 per cent adjustment of support moments is permitted, provided span moments are modified accordingly, an overall reduction in design moments through the entire three-span beam may be possible. Case *a*, for example, produces an elastic maximum span moment in the exterior spans of 109 ft-kips. Corresponding to this is an elastic negative moment of 82 ft-kips at the interior support. Adjusting the support moment upward by 20 per cent, one obtains a negative moment of 98 ft-kips, which results in a downward adjustment of the span moment to 101 ft-kips.

Now consider case *b*; by a similar redistribution of moments, a reduced middle-span moment of 57 ft-kips is obtained through increase of the support moment from 78 to 93 ft-kips.

The moment obtained at the first interior support for loading case *c* can be adjusted in the reverse direction; i.e., the support moment is decreased by 20 per cent to 107 ft-kips, with the positive moments increased in the adjacent spans to 96 ft-kips and 63 ft-kips in the exterior and interior spans, respectively.

Now, it will be observed that the reduction obtained for the span moments in cases *a* and *b* were achieved at the expense of increasing the moment at the first interior support. However, the increased support moment in each case was less than the moment for which that support would have to be designed based on the loading *c*, which produced maxi-

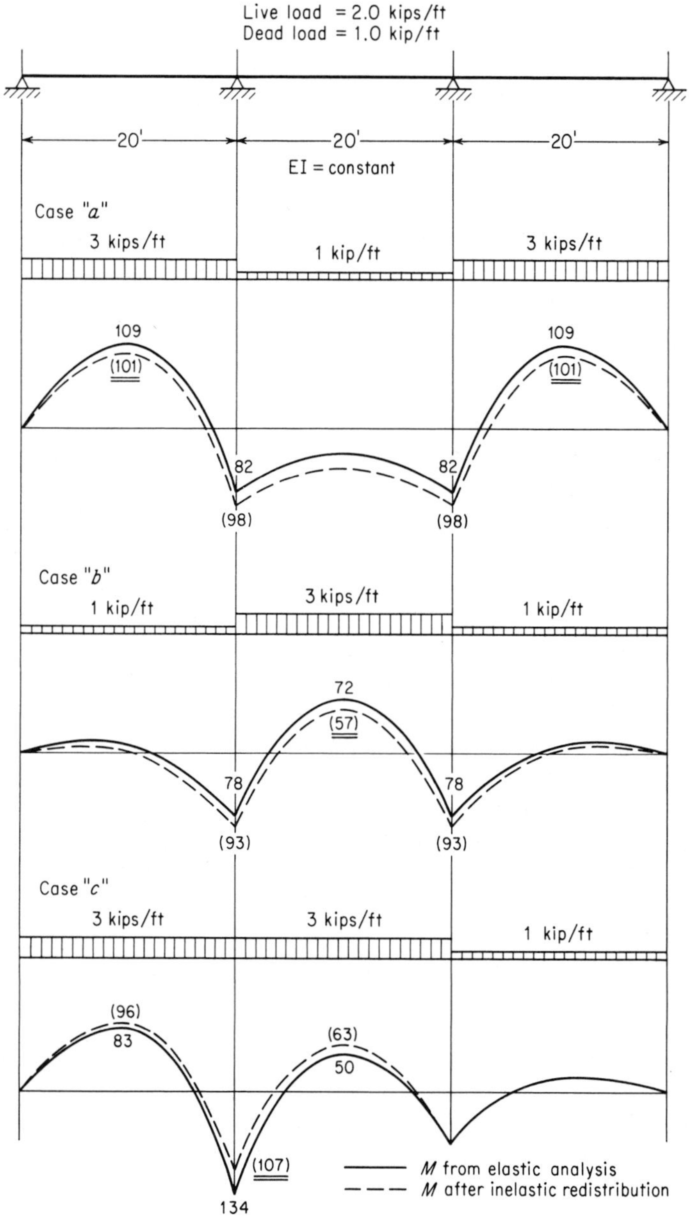
Live load = 2.0 kips/ft
Dead load = 1.0 kip/ft
20'
20'
20'
EI = constant
Case "a"
3 kips/ft
1 kip/ft
3 kips/ft
109
(101)
109
(101)
82
82
(98)
(98)
Case "b"
1 kip/ft
3 kips/ft
1 kip/ft
72
(57)
78
78
(93)
(93)
Case "c"
3 kips/ft
3 kips/ft
1 kip/ft
(96)
83
(63)
50
(107)
134
M from elastic analysis
M after inelastic redistribution

Fig. 8.25

mum support moment. Similarly, the reduction in support moment in case *c* was taken at the expense of an increase in span moments in the two adjacent spans. But in each case, the increased span moments were less than the maximum span moments obtained for other loading conditions. The final design moments at all critical sections are underlined in Fig. 8.25. It may be seen, then, that the net result is a reduction in design moments over the entire beam. This modification of moments does not mean a reduction in safety factor below that implied in code safety provisions; rather, it means a reduction of the *excess* strength which would otherwise be present in the structure because of the actual redistribution of moments that would occur before failure. It reflects the fact that the maximum design moments are obtained from alternative load patterns, which could not exist concurrently. The end result is a more realistic appraisal of the actual collapse load of the indeterminate structure.

At the time of writing, sufficient evidence is not available to justify the adoption of a complete limit-analysis theory for reinforced concrete. Accordingly, *the present ACI Building Code permits only a limited redistribution of elastic moments.* A 10 per cent adjustment of negative support moments (upward or downward) is permitted, with a statically compatible adjustment in span moments, for beams in which the reinforcement ratio is equal to or less than 50 per cent of the balanced ratio p_b.[1] This ensures adequate rotation capacity and only unobjectionable cracking. It is probable that future editions of the Code will not be so restrictive, as additional information becomes available regarding (1) rotation capacities of concrete members, (2) detrimental effects of cracking at hinges, (3) effect of high shear on the formation of hinges, (4) effect of rotations on deflection at service loads, and (5) effort of triaxiality of stress at the columns on the formation of hinges.

REFERENCES

The methods of analysis discussed in this chapter furnish the tools for dealing with the most common types of continuous concrete structures. They are limited, however, to structures composed of straight, prismatic members, in which all members are either in line or meet at right angles. For conditions other than these, modified methods must be employed. Their discussion is beyond the scope of this text. For a more elaborate treatment of the topics discussed, and for further information on the analysis of more complicated forms, the reader is referred to the following publications:

[1] While, in the case of doubly reinforced beams, the ACI Code requires only that $(p - p')$ be less than 0.50 p_b, or equivalently, that $p_{max} = 0.50\ p_b + p'$, in order to ensure the same rotation capacity in doubly reinforced beams as in singly reinforced beams, one should have $p_{max} = 0.50(p_b + p')$. Similarly, in the case of T beams, the Code requirement that $p_{w,max} = 0.50\ p_b + p_f$ might better be stated as $p_{w,max} = 0.50(p_b + p_f)$.

8.1 J. S. Kinney: "Indeterminate Structural Analysis," Addison-Wesley Publishing Company, Inc., Reading, Mass., 1957.
8.2 J. I. Parcel and R. B. B. Moorman: "Analysis of Statically Indeterminate Structures," John Wiley & Sons, Inc., New York, 1955.
8.3 C. K. Wang: "Statically Indeterminate Structures," McGraw-Hill Book Company, Inc., New York, 1953.
8.4 "Continuity in Concrete Building Frames," Portland Cement Association, Chicago.
8.5 "Handbook of Frame Constants," Portland Cement Association, Chicago.
8.6 "Working Stress Design Handbook," American Concrete Institute, Detroit, 1964.
8.7 G. C. Ernst and A. R. Riveland: Ultimate Loads and Deflections from Limit Design of Continuous Structural Concrete, *J. ACI*, October, 1959.
8.8 A. H. Mattock: Limit Design for Structural Concrete, *Portland Cement Assoc. Res. Develop. Lab. Develop. Dept. Bull.*, May, 1959.

chapter 9

REINFORCED-CONCRETE BUILDINGS

9.1 Introduction In the conceptual stages of the design of reinforced-concrete structures, it should be borne in mind that reinforced concrete is a material in its own right, with its own unique features and characteristics. To use the material in structural systems which are patterned after articulated structures of steel or timber betrays a lack of design imagination and denies the monolithic nature of concrete construction. From a practical point of view, such imitative design will usually fail to realize the true potential of the material and will often result in highly uneconomical structures.

The advantages of reinforced-concrete construction for buildings are many, but the more significant points are summarized as follows:

Versatility of form Usually placed in the structure in the fluid state, the material is readily adaptable to a wide variety of architectural and functional requirements.

Durability With proper concrete protection of the steel reinforcement, the structure will have long life even under highly adverse climatic or environmental conditions.

Fire resistance With proper protection for the reinforcement, a reinforced-concrete structure provides the maximum in fire protection.

Speed of construction In terms of the entire period from the date of approval of the contract drawings to the date of completion, a concrete building may often be completed in less time than a steel structure. While the field erection of a steel building is more rapid, this phase must necessarily be preceded by prefabrication of all parts in the shop.

Cost In many cases the first cost of a concrete structure is less than that of a comparable steel structure. In almost every case, maintenance costs are less.

Availability of labor and material It is always possible to make use of local sources of labor, and in many inaccessible areas a nearby source of good aggregate can be found, so that only the cement and reinforcement need be brought in from a remote source.

9.2 Floor and Roof Loads The minimum live loads for which the floors and roof of any building should be designed are usually specified in the building code that governs at the site of construction. There are local municipal codes, state codes, and regional codes, as well as "model" codes proposed for general usage. Representative values of minimum live loads to be used in the design of a wide variety of buildings are found in the recommendations of the American Standards Association publication, "Minimum Design Loads in Buildings and Other Structures," a portion of which is reprinted in Table 9.1.

In addition to these uniformly distributed loads, it is recommended, as an alternative to the uniform load, that floors be designed to support safely certain concentrated loads, if these produce a greater stress. For example, office floors are to be designed to carry a load of 2000 lb distributed over an area $2\frac{1}{2}$ ft square, to allow for the weight of a safe or other heavy equipment, and stair treads must safely support a 300-lb load applied on the center of the tread. The specified uniform and concentrated loads are assumed to include adequate allowance for ordinary impact loading. Certain reductions are permitted in live load of 100 psf or less for members supporting 150 ft^2 of floor or more, on the premise that it is not likely that the entire area would be fully loaded at one time. The reduction specified is at the rate of 0.08 per cent per square foot of area supported by the member, except that no reduction is permitted in places of public assembly. The reduction is not to exceed 60 per cent nor the percentage

$$100\,\frac{D+L}{4.33L}$$

***Table* 9.1 Minimum uniformly distributed live loads**

Occupancy or use	Live load, psf
Apartments (see Residential)	
Armories and drill rooms	150
Assembly halls and other places of assembly:	
Fixed seats	60
Movable seats	100
Balcony (exterior)	100
Bowling alleys, poolrooms, and similar recreational areas	75
Corridors:	
First floor	100
Other floors, same as occupancy served except as indicated	
Dance halls	100
Dining rooms and restaurants	100
Dwellings (see Residential)	
Garages (passenger cars)	100
Floors shall be designed to carry 150 per cent of the maximum wheel load anywhere on the floor.	
Grandstands (see Reviewing stands)	
Gymnasiums, main floors, and balconies	100
Hospitals:	
Operating rooms	60
Private rooms	40
Wards	40
Hotels (see Residential)	
Libraries:	
Reading rooms	60
Stack rooms	150
Manufacturing	125
Marquees	75
Office buildings:	
Offices	80
Lobbies	100
Penal institutions:	
Cell blocks	40
Corridors	100
Residential:	
Multifamily houses:	
Private apartments	40
Public rooms	100
Corridors	60
Dwellings:	
First floor	40
Second floor and habitable attics	30
Uninhabitable attics	20
Hotels:	
Guest rooms	40
Public rooms	100
Corridors serving public rooms	100
Public corridors	60
Private corridors	40
Reviewing stands and bleachers	100
Schools:	
Classrooms	40
Corridors	100
Sidewalks, vehicular driveways, and yards subject to trucking	250
Skating rinks	100
Stairs, fire escapes, and exitways	100
Storage warehouse, light	125
Storage warehouse, heavy	250
Stores:	
Retail:	
First floor, rooms	100
Upper floors	75
Wholesale	125
Theaters:	
Aisles, corridors, and lobbies	100
Orchestra floors	60
Balconies	60
Stage floors	150
Yards and terraces, pedestrians	100

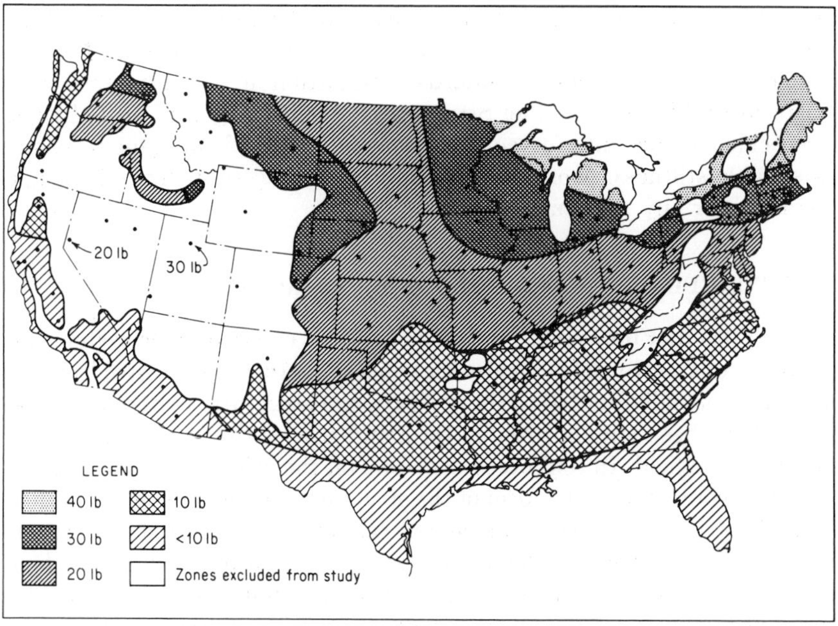

***Fig.* 9.1** Estimated weight of seasonal snowpack equalled or exceeded one year in ten. (*From "Minimum Design Loads in Buildings and Other Structures," American Standards Association,* 1955.)

in which D is the dead load per square foot of area supported by the member, and L is the live load. No reduction is permitted for loads over 100 psf (characteristic of warehouses and factories, in which cases it is not unlikely that the entire area may be loaded at one time), except that column loads may be reduced 20 per cent.

The specified minimum live loads cannot always be used. The type of occupancy should be considered, and the probable loads computed as accurately as possible. Warehouses for heavy storage may be designed for loads as high as 500 psf or more; unusually heavy operations in manufacturing buildings may require a large increase in the 125-psf value specified in Table 9.1; special provision must be made for all definitely located heavy concentrated loads.

In all cases, the dead weight of the floor must be included in the total design load. When plastered ceilings are specified, an additional allowance of about 10 psf is usual. Floor fill and finish floors together with suspended loads such as piping and lighting fixtures also must be included. If the locations of partitions are not definitely established, an extra allowance of from 10 to 20 psf may be in order.

Snow loads for the design of building roofs are likewise generally specified by local codes. They are preferably based on statistical studies, over an extended period, of the local depth and density of snowfall. Such a set of data has resulted in the snow-load map shown in Fig. 9.1, published by the American Standards Association in "Minimum Design Loads in Buildings and Other Structures." A minimum roof load of 20 psf is specified to provide for construction and repair loads and to ensure reasonable stiffness. More detailed information on snow loads is usually available for any particular locality.

REINFORCED - CONCRETE FLOORS AND ROOFS

9.3 Types of Floor Systems The types of concrete floor systems are so numerous as to defy concise classification. In steel construction the designer is usually limited to the utilization of structural plates and shapes which have been standardized in form and size by the relatively few producers in the field. In reinforced concrete, on the other hand, the engineer has more control over the form of the structural components of a building. In addition, many small producers of reinforced-concrete structural elements and construction accessories can compete profitably in this field, since plant and equipment requirements are not excessive. This has resulted in the development of a wide variety of concrete floor systems. Only the more common types can be mentioned in this text.[1]

In general, the commonly used reinforced-concrete floor systems can be classified as follows:

1. One-way reinforcing systems (in which the main reinforcement in each structural element runs in one direction)
   a. One-way solid slabs
      (1) Slab supported on monolithic concrete beams and girders
      (2) Slab supported on steel beams (shear connectors may be used to provide for composite action)
      (3) Slab with light-gage steel decking which serves as form and reinforcement for the concrete
   b. One-way ribbed slabs (also known as concrete joist floors)
   c. Precast systems, including precast slab or beams or both
2. Two-way reinforcing systems (in which the main reinforcement in at least one of the structural elements runs in two directions)
   a. Two-way solid slabs
      (1) Slab on monolithic concrete beams
      (2) Slab on steel beams
   b. Two-way ribbed slab on concrete or steel beam supports
   c. Flat-slab systems

[1] For illustrations of several other types of floor systems, see C. G. Ramsey and H. R. Sleeper, "Architectural Graphic Standards," 5th ed., John Wiley & Sons, Inc., New York, 1956.

(1) Flat slab with drop panels or column capitals or both
(2) Flat-plate floor with no drop panels or column capitals (may be precast and lifted to final elevation)
(3) Ribbed flat-slab or flat-plate systems

Each of these types is described in the following articles.

9.4 Monolithic Solid-slab Beam-and-girder Floor A solid-slab beam-and-girder floor consists of a series of parallel beams supported at their extremities by girders which in turn frame into concrete columns placed at more or less regular intervals over the entire floor area. This framework is covered by a one-way reinforced-concrete slab, the load from which is transmitted first to the beams and thence to the girders and columns. The beams are usually spaced so that they come at the midpoints, at the third points, or at the quarter points of the girders, as shown in Fig. 9.2. The arrangement of beams and spacing of columns should be determined by economical and practical considerations. These will be affected by the use to which the building is to be put, the size and shape of the ground area, and the load which must be carried. A comparison of a number of trial designs and estimates should be made if the size of the building warrants, and the most satisfactory arrangement selected. As the slabs, beams, and girders are built monolithically, the beams and girders are designed as T beams, and advantage is taken of continuity.

Beam-and-girder floors, as they are usually called, are adapted to any loads and to any spans that might be encountered in ordinary building construction. The normal maximum spread in live-load values is from 40 to 400 psf, and the normal range in column spacings is from 16 to 32 ft. A complete design of a typical beam-and girder floor panel is given in Arts. 9.23 to 9.26.

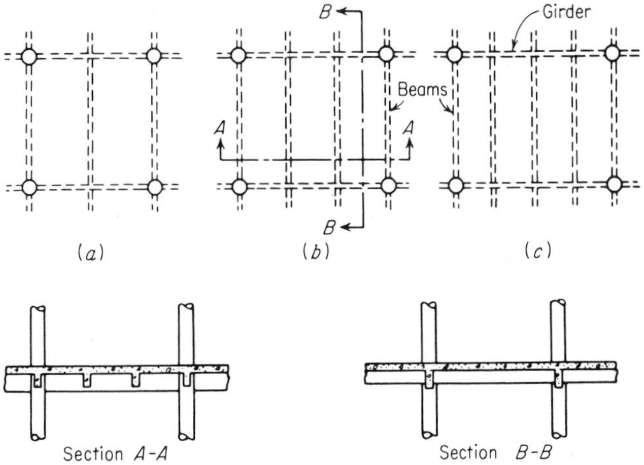

***Fig.* 9.2** Framing of beam-and-girder floors.

In normal beam-and-girder construction the depth of a beam is about twice its stem width. For light loads, however, it may be economical to omit the intermediate beams and deep column-line girders entirely and to have the one-way slab supported by wide, shallow beams which are centered on the column lines and which frame directly into the columns. The interior beam becomes little more than a thickened portion of the slab; this form of construction, in fact, is commonly referred to as *slab-band* construction. There are a number of advantages associated with its use. In the slab span, a haunch is created which aids in resisting the relatively high negative moments that will be present over the interior support. This will both reduce the positive slab moment and the critical negative slab moment at the face of the haunch. While beam steel will be increased because of the reduced effective depth as compared with a beam of normal proportions, cost comparisons have shown that this may often be outweighted by savings in slab steel. Other advantages include a reduced depth of construction, permitting a reduction in overall height of the building, and greater flexibility in locating columns. Formwork is simplified because of the reduction in the number of framing members. In Fig. 9.3 are shown comparative sections through conventional and slab-band floors.

9.5 Concrete-slab Floors on Steel Beams One-way reinforced-concrete slabs are also frequently used in structural-steel framed buildings. Spacing of the steel beams is usually about 6 to 8 ft. Often the slab is poured so that its underside is flush with the underside of the top flange of the beam, as shown in Fig. 9.4*a*. This simplifies construction to a certain extent, as the plywood slab form can be wedged between the upper and lower flanges of the steel beam. Of even greater significance is the fact that positive bracing against lateral buckling is provided for the compressive flange of the beam, whereas if the bottom of the slab were flush with the top of the steel, one would have to rely upon adhesion between the concrete and steel to prevent lateral movement.

Increasingly in recent years buildings are being designed for composite

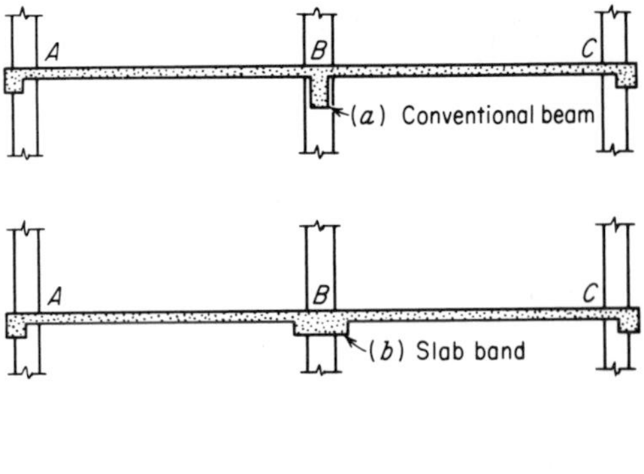

***Fig.* 9.3** Comparison of sections through conventional and slab-band floors.

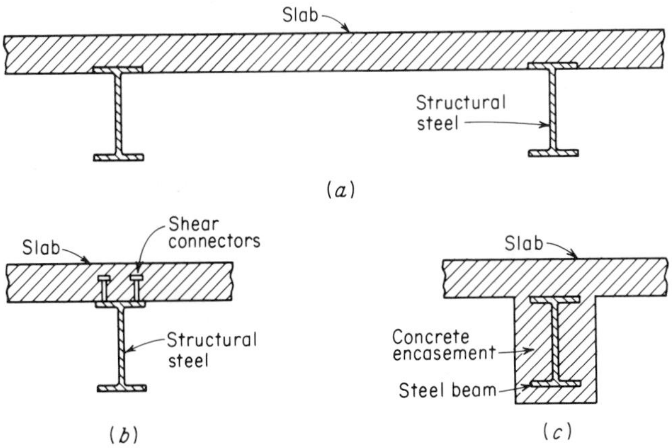

Fig. 9.4 Slab floors with steel beams.

action. Shear connectors are welded to the top of the steel beam and are embedded in the concrete slab, as shown in Fig. 9.4*b*; they prevent relative movement between the concrete and steel in the direction of the beam axis. The entire cross section, consisting of the concrete slab and the steel beam, then acts together in resisting longitudinal flexural stress. Shallower sections can be used which are nevertheless stiffer than their deeper, noncomposite counterparts. The design of composite steel-concrete members is discussed in detail in Chap. 12.

If it is necessary to fireproof a steel frame building, a form may be built around the beam, and the steel encased in concrete as shown in Fig. 9.4*c*. While some composite action undoubtedly exists, this may not be reliable for various reasons, such as the presence of a paint film between the concrete and steel, and the contribution of the concrete is usually disregarded. As an alternative to the solid encasement of the steel, it my be wrapped with expanded-metal lath or wire mesh, which is then troweled or sprayed with a fireproofing vermiculite plaster, affording a substantial reduction in dead load.

9.6 Concrete-slab Floors with Light-gage Steel Decking In recent years considerable use has been made of light-gage steel deck covered with a concrete slab for floors and roofs in steel frame office and apartment buildings. Examples of this type of construction are shown in Figs. 9.5 and 9.6. The steel deck in this case serves a double purpose: (1) it provides a form for the wet concrete, eliminating the necessity for temporary wood forms, and (2) it provides tensile reinforcement for the hardened slab. Often a light welded wire mesh is used in conjunction with the steel deck, to reinforce for shrinkage and temperature stresses in the

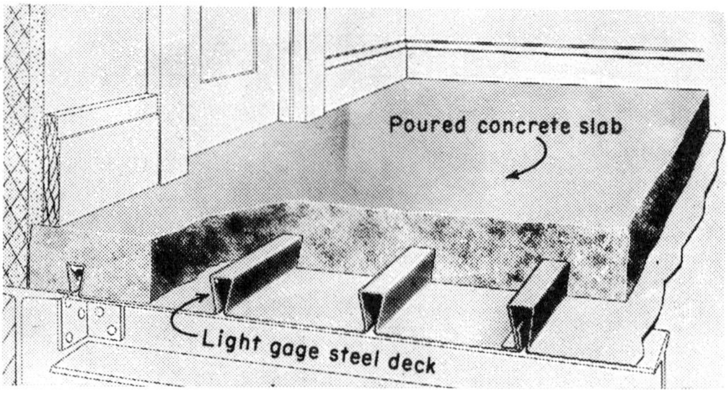

Fig. 9.5 Concrete slab with steel deck reinforcing. (*Fenestra, Inc., Holorib deck.*)

direction perpendicular to the deck ribs. In one case, transverse wires are welded to the ridges of corrugated sheet steel, reinforcing shrinkage and temperatures stress as well as improving bond between the panels and the concrete. In some installations, additional negative steel bars are placed over supports; in other cases, the temperature mesh, while not adequate to reinforce for full negative moment, will at least control the cracking which will occur over supports.

The design of steel-deck-reinforced concrete slabs follows the same principles as that of any one-way slab. The steel is assumed to be concentrated at the level of the centroid of the deck cross section. The question of bond between the deck and the concrete becomes of particular

Fig. 9.6 Placing corrugated sheet reinforcing for floor slab. (*Granco Steel Products Co., Cofar deck.*)

importance, and precautions must be taken to ensure that the panels are free of oil film or dirt prior to pouring the slab.

9.7 One-way Ribbed Slabs A ribbed floor consists of a series of small, closely spaced reinforced-concrete T beams, framing into girders which in turn frame into the supporting columns. The T beams (called *joists* or *ribs*) are formed by creating void spaces in what otherwise would be a solid slab. The voids may be formed using wood or specially waterproofed cardboard, but usually special steel pans are used. The girders which support the joists are built as regular T beams.

Since the strength of concrete in tension is small and is commonly neglected in design, elimination of much of the tension concrete in a slab by the use of pan forms results in a saving of weight with little alteration in the structural characteristics of the slab. Ribbed floors are economical for buildings such as apartment houses, hotels, and hospitals, where the live loads are fairly small and the spans comparatively long. They are

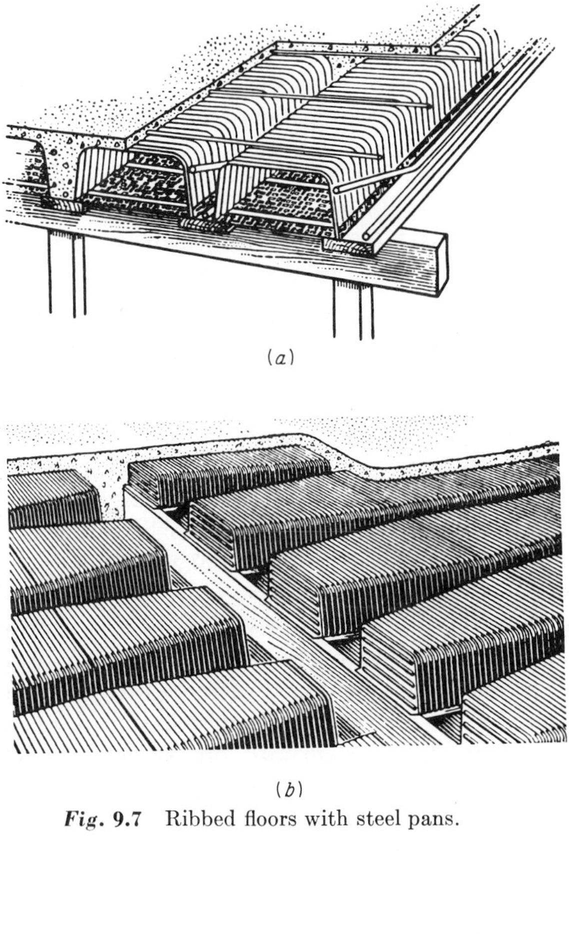

(a)

(b)

Fig. 9.7 Ribbed floors with steel pans.

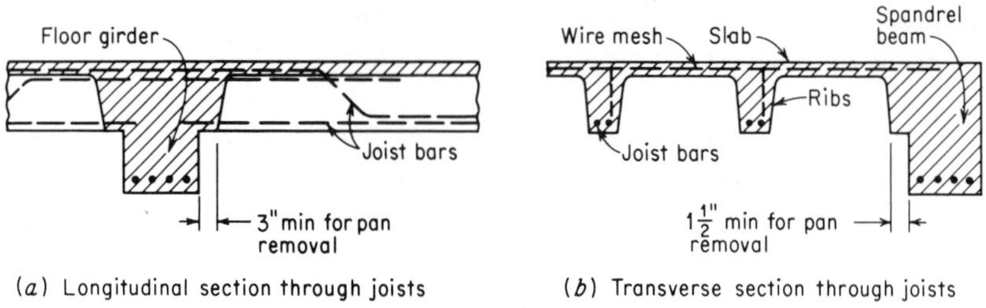

Fig. 9.8 Ribbed-floor cross sections.

not suitable for heavy construction, such as in warehouses, printing plants, and heavy manufacturing buildings.

Steel pan forms are available in depths of 6, 8, 10, 12, and 14 in. They are tapered in cross section, as shown in Fig. 9.7, to facilitate removal and are usually provided with a bottom width of 20 in., although 10- and 30-in. pans are available. Any width of joist may be obtained by varying the width of the soffit form. Figure 9.7*a* and *b* shows steel pan forms in place on wooden falsework. The tapered end pans shown in Fig. 9.7*b* are used where it is desired to obtain a wider joist width near the end supports, because of high shear or negative bending moment.

Concrete is placed on the soffit boards in the space between rows of steel pans, and above the pans to form a slab 2 in. or more thick.[1] After the concrete has hardened, the steel pans are generally removed for reuse. The reinforcement of the joists usually consists of two bars, one bent and one straight. The slab is reinforced, primarily for temperature and shrinkage stresses, with wire mesh or small bars placed at right angles to the joists; the area of the reinforcement is usually about 0.25 per cent of the cross-sectional area of the slab.

The girders which support the joists are rectangular beams or T beams with a maximum flange thickness equal to the total floor thickness, as shown in Fig. 9.8. The rows of pans are stopped at the proper distance from the stem of the girder. End caps are used at each end of each row of pans to form the sides of the girder flange. Figure 9.8 shows transverse and longitudinal cross sections of a typical ribbed-slab floor. A complete ribbed-slab floor design is given in Arts. 9.27 to 9.31.

9.8 Precast-concrete Floor Systems Precast concrete has accounted for a significant portion of building construction in recent years. Although in many cases prestressing is combined with precasting, this is not always so. Many manufacturers produce standard precast members which utilize ordinary reinforcing bars. In general, precast-concrete units can be

[1] The ACI Code specifies a minimum slab thickness of 2 in., but not less than one-half the clear distance between joists.

divided into two categories: (1) those produced as a stock item and adaptable for use under a wide variety of conditions and for many jobs and (2) those produced to a specific shape for a specific job.

Figure 9.9 shows two types of precast members which have become standard in building construction. The concrete joists of Fig. 9.9*a* are commonly available in depths from 6 to 14 in. and are used for spans from 8 to 36 ft. Reinforcement usually consists of a pair of tension bars in the bottom flange, a pair of smaller compression bars in the top flange, and inclined stirrups which are welded to the longitudinal steel. These may be used from about 4 to 8 ft on centers, with either a cast-in-place slab or precast slab units.

Another widely used, standardized precast product is the channel slab shown in Fig. 9.9*b*, which provides a usable floor or roof surface in addition to providing structural strength. A 24-in. width is standard; depths vary, depending upon the span, which may be from 8 to 30 ft, but the shorter-span planks of $2\frac{3}{4}$- or $3\frac{1}{2}$-in. thickness are most widely used. Main reinforcement consists of one or two longitudinal bars at the bottom of each flange of the channel. A light wire mesh is used to reinforce the channel web.

Precast planks are also provided in rectangular cross section. In some cases, internal longitudinal voids are cast in the rectangular planks by means of collapsible rubber tubes which are withdrawn after the concrete has hardened, thus reducing dead load. In many cases, a lightweight concrete is used.

In contrast to the more or less standard shapes just described, a building may be designed around a precast section or sections that are unique to that particular job. Figure 9.10, for example, shows an unusual precast-concrete load-bearing grill being installed for a large office building in Los Angeles. The units were cast in plastic forms, trucked to the site, and hoisted into final position. In addition to providing an exterior

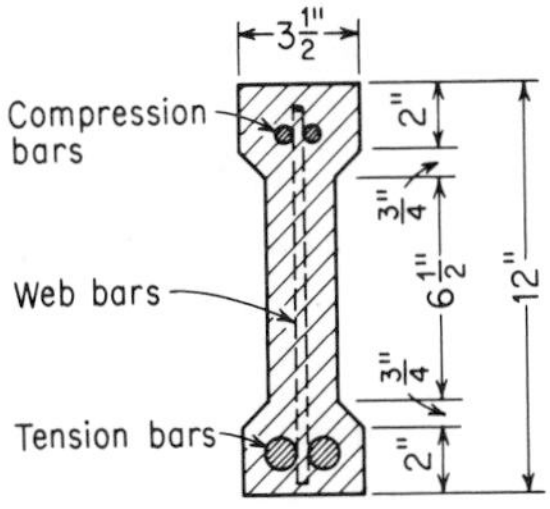

(*a*) Precast joist section

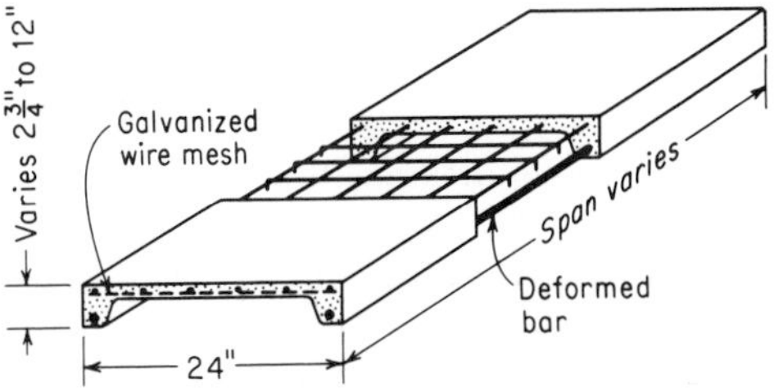

(*b*) Precast channel plank

Fig. **9.9** Precast-concrete sections.

Fig. 9.10 Precast-concrete load-bearing grill, American Cement Corp. Building. (*Courtesy of Daniel, Mann, Johnson, and Mendenhall, Architect-Engineers, Los Angeles.*)

wall effective in resisting both gravity and seismic loads, they present an attractive facade and desirable shading of sunlight, a requirement overlooked in many contemporary buildings.

Precast units are designed by standard reinforced-concrete theory. In some cases, a relaxation of the usual requirements for concrete cover around bars may be justified when the units are made by carefully controlled factory methods.[1] Higher-strength concrete is more easily obtained under these conditions also.

9.9 Two-way Solid Slabs Two-way solid slabs supported by beams on all four sides, with main reinforcement running in two directions, have been discussed in detail in Chap. 4. The perimeter beams may be either concrete poured monolithically with the slab or structural steel, often

[1] See ACI 711-58, "Precast Concrete Floor and Roof Units."

encased in concrete. Such two-way systems are suitable for intermediate and heavy loads on spans up to about 30 ft. The range of usefulness of two-way slabs corresponds generally to that of flat slabs, described below. The latter are often preferred because of the complete elimination of beams in a flat-slab system. In many concrete buildings designed for other types of reinforcing systems, there occur isolated floor panels which are ideally suited to two-directional reinforcement. An example of this is the floor or roof of a penthouse one bay wide in each direction.

9.10 Two-way Ribbed-slab Floors and Roofs As in one-way slab systems, the dead weight of two-way slabs can be reduced considerably by creating void spaces in what would otherwise be a solid slab. For the most part, the concrete removed is in tension and ineffective, so that the lighter floor will have virtually the same structural characteristics as the corresponding solid floor. Voids are usually formed using dome-shaped steel forms (Fig. 9.11) which are removed after the concrete slab has hardened. The lower flange of each dome contacts that of the adjacent dome, so that the concrete is poured entirely against a metal surface, resulting in good finished appearance of the slab. A waffle-like appearance is imparted to the underside of the floor or roof. Floors of this type are designed as ordinary two-way slabs.

9.11 Flat-slab Floors and Roofs While most slabs dealt with in structural practice are flat, the term *flat-slab* is reserved for a particular form of construction in which the reinforced-concrete slab is supported directly on columns without the aid of beams or girders. Figure 9.12 shows a typical flat-slab floor. Note the thickened portion of the slab, termed a *drop panel*, at the columns and the enlarged sections at the tops of the columns, called *column capitals*. Both the drop panels and column capitals serve the double purpose of reducing shear stress in the slab near the column supports and providing greater effective depth for negative bending moment.

In general, flat-slab construction is economical for live loads of 100 psf

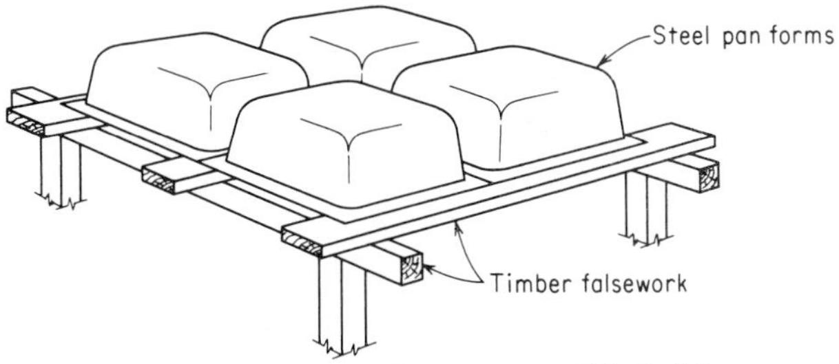

Fig. **9.11** Forms for two-way ribbed slab.

or more and for spans up to about 30 ft. For lighter loads, such as are found in apartment houses, hotels, and office buildings, some form of ribbed floor construction will usually be less expensive than a flat-slab floor, although in recent years flat slabs have been used economically for a wide range of loading. For spans longer than about 30 ft, beams and girders are desirable because of improved stiffness.

Flat-slab floors are discussed in detail in Chap. 4, and a design example is presented in Arts. 9.32 to 9.46.

9.12 Flat-plate Construction A flat-plate floor is essentially a flat-slab floor with the drop panels and column capitals omitted, so that a floor slab of uniform thickness is carried directly by prismatic columns. Flat-plate floors have been found economical and otherwise advantageous for such uses as apartment buildings, as shown in Fig. 9.13, where the spans are moderate, and the loads relatively light. Construction depth for each floor is held to the absolute minimum, with resultant savings in the overall height of the building. The smooth underside of the slab can be painted directly and left exposed for ceiling, or plaster can be applied to the concrete.

***Fig.* 9.12** Flat-slab garage floor. (*Courtesy Portland Cement Association.*)

***Fig.* 9.13** Flat-plate floor construction. *(Courtesy Portland Cement Association.)*

Flat-plate construction is singularly adapted to the precasting of entire floors at ground level. The slabs are cast in layers over the basement or ground-floor slab, with a bond-parting agent between. After the concrete has attained its strength, the slabs are raised to their final elevation by means of jacks set on the columns. With the exception of edge forms, all falsework and forming is eliminated. This is known as *lift-slab* construction.

Certain problems are inherent in flat-plate construction. One of these is the fact that shear stresses in the concrete may be very high near the columns. Often special reinforcement is required in this area in the form of flanged steel weldments, steel beam stubs embedded in the slab, or wire-cage reinforcement. Problems with excessive longtime deflections of the relatively thin slab sections have arisen in a number of recent installations of this type.

9.13 Ribbed Flat-slab Construction The dome forms described in Art. 9.10 have also been used successfully for flat-slab and flat-plate floors, as shown in Fig. 9.14. Inactive tension concrete is removed, with a resultant saving in dead load. A wafflelike appearance results, which has in many instances been used to architectural advantage.

Commonly, dome forms are omitted near the columns, providing a section better able to resist negative bending moment and high shear in that region.

9.14 Floor Surfaces Many types of wearing surfaces are used on concrete floors. Concrete topping $\frac{3}{4}$ to 2 in. thick is frequently used. Such topping may be either monolithic or bonded. Monolithic finishes should be placed within 45 min after the base slab is poured; bonded finishes are placed on a fully hardened base slab. In order to obtain an effective bond in the latter case, the base slab should be rough, and it should be thoroughly wetted and coated with a neat cement paste before placing the finish. Mix proportions vary, and quite often an artificial hardening agent is added.[1]

A wooden floor may be provided for, if desired, by embedding beveled nailing strips or "sleepers," usually 2 by 4's laid flat, in a layer of cinder concrete on top of the main slab, as shown in Fig. 9.15. A spacing of 16 in. for the sleepers has been found satisfactory for the ordinary floor.

Small vitrified-clay flat tiles embedded in a 2-in. layer of portland-cement mortar also provide a satisfactory floor surface. Asphalt or linoleum tile placed over a smooth cement base is also frequently used.

[1] See Portland Cement Association bulletins "Surface Treatments for Concrete Floors" and "Specifications for Heavy-duty Floor Concrete Floor Finish" for more complete coverage of this important topic.

Fig. 9.14 Ribbed flat-slab floor or grid slab.

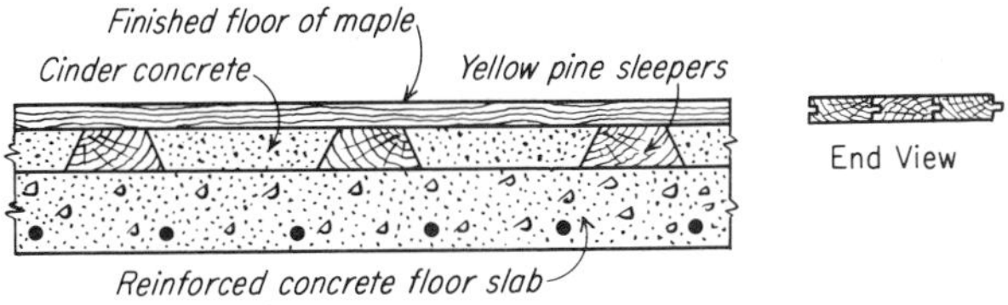

Fig. **9.15** Details of a wooden floor on a concrete slab.

The durability of any wearing surface depends in a large measure upon the method of placing the surface. If not properly constructed, the concrete finish might spall, the wood floor "dry-rot," the tiles curl, and the linoleum crack. In order to ensure the maximum degree of serviceability from a given type of floor surface, a special study of methods which have proved successful for laying that particular type of floor should be made.

9.15 Concrete Roofs The design of roofs is similar to the design of floors. In addition to the structural requirements, however, the roofs must be impervious to the passage of water, provide for adequate drainage, and furnish protection against condensation.

In order to provide adequate drainage, the roof slab may be pitched slightly, or a filling of some light material such as cinder concrete, covered with a suitable roofing material, may be used, the thickness of the filling being varied so as to give the required slope to the roof surface. The amount of slope required for drainage will depend upon the smoothness of the exposed surface. A value of $\frac{1}{8}$ in. per ft might be used with a surface of hard tile. Felt and gravel roofs should have a pitch of at least $\frac{1}{4}$ in. per ft. Some form of flashing is required along the parapets to prevent the drainage from seeping into the building at the edges of the roof slab.

Condensation may best be guarded against by proper ventilation and insulation. The form of insulation to be used will depend upon the particular class of building under consideration.

Imperviousness may best be provided for by the application of some form of separate roof covering, such as a combination of felt and gravel in alternate layers cemented together and to the slab by means of coal-tar pitch or asphalt, vitrified tile embedded in asphalt, or any of the commercial types of built-up roofings. Tin, corrugated iron, or copper roofings are sometimes placed on reinforced-concrete buildings but are usually more expensive and less permanent than other types of coverings.

WALLS AND PARTITIONS

9.16 Panel and Curtain Walls As a general rule, the exterior walls of a reinforced-concrete building are supported at each floor by the skeleton framework, their only function being to enclose the building. Such walls are called *panel* walls. They may be made of concrete (often precast), cinder concrete block, brick, tile blocks, or insulated metal panels. The latter may be faced with aluminum, stainless steel, or a porcelain-enamel finish over steel, backed by 1 or 2 in. of insulating material and an inner surface sheathing. The thickness of each of these types of panel walls will vary according to the material, type of construction, climatological conditions, and the building requirements governing the particular locality in which the construction takes place.

The pressure of the wind is usually the only load that is considered in determining the structural thickness of a wall panel, although in some cases exterior walls are used as diaphragms to transmit forces caused by horizontal loads down to the building foundations.

Curtain walls are similar to panel walls except that they are not supported at each story by the frame of the building, but are self-supporting. However, they are often anchored to the building frame at each floor to provide lateral support.

9.17 Bearing Walls A bearing wall may be defined as one which carries any vertical load in addition to its own weight. Such walls may be constructed of stone masonry, brick, concrete block, or reinforced concrete. Occasional projections or pilasters add to the strength of the wall and are often used at points of load concentration. In small commercial buildings bearing walls may be used with economy and expediency. In larger commercial and manufacturing buildings, when the element of time is an important factor, the delay necessary for the erection of the bearing wall and the attending increased cost of construction often dictate the use of some other arrangement.

Bearing walls may be of either single or double thickness, the advantage of the latter type being that the air space between the walls renders the interior of the building less liable to temperature variations and makes the wall itself more nearly moistureproof. On account of the greater gross thickness of the double wall, such construction reduces the available floor space. This feature is often sufficient in itself to warrant the selection of the solid wall unless the factors of condensation and temperature are of great importance. Cavity wall construction is usually limited to a total height of about 40 ft.

The thickness of bearing walls varies with the height. The New York City Building Code requires that, for bearing walls made of solid masonry units (brick, stone, concrete brick, etc.) and not more than 75 ft in height, the thickness of the uppermost 55 ft of height shall be at least 12 in., and the thickness below this shall be at least 16 in., except that for walls in buildings of one, two, and three stories the top-story thickness in each case may be 8 in. In computing wall thicknesses, a maximum story height of 13 ft shall be assumed.

According to the ACI Code, the allowable compressive stress in reinforced-concrete bearing walls shall be

$$f_c = 0.225f'_c\left[1 - \left(\frac{h}{40t}\right)^3\right] \tag{9.1}$$

in which h is the vertical distance between supports, and t is the thickness of the wall. When the reinforcement in bearing walls is designed, placed, and anchored in position as for tied columns, the allowable stresses shall be those for tied columns, in which the ratio of vertical reinforcement shall not exceed 0.04. For design by ultimate-strength methods, the values from Eq. (9.1) shall be multiplied by 1.9. In the case of concentrated loads, the length of the wall to be considered as effective for each shall not exceed the center-to-center distance between loads, nor shall it exceed the width of the bearing plus 4 times the wall thickness. Reinforced-concrete bearing walls shall have a thickness of at least $\frac{1}{25}$ the unsupported height or width, whichever is shorter. Reinforced-concrete bearing walls of buildings shall be not less than 6 in. thick for the uppermost 15 ft of their height; for each successive 25 ft downward, or fraction thereof, the minimum thickness shall be increased 1 in.

9.18 Basement Walls In determining the thickness of basement walls, the lateral pressure of the earth, if any, must be considered in addition to other structural features. If part of a bearing wall, the lower portion may be designed either as a slab supported by the basement and first floors, or as a retaining wall, depending upon the type of construction. If columns and wall beams are available for support, each basement wall panel of reinforced concrete may be designed to resist the earth pressure as a simple slab reinforced in either one or two directions.

A minimum thickness of 8 in. is generally specified for reinforced-concrete basement walls. In wet ground a minimum thickness of 12 in. should be used. In any case, the thickness cannot be less than that of the wall above.

Care should be taken to brace a basement wall thoroughly from the inside if the earth is backfilled before the wall has obtained sufficient strength to resist the lateral pressure without such assistance or if it is placed before the first-floor slab is in position.

9.19 Partition Walls Interior walls used for the purpose of subdividing the floor area may be made of cinder block, brick, precast concrete, metal lath and plaster, clay tile, or metal. The type of wall selected will depend upon the fire resistance required, flexibility of rearrangement, ease with which electrical conduits, plumbing, etc., can be accomodated, and architectural requirements.

STAIRWAYS

9.20 Types of Concrete Stairs The simplest form of reinforced-concrete stairway consists of an inclined slab supported at the ends upon beams, with steps formed upon its upper surface. Such a stair slab is usually designed as a simple slab with a span equal to the horizontal distance between supports. This method of design requires steel to be placed only in the direction of the length of the slab. Transverse steel, usually one bar to each tread, is used only to assist in distribution of the load and to provide temperature reinforcement. It sometimes becomes necessary to include a platform slab at one or both ends of the inclined slab. Many successful designs made as outlined above for the simple inclined slab indicate that the effect of the angle that occurs in a slab of this type can safely be disregarded.

It is advisable to keep the unsupported span of a stair slab reasonably short. If no break occurs in the flight between floors, intermediate beams, supported by the structural framework of the building, may be employed. If the stair between floors is divided into two or more flights, beams as described above may be used to support the intermediate landing, with these in turn supported as above for the long straight flight, or the intermediate slab may be suspended from a beam at the upper floor level by means of rod hangers. Where conditions permit, the intermediate slab may be supported directly by the exterior walls of the building.

9.21 Building-code Requirements The required number of stairways, and many of the details, are governed to a large extent by the provisions of the governing building code. Among other things, these provisions stipulate the maximum distance from the most remote point in the floor area to the stairway, the minimum width of stairway, the maximum height of any straight flight, the maximum height (or rise) of a single step, the minimum distance (the run) between the vertical faces of two consecutive steps, and the required relation between the rise and the run to give safety and convenience in climbing.

In most codes the minimum width of any stair slab and the minimum dimension of any landing are about 44 in. The maximum rise of a stair step is usually specified as about $7\frac{3}{4}$ in., and the minimum run or tread width, exclusive of nosing, $9\frac{1}{2}$ in. A rise of less than $6\frac{1}{2}$ in. is not considered generally satisfactory. In order to give a satisfactory and comfortable ratio of rise to run, various rules have been adopted. One requires that for steps without nosings, the sum of the rise and run shall be $17\frac{1}{2}$ in., but the rise shall not be less than $6\frac{1}{2}$ in. or more than $7\frac{3}{4}$ in.

The maximum height of a straight flight between landings is generally 12 ft, except for stairways serving as exits from places of assembly, where a maximum of 8 ft is normally specified.

The number of stairways is governed by the width of the stair slab, the number of probable occupants on each floor, and the dimensions of the floor area. One typical code specification is that the distance from any point in an open floor area to the nearest stairway or exit shall not exceed 100 ft, that the corresponding distance along corridors in a particular area shall not exceed 125 ft, and that the combined width of all stairways in any story shall be such that the stairs may accommodate at one time the total number of persons occupying the largest floor area served by such stairs above the floor area under consideration on the basis of one person for each 22 in. of stair width and $1\frac{1}{2}$ treads on the stairs, and one person for each $3\frac{1}{2}$ ft^2 floor area on the landings and halls within the stairway enclosure.

In all buildings over 40 ft in height, and in all mercantile buildings regardless of height, the required stairways must be completely enclosed by fireproof partitions, and at least one stairway must continue to the roof. An open ornamental stairway can be used from the main entrance floor to the floor next above, provided it is not the only stairway.

9.22 Construction Details The usual practice is to construct the stairways after the main structural framework of the building has been completed, in which event recesses should be left in the beams to support the stair slab, and dowels should be provided to furnish the necessary anchorage. Occasionally, however, the stairs are poured at the same time as the floors, in which event negative-moment reinforcement should be furnished over the supports of the stair slab, as in any continuous-beam construction. The steps are usually poured monolithically with the slab, but they may be molded after the main slab is in place. In the latter instance, provision must be made for securing the step to the slab.

DESIGN OF A BEAM - AND - GIRDER FLOOR

9.23 Data and Specifications In order to illustrate the application of the principles of reinforced-concrete design to the design of a concrete floor of the slab–beam-and-girder type, typical portions of the second floor of the building shown in Figs. 9.17 and 9.18 will be designed. The building is to sustain a live load of 200 psf. The ACI moment coefficients of Table 8.2 are applicable and will be used for this example, although improved economy would undoubtedly result from an elastic analysis of the building frame. The outside faces of all the exterior columns will be kept in the same plane so that the pilasters will have smooth faces, and all the wall beams and girders will be placed flush with the outer face of the pilasters so that the entire outer walls, except for the windows, will be in one plane. A 1-in. bonded wearing surface, which will add to the dead load but will not be considered as part of the effective depth, will be placed on the slab. Steel reinforcement with a yield stress $f_y = 40{,}000$ psi will be used with concrete of strength $f'_c = 3000$ psi. A maximum steel ratio of $p = 0.18f'_c/f_y$ will be adopted.

For purposes of illustration, most of the computations for this design will be presented on computation sheets of the type that are typical in design office practice.

9.24 Design of the Slabs The computations for the design of the floor slabs *S*1 and *S*2 are shown in Computation Sheet 9.1. The clear spans were obtained from the assumptions that the exterior basement columns will be 24 in. deep from the face of the basement wall and that the floor beams will be 8 in. in width. In computing the negative moments at the faces of supports, the average of the two adjacent clear spans was used. A negative-moment coefficient at the interior face of the exterior support of $\frac{1}{24}$ was taken in accordance with Table 8.2. Reinforcing steel is placed with centers 1 in. from the top or bottom of the slab.

From Graph 11, Appendix B:

*S*1:

Fifty per cent positive-moment reinforcement required for

$$0.23 \times 7 \text{ ft} - 12 \times \tfrac{3}{8} \text{ in.} = 1 \text{ ft } 3 \text{ in.}$$

from support, bent at 45°, reaching top at 1 ft 1 in. from support. Negative-moment reinforcement required at top,

$$0.09 \times 7 \text{ ft} + 4\tfrac{1}{2} \text{ in.} = 1 \text{ ft } 0 \text{ in.}$$

from outer support. At continuous end, 50 per cent positive-moment reinforcement required for 1 ft 3 in. from support, and 50 per cent negative-moment reinforcement at

$$0.09 \times 7 \text{ ft} + 4\tfrac{1}{2} \text{ in.} = 1 \text{ ft } 0 \text{ in.}$$

*S*2:

Fifty per cent of positive-moment reinforcement required at

$$0.25 \times 6 \text{ ft } 4 \text{ in.} - 4\tfrac{1}{2} \text{ in.} = 1 \text{ ft } 2\tfrac{1}{2} \text{ in.}$$

Design of floor slab

Live load	200.0 × 1.8 = 360 psf
Dead load (assume 4″ slab + 1″ finish)	62.5 × 1.5 = 94
	Total = 454 psf

Clear span for *S*-1 = 7′0″
Clear span for *S*-2 = 6′4″
} Avg clear span = 6′8″

*S*1

Center:
$M = +\frac{1}{14}(454)(7.0)^2(12) = 19{,}000$ in.-lb
At continuous end:
$M = -\frac{1}{12}(454)(6.67)^2(12) = -20{,}200$ in.-lb
At wall end:
$M = -\frac{1}{24}(454)(7.0)^2(12) = -11{,}050$ in.-lb
From Graph 1

$$\frac{M_u}{\phi bd^2} = 483$$

$$d^2 = \frac{20{,}200}{0.9 \times 12 \times 483} = 3.88 \text{ in.}^2$$

$d = 1.97$ in.
Use a minimum d of 3 in.
Slab thickness = 4 in. as assumed.
Center:

$$\frac{M_u}{\phi bd^2} = \frac{19{,}000}{0.9 \times 12 \times 9} = 196$$

From Graph 1
$p = 0.0051$
$A_s = 0.0051 \times 12 \times 3 = 0.183$ in.²
At continuous end:

$$\frac{M_u}{\phi bd^2} = \frac{20{,}200}{0.9 \times 12 \times 9} = 208$$

$p = 0.0054$
$A_s = 0.0054 \times 12 \times 3 = 0.194$ in.²
At wall end:

$$\frac{M_u}{\phi bd^2} = \frac{11{,}050}{0.90 \times 12 \times 9} = 114$$

$p < p_{min} = 0.005$
$A_s = 0.005 \times 12 \times 3 = 0.18$ in.²

*S*2

Center:
$M = +\frac{1}{16}(454)(6.33)^2(12) = 13{,}600$ in.-lb
At first interior support:
$M = -\frac{1}{12}(454)(6.67)^2(12) = 20{,}200$ in.-lb
At all other interior supports:
$M = -\frac{1}{12}(454)(6.33)^2(12) = 18{,}100$ in.-lb
Use 4-in. slab thickness throughout.

Center:

$$\frac{M_u}{\phi bd^2} = \frac{13{,}600}{0.9 \times 12 \times 9} = 140$$

$p < p_{min}$
$A_s = 0.005 \times 12 \times 3 = 0.18$ in.²

At first interior support:

$$\frac{M_u}{\phi bd^2} = \frac{20{,}200}{0.9 \times 12 \times 9} = 208$$

$p = 0.0054$
$A_s = 0.0054 \times 12 \times 3 = 0.19$ in.²
At other interior supports:

$$\frac{M_u}{\phi bd^2} = \frac{18{,}100}{0.9 \times 12 \times 9} = 186$$

$p < p_{min}$
$A_s = 0.18$ in.²

Outer support	*S*1 center	First interior support	*S*2 center	Other supports
0.18	0.18	0.19	0.18	0.18
#3 straight @ 14″ #3 bent @ 14″	#3 straight @ 14″ #3 bent @ 14″	#3 bent @ 7″	#3 bent @ 14″ #3 straight @ 14″	#3 bent @ 7″
$A_s = 0.19$	$A_s = 0.19$	$A_s = 0.19$	$A_s = 0.19$	$A_s = 0.19$

Temperature steel
$A_s = 0.002(12)(4) = 0.096$ in.² Use #3 @ 13″

***Computation Sheet* 9.1** Beam-and-girder floor.

from support. Fifty per cent of negative-moment reinforcement required at

$$0.09 \times 6 \text{ ft } 4 \text{ in.} + 4\tfrac{1}{2} \text{ in.} = 0 \text{ ft } 11\tfrac{1}{2} \text{ in.}$$

from support. Number 3 bars at bottom 14 in. center to center are carried into exterior support 6 in. and are continuous over other supports. Alternate No. 3 bars 14 in. center to center are bent up 1 ft 2 in. from face of all supports. Bent-up bars must be extended into the adjacent span a length of

$$0.21 \times 7 \text{ ft} + 4\tfrac{1}{2} \text{ in.} = 1 \text{ ft } 10 \text{ in.}$$

All details for the slab are shown in Fig. 9.17.

9.25 Design of the Beams The computations for the design of beams $B1$ and $B2$ are shown in Computation Sheets 9.2 and 9.3. The clear spans for the beams were obtained using the same assumptions made in the design of the slab, with the further assumption that the beams will be framed into girders 12 in. in width. The beams framing into girders were designed, since these beams have clear spans slightly longer than those framing into columns; however, to simplify the construction, all beams are

Design of beams:

Uniform load per foot from floor	$7 \times 454 = 3175$ plf
Dead load of stem (assumed)	$210 \times 1.5 = 315$
	Total $= 3490$ plf

Clear span for $B1 = 22'6''$ and clear span for $B2 = 22'0''$: Avg clear span $= 22'3''$

B1

Center:

$M = +\frac{1}{14}(3490)(22.5)^2 12 = 1{,}520{,}000$ in.-lb

At continuous end:

$M = -\frac{1}{10}(3490)(22.25)^2 12 = 2{,}080{,}000$ in.-lb

At wall ends:

$M = -\frac{1}{24}(3490)(22.5)^2 12 = 885{,}000$ in.-lb

$V_{max} = \frac{1}{2}(1.15)(3490)22.5 = 45{,}200$ lb

At continuous end:

$p = 0.18 \times \frac{3}{40} = 0.0135$

$$\frac{M_u}{\phi bd^2} = 483$$

$$bd^2 = \frac{2{,}080{,}000}{0.9 \times 483} = 4790$$

Use $b = 12$ in., $d = 20$ in.

$A_s = 0.0135 \times 12 \times 20 = 3.24$ in.^{2}

At wall end:

$$\frac{M_u}{\phi bd^2} = \frac{885{,}000}{0.9 \times 4790} = 206$$

$p = 0.0054$

$A_s = 0.0054 \times 240 = 1.30$ in.^{2}

Center:

$$A_s = \frac{1{,}520{,}000}{0.9 \times 40{,}000(20 - 2)} = 2.35 \text{ in.}^2$$

$$a = \frac{2.35 \times 40}{0.85 \times 3 \times 67.5} = 0.58 \text{ in.}$$

Revised $A_s = 2.35 \times 18/19.71 = 2.14$ in.^{2}

B2

Center:

$M = +\frac{1}{16}(3490)(22)^2 12 = 1{,}269{,}000$ in.-lb

At first interior support:

$M = -\frac{1}{11}(3490)(22.25)^2 12 = 1{,}866{,}000$ in.-lb

At all other interior supports:

$M = -\frac{1}{11}(3490)(22)^2 12 = 1{,}842{,}000$ in.-lb

$V_{max} = \frac{1}{2}(3490)22 = 38{,}400$ lb

Beam dimensions will be kept the same throughout.

At first interior support:

$$\frac{M_u}{\phi bd^2} = \frac{1{,}866{,}000}{0.9 \times 4790} = 433$$

$p = 0.012$

$A_s = 0.012 \times 240 = 2.88$ in.^{2}

At all other interior supports:

$$\frac{M_u}{\phi bd^2} = \frac{1{,}842{,}000}{0.9 \times 4790} = 428$$

$p = 0.0118$

$A_s = 0.0118 \times 240 = 2.84$ in.^{2}

Center:

$$A_s = \frac{1{,}269{,}000}{0.9 \times 40{,}000(20 - 2)} = 1.96 \text{ in.}^2$$

$a = 0.48$

Revised $A_s = 1.96 \times 18/19.76 = 1.79$ in.^{2}

***Computation Sheet* 9.2** Beam-and-girder floor.

*B*1

Shear (use #3 U stirrups):

At wall end:

$V = 39{,}200$ lb

$V_c = 2 \times 0.85\sqrt{3000}\,(12)(20) = 22{,}400$ lb

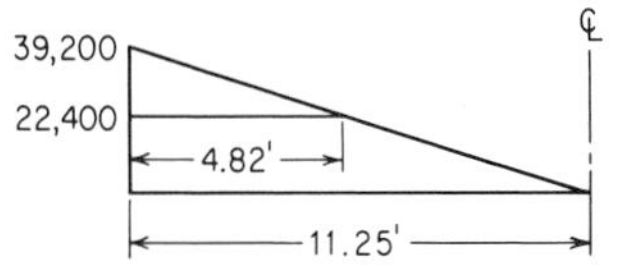

$s_{max} = 20/2 = 10$ in.

$s_{max} = 0.22/0.0015 \times 12 = 12.2$ in.

At distance *d*:

$V' = 16{,}800 \times 3.15/4.82 = 11{,}000$ lb

$$s_d = \frac{0.22 \times 0.85 \times 40{,}000 \times 20}{11{,}000} = 13.6 \text{ in.} > s_{max}$$

Space 1 @ 5″, 8 @ 10″.

At continuous end:

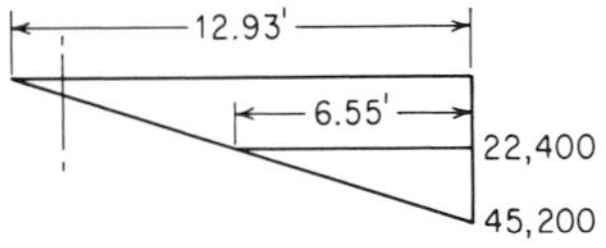

At distance *d*:

$V' = 22{,}800 \times 4.88/6.55 = 17{,}000$ lb

$$s_d = \frac{0.22 \times 0.85 \times 40{,}000 \times 20}{17{,}000} = 8.80 \text{ in.}$$

Space 1 @ 4″, 4 @ 8″, 7 @ 10″.

*B*2

At either end:

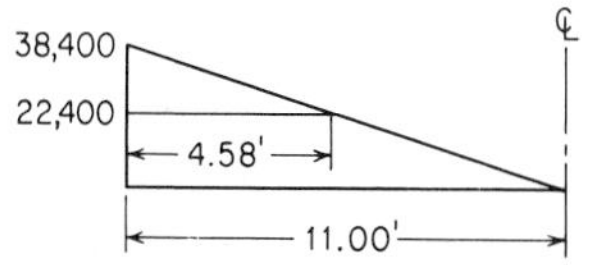

At distance *d*:

$V' = 16{,}000 \times 2.91/4.58 = 10{,}200$ lb

$$s_d = \frac{0.22 \times 0.85 \times 40{,}000 \times 20}{10{,}200} = 14.7 \text{ in.} > s_{max}$$

Space 1 @ 5″, 8 @ 10″.

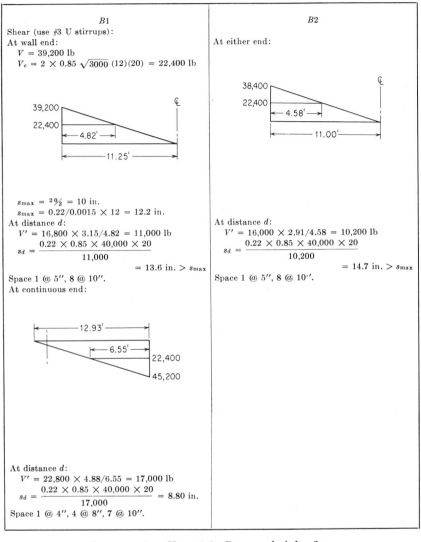

***Computation Sheet* 9.3** Beam-and-girder floor.

of the same dimensions. Beams will be proportioned for a maximum steel ratio of $0.18f'_c/f_y$. While a portion of the bottom steel will be bent up in each beam, stirrups will be provided to take all the diagonal tensile stresses.

On the basis of Computation Sheets 9.2 and 9.3, the positive steel requirement of 2.14 in.^{2} for *B*1 will be provided using four No. 7 bars ($A_s = 2.41$). Two of these will be bent up at each end. At the wall end of

*B*1, the required area of 1.30 in.^{2} will be met by adding one No. 5 bar to the two No. 7 bent bars (A_s = 1.51 in.^{2}). In beam *B*2, the positive steel requirement of 1.79 in.^{2} will be provided by four No. 6 bars (A_s = 1.77 in.^{2}), two of which are bent up at each end. At the first interior support, the total requirement is 3.24 in.^{2} Two No. 7 straight bars will be added to the two No. 6 and two No. 7 bent bars (A_s = 3.29 in.^{2}). At typical interior supports, where the steel requirement is 2.84 in.^{2}, two No. 7 straight bars are added to the two No. 6 bars bent up from each side (A_s = 2.97 in.^{2}).

From Graph 11, Appendix B:

*B*1:

Two No. 7 bars can be bent up at

$$0.23 \times 22.5 \times 12 - 20 = 42 \text{ in.}$$

from the face of either support. The remaining two No. 7 bars are continued 6 in. into the support faces. At the wall end, the No. 5 straight bar is continued a distance d beyond the point of inflection and is cut off at

$$0.12 \times 22.5 \times 12 + 20 = 52 \text{ in.}$$

from the support face. At the continuous end, straight bars are cut off at

$$0.28 \times 22.5 \times 12 + 20 = 96 \text{ in.}$$

from the support face.

*B*2:

Two No. 6 bars are bent up at

$$0.25 \times 22 \times 12 - 20 = 46 \text{ in.}$$

from the support faces. The remaining two No. 6 bars are continued 6 in. into the face of the supports. At the first interior support, the four No. 7 straight bars are cut off at

$$0.24 \times 22.25 \times 12 + 20 = 84 \text{ in.}$$

beyond the support face. At all other interior supports, the two No. 7 and two No. 6 straight bars are cut off at

$$0.24 \times 22 \times 12 + 20 = 84 \text{ in.}$$

from the support face.

By inspection of Table 8, Appendix B, it is evident that adequate development length is provided for all bars; therefore, according to Code, flexural bond stress need not be checked.

9.26 Design of the Girders A portion of the sample computations for the design of the girders is shown in Computation Sheets 9.4 and 9.5.

Design of girders

Load from floor beams = 76,800 lb

Live load on girder		360 plf
Dead load of floor finish on girder		19
Dead load of girder (assumed)	$500 \times 1.5 =$	750
	Total $=$	1129 plf

Clear span of $G1$ = 20′2″
Clear span of $G2$ = 19′8″ } Avg clear span used = 19′11″

Simple span maximum moment

$$\tfrac{1}{8}(1129)(19.92)^2 12 = 672{,}000 \text{ in.-lb}$$
$$76{,}800(6.58)12 = 6{,}020{,}000$$
$$M_s = 6{,}692{,}000 \text{ in.-lb}$$

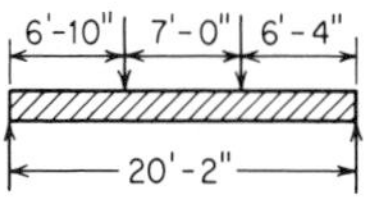

G1

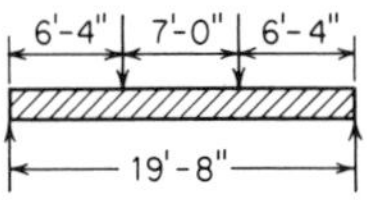

G2

G1

Center:

$M = +\frac{8}{14}M_s = 3{,}820{,}000$ in.-lb

At continuous end:

$M = -\frac{8}{10}M_s = -5{,}350{,}000$ in.-lb

At wall end:

$M = -\frac{8}{16}M_s = -3{,}340{,}000$ in.-lb

$$V_{\max} = 1.15\left[76{,}800 + 1129\frac{20.2}{2}\right] = 101{,}000 \text{ lb}$$

Use $p = 0.18 \times \frac{3}{40} = 0.0135$.

At continuous end:

$$\frac{M_u}{\phi b d^2} = 483$$

$$bd^2 = \frac{5{,}350{,}000}{0.9 \times 483} = 12{,}310$$

Use b = 18 in., d = 26.5 in.

$A_s = 0.0135 \times 18 \times 26.5 = 6.45$ in.^{2}

At wall end:

$$\frac{M_u}{\phi b d^2} = \frac{3{,}340{,}000}{0.9 \times 12{,}310} = 301$$

$p = 0.0080$

$A_s = 0.0080 \times 18 \times 26.5 = 3.83$ in.^{2}

At center (b = 60.5 in.):

$$A_s = \frac{3{,}820{,}000}{0.9 \times 40{,}000(26.5 - 2)} = 4.33 \text{ in.}^2$$

$$a = \frac{4.33 \times 40}{0.85 \times 3 \times 60.5} = 1.12 \text{ in.}$$

Revised $A_s = 4.33 \times 24.50/25.94 = 4.10$ in.^{3}

G2

Center:

$M = +\frac{8}{16}M_s = 3{,}340{,}000$ in.-lb

At ends:

$M = -\frac{8}{11}M_s = -4{,}860{,}000$ in.-lb

$$V_{\max} = 76{,}800 + 1129\frac{19.67}{2} = 87{,}500 \text{ lb}$$

Girder dimensions will be kept the same throughout.

At supports:

$$\frac{M_u}{\phi b d^2} = \frac{4{,}860{,}000}{0.90 \times 12{,}310} = 439$$

$p = 0.0121$

$A_s = 0.0121 \times 18 \times 26.5 = 5.77$ in.^{2}

At center:

$$A_s = \frac{3{,}340{,}000}{0.9 \times 40{,}000(26.5 - 2)} = 3.78 \text{ in.}^2$$

$$a = \frac{3.78 \times 40}{0.85 \times 3 \times 60.5} = 0.975 \text{ in.}$$

Revised $A_s = 3.78 \times 24.50/26.01 = 3.56$ in.

Computation Sheet 9.4 Beam-and-girder floor.

The clear spans here were obtained by making use of all previous assumptions and further assuming that the exterior columns supporting the second floor have a depth of 14 in., measured from the face of the wall, and that the interior first-floor columns are 16 in. in diameter. The average clear span was used in computing moments caused by the uniformly distributed load, and the average distance between beams and adjacent columns in *G*1 for computing moments caused by concentrated loads. These assumptions are justifiable since they produce moments slightly larger than those which actually exist in either span. The inherently approximate nature of calculations of this sort does not warrant closer refinement in computations.

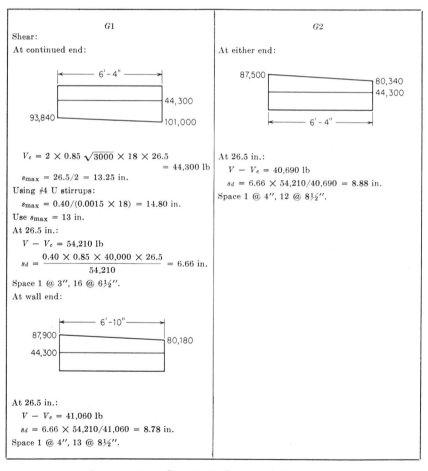

*G*1

Shear:

At continued end:

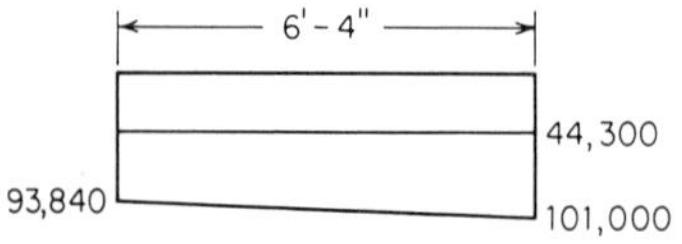

$V_c = 2 \times 0.85\sqrt{3000} \times 18 \times 26.5 = 44{,}300$ lb

$s_{max} = 26.5/2 = 13.25$ in.

Using #4 U stirrups:

$s_{max} = 0.40/(0.0015 \times 18) = 14.80$ in.

Use $s_{max} = 13$ in.

At 26.5 in.:

$V - V_c = 54{,}210$ lb

$$s_d = \frac{0.40 \times 0.85 \times 40{,}000 \times 26.5}{54{,}210} = 6.66 \text{ in.}$$

Space 1 @ 3″, 16 @ 6½″.

At wall end:

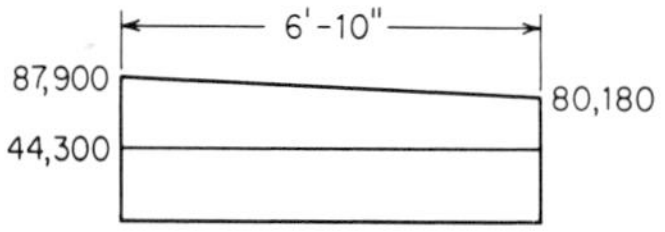

At 26.5 in.:

$V - V_c = 41{,}060$ lb

$s_d = 6.66 \times 54{,}210/41{,}060 = 8.78$ in.

Space 1 @ 4″, 13 @ 8½″.

*G*2

At either end:

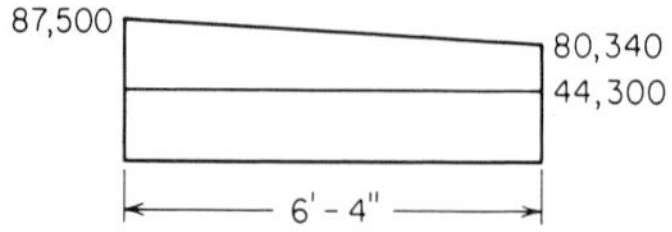

At 26.5 in.:

$V - V_c = 40{,}690$ lb

$s_d = 6.66 \times 54{,}210/40{,}690 = 8.88$ in.

Space 1 @ 4″, 12 @ 8½″.

***Computation Sheet* 9.5** Beam-and-girder floor.

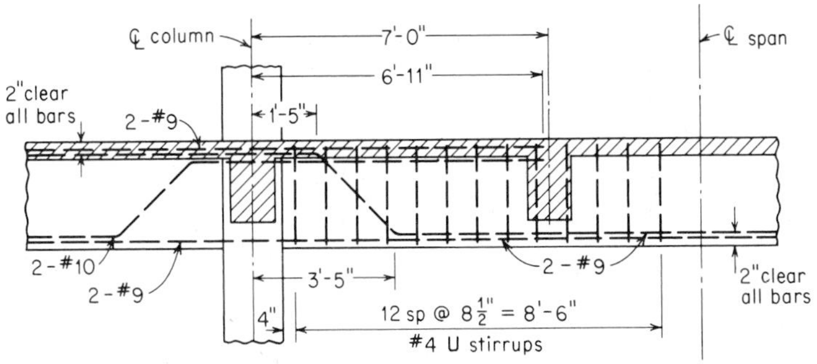

Fig. 9.16 Details of girder.

From Computation Sheets 9.4 and 9.5, the positive steel-area requirement for $G1$ of 4.10 in.^{2} will be provided by two No. 9 straight bars and two No. 10 bent bars ($A_s = 4.53$ in.^{2}). At the wall end of $G1$, the requirement of 3.83 in.^{2} is closely met by adding one No. 10 straight bar to the two No. 10 bent bars ($A_s = 3.79$ in.^{2}). In girder $G2$, the positive requirement of 3.56 in.^{2} calls for two No. 9 straight bars and two No. 9 bent bars ($A_s = 4.00$ in.^{2}). At the first interior support, adding two No. 9 straight bars to the two No. 10 and two No. 9 bent bars provides an area of 6.53 in.^{2}, very close to the required 6.45 in.^{2} At the typical interior supports, two No. 9 straight bars are added to the two No. 9 bent bars from each adjacent span, providing 6.00 in.^{2}, slightly in excess of the required 5.77 in.^{2}

The points at which the bars may be bent up are determined by assuming that the positive moment is zero at a distance of $\frac{2}{3}L/3$ from the concentrated load to the center line of the support, measured toward the support, and that the moment diagram is a straight line between the maximum and zero values. The latter assumption is in error only because of the uniformly distributed weight of the girder; this is very small in comparison with the large concentrated loads. The two No. 9 bars in $G2$ may be bent up at a distance of

$$\tfrac{1}{2} \times \tfrac{2}{3} \times \frac{21 \times 12}{3} = 28 \text{ in.}$$

to the left of the first concentrated load.

A similar assumption for the negative-moment variation can be made; the point of zero negative moment is, therefore, $\frac{2}{3}L/3$ from the center line of the support. The overlapping of the positive and negative moment diagrams which results from these assumptions provides for any variation in the moments that might result from unequal placing of the live load on adjoining spans. The two No. 9 bars at the first interior support of $G2$

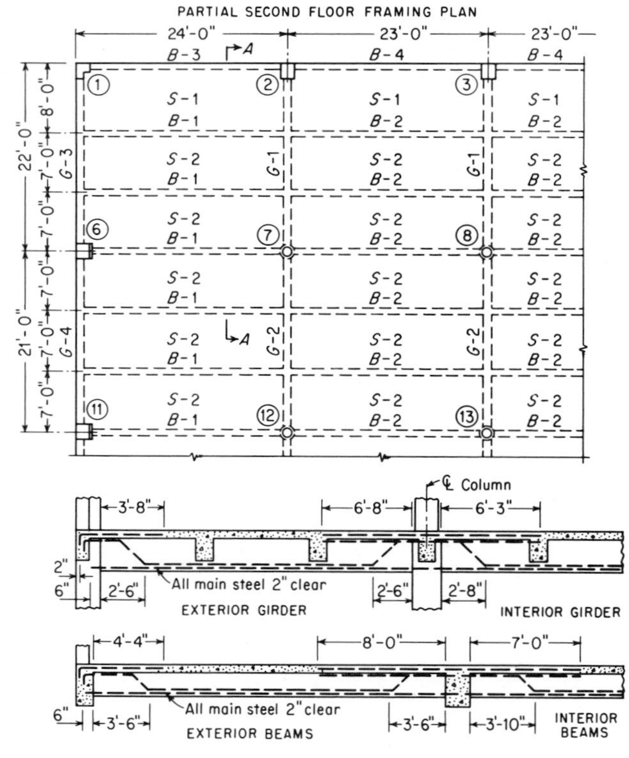

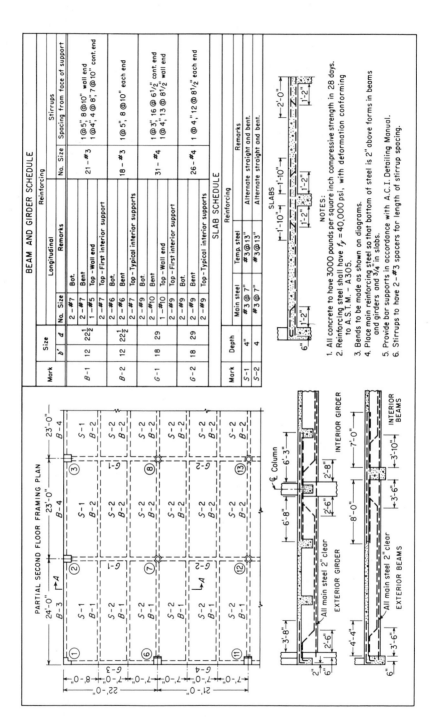

BEAM AND GIRDER SCHEDULE

Mark	Size		Reinforcing			
			Longitudinal		Stirrups	
	b'	d	No. Size	Remarks	No. Size	Spacing from face of support
B-1	12	$22\frac{1}{2}$	2 - #7	Bot.	21 - #3	1 @ 5", 8 @ 10" wall end 1 @ 4", 4 @ 8", 7 @ 10" cont. end
			2 - #7	Bent		
			1 - #5	Top - Wall end		
			2 - #7	Top - First interior support		
B-2	12	$22\frac{1}{2}$	2 - #6	Bot.	18 - #3	1 @ 5", 8 @ 10" each end
			2 - #6	Bent		
			2 - #7	Top - Typical interior supports		
G-1	18	29	2 - #9	Bot.	31 - #4	1 @ 3", 16 @ $6\frac{1}{2}$" cont. end 1 @ 4", 13 @ $8\frac{1}{2}$" wall end
			2 - #10	Bent		
			1 - #10	Top - Wall end		
			2 - #9	Top - First interior support		
G-2	18	29	2 - #9	Bot.	26 - #4	1 @ 4", 12 @ $8\frac{1}{2}$" each end
			2 - #9	Bent		
			2 - #9	Top - Typical interior supports		

SLAB SCHEDULE

Mark	Depth	Reinforcing		
		Main steel	Temp. steel	Remarks
S-1	4"	#3 @ 7"	#3 @ 13"	Alternate straight and bent.
S-2	4	#3 @ 7"	#3 @ 13"	Alternate straight and bent.

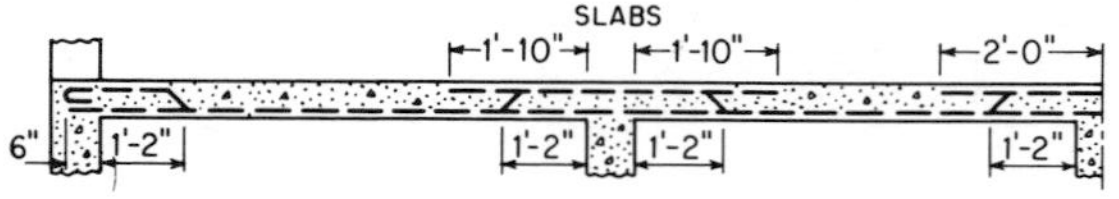

NOTES:

1. All concrete to have 3000 pounds per square inch compressive strength in 28 days.
2. Reinforcing steel shall have $f_y = 40,000$ psi, with deformation conforming to A.S.T.M. - A305.
3. Bends to be made as shown on diagrams.
4. Place main reinforcing steel so that bottom of steel is 2" above forms in beams and girders and 3/4" in slabs.
5. Provide bar supports in accordance with A.C.I. Detailing Manual.
6. Stirrups to have 2 - #3 spacers for length of stirrup spacing.

Fig. 9.17 Engineering drawing of beam-and-girder floor.

Fig. 9.18

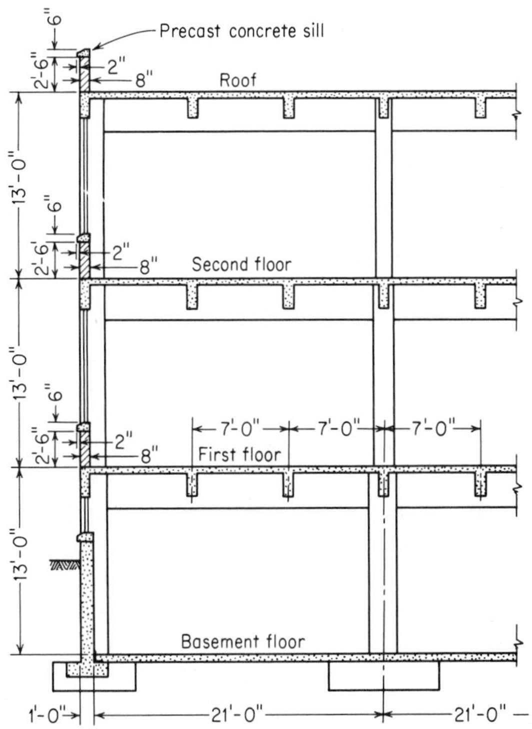

Section *A-A* Partial cross section

may be bent down at a distance of

$$\frac{2.00}{6.53}\,\frac{2}{3}\,\frac{21 \times 12}{3} = 17 \text{ in.}$$

from the support. Actual bend points are located to satisfy these requirements and are shown in Fig. 9.16. The remaining top bars are carried a distance d past the extreme position of the point of inflection and are cut off

$$\frac{2}{3}\,\frac{21 \times 12}{3} + 26.5 = 83 \text{ in.}$$

from the support as shown. A check of development length for all bars (Table 8, Appendix B) indicates that flexural bond stresses need not be checked.

Vertical No. 4 U stirrups are provided to accommodate all the diagonal tensile stresses, in neglect of the contribution of the bent bars. With reference to the shear diagrams of Computation Sheet 9.5, the excess shear is very nearly constant from the support face to the center line of the concentrated load. In each case, the spacing required at the critical section a distance *d* from the support face is used through the entire region in which stirrups are required.

Complete engineering details for the portion of the building designed above are shown in Figs. 9.17 and 9.18.

DESIGN OF A RIBBED FLOOR WITH STEEL PAN FORMS

9.27 Dead Loads The weight of a ribbed floor can be computed from the known concrete dimensions. The general form of the cross section of the steel tiles must be known, since the taper of the sides and the chamfering of the upper corners affect the volume of concrete in the ribs or joists. The cross section can be obtained from the manufacturers' catalogues. The average values in Table 9.2 can be used for joists (or ribs) 5 in. wide at the bottom and 25 in. on centers.

The values given in this table do not include the weight of an extra floor finish or a plastered ceiling below the floor. The former can be computed from the specified thickness of finish or type of floor surface. In computing design loads, an allowance of 10 psf is usually made for a plastered ceiling. An additional allowance of from 10 to 20 psf is made for the weight of partitions not definitely located on the architect's plans, or where there is a possibility of future rearrangement of partitions. The latter condition is very likely to occur in buildings of the types to which

***Table* 9.2 Weight of concrete in ribbed floors with steel pan fillers**

Depth of joist below slab, in.	Thickness of slab, in.	Average weight of floor, psf
6	2	42
	$2\frac{1}{2}$	48
8	2	48
	$2\frac{1}{2}$	54
10	2	55
	$2\frac{1}{2}$	61
12	2	61
	$2\frac{1}{2}$	67
	3	73
14	2	69
	$2\frac{1}{2}$	75
	3	81

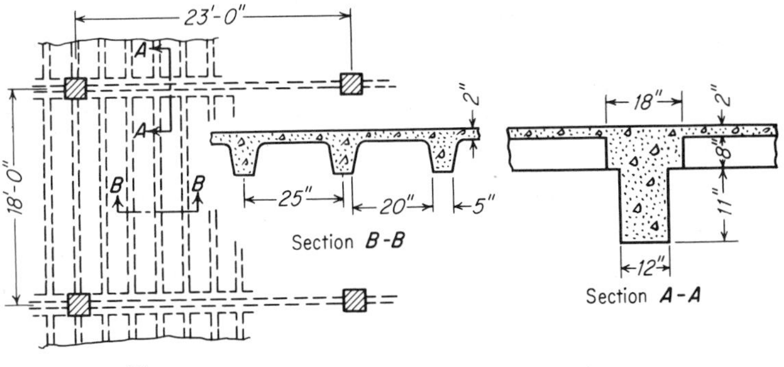

Fig. **9.19** Details of ribbed floor with removable steel pans.

ribbed-floor construction is adapted. When definitely located partitions are parallel with the joists, a joist thicker than the normal 5 in. is usually placed under these partitions, or, if the partition is located between two joists, both these joints are made thicker than the others, and the slab thickness between them is increased. The increased slab thickness is obtained by using shallower pans in the one row, or by lowering the pans in that row. When definitely located partitions are perpendicular to the joists, the partition weight is considered as a concentrated load in designing the joists. Transverse bridging ribs 4 in. wide and the same depth as the joists are commonly used at the center of span of less than 24 ft and at the third points of a longer span to stiffen the joists and distribute concentrated floor loads to adjacent joists.

9.28 Data for Design A typical interior panel of a hotel floor is to be built as a ribbed floor, using removable steel pan forms. The joists are to be supported at the ends on concrete girders, as shown in Fig. 9.19. The span of the girders is 23 ft 0 in., and the distance center to center of girders is 18 ft 0 in. The live load is 50 psf, and allowances for dead loads other than the weight of the concrete are to be made as follows: partitions, 10 psf; plastered ceiling, 10 psf; wood floor, with sleepers in cinder-concrete fill, 15 psf. A 4000-psi concrete is to be used in the floor, with bars for which f_y = 60,000 psi. It is required to design the panel.

9.29 Design of Joists: ***Computation of moments and shears*** The joists are designed as regular continuous T beams, with a flange width equal to the distance center to center of joists. In order to compute the weight of the floor, the depth of the joists below the slab and the thickness of the slab must be assumed. A combination of 8-in. joists and 2-in. slab will be tried. The weight of the concrete per square foot of floor is 48 psf, and the total ultimate dead load is $(20 + 10 + 15 + 48)1.5 = 140$ psf. The ultimate live load is $50 \times 1.8 = 90$ psf, and the total ultimate load is $140 + 90 = 230$ psf. With 5-in. joists spaced 25 in. on centers, each joist supports $^{25}/_{12} = 2.08$ ft² of floor per foot of joist, and the total ultimate load on each joist is

$$230 \times 2.08 = 478 \text{ plf}$$

The panel is fully continuous, and the effective span for moment is equal to the clear distance between the stems of the girders. If the width of the girder stems is assumed as 12 in., the joist span is 17 ft. The maximum negative moment at the face of the support is

$$M = \tfrac{1}{11} \times 478 \times 17^2 \times 12 = 151{,}000 \text{ in.-lb}$$

and the maximum positive moment at the center of the span is

$$M = \tfrac{1}{16} \times 478 \times 17^2 \times 12 = 104{,}000 \text{ in.-lb}$$

The shear at the face of the supporting girder is

$$V_u = 478 \times \tfrac{17}{2} = 4070 \text{ lb}$$

Design for shear It is rather difficult to place stirrups in narrow joists, such as are used in this form of construction; hence the shearing unit stress should be kept below the value permitted on the concrete web. Taking this as $v_c = 2\phi\sqrt{f'_c}$, one obtains

$$v_u = 2 \times 0.85\sqrt{4000} = 108 \text{ psi}$$

The effective shearing width of a joist is taken as the width at the bottom of the joist; the increased section due to the side slope of the pans is neglected. If necessary, tapered pans can be used at the ends of each row to increase the shearing area, or deeper joists can be used to serve the same purpose. At the critical section for shear, a distance d (estimated as 8 in.) from the face of supports, the ultimate shear is

$$V_u = 4070 - 478 \times \tfrac{8}{12} = 3750 \text{ lb}$$

The minimum web area is

$$b'd = \frac{V_u}{v_u} = \frac{3750}{108} = 34.7 \text{ in.}^2$$

If straight end pans are used, with $b' = 5$ in., the minimum effective depth is 6.95 in. With 8-in. joists under a 2-in. slab, the effective depth is $10 - 1\tfrac{1}{8} = 8.87$ in. This will be satisfactory and will allow for a minimum clear insulation under the bars of about $\tfrac{3}{4}$ in.

If the problem of deciding whether to use tapered end pans or deeper pans throughout arises, it should be remembered that the steel area required decreases with an increase in the depth of the joists, and both the cost of the steel and the cost of the concrete should be considered. The cost of the forms can be omitted from the comparison, because this cost does not vary materially.

Computation of steel area At the face of the girder stem, the negative joist moment is 151,000 in.-lb. Then

$$\frac{M_u}{\phi b'd^2} = \frac{151{,}000}{0.9 \times 5 \times 8.87^2} = 427$$

From Graph 1, Appendix B, $p = 0.0076$. Then

$$A_s = pb'd = 0.0076 \times 5 \times 8.87 = 0.33 \text{ in.}^2$$

At midspan, assuming a stress-block depth equal to the slab thickness,

$$\text{Trial } A_s = \frac{M_u}{\phi f_y(d - t/2)} = \frac{104{,}000}{0.9 \times 60{,}000 \times 7.87} = 0.25 \text{ in.}^2$$

The corresponding stress-block depth is

$$a = A_s f_y / 0.85 f'_c b = 0.25 \times 60/(0.85 \times 4 \times 25) = 0.177 \text{ in.}$$

The revised lever arm is 8.78 in., and

$$A_s = 0.25 \times 7.87/8.78 = 0.22 \text{ in.}^2$$

Arrangement of reinforcement As shown in Fig. 9.20, two No. 3 bars ($A_s = 0.22$ in.²) will be used for positive-moment reinforcement. Bending up one bar in each span and adding one No. 3 straight top bar will provide sufficient steel ($A_s = 0.33$ in.²) to meet the negative-moment requirements. In accordance with Graph 11, Appendix B, the positive steel will be bent up at 3.50 ft from the support face and, together with the added straight bars, will be continued a distance of 5.14 ft beyond the

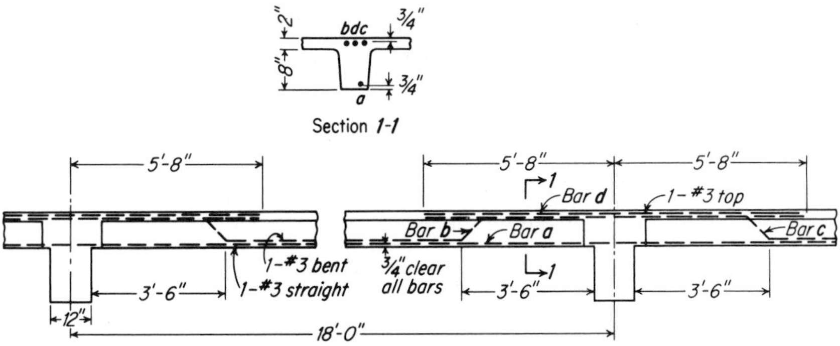

Fig. 9.20 Joist details.

far face of the supports. The remaining positive steel will be carried 6 in. into the face of supports. From Table 8, Appendix B, it is evident that adequate development length is provided for both top and bottom steel, so that it is unnecessary to check flexural bond stresses.

9.30 Design of Girder: ***Computation of loads*** The loads which are brought to the girder from the joists are theoretically concentrated at the points at which the joists frame into the girder. They are spaced so closely, however, that they may be considered as uniformly distributed throughout the length of the girder without materially affecting the maximum moment in the girder. Each pair of adjoining joists, one on either side of the girder, transmits a load to the girder equal to twice the end shear of one joist, or $2 \times 4070 = 8140$ lb. Since the joists are 25 in., or 2.08 ft, on centers, the uniform load per foot of girder is $8140/2.08 = 3910$ plf. To this must be added the weight of the girder and the floor and ceiling loads directly over and under the girder. With total girder depth assumed to be 22 in., and width 12 in., the weight of the girder is

$$12 \times 22 \times {}^{150}\!/_{144} = 276 \text{ plf}$$

The weights of partitions, ceiling, and fill over the 12-in. girder width add 45 plf. The ultimate dead load is then

$$(276 + 45)1.5 = 480 \text{ plf}$$

The additional ultimate live load directly over the girder is

$$50 \times 1.8 = 90 \text{ plf}$$

and the total ultimate load is

$$3910 + 480 + 90 = 4480 \text{ plf}$$

Computation of moment and shear The girder is continuous at both ends, so that with 18-in. columns the effective span is

$$23 - {}^{18}\!/_{12} = 21.5 \text{ ft}$$

The maximum negative moment at the face of the support is

$$M = {}^{1}\!/_{11} \times 4480 \times 21.5^2 \times 12 = 2{,}260{,}000 \text{ in.-lb}$$

and the maximum positive moment at the center of the span is

$$M = {}^{1}\!/_{16} \times 4480 \times 21.5^2 \times 12 = 1{,}560{,}000 \text{ in.-lb}$$

The maximum shear is

$$V = 4480 \times 21.5/2 = 48{,}200 \text{ lb}$$

Design at supports A maximum steel ratio of

$$0.18\frac{f'_c}{f_y} = 0.18 \times \frac{4}{60} = 0.012$$

will be adopted. Then, from Graph 1,

$$\frac{M_u}{\phi bd^2} = 643$$

from which

$$bd^2 = \frac{M_u}{643\phi} = \frac{2{,}260{,}000}{643 \times 0.9} = 3900 \text{ in.}^3$$

For a girder width of 12 in., the required effective depth is 18.0 in. An effective depth of 18.5 in. will be used, providing an overall girder depth of 21 in. No revision in the assumed dead load is required. The total tension steel required is

$$A_s = 0.012 \times 12 \times 18.0 = 2.59 \text{ in.}^2$$

Design at center The girder is a T beam, but because of the comparatively thick flange, the neutral axis will probably be in the flange, and the girder can be designed for moment as a rectangular beam with a width equal to the width of the flange. Accordingly,

$$\frac{M_u}{\phi bd^2} = \frac{1{,}560{,}000}{0.9 \times 18 \times 18.5^2} = 281$$

From Graph 1, $p = 0.0048$, and

$$A_s = 0.0048 \times 18 \times 18.5 = 1.60 \text{ in.}^2$$

Checking the location of the neutral axis,

$$a = \frac{1.60 \times 60}{0.85 \times 4 \times 18} = 1.57 \text{ in.}$$

well within the depth of the flange as assumed.

The positive-moment requirement of 1.60 in.^{2} will be provided using two No. 6 and one No. 8 bars ($A_s = 1.67$ in.^{2}). The single No. 8 bar will be bent up 4.00 ft from the face of the column, in accordance with Graph 11. At the support, the required area of 2.59 in.^{2} will be provided by adding a single No. 10 straight bar to the two bent-up No. 8 bars ($A_s = 2.84$ in.^{2}). The bent-up bars and the straight bar will be continued 6.75 ft beyond the face of the column.

Adequate development length is provided for all top and bottom bars, so that it is unnecessary to check flexural bond stresses in the girder.

Design of web reinforcement Resistance to diagonal tension will be provided using vertical stirrups, in neglect of the contribution of the bent No. 8 bars. The computations are the same as for any uniformly loaded, continuous beam; a typical example is given in Art. 9.25.

9.31 Detail Drawings Each floor plan must show the number of ribs, or joists, in each panel, the number of rows of pans, and the arrangement of the joists. All identical joists are given the same mark, which consists of a numeral indicating the floor, the letter R or J indicating ribs or joists, and a final numeral which is the mark of identity. Thus, $1R22$ would designate first-floor joist No. 22. The outlines of the rows of pans are shown by dotted lines. Where there are several adjacent identical rows forming identical joists, only the end rows and joists in the group are shown, and the numbers of rows and joists are placed on dimension lines with arrows pointing to the boundaries of the group. The depth of the stems of the joists and the thickness of the slab are also given on the floor plan. Temperature steel, usually about No. 2 bars at 10 in. on centers, is placed in the slab at right angles to the joists; this is detailed on the plan in the usual manner. Quite often welded wire mesh is used to reinforce the slab.

A detail floor plan for the typical interior panel which was designed in the preceding articles is shown in Fig. 9.21. The girders are marked on the plan in the usual manner. At least one typical cross section through the joists and through the girders should be given on the drawing. The joists $1R16$ between the columns of Fig. 9.21 are 7 in. wide at the bottom instead of 5 in., in order to fill up the panel. It is usually desirable to have a joist such as $1R16$ between the columns, in order to stiffen the columns in this direction. In tall structures subject to wind pressure, a deeper beam would be used in place of the joist $1R16$ to add to the rigidity of the entire structure.

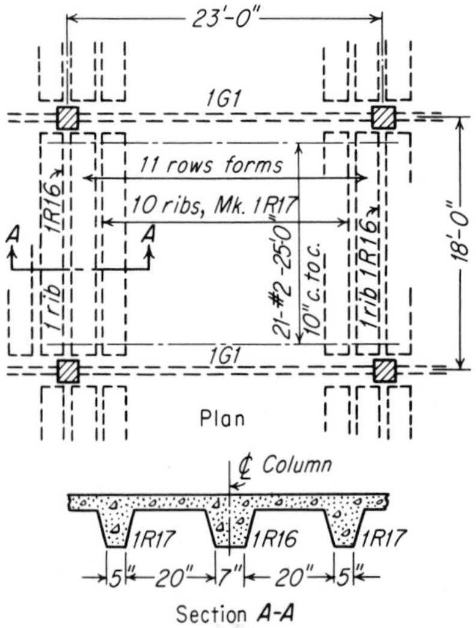

Fig. 9.21 Method of detailing ribbed floors with concrete girders.

DESIGN OF A FLAT-SLAB BUILDING

9.32 Data and Specifications The method of design of flat-slab floors and other details involved in a reinforced-concrete building are illustrated in the following articles, which contain the complete design of a building 66 by 105 ft in plan, consisting of two upper stories and a basement. The height of the upper stories, floor to floor, is 12 ft 0 in., and that of the basement is 10 ft 0 in. The floor plan is shown in Fig. 9.33. The live load to be supported by the floors is 200 psf, and by the roof 40 psf. An additional load of 40 psf is to be considered in the dead weight of the roof, to provide for a cinder-concrete fill and for the roof covering. Adequate drainage will be provided by inclining the exterior slabs in the short direction of the building and by varying the thickness of the surfacing over the middle panel. A 3000-psi concrete will be used for all the construction. The ACI Code will be used in the design of the floor and roof slabs, beams, columns, and footings. Steel of 40,000-psi strength will be used, at a working stress of 20,000 psi.

9.33 Design of Interior Floor Panel: ***Slab*** The thickness of the slab exclusive of the drop panel is

$$t_2 = 0.024 \times 22\left(1 - \frac{2 \times 4.5}{3 \times 22}\right)\sqrt{\frac{300}{3000/2000}} + 1 = 7.33 \text{ in.}$$

A thickness of 8 in. will be tentatively adopted.

Capital Metal cap forms will be used, standard diameters being multiples of 6 in. A diameter c of cap of approximately 0.20 times the average span of the panel will be used.

$$0.20 \times 21.5 \times 12 = 51.6 \text{ in.}$$

Use 4 ft 6 in.

Drop The length of each side of the drop panel will be made approximately equal to 0.33 times the longer span.

$$0.33 \times 22 \times 12 = 87 \text{ in.}$$
$$0.33 \times 21 \times 12 = 83 \text{ in.}$$

A drop 7 ft 6 in. by 7 ft 6 in. will be used.

The thickness of the drop panel will be made 4 in., which is the maximum thickness that can be used in determining the required amount of negative reinforcement in the column strip.

Shearing stresses Article 2102(c)2, Appendix A. The unit shearing stress ($v = V/b_0d$) on a vertical section a distance $d/2$ from the edge of the capital, and concentric with it, shall not exceed $2\sqrt{f'_c} = 110$ psi.

$$\frac{d}{2} = \frac{10.5}{2} = 5.25 \text{ in.} = 0.437 \text{ ft}$$

$$4.50 + 2 \times 0.437 = 5.38 \text{ ft}$$

The total load on the panel is

$$300 \times 21 \times 22 + \tfrac{4}{12} \times 150(7.50)^2 = 141{,}300 \text{ lb}$$

At the section described above,

$$V = 141{,}300 - 350 \frac{\pi \times 5.38^2}{4} = 133{,}400$$

$$v = \frac{133{,}400}{(\pi \times 5.38 \times 12) \times 10.5} = 62 \text{ psi} < 110 \text{ psi}$$

The unit shearing stress on a vertical section a distance $d/2$ from the edge of the drop panel and parallel with it shall not exceed 110 psi.

$$\frac{d}{2} = \frac{6.5}{2} = 3.25 \text{ in.} = 0.27 \text{ ft}$$

$$750 + 2 \times 0.27 = 8.04 \text{ ft}$$

$$V = (21 \times 22 - 8.04^2)300 = 119{,}000 \text{ lb}$$

$$v = \frac{119{,}000}{(4 \times 8.04 \times 12) \times 6.5} = 48 \text{ psi} < 110 \text{ psi}$$

In checking the unit shearing stress in the slab acting as a wide beam [ACI Code, Art. 1207(*a*)1], the presence of the drop panel over a portion of the width is neglected. The load per foot of slab in the 22-ft span direction is $300 \times 21 = 6300$ plf, and the column reaction is $6300 \times 22/2 = 69{,}300$ lb. At a distance d past the column capital (2.80 ft from the column center line) the shear is

$$69{,}300 - 6300 \times 2.80 = 51{,}600 \text{ lb}$$

and the unit shear is

$$v = \frac{51{,}600}{21 \times 12 \times 6.5} = 32 \text{ psi}$$

The allowable shear stress at this section [Art. 1201(*c*)] is

$$1.1\sqrt{3000} = 61 \text{ psi} > 32 \text{ psi}$$

The assumed dimensions of the capital and drop need no revision.

Bending moments Table 2104(*f*). Since the panel is nearly square, moments and steel areas will be computed for the long direction, and the same steel will be placed in the short direction.

$W = 141{,}300$ lb $\quad l = 22.0$ ft $\quad c = 4.5$ ft

$$M_0 = 0.09WLF\left(1 - \frac{2c}{3L}\right)^2 = 0.09 \times 141{,}300 \times 22.0\left(1 - \frac{2 \times 4.5}{3 \times 22.0}\right)^2$$
$$= 209{,}000 \text{ ft-lb} = 2{,}510{,}000 \text{ in.-lb}$$

Column strip, positive moment: $M = +0.20 \times 2{,}510{,}000 = +502{,}000$ in.-lb

Column strip, negative moment: $M = -0.50 \times 2{,}510{,}000 = -1{,}256{,}000$ in.-lb

Middle strip, positive moment: $M = +0.15 \times 2{,}510{,}000 = +376{,}000$ in.-lb

Middle strip, negative moment: $M = -0.15 \times 2{,}510{,}000 = -376{,}000$ in.-lb

Steel areas In computing steel areas required for those moment sections in which bars are placed in two directions (i.e., the positive-moment section of the middle strip and the negative-moment section of the column strip), the governing row will be assumed as that row farthest from the tension face of the slab. This removes all restrictions as to the order of placing the steel in the two directions. Values of j are obtained from Table 5, Appendix B: $f_s = 20{,}000$; $f_c = 0.45 \times 3000 = 1350$ psi; $n = 9$.

COLUMN-STRIP, POSITIVE-MOMENT SECTION. For No. 5 bars and ¾-in. clear insulation, $d = 8 - 1\frac{1}{16} = 6\frac{15}{16}$ in.

$$A_s = \frac{502{,}000}{20{,}000 \times 0.874 \times 6.93} = 4.16 \text{ in.}^2$$

Fourteen No. 5 bars furnish 4.30 in.²

COLUMN-STRIP, NEGATIVE-MOMENT SECTION. For No. 5 bars and ¾-in. clear insulation, $d = 12 - 1\frac{11}{16} = 10\frac{5}{16}$ in.

$$A_s = \frac{1{,}256{,}000}{20{,}000 \times 0.874 \times 10.31} = 6.96 \text{ in.}^2$$

Twenty-three No. 5 bars furnish 7.06 in.²

Nine bars, or slightly less than two-thirds of the total required for positive moment, will be bent up to provide resistance to negative moment. Hence at each negative-moment section a total of 18 bars is furnished from the two adjacent positive areas. Five straight bars in the top of the slab over the column head are sufficient to complete the steel area required at the negative-moment section (see Fig. 9.22).

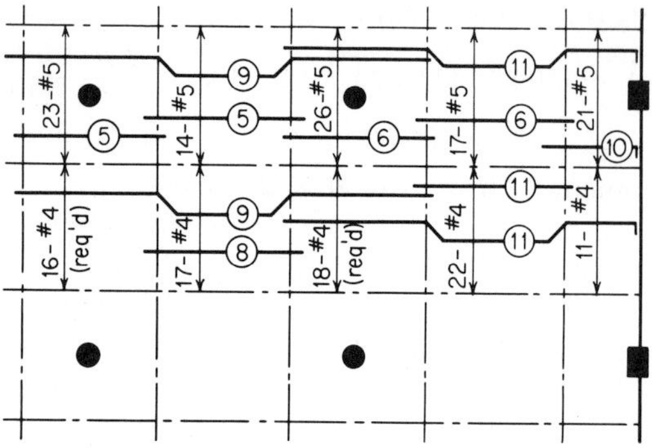

Fig. **9.22** Arrangement of reinforcement in floor slab.

MIDDLE-STRIP, POSITIVE-MOMENT SECTION. For No. 4 bars and ¾-in. clear insulation, $d = 8 - 1\frac{1}{2} = 6\frac{1}{2}$ in.

$$A_s = \frac{376{,}000}{20{,}000 \times 0.874 \times 6.5} = 3.31 \text{ in.}^2$$

Seventeen No. 4 bars furnish 3.33 in.²

MIDDLE-STRIP, NEGATIVE-MOMENT SECTION. For No. 4 bars and ¾-in. clear insulation, $d = 8 - 1 = 7$ in.

$$A_s = \frac{376{,}000}{20{,}000 \times 0.874 \times 7} = 3.08 \text{ in.}^2$$

According to Table 2104(*g*)2, Appendix A, not less than five-tenths of the steel required in the positive-moment section of the middle strip should be bent up at both ends so as to reinforce the two adjacent negative-moment sections. Bending 9 of the 17 bars required in the positive-moment section provides a total of 18 bars in each negative-moment section, which is more than ample in the present case.

Fiber stress in the concrete The critical section is in the negative-moment portion of the column strip. According to Art. 2102(*c*)1, Appendix A, the effective width of the column head section, for compression, shall be taken as three-fourths the width of the dropped panel, 67.5 in.

$$p = \frac{7.06}{67.5 \times 10.31} = 0.0102$$

From Table 5, Appendix B, $k = 0.347$ and $j = 0.885$.

$$f_c = \frac{2 \times 1{,}256{,}000}{0.347 \times 0.885 \times 67.5 \times 10.31^2} = 1140 \text{ psi}$$

The allowable stress is $0.45 \times 3000 = 1350$ psi.

9.34 Design of Exterior Floor Panel From Table 2104(*f*), Appendix A, the following percentages of the interior panel moments are to be used in the exterior panel:

Column-strip negative moment at wall or spandrel: 88
Column-strip negative moment at first row of columns: 112
Column-strip positive moment: 120
Middle-strip negative moment at wall or spandrel: 67
Middle-strip negative moment at first row of columns: 113
Middle-strip positive moment: 133

Hence, the steel areas required at the various sections in the exterior panel (for bands perpendicular to the wall) may be obtained by multiplying the corresponding interior-panel required areas by the above percentages, as follows:

Middle-strip, positive-moment section:

$A_s = 1.33 \times 3.31 = 4.40$ in.^{2}
Twenty-two No. 4 bars furnish 4.32 in.^{2}

Middle-strip, negative-moment section at wall:

$A_s = 0.67 \times 3.08 = 2.06$ in.^{2}
Eleven No. 4 bars furnish 2.16 in.^{2}

Middle-strip, negative-moment section at first interior support:

$A_s = 1.13 \times 3.08 = 3.48$ in.^{2}
Eighteen No. 4 bars furnish 3.54 in.^{2}

Column-strip, positive-moment section:

$A_s = 1.20 \times 4.16 = 5.00$ in.^{2}
Seventeen No. 5 bars furnish 5.22 in.^{2}

Column-strip, negative-moment section at wall:

$A_s = 0.88 \times 6.96 = 6.14$ in.^{2}
Twenty-one No. 5 bars furnish 6.45 in.^{2}

Column-strip, negative-moment section at first interior support:

$A_s = 1.13 \times 6.96 = 7.86$ in.^{2}
Twenty-six No. 5 bars furnish 7.98 in.^{2}

9.35 Arrangement of Reinforcement The proposed method of placing and bending the steel so as to furnish the necessary areas at the various sections in both the interior and exterior panels is shown diagrammatically in Fig. 9.22. The points at which the bars are bent are obtained from Fig. 2104(*g*), Appendix A. The minimum spacing is governed by the necessity of allowing space for the concrete to be deposited conveniently and effectively. A minimum spacing of about 3 in. center to center of bars should be maintained if possible. Bars less than ½ in. in diameter are difficult to handle because of their lack of stiffness, and bars greater than ¾ in. in diameter cannot be bent in place.

A complete engineering drawing for the floor slab is shown in Fig. 9.33. This drawing follows the recommendations in the American Concrete Institute "Manual of Standard Practice for Detailing Reinforced Concrete Structures" (ACI 315-57).

9.36 Design of Roof Slab The design of the interior and exterior panels of the roof slab is carried out in a manner similar to that used in the design of the floor slab. The total load on the roof includes the live load (40 psf), the weight of the roofing material (40 psf), and the dead weight of the slab itself. The thickness of slab beyond the drop is 6½ in., and the total thickness through the dropped panel is 10 in. The diameter of the capital is 4 ft 6 in., and the drop is 7 ft 6 in. square in plan.

The number of ½-in. round bars required in the various sections of the slab and the proposed method of placing and bending the bars so as to furnish the required steel areas at all sections are shown diagrammatically in Fig. 9.23. It has been assumed, for simplicity, that the stairway and elevator shaft openings do not extend through the roof.

9.37 Design of Interior Columns The interior columns are to be made of 3000 psi concrete, with reinforcement having $f_y = 40{,}000$ psi. They are to be round, with spirals, and designed in accordance with the ACI specifications. The fundamental principles involved in the design are explained in Chap. 5. In flat-slab construction the columns are an important factor in adding to the rigidity of the slab, and many codes specify a

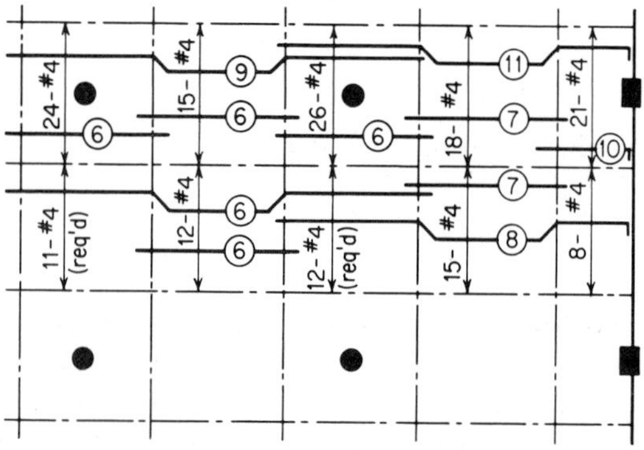

Fig. **9.23** Arrangement of reinforcement in roof slab.

***Table* 9.3 Interior columns: design for direct load only**

Column	Load from	Amount of load, kips	Diameter and area of column	Vertical bars	Spirals (Table 10, Appendix B)	Load carried by concrete, kips	Load carried by steel, kips	Total load, kips
Top	Roof Column Capital Total	76 2 2 80	16 in. 201 in.^{2}	5-#6 2.21 in.^{2} $p_g = 0.0110$	No. 3-1¾ in.	136	35	171
Intermediate	Floor Column Capital Total	141 3 2 226	20 in. 314 in.^{2}	8-#6 3.53 in.^{2} $p_g = 0.0112$	No. 3-1¾ in.	212	56	264
Basement	Floor Column Capital Total	141 4 2 373	24 in. 452 in.^{2}	8-#7 4.81 in.^{2} $p_g = 0.0106$	No. 3-2 in.	305	76	381

minimum column size greater than the usual minimum for beam-and-girder floors. For columns supporting heavily loaded floors, a minimum overall dimension of one-fifteenth the average span of the panel is considered satisfactory. Roof columns may be somewhat lighter; one-eighteenth the average span is specified by some codes as a minimum diameter. In the present case $\frac{1}{15} \times 21.5 \times 12 = 17.2$, or 18 in., will be taken as the minimum size for floor columns, and 16 in. for columns supporting the roof.

According to the ACI Code, values of p_g may vary from 0.01 to 0.08 for columns with spirals, but values greater than 0.02 to 0.025 are normally inadvisable because of the crowding of the steel which occurs just above the floor line, where the bars are spliced by lapping. In general, greater overall economy is obtained by the use of the smaller values of p_g. Steel ratios approaching the maximum may be necessary, however, in heavily loaded columns, in order to keep the size of the columns within reasonable limits. In some cases architectural limitations may require a smaller column with the resulting greater steel ratio. Metal column forms, which are generally used for round columns, are available in multiples of 2 in., and column sizes should be selected accordingly.

Table 9.3 gives a summary of the loads (to the nearest thousand pounds) which are carried in each tier of columns. The excess strength of the top column cannot be avoided, since minimum-size columns and the minimum percentage of reinforcement have been used. The excess strength of the intermediate column is required to provide for bending stresses, as shown by the investigation in Art. 9.48.

9.38 Investigation for Bending Stresses Bending stresses due to unequally loaded panels are not apt to affect the design of the interior columns, except possibly in the upper tiers. This is because the bending is usually caused by the live load only, and thus the maximum unit stress due to bending is in most cases less than the allowable *increase* in fiber stress as compared with the stress permitted when no bending is considered.

The method of investigation of bending of columns is explained in Chap. 5. With unequally loaded panels the amount of bending moment transferred to the columns depends upon the relative stiffness of the slab on both sides of the column and the columns themselves. The ACI Code [Art. 2104(*b*)2, Appendix A] states that a bending moment[1] of $\frac{1}{40}W_LL$ shall be distributed without further reduction between the columns above and below the floor or roof line under consideration in direct proportion to their stiffness, where W_L is the total live load on one panel, and L the span of the panel.

The maximum combined stress occurs only when the panels at the floor line under consideration are unequally loaded, with a full live load on alternate panels and no load on the remaining panels. A full live load is assumed on all floors above the one considered. In the investigation for the combined stress at the top of any column, the total direct load is equal to the load in Table 9.3 (the full load) minus the weight of the column and minus one-half a live panel load.

Table 9.4 contains a summary of computations which are necessary to determine the adequacy of the interior columns.
For the roof,

$$M = \frac{1}{40} \times 40 \times 21 \times 22 \times 21.5 \times 12 = 119{,}000 \text{ in.-lb}$$

[1] The recommended moment of $\frac{1}{40}W_LL$ is based on the following analysis: Due to live load only, the negative moment in a column strip, for two-way slabs with drops and with $c = 0.225L$ (a representative value), is $0.0325W_LL$. This unbalanced moment (assuming live load to be placed only on one side of the columns under consideration) is resisted by the slab on the unloaded side and the columns above and below the floor, more or less in direct proportion to the stiffness factors (I/h) of these members. Assuming that the stiffness factor of the slab is one-third the sum of the stiffness factors of the two columns, the moment to be resisted by the two columns is

$$\frac{3}{4} \times 0.0325W_LL = 0.0244W_LL$$

or approximately $\frac{1}{40}W_LL$.

In the investigation of the exterior columns (see Art. 9.49), since there is no slab beyond the wall the entire negative moment in the column strip at the wall is resisted by the two columns. For $c = 0.225L$ this moment is $0.0325WL$, or approximately $\frac{1}{30}WL$. Here the full load (dead plus live) on the panel is used, because both the dead and live loads are unbalanced loads. The total moment of $\frac{1}{30}WL$ is distributed to the columns in direct proportion to the stiffness factors.

***Table* 9.4 Interior columns: bending and axial load**

Column	Point	A_g, in.²	N, kips	M, in.-kips	$\frac{e}{t}$	I_t, in.⁴	F_a, psi	F_b, psi	f_a, psi	f_b, psi	$\frac{f_a}{F_a}$	$\frac{f_b}{F_b}$	Cols. 12 + 13
(1)	(2)	(3)	(4)	(5)	(6)	(7)	(8)	(9)	(10)	(11)	(12)	(13)	(14)
Top	Top	201	69	119	0.108	3787	1200	1350	343	252	0.286	0.187	0.473
	Bottom		80	173	0.135				398	366	0.332	0.270	0.602
Intermediate	Top	314	177	423	0.119	9534	1200	1350	564	449	0.366	0.332	0.689
	Bottom		226	167	0.037				720	175	0.600	0.130	0.730
Basement	Top	452	323	429	0.055	19,970	1120	1350		258	0.595	0.191	0.786
	Bottom		373	0					825	0	0.686	0	0.686

For the other floors,

$$M = \tfrac{1}{40} \times 200 \times 21 \times 22 \times 21.5 \times 12 = 596{,}000 \text{ in.-lb}$$

In the present case, the investigation for bending and direct stress shows that no revision of the original columns, as designed for direct load only, is necessary. It should be noted, however, that in the original selection, some excess strength was intentionally provided in the intermediate column. The amount there provided is shown to be sufficient for the bending. The design as shown in Tables 9.3 and 9.4 is therefore satisfactory.

9.39 Design of Exterior Columns The exterior columns are to be rectangular in section. In addition to the load from the floors, the exterior columns must support the weight of the walls enclosing the story next above. In estimating the weight of the enclosure walls, the wall beams and brick spandrels underneath the windows are assumed 12 in. thick, the spandrel 2 ft 6 in. deep, and the wall beam 2 ft 0 in. deep. The brick parapet wall at the roof is assumed 12 in. thick and 3 ft 6 in. deep. The weight of windows, including sash, is taken as 8 psf. The weight of the brick masonry is assumed as 120 pcf. The general arrangement of a typical wall panel is shown in Fig. 9.24.

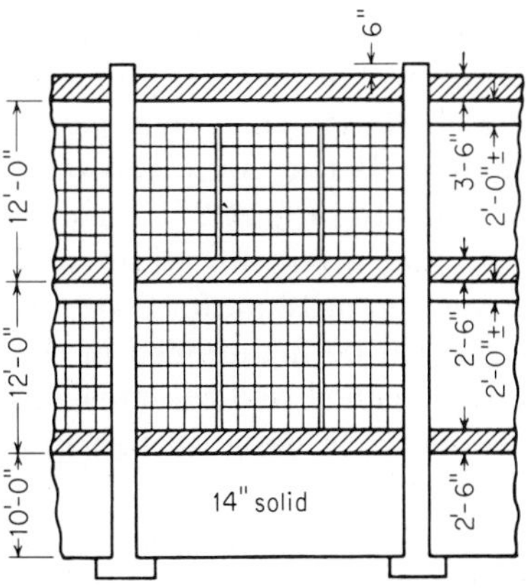

***Fig.* 9.24**

Bending stresses should always be considered in the design of the exterior columns, especially in the upper tiers. The direct loads on these columns are comparatively small, and the bending moments due to unsymmetrical loading are large since live load and dead load act together in causing these moments. According to Code, the wall columns in flat-slab construction shall be designed to resist a bending moment from the slab of $\frac{1}{30}WL$, where W is the total load (dead and live) on one panel, and L is the average span of the panel. In the present design, at the first- and second-floor levels, $W = 141$ kips, $L = 21.5$ ft, and

$$M = \tfrac{1}{30}(141 \times 21.5 \times 12) = 1215 \text{ in.-kips}$$

At the roof level $W = 76$ kips, and

$$M = \tfrac{1}{30}(76 \times 21.5 \times 12) = 654 \text{ in.-kips}$$

Countermoments due to the weight of the structure that projects beyond the column center lines and countermoments due to the eccentricity of one column with respect to the column beneath may be deducted from the value of $\frac{1}{30}WL$, and the resulting reduced moment is then divided between the two columns immediately above and below a given floor line in proportion to the stiffness factors (I/h) of these columns.

Inasmuch as bending stresses constitute a large proportion of the total stresses in exterior columns, particularly in the upper tiers, it is of no use to design the columns first for direct load only. The general procedure is to assume column sizes and reinforcement, compute the combined extreme fiber stresses, including bending, and then revise the assumed sizes if necessary. Where the concrete is to be left exposed on the exterior face, the dimension along that face should be the same for all tiers of columns and of sufficient amount to give a satisfactory architectural appearance to the face. If this dimension is too small, the building will appear to be unstable or insecure. If it is too large, the building will appear squatty, and the design will be needlessly uneconomical. An elevation drawn to scale, as in Fig. 9.30, will show whether or not an assumed face dimension is satisfactory. Better architectural appearance is obtained by allowing the columns to project 2 in. or more beyond the face of the wall. In the present case, a column width of 22 in. is selected. The minimum required dimension of 18 in. for floor columns and 16 in. for roof columns (see Art. 9.37) will be maintained in the direction perpendicular to the wall. For axially loaded tied columns, steel ratios may vary from 0.01 to 0.04. For tied columns designed to withstand combined bending and axial stress, the steel ratio may vary from 0.01 to 0.08, provided that the amount of steel spliced by lapping shall not exceed a steel ratio of 0.04 in any 3-ft length of column. As stated before, the smaller ratios of reinforcement usually result in more economical designs. Where it is desirable to keep

***Table* 9.5 Exterior columns: computation of loads**

Column	Load from	Amount of load, kips	Size of column, in.	Vertical steel	Load by concrete, kips	Load by steel, kips	Total load, kips
Top	Roof Parapet* Column† Total	38 14 6 58	22 × 16 A_g = 352 in.²	6-#7 A_s = 3.61 in.² p_g = 0.01025	190	46	236
Intermediate	Floor Wall Column Total	71 12 5 146	22 × 18 A_g = 396 in.²	6-#8 A_s = 4.71 in.² p_g = 0.0119	214	61	275
Basement	Floor Wall Column Total	71 12 4 233	22 × 20 A_g = 440 in.²	6-#8 A_s = 4.71 in.² p_g = 0.0107	238	60	298

* This value includes the weight of the stem of the wall beam.

† This value includes the weight of the column above the roof (see Fig. 9.24). The weight of the bracket in each tier has been neglected, since it varies only from about 300 lb for the basement column to 500 lb for the top column.

the column sizes small, larger percentages may be used. The column dimensions and steel areas ultimately selected for trial are shown in Table 9.5.

The countermoment at the top of the intermediate column is equal to the product of the wall load and the distance from the center of the wall beam to the center of the column, plus the moment due to column eccentricity, which is equal to the load on the top column multiplied by the distance between column centers. In the design under consideration, the wall beams are set back 2 in. from the faces of the columns, as shown in Fig. 9.25. At the top of the basement columns the countermoment due to column eccentricity is equal to the load on the intermediate column multiplied by the distance between the column centers, which is $\frac{1}{2}(20 - 18) = 1$ in. In this design the countermoment at the second-floor level is 70,000 in.-lb, and that at the first-floor level is 170,000 in.-lb.

Fig. **9.25**

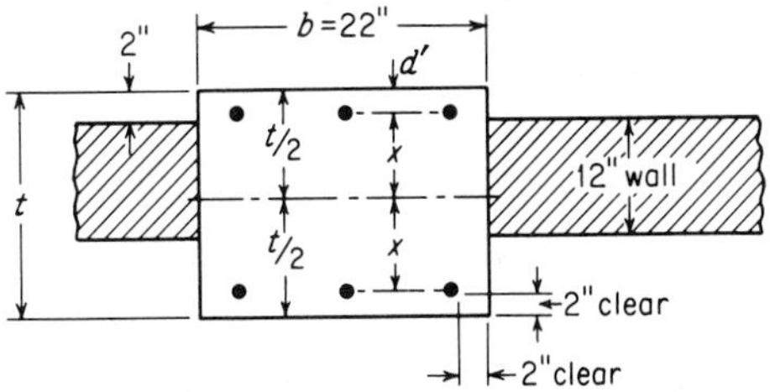

Table 9.6 **Exterior columns: bending and axial load**

Column	Point	A_g, in.²	N, kips	M, in.-kips	$\frac{e}{t}$	I_t, in.⁴	F_a, psi	F_b, psi	f_a, psi	f_b, psi	$\frac{f_a}{F_a}$	$\frac{f_b}{F_b}$	Cols. 12 + 13
(1)	(2)	(3)	(4)	(5)	(6)	(7)	(8)	(9)	(10)	(11)	(12)	(13)	(14)
	Top		54	656	0.759				*				
Top		352				9,342	1185	1350	*				
	Bottom		58	472†	0.491				*				
	Top		141	673	0.270				*				
Intermediate		396				14,052	1210	1350					
	Bottom		146	386	0.148				369	247	0.274	0.183	0.457
	Top		229	659	0.143				520	342	0.436	0.254	0.690
Basement		440				19,164	1190	1350					
	Bottom		233	0	0				530	0	0.445	0	0.445

* Tension governs. Analysis follows the methods of Chap. 5 and indicates the trial column sizes to be satisfactory.

† (Moment from slab) − (countermoment) = 1215 − 70 = 1145 in.-kips

$$\frac{66.4}{(66.4 + 94.6)} \times 1145 = 472 \text{ in.-kips}$$

Tables 9.5 and 9.6 contain a summary of the design. The complete column details are shown in Fig. 9.26.

9.40 Design of Interior-column Footings The interior-column footings are to be square and reinforced in two directions. The allowable soil pressure is 4000 psf.

The interior basement column is a 24-in. round column, with a total load of 373,000 lb. In the design of the footing the round column must be replaced with a square column of the same area. The equivalent square has a side dimension equal to

$$\sqrt{452} = 21.3 \text{ in.} = 1.78 \text{ ft}$$

The bearing area required is

$$(373{,}000 + 28{,}000)/4000 = 100 \text{ ft}^2$$

A base 10 ft 0 in. square is selected. The net upward pressure is

$$\frac{373{,}000}{100} = 3730 \text{ psf}$$

$$M = 3730 \times 10.00 \times 49.3/12 \times 24.6 = 3{,}780{,}000 \text{ in.-lb}$$

$$d = \sqrt{\frac{3{,}780{,}000}{10.00 \times 12 \times 223}} = 11.9 \text{ in.}$$

Assume that, for shear, an effective depth of 19 in. will be adequate.

According to Code, the critical section for shear, with the footing considered to be acting as a broad beam, is at a distance d from the face of the column, that is, $5.00 - (1.78/2 + 19/12) = 2.53$ ft from the edge of the footing. At that section the shear is

$$V = 3730 \times 10 \times 2.53 = 94{,}400 \text{ lb}$$

and the unit shear stress is

$$v = \frac{V}{bd} = \frac{94{,}400}{10 \times 12 \times 19} = 42 \text{ psi}$$

This is well below the allowable shear stress of $1.1\sqrt{3000} = 60$ psi at this section. Alternatively, the shear is computed on a perimeter a distance $d/2$ from the face of the column. The total shearing force is

$$V = 3730(100 - 3.36^2) = 331{,}000 \text{ lb}$$

and the unit shear stress is

$$v = \frac{V}{b_0 d} = \frac{331{,}000}{4 \times 3.36 \times 12 \times 19} = 108 \text{ psi}$$

The allowable shearing stress at this section is $2\sqrt{3000} = 110$ psi. The assumed value of 19 in. may be considered satisfactory. The total thick-

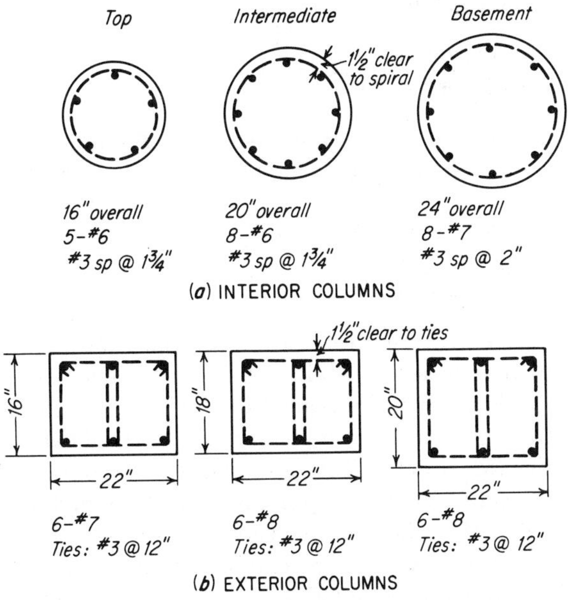

Fig. 9.26 Details of columns.

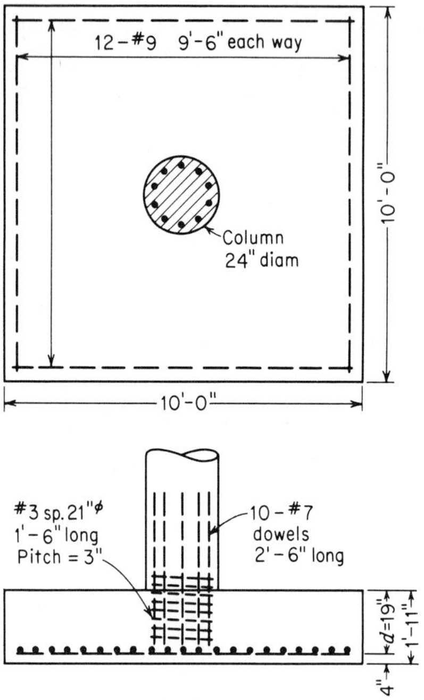

Fig. 9.27 Details of interior-column footing.

ness of the footing is then 23 in., and the weight is 28,800 lb, which agrees with the assumed weight.

$$A_s = \frac{3{,}780{,}000}{20{,}000 \times 0.9 \times 19} = 11.05 \text{ in.}^2$$

The allowable unit bond stress, using No. 9 bars, is 233 psi, and the maximum shear to be used in the equation for unit bond stress is

$$3730 \times 10.00 \times 4.11 = 153{,}000 \text{ lb}$$

$$\Sigma_0 \text{ (required)} = \frac{153{,}000}{233 \times 0.9 \times 19} = 38.4 \text{ in.}$$

Twelve No. 9 bars are selected; $A_s = 12.0$ in.², and $\Sigma_0 = 42.5$ in. The spacing of the bars is about 9½ in., which is satisfactory.

Ten No. 7 dowels will be placed in the footing. The dowels should extend into the columns 20 bar diameters or, for No. 7 bars, approximately 18 in. The embedment in the footing should be sufficient to develop the full working stress of 13,600 psi, or approximately 12.5 in. This length can be accommodated within the footing; therefore no pedestal is required. A total length of 30 in. will be used. The bearing stress, 373,000/452 = 825 psi, is less than the allowable value of 1125 psi. The complete details of the footing are shown in Fig. 9.27.

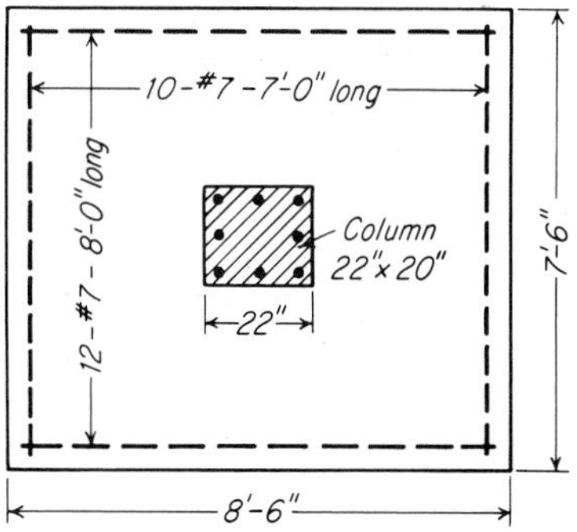

***Fig.* 9.28** Plan of exterior-column footing.

9.41 Design of Exterior-column Footings The design of the exterior-column footings follows closely the procedure for the interior-column footings. A rectangular concrete block with horizontal dimensions 7.50 × 8.50 ft is used. An effective depth of 15 in. results in a total footing depth of 19 in. Twelve No. 7 bars are used in the long direction of the footing, and ten No. 7 bars in the short direction.

Eight No. 8 dowels 3 ft long are required in each footing. They will project into the footing 15 in., which is sufficient to develop the full working value of each bar. The unit bearing stress at the base of the column is 233,000/22 × 20 = 530 psi, which is much less than the allowable value of 1125 psi. Complete details of the footing are shown in Figs. 9.28 and 9.29.

9.42 Design of Wall Beams With the proposed framing as shown in Figs. 9.30 and 9.33, the unsupported spans of the end wall beams are 19 ft 3 in. and 18 ft 3 in., while those of the intermediate wall beams are 20 ft 2 in. and 19 ft 2 in. for the short and long sides of the building, respectively. Since it is desirable to keep the depth of the wall beams constant throughout the building for architectural appearance, it is first necessary to determine the cross section required for the maximum moment and shear. The width of the beams is taken as 12 in. in all cases.

The maximum shear occurs in the first- and second-floor intermediate

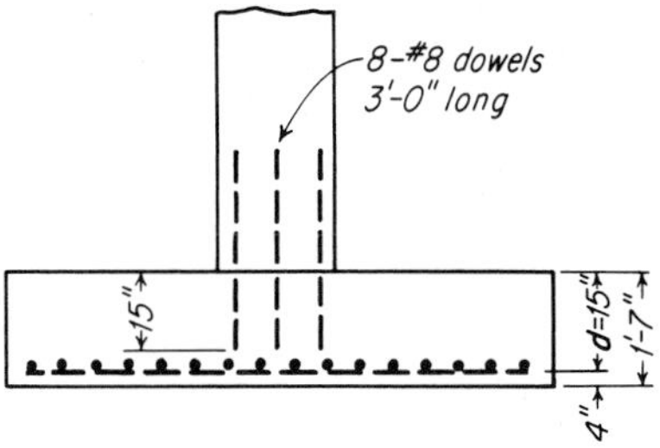

***Fig.* 9.29** Elevation of exterior-column footing.

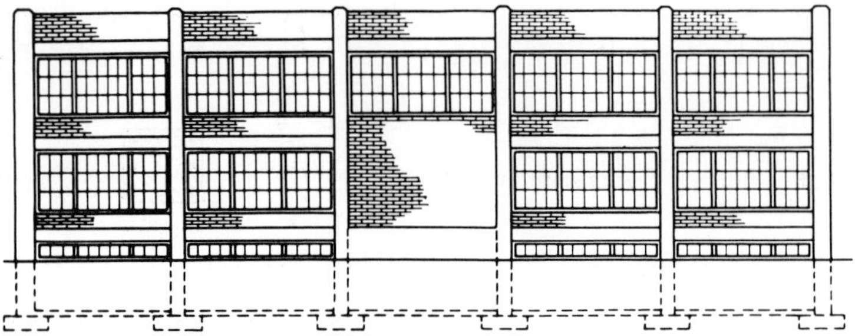

REAR ELEVATION

Fig. 9.30 Rear elevation.

beams along the short side of the building. According to Table 1004(f), Appendix A, a marginal beam having a depth greater than $1\frac{1}{4}$ and less than 3 times the minimum slab thickness shall carry that proportion of the panel load obtained by interpolation between the proportions assigned to the shallower and deeper beams. In this case the value is 36 per cent. The total load on the wall beam per linear foot is therefore

Brick sill: $2.5 \times 1 \times 120$	=	300 lb
Windows: 7.5×8	=	60 lb
Stem of beam, assumed	=	170 lb
Floor load: $0.36 \times 300 \times 21$	=	2270 lb
Total		2800 lb

The maximum shear occurs at the interior supports of the end spans on the short side of the building:

$$V = 1.15 \times 2800 \times 19.25/2 = 31{,}000 \text{ lb}$$

Assuming that web reinforcement will be used, and that the effective depth of the beam is 18 in.,

$$d \text{ (for shear)} = \frac{31{,}000 - \frac{18}{12} \times 2800}{5\sqrt{3000} \times 12} = 8.15 \text{ in.}$$

The maximum moment occurs in the end spans on the short side of the building. These beams are continuous over one support only and are designed for a negative moment of $\frac{1}{10}wl'^2$, where l' is the average of the two clear spans (see Table 8.2).

$$M = \tfrac{1}{10} \times 2800 \times 19.71^2 \times 12 = 1{,}305{,}000 \text{ in.-lb}$$

Since the beams are, in effect, T beams with the tee on one side only, the effective width of flange, according to the ACI Code, is

$$b = \tfrac{1}{12} \times 19.25 \times 12 + 12 = 31.25 \text{ in.}$$

On account of the relatively thick flange, the neutral axis will undoubtedly be in the flange. Under this assumption, the beam must be designed as a rectangular beam 31.25 in. wide, and the required depth is

$$d \text{ (for moment)} = \sqrt{\frac{1{,}305{,}000}{223 \times 31.25}} = 13.5 \text{ in.}$$

In order to give the desired architectural appearance, a total height of 21 in. is adopted for all the wall beams. The effective depth at the center of the beam, allowing for one row of steel with $2\frac{1}{2}$ in. insulation, is $18\frac{1}{2}$ in., and with the proposed arrangement of the steel (Fig. 9.33) the effective depth at the support is 19 in. The weight of the stem per foot is then 165 lb, as assumed.

9.43 Design of $L1$ and $L2$ Since it has been determined above that a cross section of 12 × 21 in. is satisfactory for all wall beams, it is now merely necessary to determine the area of steel required for each beam and to provide for shearing stresses.

The design positive moment in the end beam $L1$ is

$$M = \tfrac{1}{14} \times 2800 \times 19.25^2 \times 12 = 889{,}000 \text{ in.-lb}$$

and the positive moment in the interior beam $L2$ is

$$M = \tfrac{1}{16} \times 2800 \times 20.17^2 \times 12 = 853{,}000 \text{ in.-lb}$$

Assuming $j = 0.9$, the required steel areas are as follows:

Beam $L1$, positive-moment section:

$$A_s = \frac{889{,}000}{20{,}000 \times 0.9 \times 18.5} = 2.67 \text{ in.}^2$$

Beam $L1$, interior support:

$$A_s = \frac{1{,}305{,}000}{20{,}000 \times 0.9 \times 19} = 3.81 \text{ in.}^2$$

Beam $L2$, positive-moment section:

$$A_s = \frac{853{,}000}{20{,}000 \times 0.9 \times 18.5} = 2.56 \text{ in.}^2$$

Two No. 7 and two No. 8 bars will be placed in the bottoms of the beams $L1$ and $L2$, providing 2.77 in.^{2} for the positive moment. By bending up the No. 8 bars from each beam and carrying them over the interior support, an area of 3.14 in.^{2} is provided for the negative moment. One more No. 8 bar will provide the additional negative steel required. The No. 8 bars in $L1$ will be bent up at the exterior support, and one No. 9 bar will be added to provide for a negative moment of $\frac{1}{16}wl'^2$. The points at which the bars may be bent and cut off are obtained from Fig. 3.19. The arrangement is shown in Fig. 9.33. The straight bars are carried 6 in. into the columns. A check against Table 8, Appendix B, indicates that adequate development length in bond is provided for all bars.

Since only two bars are bent up in each beam, and these at one place, their strength is disregarded in providing for diagonal tension. Stirrups are placed at suitable intervals to furnish the necessary web strength. With 3000-psi concrete, $V_c = 1.1\sqrt{3000} \times 12 \times 19 = 13{,}700$ lb. At the interior end of $L1$, the distance from the edge of the column in which stirrups are theoretically required is

$$11.1\,\frac{31{,}000 - 13{,}700}{31{,}000} = 6.20 \text{ ft}$$

For No. 3 U stirrups, the maximum spacing is $d/2 = 9.50$ in., but not to exceed $0.22/(0.0015 \times 12) = 12.2$ in. A maximum spacing of 9 in. will be adopted. At a distance d from the face of support, the excess shear is 12,900 lb, and the required stirrup spacing is

$$s = \frac{0.22 \times 20{,}000 \times 19}{12{,}900} = 6.50 \text{ in.}$$

By prorating, the spacing at a point 3 ft from the support is calculated as 9.55 in., which exceeds the maximum spacing. The first stirrup will be placed 4 in. from the support face and followed by four stirrups at $4\frac{1}{2}$ in., three at $6\frac{1}{2}$ in., and six at 9 in., providing web reinforcement over a distance slightly in excess of the theoretical distance plus d as required by Code. At the exterior end of $L1$, the first stirrup is placed 4 in. from the support and followed by nine spaces at 9 in.

In each end of the interior span $L2$, similar calculations indicate spacing from the support face of 4 in., then four spaces at $5\frac{1}{2}$ in., and six at 9 in.

The areas of steel required in the other wall beams, floor, and roof and the arrangement of the web reinforcement are determined in a similar manner. The roof wall beams are made the same depth as those at the second-floor level for architectural reasons. In investigating the beams on the long side of the building, it should be borne in mind that the first interior supports of the line are designed for a moment of $\frac{1}{10}wl'^2$, while at the other interior supports a coefficient of $\frac{1}{11}$ is used. The end supports at the corners of the building are reinforced for negative moments of $\frac{1}{16}wl'^2$. The necessary steel details are shown in Fig. 9.33.

9.44 Design of Stairway Slab The stairway, which extends from the basement to the second-floor level, is located as shown in Fig. 9.33. The opening made by the stairwell and the future elevator shaft is framed by beams as shown. In order to keep the thickness of the stair slab down to a reasonable minimum, beam *B*9 is placed at the edge of the floor-level landing slab. The stair slab is designed as a simple slab with a span equal to the horizontal distance from the middle of beam *B*9 to the middle of the wall support of the intermediate landing slab.

The dead load on the stair slab is made up of the weight of the intermediate landing slab, the weight of the inclined slab, and the weight of the treads. For purposes of computation it is sufficiently accurate to assume that this total dead load is uniformly distributed over the horizontal span. The live load is assumed as 100 psf of horizontal surface.

The widths of the stair slabs and landing slabs as shown in Fig. 9.35 will prove satisfactory in the ordinary building of this size. With 6-in. bearing allowed on the brick exterior wall, the horizontal span of the stair slab is 12 ft 1 in. The total length of slab between supports is

$$\sqrt{6^2 + 7.66^2} + 3.83 = 13.5 \text{ ft.}$$

Assuming the weight of the slab to be 69 psf, the total load on a 1-ft strip of slab is

$$\begin{aligned}
&\text{Treads:}\quad 9 \times \frac{7.19 \times 10.25}{2 \times 144} \times 150 &&= 350 \text{ lb}\\
&\text{Slab:}\quad 13.5 \times 69 &&= 940\\
&\text{Live load:}\quad 12 \times 100 &&= 1200\\
&\quad\text{Total} &&= 2490 \text{ lb}
\end{aligned}$$

$$M = \tfrac{1}{8} \times 2490 \times 12.1 \times 12 = 45{,}300 \text{ in.-lb}$$

$$d = \sqrt{\frac{45{,}300}{223 \times 12}} = 4.11 \text{ in.}$$

An effective depth of 4½ in. is selected; with 1-in. insulation the total slab thickness is 5½ in., and the weight is 69 psf, as assumed.

$$A_s = \frac{45{,}300}{20{,}000 \times 0.874 \times 4.50} = 0.575 \text{ in.}^2 \text{ per ft of width}$$

This area is furnished by No. 5 bars, 6 in. center to center. One No. 5 bar, 3 ft 8 in. long, is placed under each tread at right angles to the main reinforcement, as shown in Fig. 9.35.[1]

[1] The detailing shown in Fig. 9.35 assumes that the stairway slab will be poured with the structural frame. A more widely used method of construction places the stair slab after the main structure has been completed. In such cases, recesses must be left in beams *B*9 and in the brick wall in order to furnish support for the future stair slabs, and dowels must be placed in beams *B*9 to project into the stair slabs when they are poured.

The floor-level landing slab is made 8 in. thick, and every other bar of the stair-slab reinforcement is continued across this slab. Two No. 5 bars are placed in the intermediate landing slab, at right angles to the main reinforcement, to assist in distributing the load on that slab and to provide for temperature stresses. Negative-moment stresses in the stair slabs across beams *B*9 are provided for by means of short bent bars placed in the tops of the slabs at these points, as shown in Fig. 9.35.

9.45 Design of Beams Framing Stairwell: ***Beam B9*** (See Fig. 9.31). This beam supports a uniform load along its entire length, consisting of one-half of the stairway-slab load and one-half of the floor-level landing-slab load in addition to its own weight. The span of the beam is 9 ft 5 in.,

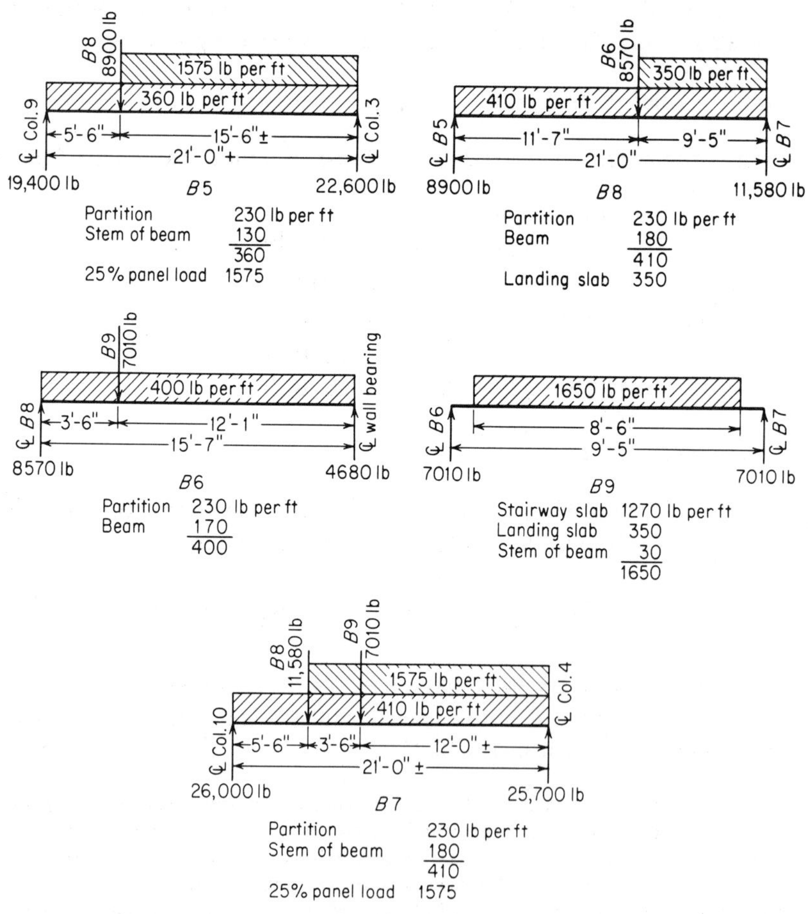

***Fig.* 9.31** Loading diagrams for beams framing stairwell.

the distance center to center of beams $B6$ and $B7$. The beam is designed as a T beam with the tee on one side only; this is necessary because of the break between the up and down stair slabs at the landing.

Beam B6 This is a simply supported rectangular beam loaded by the weight of a 4-in. hollow tile partition and the concentrated load from $B9$ in addition to its own weight.

Beam B8 This beam carries the concentrated load from beam $B6$, one-half of the load from the landing slab, and the weight of a 4-in. hollow-tile partition, in addition to its own weight. Beam $B8$ has been placed at the edge of the column strip. This fact, together with the improbability of having the full live load on the portion of the floor near it, justifies the assumption that no floor load is supported by $B8$.[1] Because of the open shaft on one side of the beam at the point of maximum moment, it must be designed as a T beam with the tee on one side only. In order to illustrate the method of design when such irregular loads are involved, the design of $B8$ is included below.

The loads on the beam (see Figs. 9.31 and 9.33) are as follows:

Uniform load over entire length of beam:

Partition:	20×11.5	= 230 plf
Weight of beam		= 180 plf
Total		= 410 plf

Additional uniform load from stairway landing slab:

$$\tfrac{1}{2} \times 3.5 \times 200 = 350 \text{ plf}$$

Concentrated load from $B6$ in 8570 lb:

$$R_L = \frac{8570 \times 9.42 + 350 \times 9.42^2/2 + 410 \times 21^2/2}{21} = 8900 \text{ lb}$$

$$R_R = 11{,}580 \text{ lb}$$

The point of zero shear, which locates the point of maximum moment, occurs under the concentrated load. The maximum moment is

$$M = (8900 \times 11.5 - 410 \times 11.58^2/2)12 = 900{,}000 \text{ in.-lb}$$

According to the ACI Code, the effective width of flange is equal to $10 + \tfrac{1}{12} \times 21 \times 12 = 31$ in. Because of the relatively large thickness of

[1] Since beam $B8$ and the slab adjacent to it are poured at the same time, they cannot act independently of each other. A more conservative design would assume that a part of the adjacent slab load is supported by $B8$.

the flange, it is reasonable to assume that the neutral axis is in the flange, in which case the equations for rectangular beams apply:

$$d = \sqrt{\frac{900{,}000}{31 \times 223}} = 11.4 \text{ in.}$$

An effective depth of 14 in. will be used, in order to avoid interference with the bars in *B*6:

$$b' = \frac{11580 - 1.17 \times 760}{5\sqrt{300} \times 14} = 2.78 \text{ in.}$$

A width of stem of 10 in. will be used, in order to give a reasonable amount of resistance to torsional stresses. With 3 in. of insulation, to provide for two rows of bars, the total height of the beam is 17 in., and the weight per foot is 180 lb, as assumed.

$$A_s = \frac{900{,}000}{20{,}000 \times 0.875 \times 14} = 3.66 \text{ in.}^2$$

Six No. 7 bars are selected (3.61 in.^{2}). With

$$np = \frac{9 \times 3.61}{31 \times 14} = 0.077$$

and $t/d = 1\frac{4}{8} = 0.57$, Graph 12, Appendix B, shows that the neutral axis is in the flange, so that, from Table 6, Appendix B, with

$$p = \frac{3.61}{31 \times 14} = 0.0085$$

$j = 0.893$, and the revised steel area required is 3.59 in.^{2}. The six No. 7 bars are satisfactory.

Since this beam is poured monolithically with the beams supporting it, there will exist some negative moment at the supports. The amount of this bending moment is dependent upon too many factors to permit any accurate determination. In order to provide for the stresses of negative moment, one-half the steel is bent up and hooked over the support.

Since only three bars are bent up, and since these are bent at a single point, they will not be depended upon for diagonal tension resistance, and vertical stirrups will be used wherever web reinforcement is required. The total shear that the concrete can resist is

$$V_c = 1.1\sqrt{3000} \times 10 \times 14 = 8400 \text{ lb}$$

The stirrups will be designed to resist all the shear in excess of this amount.

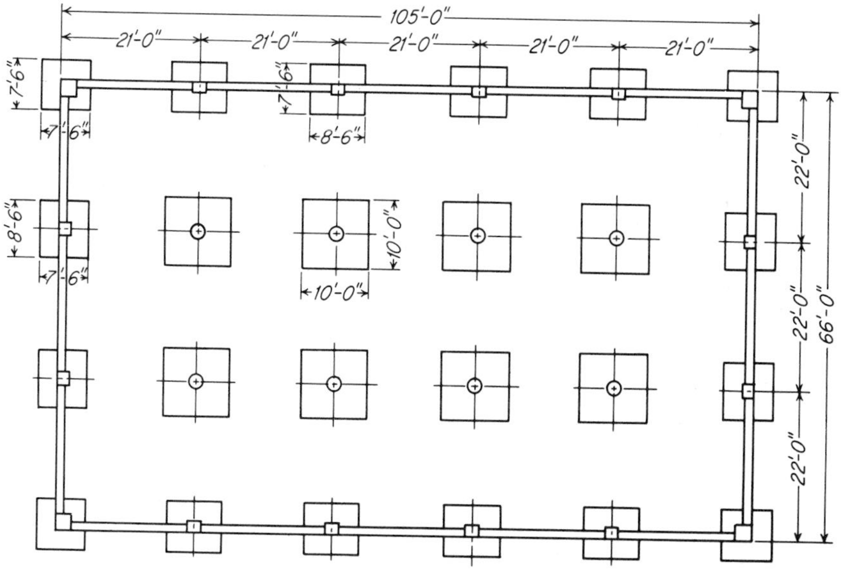

FOUNDATION PLAN

Fig. **9.32**

With ¼-in. U stirrups, the required stirrup spacing at the right end of the span is 3 in., followed by 11 spaces at 7 in. At the left end, the first stirrup is placed at 3 in., with four additional stirrups at 7 in.

Beam B5 In addition to supporting the concentration from beam *B*8 and its own weight, beam *B*5 must be designed to support the partition as shown and the required proportion of the floor load. The beam is a T beam, with the tee on one side only.

Beam B7 This beam supports the same loads as beam *B*5, in addition to the concentrated load from beam *B*9. It is a T beam, with the tee on one side only. The complete framing details of the stairway beams are shown in Fig. 9.33.

9.46 Engineering Drawings Figure 9.33 is an engineering drawing of the second floor, giving the necessary information on the concrete and steel for the slab and beams at that floor. This is the type of drawing which would be prepared in the design office. The reinforcing-bar fabricator would use this drawing as a basis for preparing a complete detail drawing showing bar lengths and bends and placing instructions. The "Manual of Standard Practice for Detailing Reinforced Concrete Structures" (ACI 315–57) of the American Concrete Institute is usually followed in the preparation of both engineering drawings and fabricator's detail drawings.

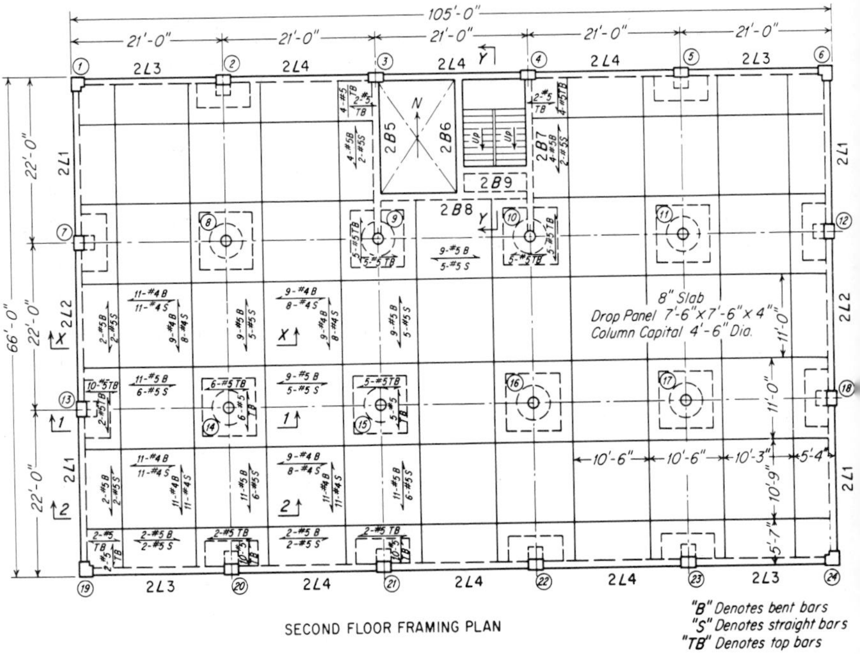

SECOND FLOOR FRAMING PLAN

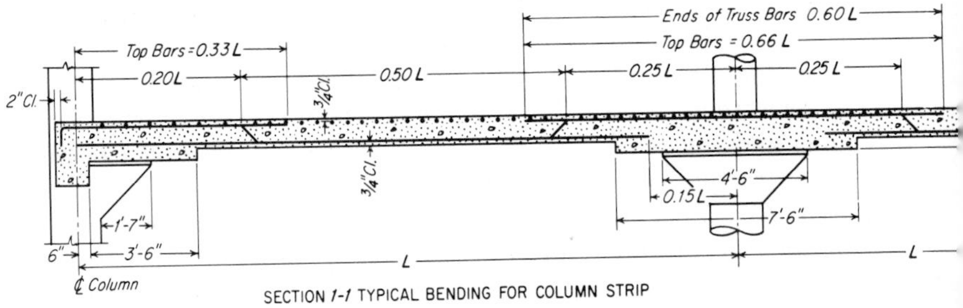

SECTION *1-1* TYPICAL BENDING FOR COLUMN STRIP

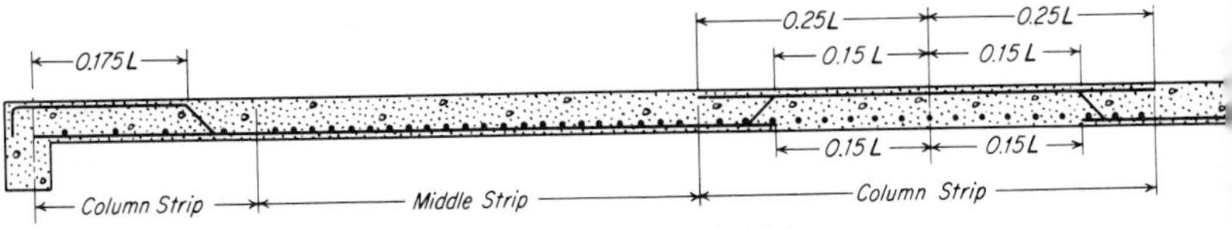

SECTION *2-2* TYPICAL BENDING FOR MIDDLE STRIP

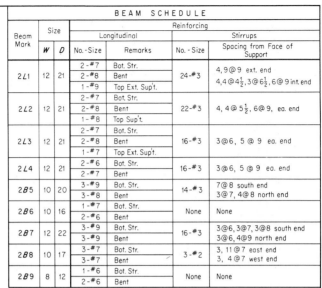

BEAM SCHEDULE						
Beam Mark	Size		Reinforcing			
			Longitudinal		Stirrups	
	W	D	No.-Size	Remarks	No.-Size	Spacing from Face of Support
2L1	12	21	2-#7	Bot. Str.	24-#3	4, 9@9 ext. end 4, 4@4½, 3@6½, 6@9 int. end
			2-#8	Bent		
			1-#9	Top Ext. Sup't.		
2L2	12	21	2-#7	Bot. Str.	22-#3	4, 4@5½, 6@9, ea. end
			2-#8	Bent		
			1-#8	Top Sup't.		
2L3	12	21	2-#7	Bot. Str.	16-#3	3@6, 5@9 ea. end
			2-#8	Bent		
			1-#7	Top Ext. Sup't.		
2L4	12	21	2-#6	Bot. Str.	16-#3	3@6, 5@9 ea. end
			2-#7	Bent		
2B5	10	20	3-#9	Bot. Str.	14-#3	7@8 south end 3@7, 4@8 north end
			3-#8	Bent		
2B6	10	16	1-#7	Bot. Str.	None	None
			2-#6	Bent		
2B7	12	22	3-#9	Bot. Str.	16-#3	3@6, 3@7, 3@8 south end 3@6, 4@9 north end
			3-#9	Bent		
2B8	10	17	3-#7	Bot. Str.	3-#2	3, 11@7 east end 3, 4@7 west end
			3-#7	Bent		
2B9	8	12	1-#6	Bot. Str.	None	None
			2-#6	Bent		

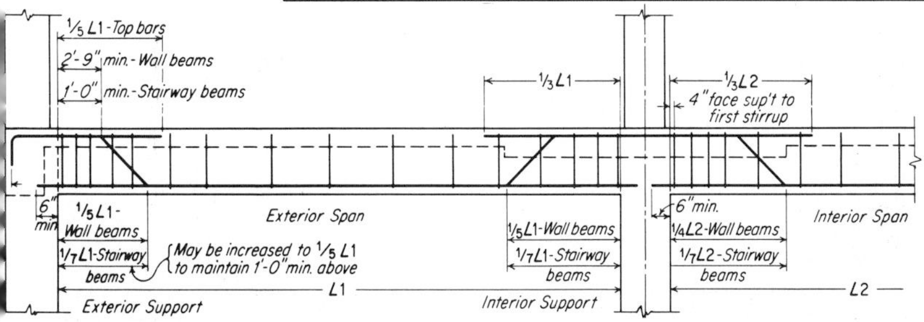

TYPICAL BEAM BENDING

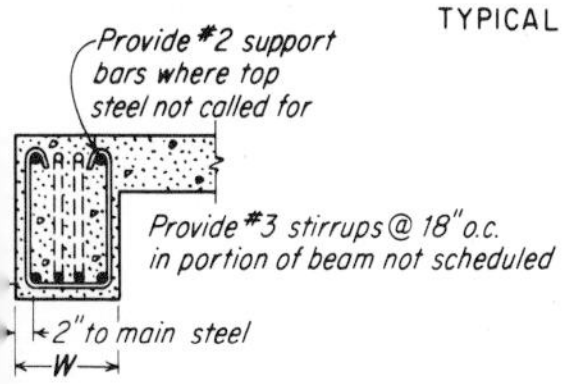

ICAL SECTION
ROUGH BEAM

NOTES:

1. *All concrete to have 3000 p.s.u. compressive strength at 28 days.*
2. *Reinforcing steel to have f_y = 40,000 psi, with deformations conforming to A.S.T.M. - A305.*
3. *Bends to be made as per diagrams.*
4. *Terminate non-continuous bent bars in accordance with ACI Code by a hook if required embedment cannot be obtained.*
5. *Place main reinforcing steel so that bottom of steel is 2" above forms in beams and 3/4" in slabs.*
6. *All slab and beam steel shall have a minimum extension into the support in accordance with ACI Code.*
7. *Provide bar supports in accordance with ACI Detailing Manual.*

FLAT SLAB BUILDING SECOND FLOOR FRAMING PLAN
FIG. 9.33

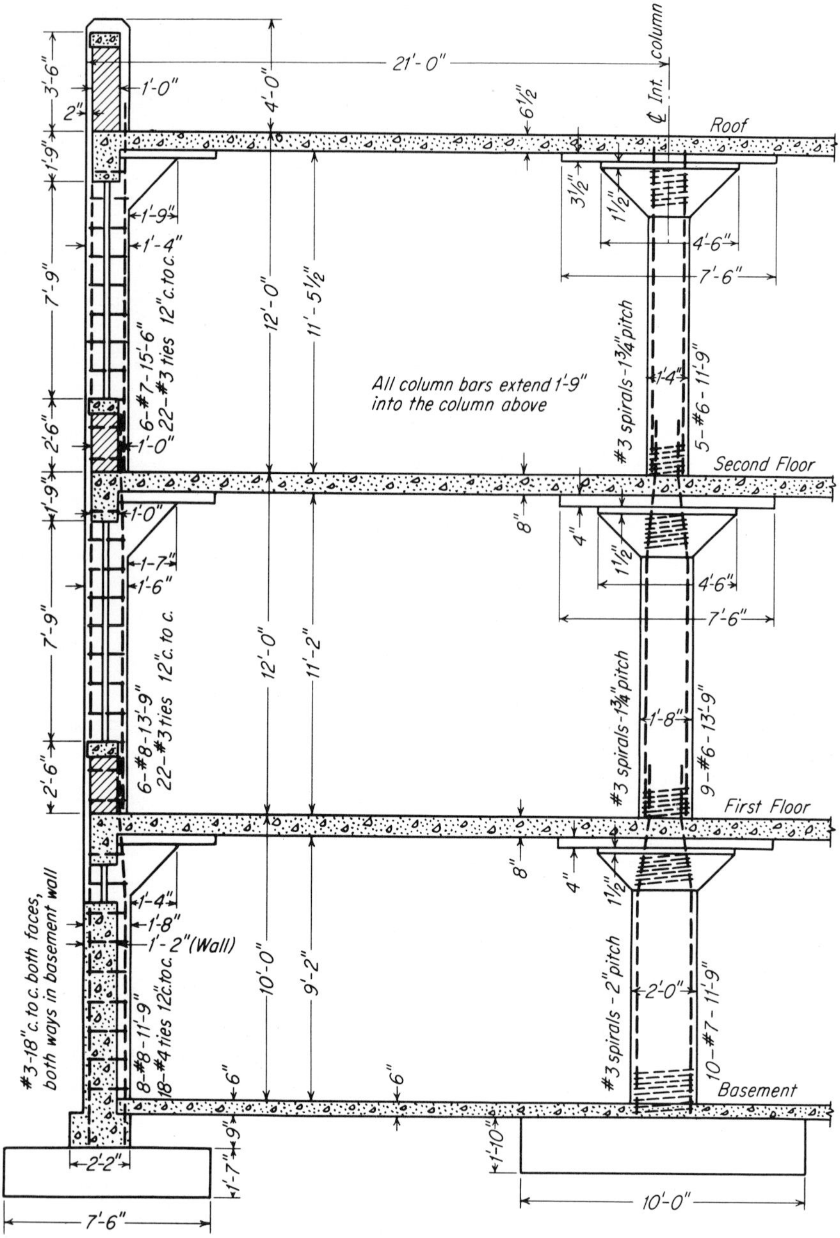

PARTIAL CROSS SECTION

SECTION X-X

Showing Column Steel

Fig. 9.34

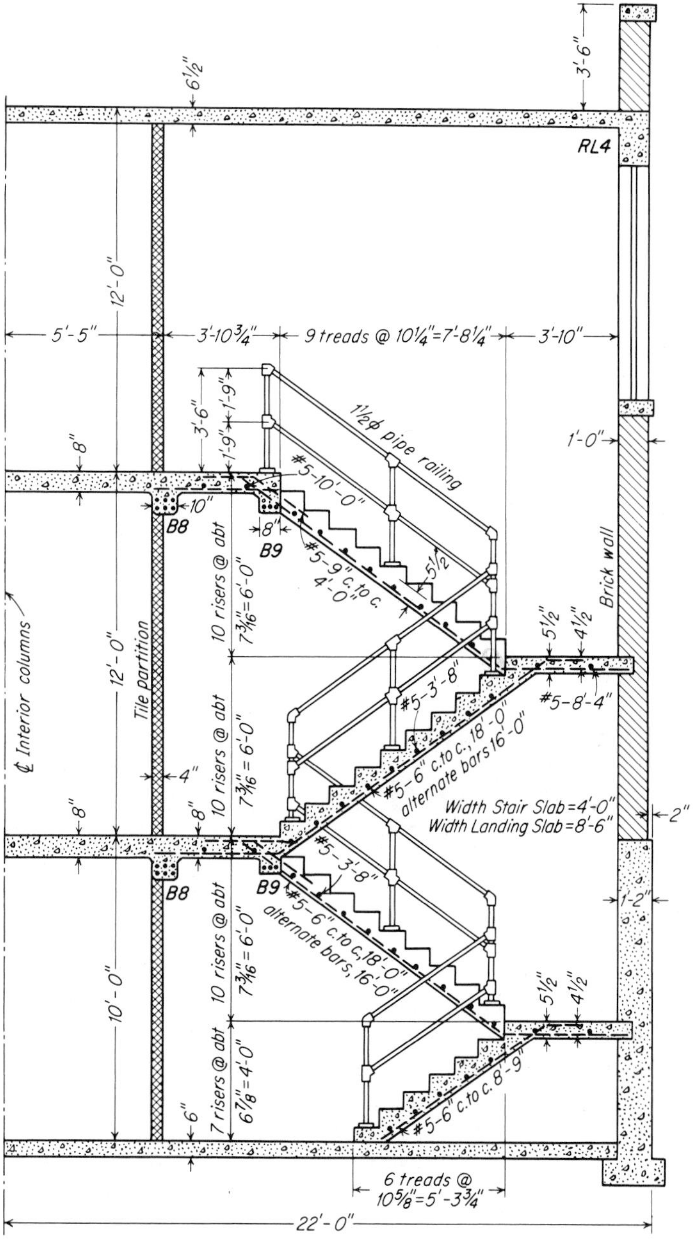

DETAIL OF STAIRWAY
SECTION Y-Y

Fig. 9.35

chapter 10

ARCH AND SHELL ROOFS

10.1 Introduction The search for structures which cover long spans and large areas without intermediate support, and which do so using a minimum of material, has long occupied the attention of the structural-engineering profession. When a plane roof surface is not necessary to meet the functional requirements of the structure, a singly or doubly curved roof form will normally be found to be the most economical of material. These nonlinear, nonplanar systems owe their economy to their unique capacity to resist applied loads primarily by direct stress, as opposed to flexural and shear stress.

In this connection, it is pertinent to observe that the beam is one of the least efficient of structural forms. Commonly, only one cross section of a beam is subjected to the maximum design moment, and consequently, if the member is prismatic, only one cross section of the beam is working at the maximum allowable stress at design load. What is worse, at design load only the extreme fiber of thatunique cross section is stressed to the maximum; all the other fibers are understressed. It is acknowledged that this situation is somewhat improved by continuity, by virtue of which two sections may be subjected to the maximum moment. The situation is further improved by the plasticity of concrete and steel, which results in a nonlinear distribution of stress in the cross section, and which may permit a redistribution of moments to occur within the member which will more fully utilize the prismatic beam. But it is still impossible to compete for efficiency with the simple compression strut, for example, in which every cross section along the length is stressed to the full allowed value over its entire width and depth.

This leads one to select, for those design situations which permit it, a structural form in which direct stress (in the case of concrete, compressive stress) is dominant over flexural and shear stress. The degree to which this is accomplished is a measure of the structural efficiency of the design.

10.2 Arches The use of arches is the oldest structural method for bridging spans too large for straight beams. Arches were introduced by the Romans for their bridges, aqueducts, and large public buildings more than 2000 years ago. Constructed of masonry, concrete, steel, and timber, they have been in wide use ever since.

Modern arches are of three types: the fixed arch, which is rigidly connected to the abutments, the two-hinged arch, which is supported at each end by a hinge resting on the abutment, and the three-hinged arch, which has an additional hinge at the crown. Reinforced-concrete arches are mostly of the first two types.

The structural action and advantage of arches are easily recognized by considering a two-hinged arch. Figure 10.1*a* shows a uniformly loaded simple beam with $M_{\max} = wL^2/8$, $V_{\max} = wL/2$, and axial force $N = 0$. If this beam is curved, as in Fig. 10.1*b*, $M_{\max}$ is the same as before. The

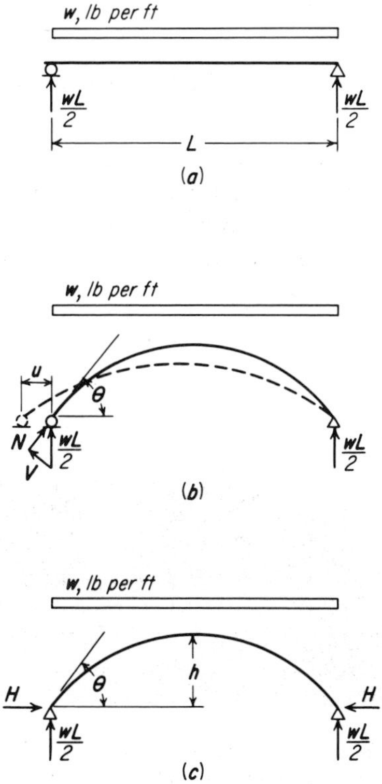

Fig. 10.1

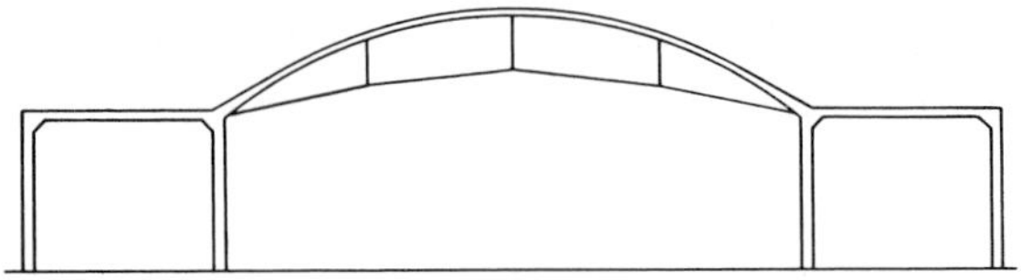

***Fig.* 10.2** Two-hinged roof arch with cambered tie rod.

shear at the support, however, is decreased to $V_{max} = (wL/2) \cos \theta$; in addition, an axial force is now present in the member which, at the supports, equals $N = (wL/2) \sin \theta$. This curved beam tends to straighten under load since, owing to bending, the bottom fibers are stretched and the top fibers compressed. This action tends to increase the span, as shown in Fig. 10.1*b*. To maintain the original span, as in the two-hinged arch with immovable supports (Fig. 10.1*c*), a horizontal reaction H must be applied. In this two-hinged arch

$$M_{max} = \frac{wL^2}{8} - Hh$$

$$V_{max} = \frac{wL}{2} \cos \theta - H \sin \theta$$

$$N = \frac{wL}{2} \sin \theta + H \cos \theta$$

It is seen that, in comparison with the simple beam, the bending moment and the shear force in the arch are greatly decreased. On the other hand, an axial compression force N, not present in the beam, acts in the arch. It is exactly this state of affairs which is desirable in reinforced concrete,

***Fig.* 10.3** Hangar at Chicago Municipal Airport. Fixed arches spaced at 28 ft 11½ in., clear span 257 ft, height at center 60 ft, thickness of concrete shell between arches varies from 3½ to 6 in. (*Courtesy of Ammann and Whitney.*)

since concrete is relatively weak in tension and shear but strong in compression.

The choice of two-hinged or fixed arches depends on the particular conditions of design. Fixed arches require immovable abutments which prevent not only vertical and horizontal motion, but also rotation of the support. For roof arches resting on columns or walls, it is obviously impossible to fix the supports against rotation, since the rigidity of the supporting structure is not sufficient for this purpose. Two-hinged arches, on the other hand, are insensitive to rotations and to moderate differential settlements of the abutments, which, for this reason, can often be made less substantial than for fixed arches. Tie rods are often provided in two-hinged arches to resist the horizontal reaction H; hence the supports have to resist vertical reactions only, with a corresponding further decrease in their cost. Tied two-hinged arches are obviously advantageous in roof structures of the type shown in Fig. 10.2, where large horizontal reactions would require much heavier columns and frames. Large hangars and halls of the type of Fig. 10.3 have been built both with fixed arches and with tied two-hinged arches; in the latter case tie rods were located below the floor. Effective hinges can be constructed at reasonable cost, provided that the reactions are not excessively large. They may be architecturally undesirable, however, and represent a maintenance problem in some cases. A well-considered decision on the type of arch to be used in a given design depends, therefore, on a balanced evaluation of factors such as those just enumerated.

In contrast to the arch ribs of the previous illustrations, ribless barrel-arch roofs of the type shown in Fig. 10.4 can be used for moderate spans. A strip of unit width may be designed as either a fixed or two-hinged arch.

As was noted in the general discussion of arch action (Fig. 10.1), arch ribs or barrels are subject to compression and bending, and usually only small shear. They are, therefore, designed and analyzed in the same manner as eccentrically compressed columns, with one layer of steel being located near the top surface and another near the bottom. It is economical to keep steel percentages small, on the order of 1 to 2 per cent. Lateral ties for the reinforcement are used in arch ribs as in columns. In barrel arches, transverse reinforcement normal to the main steel is placed near both surfaces and is tied to the main longitudinal steel. This distributes localized loads and acts as temperature and shrinkage reinforcement.

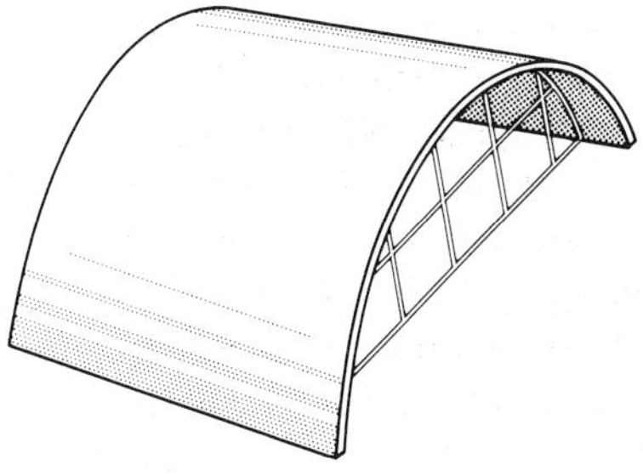

***Fig.* 10.4** Barrel-arch roof.

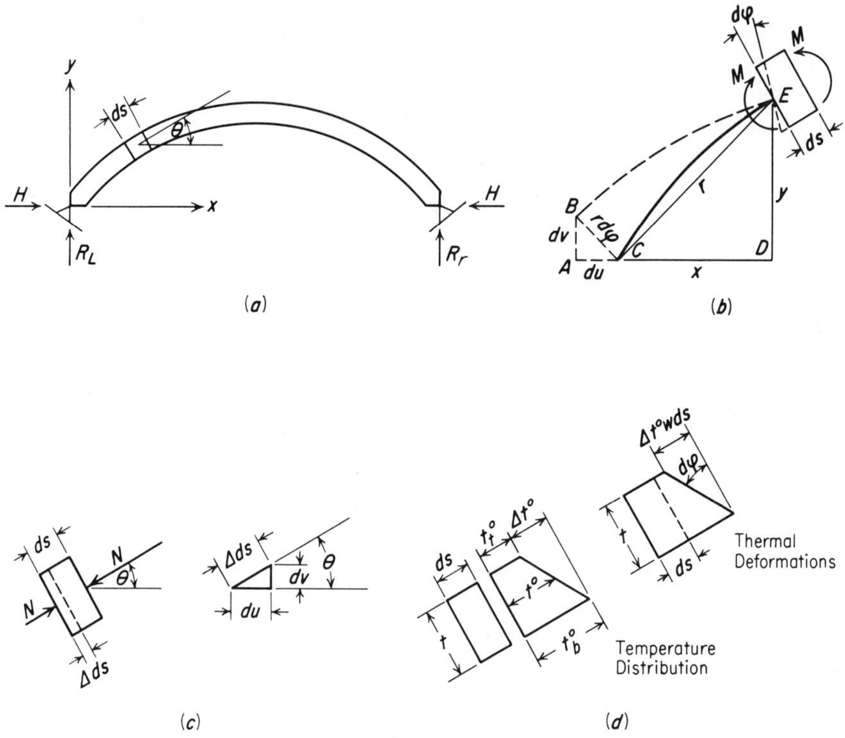

Fig. **10.5**

10.3 Theory of Symmetrical, Two-hinged Arches The two-hinged arch (Fig. 10.1*c*) differs from a curved simple beam (Fig. 10.1*b*) in that horizontally immovable hinges or tie rods prevent the spread of supports. The forces in such an arch can be analyzed by introducing a fictitious roller support at one of the hinges, which converts the arch into a simple beam. The horizontal displacement u can then be determined. To convert this fictitious beam into the actual arch, a horizontal force H must be introduced of sufficient magnitude to produce a displacement equal and opposite to u. In other words, this force brings the fictitious roller support back to its original position as it actually is in the arch.

To determine the horizontal displacement u, take a small element ds (Fig. 10.5*a*) of the arch, and consider the effect of the deformation of this one element on the deformation of the arch as a whole. Thus all parts of the arch with the exception of this one element are considered as rigid. The contribution of the deformation of the element ds to the total displacement can be determined as follows. A bending moment M, considered as constant over the small length ds, will cause the left cross section to rotate with respect to the right one by an amount $d\phi$ which can be determined by the moment-area principle, i.e., from the fact that the rotation of one section with respect to another is equal to the area of the moment curve between them divided by EI. Hence

$$d\phi = \frac{M\,ds}{EI} \tag{10.1}$$

The entire left portion of the arch, rigidly attached as it is to the cross section, will likewise rotate through an angle $d\phi$, as represented by the dotted position of the axis in Fig. 10.5*b*. Consequently, the left end of the arch describes an arc $r\,d\phi$. It will be noted that triangle ABC is similar to triangle CDE. Hence, from simple proportions, $du/r\,d\phi = y/r$, and the horizontal displacement is

$$du = y\,d\phi = \frac{My\,ds}{EI} \tag{10.1a}$$

This is the contribution made to the total displacement u by the angular deformation due to bending of the single element ds. To obtain u itself, it is only necessary to sum these contributions for all elements ds along the arch, or

$$u = \int_0^s \frac{My\,ds}{EI} \tag{10.2}$$

Let M_0 represent the bending moment due to any external arch loads caused in the fictitious simple curved beam, as in Fig. 10.1*b*. These moments, of course, are the same as those in the straight beam (Fig. 10.1*a*). Then the outward displacement due to these "simple beam moments" is

$$u_{M_0} = \int_0^s \frac{M_0 y\,ds}{EI} \tag{10.2a}$$

The sign convention is the same as in beam analysis; i.e., moments are considered positive if they produce tension in the bottom fiber. In addition to M_0, the horizontal reaction H causes a moment at section x which is equal to

$$M_H = -Hy$$

and the inward displacement caused by these moments is

$$u_{M_H} = -H \int_0^s \frac{y^2\,ds}{EI} \tag{10.2b}$$

Since, actually, no displacement occurs at the immovable hinge,

$$u_{M_0} = -u_{M_H}$$

from which one obtains the magnitude of the horizontal reaction:

$$H = -\frac{\int_0^s (M_0 y\, ds/EI)}{\int_0^s (y^2\, ds/EI)} \tag{10.3}$$

If displacements u were caused exclusively by bending, Eq. (10.3) would furnish all the information necessary for analyzing a two-hinged arch. Since such an arch, as is seen from Fig. 10.1, has only one statically indeterminate reaction H, it is now possible to find moments, shears, and axial forces at any point in the arch from equilibrium conditions only, since the previously unknown force H is given by Eq. (10.3). However, other factors in addition to bending moments may contribute significantly to the magnitude of u and must therefore be considered in determining H.

In addition to bending moments, shear forces and axial thrusts act on element ds. Deformations due to shear in arches are even smaller, relatively, than in beams and can therefore be neglected. Those caused by axial compression forces N, on the other hand, may affect the magnitude of H significantly and must be considered.

Consider an element ds with a concentric force N on both faces, as shown in Fig. 10.5*c*. The axial shortening $\Delta\, ds$ caused by the normal force N_0 is $N_0\, ds/EA$. N_0 is the component, parallel to the arch axis at the element ds, of all external forces and reactions on the fictitious curved beam to the right or left of the element ds. The component of $\Delta\, ds$ in the direction of u is

$$du = \Delta\, ds \cos\theta \tag{10.4}$$

Hence

$$du_{N_0} = \frac{N_0 \cos\theta\, ds}{EA}$$

and the total displacement due to N_0 is

$$u_{N_0} = -\int_0^s \frac{N_0 \cos\theta\, ds}{EA} \tag{10.5}$$

The minus sign indicates that this displacement is inward, in contrast to the outward displacement u_{M_0}. On the other hand, the horizontal reaction H results in an axial compression, at any point of the arch, of magnitude $H \cos\theta$; thus the inward displacement caused by this action is

$$u_{N_H} = -H \int_0^s \frac{\cos^2\theta\, ds}{EA} \tag{10.6}$$

Temperature changes which may occur in roof arches produce further deformation of the arch. A uniform temperature increase of $t°$ causes the arch element ds to increase in length by the amount

$$\Delta\, ds = \omega t°\, ds$$

where ω is the temperature coefficient of expansion. Substitution of this expression in Eq. (10.4) and integration over the entire arch give the total support displacement due to a uniform temperature increase:

$$u_t = \omega t° \int_0^s \cos\theta\, ds = \omega t° l \tag{10.7}$$

Another factor which results in inward displacement u is the inevitable shrinkage of concrete. It has been shown, however, that the unfavorable effect of shrinkage is greatly decreased by the longtime plastic flow of concrete, which allows the structure to adapt itself to those stresses which are caused by change of shape, such as shrinkage, rather than by external loads. It has been proposed that limited effect of shrinkage can be accounted for by an equivalent drop in temperature of 15°F added to the actual seasonal temperature drop for which the arch is designed. The temperature coefficient may be taken as $\omega = 5.5 \times 10^{-6}$ per °F.

In addition to the uniform temperature change just considered, a temperature differential may exist between the inside and outside surfaces in roof arches, particularly if, as in the hangar of Fig. 10.3, the roof slab or shell is placed at middepth of the arch ribs. The total temperature changes and corresponding deformations may then be represented as in Fig. 10.5*d*. The amount by which the bottom fiber ds expands more than the top fiber is $\Delta t°\, \omega\, ds$. It is seen that this results in

$$d\phi = \frac{\Delta t°\, \omega\, ds}{t} \tag{10.8}$$

If this value is substituted in the left equality of Eq. (10.1*a*), and the result integrated over the arch, the total displacement caused by the temperature gradient becomes

$$u_{\Delta t°} = \omega\, \Delta t° \int_0^s \frac{y\, ds}{t} \tag{10.9}$$

These are all the types of displacements that occur in an arch with immovable hinges. In arches with tie rods, hinges are not immovable, since the force H in the tie rod causes it to stretch. For a tie rod of area A_{tr} and modulus E_{tr}, this stretch amounts to

$$u_{tr} = H \frac{l}{E_{tr} A_{tr}} \tag{10.10}$$

For a tied arch, the sum of all other displacements must be equal to the stretch of the tie; i.e.,

$$u_{M_0} + u_{M_H} + u_{N_0} + u_{N_H} + u_{t^\circ} + u_{\Delta t^\circ} = u_{tr}$$

If the proper values are substituted in this equation, the unknown horizontal force H may be found:

$$H = \frac{\int_0^s \frac{M_0 y\,ds}{I} - \int_0^s \frac{N_0 \cos\theta\,ds}{A} + E\omega\left(t^\circ l + \Delta t^\circ \int_0^s \frac{y\,ds}{t}\right)}{\int_0^s \frac{y^2\,ds}{I} + \int_0^s \frac{\cos^2\theta\,ds}{A} + \frac{El}{E_{tr}A_{tr}}} \tag{10.11}$$

This lengthy expression can usually be simplified by omitting terms which are zero or negligibly small, depending on the particular condition. Thus, for an arch without tie rod the last term in the denominator drops out, since $u_{tr} = 0$. If no temperature gradient can occur between inside and outside surfaces, such as in roof arches located below a well-insulated surface, the term containing Δt° is zero. Furthermore, in many cases the displacements u_{N_0} and u_{N_H} caused by axial compression are very small compared to those caused by bending moments (u_{M_0} and u_{M_H}). For a parabolic arch, S. Timoshenko[1] has computed the amount of error obtained by neglecting the influence of axial compression in determining H. His results are given in the table below, in which t_c is the thickness at the crown:

h/l	1/12			1/8			1/4		
t_c/l	1/10	1/20	1/30	1/10	1/20	1/30	1/10	1/20	1/30
Error, %	17.1	5.1	2.4	8.4	2.2	1.0	1.8	0.4	0.2

Since the usual accuracy of engineering designs is hardly greater than 5 per cent on account of uncertainties of loading, materials properties, and various other factors, the influence of axial compression can be neglected in all but very flat or unusually thick arches. Normally then, the second term in both the numerator and denominator can be dropped as being negligibly small. Hence, for an arch of usual dimensions without tie rod and without temperature gradient, H can be determined with sufficient accuracy from

$$H = \frac{\int_0^s (M_0 y\,ds/I) + E\omega t^\circ l}{\int_0^s (y^2\,ds/I)} \tag{10.11a}$$

[1] S. Timoshenko, "Strength of Materials," part 1, p. 397, D. Van Nostrand Company, Inc., Princeton, N.J., 1956.

The determination of the integrals in the equation for H is simple, provided that M_0, N_0, I, A, h, and y can be expressed as functions of s and that these functions can be integrated. Ordinarily this is possible for only a few very simple cases in which the arch axis is either a parabola or a circular arc. In most other cases it becomes necessary to approximate these integrals with a finite sum of numerical terms. The details of this procedure will be given after the theory of fixed arches is developed.

10.4 Theory of Symmetrical Fixed Arches The fixed arch shown in Fig. 10.6*a* has a total of six reactions, i.e., a vertical and a horizontal reaction and a moment at each springing. There are, then, three redundant reactions to be determined. If no horizontal loads are present, the condition that the sum of horizontal forces be zero results in $H_l = H_r$.

For purposes of analysis the arch is cut through the crown, and each half arch is regarded as a statically determinate cantilever fixed at its springing. In the plane of separation, in general, a horizontal and a vertical force H_c and V_c and a bending moment M_c will act from one half onto the other. These three quantities are taken as the redundants. They are shown, in Fig. 10.6*b*, acting in the direction and sense which will be assumed as positive in the following derivations. In any other cross section of the structure, M, N, and V will be assumed positive, as shown in Fig. 10.6*b*. If M_c, H_c, and V_c are known, M, N, and V at any point can be determined from statics.

The crown sections of the separate halves, through the action of loads,

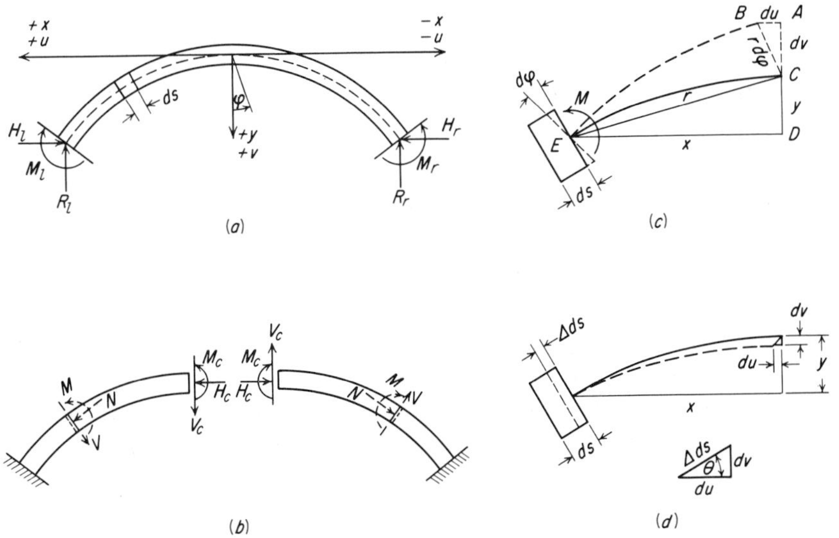

Fig. 10.6

temperature, and other influences, will be displaced from their original positions. In general, there will be a horizontal displacement u, a vertical displacement v, and a rotation of the normal to the crown section ϕ. The assumed positive directions of these displacements are shown in Fig. 10.6*a*. If the structure in fact consisted of two independent cantilevers, u, v, and ϕ would, in general, be different for the two halves. Since, actually, the arch is one continuous structure, these displacements must be equal in magnitude and sign. Consequently,

$$u_l = u_r \qquad v_l = v_r \qquad \phi_l = \phi_r \tag{10.12}$$

where the subscripts l and r refer to the left and right half arch, respectively. These three equations permit the determination of the redundants H_c, V_c, and M_c. In other words, in the arch these three quantities must be of such magnitude as to join the left and the right cantilevers into one continuous structure.

Isolating an element ds of the arch (Fig. 10.6*c*), one can determine the contributions du, dv, and $d\phi$ made to the total displacements u, v, and ϕ by the deformations of this single element. The bending moment M causes a rotation $d\phi$ which is determined by Eq. (10.1). The part of the arch between the section and the crown, considered rigid and represented by its axis in Fig. 10.6*c*, rotates through the same angle $d\phi$, which, consequently, also represents the rotation of the crown section caused by the deformation of the element ds. Furthermore, since the triangles ABC and CDE are similar, it is seen that

$$\frac{du}{r\,d\phi} = \frac{y}{r} \qquad \text{and} \qquad \frac{dv}{r\,d\phi} = \frac{x}{r}$$

from which

$$du = y\,d\phi \qquad dv = x\,d\phi \tag{10.13}$$

Substituting $d\phi$ from Eq. (10.1), one obtains

$$du = \pm\frac{My\,ds}{EI} \qquad dv = \mp\frac{Mx\,ds}{EI} \qquad d\phi = \pm\frac{M\,ds}{EI} \tag{10.13a}$$

In these and the following expressions, if two signs are shown, the upper refers to the left half arch, and the lower to the right.

In addition to the angular rotation $d\phi$, the elements ds will be uniformly compressed or stretched by normal forces N, temperature variations, and shrinkage. If $\Delta\,ds$ is the change of ds due to any of these actions, it is seen, from Fig. 10.6*d*, that

$$du = \Delta\,ds\cos\theta \qquad dv = \Delta\,ds\sin\theta \tag{10.14}$$

An axial force N results in $\Delta\, ds = N\, ds/EA$, and hence in horizontal and vertical displacements

$$du = \frac{N\, ds \cos \theta}{EA} \qquad dv = \frac{N\, ds \sin \theta}{EA} \tag{10.14a}$$

At any point of the arch, x, y, the moment M, and the axial force N are the resultant effects of the three crown quantities M_c, H_c, and V_c and of the external loads acting on the half-arch cantilever in which the particular section is located. They can be calculated by statics (see Fig. 10.6*b*) and are tabulated below:

Force and moment at section x, y

Due to......	M_c	H_c	V_c	External loads
M	M_c	$H_c y$	$-V_c x$	M_0
N	0	$H_c \cos \theta$	$V_c \sin \theta$	N_0

The signs in this table are valid for both halves of the arch. In this connection it is important to note that for the right half arch x and θ are negative, whereas y is positive by the sign convention given in Fig. 10.6*a*. It should also be noted that external gravity loads result in negative M_0 (see Fig. 10.6*b*). N_0 at any section is the component, in the direction of the tangent to the arch axis, of all the external loads located between that section and the crown; gravity loads therefore result in positive N_0.

By substituting the values M and N from the table into Eqs. (10.13*a*) and (10.14*a*) and integrating for the left half from 0 to $+s/2$, and for the right half from 0 to $-s/2$, one obtains separately the crown displacements u and v for either half. If these are substituted in Eqs. (10.12), they result in three simultaneous equations for H_c, M_c, and V_c. If any particular action, for example, that of H_c, results in equal displacements for both halves, these can obviously be omitted from Eqs. (10.12), since equal terms on both sides of an equation cancel. For example, H_c results in equal vertical displacements v_l and v_r, as is seen directly from Fig. 10.6*c* (the corresponding behavior of the right half is obtained by mirroring the entire figure about the vertical axis through the crown). Hence, the contribution of H_c to the vertical displacements can be omitted in the second of Eqs. (10.12). On the other hand, the horizontal crown displacements caused by H_c are equal in magnitude but opposite in sign, since the crown section of the left cantilever is displaced to the left (see Fig. 10.6*b*), and that of the right cantilever to the right. Hence, these displacements must be entered in the first of Eqs. (10.12).

Table 10.1 Crown displacement of half arch of Fig. 10.7: All integrals $\int_0^{+s/2}$ for left half; $\int_0^{-s/2}$ for right half; multiply by $1/E$

Caused by bending

	$+M_c$	$+H_c$	$+V_c$	$+M_0$
u	$\pm M_c \int \frac{y\,ds}{I}$*	$\pm H_c \int \frac{y^2\,ds}{I}$	Cancels	$\pm \int \frac{M_0 y\,ds}{I}$
v	Cancels	Cancels	$\pm V_c \int \frac{x^2\,ds}{I}$	$\mp \int \frac{M_0 x\,ds}{I}$
ϕ	$\pm M_c \int \frac{ds}{I}$	$\pm H_c \int \frac{y\,ds}{I}$*	Cancels	$\pm \int \frac{M_0\,ds}{I}$

Caused by arch shortening and temperature

	$+H_c$	$+V_c$	$+N_0$	$+t°$	$+\Delta t°$
u	$\pm H_c \int \frac{\cos^2\theta\,ds}{A}$	Cancels	$\pm N_0 \int \frac{\cos\theta\,ds}{A}$	$\mp \omega t° E \int \cos\theta\,ds$	Cancels
v	Cancels	$\pm V_c \int \frac{\sin^2\theta\,ds}{A}$	Cancels	Cancels	$\mp \Delta t°\,\omega E \int \frac{x\,ds}{t}$
ϕ	0	0	0	0	$\pm \Delta t°\,\omega E \int \frac{ds}{t}$

* These expressions are zero when x and y are measured from the elastic center.

In Table 10.1 are given the crown displacements caused by the various actions, separately for both halves. They must be substituted in Eqs. (10.12) to determine the three redundants. In this table the notation "cancels" designates displacements equal in sign and magnitude for both halves, which cancel if substituted in Eqs. (10.12). For simplicity, all values in the table are multiplied by E.

In addition to the displacements caused by the crown forces and the external loads (which include the weight of the arch), those resulting from temperature changes and shrinkage must be considered just as in the case of the two-hinged arch. In fact, these influences are of more consequence for the fixed than for the two-hinged arch, since the latter, being free to rotate at the supports, is better able to accommodate itself to changes in shape without excessive stress.

A uniform temperature increase of amount $t°$ causes an elongation $\Delta\,ds = \omega t°\,ds$ which, if substituted in Eqs. (10.14) and integrated over the respective half arches, gives the corresponding crown displacements. Likewise, a temperature differential between top and bottom fiber (Fig. 10.5*d* and *e*) results in a rotation $d\phi$, given by Eq. (10.8). This must be substituted in Eqs. (10.13) and similarly integrated to result in the corresponding crown displacements. These values are shown in Table 10.1. The general information as to range of temperature and method of accounting for shrinkage given in the article on two-hinged arches is valid for the fixed arch.

If the displacements of the table are substituted in Eqs. (10.12), the second equation contains only V_c as an unknown and hence can be solved for this quantity. The first and third equations, however, contain both H_c and M_c, resulting in two simultaneous equations which are awkward to solve and, when solved, lead to rather lengthy expressions for these two quantities. This complication can be overcome by a suitable transformation of coordinates.

Consider the first term of the first row and the second term of the third row of the displacement table; if $\int y\, ds/I$ could be made zero, the first of Eqs. (10.12) would contain only H_c as an unknown, and the third only M_c. Obviously, for the location of the coordinate axes shown in Fig. 10.6*a*, this integral is not zero, since y is positive throughout. It is possible, however, to shift the origin to a position which will make this integral vanish. To visualize the meaning of this shift, assume the arch axis to be loaded by fictitious loads equal to $1/I$ at every point, as shown in Fig. 10.7*a*. Then, since y_1 is the lever arm of any of these forces about the origin, $\int y_1\, ds/I = 0$ shows that the sum of the moments of all these forces about the x axis is to be zero; i.e., the axis is to pass through the center of these forces or is to be coincident with their resultant. The coordinate origin determined in this manner is known as the *elastic center* of the arch. By the general formula for the location of the resultant of parallel forces,

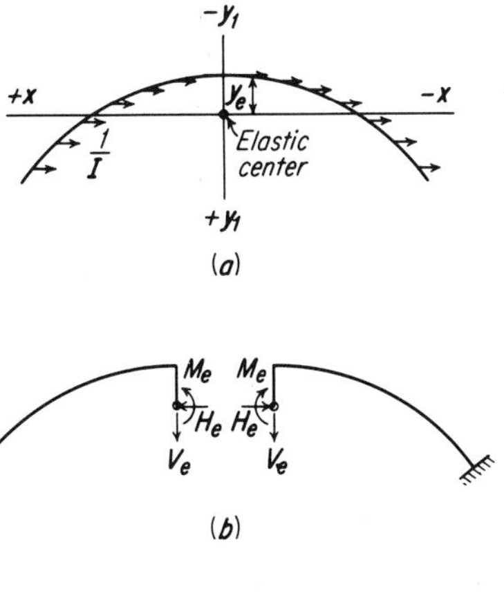

Fig. 10.7

the distance y_e of the elastic center from the center of the crown is then found from

$$y_e = \frac{\int_0^{s/2} (y\,ds/I)}{\int_0^{s/2} (ds/I)} \tag{10.15}$$

By symmetry these integrals need be extended only over the half arch.

Let y_1 designate the ordinate of any point on the arch axis measured from this new origin, as shown in Fig. 10.7*a*. Now, assume that the elastic center is joined to the crown section by a rigid, fictitious lever, as shown separately for each half in Fig. 10.7*b*. Instead of introducing the three unknown quantities M_c, H_c, and V_c at the crown, introduce three similar quantities M_e, H_e, and V_e at the ends of these fictitious levers, positive as shown. Then the previously tabulated expressions for u, v, and ϕ refer to the new origin (end of levers) if, in them, y is replaced by y_1, and M_c, H_c, and V_c by M_e, H_e, and V_e. Equations (10.12) are now valid for the ends of these levers. Since the levers are regarded as rigidly connected to their respective crown sections, and the two halves are fitted together to form the complete arch, the ends of the two levers cannot separate, no matter how the arch deforms. Thus the displacements u, v, and ϕ must be the same for the ends of both levers.

Since the origin is now chosen such that $\int y_1\,ds/I = 0$, the first term of the first row and the second term of the third row in Table 10.1 vanish. (These terms are indicated by asterisks in the table.) Hence, if the remaining terms of the first, second, and third rows of the table are substituted, respectively, in the first, second, and third of Eqs. (10.12), each results in one equation with one unknown, H_e, V_e, and M_e in that order. Since in each individual expression the respective integral for the left half arch is added to that for the right half, integration can be extended directly from $-s/2$ to $+s/2$, rather than writing two integrals for each term. The three redundant quantities, referred to the elastic center, then become

$$H_e = \frac{-\int_{-s/2}^{s/2} \frac{M_0 y_1\,ds}{I} - \int_{-s/2}^{s/2} \frac{N_0 \cos\theta\,ds}{A} + Et^\circ\omega l - E\,\Delta t^\circ\,\omega \int_{-s/2}^{s/2} \frac{y_1\,ds}{t}}{\int_{-s/2}^{s/2} \frac{y_1^2\,ds}{I} + \int_{-s/2}^{s/2} \frac{\cos^2\theta\,ds}{A}} \tag{10.16}$$

$$V_e = \frac{\int_{-s/2}^{s/2} (M_0 x\,ds/I) - \int_{-s/2}^{s/2} (N_0 \sin\theta\,ds/A)}{\int_{-s/2}^{s/2} (x^2\,ds/I) + \int_{-s/2}^{s/2} (\sin^2\theta\,ds/A)} \tag{10.17}$$

$$M_e = \frac{-\int_{-s/2}^{s/2} (M_0\,ds/I) - E\,\Delta t^\circ\,\omega \int_{-s/2}^{s/2} (ds/t)}{\int_{-s/2}^{s/2} (ds/I)} \tag{10.18}$$

where all integrals extend over the entire arch, as indicated.

Once these quantities are determined, it is more convenient to work with crown moments and forces (Fig. 10.6b) than with those referred to the elastic center (Fig. 10.7b). As is seen directly from this figure,

$$H_c = H_e \qquad V_c = V_e \qquad M_c = M_e - H_e y_e \tag{10.19}$$

Equations (10.16) to (10.18) account for all influences that act on symmetrical fixed arches. In any particular design it will often be found that certain of these influences are small compared with others and can be neglected. The analogous situation for the two-hinged arch was discussed in Art. 10.3. As in that case, the influence of rib shortening caused by axial forces N is small except for unusually flat and thick arches. Except for such cases, therefore, the second term in both numerator and denominator of Eqs. (10.16) and (10.17) can be omitted. The last term in the numerator of Eq. (10.16) will often be found to be small in comparison with other terms. Indeed, for an arch with constant cross section this term vanishes. It does so because the elastic center was chosen such that $\int y_1\,ds/I = 0$, which, for constant I, is the same as $\int y_1\,ds = 0$. This makes $\int y_1\,ds/t = 0$ if t is constant. It is seen, therefore, that the magnitude of that term in Eq. (10.16) depends essentially on the ratio of the depths at springing and crown and will usually be negligible. Finally, the term containing $\Delta t°$ in Eq. (10.18) must be included only in the rather rare case of a roof arch not insulated at the top.

Hence, the following simplified expressions are usually accurate enough for purposes of design:

$$H_e = \frac{-\int_{-s/2}^{s/2} (M_0 y_1\,ds/I) + Et°\omega l}{\int_{-s/2}^{s/2} (y_1^2\,ds/I)} \tag{10.16a}$$

$$V_e = \frac{\int_{-s/2}^{s/2} (M_0 x\,ds/I)}{\int_{-s/2}^{s/2} (x^2\,ds/I)} \tag{10.17a}$$

$$M_e = \frac{-\int_{-s/2}^{s/2} (M_0\,ds/I)}{\int_{-s/2}^{s/2} (ds/I)} \tag{10.18a}$$

A word of warning should be included in connection with these simplified equations. Although under the specific conditions which were enumerated, the omitted terms are usually negligibly small, there is no way of definitely ascertaining this fact except by computing them. It is therefore suggested, particularly for closely designed arches of significant spans, that the simplified equations be used for preliminary design but that in computing final stresses the influence of the omitted terms be at least estimated numerically and included in the final expressions if found significant.

10.5 Evaluation of Integrals The integrals which occur in the expressions for the redundants of both the two-hinged arch [Eqs. (10.11) and (10.11*a*)] and the fixed arch [Eqs. (10.16) to (10.18) and (10.16*a*) to (10.18*a*)] can be evaluated by direct integration only in a few simple cases. For this reason it is necessary, in general, to approximate the integrals with sums of a finite number of terms.

For this purpose the arch axis (not the span) is generally divided into a number of equal intervals Δs. A maximum of 10 intervals for the half arch is generally sufficient; 6 to 8 intervals may often be used for small, secondary structures. The pertinent quantities entering a particular integral, such as y_1, M_0, and I for $\int M_0 y_1\, ds/I$, are then computed for the midpoint of each individual interval Δs. Then

$$\int \frac{M_0 y_1\, ds}{I} \cong \sum \frac{M_{0n} y_{1n}}{I_n} \Delta s$$

where the subscript n refers to the values M_0, y_1, and I at the midpoint of the nth interval. The other integrals in Eqs. (10.11) and (10.16) to (10.18) are computed in a similar manner by summation. Attention must be paid to the signs of the various quantities. Thus, y_1 is negative if measured upward from the elastic center of the fixed arch (see Fig. 10.7*a*); x is negative if measured to the right of the crown of the fixed arch, but is positive throughout for the two-hinged arch, as is evident from Figs. 10.7*a* and 10.5*a*. The importance of this is evident, for instance, in connection with Eq. (10.17). If an arch is symmetrically loaded, M_0 and N_0 are equal at corresponding points of the two half arches. On the other hand, for the left half arch x and $\sin \theta$ are positive, whereas for the right half they are negative. Each contribution to the sums of both numerator integrals made by an element on the left half is, therefore, canceled by the equal and opposite contribution made by the corresponding element on the right. Consequently, V_e (and thereby V_c) is zero for symmetrical loads, in analogy with a simple beam which has zero shear at midspan, if symmetrically loaded.

For fixed arches, the location of the elastic center [Eq. (10.15)] is likewise calculated by replacing the integrals with corresponding sums. The computation of these sums is best arranged in tabular form, as demonstrated in the design example of Art. 10.8.

Moments of inertia can be computed for the entire concrete section, including the tension portion, without regard to reinforcement.

10.6 Preliminary Arch Design The analysis discussed in the preceding articles can be carried out only if loads, as well as all dimensions of the arch, are definitely known. Before such an analysis can be made, it is therefore necessary to determine the shape and weight of the arch by a preliminary design. In general, only the span, the rise, and the loads superimposed on the arch are known. (In cases in which the designer is free to select the rise it is important to consider that the horizontal thrust decreases as the ratio of rise to span increases, with a consequent saving in cost of abutments.) It is then required to determine the shape of the arch axis and the dimensions of the cross sections at various points and, from these, to find the weight of the arch proper. Once these quantities are preliminarily determined, an exact stress analysis can be made. Should this analysis indicate the necessity for a considerable change in the assumed dimensions, a second, final analysis must be made, based on the corrected dimensions. Since such computations are very time-consuming, it is desirable to determine the shape of the arch by preliminary design as accurately as possible, so that subsequent corrections are held to a minimum.

The axis of the arch is often made to coincide with the equilibrium or string polygon for dead load. If this is done, bending moments are caused by live load only. This polygon can be drawn only after the weight of the arch is determined. For roof arches, in which dead loads are mostly uniform along the axis the parabola is a close approximation to the dead-load polygon, and, with the designations of Fig. 10.9, the equations of the axis and the slope are

$$y = 4rlc^2 \tag{10.19a}$$

$$\tan \theta = 8rc \tag{10.19b}$$

Next it is necessary to obtain an estimate of the maximum moments, thrusts, and shears for the purpose of determining the required cross section. To this end superimposed loads are determined, and a rough estimate is made of the weight of the arch proper. If temperature stresses need consideration, the limiting temperatures are also determined. With these data it is possible to determine M, V, and H from Tables 10.2 and 10.3.

For roof arches, the dead load is generally approximately uniformly distributed along the arch axis. The load per horizontal foot of span is therefore distributed as shown in Fig. 10.9. In order that Tables 10.2 and 10.3 may be used this load can be divided into a uniform load g and a variable load of maximum intensity g' at the springing. The tables then allow one to compute separately the influences of each of these two loads,

Fig. 10.8

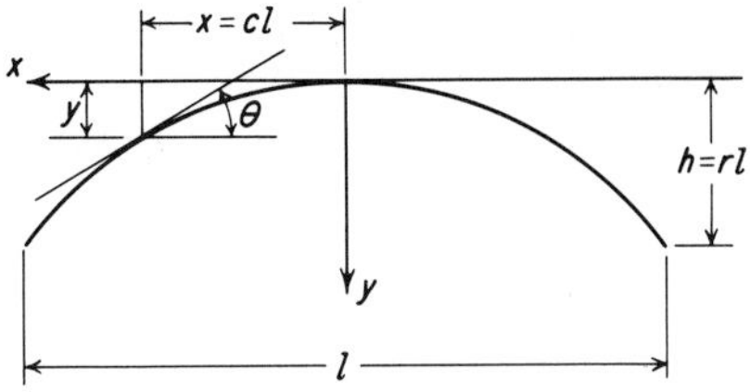

Table 10.2 **Moments and reactions of two-hinged parabolic arches***

	Case I	Case II	Case III	Case IV	Case V	Case VI	Case VII	Case VIII	Case IX
		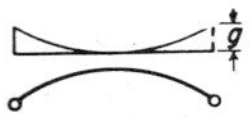	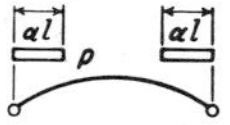	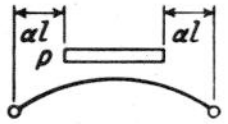	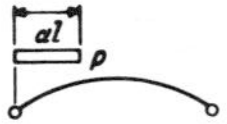	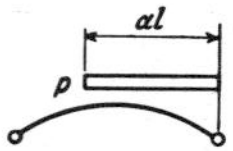	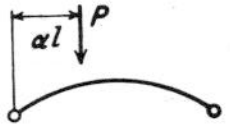	Uniform temperature change	Temperature differential of Δt°
R_l	$\frac{gl}{2}$	$\frac{g'l}{6}$	$p\alpha l$	$\frac{pl}{2}(1-2\alpha)$	$\frac{p\alpha l}{2}(2-\alpha)$	$\frac{p\alpha^2 l}{2}$	$P(1-\alpha)$	None	None
R_r	$\frac{gl}{2}$	$\frac{g'l}{6}$	$p\alpha l$	$\frac{pl}{2}(1-2\alpha)$	$\frac{p\alpha^2 l}{2}$	$\frac{p\alpha l}{2}(2-\alpha)$	$P\alpha$	None	None
H	$\frac{gl^2}{8h}$	$\frac{g'l^2}{42h}$	$\frac{pl^2}{8h}\alpha^2(2\alpha^3-5\alpha^2+5)$	$\frac{-pl^2}{8h}(2\alpha^5-5\alpha^4+5\alpha^2-1)$	$\frac{pl^2}{16h}\alpha^2(2\alpha^3-5\alpha^2+5)$	$\frac{pl^2}{16h}\alpha^2(2\alpha^3-5\alpha^2+5)$	$\frac{5Pl}{8h}\alpha(\alpha^3-2\alpha^2+1)$	$\frac{15EI_c\omega t^\circ}{8h^2}$	$\frac{5EI_{c\omega}\,\Delta t^\circ}{4t_c h}$
M_c	None	$-\frac{g'l^2}{338}$	$\frac{-pl^2}{8}\alpha^2(2\alpha^3-5\alpha^2+1)$	$\frac{pl^2}{8}\alpha^2(2\alpha^3-5\alpha^2+1)$	. . . .	. . . .	$\frac{(1-\alpha)l}{8}P(5\alpha^3-5\alpha^2-5\alpha+4)$	$\frac{-15EI_c\,\omega t^\circ}{8h}$	$\frac{-5EI_{c\omega}\,\Delta t^\circ}{4t_c}$
$M_{l/4}$	None	$\frac{g'l^2}{234}$	. . . .	. . . .	$\frac{-pl^2}{64}(6\alpha^5-15\alpha^4+23\alpha^2-16\alpha+2)$ †	$-\frac{pl^2}{64}\alpha^2(6\alpha^3-15\alpha^2+7)$ ‡	$\frac{1}{4}(R_r l-Hh)$ ¶ $\frac{1}{4}(R_l l-Hh)$ ¶	$\frac{-45EI_c\,\omega t^\circ}{32h}$	$\frac{-15EI_{c\omega}\,\Delta t^\circ}{16t_c}$

* According to Eqs. (10.19).

† $\frac{l}{4}\le \alpha l \le \frac{l}{2}$

‡ $\frac{l}{2}\le \alpha l \le \frac{3l}{4}$

¶ $\alpha l \le l/4$

¶ $\alpha l \ge l/4$

Table 10.3 Moments and reactions of fixed parabolic arches*

	Case I	Case II	Case III	Case IV	Case V	Case VI	Case VII	Case VIII	Case IX
		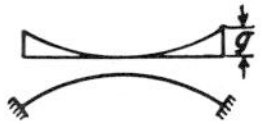	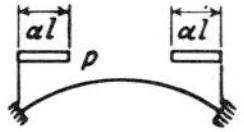	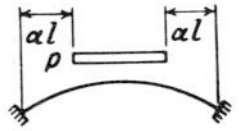	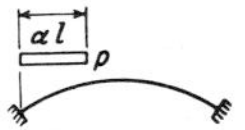	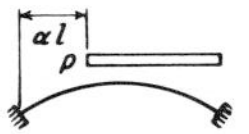	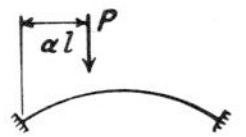	Uniform temperature change	Temperature differential of Δt°
R_l	$\frac{gl}{2}$	$\frac{g'l}{6}$	$p\alpha l$	$\frac{pl}{2}(1-2\alpha)$	$\frac{pl}{2}\alpha(\alpha^3-2\alpha^2+2)$	$\frac{pl}{2}(1+\alpha)(1-\alpha)^3$	$P(1-\alpha)^2(1+2\alpha)$	None	None
R_r	$\frac{gl}{2}$	$\frac{g'l}{6}$	$p\alpha l$	$\frac{pl}{2}(1-2\alpha)$	$\frac{pl}{2}\alpha^3(2-\alpha)$	$\frac{pl}{2}(1-2\alpha^3+\alpha^4)$	$P\alpha^2(3-2\alpha)$	None	None
H	$\frac{gl^2}{8h}$	$\frac{g'l^2}{56h}$	$\frac{pl^2}{4h}\alpha^3(6\alpha^2-15\alpha+10)$	$\frac{-pl^2}{8h}(12\alpha^5-30\alpha^4+20\alpha^3-1)$	$\frac{pl^2}{8h}\alpha^3(6\alpha^2-15\alpha+10)$	$\frac{pl^2}{8h}(1-\alpha)^3(6\alpha^2+3\alpha+1)$	$\frac{15}{4}\frac{Pl}{h}\alpha^2(1-\alpha)^2$	$\frac{45EI_c\omega t^\circ}{4h^2}$	None
M_{ls}	None	$\frac{-g'l^2}{210}$	$-\frac{pl^2}{2}\alpha^2(1-\alpha)^2(1-2\alpha)$	$\frac{pl^2}{2}\alpha^2(1-\alpha)^2(1-2\alpha)$	$-\frac{pl^2}{2}\alpha^2(1-\alpha)^3$	$\frac{pl^2}{2}\alpha^2(1-\alpha)^3$	$-\frac{Pl}{2}\alpha(1-\alpha)^2(2-5\alpha)$	$\frac{15EI_c\omega t^\circ}{2h}$	$\frac{-EI_c\omega\,\Delta t^\circ}{t_c}$
M_{rs}	None	$\frac{-g'l^2}{210}$	$-\frac{pl^2}{2}\alpha^2(1-\alpha)^2(1-2\alpha)$	$\frac{pl^2}{2}\alpha^2(1-\alpha)^2(1-2\alpha)$	$\frac{pl^2}{2}\alpha^3(1-\alpha)^2$	$-\frac{pl^2}{2}\alpha^3(1-\alpha)^2$	$\frac{Pl}{2}\alpha^2(1-\alpha)(3-5\alpha)$	$\frac{15EI_c\omega t^\circ}{2h}$	$\frac{-EI_c\omega\,\Delta t^\circ}{t_c}$
M_c	None	$-\frac{g'l^2}{560}$	$-\frac{pl^2}{4}\alpha^3(1-2\alpha)(2-\alpha)$	$\frac{pl^2}{4}\alpha^3(1-2\alpha)(2-\alpha)$	$-\frac{pl^2}{8}\alpha^3(1-2\alpha)(2-\alpha)$ †	$\frac{pl^2}{8}\alpha^3(1-2\alpha)(2-\alpha)$ ‡	$-\frac{Pl}{4}\alpha^2(5\alpha^2-10\alpha+3)$	$\frac{15EI_c\omega t^\circ}{4h}$	$\frac{-EI_c\omega\,\Delta t^\circ}{t_c}$

* According to Eqs. (10.19).

† $0 \leqq \alpha l \leqq \frac{l}{2}$

‡ $0 \leqq \alpha l \leqq \frac{l}{2}$

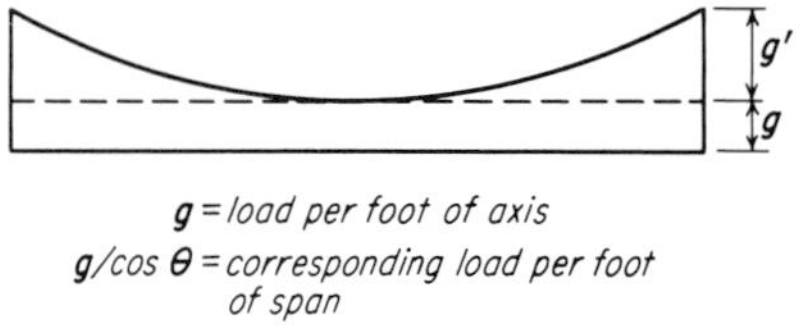

Fig. **10.9**

which must be added to result in the final M, V, and H. Live load must be so placed as to give maximum moments or forces; this will generally require partial loading of the span. The necessary formulas for partial loading are included in the tables; the load positions, determined by $\alpha = a/l$, are as shown in the sketches. Positions of loads and values of α which result with good accuracy in maximum moments at the crown, quarter point, or springing are given for both types of arches in Fig. 10.10.

In order to obtain simple expressions for Tables 10.2 and 10.3, it was assumed that

$$I = \frac{I_c}{\cos\theta}$$

Even considerable deviation from this relationship has relatively little influence and leads to satisfactory accuracy.

The length of the *half axis* s for parabolic arches is very nearly

$$s = \frac{l}{2}\left(1 + \tfrac{8}{3}r^2\right) \tag{10.20}$$

Once approximate values of M, N, and H are found for the critical sections from Table 10.2 or 10.3, the required cross-sectional dimensions are determined in the usual manner for bending plus axial thrust. Reinforcement is usually provided symmetrically near both faces. For reasons

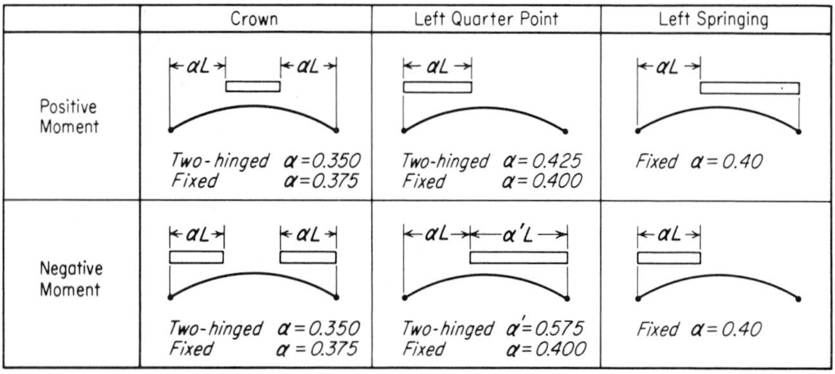

Crown
Left Quarter Point
Left Springing
Positive Moment
αL αL
Two-hinged α=0.350
Fixed α=0.375
αL
Two-hinged α=0.425
Fixed α=0.400
αL
Fixed α=0.40
Negative Moment
αL αL
Two-hinged α=0.350
Fixed α=0.375
αL α'L
Two-hinged α'=0.575
Fixed α=0.400
αL
Fixed α=0.40

Fig. **10.10** Live-load positions for maximum moment.

of appearance the depth is often increased gradually from crown to springing or held constant, but it is hardly ever decreased toward the springing.

With dimensions of the cross sections determined as required by strength and appearance, the weight of the arch is computed. If the new total dead load differs materially from that assumed in the beginning, the preliminary design procedure is repeated with adjusted loads, and dimensions are correspondingly corrected.

Since, at this stage, all loads are known, it is now possible to obtain the final location of the arch axis by passing a string polygon for dead load through the midpoints of the crown and springing sections. For this purpose, as well as for the subsequent exact analysis, the half axis is generally divided into six to ten equal sections (see Art. 10.5), and the dead load of each section applied at its center. A smooth curve which is tangent to this string polygon then represents the final location of the arch axis. Accurate values of M, N, and V are now determined by elastic analysis at the crown, quarter point, and springing, and at such additional points as may be necessary. The difference between these accurate values and the approximate ones obtained from the preliminary design will require minor adjustments of cross-sectional dimensions, which can often be made merely by changing the reinforcement without alteration of overall size. Even if the thickness and width of the arch are changed in this stage of design, the elaborate elastic analysis need not be repeated for the adjusted sections unless these adjustments are quite sizable. This is due to the fact that the magnitudes of M, N, and V caused by external loads depend primarily on the ratios of the moments of inertia along the arch to that at the crown, rather than on their absolute values. Only the stresses due to rib shortening and temperature depend directly on the absolute size of the cross section and may have to be recomputed if the dimensions change significantly. The design of a simple roof arch in Art. 10.8 illustrates the above procedure.

10.7 Hinges in Reinforced-concrete Structures It is the function of hinges to transmit safely the thrust N and the shear force S and, at the same time, to offer little resistance to rotation. An ideal hinge should be entirely free to rotate, since only then will the bending moment at the hinge be zero, as assumed in the analysis of hinged structures. Such ideal hinges cannot be constructed, since friction or other inevitable restraining factors cannot be avoided. Practically, however, it is only necessary to ensure that the flexibility of the hinge be considerably greater than that of any other portion of the structure of which it is a part. This will result in very small moments in the hinge as compared to the moments in the structure proper and, therefore, will lead only to negligible errors. The use of hinges is not restricted to arches. They are equally useful in rigid frames,

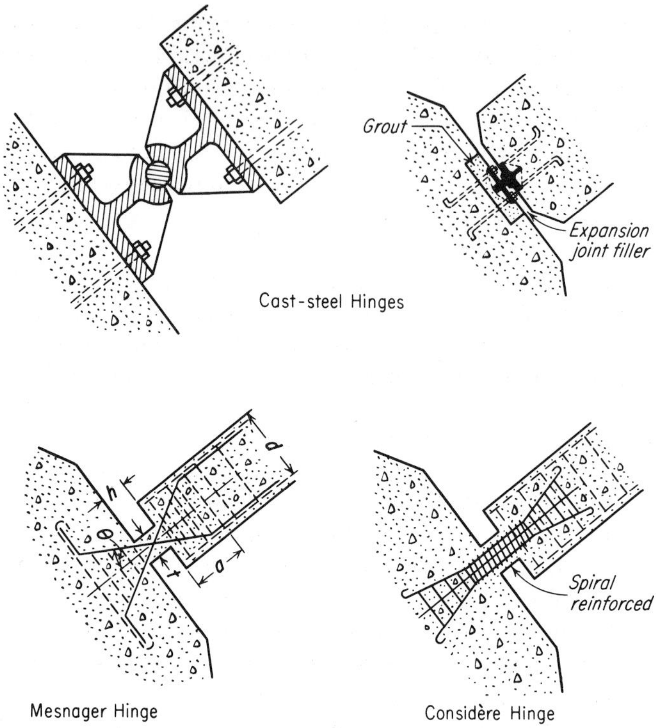

***Fig.* 10.11** Hinges for concrete structures.

in bridges as well as in buildings, particularly for long-span single-story frames. They reduce or, in the case of three-hinged spans, eliminate the stresses caused by rib shortening, by temperature, and by slight foundation movements. For these reasons a considerable reduction in the dimensions and weight of the structure and foundation can often be achieved by their use.

The main practical types of hinges for concrete structures are given in Fig. 10.11. The steel hinges shown there result in more perfect hinge action than the concrete hinges, but are considerably more expensive. Their use, today, is restricted to unusually heavy structures. Of the two types of concrete hinges, named after the French engineers who developed them, the Mesnager hinge ensures greater freedom of rotation and, except for very large thrusts, is the most satisfactory hinge presently in use.

In order to obtain maximum flexibility in a Mesnager hinge, it has been recommended that the hinge opening h should at least be equal to the concrete thickness t. A value $h = 1.3t$ is recommended by some. However, hinges with smaller openings have been used successfully. For the same purpose of maximum flexibility, the crossed steel bars should not be too thick and short. On the other hand, if their diameter were too small in relation to their length, they would be likely to buckle. For this reason the slenderness ratio L/r of the hinge bars should be between the limits of 20 and 40, L being the length of the inclined bar between concrete faces (that is, $h/\cos\theta$), and r the radius of gyration of the bar (that is, $D/4$ for round bars of diameter D). The length of embedment of the hinge bars on either side of the hinge should be at least equal to that prescribed for dowels connecting columns to footings.

To find the required area of the hinge bars, it is assumed that they form a triangular truss which transmits the normal and shear forces N and S, as shown in Fig. 10.12. It is easily seen that the compression stress in bars 1 is equal to

$$f_s' = \frac{N}{A_s' \cos\theta} + \frac{S}{A_s' \sin\theta} \tag{10.21}$$

where A_s' is the total combined area of all hinge bars. This stress should not exceed 30 per cent of the yield point of the hinge bars. The large factor of safety, $1/0.3 = 3.33$, is introduced for the following reason: Even though, by the above procedure, the bars are assumed to be subjected only to axial compression, like members of a truss, any rotation actually occurring at the hinge bends the bars and induces corresponding flexural stresses. Such rotations actually do take place during the lifetime of the structure and are caused primarily by changes in live load and in temperature. These flexural stresses superpose on the computed compression and correspondingly increase the values of the actual maximum stresses in the bars. Rather than to attempt computing these additional stresses, it is generally satisfactory to keep the compression stress f_s' sufficiently low so that the bars will not be overstressed by superposed bending.

The inclined bars, transmitting their forces to the concrete by bond along the embedded length, exert a bursting force which must be resisted by lateral reinforcement (stirrups and ties), as shown in Fig. 10.11. Only the part of the lateral reinforcement within a distance $a = 8D$ from the face of the concrete is considered effective in resisting the bursting force. The stress in the lateral reinforcement can be computed from

$$f_s'' = \frac{(N/2)\tan\theta + Sa/jd}{0.005ab + A_s''} \tag{10.22}$$

where, in addition to previously defined quantities, A_s'' is the combined area of lateral stirrups or ties located within $a = 8D$ from the free face of the hinge, j

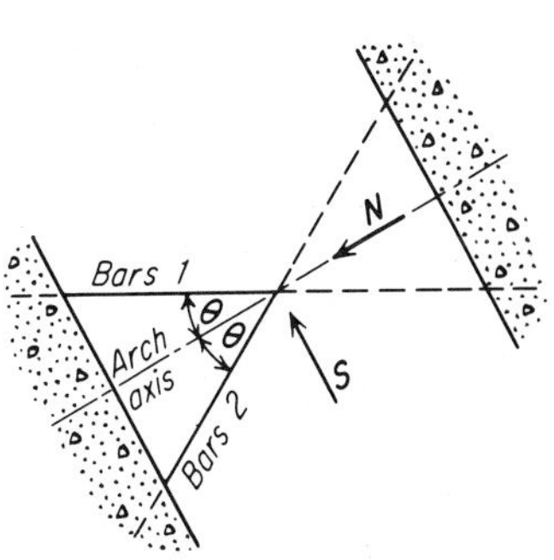

Fig. 10.12

can be taken as 0.9, d is shown in Fig. 10.11, and b is the horizontal width of the hinge, equal, in most cases, to the width of the arch rib.

More detailed information on concrete hinges can be found in a paper by G. C. Ernst; most texts on steel bridges give adequate data on steel hinges of the type used for both steel and concrete arches and frames.

10.8 Design of Two-hinged, Tied Roof Arch Arches of the type shown in Fig. 10.2 with 90-ft span are to be spaced at 20-ft intervals, to support a fireproof, insulated roof. The roof itself is to consist of precast slabs spanning between arches and weighing 40 psf. Four-ply tar and gravel roofing to cover the slabs weighs 5 psf. To account for the effects of wind and snow a live load of 35 psf is assumed.

The columns of Fig. 10.2 supporting the arch cannot develop sufficient rigidity to serve as fixed supports. A two-hinged arch is therefore indicated. In addition, if the horizontal thrust were transmitted to the supporting columns and frames, they would become excessively heavy and costly. For this reason a tied arch of the type shown in Fig. 10.13 will be used. A 15-ft rise has been selected, resulting in a rise-span ratio of $\frac{1}{6}$.

The sample design that follows is abbreviated for reasons of clarity and space. Computations of moments, etc., caused by small secondary loads, such as from the weight of the tie rod and the hangers, have been omitted, since they would complicate and lengthen the illustrative computations without adding new features. In actual design practice the influence of such loads should be included in the computations.

Preliminary design The loads per linear foot of arch axis are:
Dead load:

Concrete slabs: 40 × 20	=	800 lb per ft
Roofing: 5 × 20	=	100 lb per ft
Arch (assumed)	=	300 lb per ft
Total	=	1200 lb per ft

Live load:

Snow plus wind: 35 × 20 = 700 lb per ft

The load, uniform along the axis, results in distribution along the span as shown in Fig. 10.9. With θ computed from Eq. (10.19b), $g' = 380$ lb per ft for dead plus live load, and $g' = 240$ lb per ft for dead load alone. From the information of Table 10.2, the following moments and forces are obtained for the trial design:

Maximum horizontal reaction (loading Fig. 10.14a):

$$H = \frac{gl^2}{8h} + \frac{g'l^2}{42h} = 133 \text{ kips}$$

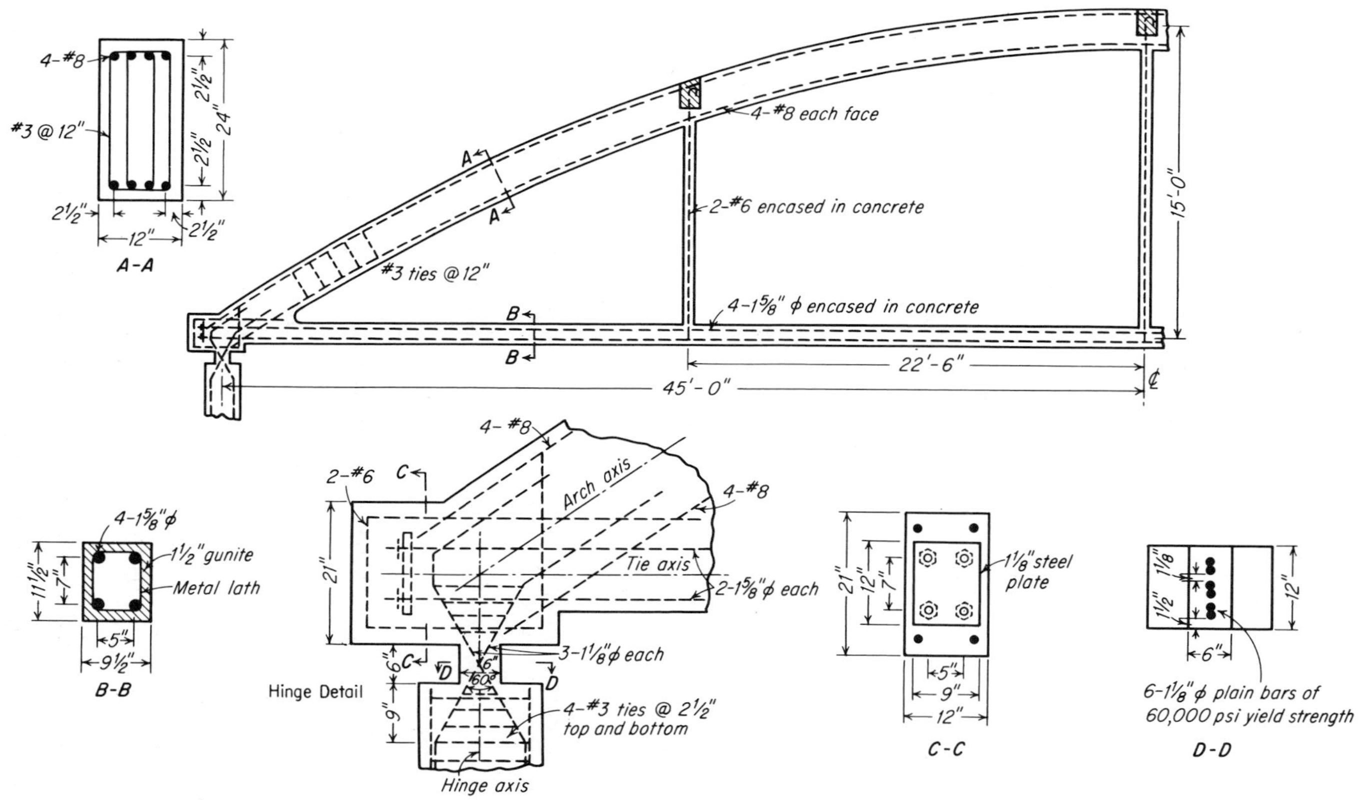

Fig. 10.13 Two-hinged, tied roof arch.

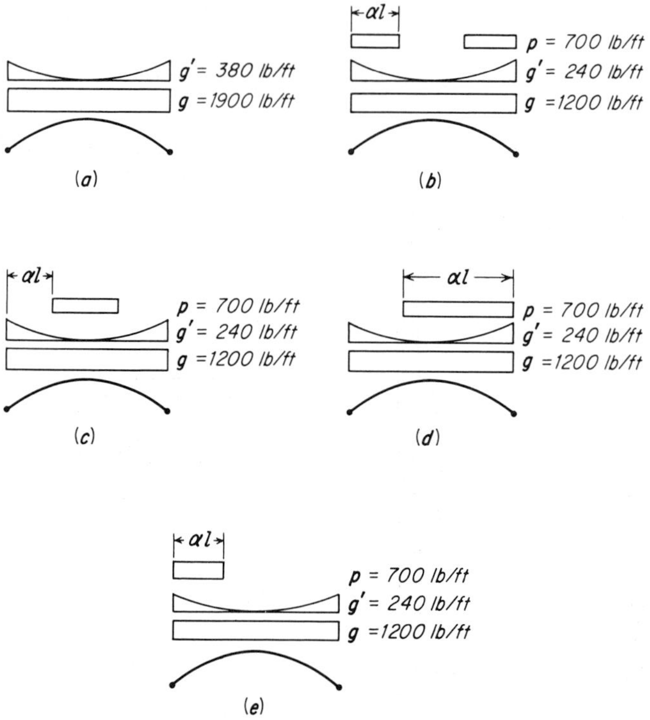

Fig. 10.14

Maximum negative crown moment (Fig. 10.14*b*; $\alpha = 0.35$ from Fig. 10.10):

$$M_c = -0.00296g'l^2 - 0.00725pl^2 = -46.5 \text{ ft-kips}$$

combined with

$$H = \frac{gl^2}{8h} + \frac{g'l^2}{42h} + 0.0685\,\frac{pl^2}{h} = 109.7 \text{ kips}$$

Maximum positive crown moment (Fig. 10.14*c*; $\alpha = 0.35$):

$$M_c = -0.00296g'l^2 + 0.00725pl^2 = 35.0 \text{ ft-kips}$$

combined with

$$H = \frac{gl^2}{8h} + \frac{g'l^2}{42h} + 0.0564\,\frac{pl^2}{h} = 105.5 \text{ kips}$$

Maximum negative quarter-point moment (Fig. 10.14*d*; $\alpha = 0.575$):

$$M_{l/4} = 0.00428g'l^2 - 0.0164pl^2 = -84.2 \text{ ft-kips}$$

combined with

$$H = \frac{gl^2}{8h} + \frac{g'l^2}{42h} + 0.0760 \frac{pl^2}{h} = 111 \text{ kips}$$

$$R_l = \frac{p\alpha^2 l}{2} + \frac{g'l}{6} + \frac{gl}{2} = 75 \text{ kips}$$

$V_{l/4}$ = vertical shear at quarter point
$= 75 - 22.5 \times 1.2 - 0.240 \times {}^{90}\!/_{8} = 45$ kips

The inclination $\theta = 18°25'$ is determined from Eq. (10.19*b*). Then

$T_{l/4}$ = axial thrust at quarter point
$= V_{l/4} \sin\theta + H \cos\theta$
$= 45 \times 0.316 + 111 \times 0.95 = 119.3$ kips

Maximum positive moment at quarter point (Fig. 10.14*e*; $\alpha = 0.425$):

$$M_{l/4} = 0.00428g'l^2 + 0.0164pl^2 = 100.8 \text{ ft-kips}$$

combined with

$$H = \frac{gl^2}{8h} + \frac{g'l^2}{42h} + 0.0435 \frac{pl^2}{h} = 100.6 \text{ kips}$$

$$R_l = p\alpha l\left(1 - \frac{\alpha}{2}\right) + \frac{gl}{2} + \frac{g'l}{6} = 86 \text{ kips}$$

$V_{l/4} = 86 - 22.5 \times 1.9 - 0.240 \times {}^{90}\!/_{8} = 41$ kips
$T_{l/4} = 41 \times 0.316 + 102.5 \times 0.95 = 110.5$ kips

Maximum axial thrust at springing (Fig. 10.14*a*):

$H = 133$ kips (as previously computed)
$R_l = 45 \times 1.9 + 15 \times 0.380 = 92.6$ kips
$T_l = R_1 \sin\theta + H \cos\theta$
$= 92.6 \times 0.538 + 133 \times 0.834 = 162$ kips

Maximum force in ties: $H = 133$ kips
Maximum crown moment: $M_c = -46.5$ ft-kips
Accompanying crown thrust: $T_c = 109.7$ kips
Maximum quarter-point moment: $M_{l/4} = 100.8$ ft-kips
Accompanying quarter-point thrust: $T_{l/4} = 110.5$ kips
Maximum thrust at springing: $T = 162$ kips

In a structure of this type, in which the entire arch rib is located below an insulated roof, no temperature differential will arise in the rib. In addition, the arch and the tie are always at substantially the same temperature. Any temperature change in the enclosed space will therefore cause the arch and the tie to expand or contract by the same amount and, for this reason, will not cause any temperature stresses in the structure.

For simplicity of formwork and for good appearance, an arch of constant cross section will be used. It is consequently only necessary to design the most critical section, which is seen to be that at the quarter point. A concrete with $f'_c = 3000$ psi and intermediate-grade steel will be used.

For a 14 × 22 in. cross section with eight No. 8 bars, $p_g = 0.0204$, $m = 15.7$, and $e_b = 7.51$ in. At the quarter point,

$$e = \frac{100.8 \times 12}{110.5} = 10.95 > e_b$$

indicating that the allowable load is controlled by tension. Following the recommended methods of the ACI Code as described in Art. 5.8, $F_a = 1350$ psi and $F_b = 1350$ psi. These values, together with e_b and I_{ut}, are used in the column-interaction equation to obtain $N_b = 184$ kips and $M_b = 115$ ft-kips. If the given cross section were subjected to pure flexure, M_0 would be 71.4 ft-kips. Accordingly, the axial load of 110.5 kips will permit an allowable moment of 98 ft-kips. While this is slightly below the estimated applied moment of 100.8 ft-kips, the small difference does not justify revision at this stage in the analysis. The weight of this arch rib is 320 lb per ft, as compared with the assumed weight of 300 lb per ft. Since the final location of the arch axis obtained by means of a string polygon is likely to result in a smaller required cross section than determined in this preliminary design, 300 lb per ft will be used for the final analysis.

The tie rod must resist $H_{max} = 133{,}000$ lb. To reduce the stretch of the tie, a low unit stress of about 15,000 psi will be used. Consequently, the required tie area is $A_{tr} = 133{,}000/15{,}000 = 8.9$ in.^{2} Since the final design is likely to result in a smaller H_{max}, four 1⅝-in. plain round bars with upset threaded ends will be used, furnishing an area $A_{tr} = 8.3$ in.^{2}

Final design Since the preliminary design did not result in any change of the weight of the arch rib, as originally assumed, the final design is carried out for the same loads as before, that is, 1200 lb per ft dead load and 700 lb per ft live load.

For the purpose of drawing the dead-load string polygon and for subsequent computations, the length of the arch axis is divided into 20 equal segments Δs. From Eq. (10.20), with $l = 90$ ft and $r = \frac{1}{6}$,

$$\Delta s = l\,\frac{1 + \frac{8}{3}r^2}{20} = \frac{96.66}{20} = 4.83 \text{ ft}$$

The dead load per segment is 1.2 × 4.83 = 5.80 kips. To draw the string polygon, it is simplest first to draw to a large scale the parabolic axis used in the preliminary analysis, which is easily done by computing a sufficient number of points by means of Eq. (10.19*a*). It is sufficient to draw half the arch, as shown in Fig. 10.15. The half axis is next divided into 10 equal parts of 4.83 ft each, and the weight of each such segment, 5.8 kips, is applied at its midpoint. An accurate string polygon for these loads is then drawn through the midpoints of crown and springing (not shown in Fig. 10.15 so as not to obscure the drawing). A curve tangent to this string polygon represents the final axis. Figure 10.15 shows that for this particular arch the final axis is very close to the original parabola. For subsequent computations the coordinates x and y of the 10 segments are accurately scaled off the drawing.

As is seen from Eq. (10.11*a*), the quantities $y\ \Delta s/I$ and $y^2\ \Delta s/I$ must be computed for the 10 segments of the half arch. For the tentative 14×22 in. section, $I = 11{,}600$ in.[4] The pertinent quantities are assembled in the first four columns of Table 10.4, which summarizes the numerical calculations.

For determining the dimensions of the arch, the tie rod, and the hinges, the forces and moments caused by the following loadings must be computed:

a. MAXIMUM VERTICAL REACTION R AND MAXIMUM FORCE IN TIE ROD H. These are obtained for full live load, being placed over the entire span, so that the load per segment, dead plus live, is 9.2 kips. The corresponding reactions are $R_l = R_r = 92.0$ kips. The beam moments M_0 and the quantities $M_0 y\ \Delta s/I$ are computed at the midpoints of the 10 segments. They are entered in Table 10.4 in the columns headed "Case *a*." By virtue of symmetry, computations can be restricted to half the arch.

b. MAXIMUM POSITIVE QUARTER-POINT MOMENT. The preliminary design has shown that the positive quarter-point moment will govern the dimensions of the arch rib. Since a constant-cross-section arch was chosen,

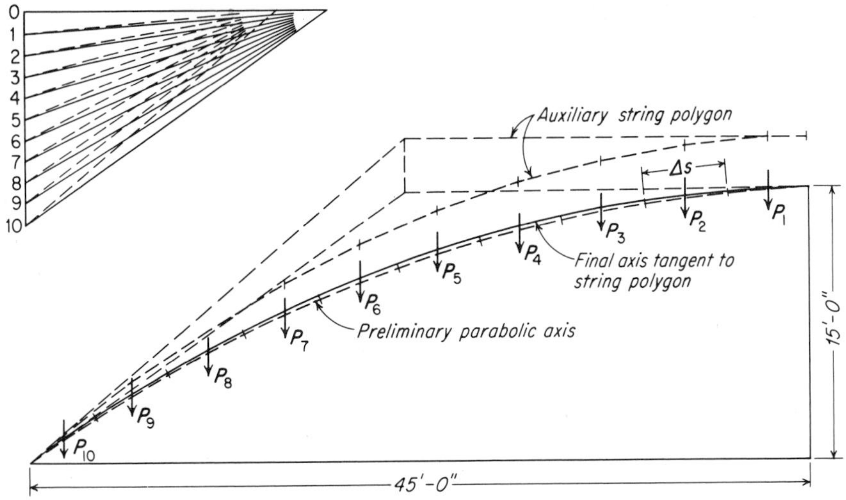

Fig. 10.15 Determination of final location of arch axis by means of dead-load string polygon.

it is sufficient for our purposes to investigate only this one loading case. For a more complete investigation, the other loading cases of the preliminary design should also be computed. This is desirable even in the case of a constant-cross-section arch, in view of the approximate character of the preliminary design. It becomes mandatory if the final arch axis differs considerably from the original parabolic shape and, of course, if rib dimensions and reinforcement are varied along the span.

The exact location of the quarter point is at $x = 22.5$ ft. This point does not happen to coincide with any of the centers of the segments. Since moments and thrusts vary only very gradually in an arch subject only to distributed loads, it will be simpler and sufficiently accurate to compute the moment at that segment center located closest to the quarter point, i.e., at $x = 23.5$ ft. According to Fig. 10.10, live load should be placed from the left springing up to $x = 0.425 \times 90 = 38.3$ ft. In the summation process it is quite inconvenient to place loads at locations other than over integer segments. For this reason the first nine segments from the left springing (i.e., up to $x = 40.2$ ft) will be subjected to live load. The error so introduced is entirely negligible. Hence, these nine segments are loaded by 9.2 kips each, the remaining eleven segments by the dead load of 5.8 kips. The corresponding reactions are $R_l = 82.0$ kips and $R_r = 64.4$ kips.

In view of unsymmetrical loading, beam moments M_0 and quantities $M_0 y\,\Delta s/I$ must be computed for both halves of the arch. They are entered in Table 10.4 in the columns headed "Case *b*."

In Table 10.4, x and y are given in feet, $y\,\Delta s/I$ in 1/in., $y^2\,\Delta s/I$ in 1/in.^{2}, M_0 in ft-kips, and $M_0 y\,\Delta s/I$ in ft-kips per in.^{2} (It is advisable to

***Table* 10.4**

x	y	$y\,\Delta s/I$	$y^2\,\Delta s/I$	Case a		Case b			
						Left half		Right half	
				M_0	$M_0 y\,\Delta s/I$	M_0	$M_0 y\,\Delta s/I$	M_0	$M_0 y\,\Delta s/I$
1.9	1.30	0.078	1.2	174	13	156	12	123	10
6.0	3.90	0.235	10.9	514	121	444	104	364	85
10.2	6.20	0.373	27.6	823	306	713	269	580	216
14.5	8.30	0.498	49.6	1101	553	954	475	790	394
19.0	10.20	0.613	74.9	1349	825	1159	710	976	598
23.5	11.80	0.708	100.2	1556	1102	1321	935	1138	806
28.2	13.10	0.786	123.2	1728	1358	1447	1138	1276	1002
32.9	14.10	0.847	143.2	1862	1578	1531	1298	1390	1178
37.7	14.70	0.882	155.5	1947	1718	1570	1384	1475	1301
42.5	14.95	0.897	160.8	1991	1787	1566	1402	1533	1375
Σ			847.1		9361		7727		6965

select units so as not to obtain unwieldy figures, such as millions on the one hand, or small decimal fractions on the other.)

From the general discussion of Eq. (10.11), it is evident that only the first term in the numerator and the first and last terms in the denominator of that equation need be considered for this particular roof arch. Hence, for determining H, the following equation is used:

$$H = \frac{\Sigma M_0 y \, \Delta s/I}{\Sigma y^2 \, \Delta s/I + El/E_{tr}A_{tr}}$$

The denominator then becomes

$$2 \times 848.1 + 4 \times 10^6 \times 90 \times 12/30 \times 10^6 \times 8.3 = 1709.5$$

The maximum force in the tie rod (case a) is

$$H_{\max} = \frac{2 \times 9361 \times 12}{1709.5} = 131.5 \text{ kips}$$

For the loading which results in maximum quarter-point moment (case b),

$$H = \frac{(7727 + 6965)\ 12}{1709.5} = 103.1 \text{ kips}$$

From Table 10.4 the simple beam moment M_0 at $x = 23.5$ ft is seen to be 1321 ft-kips. Hence the moment in the arch rib at that point is

$$M = M_0 - Hy = 1321 - 103.1 \times 11.80 = 103 \text{ ft-kips}$$

Since the point $x = 23.5$ ft is located at the center of the sixth arch segment, the vertical shear at that point is

$$V = 82.0 - 9.2 \times 5.5 = 31.4 \text{ kips}$$

At that point, from Eq. (10.19b), $\theta = 17°42'$. The axial thrust at that point then becomes

$$T = 31.4 \times 0.303 + 103.1 \times 0.95 = 107.4 \text{ kips}$$

It will be noticed that the values of $H_{\max}$, M, and T are quite close to those obtained in the preliminary design. Such good coincidence obtains only when, as in this case, the final location of the axis is very close to that used in the preliminary design. Even then, significant differences between preliminary and final results are not infrequent; therefore the accurate analysis by summation should always be carried out.

A 12 × 24 in. section with eight No. 8 bars, shown in Fig. 10.13, is selected for the arch rib. By the methods of Art. 5.8, $p_g = 0.0218$, $m = 15.7$, and $e_b = 8.58$ in. For $M = 103$ ft-kips and $T = 107.4$ kips, $e = 11.5$ in. $> e_b$, indicating tension failure. From the column-interaction equation, with $F_a = 1370$ psi and $F_b = 1350$ psi, $N_b = 173$ kips and $M_b = 124$ ft-kips. If pure bending were applied to the section, M_0 would be 79.5 ft-kips. By adopting a straight-line variation of moment from $N = 0$ to $N = N_b$, it is found that for the actual axial load of 107.4 kips, a moment of 107 ft-kips is allowed. This is very close to, and conservatively above, the applied moment of 103 ft-kips, indicating that the section chosen is satisfactory.

With four $1\frac{5}{8}$-in. round bars for the tie rod, as obtained in the preliminary design, the stress in the tie is $131{,}500/8.3 = 15{,}850$ psi. The ends of the tie rods are upset and threaded. The long diameter of the nuts for bars of this size is $3\frac{1}{2}$ in. To accommodate the wrench for tightening the nuts, a 5-in. minimum center-to-center spacing of tie bars is selected.

To transmit the pull of the tie to the concrete, an anchor plate $9 \times 12 \times 1\frac{1}{8}$ in. is provided. Actually, a considerable part of the pull will be transmitted to the concrete by bond over the embedded length of the tie bars; this will be discounted, however, and the anchor designed for the entire pull. The bearing surface is $9 \times 12 - 4 \times 2.1 = 99.6$ in.², and the bearing pressure is $131{,}500/99.6 = 1320$ psi. As is easily computed from the dimensions of Fig. 10.13, the bearing surface represents 39.5 per cent of the cross section of the arch extension in which the anchor is located. For this percentage the ACI Code allows a bearing pressure of 1370 psi. The bending stresses in the anchor plate are investigated in the long direction for a strip 1 in. wide. The maximum negative moment of the portion projecting beyond the center line of the anchors is $1320 \times 2.5^2/2 = 4120$ in.-lb, while the maximum positive moment at the center line of the plate is

$$1320 \times 7^2/8 - 4120 = 3960 \text{ in.-lb}$$

With the section modulus equal to $1.125^2/6 = 0.210$, the maximum bending stress is $4120/0.210 = 19{,}600$ psi, which is slightly smaller than 20,000 psi, the permissible bending stress for structural steel.

The hinges transmit only the vertical reaction $V = 92$ kips, since the horizontal component is resisted by the tie. To reduce the number and size of the hinge bars so as to accommodate them in the limited width, a steel with 60,000-psi yield point will be used, so that the allowable compression stress is $f_s' = 0.3 \times 60{,}000 = 18{,}000$ psi. With an angle $\theta = 30°$ (Fig. 10.12), the required area of hinge bars is computed from Eq. (10.21), that is, $A_s' = 92{,}000/(18{,}000 \times 0.866) = 5.9$ in.² Six No. 9 bars are provided, furnishing an area of 5.95 in.² With a hinge opening of 6 in., as shown in Fig. 10.13, the free length of the hinge bars is $L = 6/0.866 = 6.93$ in., while the radius of gyration is

$$r = 1.125/4 = 0.281$$

Hence the ratio $L/r = 24.7$ is within the limits recommended in Art. 10.7.

The required lateral reinforcement is obtained from Eq. (10.22) where, in this case, $a = 8 \times 1.125 = 9.0$ in., $b = 12$ in., $N = 92{,}000$ lb, and $S = 0$. With an allowable stress $f_s'' = 20{,}000$ psi, the required area becomes $A_s'' = 0.79$ in.^{2} It is seen from Fig. 10.13 that within the length $a = 9$ in. four No. 3 closed ties are provided, which furnish an area of $8 \times 0.11 = 0.88$ in.^{2}

The required length of embedment for the hinge bars is

$$24 \times 1.125 = 27 \text{ in.}$$

beyond the faces of the concrete at either side of the hinge.

In order to avoid bending moments caused by eccentricities, the axes of the arch, the tie, and the hinge must be made to intersect at one common point, as shown in the hinge detail of Fig. 10.13.

10.9 Cylindrical Shells As a further development of the arch principle, shell surfaces provide a structurally efficient solution to the problem of carrying roof loads over long spans. These three-dimensional forms owe their efficiency to the translation of applied loads into tensile and compressive stress and shear stress in the plane of their surface. These are termed *membrane* stresses, and the degree to which membrane stresses are dominant over stresses due to out-of-plane flexure is generally a measure of the structural economy of the system.

One common form of shell surface is the cylindrical shell. This is a developable surface, superficially similar to the barrel arch described in Art. 10.2, but quite different in nature and behavior. While the barrel arch normally has continuous support along the lower edges and performs as a true arch, the cylindrical shell is supported only by transverse diaphragms or ribs, the longitudinal edges being free. Precast units of a cylindrical shell roof are shown in Fig. 10.16. Figure 10.17 shows several of the characteristic types of cylindrical shells. Such shells may be used as single units (Fig. 10.17*a*) supported at the ends and free along the long edges, or as multiple units (Fig. 10.17*b*) joined along the long edges. They may be continuous over one or more intermediate supports (Fig. 10.17*c*). If transverse spans are long, the use of a ribbed cylindrical shell (Fig. 10.17*d*) may be indicated.

Since a cylindrical shell is a space structure, with its internal forces acting in three directions, its analysis becomes quite complicated. However, a qualitative understanding of the fundamental nature of shell behavior can be gained without detailed mathematical analysis. A small element of the shell surface, shown in Fig. 10.18*a* to *c*, must be in equilibrium under the action of the applied load, the membrane forces acting in the plane of the surface, and the out-of-plane shears and moments causing bending in the shell (shown separately in Fig. 10.18*c* for clarity). It

***Fig.* 10.16** Cylindrical-shell roof.

will be found for most cylindrical shells that the quantities N_x, N_ϕ, M_x, and $M_{x\phi}$ are so small as to be considered negligible, so that the quantities of principal concern are the membrane forces, shown in Fig. 10.8*b*, and the transverse moment M_ϕ. By summing forces in the radial direction, it becomes apparent that the radial component of the load W must be resisted by the radial component of the tangential thrust T_ϕ, while the tangential component must be resisted by the difference between the shears S acting on the two opposite faces of the element, plus the difference in tangential thrust T_ϕ acting on opposite faces. Conditions of equilibrium can be satisfied by the membrane forces alone, so that any load can be resisted by direct stresses acting wholly in the plane of the surface. Note that it is the presence of the membrane shear stresses which distinguishes shell behavior from that of an arch; because of these shear stresses, a shell can carry loads by direct stress regardless of its shape or the distribution of the loads, while the arch can carry by direct stress only one unique loading. The longitudinal membrane forces T_x are similar to the fiber stress resulting from bending of a beam; in fact, for shells with a suffi-

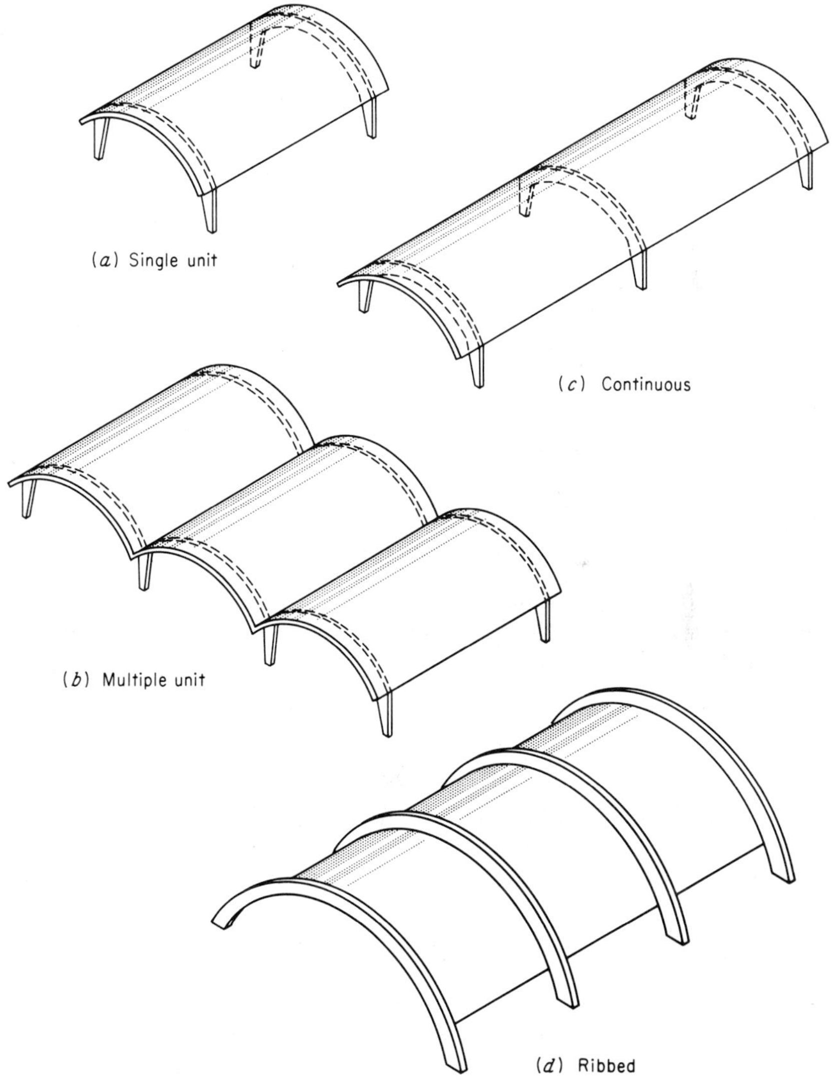

***Fig.* 10.17** Cylindrical shells.

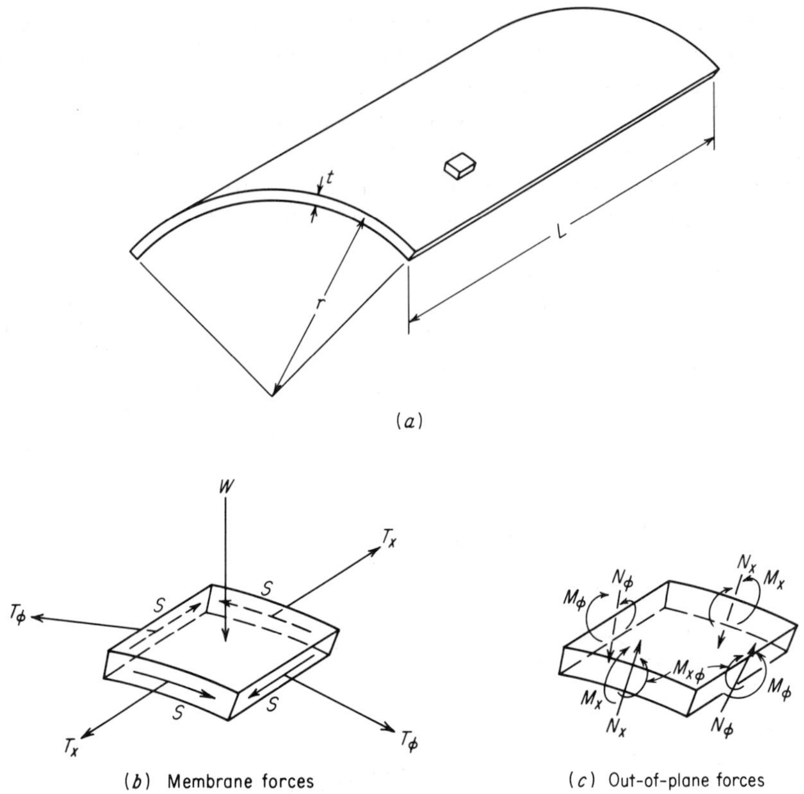

Fig. 10.18

ciently high ratio L/r, these stresses can be closely calculated using the familiar beam equation

$$f_x = \frac{T_x}{t} = \frac{My}{I} \tag{10.23}$$

with section properties calculated for the shell as for any beam of curved cross section (see Fig. 10.19*b*). The distribution of tangential shear stress (which must be the same as the longitudinal shear-stress distribution) can then be found from the usual expression,

$$v = \frac{S}{t} = \frac{VQ}{Ib} \tag{10.24}$$

(For shorter shells, the T_x and S forces will deviate from those found by beam theory, increasingly so as L/r becomes smaller.) As long as membrane shear forces and transverse thrust are provided for each small element of the surface, the shell will carry its load almost entirely by membrane stress. But along the free edges, these requirements are no longer met, and it is this condition which brings about the out-of-plane bending forces, principally M_ϕ.

Once the distribution of shear is obtained from beam theory, the transverse moment M_ϕ is calculated from equilibrium of the shell element dx shown in Fig. 10.19*a* and *c*. It is seen that M_ϕ must be equal to the moment of the external load minus the moment of the net tangential shear. It will be found that the difference between these two quantities is small and usually is such as to produce circumferential tension in the top fibers, i.e., the free longitudinal edge will deflect downward and inward under load. It is this relative movement with respect to the crown point which causes the longitudinal stresses T_x, in turn, to deviate from those found by beam theory. Since the free edge deflects more than the crown,

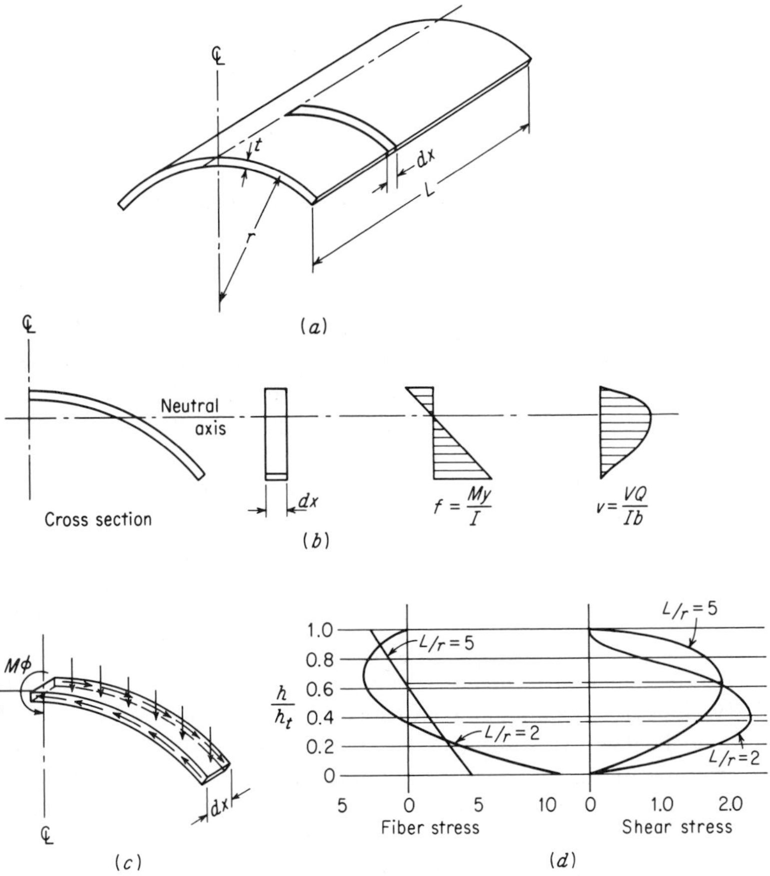

Fig. 10.19

the tensile strains must be larger than those found by beam theory; consequently the tension along the free edge must be increased. But for horizontal equilibrium the compressive stresses above the neutral axis must be increased as well, although the internal moment of these forces must be the same as before. This indicates that the lever arm between the two must decrease; i.e., the center of compression must move down, as must the neutral axis. This effect increases with decreasing L/r, as is shown in Fig. 10.19*d*, which contrasts the longitudinal stress distribution in a shell with $L/r = 5$ with that for a shell with $L/r = 2$.

The change in the longitudinal stress will, in turn, mean a variation in longitudinal (and tangential) shear distribution from that obtained from simple beam theory. Figure 10.19*d* shows the change in shear stress distribution as the L/r ratio is reduced from 5 to 2.

The foregoing qualitative discussion of cylindrical-shell behavior suggests the possibility of a method of solution which has been referred to as the *beam method*. Originally proposed by Lundgren, it is described in detail in Ref. 10.4. In addition to the usual assumptions associated with elastic flexural analysis, Lundgren's method assumes (1) that all points on a transverse cross section deflect the same amount vertically and do not deflect horizontally and (2) that radial moments, torsional moments, and radial shears on transverse cross sections are all negligible. Consistent with these assumptions, it has been observed (Refs. 10.5, 10.6) that the beam method should not be applied to single cylindrical shells with L/r less than about 5, nor to interior units of multiple cylindrical shells with L/r less than about 2. With these conditions satisfied, the solution requires only the calculation of T_x, S, T_ϕ, and M_ϕ, the first two obtained from a beam calculation, and the latter two obtained from what Lundgren terms the *arch calculation*. The method has the advantage that it permits easy visualization of the structural action of the shell in resisting loads; in addition, it can be applied to cross sections of any shape, of variable thickness, with or without stiffening ribs.

Alternatively, cylindrical shells can be analyzed by direct application of the theory of elasticity. The solution is analogous to that of a conventional indeterminate frame by superposition, in which the structure is reduced to a determinate frame by the removal of redundant restraints, which are then reintroduced in turn and adjusted in value in order to satisfy the stated boundary conditions of the original frame. In the case of the shell, it is first assumed that the surface loads are transmitted to the supports by direct stress only. This is the membrane solution, equivalent to assuming the structure to be statically determinate. This assumption generally leads to displacements and reactions along the long edges which are inconsistent with the stated boundary conditions. To correct this situation, line loads must be applied along the long edges; the stresses resulting from these line loads are then superimposed on those obtained from the membrane solution to obtain the final stresses in the shell.

The mathematical labor associated with this procedure is greatly reduced by use of data and coefficients available in "Manual of Engineering Practice No. 31—Design of Cylindrical Concrete Shell Roofs," published by the American Society of Civil Engineers in 1952 (Ref. 10.7). This publication includes a set of tables and charts which permit a solution for internal stresses for shells of common proportions and includes a valuable presentation of design theory and a number of detailed examples. In addition to this publication, the reader will find design data of interest in "Coefficients for Design of Cylindrical Concrete Shell Roofs," published by the Portland Cement Association (Ref. 10.8), which extends the "Manual 31" tables, thus avoiding interpolation. Additional discussion and examples are available in Ref. 10.9.

With regard to the reinforcement of the shell, while the analysis is carried out assuming a homogeneous, isotropic material, the concrete has tensile strength so low that it is disregarded, and steel is included to carry all the tension. The bars are in some cases curved to follow the lines of principal stress. While this is theoretically the best arrangement, it leads to difficulty in the field, particularly since fairly large bars may be required. More commonly, the steel is arranged in a rectangular pattern; generally the principal tensile reinforcement is concentrated as near to the lower edge (valley) as possible for greatest economy. Often welded wire mesh is used to provide for transverse moment and thrust. Diagonal bars are used near the ends of the span, in order to provide more efficiently for diagonal tension in those areas. Minimum reinforcement in any direction of about ¼ per cent of the concrete section is used to control shrinkage and temperature cracking. Particular attention should be given to the region in which the thin shell surface joins the more massive end diaphragms or supporting frames, where differential expansion and contraction may require additional reinforcement.

10.10 Folded Plates In an attempt to simplify formwork and yet retain many of the advantages characteristic of cylindrical shells, the folded-plate structure has evolved. These surfaces have a deep corrugated form similar to that of cylindrical shells, except that plane elements are used, intersecting in "fold lines" parallel to the span direction. Folded-plate structures have been built, using very thin slabs, spanning clear distances greater than 100 ft. They are not ideal shells, because flexural stresses may have considerable influence on their dimensions and design, but they offer the sizable advantage of simplified formwork as compared to curved shell surfaces.

Folded-plate construction appears to have originated in Germany in

***Fig.* 10.20** Folded-plate roof.

the 1920's. Following the construction of a number of bunker-type structures using the folded-plate principle, a design theory was developed and published in Europe. The first technical publication on folded plates in the United States was a paper by Winter and Pei (Ref. 10.11) published in 1948. The past 15 years have seen numerous applications of the principles set forth. Figure 10.20 illustrates a recently constructed folded-plate roof of 125-ft span which, in addition to carrying ordinary roof loads, carries the second floor as well from a system of cable hangers. The ground floor is thus kept free of columns.

The action of a folded-plate structure in carrying its loads is illustrated by Fig. 10.21. A surface load applied to the folded-plate structure shown in Fig. 10.21*a* would tend to deflect the individual plates, as indicated by the dotted lines for plate 1, if each plate were free to act independently, the plates spanning as one-way slabs between end diaphragms. The upper edges of plates 1 and 2, for example, would deflect in the directions CC' and CC'', respectively, as in Fig. 10.21*b*. The plates cannot act independently, however. The final location of the deflected edge C must lie at some singular position C_1. This necessitates that plates 1 and 2 undergo deflections Δ_1 and Δ_2, respectively, in their own planes. While the plates have negligible torsional and flexural stiffness in resisting the deflection components perpendicular to their own planes, they are extremely stiff in resisting in-plane deflections. This resistance to bending about each plate's strong axis results in effective support for the slab along any fold line. A fold line cannot deflect without causing in-plane deflection of one or both of the adjacent plates, a type of deformation which the plates are able to resist effectively. Consequently the plates, rather than spanning in the

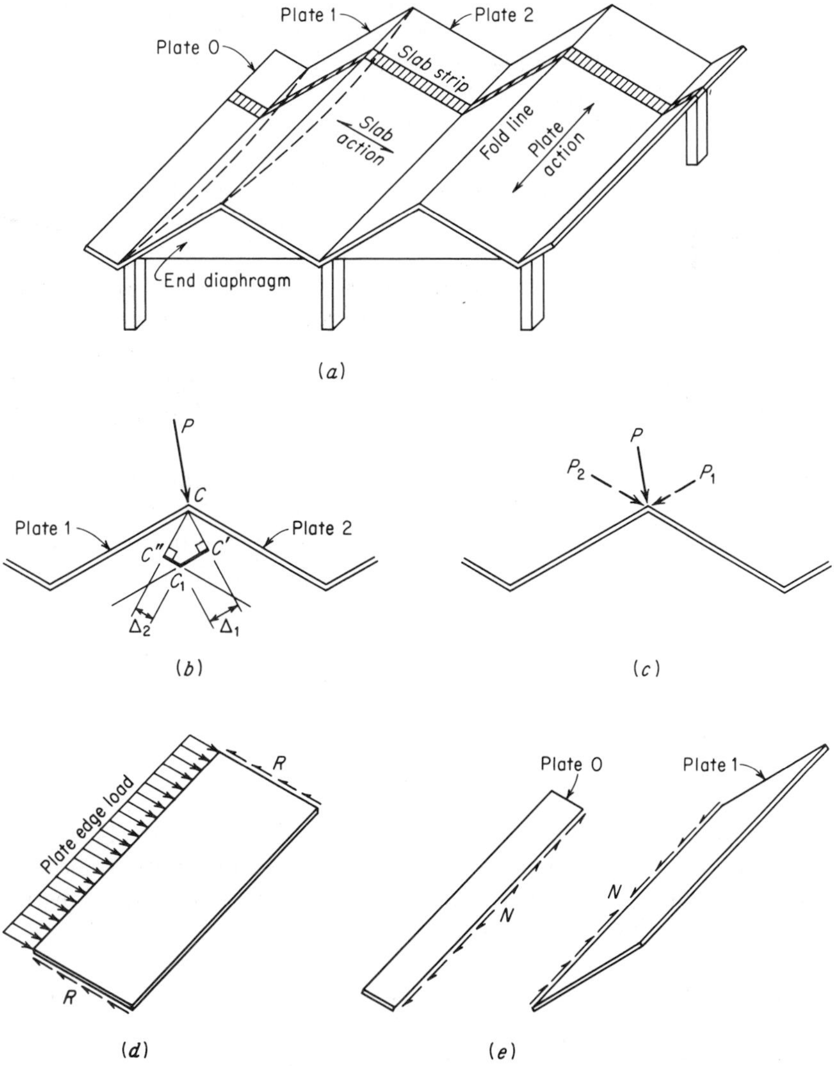

Fig. **10.21**

long direction of the structure, act as slabs supported at the fold lines as well as the end diaphragms. For most folded plates, the ratio of plate length to width is sufficiently large, in fact, that it is satisfactory to consider all the surface load as carried by the plate in the direction perpendicular to the fold lines. This is termed *slab action*. A typical transverse slab strip is shown in Fig. 10.21*a*.

The reactions from such slab strips are applied as line loads to the fold lines. Because of the negligible torsional and out-of-plane flexural resistance of the plates, the only direction in which each plate can apply a reactive force to resist this line load is parallel to its own surface. The resultant line load P (see Fig. 10.21*c*) therefore resolves into components parallel to the two adjacent plates. The plates in turn carry this edge loading longitudinally between end diaphragms by plate action, as shown in Fig. 10.21*d*. Their behavior may be likened to that of deep, inclined-web girders, laterally braced by adjacent plates. Longitudinal membrane stresses T_x can be found as for any beam. These are termed the *free-edge* stresses.

If conditions are such that the free-edge stresses are the same on both sides of all fold lines, then they are identical with the final stresses. This would be the case, for example, at the edges of an interior unit of a roof consisting of many identical units. If, on the other hand, the initial plate analysis indicates a stress difference on either side of a fold line, an incompatibility is indicated which cannot actually exist, because the strains on either side of a given fold line must be equal. This indicates the presence of longitudinal shears acting along the joint as shown in Fig. 10.21*e*.

For plate 0, the longitudinal stresses at the top and bottom edges, f_{t0} and f_{b0}, resulting from the application of an edge shear N acting as shown, are

$$f_{t0} = -\frac{2N}{A_0} \qquad (a)$$

$$f_{b0} = +\frac{4N}{A_0} \qquad (b)$$

with $+$ and $-$ indicating tension and compression, respectively, and A_0 indicating the cross-sectional area of the plate. Similarly, the same edge shear N applied to the lower edge of plate 1 in the opposite direction produces the following stresses in plate 1:

$$f_{b1} = -\frac{4N}{A_1} \qquad (c)$$

$$f_{t1} = +\frac{2N}{A_1} \qquad (d)$$

The edge shear force N must be of such magnitude as to eliminate completely any difference in longitudinal free-edge stresses at the fold line. The total required stress change is therefore equal to

$$f_{b0} - f_{b1} = \frac{4N}{A_0} + \frac{4N}{A_1}$$

The proportion of this change which occurs in plate 0 is

$$\frac{+4N/A_0}{4N/A_0 + 4N/A_1} = \frac{A_1}{A_0 + A_1} = K_0 \qquad (e)$$

while that assigned to plate 1 is

$$\frac{4N/A_1}{4N/A_0 + 4N/A_1} = \frac{A_0}{A_0 + A_1} = K_1 \qquad (f)$$

The factors K_1 and K_2 are known as the *stress-distribution factors* and are applied to any difference in free-edge stresses to determine the stress change due to edge shear. Similar factors are found for all other joints.

Additionally, it is evident from Eqs. (*a*) through (*d*) that an edge shear causing a given stress change at the near edge of a plate will cause a stress change of one-half that amount, of opposite sign, at the far edge. Thus a *stress carry-over factor* of $-\frac{1}{2}$ is obtained. Stress-distribution factors and stress carry-over factors are applied to the free-edge stresses, in an iterative procedure exactly analogous to the familiar Cross method of moment distribution, to obtain T_x stresses corrected for the presence of edge shears.

In many cases the above analysis is a sufficient basis for design. In other cases, because of the geometry of the structure or the nature of the loads, it is necessary to correct for the relative displacement of the fold lines. This relative displacement amounts to support settlement for the slab strips. While it will usually have little effect on the T_x stresses, there may be a significant change in slab moments M_ϕ and slab shears N_ϕ.

There are several methods for determining the effect of joint translation. The method which is simplest conceptually is an iterative procedure in which the fold-line deflections for the initial plate stresses, calculated as described above, are determined. Slab moments and shears and joint loads resulting from such deflections are found, and the plate stresses resulting from these joint loads are calculated. The associated plate deflections are determined, and the cycle is repeated until sufficient accuracy is obtained. While quite straightforward, the method has the disadvantage that it may converge very slowly under certain circumstances.

Alternatively, a method analogous to the sidesway analysis of a multistory building is used. Each plate is given an arbitrary rotation in turn, and slab reactions, plate loads, plate stresses, and deflections are found for that rotation. A geometrical relation is established between plate deflection and plate rotation which permits the writing of a set of simultaneous equations. From these equations, constants are found which are applied to each of the arbitrary rotation solutions. Final moments and stresses are then found by superposition.

Other methods of solution are available, many particularly adapted for use with digital computers. Additional information of interest to the designer will be found in Refs. 10.13 to 10.15.

10.11 Hyberbolic Paraboloids The possibilities of doubly curved shell roofs have been increasingly exploited in recent years. With both main curvatures in the same direction, say concave downward, such surfaces are termed *synclastic;* with the main curvatures in opposite directions, such as in a saddle surface, they are termed *anticlastic.* The hyperbolic-paraboloid surface is an anticlastic form that has achieved great popularity owing to its economical use of material, relative simplicity of structural action, relatively easy forming, and interesting architectural effect.

With reference to Fig. 10.22, the surface is defined by two intersecting systems of straight-line generators, a and b. The lines AB and CD are termed the *directrixes;* both are parallel to the director plane YOZ, but they are not parallel to each other. The generators a intersect both directrixes and are at the same time parallel to the second director plane XOZ. Similarly, the second set of generators b intersect the directrixes EF and GA and are parallel to the director plane YOZ. The intersection

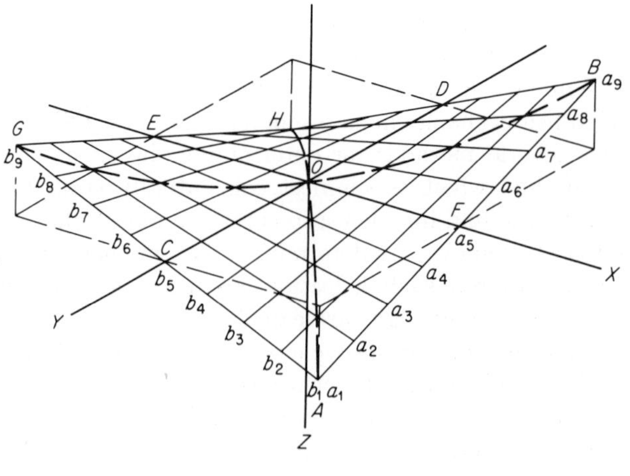

Fig. 10.22

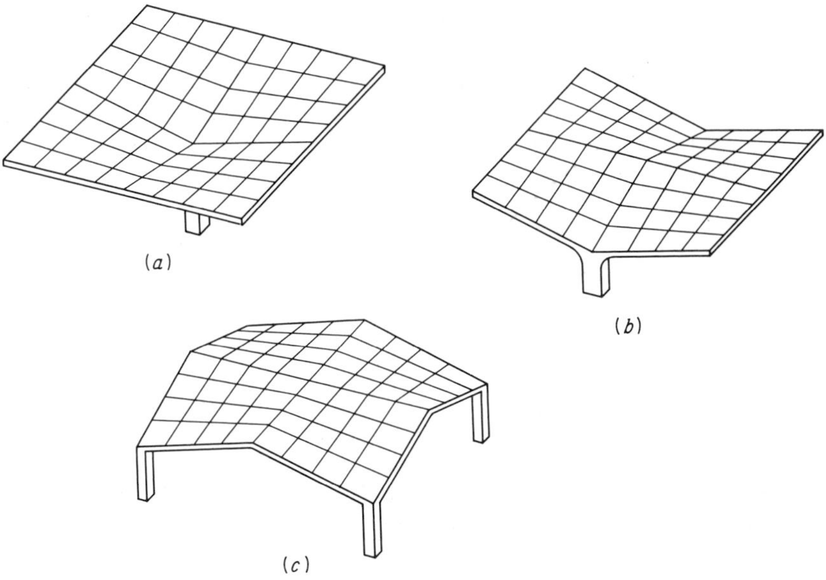

Fig. **10.23**

of the two director planes XOZ and YOZ is usually, but not necessarily, a right angle.

In describing the surface, it is convenient to take as coordinate axes the two generators OF and OC, passing through the crown of the surface, and the intersection line OZ of the two director planes. The line OZ is always perpendicular to the plane XOY. The equation of the surface is then

$$z = kxy \tag{10.25}$$

where k is a constant representing the slope of the surface. It is evident that plane sections parallel to the two bisecting planes of the dihedral angle XOY are parabolic; these are termed the *principal parabolas*. They are respectively curved upward (GOB) and downward (AOH); the surface is anticlastic. Plane sections parallel to the plane XOY are hyperbolic; hence the name *hyperbolic paraboloid*.

The geometry of the surface described is most convenient in the building of forms. It is evident that the surface can be formed using straight elements, say 2 by 6's on edge, placed along either system of generators, over which can be laid plank or plywood sheathing thin enough to conform to the warped surface. Many different roof forms can be created either by use of the entire surface or by combining parts of it in various ways. For example, the surface of Fig. 10.22 can be used in its entirety, with a buttress support at A and H; Fig. 10.24 illustrates such an application. Alternatively, segments of the surface can be combined in a number of arrangements, a few of which are shown in Fig. 10.23. In most cases, stiffening ribs are required along the lines of intersection of the segments and along the free edges of the shell to accommodate the substantial thrusts developed.

In analyzing the hyperbolic paraboloid, it is convenient to work with X' and Y' axes, each rotated 45° in a horizontal plane from the original X or Y axis; thus the axes are in the planes of the principal parabolas. The equation of the warped surface then becomes

$$z = 0.5k(x'^2 - y'^2) \tag{10.26}$$

The means by which a hyperbolic paraboloid carries its load may be apparent from its geometry. With two mutually perpendicular sets of parabolic strips, all of exactly the same curvature, it is reasonable to suppose that a load applied to a unit of surface area will be divided equally, half carried by each of the intersection parabolic arch strips. The concave-downward strip carries its share by compression, while the concave-upward strip acts in tension. Since the parabolic axes correspond with the equilibrium polygons for a load distributed uniformly, no bending mo-

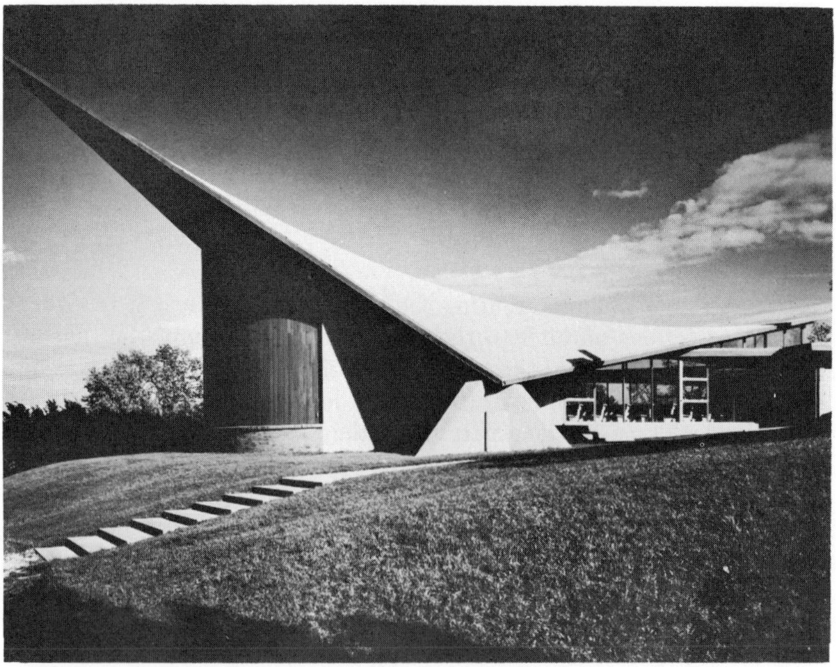

Fig. 10.24 Hyperbolic-paraboloid shell, St. Edmund's Episcopal Church.

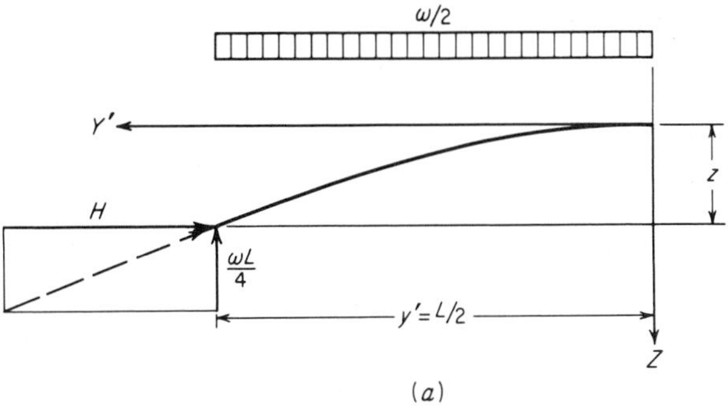

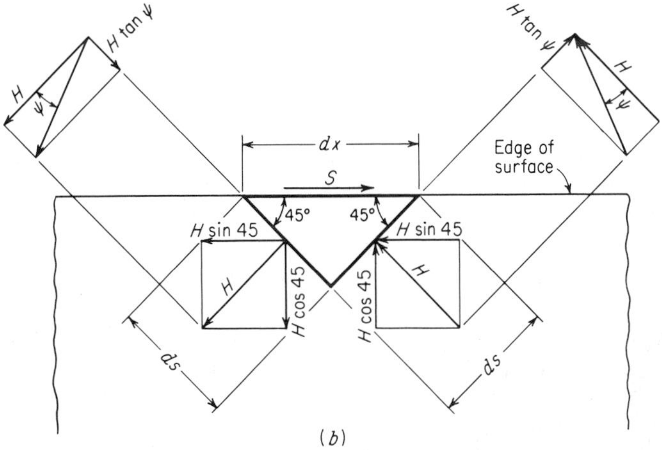

Fig. **10.25**

ments or radial shears are developed; that is, the direction of thrust must at any point be tangent to the axis of the parabolic strip. Figure 10.25*a* shows a parabolic compression strip, with a surface load $w/2$ producing a thrust at point (z,y'), with a horizontal component H and a vertical component $wL/4$. With x' a constant value, the equation of the curve is obtained from Eq. (10.26) and is

$$z = k_1 - 0.5ky'^2 \tag{a}$$

where k_1 is a new constant, simply defining the elevation of the vertex. Consider for convenience the parabola which passes through the origin (Fig. 10.22); k_1 is zero, and

$$z = -0.5ky'^2 \tag{b}$$

The slope of the parabola at any point is obtained by differentiation:

$$\frac{dz}{dy'} = -1.0ky' \tag{c}$$

At $y' = L/2$, the slope is $-kL/2$. Since the slope of the resultant thrust must coincide with that of the parabola,

$$\frac{wL/4}{H} = \frac{kL}{2}$$

and

$$H = \frac{w}{2k} \tag{10.27}$$

Equation (10.27) is an expression for the horizontal component of tensile or compressive thrust produced in the shell at any point due to a uniform load.

The above analysis is predicated upon the presence of a suitable restraining force, acting on each elemental unit of surface from those adjacent. At the edges of the shell, a special situation obtains. The equilibrium of the small triangular element taken at the edge of the surface (Fig. 10.25*b*) demonstrates the need for edge members to take the thrust that is developed along the free edges. Consider first the horizontal component of thrust, and break that into components perpendicular and parallel to the edge; it is seen that the vectors normal to the edge are equal and act in opposite directions; hence they cancel, and no net force results normal to the free edge. The tangential components are additive, however. If S is the intensity of shear force per unit length along the edge,

$$2H\ ds \sin 45 = S\ dx$$

$$S = 2H \sin 45 \frac{ds}{dx} = 2H \sin^2 45$$

But $H = w/2k$, and $\sin^2 45 = 0.50$, so that

$$S = \frac{w}{2k} \tag{10.28}$$

In considering the effects of the vertical components of thrust, one must take separately the case of an element along a horizontal edge OF or OC (Fig. 10.22) and an element along a sloping edge AF or AC. Along the horizontal edges, since the slope of the axis of one parabola is equal to that of the intersecting parabola but of opposite sign, the vertical components cancel one another (see Fig. 10.25*b*). Consequently, the edge member must resist only a force parallel to its axis. Along the sloping edges, the vertical components do not cancel but rather add, and it is easily shown that the net vertical force is such that, when combined with the horizontal shear, it will produce a force acting along the sloping edge; again an edge member is required to resist axial load only.

The membrane analysis described provides the basis for the principal shell reinforcement. In large hyperbolic paraboloids, careful attention must be given to the question of secondary stresses. These are due to several causes. There are characteristically flat regions in most hyperbolic-paraboloid shells which give rise to significant bending stresses. In addition, the membrane analysis results in an indicated strain incompatibility adjacent to edge members, which may be in compression while the adjacent monolithic shell surface is loaded primarily in shear. The result of this is the development of flexural and shearing stresses in the shell adjacent to the boundary members. Also, concentrated-load effects require special consideration, as well as the effects of temperature changes and support movements. The reader will find further information on hyperbolic-paraboloid shells in Refs. 10.3 and 10.16 to 10.18.

10.12 Spherical Domes Another form of three-dimensional curved roof which has found frequent application is the spherical dome, generated by rotating an arc of a circle about a vertical axis through the center of the circle. The circular arc is termed a *meridian* (see Fig. 10.26*a*), and its plane a *meridian plane*. The movement of a point on the circular arc, as it rotates about the axis of the dome, describes a *parallel*, or a *circle of*

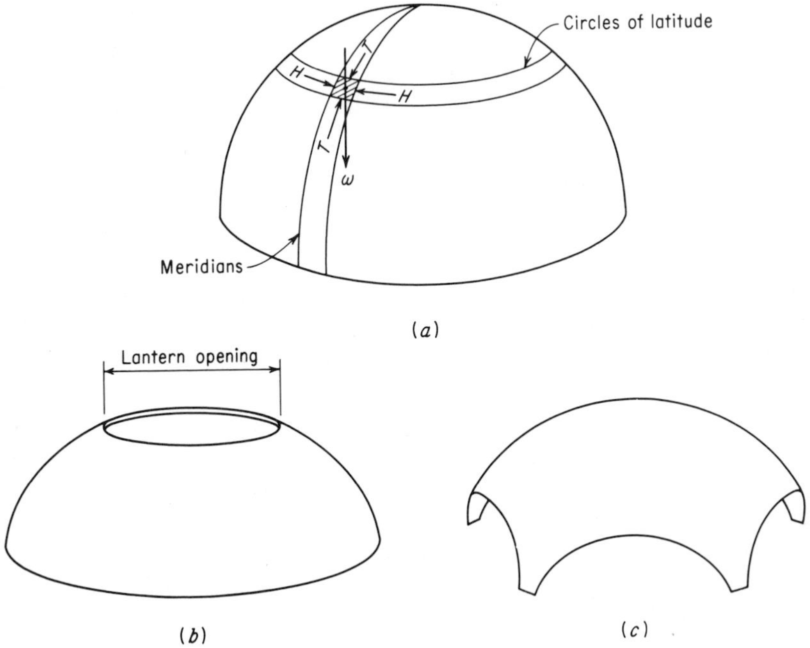

Fig. **10.26**

Fig. 10.27 Spherical shell, Kresge Auditorium.

latitude. While simpler to describe geometrically than the hyperbolic-paraboloid surface, the dome is considerably more complicated to build, because in the case of the dome there are no straight generators. The forming joists as well as the sheathing must be curved to fit the surface, which adds considerably to the difficulty of construction and cost of such structures.

In spite of this, the economy of material associated with spherical domes has led to their choice in preference to other solutions in many cases. Spherical domes need not be completely closed, as shown in Fig. 10.26*a*, but may include "lantern openings" at the top for purposes of skylighting (Fig. 10.26*b*) or arched openings along the lower edge (Fig. 10.26*c*). A recently completed spherical dome which has attracted considerable attention is the Kresge Auditorium at M.I.T., shown in Fig. 10.27, which is supported at only three points at ground level.

As is the case for hyperbolic paraboloids, domes carry their load almost entirely by membrane stress in the plane tangent to surface, over the greater part of the shell. As a consequence, the shell can be made very thin, even for long spans. Flexural stresses become significant only after axial strains of considerable magnitude occur. In Fig. 10.28*a*, the surface of an annular ring formed by rotating $r\,d\phi$ about the axis is

$$r\,d\phi\;2\pi r \sin\phi \qquad (a)$$

The total surface of the shell above the level of point 1 is found by integrating this expression between the limits zero and ϕ to obtain

$$A = 2\pi r^2(1 - \cos\phi_1) \tag{b}$$

If the load w per unit of surface area is constant, the total load above level 1 is then

$$W = 2\pi r^2 w(1 - \cos\phi_1) \tag{c}$$

If the total load on the shell above any specified circle of latitude is

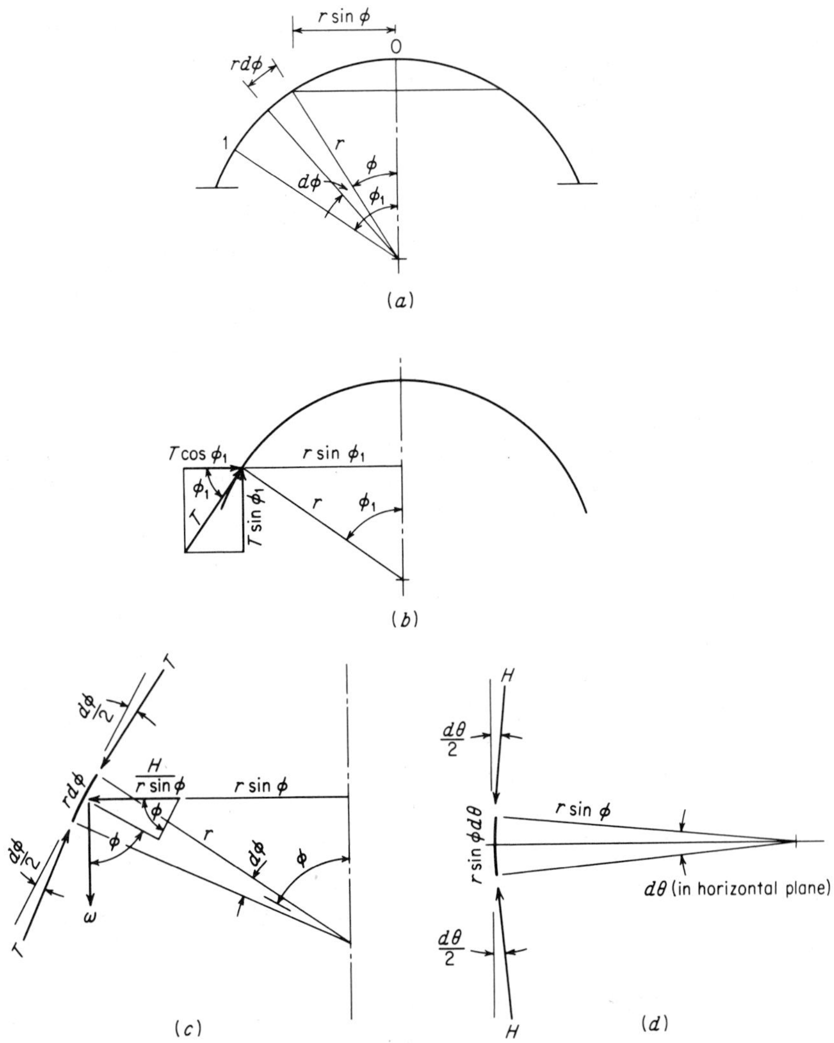

Fig. 10.28

known, the meridianal thrust can be calculated from a consideration of the vertical equilibrium of that portion of the shell. In Fig. 10.28*b*, let W be the total weight of the shell above the level concerned, and let T be the meridianal thrust per unit of length. Then

$$W = -2\pi r \sin \phi_1 \, T \sin \phi_1 \tag{d}$$

and

$$T = -\frac{W}{2\pi r \sin^2 \phi_1} \tag{10.29}$$

It is noted that the meridianal thrust is always compressive. If the dome is hemispherical, the thrust reaches a maximum value of $W/2\pi r$ at $\phi_1 = 90°$.

The circumferential stress is obtained from the equilibrium of the small element shown shaded in Figs. 10.26*a* and 10.28*c* and *d*. Summing forces in a radial direction, one obtains

$$H = -T - wr \cos \phi_1 \tag{10.30}$$

relating H and T. If one considers the particular case of a dome of uniform thickness and load, one will find that the meridianal thrust, always compressive, varies from a minimum of $-wr/2$ at the crown to $-wr$ if ϕ becomes as large as 90°. The circumferential stress varies from $wr/2$ (compression) at the crown to wr (tension) at $\phi = 90°$. The transition point, at which circumferential stress is zero, occurs at $\phi = 51°50'$.

If the shell is terminated such that ϕ_1 is smaller than 90°, the meridianal thrust will have an outward component which must be resisted by a ring girder subjected to an outward radial force of $T \cos \phi_1$ per unit length. The resulting ring tension is found from the hoop-tension expression and is

$$P_T = \frac{W \cos \phi_1}{2\pi \sin \phi_1} \tag{10.31}$$

Note that the ring tensile stress bears no direct relation to the circumferential stress present in the shell. In fact, as has been noted, for a uniformly loaded shell with ϕ_1 less than $51°50'$, the shell circumferential stresses are compressive, although the stress in the ring girder must be tensile. Hence one has an incompatibility of strains near the base ring, which results in local bending and shearing stresses in the shell.

It should be kept in mind that the above pertains to an analysis of the spherical shell for membrane stress conditions. While the results will be close to the actual stresses over the greater part of uniformly loaded shells, particular attention must be directed to stresses resulting from concentrated loads, unbalanced loading, temperature and shrinkage effects, and discontinuity along the edges. For additional information with regard to these and other matters, the reader should consult Refs. 10.2, 10.3, 10.19, and 10.20.

10.13 Conclusion The possibilities of curved two- and three-dimensional structures of reinforced concrete have not yet been fully explored. Great spans can be achieved, and genuine material economy realized; as builders become more familiar with arch and shell construction methods, and as precasting and prestressing techniques are developed more fully, it is to be expected that cost economy will more closely follow economy of material.

While no one would suggest that curved structures offer the best solution to every structural situation, some rather startling and ingenious applications have been found. Already discussed (Fig. 10.20) is a retail store in Florida in which a plane floor system is suspended by cables from a shell roof of 125-ft span. Recently a multistory apartment building was framed using nearly flat hyperbolic paraboloids. Responsible engineers have proposed a concrete building 90 stories high, incorporating thin folded plates in the space between ceiling and floor above to provide long clear spans and using the cellular voids for lighting and utility space. Numerous other possibilities suggest themselves.

The practicing engineer should not be alarmed at the mathematical complications, which in most cases are not as great as supposed. New techniques of analysis are available, as are methods making use of electronic computers, which will greatly abbreviate the labor associated with the solution of stresses in shells. Available also to the structural engineer in general practice are the services of an increasing number of consultants who have made a special study of roof structures and who can, in collaboration with the principal engineer, produce designs of great originality which can be built at a reasonable price.

REFERENCES

10.1 G. C. Ernst: Design of Hinges and Articulations in Reinforced Concrete Structures, *Trans. ASCE*, vol. 106, p. 862, 1941.

10.2 S. Timoshenko and S. Weinowsky-Krieger: "Theory of Plates and Shells," McGraw-Hill Book Company, Inc., New York, 1940.

10.3 A. Pflüger: "Elementary Statics of Shells," McGraw-Hill Book Company, Inc., New York, 1961.

10.4 H. Lundgren: "Cylindrical Shells," vol. 1, Danish Technical Press, Copenhagen, 1951.

10.5 J. Chinn: Cylindrical Shell Analysis Simplified by Beam Method, *J. ACI*, May, 1959.

10.6 M. S. Ketchum, A. L. Parme, H. W. Connor, A. Siev, A. Tedesko, and A. Zweig: Discussion of Ref. 10.5, *J. ACI*, December, 1959.

10.7 "Design of Cylindrical Concrete Shell Roofs," American Society of Civil Engineers Manual of Engineering Practice No. 31, 1952.

10.8 "Coefficients for Design of Cylindrical Concrete Shell Roofs," Portland Cement Association, 1959.

10.9 "Design of Barrel Shell Roofs," Portland Cement Association Bull. ST77, 1954.

10.10 A. L. Parme and H. W. Connor: Design Constants for Interior Cylindrical Concrete Shells, *J. ACI*, July, 1961.

10.11 G. Winter and M. Pei: Hipped Plate Construction, *J. ACI*, January, 1947.

10.12 H. Simpson: Design of Folded Plate Roofs, *J. Struct. Div. ASCE*, January, 1958.

10.13 C. S. Whitney, B. G. Anderson, and H. Birnbaum: Reinforced Concrete Folded Plate Construction, *J. Struct. Div. ASCE*, October, 1959.

10.14 E. Traum: The Design of Folded Plates, *J. Struct. Div. ASCE*, October, 1959.

10.15 A. C. Scordelis: Matrix Formulation of the Folded Plate Equations, *J. Struct. Div. ASCE*, October, 1960.

10.16 "Elementary Analysis of Hyperbolic Paraboloid Shells," Portland Cement Association Bull. ST85, 1960.

10.17 A. L. Parme: Shells of Double Curvature, *Proc. ASCE*, vol. 123, p. 989, 1958.

10.18 F. Candella: General Formulas for Membrane Stresses in Hyperbolic Paraboloidical Shells, *J. ACI*, October, 1960.

10.19 "Design of Circular Domes," Portland Cement Association Bull. ST55.

10.20 J. S. Terrington: "Design of Domes," Concrete Publications, Ltd., London, 1946.

chapter 11

PRESTRESSED CONCRETE

11.1 General Modern structural engineering tends to progress toward more economical structures through gradually improved methods of design and the use of higher-strength materials. This results in a reduction of cross-sectional dimensions and consequent weight savings. Such developments are particularly important in the field of reinforced concrete, where the dead load represents a substantial part of the total design load. Also, in multistory buildings, any saving in depth of members, multiplied by the number of stories, can represent a substantial saving in total height, load on foundations, length of heating and electrical ducts, plumbing risers, and wall and partition surfaces. Significant savings can be achieved by the use of high-strength concrete and steel in connection with ultimate-strength design.

However, as was discussed in Art. 2.9, there are limitations to this development, due primarily to the presence of tension cracks which occur under service load conditions and which affect the value of ultimate load. Undesirable features associated with such cracking may be summarized as follows:

1. In flexural members, all concrete on the tension side of the neutral axis, roughly two-thirds of the total volume, does not participate in resisting bending and, in this sense, is wasted.

2. The size of a member is often governed by diagonal tension, a type of stress which concrete is not well suited to resist.

3. The deflection of cracked members is substantially larger than that of uncracked members.

4. The efficient use of high-strength steel is limited by the fact that the amount of cracking (width and number of cracks) is about proportional to the strain, and therefore the stress, in the steel.

These undesirable characteristics of ordinary reinforced concrete have been largely overcome by the development of prestressed concrete. A prestressed-concrete member has been defined as one in which there have been introduced internal stresses of such magnitude and distribution that the stresses resulting from the given external loading are counteracted to a desired degree. Concrete is basically a compressive material, with its strength in tension a low and unreliable value. Prestressing applies a precompression to the member which reduces or eliminates undesirable tensile stresses that would otherwise be present. The entire cross section can be used to resist bending, and cracking under service load conditions can be minimized or even avoided entirely. In addition, it will be shown later that longitudinal precompression greatly reduces the diagonal tension in prestressed-concrete beams.

The first suggestions for prestressing seem to have been made between 1886 and 1908 by the Americans P. H. Jackson and G. R. Steiner, the Austrian J. Mandl, and the German J. Koenen. The use of high-strength steel was first suggested by the Austrian F. von Emperger in 1923, while at about the same time the American R. H. Dill proposed "full prestressing" to eliminate cracks completely. While these proposals remained mainly on paper, the actual development of prestressed reinforced-concrete structures abroad is chiefly due to E. Freyssinet (France, 1928), E. Hoyer (Germany, 1938), and more recently G. Magnel in Belgium. These methods have found very wide application in Europe for bridges with spans of 200 ft and more, floors and roofs, piles, railroad ties, etc. Moderate-sized elements such as prestressed joists, beams, and slabs are successfully mass produced by precasting. In a different field, an independent American method, originated by W. H. Hewitt in 1923, has found wide application. This consists in precompressing the cylindrical shells of water tanks and pipes by surrounding a concrete shell with hoops of steel which are tightened to a predetermined tension and then covered with a protective concrete layer.

The development in this country has been slower, not for technical but for economic reasons. The European methods achieve great savings of materials, but the methods of prestressing require a great amount of highly qualified labor. This is no particular disadvantage under the high European ratio of material to labor cost. The American ratio is exactly the reverse, which required the development of somewhat different methods more adapted to cost factors in this country. Rapid development in recent years has furnished such techniques, and at the present time considerable quantities of prestressed concrete compete economically with ordinary reinforced concrete and with other materials.

11.2 Sources of Prestress Force Prestress force can be applied to a concrete beam in many ways. Perhaps the most obvious method of precompressing is to use jacks reacting against abutments, as shown in Fig. 11.1*a*. Such a scheme has been employed for large projects. Many variations are possible, including replacing the jacks with compression struts after the desired stress in the concrete is obtained or the use of inexpensive jacks which remain in place in the structure, in some cases with a cement grout used as the hydraulic fluid. The principal difficulty associated with such a system is that even a slight movement of the abutments will drastically reduce the prestress force.

In most cases the same result is more conveniently obtained by tying

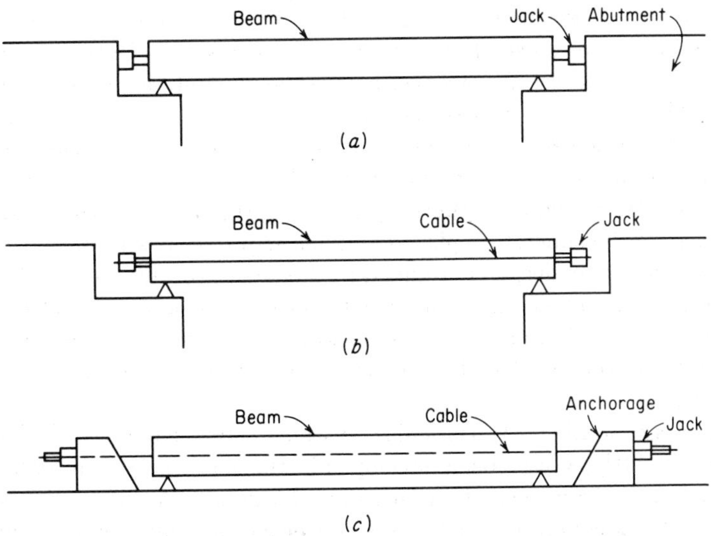

Fig. 11.1

the jack bases together with wires or cables, as shown in Fig. 11.1*b*. These wires or cables may be external, located on each side of the beam; more usually they are passed through a hollow conduit embedded in the concrete beam. Usually one end of the prestressing tendon is anchored, and all the force is applied at the other end. After attainment of the desired amount of prestress force, the wires are wedged against the concrete, and the jacking equipment is removed for reuse. Note that, in this type of prestressing, the entire system is self-contained and is independent of relative displacement of the supports.

Another method of prestressing which is widely used is illustrated by Fig. 11.1*c*. The prestressing strands are tensioned between massive abutments in a casting yard prior to placing the concrete in the beam forms. The beam is poured around the tensioned strands, and after the concrete has attained sufficient strength, the jacking pressure is released. This transfers the prestressing force to the concrete by bond and friction along the strands, chiefly at the outer ends.

Other means for introducing the desired prestressing force have been attempted on an experimental basis. Thermal prestressing can be achieved by preheating the steel by electrical or other means. Anchored against the ends of the concrete beam while in the extended state, the steel cools and tends to contract. The prestress force is developed through the restrained contraction. The use of expanding cement in concrete members has been tried with varying success. The volumetric expansion, restrained by steel strands or by fixed abutments, produces the prestress force.

Most of the patented systems for applying prestress in current use are variations of those shown in Fig. 11.1*b* and *c*. Such systems can generally be classified as *pretensioning* or *posttensioning* systems. In the case of pretensioning, the wires are stressed before the concrete is placed, as in Fig. 11.1*c*. This system is well suited for mass production, since casting beds can be made several hundred feet long, the entire length cast at once, and individual beams cut to the desired length from the long casting.

In posttensioned construction, shown in Fig. 11.1*b*, the wires are tensioned after the concrete is placed and has acquired its strength. Usually a hollow conduit or sleeve is provided in the beam, through which the wires are passed. In some cases, hollow box-section beams are used, as are external posttensioning wires. The jacking force is usually applied against the ends of the hardened concrete, eliminating the need for massive abutments.

A large number of pasticular systems, steel elements, jacks, and anchorage fittings have been developed in this country and abroad, many of which differ from each other only in minor details. As far as the designer of prestressed-concrete structures is concerned, it is unnecessary and perhaps even undesirable to specify in detail the technique that is to be followed and the equipment to be used. It is frequently best to specify only the magnitude and line of action of the prestress force. The contractor is then free, in bidding the work, to receive quotations from several different prestressing subcontractors, with resultant cost savings. It is evident, however, that the designer must have some knowledge of the details of the various systems contemplated for use, so that in selecting cross-sectional dimensions any one of several systems can be accommodated.

As noted in Art. 2.9, the magnitude of prestress force in concrete members is not constant, but diminishes with time at a gradually decreasing rate. The reduction of the initial prestress force P_i to the final effective value P is due to a number of causes. The most significant are elastic shortening of the concrete, concrete creep under sustained load, concrete shrinkage, relaxation of the stress in the steel, frictional loss between the tendons and the concrete during the stressing operation, and loss due to slip of the steel strands as stress is transferred from the prestressing jacks to the anchorages at the ends of the beam. The approximate magnitudes of the various losses and means for predicting stress loss will be discussed in detail in Art. 11.9.

11.3 Prestressing Steels Early attempts at prestressing concrete were unsuccessful because steel of ordinary structural strength was used. The low prestress obtainable in such rods was quickly lost by shrinkage and creep in the concrete.

Such changes in length of concrete have much less effect on prestress force if that force is obtained using highly stressed steel wires or cables. In Fig. 11.2*a*, a concrete beam of length L is prestressed using steel bars with a yield stress of 40,000 psi, at a working stress of 20,000 psi. With $E_s = 29 \times 10^6$ psi, the unit strain ϵ_s required to produce the desired stress of 20,000 psi is

$$\epsilon_s = \frac{\Delta L}{L} = \frac{f_s}{E_s} = \frac{20{,}000}{29 \times 10^6} = 6.9 \times 10^{-4}$$

But the long-term strain in the concrete due to shrinkage and creep alone may be of the order of 8.0×10^{-4}, which would be sufficient to completely relieve the steel of all stress.

Alternatively, suppose that the beam is prestressed using high-tensile wire with an ultimate strength of 250,000 psi, at a working stress of 150,000 psi. The elastic modulus of steel does not vary greatly, and the same value of 29×10^6 psi will be assumed. Then in this case the unit strain required to produce the working stress in the steel is

$$\epsilon_s = \frac{150{,}000}{29 \times 10^6} = 51.7 \times 10^{-4}$$

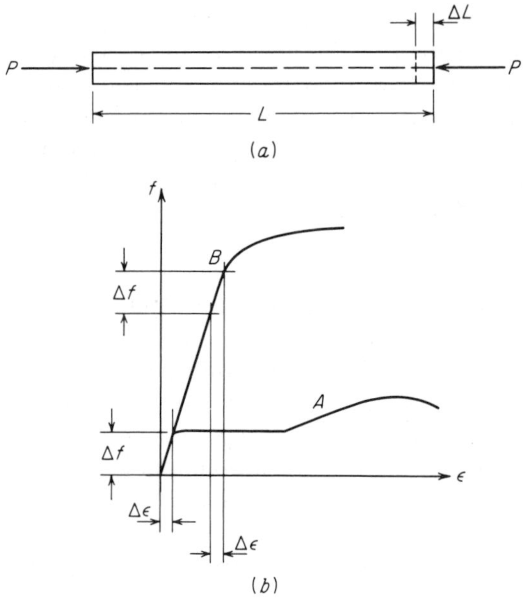

Fig. 11.2

If shrinkage and creep strain are the same as before, the net strain in the steel after these losses is

$$\epsilon_s' = (51.7 - 8.0)10^{-4} = 43.7 \times 10^{-4}$$

and the corresponding stress after losses is

$$f_s = \epsilon_s' E_s = 43.7 \times 10^{-4} \times 29 \times 10^6 = 127{,}000 \text{ psi}$$

This represents a stress loss of about 15 per cent, compared with 100 per cent loss in the beam using ordinary steel. It is apparent that the amount of stress lost because of shrinkage and creep is independent of the original stress in the steel. Therefore, the higher the original stress, the lower will be the percentage loss. This is illustrated graphically by the stress-strain curves of Fig. 11.2*b*. Curve *A* is representative of ordinary reinforcing rods, with a yield stress between 40,000 and 60,000 psi, while curve *B* represents high-tensile wire, with an ultimate stress of about 250,000 psi. The stress change Δf resulting from a certain change in strain $\Delta\epsilon$ is seen to have much less effect when high steel-stress levels are attained.

Prestressing steel is most commonly used in the form of individual wires of high tensile strength, stranded cable made up of seven or more individual wires, and alloy-steel bars. Prestressing wire is made by rolling steel billets into round rods, which are then passed through dies to reduce the diameter and to produce the required strength. In addition to reducing the diameter of the wire, the drawing operation changes the internal structure of the wire from crystalline to fibrous and gives the wire great strength through cold-working and strain-hardening. The end product is known as *cold-drawn* wire. For use in prestressing it is almost always subjected to a stress-relieving process. This stress-relieving is not sufficient to reduce materially the strength of the wire, but it does eliminate most of the internal stresses resulting from the drawing operation. A typical stress-strain curve for cold-drawn wire is shown in Fig. 11.3, together with curves for seven-wire stranded cable and for alloy-steel bars. The lack of a well-defined yield point for these materials is apparent, and it is convenient to refer to the "proof-stress" value, established arbitrarily as that stress which will produce a residual strain of 0.2 per cent.

Stranded cable is usually laid up using seven wires, with the outer six being wound around a seventh wire of slightly larger diameter. The wires may be galvanized (usual for posttensioned construction) or uncoated (usual for pretensioned construction). In the case of stranded cable, stress-relieving is conducted on the finished cable; this eliminates in one operation the internal stresses resulting from both cold-drawing and stranding.

Alloy-steel bars, having a tensile strength somewhat lower than that of cold-drawn wires or stranded cable, are produced by alloying high-carbon steel with other elements, principally manganese and silicon. In addition, cold work is done on the bars during production, further increasing their proportional limit.

A property of steel which is of particular significance in prestressing operations is known as *relaxation*. Most stress-strain curves are obtained from tests conducted at a fairly rapid rate of loading. It is generally

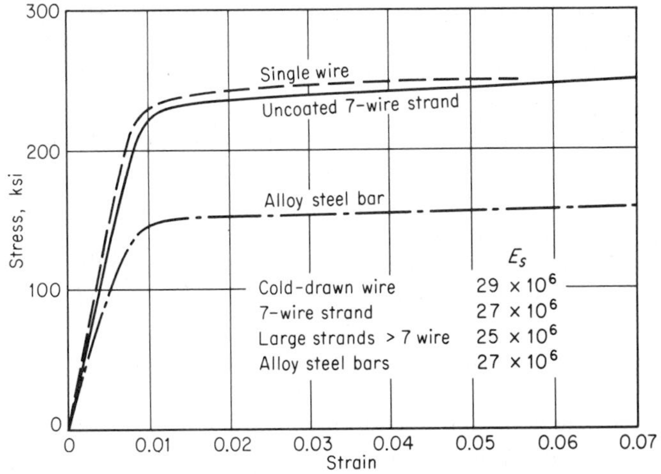

Fig. 11.3 Stress-strain curves for prestressing steels.

***Table* 11.1 Allowable stresses in prestressing steel**

a. *Temporary stresses*	
1. Due to temporary jacking force but not greater than the maximum value recommended by the manufacturer of the steel or of the anchorages	$0.80f'_s$
2. Pretensioning tendons immediately after transfer, or posttensioning tendons immediately after anchoring	$0.70f'_s$
b. *Effective prestress*	$0.60f'_s$ or $0.80f_{sy}$ whichever is smaller

known that if the specimen, be it in the form of wire, strand, or alloy bar, is held at a constant high strain, there will be a gradual reduction in stress, which approaches some limiting value asymptotically. This phenomenon of relaxation is closely related to, but not quite the same as, creep, which is defined as a gradually changing strain at constant stress. In prestressed beams, the steel undergoes a slightly modified form of relaxation, since the strain is essentially constant but not completely so, as there is a slight reduction in steel strain due to shrinkage and creep of the concrete.

In general, relaxation loss of stress will be higher for high-stress levels than for low. Most present prestressing steel shows only negligible relaxation loss if the stress is below about 50 per cent of ultimate; however, higher stress than this is usually permitted in design. Consequently it is necessary to make some allowance for loss of stress due to relaxation, in addition to other causes.

The tensile stress permitted by the ACI Code in prestressing wires, strands, or bars is dependent upon the stage of loading. With f'_s defined as the ultimate strength of the prestressing steel, and f_{sy} as the nominal yield strength (proof strength), allowable stresses are as shown in Table 11.1.

The justification for higher allowable stresses during the jacking operation and immediately after transfer (the moment at which the wires are cut free of abutments in the case of pretensioning, or when the wires are wedged and jack pressure is removed in the case of posttensioning) lies in the fact that the steel stresses are known quite precisely at this stage. Hydraulic jacking pressure and total steel strain are quantities that are easily measured. In addition, if an accidentally deficient cable should break, it could easily be replaced at small cost; in effect, the tensioning operation is a performance test of the material. The allowable effective prestress, after essentially all losses in stress have occurred, is limited to a more conservative value.

The strength and other characteristics of prestressing wire, strands, and bars very somewhat among manufacturers, as do the methods of grouping the tendons and anchoring them. Typical information is given for illustration in Table 11, Appendix B.

11.4 Concrete for Prestressed Construction Ordinarily, concrete of substantially higher compressive strength is used for prestressed structures than for those constructed of ordinary reinforced concrete. Most prestressed construction in the United States at the present time is designed for a 28-day compressive strength between 4000 and 5000 psi. There are several reasons for this:

1. High-strength concrete normally has a higher modulus of elasticity (see Fig. 1.3). This means a reduction in initial elastic strain under application of prestress force and a reduction in creep strain, which is approximately proportional to elastic strain. This results in a reduction in loss of prestress.

2. In posttensioned construction, high bearing stresses result at the ends of beams, where prestressing force is transferred from the tendons to anchorage fittings, which bear directly against the concrete. This problem can be met by increasing the size of the anchorage fitting or by increasing the bearing capacity of the concrete by increasing its compressive strength. The latter is usually more economical.

3. In pretensioned construction, where transfer by bond is customary, the use of high-strength concrete will permit the development of higher bond stresses.

4. A substantial part of the prestressed construction in the United States is precast, with the concrete mixed, placed, and cured under carefully controlled conditions which facilitate the obtaining of higher strengths.

The strain characteristics of concrete under short-time and sustained loads assume an even greater importance in prestressed structures than in reinforced-concrete structures, because of the influence of strain on loss of prestress force. Strains due to stress, together with volume changes due to shrinkage and temperature changes, may have considerable influence on prestressed structures. In this connection, it is suggested that the reader review Arts. 1.7 to 1.9, which discuss in some detail the compressive and tensile strengths of concrete under short-time and sustained loads and the changes in concrete volume that occur owing to shrinkage and temperature change.

As is the case for prestressing steels, the allowable stresses in the concrete, according to the ACI Code, are dependent upon the stage of loading. These stresses are given in Table 11.2. Here f'_{ci} is the compressive strength of the concrete at the time of initial prestress, f'_c the 28-day compressive strength of the concrete, A_b the bearing area of the anchor plate of the posttensioning steel, and A'_b the maximum area of the portion of the anchorage surface that is geometrically similar to and concentric with the area of the anchor plate of the posttensioning steel.

***Table* 11.2**

a. Temporary stresses immediately after transfer, before losses due to creep and shrinkage, shall not exceed the following:

1. Compression . . . . $0.60f'_{ci}$
2. Tension stresses in members without auxiliary reinforcement (unprestressed or prestressed) in the tension zone . . . . $3\sqrt{f'_{ci}}$

   Where the calculated tension stress exceeds this value, reinforcement shall be provided to resist the total tension force in the concrete computed on the assumption of an uncracked section.

b. Stresses at design loads, after allowance for all prestress losses, shall not exceed the following:

1. Compression . . . . $0.45f'_c$
2. Tension in the precompressed tension zone:

   Members, not exposed to freezing temperatures nor to a corrosive environment, which contain bonded prestressed or unprestressed reinforcement located so as to control cracking . . . . $6\sqrt{f'_c}$

   All other members 0

   These values may be exceeded when not detrimental to proper structural behavior as provided in Art. 104 of ACI Code.

c. The bearing stress on the concrete created by the anchorage in posttensioned concrete with adequate reinforcement in the end regions shall not exceed

$$f_{cp} = 0.6f'_{ci}\sqrt[3]{\frac{A'_b}{A_b}}$$

but not greater than . . . . f'_{ci}

11.5 General Equations for Flexural Design It is convenient in treating prestressed members to think of the prestressing forces as a system of external forces acting on the concrete member, which must be in equilibrium under the action of those forces. Figure 11.4*a* shows a simple-span prestressed beam with curved cables, typical of many posttensioned installations. The portion of the beam to the left of a vertical cutting plane x-x is taken as a free body, with forces acting as shown in Fig. 11.4*b*. The force P at the left end is exerted on the concrete through the cable anchorage, while the force P at the cutting plane x-x results from combined shear and normal force acting on the concrete surface at that location. The direction of P is tangent to the curve of the cable at each location. Note the presence of the force N, acting on the concrete from the cable, due to cable curvature. This force will be distributed in some manner along the length of the cable, the exact distribution depending upon the cable profile. Its resultant, and the direction in which the resultant acts, can be found from the force diagram of Fig. 11.4*c*.

It is convenient in working with the prestressing force P to divide it into its components in the horizontal and vertical directions. The horizontal component (Fig. 11.4*d*) is $H = P\cos\theta$, and the vertical component is $V = H\tan\theta = P\sin\theta$, where θ is the angle of inclination of the cable centroid at the particular section. Since the slope angle is normally quite small, the cosine of θ is very close to unity, and it is sufficient for most calculations to take $H = P$.

In developing equations for flexural stress, the effects of prestress force, dead-load moment, and live-load moment are calculated separately, and the separate stresses are superimposed. When the prestress force P is applied with an eccentricity e below the neutral axis of the cross section with area A and top and bottom fiber distances c_1 and c_2, respectively, it causes the compressive stress $-P/A$ and the bending stresses $+Pec_1/I$ and $-Pec_2/I$ in the top and bottom fibers, respectively (compressive stresses are designated as negative, tensile stresses as positive), as shown in Fig. 11.5*a*. Then, at the top fiber, the stress is

$$f_{1p} = -\frac{P}{A} + \frac{Pec_1}{I} = -\frac{P}{A}\left(1 - \frac{ec_1}{r^2}\right) \tag{11.1}$$

and at the bottom fiber

$$f_{2p} = -\frac{P}{A} - \frac{Pec_2}{I} = -\frac{P}{A}\left(1 + \frac{ec_2}{r^2}\right) \tag{11.2}$$

where r is the radius of gyration of the concrete section. When the dead load of the girder w_g is added, causing additional moment M_g, the total top and bottom fiber stresses become

$$f_{1d} = f_{1P} - \frac{M_g c_1}{I} \tag{11.3}$$

$$f_{2d} = f_{2P} + \frac{M_g c_2}{I} \tag{11.4}$$

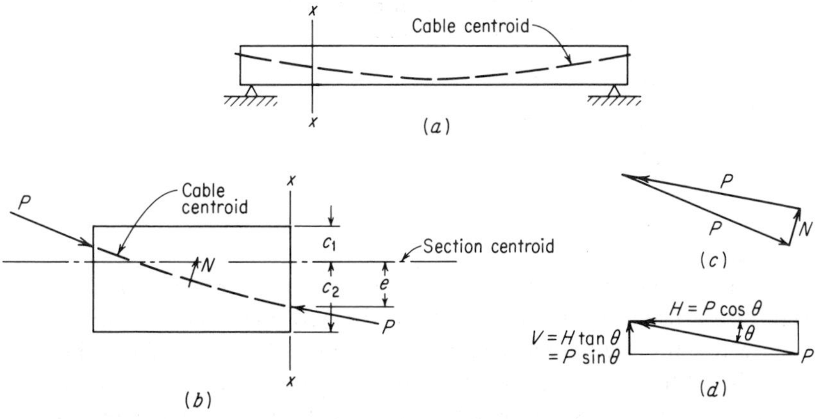

Fig. 11.4

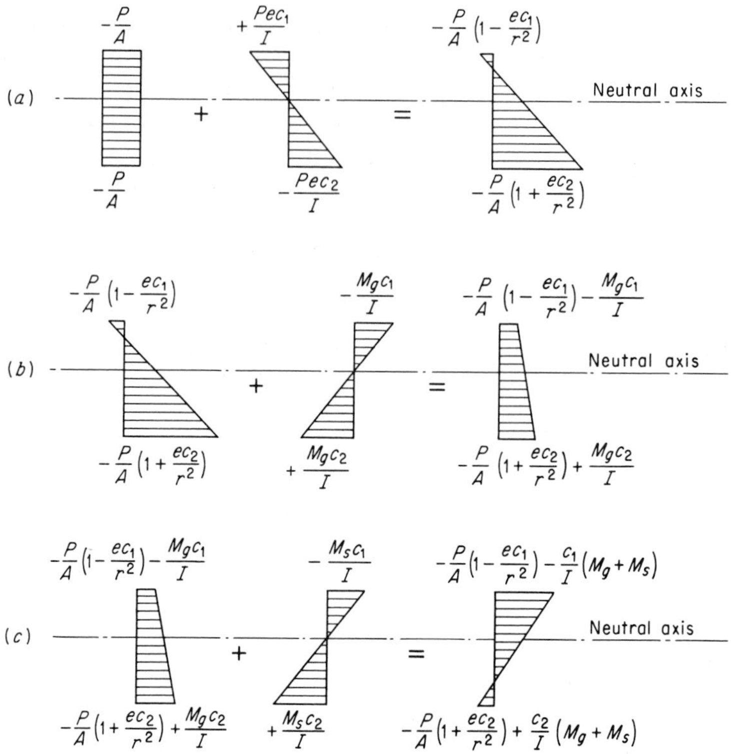

Fig. 11.5 Stress distribution in beams: (*a*) effect of prestress; (*b*) effect of prestress and girder dead load; (*c*) effect of prestress, girder dead load, and service load.

as shown in Fig. 11.5*b*. When the girder is installed and subjected to the service load (dead loads in addition to girder dead load, plus design live load) the stresses in the top and bottom fiber are

$$f_{1s} = f_{1d} - \frac{M_s c_1}{I} \tag{11.5}$$

$$f_{2s} = f_{2d} + \frac{M_s c_2}{I} \tag{11.6}$$

as in Fig. 11.5*c*.

It is necessary, in a review of the adequacy of a cross section or in the design of a section, that the stresses in the extreme fibers remain within the allowable limits under any loading or combination of loadings that can occur. Normally the stress distribution at the section of maximum moment in a properly designed beam will range between the extreme states shown in Fig. 11.6 as the beam passes from the unloaded state to the

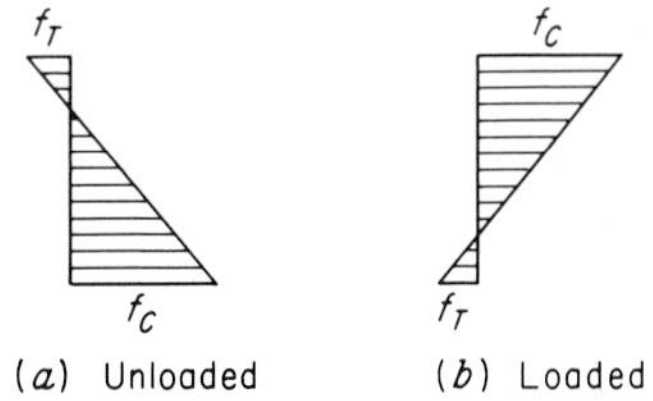

***Fig.* 11.6** Stress limits.

loaded state, where f_c is the allowable stress in compression, and f_t the allowable stress in tension.

In calculating the section properties A, I, etc., to be used in the design equations, it is relevant that, in posttensioned construction, the cables are usually grouted in the conduits after tensioning. Before grouting, stresses should be based on the net section with holes deducted. After grouting, the transformed section should be used, with holes considered filled with concrete, and with the steel replaced with an equivalent area of concrete. However, it is satisfactory, unless the holes are quite large, to compute section properties on the basis of the gross concrete section. This tends to underestimate stresses due to prestress and overestimate stresses caused by applied loads; however, each error is small, and the two tend to compensate each other. Similarly, while in pretensioned beams the properties of the transformed section should be used, it makes little difference if calculations are based on properties of the gross concrete section.[1]

In some cases, in the design of prestressed-concrete beams it is useful to establish the location of the upper and lower *kern points* of a cross section. These are defined as the limiting points inside which the prestress-force resultant may be applied without causing tension anywhere in the cross section. Their locations are obtained by writing the expression for the tensile fiber stress due to application of an eccentric prestress force acting alone and setting this expression equal to zero to solve for the required eccentricity. In Fig. 11.7, to locate the upper kern-point distance k_1 from the neutral axis, let the prestress-force resultant P act at that point. Then the bottom fiber stress is

$$f_b = -\frac{P}{A}\left(1 - \frac{ec_2}{r^2}\right) = 0$$

[1] The ACI Code states: "In calculations of section properties prior to bonding of tendons, areas of the open ducts shall be deducted. The transformed area of bonded tendons may be included in pretensioned members and in posttensioned members after grouting."

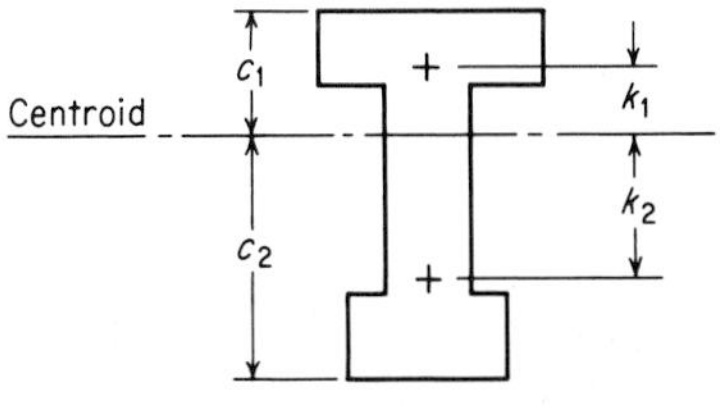

***Fig.* 11.7** Location of kern points.

Set

$$1 - \frac{ec_2}{r^2} = 0$$

and solve for

$$e = k_1 = \frac{r^2}{c_2} \tag{11.7}$$

Similarly, the lower kern-point distance k_2 is

$$k_2 = \frac{r^2}{c_1} \tag{11.8}$$

The region between these two limiting points is known as the *kern*, or in some cases the *core*, of the section.

11.6 Application of Flexural Equations As in reinforced concrete, problems in prestressed concrete can be separated generally into review problems and design problems. For the former, with the applied loads, the concrete cross section, and the amount and point of application of the prestress-force resultant known, the equations of Art 11.5 permit the direct calculation of the resulting stresses. However, if the dimensions of a section and the amount and location of the prestress force are to be found, given the loads and allowable stresses, the problem is more complicated because of the several interrelated variables. More detailed study of these equations will reveal some significant points.

Consider first a simple-span prismatic beam with straight tendons typical of many types of pretensioned construction. Let the allowable concrete stress in tension be f_t, and that in compression f_c.* Straight tendons used with a straight beam result in a constant eccentricity of prestress force below the neutral axis throughout the length of the beam. At the cross section over the supports, neither dead- nor live-load moment is present, and the stresses are due only to the thrust and moment of the prestress force. Using Eqs. (11.1) and (11.2) and setting the top and bottom fiber stresses equal to the maximum allowable tension and compression, respectively,

$$f_{1p} = -\frac{P}{A} + \frac{Pec_1}{I} = f_t$$

$$f_{2p} = -\frac{P}{A} - \frac{Pec_2}{I} = f_c$$

* In writing statements of inequality, it is convenient to designate tensile stress as being larger than zero, and compressive stress smaller than zero. Thus +450 > −1350, −600 > −1140, etc.

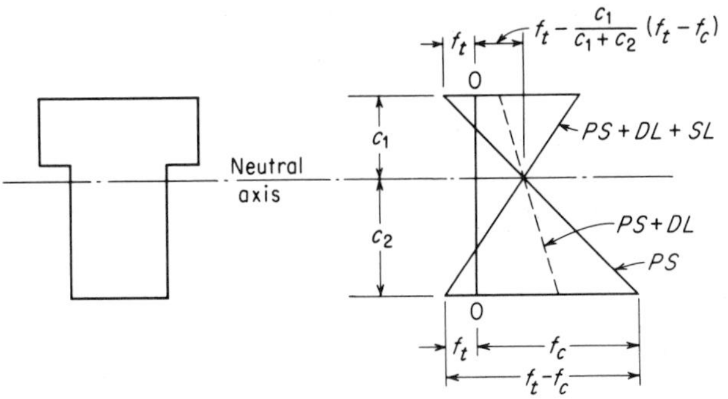

Fig. **11.8**

The resulting stress distribution PS is shown in Fig. 11.8. For a given cross section and known allowable stresses, the unknowns in these two equations are P/A and e. Solving simultaneously for these quantities,

$$e = \frac{(f_t - f_c)I}{P(c_1 + c_2)} \tag{a}$$

$$-\frac{P}{A} = f_t - \frac{c_1}{c_1 + c_2}(f_t - f_c) \tag{b}$$

The required prestress force P can be found from Eq. (*b*) as the product of the area times the concrete stress at the section centroid (see Fig. 11.8), and that value of P may be substituted in Eq. (*a*) to obtain the eccentricity.

The section of maximum moment of the beam (usually midspan) will be investigated next under the action of eccentric prestress force and girder dead load. From Eqs. (11.3) and (11.4) the top and bottom fiber stresses are

$$f_{1d} = f_t - \frac{M_g c_1}{I} \qquad f_{2d} = f_c + \frac{M_g c_2}{I}$$

The resulting stress distribution $PS + DL$ is shown in Fig. 11.8. It is evident that, for the type of beam under discussion, this loading state will never be critical, but only represents an intermediate condition between two limiting values which control.

Considering now the maximum-moment section under the action of eccentric prestress force and full service load; from Eqs. (11.5) and (11.6) the top and bottom fiber stresses are

$$f_{1s} = f_{1d} - \frac{M_s c_1}{I} = f_t - \frac{c_1}{I}(M_g + M_s)$$

$$f_{2s} = f_{2d} + \frac{M_s c_2}{I} = f_c + \frac{c_2}{I}(M_g + M_s)$$

These stresses must be within the specified allowable stress limits. Thus (designating the section moduli $S_1 = I/c_1$ and $S_2 = I/c_2$) one obtains

$$f_t - \frac{1}{S_1}(M_g + M_s) \geq f_c$$

$$f_c + \frac{1}{S_2}(M_g + M_s) \leq f_t$$

from which

$$S_1 \geq \frac{M_g + M_s}{f_t - f_c} \qquad (c)$$

$$S_2 \geq \frac{M_g + M_s}{f_t - f_c} \qquad (d)$$

That is, the section moduli of both top and bottom fibers must be at least equal to the total moment $(M_g + M_s)$ divided by the available stress range. The resulting stress distribution $PS + DL + SL$ is shown in Fig. 11.8.

In summary, the significant points of this discussion of prismatic beams with straight tendons are:

1. The required prestress force is the product of the concrete area and the concrete stress at the section centroid.

2. At no place in the beam can the tendon eccentricity be larger than its value at the supports, where only the eccentric prestress force acts.

3. The required section modulus depends upon the sum of the girder moment and service-load moment.

In most cases in actual construction, the prestress force does not act alone on a concrete beam. As the eccentric prestress force is applied, the beam cambers off the supporting form, and stresses due to girder dead load are immediately superimposed on those due to prestress. If straight tendons are used, resulting in a constant eccentricity, it is not possible to take advantage of the superposition of prestress and girder dead-load stresses, because the maximum eccentricity is controlled by the situation at the support, where no dead-load moment acts. On the other hand, if a variable eccentricity is possible, that eccentricity can be made larger near midspan, such that the superimposed prestress and girder dead-load stress distributions will utilize the full stress range from f_t (tension) to f_c (compression).

This is easily done for posttensioned beams by using a curved tendon conduit, wired to the stirrups in the desired profile prior to pouring the concrete. It can also be accomplished (but with somewhat more difficulty) in pretensioned beams, by the use of cable tie-down bars at intervals along the span.

Consider now a simple-span prismatic beam with curved tendons providing a variable eccentricity. All other conditions are the same as in the previous illustration. At the support sections, conditions will be the same as before, with stresses due to prestress force alone, and

$$f_{1p} = -\frac{P}{A} + \frac{Pe_sc_1}{I} = f_t$$

$$f_{2p} = -\frac{P}{A} - \frac{Pe_sc_2}{I} = f_c$$

Accordingly, at the supports,

$$e_s = \frac{(f_t - f_c)I}{P(c_1 + c_2)} \tag{e}$$

$$-\frac{P}{A} = f_t - \frac{c_1}{c_1 + c_2}(f_t - f_c) \tag{f}$$

At the maximum-moment section, girder dead-load stresses are superimposed. The eccentricity of prestress force can therefore be increased such that the limiting stress conditions are attained only under the superimposed load of the girder. Then, at midspan,

$$f_{1d} = -\frac{P}{A} + \frac{Pe_mc_1}{I} - \frac{M_gc_1}{I} = f_t$$

$$f_{2d} = -\frac{P}{A} - \frac{Pe_mc_2}{I} + \frac{M_gc_2}{I} = f_c$$

Solving these two equations simultaneously for the unknowns P/A and e_m,

$$-\frac{P}{A} = f_t - \frac{c_1}{c_1 + c_2}(f_t - f_c) \tag{g}$$

as before, and

$$e_m = \frac{(f_t - f_c)I}{P(c_1 + c_2)} + \frac{M_g}{P} \tag{h}$$

By comparing this expression for e_m with that for e_s at the supports, it is seen that an additional eccentricity in the amount M_g/P has been introduced which will produce a moment due to prestress just equal to the dead-load moment but of opposite sign. The stress distribution $PS + DL$ due to superimposed prestress and girder dead-load stress is shown in Fig. 11.9. The distribution PS due to prestress alone does not exist where dead-load moments act.[1]

[1] In designing on this basis, care must be taken to ensure that the assumed conditions will actually be obtained. For example, a beam cast on soft ground would receive some support along its length even after prestress is applied. A precast beam laid flat on its side during handling would obviously have no dead-load stresses superimposed.

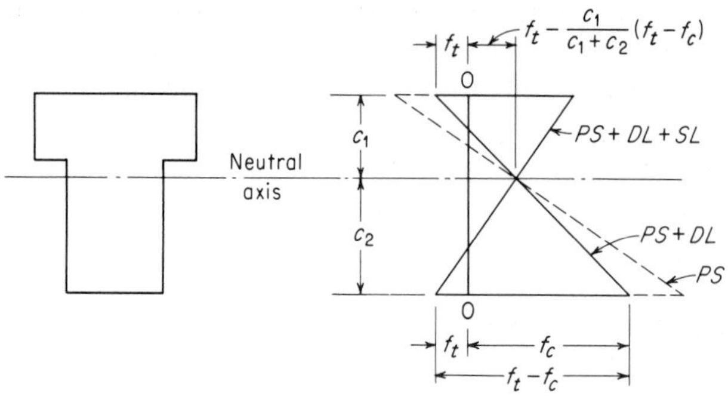

***Fig.* 11.9**

Now, investigating the maximum-moment section under the action of eccentric prestress force and full service load, the top and bottom fiber stresses are

$$f_{1s} = f_{1d} - \frac{M_s c_1}{I} = f_t - \frac{M_s c_1}{I}$$

$$f_{2s} = f_{2d} + \frac{M_s c_2}{I} = f_c + \frac{M_s c_2}{I}$$

These stresses must be within the limits of f_t (tension) and f_c (compression). Thus

$$f_t - \frac{M_s}{S_1} \geq f_c \qquad f_c + \frac{M_s}{S_2} \leq f_t$$

from which

$$S_1 \geq \frac{M_s}{f_t - f_c} \tag{i}$$

$$S_2 \geq \frac{M_s}{f_t - f_c} \tag{j}$$

The section moduli in this case must be at least equal to the superimposed load moment M_s divided by the available stress range. The resulting stress distribution $PS + DL + SL$ is shown in Fig. 11.9.

In summary, the more significant aspects of the second illustration, pertaining to prismatic beams with curved tendons, are:

1. The required prestress force is the product of the concrete area and the concrete stress at the section centroid. (Note that the centroidal stress does not change as moment is applied to the beam.)

2. Conditions at the supports are the same as for beams with straight cables; here prestress force acts alone.

3. Elsewhere along the span, by depressing the centroid of prestress force an amount M_g/P below its lowest possible location at the supports, the dead load of the beam may be fully compensated.

The last feature is of the greatest importance; it explains a large part of the economy of prestressed-concrete members, particularly for long spans. The dead load of the girder is carried entirely "free," at no cost of additional concrete, steel, or prestress force, and the full stress capacity of the material is used in resisting useful load.

Example A simply supported rectangular beam is to span 30 ft and must carry a load, in addition to its own weight, of 500 plf. Allowable concrete stresses are 1800 psi in compression and 200 psi in tension. A prismatic beam with straight, posttensioned wires is to be used. Find the required dimensions of the concrete section, the magnitude of the required prestress force, and the location of the cable centroid.

It is necessary in this case to estimate the dead load of the beam. Assuming a section 12 in. wide and 15 in. deep,

$$w_g = \frac{12 \times 15}{144} 150 = 188 \text{ plf}$$
$$M_g = \tfrac{1}{8} \times 188 \times 30^2 = 21{,}200 \text{ ft-lb}$$
$$w_l = 500 \text{ plf}$$
$$M_s = \tfrac{1}{8} \times 500 \times 30^2 = 56{,}300 \text{ ft-lb}$$

In this case, since straight tendons are specified, the prestress eccentricity can be no larger than that value permissible at the supports, where no girder moments act, and the section modulus depends upon the sum of girder moment and superimposed load moment. Thus

$$S = \frac{M_g + M_s}{f_t - f_c} = \frac{(21{,}200 + 56{,}300)12}{200 + 1800} = 465 \text{ in.}^3$$
$$\frac{bh^2}{6} = 465$$
$$bh^2 = 2790$$

A concrete section 12 in. wide and 15.2 in. deep is selected; the assumed dead load is satisfactory. (In practice, dimensions would be rounded, probably to the next larger inch; however, for the sake of clarity in this example and for comparison with later results, theoretical dimensions will be retained.) Then

$$A = 12 \times 15.2 = 182 \text{ in.}^2$$
$$I = \frac{12 \times 15.2^3}{12} = 3510 \text{ in.}^4$$
$$P = -\left[f_t - \frac{c_1}{c_1 + c_2}(f_t - f_c)\right] A$$
$$= (-200 + \tfrac{1}{2} \times 2000)182 = 146{,}000 \text{ lb}$$
$$e = \frac{(f_t - f_c)I}{P(c_1 + c_2)} = \frac{2000 \times 3510}{146{,}000 \times 15.2} = 3.16 \text{ in.}$$

Using stress-relieved solid wires of 0.250-in. diameter (see Table 11, Appendix B) with an effective prestress of 0.60 of the ultimate value, the number of wires required is

$$N = \frac{146{,}000}{0.60 \times 11{,}800} = 20.6$$

Twenty-one wires will be used. A check of top and bottom fiber stresses using Eqs. (11.1) to (11.6) verifies that the specified stress limits have not been exceeded.

Example Design a beam for the same span, load, and stress conditions as for the preceding example; use curved tendons to permit a variable eccentricity.

Under the assumption that dead-load moment can be compensated by additional prestress eccentricity, it is unnecessary to estimate the dead load. The required section modulus is

$$S = \frac{M_s}{f_t - f_c} = \frac{56{,}300 \times 12}{200 + 1800} = 338 \text{ in.}^3$$

$$\frac{bh^2}{6} = 338$$

$$bh^2 = 2030$$

A section 12 in. wide and 13 in. deep is selected, for which

$$A = 12 \times 13 = 156 \text{ in.}^2$$

$$I = \frac{12 \times 13^3}{12} = 2200 \text{ in.}^4$$

$$w_g = {}^{156}\!/_{144} \times 150 = 163 \text{ plf}$$

$$M_g = {}^{1}\!/_{8} \times 163 \times 30^2 = 18{,}400 \text{ ft-lb}$$

Then

$$P = -\left[f_t - \frac{c_1}{c_1 + c_2}(f_t - f_c)\right]A$$

$$= (-200 + {}^{1}\!/_{2} \times 2000)156 = 125{,}000 \text{ lb}$$

$$e_s = \frac{(f_t - f_c)I}{P(c_1 + c_2)} = \frac{2000 \times 2200}{125{,}000 \times 13} = 2.71 \text{ in.}$$

$$e_m = e_s + \frac{M_g}{P} = 2.71 + \frac{18{,}400 \times 12}{125{,}000} = 4.48 \text{ in.}$$

In this case, the required number of wires of 0.250 in. diameter is

$$N = \frac{125{,}000}{0.60 \times 11{,}800} = 17.7$$

Eighteen wires will be used. A check of top and bottom fiber stresses, both at the supports and at midspan, indicates that the desired stresses have been attained. In a comparison of these results with those of the previous example, the advantage of curved tendons becomes obvious. By the simple expedient of depressing the centroid of the wires at midspan 1.77 in. below its location at the supports, a saving of over 14 per cent in both concrete and steel is obtained. For longer spans, with a higher ratio of dead to live load, the saving would be considerably larger.

Example Design a beam with specifications as in the first two examples, except that the span is increased to 60 ft. Use curved tendons to permit a variable eccentricity. The live load is 500 plf, and allowable stresses are 1800 psi in compression and 200 psi in tension as before.

Proceeding as in the second example,

$$M_s = \tfrac{1}{8} \times 500 \times 60^2 = 225{,}000 \text{ ft-lb}$$

$$S = \frac{M_s}{f_t - f_c} = \frac{225{,}000 \times 12}{200 + 1800} = 1350 \text{ in.}^3$$

$$\frac{bh^2}{6} = 1350$$

$$bh^2 = 8110$$

A section 15 in. wide and 23.2 in. deep is selected, for which

$$A = 15 \times 23.2 = 348 \text{ in.}^2$$

$$I = \frac{15 \times 23.2^3}{12} = 15{,}600 \text{ in.}^4$$

$$w_g = \tfrac{348}{144} \times 150 = 362 \text{ plf}$$

$$M_g = \tfrac{1}{8} \times 362 \times 60^2 = 163{,}000 \text{ ft-lb}$$

Then

$$P = -\left[f_t - \frac{c_1}{c_1 + c_2}(f_t - f_c)\right] A$$

$$= (-200 + \tfrac{1}{2} \times 2000)348 = 279{,}000 \text{ lb}$$

$$e_s = \frac{(f_t - f_c)I}{P(c_1 + c_2)} = \frac{2000 \times 15{,}600}{279{,}000 \times 23.2} = 4.72 \text{ in.}$$

$$e_m = e_s + \frac{M_g}{P} = 4.72 + \frac{163{,}000 \times 12}{279{,}000} = 11.74 \text{ in.}$$

Note that the half depth of the proposed beam is only 11.60 in., indicating that the centroid of the wire group would have to be outside the cross section in order to satisfy the stated stress conditions. This is obviously not possible, and either the proportions of the beam must be changed or, if the section dimensions are for some reason restricted, the dead load cannot be fully compensated by additional eccentricity of prestress force. Proceeding on the basis that there is no restriction on section dimensions,

$$w_g = \frac{bh}{144}150 = 1.04bh \qquad \text{plf}$$

$$M_g = \tfrac{1}{8} \times 1.04bh \times 60^2 = 468bh \qquad \text{ft-lb}$$

$$P = (-200 + \tfrac{1}{2} \times 2000)bh = 800bh \qquad \text{lb}$$

Then

$$\frac{M_g}{P} = \frac{468bh \times 12}{800bh} = 7.03 \text{ in.}$$

It is interesting to observe here that the added eccentricity M_g/P required to compensate for girder dead load is independent of beam dimensions and depends only on the weight of the material, the span, and the stress at the section centroid. Then

$$e_s = \frac{(f_t - f_c)I}{P(c_1 + c_2)} = \frac{2000bh^3/12}{800bh^2} = 0.208h$$

At this point, it is necessary to establish the amount of concrete that will be required from the tendon centroid to the bottom fiber of the beam. This will depend not only upon the amount of concrete protection needed for the lowest wires (usually 1½ in.), but on the number and arrangement of the wires as well. For present purposes, this distance will be assumed to be 0.10h. Then

$$e_s + \frac{M_g}{P} + 0.10h = 0.50h$$

$$0.208h + 7.03 + 0.10h = 0.50h$$
$$h = 36.6 \text{ in.}$$

and the corresponding width is

$$b = \frac{6 \times 1350}{36.6^2} = 6.05 \text{ in.}$$

A concrete section 6.05 in. wide and 36.6 in. deep will be used. At the supports, the cable eccentricity is $0.208 \times 36.6 = 7.62$ in., and at midspan it is $7.62 + 7.03 = 14.65$ in. The total prestress force required is $800 \times 6.05 \times 36.6 = 177{,}000$ lb.

It is apparent from this example that, for a given span, load, and allowable stress, there is a certain minimum permissible depth which will allow all the dead load to be carried "free." If the section proportions can be modified at will, this is the economical depth to use. If, on the other hand, there are restrictions on maximum depth, as is often the case, or if the ratio of width to depth is limited by other considerations such as lateral stability, then it may be impossible to utilize the full allowable stress under both load conditions, dead load and dead plus live load. This means in turn that the section modulus must be increased to carry at least a portion of the dead-load moment, as well as the live-load moment.

PROBLEMS

1. A rectangular prestressed beam is to be simply supported on a 40-ft span and must carry a superimposed load of 1000 plf. The beam will be pretensioned, using straight cables. Concrete of $f_c' = 4000$ psi will be used. The allowable stress in compression is 1800 psi and that in tension is 380 psi. Find the required concrete dimensions, the magnitude of the required prestress force, and the location of the cable centroid.

2. Redesign the beam of Prob. 1 as a posttensioned beam with curved cables permitting a variable eccentricity.

3. A rectangular prestressed beam is to be simply supported on a 60-ft span and must carry a superimposed load of 1000 plf. The beam will be posttensioned with curved cables. Concrete having $f'_c = 4000$ psi will be used at allowable stresses of 1800 psi in compression and 380 psi in tension. Find the required concrete dimensions, the magnitude of the required prestress force, and the location of the cable centroid at the supports and at midspan. Assume that the minimum distance from the tendon centroid to the bottom of the beam is $\frac{1}{10}$ the total beam depth. Comment on your design.

4. Redesign the beam of Prob. 3 using a maximum total depth of 40 in.

11.7 I Sections The discussion up to this point has dealt exclusively with rectangular sections. These are important not only in demonstrating most simply the basic principles of prestressing, but also because rectangular sections are often used for prestressed slabs, for small beams, and for designs in which only a few beams of given dimensions are required. Forming costs are least for rectangular beams. However, for improved material economy it is desirable to use some form of I section for prestressed members, just as in steel design the wide-flange or I shape has proved most efficient. While in ordinary reinforced-concrete design, diagonal tensile stresses restrict the possibility of reduction in web thickness, in prestressed-concrete construction this is not so. It will be demonstrated later that, because of the axial compression over the cross section, diagonal tensile stresses are much reduced. One consequence of this is that the flexurally efficient I or T section can be used. Several common shapes are shown in Figure 11.10. Generally speaking, I, T, and box sections with relatively thin webs and thin flanges are more efficient than members with thicker parts. However several factors limit the gain in efficiency which may be made in proportioning the section, such as the problem of depositing concrete in very thin sections and the question of instability of very thin overhanging compression portions. Cross sections may be either symmetrical or unsymmetrical. If it is possible to utilize the cross section fully (i.e., to achieve the full range of allowable stress in both the top and bottom fibers as the load ranges from dead load only to dead plus live load), then the section should be symmetrical, since it is desirable that $(f_t - f_c) = M_s/S$ should obtain at both top and bottom of the section for

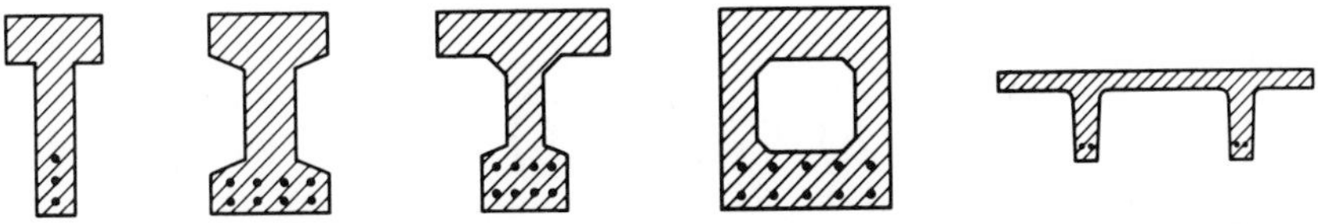

***Fig.* 11.10** Typical nonrectangular sections.

the two extreme load conditions. If the situation is such that the dead load cannot be fully counteracted by cable eccentricity, then there may be good reason to use an unsymmetrical section. A section with a high centroid location, providing sufficient depth below the neutral axis to accommodate the cable eccentricity, would be indicated.

In selecting the dimensions of I sections, it is often convenient to choose the relative proportions of the section and let all the dimensions vary with one, say the depth, so that all the properties of the section can be expressed as a numerical constant times some power of the depth. The design then closely follows the procedures outlined for rectangular sections.

11.8 Cable Profiles The previous discussion has dealt only with critical sections (usually midspan and support sections) in establishing cable centroid locations. Most present prestressed construction uses members that are essentially prismatic and employs a constant prestressing force from one end of the beam to the other, although curved or draped tendons are often used. In determining the best location for the centroid of such steel through the length of the beam, it is only necessary to ensure that the limiting stress states, such as are shown in Fig. 11.6, are nowhere violated under any anticipated loading. For a member which is properly designed at the critical sections, it is sufficient elsewhere to ensure that the tendon eccentricity is such that the allowable tensile stress in the concrete is not exceeded.

With no transverse loading applied to a beam, the center of compression at any cross section will coincide with the center of tension, i.e., the centroid of the prestressing steel. It has been shown that when the girder load is applied, the center of compression will move upward an amount M_g/P. Similarly, it can be shown that when the total load is applied, the center of compression will rise an amount $(M_g + M_s)/P$ above its original location.

The upper limit position of the compressive resultant, y_1 above the neutral axis, is such that it produces a tensile stress f_t at the bottom fiber of the section. With the compressive resultant at that limiting point, the bottom fiber stress is

$$-\frac{P}{A} + \frac{Pec_2}{I} = f_t$$

from which

$$e = y_1 = \frac{I}{Pc_2}\left(\frac{P}{A} + f_t\right) = \frac{Ar^2}{Pc_2}\left(\frac{P}{A} + f_t\right)$$

$$y_1 = \frac{r^2}{c_2}\left(1 + \frac{Af_t}{P}\right) \tag{11.9}$$

Similarly, the lower limit position of the compressive resultant, y_2 below the neutral axis, is such that it produces the allowable tensile stress f_t at the top fiber, and its location relative to the neutral axis is

$$y_2 = \frac{r^2}{c_1}\left(1 + \frac{Af_t}{P}\right) \tag{11.10}$$

With reference to Fig. 11.11, the location of the steel centroid must therefore be such that it is no less than $(M_g + M_s)/P$ below the level defined by y_1, and no more than M_g/P below the level defined by y_2. In this way the possible range of steel-centroid locations is established. The procedure should be repeated at sufficient intervals along the member to establish cable-centroid envelope curves. Note that, ideally, the upper and lower locations of the steel centroid, found in this way, will coincide. Only for this condition will the full efficiency of the cross section be obtained; i.e., the full allowable stress range will be utilized for both the upper and lower fibers of the beam. Usually this optimum condition is obtained at only one cross section.

A saving in design time is possible if it is noted that the ordinates of the cable envelope curves, measured downward from the limit lines defined by y_1 and y_2, are directly proportional to the ordinates of the respective moment diagrams. For a prismatic beam, for example, the dead load is uniform, and the lower envelope curve will vary parabolically from one end of the span to the other. If the live load is uniformly distributed, the upper envelope curve will likewise be a parabola, passing through established points at midspan and at the two supports. Limiting profiles can be drawn as shown in Fig. 11.12. Figure 11.12*a* illustrates, by the shaded area, the possible range of cable profiles for a uniformly loaded prismatic beam such that the midspan section is fully utilized, with upper and lower cable envelopes coinciding at midspan. Any cable profile falling completely within the shaded zone will be satisfactory from the point of view of flexural stress. Figure 11.12*b* shows the cable zone for a prismatic beam with a single concentrated live load at midspan. The lower cable envelope is a continuous parabola as before, while the upper curve consists

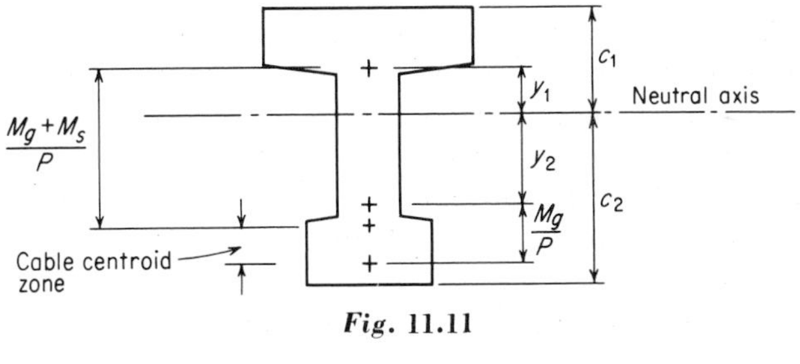

Fig. 11.11

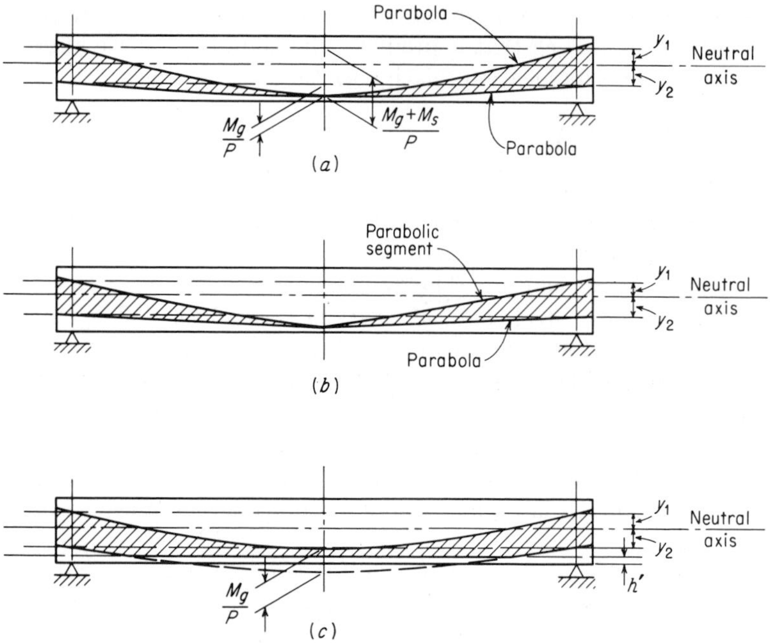

***Fig.* 11.12** Cable-profile zones.

of two parabolic segments with ordinates from the upper limit line proportional to those of the combined dead- and live-load moment diagrams. Figure 11.12*c* shows the situation for a uniformly loaded beam in which depth restrictions prevent the full compensation of dead-load moment. In this case, the distance h' represents the minimum cover to the centroid of the prestressing steel and defines the horizontal cutoff of the lower envelope parabola. As before, any cable shape falling entirely in the shaded zone will satisfy flexural requirements.

From a practical point of view, it is not always wise to adopt any arbitrary shape. In pretensioned construction, cable depressors and cable templates are used to obtain a linear segmental profile. In general, it is desirable to minimize the number of changes in slope. In posttensioned construction, curved-cable alignment can easily be obtained, but, in general, points of reversal of curvature are to be avoided, since these greatly increase losses in tension due to friction between the cable and the duct during the prestressing operation. (If such points of contraflexure cannot be avoided, there is some advantage in tensioning from both ends of the cables, rather than from one end only.) The best cable profile is that which follows the natural curve taken by the cable when it is suspended between the two end anchorages and allowed to sag until it passes through a single specified low point. To avoid displacing the conduit during concreting, it must be wired to the vertical web reinforcement.

PROBLEMS

1. Determine the cable profile for the beam of Prob. 3, Art. 11.6, giving offset dimensions from the beam centroid to the cable centroid at intervals of one-eighth the span along the beam.

2. Determine the cable profile for the beam of Prob. 4, Art. 11.6, giving offset dimensions from the beam centroid to the cable centroid at intervals of one-eighth the span along the beam.

11.9 Losses in Prestress As was previously mentioned, the prestressing force is not constant but will decrease with time, owing to a variety of causes. Most of these losses take place rapidly at first, and then at a gradually decreasing rate, approaching a limiting value asymptotically. In practice, only initial and final prestress values need be considered, final prestress being that value obtained after all important losses have occurred. It is advisable to check stresses in the member under initial prestress plus girder load, final prestress plus girder load, and final prestress plus service load. Other load combinations may at times be critical. The most important causes of loss in prestress will be discussed briefly in the following paragraphs.

a. Elastic shortening of the concrete In pretensioned members, as the cable force is transferred from the fixed abutments to the concrete beam, elastic instantaneous compressive strain will take place in the concrete, tending to reduce the stress in the bonded prestressing steel. For axially prestressed members, this can be closely estimated by

$$\Delta f_s = n\,\Delta f_c$$

where $\Delta f_c \cong P_i/A_c$ is the change in concrete stress as the prestress force is applied, and n is the modular ratio. It is recognized that the value of Δf_c can only be estimated. It will be found, however, that small errors in predicting Δf_s due to elastic shortening are of little consequence, since the loss in prestress due to that shortening will only be a small percentage of the total prestress.

In posttensioned members, if all the strands are tensioned at one time, there will be no loss due to elastic shortening, because this shortening will occur as the jacking force is applied and before the prestressing force is measured. On the other hand, if various strands are tensioned sequentially, the stress loss in each strand will vary, being a maximum in the first strand tensioned, and zero in the last strand. In such cases, it is sufficiently accurate to calculate the loss in the first cable and to apply one-half that value to all cables.

b. Creep of concrete Shortening of concrete under sustained load has been discussed in detail in Art. 1.7. It is evident that creep will result in loss of prestress force; from the previous discussion, it is known that the creep shortening may be several times the initial elastic shortening. Allowance for loss due to creep is made by using a "creep coefficient" C_c, defined as

$$C_c = \frac{\text{additional longtime deformation}}{\text{initial elastic deformation}}$$

A value of C_c of 1.5 to 2.0 will give satisfactory results under most conditions.

c. Shrinkage of concrete It is apparent that a decrease in the length of a member due to shrinkage of the concrete will be just as detrimental as length changes due to stress, creep, or other causes. As discussed in Art. 1.9, the amount of shrinkage to expect will vary widely, depending upon many factors. Adopting a shrinkage strain of 0.0003 as an average value, the stress loss due to shrinkage is

$$\Delta f_s = 0.0003E_s$$

d. Relaxation of steel The phenomenon of relaxation, similar to creep, was discussed in Art. 11.3. Loss in stress due to relaxation will vary greatly, depending upon the stress in the steel. Since an effective prestress of 60 per cent of the ultimate strength of the steel is generally used, it is apparent from the previous discussion that some allowance must be made for stress loss due to relaxation. A relaxation loss of 3 per cent is typical for steel stressed to $0.60f_s'$.

It is interesting to observe that the largest part of the relaxation loss occurs shortly after the steel is stretched. For stresses of $0.80f_s'$ and higher, even a very short period of loading will produce substantial relaxation, and this, in turn, will reduce the relaxation that will occur later at a reduced stress level. The relaxation rate can thus be artificially accelerated by temporary overtensioning. This technique has sometimes been employed to reduce losses.

e. Frictional losses Losses due to friction, as the cable is stressed in posttensioned members, are usually separated for convenience into two parts: curvature friction and wobble friction. The first is due to intentional bends in the cable profile as specified, and the second to the unintentional variation of the cable from its intended profile. It is apparent that even a "straight" cable duct will have some unintentional misalignment, so that wobble friction must always be considered in posttensioned work. Usually, curvature friction must be considered as well. The force at

***Table* 11.3**

Type of steel	Usual range of observed values		Suggested design values	
	K	μ	K	μ
Wire cables.........	0.0005–0.0030	0.15–0.35	0.0015	0.25
High-strength bars..	0.0001–0.0005	0.08–0.30	0.0003	0.20
Galvanized strand...	0.0005–0.0020	0.15–0.30	0.0015	0.25

the jacking end of the cable, P_0, required to produce the force P_x at any point x along the cable, can be found from the expression

$$P_0 = P_x \epsilon^{KL+\mu\alpha}$$

where ϵ = base of natural logarithms
L = cable length from jacking end to point x
α = angular change of cable from jacking end to point x, rad
K = wobble friction coefficient, lb per lb per ft
μ = curvature friction coefficient

There has been much research on frictional losses in prestressed construction, particularly with regard to the values of K and μ. These vary appreciably, depending on construction methods and materials used. The values in Table 11.3 are included in the ACI Code.

The loss of prestress for the entire cable length can be computed by segments, with each segment assumed to consist of either a circular arc or a length of tangent. If one accepts the approximation that the normal pressure on the duct causing the frictional force results from the undiminished initial tension all the way around the curve, then the following simplified expression for loss in tension is obtained:

$$P_0 = P_x(1 + KL + \mu\alpha)$$

where α is the angle between the tangents at the ends. The ACI Code permits the use of the simplified form if the value of $(KL + \mu\alpha)$ is not greater than 0.3.

f. Slip at the anchorages As the load is transferred to the anchorage device in posttensioned construction, a slight inward movement of the cable will occur as the wedges "seat" themselves and as the anchorage itself deforms under stress. The amount of movement will vary greatly, depending on the type of anchorage and on construction techniques. The amount of movement due to "seating" and stress deformation associated with any particular type of anchorage is best established by test. Once

Table 11.4 Summary of losses in prestress, per cent of initial prestress

Losses	Pretensioned beams		Posttensioned beams	
Before transfer	Shrinkage	3%		
At transfer	Elastic strain in concrete	3%	Elastic strain in concrete (only if multiple strands)	1%
			Anchor slip	2%
			Bending of beam (usually negligible)	
			Friction	2%
After transfer	Shrinkage	4%	Shrinkage	4%
	Concrete creep	7%	Concrete creep	4%
	Steel relaxation	3%	Steel relaxation	3%
Total		20%		16%

this amount ΔL is determined, the stress loss is easily calculated using the equation

$$\Delta f_s = \frac{\Delta L}{L} E_s$$

It is significant to note that the amount of slip is nearly independent of the cable length. For this reason, the stress loss will be large for short cables and relatively small for long cables. The practical consequence of this is that it is most difficult to posttension short wires with any degree of accuracy.

g. Summary of losses As indicated in the above discussion, the magnitude of losses in prestressed construction will vary widely, depending on conditions, and about all one can say is that losses will occur and that they must be considered. Table 11.4 presents a summary of losses for pretensioned and posttensioned beams and is included to present an order of magnitude for the various losses; individual loss figures may vary substantially from the values given.

PROBLEMS

The posttensioned prestressed beam of Fig. 11.13 (Art. 11.10) is used on a simple span of 50 ft. Nine draped strands, having a total cross-sectional area of 1.75 in.^{2}, are used. The steel centroid is 16.0 in. below the top surface of the beam at the supports and is at a 24.5-in. depth at midspan. A desired final prestress of 246,000 lb at midspan will permit a live load of 1000 plf. The average compressive stress at the level of the prestress centroid under normal conditions of loading ($PS + DL$) may be taken as 2000 psi. Strands are tensioned sequentially, at one end only, and are grouted. (1) What is your best estimate of the required initial prestress force? (2) What are the stresses in the concrete at top and bottom fibers at the supports and at midspan immediately after transfer? (3) Comment on and discuss your results. (Note that the curvature of the cable can be approximated by a circular arc in calculating losses due to curvature.)

$E_c = 4 \times 10^6$ psi
$E_s = 28 \times 10^6$ psi
Shrinkage coefficient = 0.0003
Creep coefficient = 2.5
Relaxation of the steel = 4 per cent
Slip at anchorage at transfer = 0.052 in.
$I = 25{,}170$ in.^{4}

11.10 Ultimate Flexural Strength In an ordinary reinforced-concrete beam, the stress in the tensile steel and the compressive force in the concrete increase in proportion to the applied moment up to and somewhat beyond service load, the distance between the two internal force resultants remaining essentially constant. In contrast to this behavior, in a prestressed beam, increased moment is resisted by a proportionate increase in the distance between the compressive and tensile resultant forces, the compressive resultant moving upward as the load is increased. The magnitude of the internal forces remains nearly constant up to and usually somewhat beyond service loads.

This situation is changed drastically upon tensile flexural cracking of the prestressed beam. When the beam cracks, there is a sudden increase in the stress in the steel as the tension which was formerly carried by the concrete is transferred to it. After cracking, the prestressed beam behaves essentially as an ordinary reinforced-concrete beam. The compressive resultant cannot continue to move upward indefinitely, and increasing moment must be accompanied by a nearly proportionate increase in steel stress and compressive force. The ultimate strength of a prestressed beam can therefore be predicted by the methods developed for ordinary reinforced-concrete beams, with minor modifications to account for the differing nature of the stress-strain relationship of prestressing steel as compared to ordinary reinforcing steel.

In Art. 2.9 it was shown that underreinforced prestressed beams will fall when the steel stress reaches its ultimate tensile value f'_s, at which point

$$M_u = A_s f'_s \left(d - \frac{A_s f'_s}{1.7 f'_c b}\right) = A_s f'_s d \left(1 - 0.59 p \frac{f'_s}{f'_c}\right) \qquad (2.59)$$

Whether the beam is underreinforced or overreinforced is determined by calculating the concrete strain in the extreme fiber at the instant of steel rupture. If the concrete strain ϵ_c is less than the crushing strain (usually taken equal to 0.003) when the steel has reached its breaking strain ϵ_s', then the beam is underreinforced. The concrete strain can be found from the expression

$$\epsilon_c = \epsilon_s'(\epsilon_s' - \epsilon_{se}) \frac{a/k_1}{d - a/k_1} \tag{2.60}$$

where

$$a = \frac{A_s f_s'}{0.85 f_c' b} \tag{2.58}$$

If ϵ_c, found in this way, exceeds the crushing strain of the concrete, the beam is said to be overreinforced, in which case the steel stress at failure of the beam is some value $f_{su} < f_s'$. In this case the ultimate strength of the beam can be found by successive approximations as described in detail in Art. 2.9.

The above discussion and that of Art. 2.9 pertain to prestressed beams in which the steel is bonded to the concrete continuously throughout its length. This will normally be the case in pretensioned construction and will be the case in posttensioned construction if the cables are grouted after tensioning, as is usually the case. If a posttensioned beam is not grouted, it is difficult to determine the exact steel stress at failure load. The stress will be uniformly distributed along the entire length of the tendons. Characteristically, there will be a small number of rather wide cracks. These have the effect of reducing the failure load as compared with that of an otherwise identical bonded beam.

The ACI Code states that, if the ratio pf_{su}/f_c' is not more than 0.30, the ultimate flexural strength of prestressed beams can be found from the expression

$$M_u = \phi A_s f_{su}\left(d - \frac{a}{2}\right) \tag{11.11}$$

where

$$a = \frac{A_s f_{su}}{0.85 f_c' b}$$

This is given also in the alternative form

$$M_u = \phi A_s f_{su} d\left(1 - 0.59p \frac{f_{su}}{f_c'}\right) \tag{11.11a}$$

Equation (11.11*a*) is seen to be equivalent to Eq. (2.59), with the substitution of f_{su} for f_s' and the inclusion of the understrength factor ϕ (see Art. 3.7). Where a specific stress-strain curve for the prestressing steel used is not available, the Code permits the use of the following values of f_{su}:

For bonded members: $$f_{su} = f'_s\left(1 - \frac{0.5pf'_s}{f'_c}\right) \tag{11.12a}$$

For unbonded members: $$f_{su} = f_{se} + 15{,}000 \text{ psi} \tag{11.12b}$$

where f_{se} is the effective steel prestress after losses.

According to the Code, if pf_{su}/f'_c exceeds 0.30, the ultimate moment of the member shall not be taken as greater than

$$M_u = \phi(0.25f'_cbd^2) \tag{11.13}$$

For flanged members such as I and T beams in which the neutral axis falls outside the flange,[1] the method of determining ultimate flexural strength is exactly analogous to that used for ordinary reinforced-concrete I and T beams. The total steel area is divided into two parts for computational purposes. The first part, at a stress f_{su}, balances the compression in the overhanging portion of the flange, and the remainder, at stress f_{su}, balances the compression in the web. According to Code, in applying the criterion pf_{su}/f'_c to flanged members, p is taken as the steel ratio of only that portion of the total tension-steel area which is required to develop the compressive strength of the web alone. If pf_{su}/f'_c does not exceed 0.30, then

$$M_u = \phi\left[A_{sr}f_{su}d\left(1 - \frac{0.59A_{sr}f_{su}}{b'df'_c}\right) + 0.85f'_c(b - b')t(d - 0.5t)\right] \tag{11.14}$$

where

$$A_{sf} = \frac{0.85f'_c(b - b')t}{f_{su}}$$

and

$$A_{sr} = A_s - A_{sf}$$

If pf_{su}/f'_c exceeds 0.30, then

$$M_u = \phi[0.25f'_cb'd^2 + 0.85f'_c(b - b')t(d - 0.5t)] \tag{11.15}$$

If, after a prestressed beam is designed by working-stress methods, an inadequate factor of safety against failure is obtained, it is possible to include nonprestressed reinforcement in combination with prestressed steel to improve the factor of safety. According to the ACI Code, such nonprestressed steel may be considered to contribute to the tension force in a member at ultimate moment an amount equal to its area times its

[1] This is usually the case where the flange thickness is less than $1.4dpf_{su}/f'_c$.

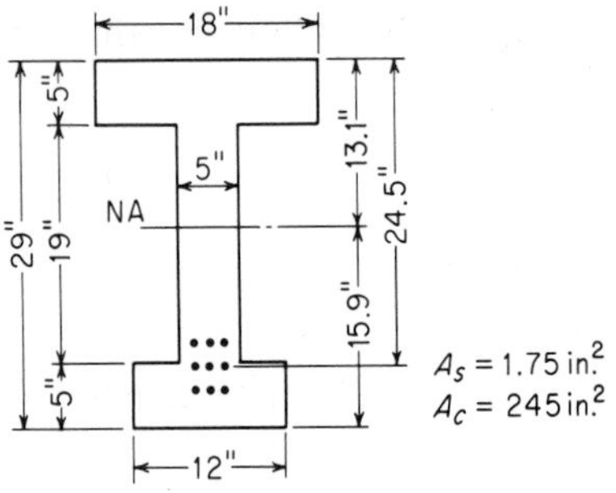

Fig. **11.13**

yield point, provided

$$p\frac{f_{su}}{f'_c} + p'\frac{f_y}{f'_c} \leq 0.30$$

where p' is the ratio of unprestressed steel A'_s/bd, and f_y is the yield stress of the unprestressed steel. It is required by Code that the total amount of prestressed and unprestressed reinforcement be adequate to develop an ultimate load in flexure at least equal to 1.2 times the cracking load, calculated on the basis of a modulus of rupture of $7.5\sqrt{f'_c}$.

Example The posttensioned, bonded, prestressed beam shown in cross section in Fig. 11.13 is stressed using wires of ultimate strength $f'_s = 275{,}000$ psi. If the concrete strength is $f'_c = 5000$ psi, what is the ultimate flexural capacity of the member?

With $f'_s = 275{,}000$ psi, the stress in the steel at ultimate load is approximately

$$f_{su} = f'_s\left(1 - \frac{0.5pf'_s}{f'_c}\right)$$

The tensile-steel ratio is

$$p = \frac{A_s}{bd} = \frac{1.75}{18 \times 24.5} = 0.00397$$

Then

$$f_{su} = 275(1 - 0.5 \times 0.00397 \times {}^{275}\!/_{5}) = 245 \text{ ksi}$$

It is next necessary to determine the location of the neutral axis. Since

$$1.4dp\frac{f_{su}}{f'_c} = 1.4 \times 24.5 \times 0.00397 \times {}^{245}\!/_{5} = 6.68 \text{ in.} > 5.0 \text{ in.}$$

it is concluded that the neutral axis is below the underside of the flange, and equations for flanged members will be used. Then

$$A_s = 0.85\frac{f'_c}{f_{su}}(b - b')t = 0.85 \times {}^{5}\!/_{245} \times 13 \times 5 = 1.13 \text{ in.}^2$$

$$A_{sr} = A_s - A_{sf} = 1.75 - 1.13 = 0.62 \text{ in.}^2$$

The ratio

$$p\frac{f_{su}}{f'_c} = \frac{0.62}{5 \times 24}\,\frac{245}{5} = 0.253$$

is less than 0.30, so the ultimate strength of the member is found from the expression

$$M_u = \phi \left[A_{sr}f_{su}d\left(1 - \frac{0.59A_{sr}f_{su}}{b'df'_c}\right) + 0.85f'_c(b - b')t\left(d - \frac{2}{t}\right)\right]$$

$$= 0.90\left[0.62 \times 245 \times 24.5\left(1 - \frac{0.59 \times 0.62 \times 245}{5 \times 24.5 \times 5}\right) + 0.85 \times 5 \times 13 \times 5 \times 22\right]$$

$$= 8340 \text{ in.-kips}$$

11.11 Shear and Diagonal Tension In prestressed-concrete beams at working loads, there are two factors which greatly reduce the intensity of diagonal tensile stress, as compared with that which would exist if no prestress force were present. The first of these results from the combination of longitudinal compressive stress and shearing stress. An ordinary tensile-reinforced concrete beam under load is shown in Fig. 11.14*a*. The stresses acting on a small element of the beam taken below the neutral axis and near the support are shown in (*b*). It is found by means of Mohr's circle of stress (*c*) that the principal stresses act at 45° to the axis of the beam (*d*) and are numerically equal to the shear-stress intensity; thus

$$t_1 = t_2 = v \qquad (a)$$

Now suppose that the same beam, with the same loads, is subjected to a precompression stress in the amount *c*, as shown in Fig. 11.15*a* and *b*. From Mohr's circle (*c*) the principal tensile stress is

$$t_1 = -\frac{c}{2} + \sqrt{v^2 + \left(\frac{c}{2}\right)^2} \qquad (b)$$

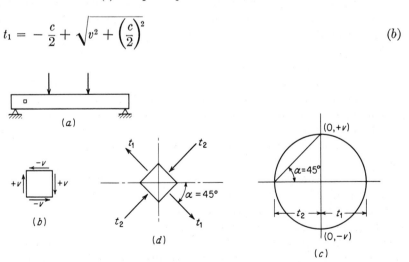

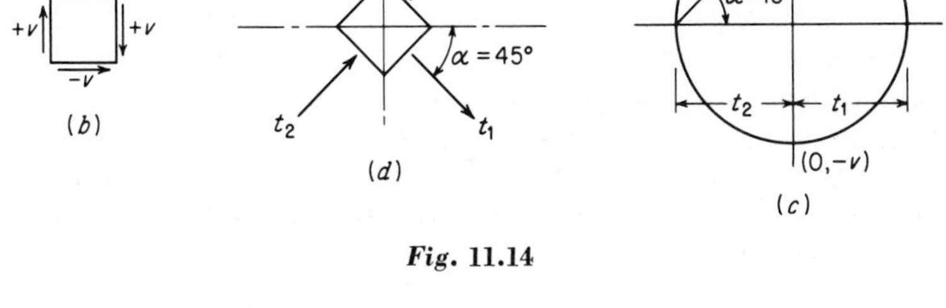

Fig. 11.14

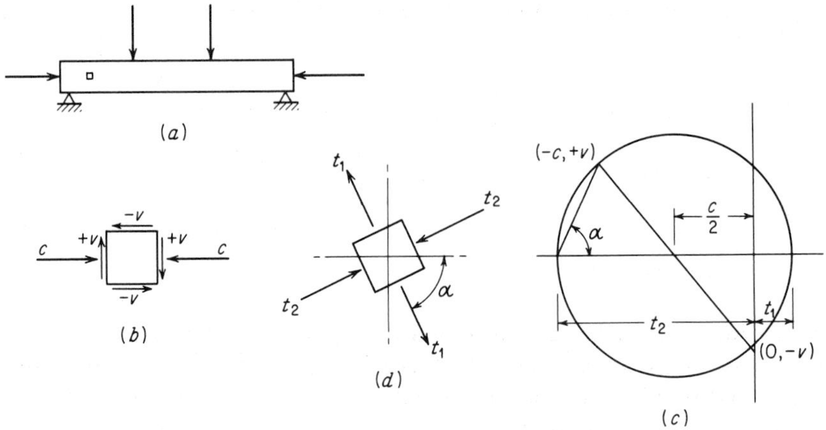

Fig. 11.15

and the direction of the principal tension with respect to the beam axis is

$$\tan 2\alpha = \frac{2v}{c} \tag{c}$$

as shown in (*d*).

Comparison of Eq. (*a*) with (*b*), and Fig. 11.14*c* with 11.15*c*, shows that, with the same shear-stress intensity, the principal tension in the prestressed beam is much reduced.

The second factor working to reduce the intensity of the diagonal tension at working loads results from the curve or slope of the tendons. Normally this slope is such as to produce a shear due to the prestress force which is opposite in direction to the load-imposed shear. The magnitude of this "countershear" is $V_p = P \sin \theta$, where θ is the slope of the tendon at the section considered (see Fig. 11.4).

It is important to note, however, that in spite of these characteristics of prestressed beams at working loads, an investigation of diagonal tensile stresses at working loads does not ensure an adequate factor of safety against failure. In Fig. 11.15*c*, it is evident that a relatively small decrease in compressive stress and increase in shear stress, which may occur when the beam is overloaded, will produce a disproportionately large increase in the resulting principal tension. In addition to this effect, if the countershear of inclined tendons is used to reduce design shear, its contribution does not increase directly with load, but much more slowly (see Art. 11.10). Consequently a small increase in total shear may produce a large increase in the net shear for which the beam must be designed. For these two reasons, it is usual to base design for diagonal tension in prestressed beams on conditions at ultimate load rather than at service load.

At ultimate load, a prestressed beam behaves essentially as an ordinary reinforced-concrete beam. According to ACI Code, the area of shear reinforcement placed perpendicular to the axis of a member is not to be less than

$$A_v = \frac{(V_u - \phi V_c)s}{\phi d f_y} \tag{11.16}$$

nor less than

$$A_v = \frac{A_s}{80}\frac{f_s'}{f_y}\frac{s}{d}\sqrt{\frac{d}{b'}} \tag{11.17}$$

where A_v = area of web reinforcement placed perpendicular to axis of member
V_u = shear due to specified ultimate load
V_c = shear carried by concrete
s = spacing of stirrups
f_y = yield stress of stirrups

The effective depth d, according to Code, is as follows:

1. In members of constant overall depth, d equals the effective depth at the section of maximum moment, and the length of the stirrups at the section under consideration shall be at least equal to the length of the stirrups at the section of maximum moment.

2. In members of varying depth, d equals hd_m/h_m, where d_m and h_m are the effective depth and total depth, respectively, at the section of maximum moment, and h is the total depth at the section under consideration. The stirrups shall extend into the member a distance d from the compression face.

It is seen that Eq. (11.16) is identical with Eq. (3.37) derived for nonprestressed-concrete beams, except that an alternative means for introducing the understrength factor ϕ is used.

The shear resistance of the concrete at ultimate load V_c is taken equal to the shear which caused the first diagonal crack to form in the prestressed beam, as was the case for reinforced-concrete beams (see Art. 2.5). In determining the magnitude of V_c, two types of diagonal tension cracks are recognized:

1. At shear V_{ci} a diagonal crack may result from high principal tension at the head of a flexural crack.

2. At shear V_{cw} a diagonal crack may result from high principal tension in a previously uncracked beam.

The shear force V_c causing cracking is taken as the smaller of V_{ci} and V_{cw}.

Consider first a diagonal tension crack which occurs as a continuation of a previously formed flexural crack (type 1 crack); the principal tensile stress which precipitates such a crack occurs near the centroid of the beam. If a 45° crack slope is assumed, a flexural crack at a distance $d/2$ from the section considered may be the initiating cause of the crack. On this basis, and on the basis of test observations, the following empirical equation for V_{ci} is derived:

$$V_{ci} = 0.6b'd\sqrt{f'_c} + \frac{M_{cr}}{(M/V - d/2)} + V_d \tag{11.18}$$

V_{ci} is not to be taken less than

$$V_{ci} = 1.7b'd\sqrt{f'_c} \tag{11.19}$$

In Eq. (11.18), M/V is the moment-shear ratio resulting from the distribution of loads causing maximum moment at the section, V_d is the shear due to dead load, and M_{cr} is the net flexural cracking moment, equal to

$$M_{cr} = \frac{I}{y}(6\sqrt{f'_c} + f_{pe} - f_d) \tag{11.20}$$

in which f_{pe} is the compressive stress in the concrete due to prestress only, after losses, at the extreme fiber of the section at which tension stresses are caused by applied loads, and f_d is the stress due to dead load at the extreme fiber of the same section.

Because a type 1 diagonal crack is initiated by flexural cracking of the beam, the formation of such a crack will not be affected by the countershear, if any, due to tendon inclination.

Now consider type 2 diagonal cracking of a previously uncracked beam section; the shear force causing diagonal tension in the beam to exceed the direct tensile capacity of the concrete can be calculated by an exact principal-stress calculation. This is permitted by Code, with the direct tensile capacity of the concrete taken equal to $4\sqrt{f'_c}$. Alternatively, the Code permits the use of the approximate expression

$$V_{cw} = b'd(3.5\sqrt{f'_c} + 0.3f_{pc}) + V_p \tag{11.21}$$

in which f_{pc} is the compressive stress in the concrete, after losses, at the centroid of the cross section or at the junction of the web and the flange when the centroid lies in the flange. In Eq. (11.21) the effective depth d is taken as the distance from the extreme compression fiber to the centroid of the tendons or as 80 per cent of the overall depth of the member, whichever is greater.

Equations (11.18) to (11.21) were developed for members constructed of normal-weight concrete (about 145 pcf). The ACI Code includes analogous expressions for members made of lightweight concrete.

Other specific provisions of the Code relative to the design of web reinforcement are:

1. Web reinforcement between the face of the support and the section at a distance $d/2$ therefrom shall be the same as that required at that section.

2. Shear reinforcement shall be provided for a distance equal to the effective depth d of the member beyond the point theoretically required.

3. Web reinforcement shall be adequately anchored at both ends.

4. Shear reinforcement not less than determined from Eq. (11.17) shall be provided at all sections and shall be spaced not farther apart than three-fourths the depth of the member or 24 in., whichever is the smaller, except when it is shown by tests that the required ultimate flexural and shear capacity can be developed when the web reinforcement is omitted.

5. A yield strength in excess of 60,000 psi shall not be considered for shear reinforcement.

6. In a pretensioned prestressed beam in which the section distant $d/2$ from the face of the support is closer to the end face of the beam than the transfer length of the wire or strand used, the reduced prestress in the concrete at sections falling within the transfer length should be considered when calculating the diagonal cracking shear V_{cw}. The prestress at the centroid of the section may be assumed to vary linearly from zero at the end face of the beam to a maximum at a distance from the end face equal to the transfer length, assumed to be 50 diam for strand and 100 diam for single wire.

Example The unsymmetrical I section shown in Fig. 11.13 carries an effective prestress force of 288 kips and supports a service load of 1000 plf on a 50-ft span in addition to its own weight of 255 plf. At the maximum moment section of the beam, the effective depth to the steel centroid is 24.5 in. If concrete of strength $f'_c = 5000$ psi and nonprestressed stirrups with $f_y = 40{,}000$ psi are to be used, what is the required spacing of stirrups at a point 5 ft from the support? At that section of the beam, the cable centroid is 19 in. below the compression face of the beam, and the cable slope is $\frac{1}{10}$.

Adopting the more conservative criterion for V_{ci} [Eq. (11.19)],

$$V_{ci} = 1.7b'd\sqrt{f'_c} = 1.7 \times 5 \times 19\sqrt{5000} = 11{,}400 \text{ lb}$$

At the section under consideration,

$$f_{pc} = 288{,}000/245 = 1180 \text{ psi}$$

and

$$V_p = 288{,}000 \times \tfrac{1}{10} = 28{,}800 \text{ lb}$$

Then

$$V_{cw} = b'd(3.5\sqrt{f'_c} + 0.3f_{pc}) + V_p$$
$$= 5 \times 0.80 \times 29(3.5\sqrt{5000} + 0.3 \times 1180) + 28{,}800 = 98{,}400 \text{ lb}$$

Thus

$$V_c = V_{ci} = 11{,}400 \text{ lb}$$

The ultimate shear at the section under consideration is

$$V_u = 1.5 \times 255(25 - 10) + 1.8 \times 1000(25 - 10) = 32{,}750 \text{ lb}$$

Using No. 3 U stirrups,

$$A_v = 2 \times 0.11 = 0.22 \text{ in.}^2$$
$$s = \frac{A_v f_y \phi d}{V_u - \phi V_c} = \frac{0.22 \times 40{,}000 \times 0.90 \times 24.5}{32{,}750 - 0.90 \times 11{,}400} = 8.62 \text{ in.}$$

Open U stirrups similar to those shown in Fig. 3.10*c* will be used, at a spacing of 8½ in.

11.12 Bond There are two separate sources of bond stress in prestressed-concrete members: (1) flexural bond, which in pretensioned construction exists between the wires and the concrete, and in grouted post-tensioned construction between the wires and grout and between conduit and concrete and (2) prestress transfer bond, usually considered in pretensioned members only.

Flexural bond The magnitude of bond stress due to flexure will depend significantly on whether or not the beam has cracked. If the beam is uncracked (usually the case at service load), flexural bond stress is low and in fact need rarely be checked in design. When the beam cracks, a sudden increase in bond stress results. The beam then behaves very much as an ordinary reinforced-concrete beam, and flexural bond stress can be calculated with the equations of Chap. 3. While bond stresses after cracking are of an order of magnitude higher than those before cracking, they will seldom be a problem in prestressed beams. According to Code, three- or seven-wire pretensioning strand shall be bonded to the concrete from the cross section under consideration for a distance in inches of not less than

$$l = (f_{su} - \tfrac{2}{3}f_{se})D \qquad (11.22)$$

where D is the nominal strand diameter in inches, and the stresses are expressed in kips per square inch. Investigation may be restricted to those cross sections nearest each end of the member that are required to develop their ultimate strength under the specified ultimate load. Equation (11.22) for minimum bonded length is an empirical one based on tests. It seems to reflect the general point of view that the actual intensity of flexural bond stress is not so important as the provision of adequate length of embedment.

Prestress transfer bond In the end regions of pretensioned beams (and in some cases for posttensioned beams), the prestress force from the cables is transferred to the concrete by bond alone. Thus there is a length of transfer at each end of the cables that serves the purpose of cable anchorage. The stress condition in the end zones of such beams is exactly the reverse of that in ordinary reinforced construction. In ordinary reinforced construction, the concrete is poured around an unstressed bar. As the bar is brought into tension, its diameter decreases at the stressed end, owing to Poisson's effect, creating tension normal to the surface of contact between the rod and the concrete. In prestressed beams, on the other hand, the wire is stretched before the concrete is poured around it. As the exposed wire end is cut loose from the anchorage, the stress at the outer end becomes zero. As a consequence, the wire expands as it attempts to regain its original diameter, causing compression normal to the surface of contact with the concrete. The stress in the wires is zero at the free end and increases progressively with distance from that end, approaching its full value at some finite distance, termed the *transfer length*. It is obvious that the free end of the wire must pull into the concrete a certain small distance and that through the extreme end region of the wire there will be relative movement between the wire and the concrete; therefore bond in this region must be completely frictional, with the frictional force enhanced because of the compression normal to the surface of contact. Farther from the free end, within the transfer zone, adhesive bond contributes to slip resistance.

There are as yet insufficient test data available to permit the accurate evaluation of required length of transfer. Fortunately, transfer length does not seem to be a problem in design, except for short members or those in which the loading conditions are such as to cause flexural cracking within the transfer zone, in which case substantial flexural bond stress may add to transfer bond stress to produce failure. The ACI Code states that the transfer length may be assumed to be 50 diam for strand and 100 diam for single wires. These values are based on (1) clean strand or wire surface, (2) gradual release of the prestressing force to the concrete, and (3) steel stress of 150 ksi after transfer. For strand or wire with a slightly rusted surface, the transfer distance can be much shorter. For sudden release of force to the concrete (such as takes place when pretensioned strands are burned through) the transfer length can be at least 20 per cent greater.

11.13 End-block Design In all the foregoing analysis, consideration has been given to resultant stress distribution in the concrete without regard for the fact that the prestress force is actually applied as a con-

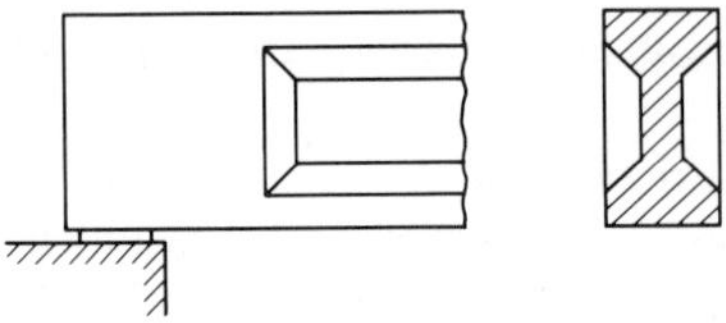

***Fig.* 11.16** End block for posttensioned beam.

centrated load or as a group of concentrated loads on the end of the member. It has been shown mathematically and experimentally that the effect of such concentration of the load becomes insignificant at a distance from the end of the member approximately equal to the member depth. In pretensioned construction, in which the prestress is normally transferred to the concrete by bond over a length which may about equal the member depth, no problem arises, because of the gradual stress input. However, in posttensioned beams, in which, in many cases, the prestress force is transferred through end anchorages and is applied in full value at the extreme end of the beam, the resulting stress concentrations require special consideration. It is customary in posttensioned I-section beams to cast a solid end block of rectangular cross section (Fig. 11.16), which may extend from the end a distance equal to anywhere from one-half the beam depth to the full beam depth, thus reducing local stresses near the anchorages.

The determination of end-block stress is a complex problem. Theoretical treatments are highly complicated, and in order to obtain workable methods one must introduce simplifications and assumptions which leave the solution at least open to question. Fortunately, one can afford to be quite conservative in reinforcing the end zone against local stress concentration. This will not significantly affect the overall economy of the construction, because even a conservative analysis will usually require only a small amount of mild-steel reinforcement to be placed in a very limited region.

Practically, the problem is to estimate the magnitude and location of the local tensile stresses, which are greatest in the direction at right angles to the prestressing force, and which may be sufficient to cause cracking or splitting of the end of the member. Y. Guyon has published an important mathematical study of end-zone stresses and has presented a set of diagrams for the transverse tension resulting from concentrated longitudinal compressive forces. Examples of such charts, in the form of *isobars,* i.e., curves of equal transverse stress, are shown in Fig. 11.17. These diagrams express the transverse unit tensile stress in terms of the average longitudinal compressive stress $p = H/A$. It is evident from these diagrams that there are two separate zones of transverse tension resulting in the end block. The first, defined as the *bursting* zone, lies deep within the block, along the line of action of the load; the second, the *spalling* zone, is at the corners of the end block. These tensile zones are separated from each other by a continuous band, shown crosshatched, in which the transverse stress is compressive.

It will be found that in many cases the transverse tensile stress is higher than that which could be tolerated by the concrete, and some form of tensile reinforcement is indicated. Usually this is in the form of ordinary bars, bent in the form of closed stirrups or hoops. The reinforcement to accommodate spalling tension should be located as close to the end face of the beam as is practical. Guyon observes that, for most practical groupings of cable load, the total transverse spalling tension will not exceed $0.03H$, where H is the total longitudinal load, and he recommends that steel be placed in the spalling zone to accommodate that amount of tension. In the bursting zone the amount of steel required to carry tension

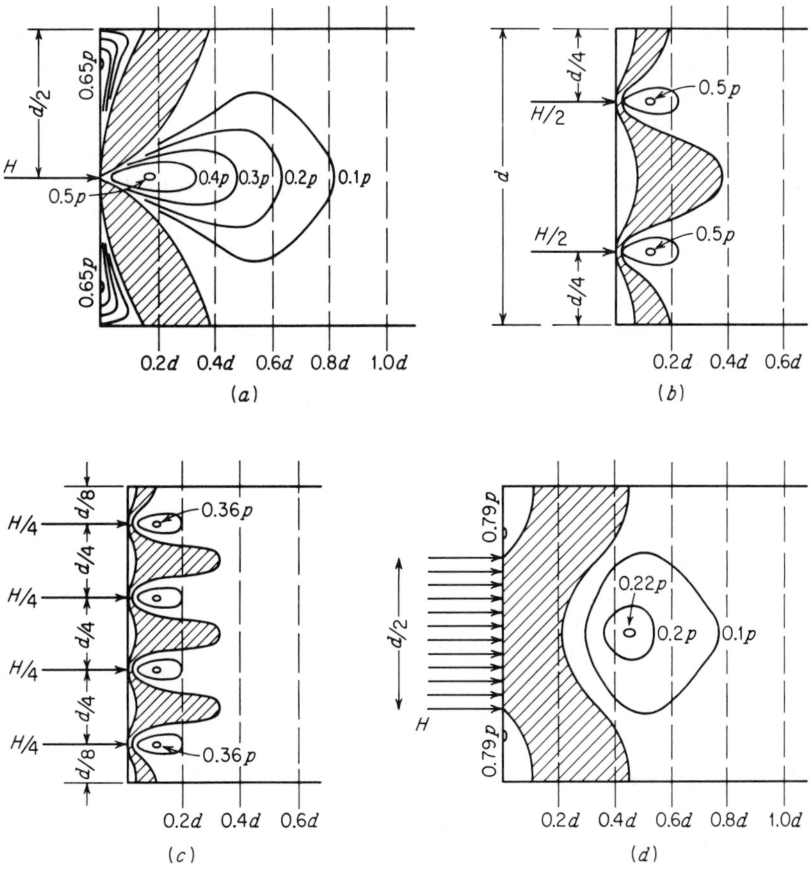

Fig. 11.17 Isobar charts. (*After Ref.* 11.1.)

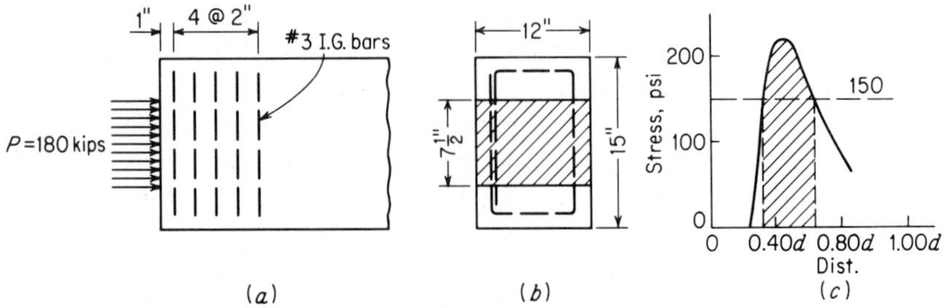

***Fig.* 11.18**

will vary considerably, depending on the pattern of loading. This total tension can be evaluated from diagrams such as Fig. 11.17. Reference 11.1 includes such diagrams covering many specific loading situations.

Example Figure 11.18*a* and *b* show the end zone of a rectangular, posttensioned, prestressed-concrete beam, 12 in. wide and 15 in. deep, stressed by a 180,000-lb prestressing force uniformly distributed over the center half of the depth. It is required to design the end-block reinforcement, with allowable tension in the concrete taken at 150 psi.

The average compressive stress is $p = 180{,}000/(12 \times 15) = 1000$ psi. Then from Fig. 11.17*d* the maximum transverse tension along the middepth center line of the beam is obtained. This is plotted against distance from the beam end in Fig. 11.18*c*. It is seen that the allowable tensile stress in the concrete is exceeded in the region from $0.32d$ to $0.64d$, a horizontal distance of 4.8 in. While the actual tensile stress varies from 150 to 220 psi in that length, use of an average value of 200 psi over the entire distance will not seriously affect the total tension, which is then obtained as

$$200 \times 4.8 \times 12 = 11{,}500 \text{ lb}$$

Number 3 stirrups in the form shown in Fig. 11.18*b*, at working stress $f_s = 20{,}000$ psi, will be used. The number of stirrups required to accommodate bursting tension is

$$N = \frac{11{,}500}{20{,}000 \times 0.22} = 2.6$$

Three stirrups will be used. The spalling tension can be obtained from Fig. 11.17*d*, but it is sufficiently accurate to estimate the total spalling tension as

$$0.03H = 0.03 \times 180{,}000 = 5400 \text{ lb}$$

The number of No. 3 stirrups necessary to accommodate this is

$$N = \frac{5400}{20{,}000 \times 0.22} = 1.23$$

Two additional stirrups are called for; the total of five No. 3 stirrups meets the requirements of spalling and bursting tension and is arranged as shown in Fig. 11.18*a*.

REFERENCES

The discussion in the preceding articles is limited to the basic features of prestressed-concrete design. A number of points have necessarily been omitted, such as design of continuous prestressed members, composite construction, deflection and camber, partial prestressing, and specific applications such as circular tanks, pipes, and piles. The important problem of selecting the optimum sectional shape for prestressed members has been dealt with only briefly. Additional information with regard to many of these questions can be obtained from the following sources:

11.1 Y. Guyon: "Prestressed Concrete," vols. 1 and 2, John Wiley & Sons, Inc., New York, 1960.
11.2 T. Y. Lin: "Prestressed Concrete Structures," 2d ed., John Wiley & Sons, Inc., New York, 1963.
11.3 F. Walley: "Prestressed Concrete Design and Construction," Her Majesty's Stationery Office, London, 1953.
11.4 P. W. Abeles: "The Principles and Practice of Prestressed Concrete," Crosby Lockwood & Son, Ltd., London, 1952.
11.5 H. K. Preston: "Practical Prestressed Concrete," McGraw-Hill Book Company, Inc., New York, 1960.
11.6 M. Chi and F. A. Biberstein: "Theory of Prestressed Concrete," Prentice-Hall, Inc., Englewood Cliffs, N.J., 1963.
11.7 T. Y. Lin: Load-balancing Method for Design and Analysis of Prestressed Concrete Structures, *J. ACI*, p. 719, June, 1963.

chapter 12

REINFORCED-CONCRETE BRIDGES

12.1 Types of Bridges Reinforced concrete is particularly adaptable for use in highway bridges because of its durability, rigidity, and economy as well as the comparative ease with which a pleasing architectural appearance can be secured. For very short spans, from about 10 to 25 ft,

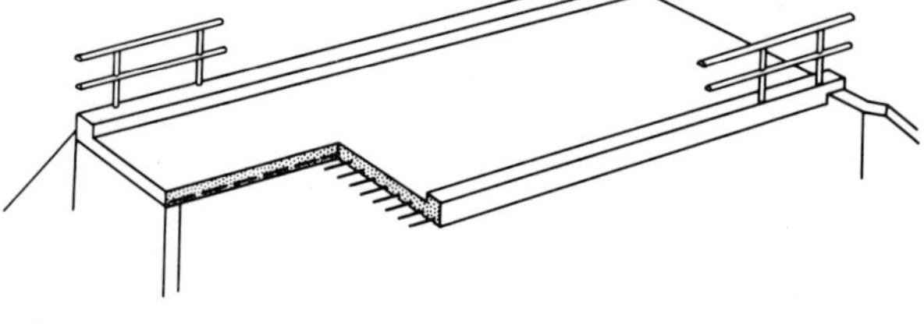

***Fig.* 12.1** Slab bridge.

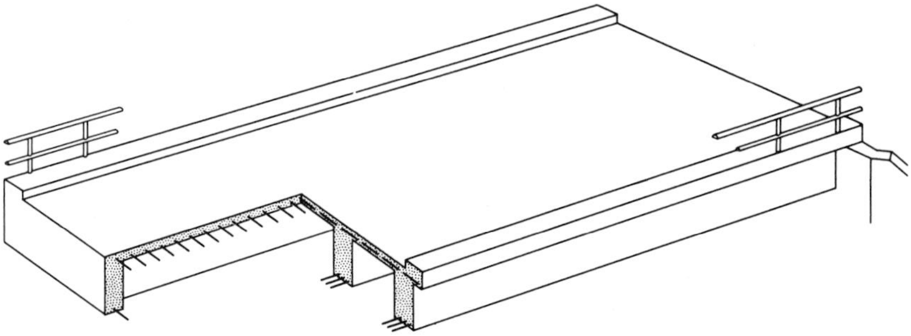

Fig. **12.2** Deck-girder bridge.

one-way slab bridges (Fig. 12.1) are economical. For somewhat longer spans, concrete girder spans (Fig. 12.2) may be used.

Probably most highway spans of medium length, from 40 to 90 ft, presently use composite steel-concrete construction (Fig. 12.3) or prestressed-concrete construction (Fig. 12.4). In composite construction with structural steel, the concrete deck is made to act integrally with supporting steel stringers by means of devices called *shear connectors,* welded to the top flange of the steel section and embedded in the slab. Although such a bridge is not strictly a reinforced-concrete structure, the design of this type of bridge will be discussed in some detail in this section because of its widespread use. Prestressed-concrete bridges frequently make use of composite section characteristics also. Commonly the girders are precast and placed into final location by crane, eliminating the necessity for obstructing traffic by falsework. The deck slab is then cast in place, bonded, and tied to the precast sections by steel dowels.

Bridge spans as long as 320 ft (Fig. 12.5) have been attained using prestressed girders. Other possibilities for long-span concrete bridges are

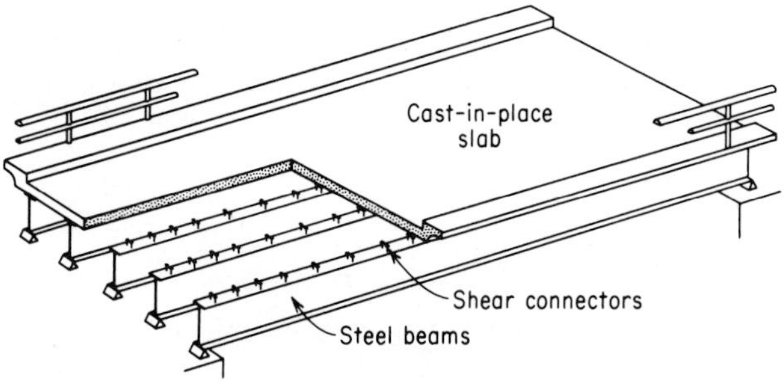

Fig. **12.3** Composite steel-concrete bridge.

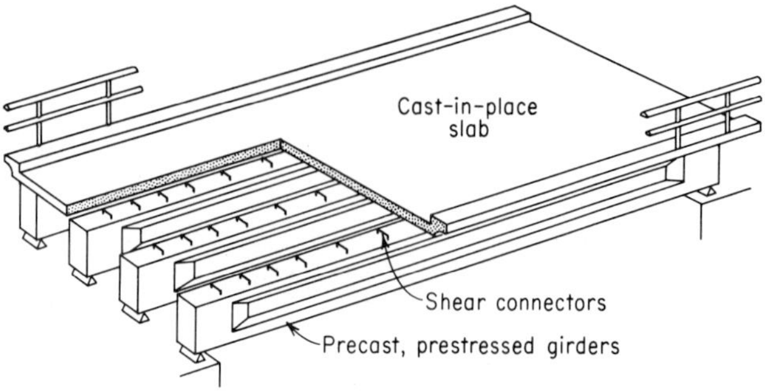

***Fig.* 12.4** Composite prestressed-concrete bridge.

the various forms of arches, including the barrel arch (Fig. 12.6) and the three-hinged arch (Fig. 12.7).

Structural steel is used more generally than reinforced concrete for bridges which are intended primarily for railroad traffic, except for the shortest spans, for which reinforced-concrete slab bridges are frequently constructed. This chapter will therefore be devoted to a discussion of the details and design of highway bridges only. It is the present practice in the United States to design reinforced-concrete highway structures by working-stress methods rather than on the basis of ultimate strength. Undoubtedly this is due to a feeling that, where repetitive loads are involved, primary attention should be focused on stress conditions at service load levels.

***Fig.* 12.5** Oneida Lake Bridge: 320-ft span, prestressed-concrete girders.

***Fig.* 12.6** Fox River Valley Bridge: five 178-ft barrel-arch spans.

***Fig.* 12.7** Salgina Bridge, Switzerland: three-hinged arch span.

12.2 Live Loads: *Truck loadings* The live loads specified by the American Association of State Highway Officials (Ref. 12.1)—whose specifications control the design of most American highway bridges—consist of standard, idealized trucks or of live loads which are equivalent to a series of trucks. Two systems of loadings are provided: the *H* loadings, as shown in Fig. 12.8, and the *H-S* loadings, as shown in Fig. 12.9. The *H* loadings represent a two-axle truck; the *H-S* loadings represent a two-axle tractor plus a single-axle semitrailer.

As shown in the figures, the highway loadings are divided into several classes. The number of the loading indicates the gross weight in tons of the truck or tractor. The gross weight is divided between the front and rear axles as shown in Figs. 12.8 and 12.9. For the *H-S* loadings the semitrailer axle load is added.

Lane loadings, which are to be used when they produce greater stress then the corresponding truck loadings, are shown in Fig. 12.10. In general,

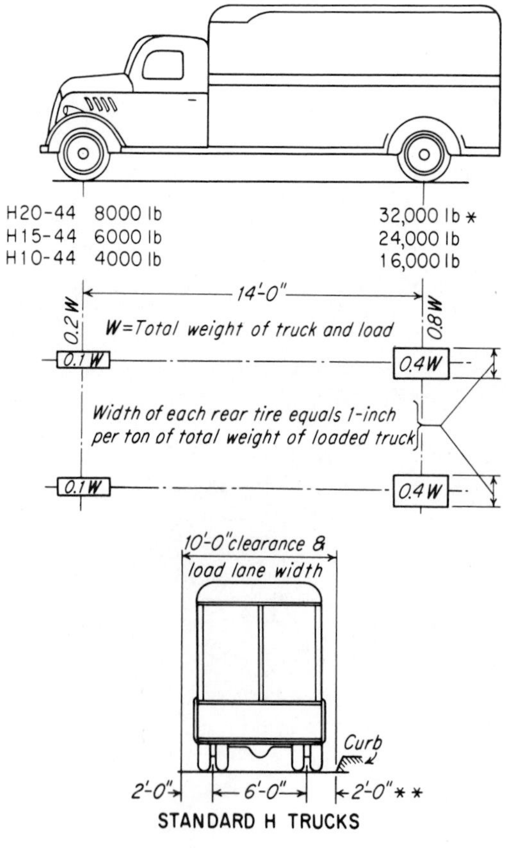

***Fig.* 12.8** Standard *H* truck loadings.

* In the design of steel grid and timber floors for *H*20 or *H*20-*S*16 loading, one axle load of 24,000 lb or two axle loads of 16,000 lb each, spaced 4 ft apart, whichever produces the greater stress, may be used instead of the 32,000-lb axle shown.

** For slab design the center line of the wheel shall be assumed to be 1 ft from the face of the curb.

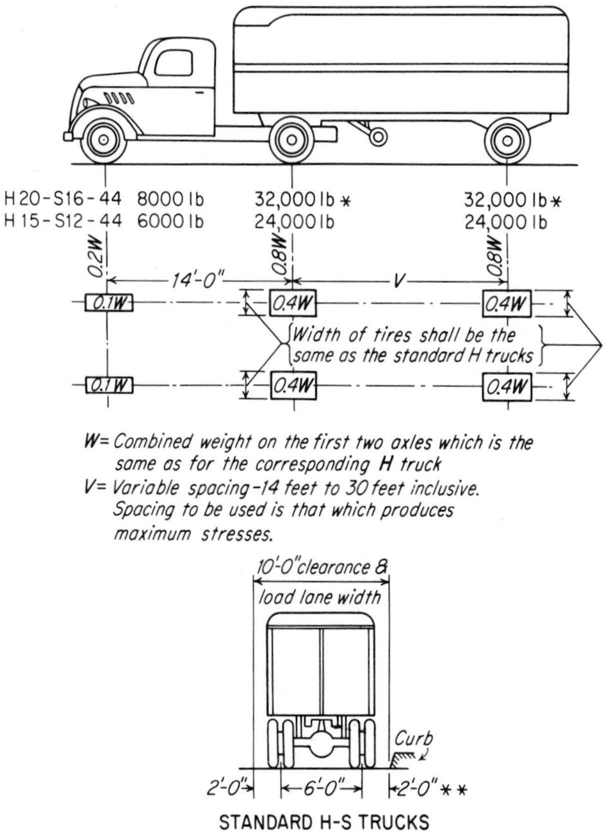

***Fig.* 12.9** Standard *H-S* truck loadings.

* In the design of steel grid and timber floors for *H*20 or *H*20-*S*16 loading, one axle load of 24,000 lb or two axle loads of 16,000 lb each, spaced 4 ft apart, whichever produces the greater stress, may be used instead of the 32,000-lb axle shown.

** For slab design the center line of the wheel shall be assumed to be 1 ft from the face of the curb.

the lane loadings, which are designed to approximate the effect of a series of trucks, govern the design of the longer-span bridges.

Other roadway loadings The possibility that the bridge may be required to carry electric railways, railroad freight cars, military vehicles, or other extraordinary vehicles should be considered in design. The class of such traffic shall determine the loads to be used.

Sidewalk loadings Sidewalk floors, stringers, and their immediate supports are usually designed for a live load of at least 85 psf of sidewalk area.

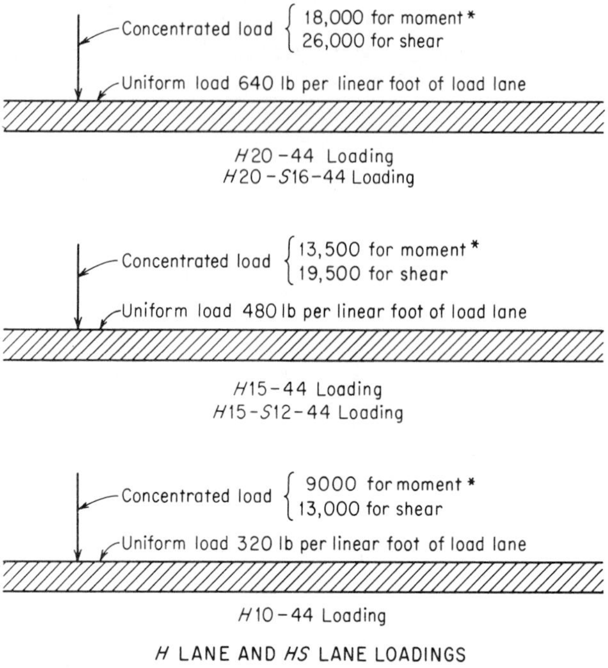

***Fig.* 12.10** Equivalent lane loadings.

* For continuous spans another concentrated load of equal weight shall be placed in one other span in the series in such a position as to produce maximum negative moment.

Selection of loadings The AASHO specifications state that for truck highways or for other highways which carry heavy truck traffic the minimum live load shall be the $H15$-$S12$ loading. It is common practice at present to design bridge spans on major highways for the $H20$-$S16$ loading, using the lighter loadings only for structures on secondary roads, on which the occurrence of heavy traffic will be negligible.

12.3 Application of Loadings Some of the more important rules for applying the selected AASHO loading follow.

1. The lane loading or standard trucks shall be assumed to occupy a width of 10 ft. They shall be assumed to occupy any position within their design traffic lane which will produce the maximum stress. The width of the design traffic lanes shall be determined from the formula

$$W = \frac{W_c}{N}$$

where W_c = roadway width between curbs, exclusive of median strip
N = number of design traffic lanes as shown in the following table
W = width of design traffic lane

W_c, *ft*	N
20–30	2
Over 30–42	3
Over 42–54	4
Over 54–66	5
Over 66–78	6
Over 78–90	7
Over 90–102	8
Over 102–114	9
Over 114–126	10

2. Each 10-ft lane loading or single standard truck shall be considered as a unit, and fractional load-lane widths or fractional trucks shall not be used.

3. The number and position of the lane loading or truck loading shall be as specified above. The type of loading to be used—lane loading or truck loading—shall be such as to produce maximum stress subject to the reduction specified below.

Reduction in load intensity Where maximum stresses are produced in any member by loading any number of traffic lanes simultaneously, the following percentages of the resultant live-load stresses shall be used in view of improbable coincident maximum loading:

Number of lanes	*Per cent*
1 or 2	100
3	90
4 or more	75

12.4 Impact Live-load stresses due to truck loading (or equivalent lane loading) are increased to allow for vibration and the sudden application of the load. The increase is computed by the formula

$$I = \frac{50}{l + 125}$$

where I = impact fraction of live-load stress
l = loaded length, ft

The maximum impact allowance to be used shall be 30 per cent.

12.5 Distribution of Loads When a concentrated load is placed on a reinforced-concrete slab, the load is distributed over an area larger than the actual contact area. For example, if a concentrated load with a bearing area of 1 ft² were placed on the slab of a through-girder bridge, it is reasonable to assume that, on account of the stiffness of the slab, the strips of slab at right angles to the girder and adjacent to the 1-ft strip in direct contact with the load would assist in carrying the load. Similarly, with the beams of a T-beam bridge spaced fairly closely, a concentrated load placed directly over one of the beams would not be carried entirely by that beam, for the concrete slab would be sufficiently rigid to transfer part of the load to adjacent beams.

No distribution is assumed in the direction of the span of the member. The effect of any such distribution would be comparatively small.

The following recommendations for the distribution of loads are taken from the specifications of the American Association of State Highway Officials.

12.6 Distribution of Wheel Loads on Concrete Slabs

The pertinent rules for the distribution of wheel loads on concrete slabs and some additional design requirements are as follows:

Span lengths For simple spans, the span length shall be the distance center to center of supports but shall not exceed clear span plus thickness of slab.

The following effective span lengths shall be used in calculating the distribution of loads and bending moments for slabs continuous over more than two supports:

Slabs monolithic with beam (without haunches): S = clear span
Slabs supported on steel stringers: S = distance between edges of flanges plus one-half the stringer flange width
Slabs supported on timber stringers: S = clear span plus one-half the thickness of the stringer

Edge distance of wheel load In designing slabs, the center line of the wheel load shall be assumed to be 1 ft from the face of the curb.

Bending moment Bending moment per foot width of slab shall be calculated according to the methods given under Cases 1 and 2. In both cases,

S = effective span length as defined under "span lengths," ft
E = width of slab over which wheel load is distributed, ft
P = load on one rear wheel of truck
P_{15} = 12,000 lb for $H15$ loading
P_{20} = 16,000 lb for $H20$ loading

Case 1: main reinforcement perpendicular to traffic (spans 2 to 24 ft inclusive) The live-load moment for simple spans shall be determined by the following formulas (impact not included):

$H20$-$S16$ loading:

$$\frac{S + 2}{32} P_{20} = \text{moment in ft-lb per ft width of slab}$$

$H15$-$S12$ loading:

$$\frac{S + 2}{32} P_{15} = \text{moment in ft-lb per ft width of slab}$$

In slabs continuous over three or more supports, a continuity factor of 0.8 shall be applied to the above formulas for both positive and negative moments.

Case 2: main reinforcement parallel to traffic Distribution of wheel loads $E = 4 + 0.6S$; maximum 7.0 ft. Lane loads are distributed over a width of $2E$. Longitudinally reinforced slabs shall be designed for the appropriate H-S loading.

For simple spans, the maximum live-load moment per foot width of slab, without impact, is closely approximated by the following formulas:

$H20$-$S16$ loading:

Spans up to and including 50 ft: L.L.M. = $900S$ ft-lb
Spans 50 to 100 ft: L.L.M. = $1000(1.30S - 20.0)$ ft-lb

$H15$-$S12$ loading:

Use three-fourths of the values obtained from the formulas for $H20$-$S16$ loading.

Moments in continuous spans shall be determined by suitable analysis using the truck or appropriate lane loading.

Edge beams (longitudinal) Edge beams shall be provided for all slabs having main reinforcement parallel to traffic. The beam may consist of a slab section additionally reinforced, a beam integral with and deeper than the slab, or an integral reinforced section of slab and curb. It shall be designed to resist a live-load moment of $0.10PS$, where P is the wheel load in pounds (P_{15} or P_{20}) and S is the span length in feet. The moment as stated is for a freely supported span. It may be reduced 20 per cent for continuous spans unless a greater reduction results from a more exact analysis.

Distribution reinforcement Reinforcement shall be placed in the bottoms of all slabs transverse to the main steel reinforcement to provide for the lateral distribution of the concentrated live loads, except that reinforcement will not be required for culverts or bridge slabs when the depth of the fill over the slab exceeds 2 ft. The amount shall be the percentage of the main reinforcement steel required for positive moment as given by the following formulas:

For main reinforcement parallel to traffic:

$$\text{Percentage} = \frac{100}{\sqrt{S}} \qquad \text{maximum} = 50 \text{ per cent}$$

For main reinforcement perpendicular to traffic:

$$\text{Percentage} = \frac{220}{\sqrt{S}} \qquad \text{maximum} = 67 \text{ per cent}$$

where S is the effective span length in feet

Shear and bond stress in slabs Slabs designed for bending moment in accordance with the foregoing shall be considered satisfactory in bond and shear.

12.7 Distribution of Wheel Loads to Stringers, Longitudinal Beams, and Floor Beams The following rules govern the distribution of wheel loads affecting longitudinal and transverse concrete beams supporting concrete slabs. The AASHO specification contains additional recommendations for steel and timber flooring which are not reproduced here.

Position of loads for shear In calculating end shears and end reactions in transverse floor beams and longitudinal beams and stringers, no lateral or longitudinal distribution of the wheel shall be assumed for the wheel or axle load adjacent to the end at which the stress is being determined. For loads in other positions on the span, the distribution for shear shall be determined by the method prescribed for moment.

Bending moment in stringers and longitudinal beams In calculating bending moments in longitudinal beams or stringers, no longitudinal distribution of the wheel loads shall be assumed. The lateral distribution shall be determined as follows:

1. *Interior stringers* supporting concrete floors shall be designed for loads determined in accordance with the following table, in which S is the average spacing of stringers in feet:

Floor system	One traffic lane, fraction of a wheel load to each stringer	Two or more traffic lanes, fraction of a wheel load to each stringer
Concrete slab on steel I-beam stringers	$S/7.0$ (S_{max} = 10 ft)*	$S/5.5$ (S_{max} = 14 ft)*
Concrete slab on concrete stringers	$S/6.0$ (S_{max} = 6 ft)*	$S/5.0$ (S_{max} = 10 ft)*
Concrete box girder	$S/8.0$ (S_{max} = 12 ft)*	$S/7.0$ (S_{max} = 16 ft)*

* If S exceeds the value in parenthesis, the load on each stringer shall be the reaction of the wheel loads, under the assumption that the flooring between the stringers acts as a simple beam.

2. The live load supported by *outside stringers* shall be the reaction of the truck wheels, under the assumption that the flooring acts as a simple beam between stringers.

3. The *combined load capacity* of all the beams in a span shall not be less than the total live and dead load in the panel.

Bending moment in floor beams (transverse) In calculating bending moments in floor beams, no transverse distribution of the wheel loads shall be assumed. If longitudinal stringers are omitted and the concrete floor is supported directly on floor beams, the fraction of wheel load allotted to each floor beam is $S/6$, where S equals the spacing of beams in feet. If S exceeds 6 ft, the load on the beam shall be the reaction of the wheel loads, under the assumption that the flooring between beams acts as a simple beam.

12.8 Abutments Bridge abutments serve to transmit the load from the superstructure to the foundation and act as retaining walls to hold back the earth fill behind them.

Bridge seats The bridge seats of abutments which support the fixed ends of concrete highway bridges are quite frequently built as horizontal surfaces without parapets or backwalls, as shown in Fig. 12.11. The slab or the beams of the deck rest directly on the bridge seat; in deck-girder bridges, transverse diaphragm walls are constructed between the beams to hold back the earth above the bridge seat. These diaphragms are thin walls, 6 or 8 in. in thickness, with a nominal amount of reinforcement.

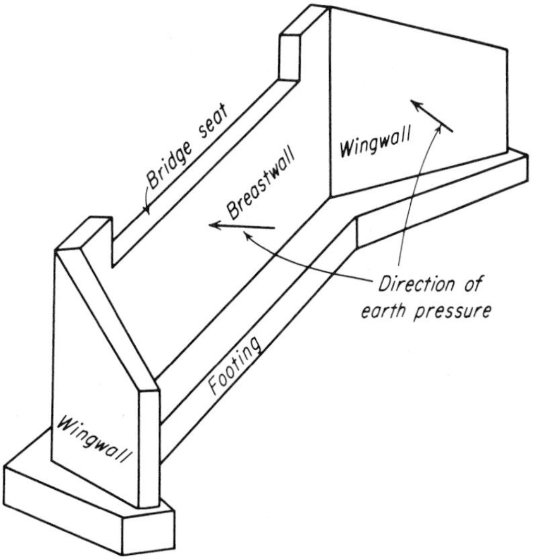

Fig. **12.11** Details of abutment without backwall.

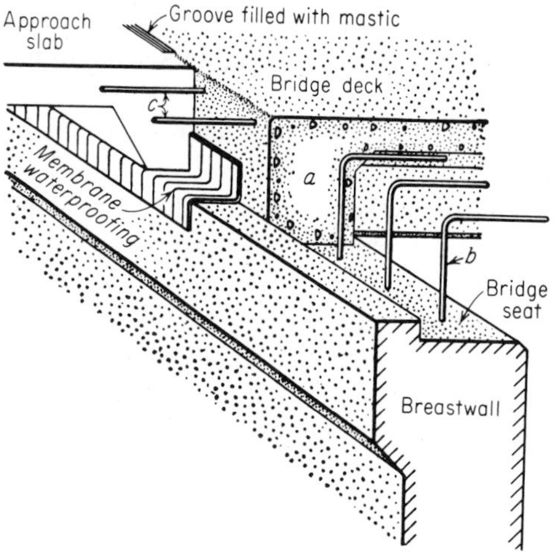

***Fig.* 12.12** Details of bridge seat with low backwall.

Figure 12.12 shows a modified form of the construction described above in which a very low backwall is used, primarily for the purpose of counteracting the tendency of the abutment to move inward under the deck. The dowels *b* and *c* shown in the abutment and in the deck construction serve to tie the deck, the abutment, and the approach slab together.

Another type of bridge seat is shown in Fig. 12.13. This type is particularly adapted to the fixed ends of deck-girder bridges. The bridge seat is constructed with notches into which the bridge beams are built. Figure 12.13 is a diagrammatic sketch and does not show the final relative positions of the deck and abutment; the two parts of the figure actually fit together as shown by the dotted lines. Ledges are provided in the abutment and at the top of the deck beams to support the approach slab, as

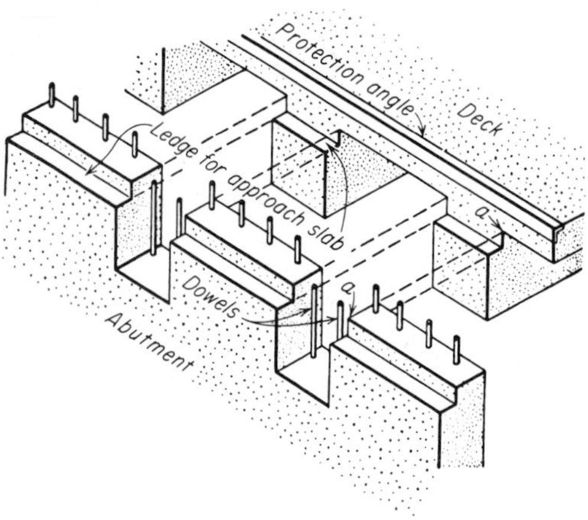

***Fig.* 12.13** Details of bridge seat with pockets for beams.

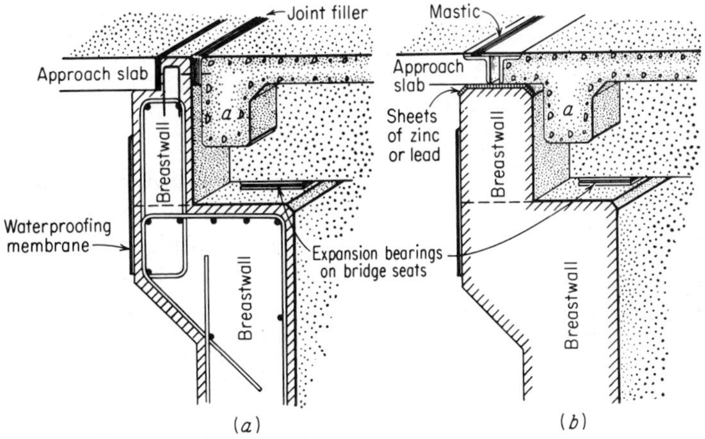

Fig. 12.14 Details of bridge seats with backwalls.

shown in the figure. Dowels are placed in the abutment in such a manner as to project up into the beams and deck slab.

A third type of bridge-seat construction is shown in Fig. 12.14. This is the usual type with backwall, used at the expansion end of the bridge. Two arrangements of joints are shown in the figure. The backwall is extended upward to the roadway surface in (*a*), while it stops at the bottom of the roadway slabs in (*b*). Type *b* is usually preferred, in that only one joint is required in the roadway surface, as compared with two joints in type *a*.

Breast walls The two most common types of breast walls are the cantilever retaining wall of reinforced concrete and the type that acts as a vertical slab supported horizontally by the deck and by the foundation. Buttressed breast walls are rarely used in short-span concrete bridges. Gravity walls of plain concrete are sometimes used, especially where the height of the abutment is not great.

The cantilever breast wall is generally used at the expansion end of the bridge. The type that is supported horizontally by the deck and the footing can be used only at the fixed end; in such cases it is always advisable to have at least a low parapet or back wall, as shown in Fig. 12.12, in order to obtain the direct horizontal resistance which is assumed to be furnished by the deck.

Wing walls Gravity or cantilever-type wing walls may be used. It is advisable to construct vertical expansion joints at the junction of the wing walls and breast wall to avoid unsightly cracks which are apt to form along these planes. Sometimes, instead of an expansion joint, a vertical groove is constructed at the joint; any crack that may develop will then

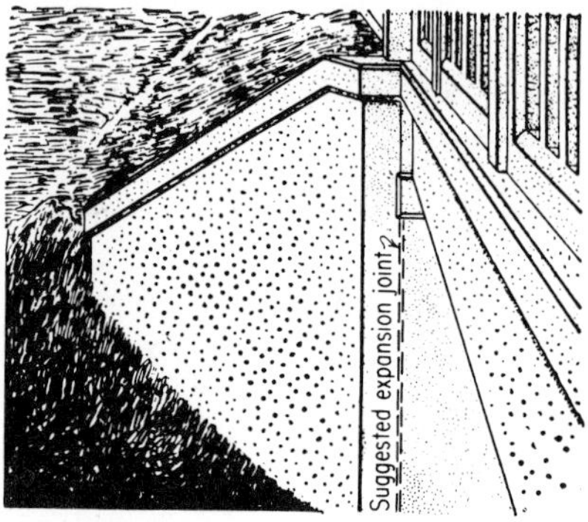

Fig. 12.15 Vertical expansion joint in breast wall.

be inconspicuous. The expansion joint or the groove should preferably be placed at the end of the bridge seat, as shown in Fig. 12.15.

12.9 Miscellaneous Construction Details: ***Diaphragms*** In deck-girder bridges, thin transverse walls called *diaphragms* are constructed between the beams at the ends of the bridge, as shown at (*a*) in Figs. 12.12 and 12.14. These diaphragms serve two purposes: first, they furnish lateral support for the beams, and second, when no parapet or back wall is built above the bridge seat, they prevent the earth fill from spilling out on the bridge seat. At the fixed ends, the diaphragms may rest directly on the bridge seat, as shown in Fig. 12.12; at the expansion ends, the diaphragms should be kept clear of the bridge seat, as shown in Fig. 12.14, so as not to develop friction which would interfere with the freedom of longitudinal movement. The diaphragms are usually from 6 to 8 in. thick, with a nominal amount of reinforcement.

Intermediate diaphragms should be constructed between the beams of deck-girder bridges with spans greater than 40 ft; the intermediate diaphragms are placed at the center or at the third points of the span.

Fixed bearings Fixed bearings can safely be used at both ends of spans up to 40 ft. Two such bearings are illustrated in Figs. 12.12 and 12.13. The dowels which serve to tie together the deck construction and the abutment are not designed to resist any appreciable amount of bending moment, and hence no joint rigidity can be assumed in the design of the deck or abutment.

Expansion bearings For spans greater than 40 ft, an expansion bearing should be provided at one end of the bridge. A suitable form of expansion bearing for spans up to 50 ft is shown in Fig. 12.14. A pair of steel plates is placed under each girder; the lower plate is anchored to the concrete in the abutment, and the upper plate is fastened to the underside of the girder. Frequently, a thin layer of graphited asbestos, zinc, or copper is placed between the plates to reduce the friction.

For the shorter spans and light loadings, frequently the only expansion device is a layer of tar paper inserted between the bridge seat and the deck. Obviously this is not desirable where provision for expansion is of any importance, because of the questionable efficiency of the construction.

In spans greater than 50 ft, the deflection of the deck may rotate the

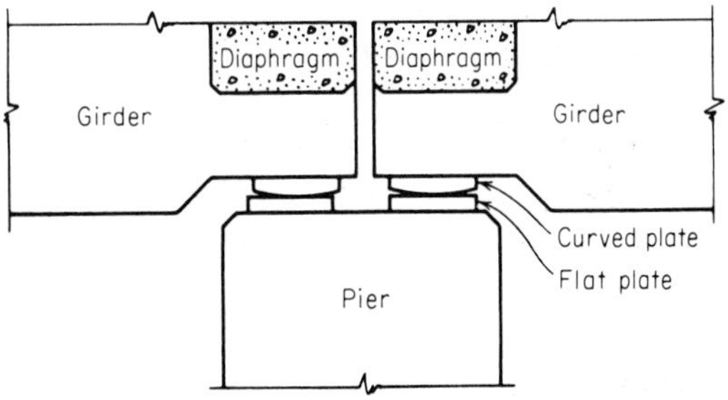

Fig. **12.16** Expansion bearings.

ends of the girders so much that the bearing pressure may become concentrated on a narrow strip along the front edge of the bridge seat and may cause local damage if flat bearing plates are used. In order to counteract this tendency, one plane and one curved plate should be used, as shown in Fig. 12.16.

Deck joints The number of expansion joints in a bridge deck should be kept as low as possible. In single-span bridges of the type under discussion, one such joint usually suffices; that joint is at one end of the bridge. A suitable detail for the joint is shown in Fig. 12.14*b*; in this detail an angle is anchored to the end of the deck slab, and a similar angle is anchored to the end of the approach slab. A tread plate is fastened, by means of rivets or tap screws, to the top of the angle at the end of the deck, and this plate bears on the angle at the end of the approach slab. The tread plate does not cover the latter angle completely, sufficient provision for expansion of the deck slab being made. The groove between the end of the tread plate and the edge of the approach slab is usually filled with mastic, as shown in Fig. 12.14*b*, in order to make the joint watertight. The mastic is soft enough to permit movement of the tread plate, but firm enough to resist displacement.

An enlarged detail of a similar joint is shown in Fig. 12.17; this applies

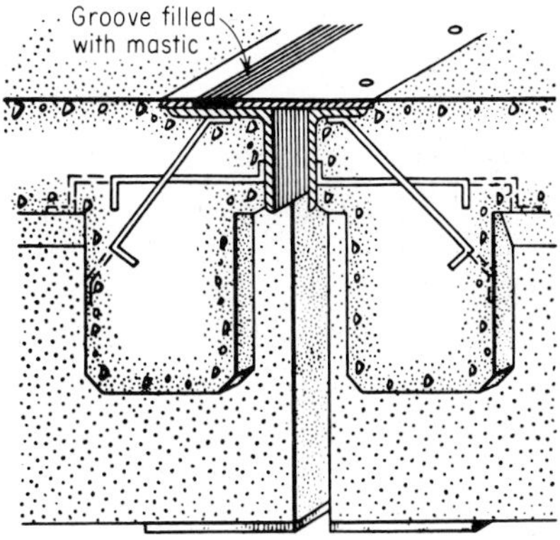

Fig. **12.17** Details of expansion joint.

Fig. **12.18** Metal strips for expansion joints.

specifically to the joint between the ends of two adjacent spans in a multispan bridge.

Thin copper or zinc strips, bent in the form of the letter T as shown in Fig. 12.18, are sometimes placed across a joint and embedded in the concrete on either side of the joint to add to the watertightness. The joint is filled with a mastic compound. A detail of this type is shown in Fig. 12.14*a*.

A joint at the fixed end of a span is made watertight by simply filling a groove at the top of the joint with mastic, as shown in Fig. 12.12. The membrane waterproofing which is shown on top of the low parapet in this figure is furnished to ensure watertightness in the horizontal joint.

Drainage Surface water on bridge decks should be disposed of as quickly and as directly as possible. This is accomplished by crowning the roadway about $\frac{1}{8}$ in. per ft and pitching the gutters to drain into inlets. In single-span bridges built on a grade, no special provision for longitudinal drainage is ordinarily necessary. The water is carried by the transverse crown to the curbs or gutters and thence to the low end of the bridge, where it can easily be deflected away from the roadway.

If the bridge is horizontal longitudinally, a longitudinal camber can be built into the bridge deck by elevating the middle portion of the span when the forms are erected. This camber will serve to carry the water in the gutters to either end of the span. A camber of about $\frac{1}{10}$ in. per ft is satisfactory for concrete decks.

When necessary, special drain inlets can be constructed by building cast-iron scuppers in the gutters. Two types are shown in Fig. 12.19. The scuppers should be so designed as to prevent the drain water from touch-

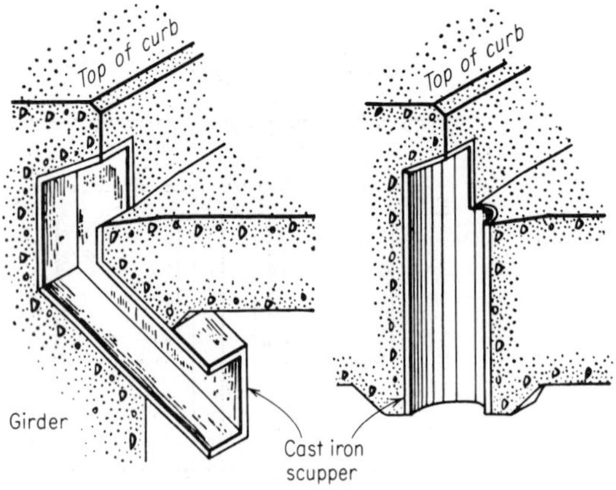

Fig. **12.19** Typical scupper details.

ing the concrete. Drain inlets are generally necessary in multispan bridges because of the impracticability of carrying the surface water to the ends of the bridge.

DESIGN OF A SLAB BRIDGE

12.10 Design of a Slab Bridge A slab bridge similar to that shown in Fig. 12.1 is to be designed according to the following data:

Clear span	15 ft
Clear width	26 ft
Live loading	*H*20–*S*16
Wearing surface	30 psf
Concrete strength f'_c	3000 psi
Intermediate-grade reinforcement	

By AASHO specifications, an allowable concrete stress of

$$f_c = 0.40f'_c = 1200 \text{ psi}$$

and an allowable steel stress of 20,000 psi will be used.

The effective span of the slab is assumed as 15 ft + 1 ft = 16 ft, and a total thickness of 12 in. is selected for trial. The total dead load per square foot is then 180 psf, and the dead-load moment is

$$\tfrac{1}{8} \times 180 \times 16^2 = 5760 \text{ ft-lb}$$

The load on each rear wheel is 16,000 lb.

$$E = 4 + 0.06S = 4 + 0.06 \times 16 = 4.96 \text{ ft}$$

The load on a unit width of slab is therefore

$$16{,}000/4.96 = 3230 \text{ lb}$$

and the live-load moment is

$$\frac{PS}{4} = \frac{3230 \times 16}{4} = 12{,}900 \text{ ft-lb*}$$

The impact coefficient is

$$I = \frac{50}{l + 125} = \frac{50}{16 + 125} = 0.355$$

which is greater than the specified maximum of 0.300. The latter will therefore be used, giving an impact moment of

$$0.300 \times 12{,}900 = 3870 \text{ ft-lb}$$

* Note that this calculation of live-load moments results in a somewhat lower value than the approximate $900S = 14{,}400$ ft-lb.

The total moment due to dead, live, and impact effects is 22,530 ft-lb.

For the unit stresses specified, $K = 197$ (Table 5, Appendix B), and

$$d = \sqrt{\frac{M}{Kb}} = \sqrt{\frac{22{,}530 \times 12}{197 \times 12}} = 10.7 \text{ in.}$$

With $t = 12$ in., less 1 in. protective covering under the main reinforcement, and less one-half of an assumed bar diameter of 1 in., an effective depth of 10.5 in. is obtained, sufficiently close to the calculated requirement. A 12-in. slab will be used.

The required main reinforcement is

$$A_s = \frac{M}{f_s jd} = \frac{22{,}530 \times 12}{20{,}000 \times 0.875 \times 10.5} = 1.47 \text{ in.}^2 \text{ per ft}$$

which is furnished by No. 8 bars 6 in. on centers ($A_s = 1.57$ in.^{2} per ft). Fifty per cent of these bars will be stopped 15 diam beyond the point at which they are no longer required for moment, or 8 in. short of the face of supports. The remainder will be carried a distance $l = A_s f_s / 2\Sigma_0 u = 9$ in. into the support, in accordance with the AASHO specification. As specified in Art. 12.6, the amount of transverse reinforcement required for proper distribution of concentrated loads (also to provide for shrinkage) is $A_s/\sqrt{S} = 1.47/\sqrt{16} = 0.37$ in.^{2}; No. 5 bars 10 in. on centers are placed directly on top of the longitudinal reinforcement.

In order to facilitate screeding off the slab, the required curbs will not be made monolithic. Required edge beams will consist of an edge slab section additionally reinforced. The dead load carried by the edge beam is

$$\frac{22 \times 24}{144} 150 = 550 \text{ plf}$$

and the dead-load moment is

$$\tfrac{1}{8} \times 550 \times 16^2 = 17{,}600 \text{ ft-lb}$$

The specified live-load moment is

$$0.10 P_{20} S = 0.10 \times 16{,}000 \times 16 = 25{,}600 \text{ ft-lb}$$

giving a total moment of 43,200 ft-lb. The resisting moment of the given section is

$$Kbd^2 = 197 \times 24 \times 10.5^2 \times \tfrac{1}{12} = 43{,}400 \text{ ft-lb}$$

which is just adequate. The steel required is

$$A_s = \frac{43{,}200 \times 12}{20{,}000 \times 0.875 \times 10.50} = 2.82 \text{ in.}^2$$

which will be provided by four No. 8 bars.

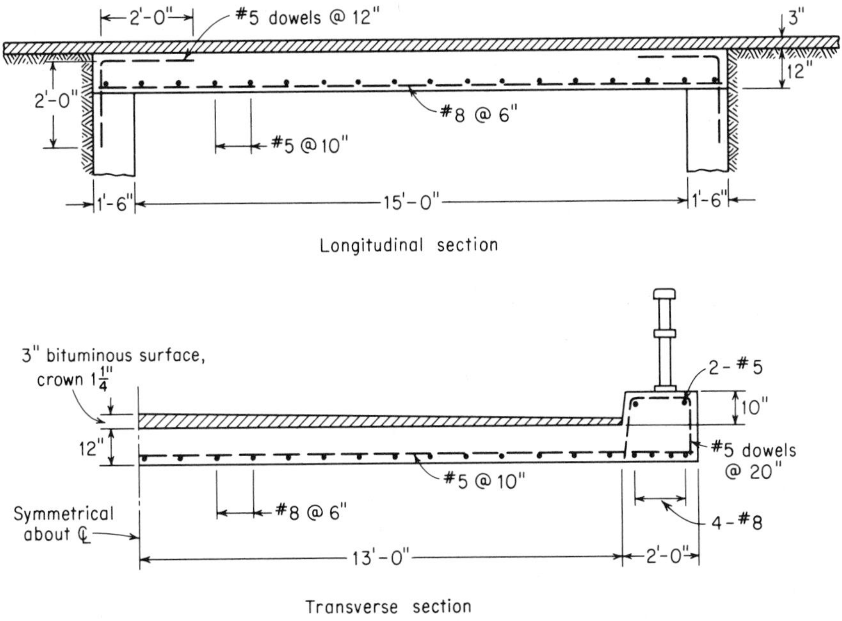

Fig. **12.20** Details of slab bridge.

The crown of the roadway is obtained by varying the thickness of the bituminous wearing surface. No expansion joints are necessary for a span of this length, and a fixed bearing is constructed at each end by placing vertical dowels in the abutment so that they will project up into the concrete deck slab. These are extended horizontally 24 in. to control the cracking that may occur near the edge of the support. The bridge seat is to be coated with a bituminous mixture before the slab is poured. Details are shown in Fig. 12.20.

DESIGN OF A T-BEAM OR DECK-GIRDER BRIDGE

12.11 Data and Specifications A T-beam or deck-girder bridge similar to that shown in Fig. 12.2 is to be designed for the following conditions:

Clear span	48 ft
Clear width	29 ft
Live loading	$H20$–$S16$
Concrete strength f'_c	3000 psi
Intermediate-grade reinforcement	

The design is to meet the AASHO specifications. The bridge will consist of six parallel girders supporting a floor slab, as shown in Fig. 12.21.

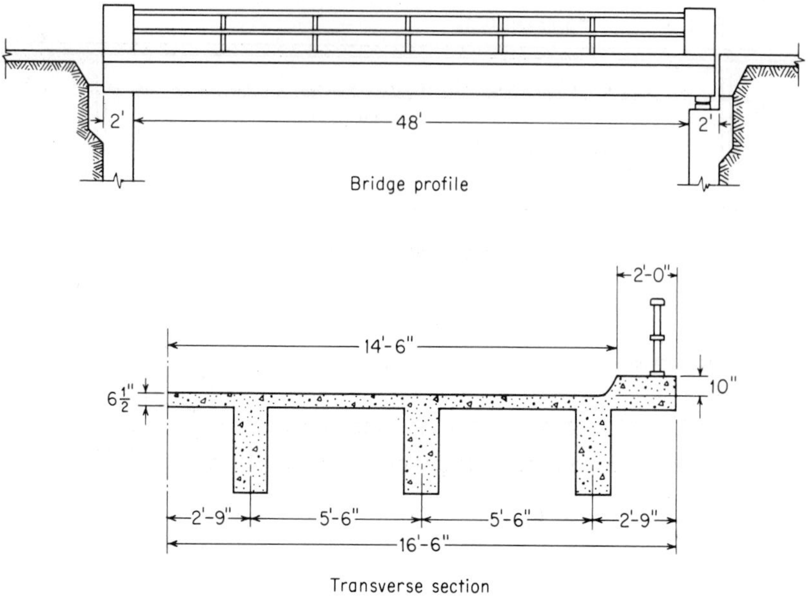

Fig. **12.21** Deck-girder bridge.

12.12 Slab Design Since the slab will be poured monolithically with the girders and will be fully continuous, the span will be taken as the clear distance between girders. Under the assumption that the girders will be 14 in. in width, the clear span will be 4 ft 4 in. For a total thickness of slab of 6 in. (including a ¾-in. wearing surface), with a 15-psf allowance for possible future protective covering, the total dead load is 90 psf. A coefficient of $\frac{1}{10}$ for positive and negative dead-load moments will be assumed in the absence of definite specification values. The dead-load positive and negative moments are

$$\tfrac{1}{10} \times 90 \times 4.33^2 = 169 \text{ ft-lb}$$

For live-load moment computations, Case 1 of Art. 12.6 applies:

$$0.80 \frac{S+2}{32} P_{20} = \frac{0.80 \times 6.33 \times 16{,}000}{32} = 2530 \text{ ft-lb}$$

Since the loaded length is small, the impact coefficient is 0.30, and the impact moment is 760 ft-lb. The total positive and negative moments are 3459 ft-lb. Then

$$d = \sqrt{\frac{3459 \times 12}{197 \times 12}} = 4.19 \text{ in.}$$

With the addition of 1 in. of protective concrete below the center of an assumed ¾-in. bar, and with the ¾-in. wearing surface (not considered structurally effective), the total thickness is 6.32 in. A 6½-in. slab will be used, with an effective depth of 4.37 in. The dead-load estimate need not be revised.

$$A_s = \frac{3459 \times 12}{20{,}000 \times 0.875 \times 4.37} = 0.54 \text{ in.}^2$$

which is furnished by No. 6 bars 10 in. on centers. In order to avoid excessive bending of bars, and since short spans are involved, straight bars will be used in the slab, with No. 6 bars at 10 in. top and bottom. This will provide a surplus of steel in some areas, but the cost of the additional steel will probably be offset by the savings in fabrication and handling of the bent bars which would otherwise be required. Temperature and distribution stresses in the perpendicular direction are provided for by placing five No. 5 bars directly on top of the main slab steel in each slab panel. Complete details of the slab are shown in Fig. 12.26.

12.13 Interior Girders The interior girders are T beams with flange width equal to the center-to-center distance of girders. The required stem dimensions are governed by either the maximum moment or maximum shear. The bridge seats will be assumed 2 ft in width, and the effective span length center to center of bearings taken as 50 ft.

Dead-load moments The weight of the slab per foot of beam is $96 \times 5.5 = 528$ plf. The stem section below the slab is assumed as 14×30 in., which adds weight of 437 plf, making the total 965 plf. The dead-load moment at the center of the span is

$$M_d = \tfrac{1}{8} \times 965 \times 50^2 = 302{,}000 \text{ ft-lb}$$

In order to determine the points at which some of the horizontal steel may be bent up, it is necessary to compute the moment at some sections between the point of maximum moment and the support. At 10 ft from the support, the dead-load moment is 192,800 ft-lb; at 20 ft, 289,000 ft-lb.

Live-load moments The absolute maximum live-load moment will occur with an *H*20-*S*16 truck on the bridge in the position[1] shown in Fig. 12.22. With the distribution of loads as specified in Art. 12.7, each interior girder must support $5.50/5.0 = 1.10$ wheel loads per wheel. Therefore the load from the rear wheel is $1.1 \times 16{,}000 = 17{,}600$ lb, and that from the front wheel is $1.1 \times 4000 = 4{,}400$ lb.

$$R_L = [17{,}600(36.6 + 22.6) + 4400 \times 8.6]\tfrac{1}{50} = 21{,}600 \text{ lb}$$
$$M_{max} = 21{,}600 \times 27.4 - 17{,}600 \times 14 = 346{,}000 \text{ ft-lb}$$

[1] For a discussion of the position of moving loads for absolute maximum moment, see any elementary text in structural theory.

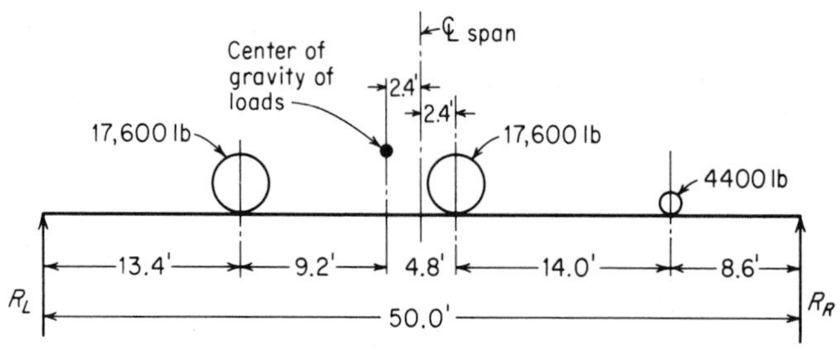

Fig. 12.22

Ten feet from the left support, the maximum live-load moment occurs with the rear trailer wheels at that point and the front wheels 38 ft from the left support. With this position of the loads,

$$R_L = [17{,}600(40 + 26) + 4400 \times 12]\tfrac{1}{50} = 24{,}400 \text{ lb}$$
$$M_{10} = 24{,}400 \times 10 = 244{,}000 \text{ ft-lb}$$

Similarly,

$$M_{20} = 330{,}000 \text{ ft-lb}$$

Impact moments In computing impact moments for a girder such as this, it is usual to consider the whole span as the loaded length. The impact coefficient is therefore $50/(50 + 125) = 0.285$, and the impact moments are as follows:

$$M_{max} = 98{,}700 \text{ ft-lb}$$
$$M_{20} = 94{,}100 \text{ ft-lb}$$
$$M_{10} = 69{,}600 \text{ ft-lb}$$

Maximum total moments The sum of the maximum dead load, live load, and impact moments is 746,700 ft-lb. The total moments at the 20 and 10-ft points are 713,100 and 506,400 ft-lb, respectively.

Dead-load shears The maximum dead-load shear at the end of the beam is $965 \times 25 = 24{,}100$ lb. Ten feet from the support, the shear is 14,450 lb; 20 ft from the support, it is 4800 lb.

Live-load shears The absolute maximum shear occurs with the truck on the span in the position shown in Fig. 12.23. The maximum live-load shear is 30,600 lb. The maximum shears at the 10-, 20-, and 25-ft points are 24,300, 16,400, and 12,700 lb, respectively.

Impact shears For loaded lengths of 50, 40, 30, and 25 ft the impact shears are as follows:

End shear	8700 lb
10-ft section	6900 lb
20-ft section	4700 lb
Midspan section	3600 lb

Total shears The total shears are as follows:

End shear.	63,400 lb
10-ft section.	45,650 lb
20-ft section.	25,900 lb
Midspan section.	16,300 lb

Determination of cross section and steel area The maximum shear stress in the beam web will be taken equal to $0.06f'_c = 180$ psi.[1] The area $b'd$ required to sustain this shear is

$$b'd = \frac{V}{vj} = \frac{63{,}400}{180 \times 0.875} = 403 \text{ in.}^2$$

If b' is taken as 14 in., the required d is 28.8 in. If three rows of No. 11 bars are assumed, with 2 in. clear between rows and $2\frac{1}{2}$ in. clear below the bottom row to allow for stirrups and concrete protection, a total depth of 35.42 in. is obtained. A 36-in. total depth will be used, resulting in an effective depth of 29.4 in. The depth of the stem below the slab is then $36 - 6\frac{1}{2} = 29\frac{1}{2}$ in. This is sufficiently close to the assumed value so that the dead-load moments need not be revised. The required tensile-steel area is then found:

$$A_s = \frac{M}{f_s(d - t/2)} = \frac{746{,}700 \times 12}{20{,}000(29.4 - 5.75/2)} = 16.90 \text{ in.}^2$$

which will be furnished by eleven No. 11 bars.

A check of the maximum stress in the concrete, using Graph 12, Appendix B, shows a maximum compression of 1190 psi, practically equal to the allowable stress of 1200 psi.

The lower four tensile bars, somewhat more than one-third the area, will be extended into the support. The upper two layers will be cut off 15 diam or one-twentieth of the span beyond the point at which they are no longer required, in accordance with the specification. The critical ex-

[1] The AASHO specification permits a unit shear as high as $0.075f'_c$ for beams with web reinforcement.

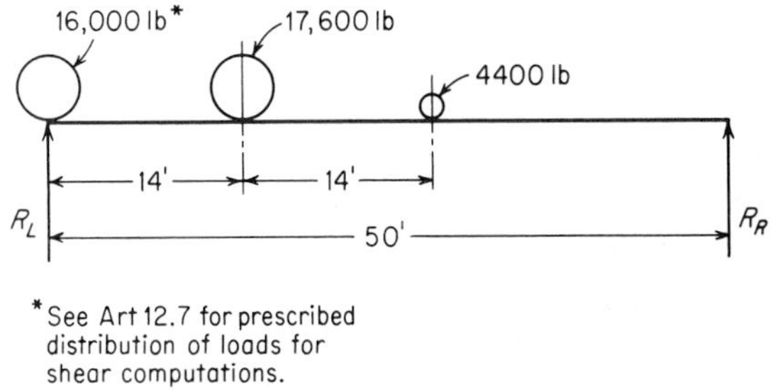

Fig. 12.23

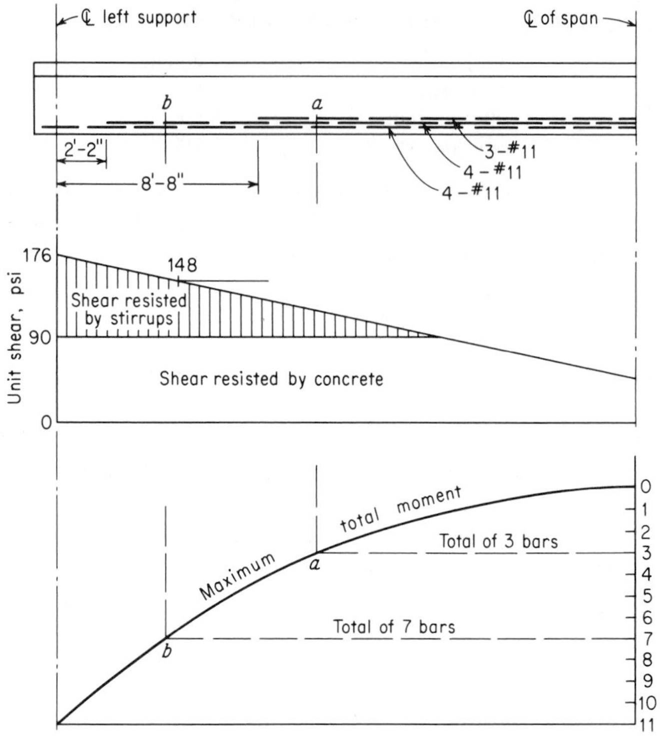

Fig. 12.24

tension in this case is one-twentieth of the span, or 30 in. Cutoff points are found graphically as in Fig. 12.24.

Checking the bond at the center line of supports, where the shear is greatest and the total bar perimeter is least, four No. 11 bars provide a perimeter of 17.7 in., and

$$u = \frac{V}{\Sigma_0 jd} = \frac{63{,}400}{17.7 \times 0.875 \times 29.4} = 139 \text{ psi}$$

which is well below the value of $0.10f'_c = 300$ psi permitted by specification.

Web reinforcement The portion of the beam through which web reinforcement is required is determined by computing the unit shears at various points on the beam. This is shown graphically in Fig. 12.24. The concrete resists a unit shear of $0.03f'_c = 90$ psi, and the remainder is taken up by stirrups. Number 5 U stirrups will be used. In the region through which web reinforcement is required, the specification calls for a maximum spacing of $d/2 = 15$ in. The excess shear corresponding to the spacing is

$$v' = \frac{A_v f_v}{sb'} = \frac{0.61 \times 20{,}000}{15 \times 14} = 58 \text{ psi}$$

and the total shear stress is 148 psi. This is attained 5 ft 3 in. from the support. The maximum spacing in the region in which stirrups are not required to carry shear is $3d/4 = 22\frac{1}{2}$ in. This will apply at a distance of 16 ft 3 in. from the support. At the support, the required spacing is

$$S = \frac{A_v f_v}{v'b} = \frac{0.61 \times 20{,}000}{86 \times 14} = 10.1 \text{ in.}$$

The first stirrup will be placed $s/2 = 5$ in. from the support center line; this will be followed by six stirrups at 10 in., nine at 15 in., and five at 20 in., filling out the distance to the center of the span.

12.14 Exterior Girders The exterior girders are identical in cross section with the interior girders, because the raised curb section will be poured separately and cannot be counted on to participate in carrying loads.

Moments In addition to the 965-plf dead load obtained for the interior girders, the safety curb adds 250 plf, producing a total dead load of 1215 plf and a maximum dead-load moment at the center of the span of 380,000 ft-lb. A portion of each wheel load which rests on the exterior slab panel is supported by the exterior girder. That portion is obtained by placing the wheels as close to the curb as the clearance diagram will permit and treating the exterior slab panel as a simple beam. The position is shown in Fig. 12.25, and the proportion of the load is $4.25/5.50 = 0.773$. The longitudinal position of the load which will produce the absolute maximum bending moment is the same as for the interior girders. The absolute maximum live-load moment can therefore be obtained by direct proportion:

$$M_{\max} = (0.773/1.10)346{,}000 = 243{,}000 \text{ ft-lb}$$

The impact moment is $0.285 \times 243{,}000 = 69{,}300$ ft-lb, and the total maximum moment is 692,300 ft-lb.

Shears The maximum dead-load shear is

$$V_D = 1215 \times 25 = 30{,}400 \text{ lb}$$

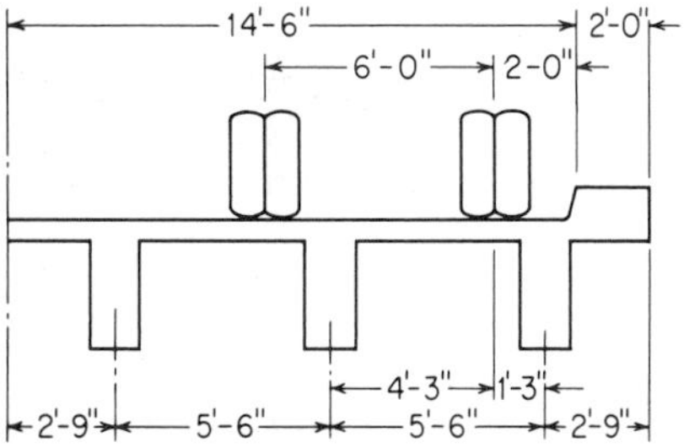

Fig. 12.25

The maximum live-load shear is proportional to the maximum live-load shear in the interior girders:

$$V_L = (0.773/1.10)30{,}600 = 21{,}500 \text{ lb}$$

The impact shear at the support is 6100 lb. The total shear at the support is then 58,000 lb. Shears at other points in the span are found similarly.

Determination of cross section and reinforcement Once the shears and moments due to dead and live loads and impact are obtained, the design of the exterior girders follows along the lines of that for the interior girders. The details will not be repeated here.

12.15 Miscellaneous Details: *Diaphragms* A transverse diaphragm (see Figs. 12.12 and 12.14) will be built between the girders at either end of the bridge. The chief function of these diaphragms is to furnish lateral support to the girders; with some abutment details, the diaphragms also

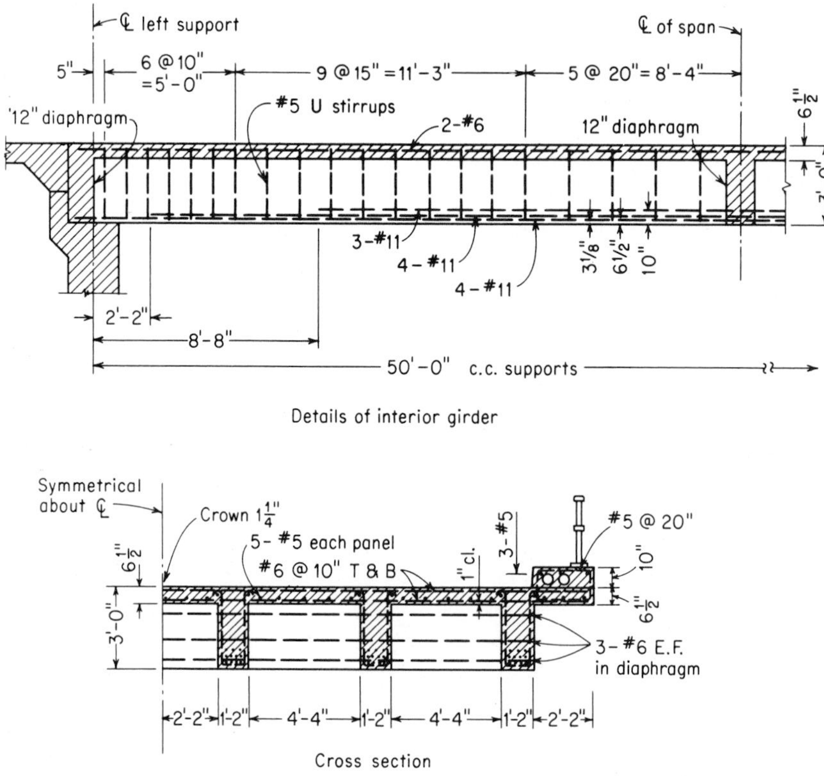

***Fig.* 12.26** Details of T-beam bridge.

serve to prevent the backfill from spilling out onto the bridge seats. A similar diaphragm will be built between the girders at midspan. Such intermediate diaphragms are recommended for all spans in excess of 40 ft and serve to ensure that all girders act together in resisting the loads.

Fixed bearing A fixed bearing similar to that in Fig. 12.13 is provided at one end. Vertical dowels are placed in the breast wall of the abutment and are bent so as to project into the longitudinal beams or deck slab. Horizontal dowels are embedded in the deck and approach slabs. The diaphragm rests directly on the bridge seat.

Expansion bearing An expansion bearing is provided at one end of the span. Its details are similar to Fig. 12.14*b*. The bottom of the diaphragm is flush with the bottoms of the beams and is not in contact with the bridge seat.

Waterproofing and drainage All joints will be filled with a mastic compound to prevent water from seeping through the joints. Removal of surface water will be accomplished by crowning the roadway 1¼ in. and pitching the gutters toward the ends by providing a camber of 2½ in. at the center. Besides facilitating drainage, this camber serves to prevent the appearance of sag that would be evident if the girders were at the same level throughout the span.

Full details are shown in Fig. 12.26.

COMPOSITE - BRIDGE CONSTRUCTION

12.16 General Description In addition to girder bridges constructed entirely of reinforced concrete, frequently bridges are constructed of longitudinal steel girders with reinforced-concrete decks. If the deck merely rests on the girders, it does not represent an integral part of the transverse cross section. That is, since no provision is made to transfer longitudinal shears from the girder to the deck, the latter does not assist in carrying longitudinal bending moments. In contrast, steel-concrete composite construction (Fig. 12.3), as used in many present-day bridges, consists essentially of three elements: (1) longitudinal steel girders, (2) a reinforced-concrete deck, and (3) devices called *shear connectors* which are welded to the top flanges of the beams and which protrude into the slab to tie slab and beam together and to force them to act as a unit in resisting girder moments and shears. Figure 12.27 shows a typical example of a completed bridge of this type. Simple spans up to about 125 ft and continuous spans up to about 175 ft have been built in this manner.

The principal advantage of this type of construction is that it utilizes the concrete deck, which in normal construction does not contribute to longitudinal strength, to assist in resisting longitudinal bending. The resulting composite section is usually shallower and lighter—but nonethe-

***Fig.* 12.27** Continuous bridge of composite construction.

less stiffer—than a comparable section of ordinary concrete-slab–steel-stringer construction in which there is no provision for composite action.

The dimension of the concrete slab in composite construction are usually determined by the transverse flexural requirements. Principal reinforcement is in the direction transverse to the axis of the bridge; in the longitudinal direction, only distribution reinforcement is used. The slab design is carried out in the same manner as for noncomposite construction.

The steel beams, spanning longitudinally between abutments or piers, may be rolled sections, rolled sections with cover plates, or built-up plate girders. Unsymmetrical steel sections, such as a rolled W.F. beam with a cover plate on the lower flange only, can be used to advantage. For longer spans, variable-depth sections are often used. The design may be continuous over several supports.

12.17 Shear Connectors Shear connectors are essential to the development of composite action. These must transfer the horizontal shear with extremely small deformation so that the structure deforms as a unit. The closest spacing of shear connectors will normally be near the support, where the shear is greatest, although recent testing indicates that this may not be necessary (Ref. 12.3).

Some of the different types of shear connectors which have been used successfully are shown in Fig. 12.28. These may take the form of a continuous spiral, as in (*a*), welded at the point of contact to the steel beam. Individual pieces of steel channel may be used, as in (*b*), set transverse to the beam axis and welded to the beam along the back and toe of the channel. The studs shown in (*c*) have been widely used in recent years. Common diameters are $\frac{5}{8}$, $\frac{3}{4}$, and $\frac{7}{8}$ in. They are granular-flux–filled and electrically welded to the steel-beam flange. Whatever the type of shear connector, it must be capable of resisting both horizontal and vertical movement between the concrete and the steel and should extend at least halfway into the slab, but not closer than 1 in. to the top of the slab. Connectors are most economically installed in the fabricating shop. However, the advantages of this procedure may be offset by the possibility of damage during shipment and the difficulty in working along the top of the beams during erection.

Since most shear connectors are of unusual shapes, the ultimate strength in shear has been established experimentally, for the various types. The following expressions are recommended by AASHO (Ref. 12.1):

1. Channels: $Q_{uc} = 180(h + \frac{1}{2}t)w\sqrt{f'_c}$
2. Welded studs with $H/d \geq 4.2$: $Q_{uc} = 330d^2\sqrt{f'_c}$
3. Welded studs with $H/d < 4.2$: $Q_{uc} = 80Hd\sqrt{f'_c}$
4. Spirals: $Q_{uc} = 3840d\sqrt[4]{f'_c}$

where Q_{uc} = ultimate-load capacity of one shear connector or one pitch of spiral bar, lb
h = maximum thickness of channel flange, measured at face of web, in.
t = thickness of web of channel shear connector, in.
w = length of channel shear connector, measured in transverse direction on flange of beam, in.
f'_c = required compressive strength of concrete at 28 days, psi
d = diameter of studs or of round bars used in spirals, in.
H = height of stud, in.

The value of Q_{uc} so obtained represents the ultimate capacity of the connector. AASHO recommends that a safety factor of 4 be applied in arriving at a safe working value Q.

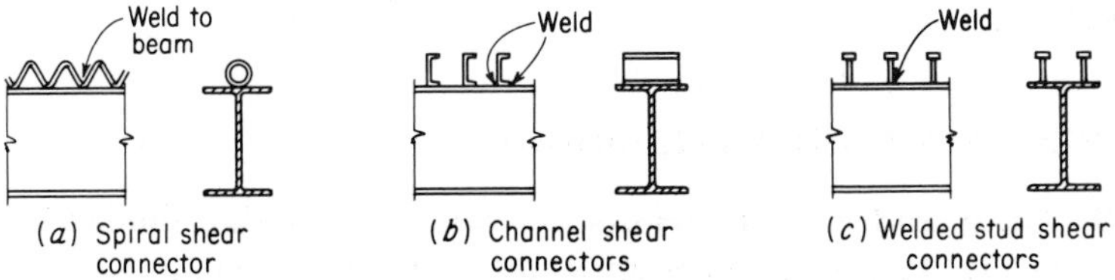

Fig. 12.28 Typical shear connectors.

12.18 Design of Composite Sections The steel stringers alone must support their own dead weight, as well as the dead weight of the formwork and fresh concrete of the deck, unless intermediate shoring is used. The usual principles of steel design apply to the design of the stringers to resist noncomposite dead loads.

A portion of the dead load and all the live load are resisted by composite action. The resisting moment of the composite section is usually computed from the properties of the transformed section obtained by substituting an equivalent amount of steel for the concrete slab.

In transforming the concrete slab into equivalent steel, the depth of the transformed area is held constant, but the width is reduced to $1/n$ times its actual value, where $n = E_s/E_c$. The value of n to be used will depend on whether the loads are long- or short-term. If loads are long-term (such as the composite portion of the dead load), the effects of creep and plastic flow are approximated by reducing E_c to one-third its normal value. Thus, when stresses due to long-term loads are dealt with, the substituted steel area is only one-third what it would otherwise have been.

AASHO recommends that the effective width of the compression-concrete flange be taken not larger than (1) one-fourth the span length of the beam, (2) the distance center to center of beams, or (3) twelve times the least thickness of the slab. For beams having a flange on one side only, the effective flange width shall not exceed one-twelfth the span length of the beam, nor 6 times the thickness of the slab, nor one-half the distance center to center of the next beam.

In composite design, the section must be selected largely by trial and error. While some tables are available giving the section properties for certain combinations of slab and steel beam (Ref. 12.2), and while methods have been developed to reduce the labor of finding an appropriate section (Ref. 12.4), it is not practical to tabulate all desirable combinations of slab width and thickness, steel-beam section, and cover-plate size. Direct design of composite sections is therefore not possible, and the design process is actually a review of an assumed section to determine if the stresses in the concrete and steel are within the allowable range. Stresses due to each type of loading are computed using the appropriate section properties, and these stresses are added algebraically to obtain final values.

DESIGN OF A COMPOSITE BRIDGE

12.19 Data and Specifications A composite bridge similar to that shown in Fig. 12.3 is to be designed for the following conditions.

Span center to center of supports	70 ft
Clear width	28 ft
Live loading	$H20$–$S16$
Wearing surface	30 psf
Concrete strength f'_c	3000 psi
ASTM A7 steel beam	
Intermediate-grade reinforcement	

Welded-stud shear connectors are specified, and a single cover plate will be used on the bottom flange and discontinued where no longer required. The bridge will consist of five parallel girders, as shown in Fig. 12.29.

12.20 Slab Design The design of the slab in the transverse direction follows the procedure presented in Art. 12.12. For the given loads and spans, a slab of 6½-in. total thickness is obtained, reinforced with No. 6 bars 8 in. on centers, top and bottom, in the direction transverse to the supporting beams. In the direction parallel to the girders, six No. 6 bars are equally spaced in each slab panel. Details of the slab are shown in Fig. 12.31.

12.21 Interior Girders The effective width of flange, in accordance with AASHO, is taken equal to the beam spacing of 81 in.

Dead-load moment on steel beams The noncomposite portion

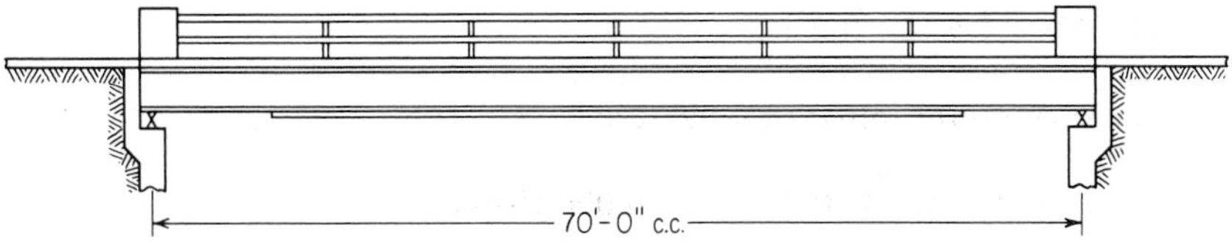

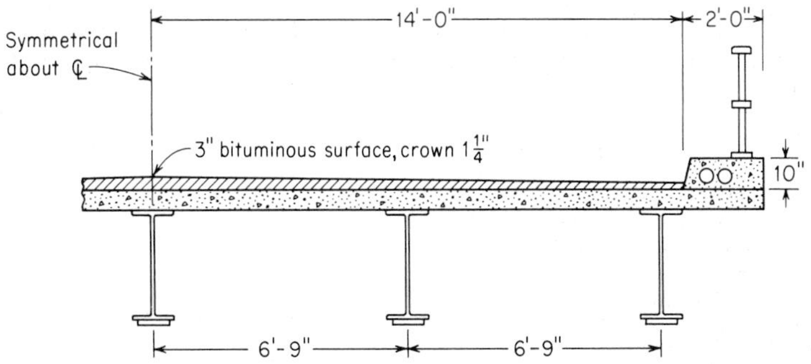

Fig. 12.29 Composite-girder bridge.

of the dead load includes the effect of the concrete slab, the estimated girder and cover-plate weight, and the estimated weight of transverse diaphragms. The total weight is estimated at 800 plf, and the noncomposite dead-load moment is

$$M_{DS} = \tfrac{1}{8} \times 800 \times 70^2 = 490{,}000 \text{ ft-lb}$$

Dead-load moment on composite beam The composite dead load includes the weight of bridge rails, safety curbs, and bituminous pavement. These sum up to 300 plf, and the composite dead-load moment is

$$M_{DC} = \tfrac{1}{8} \times 300 \times 70^2 = 184{,}000 \text{ ft-lb}$$

Live-load moment The live-load distribution factor in this case is $6.75/5.5 = 1.23$ wheel loads per wheel. The absolute maximum live-load moment will occur when an $H20$-$S16$ truck is located with one of its inner 16,000-lb wheels 2.35 ft from the span center line, and it will occur under that wheel. The live-load moment at that point is

$$M_{\max} = 494{,}000 \times 1.23 = 608{,}000 \text{ ft-lb}$$

Impact moment The impact coefficient in this case is

$$50/(70 + 125) = 0.256,$$

and the maximum impact moment is

$$M_{\max} = 608{,}000 \times 0.256 = 156{,}000 \text{ ft-lb}$$

Selection of the cross section The selection of the cover-plated cross section is necessarily a matter of trial. A section made up of a 36 W.F.150 plus a single 10 × 1¼ in. cover plate on the bottom flange, as shown in Fig. 12.30, will be tried. Section properties are calculated in Table 12.1.

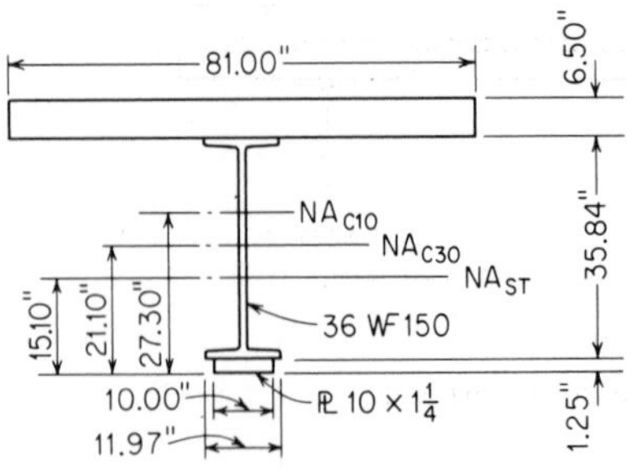

Fig. 12.30 Girder cross section.

Table 12.1 Properties of section with cover plate

	I_o	A	y_b NA to bottom	Ay_b	d CG to NA	Ad^2
Steel only:						
36 W.F.150	9012	44.16	19.17	848	4.07	730
Pl 10 × 1¼		12.50	0.63	8	14.47	2630
	9012	56.66		856		3360
						9012
						$I = 12,372$
	$\bar{y} = \frac{856}{56.66} = 15.10$			$S_b = \frac{12,372}{15.10} = 822$		
			$S_{ts} = \frac{12,372}{21.99} = 564$			
Composite with $n = 30$:						
Steel	12,372	56.66	15.10	856	6.00	2040
Slab	62	17.50	40.34	706	19.24	6480
	12,434	74.16		1562		8,520
						12,434
						$I = 20,954$
	$\bar{y} = \frac{1562}{74.16} = 21.10$			$S_b = \frac{20,954}{21.10} = 990$		
	$S_{ts} = \frac{20,954}{15.99} = 1310$			$S_{tc} = \frac{20,954}{22.49} = 929$		
Composite with $n = 10$:						
Steel	12,372	56.66	15.10	856	12.20	8450
Slab	186	52.50	40.34	2120	13.04	8940
	12,558	109.16		2976		17,390
						12,558
						$I = 29,948$
	$\bar{y} = \frac{2976}{109.16} = 27.30$			$S_b = \frac{29,948}{27.30} = 1095$		
	$S_{ts} = \frac{29,948}{9.79} = 3060$			$S_{tc} = \frac{29,948}{16.29} = 1830$		

The stresses due to various loads are shown in Table 12.2. It is seen that the bottom fiber stress is almost equal to the allowable value of 18,000 psi. The top fiber of the steel section is understressed by about 16 per cent. Since the lightest 36-in. section has been selected, the only alternative would be to use a 33-in. rolled section, which would require a heavier cover plate and which would save little if any steel. Consequently

***Table* 12.2 Total stresses**

Load	Moment	f_{sb}	f_{st}	$3nf_c$ or nf_c	f_c
M_{DS}	490,000	7170	10,400		
M_{DC}	184,000	2230	1,690	2380	80
M_{LL+I}	764,000	8370	2,990	5000	500
Totals..........		17,770	15,080		580

***Table* 12.3 Properties of section without cover plate**

	I_o	A	y_b NA to bottom	Ay_b	d CG to NA	Ad^2
Steel only...............			$S_b = 503$		$S_t = 503$	
Composite with n = 30:						
Steel..................	9012	44.16	17.92	791	5.98	1580
Slab..................	62	17.50	39.09	685	15.19	4040
	9074	61.66		1476		5620
						9074
						$I = 14,694$
		$\bar{y} = \frac{1476}{61.66} = 23.90$		$S_b = \frac{14,694}{23.90} = 616$		
		$S_{ts} = \frac{14,694}{11.94} = 1230$		$S_{tc} = \frac{14,694}{18.44} = 798$		
Composite with n = 10:						
Steel..................	9012	44.16	17.92	791	11.48	5820
Slab..................	186	52.50	39.09	2050	9.69	4920
	9198	96.66		2841		10,740
						9,198
						$I = 19,938$
		$\bar{y} = \frac{2841}{96.66} = 29.40$		$S_b = \frac{19,938}{29.40} = 678$		
		$S_{ts} = \frac{19,938}{6.44} = 3090$		$S_{tc} = \frac{19,938}{12.94} = 1540$		

the 36 W.F.150 with cover plate $10 \times 1\frac{1}{4}$ in. will be used. The concrete fiber stress is well within the allowable limit.

The cover plate on the lower flange will be discontinued where it is no longer needed to resist stress. Section properties for the beam without cover plate are computed as shown in Table 12.3. Once the section moduli of the beam without cover plate have been found, the point at which the cover plate can be discontinued without exceeding allowable stresses in the remaining section is found by trial to be 12 ft 9 in. from the support center line. In accordance with specifications, the plate will be continued far enough beyond that point toward the support to develop the capacity of the plate. A 12-in. extension will suffice in this case.

The shear connectors are designed, not for the full shear, but only for that part resulting from the composite portion of the dead load and from the live and impact loads. The horizontal shear between the slab and the top flange of the steel beam can be found from the expression

$$v = \frac{Vm}{I}$$

where V = external shear force acting at given section, lb
m = static moment of concrete cross section (transformed, with $n = 30$ or $n = 10$ as the case may be) about neutral axis of section, in.^{3}
I = moment of inertia of transformed composite section (with $n = 30$ or $n = 10$), in.^{4}
v = unit shear, lb per in.

Note that, in calculations for v, the appropriate value of n must be used in determining the transformed sections for finding m and I; this depends on whether one is dealing with composite dead load or live load.

At the left support, maximum shear is obtained with one 16,000-lb wheel at the support and 16,000- and 4000-lb wheels at 14 and 28 ft from the support, respectively. For this load condition,

$$V_{LL+I} = 44{,}700 \text{ lb}$$
$$v_{LL+I} = \frac{Vm}{I} = \frac{44{,}700 \times 52.50 \times 9.69}{19{,}938} = 1140 \text{ lb per in.}$$
$$V_D = 300 \times 70/2 = 10{,}500 \text{ lb}$$
$$v_D = \frac{10{,}500 \times 17.50 \times 15.19}{14{,}694} = 190 \text{ lb per in.}$$
$$v_{\text{total}} = 1140 + 190 = 1330 \text{ lb per in.}$$

For the present design, ¾-in. studs are selected, and, tentatively, four studs per transverse row are used, with studs 4 in. high.

$$\frac{H}{d} = 4.00/0.75 = 5.33$$
$$Q_{uc} = 330d^2\sqrt{f'_c} = 330 \times 0.75^2\sqrt{3000} = 10{,}200 \text{ lb}$$
$$Q = \frac{Q_{uc}}{SF} = \frac{10{,}200}{4} = 2550 \text{ lb}$$
$$\text{Safe load per group} = 4Q = 10{,}200 \text{ lb}$$

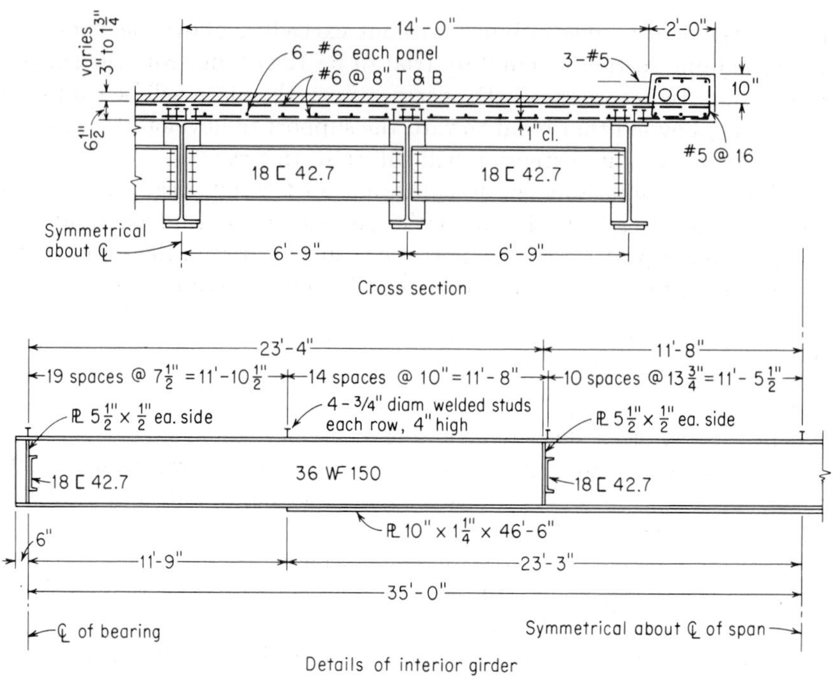

***Fig.* 12.31** Details of composite bridge.

If p is the required pitch (spacing) of connector groups, then

$$vp = 4Q \qquad p = \frac{4Q}{v}$$

and, at the support,

$$p = 10{,}200/1330 = 7.68 \text{ in.}$$

Similar calculations at 7, 14, 21, 28, and 35 ft result in required spacings at those points of 8.50, 10.70, 12.90, 16.20, and 21.80 in., respectively. The maximum spacing permitted by AASHO is 24 in. The stud spacing pattern selected, starting at the left support, is

19 spaces at 7½ in. = 11 ft 10½ in.
14 spaces at 10 in. = 11 ft 8 in.
10 spaces at 13¾ in. = 11 ft 5½ in.

making up the total of 35 ft to midspan. Details are shown in Fig. 12.31.

The spacing of the fillet welds joining the cover plate to the lower flange can likewise be increased as the shear-transfer requirement becomes less. The design method follows that for spacing of the welded studs.

12.22 Exterior Girders The design of the two exterior girders does not differ materially from that for the interior girders, and details will not be presented here. Dead and live loads will differ somewhat; transverse positioning of live load for maximum effect will follow the procedures outlined for the design of exterior girders for the deck-girder bridge (Art. 12.14).

12.23 Miscellaneous Details: ***Diaphragms*** Transverse diaphragms will be provided at the center line of supports and at the third points of the span. These will consist of 18 ⊏ 42.7 members, field-bolted to vertical ribs welded to the girder webs, as shown in Fig. 12.31. In addition to providing safety against overturning of the girders such as might be caused by lateral forces on the roadway, these transverse beams provide some distribution of vertical loads between girders, helping to ensure that the bridge acts as an integral unit.

Bearings A hinged bearing will be provided at one end of each girder, and a rocker bearing at the other, to provide for expansion and contraction of the 70-ft span. A joint detail similar to that shown in Fig. 12.14*b* will be used between the bridge decks and the approach slab.

Drainage The bituminous surface will be crowned to provide lateral drainage, with a depth of 3 in. at the bridge center line and a depth of 1¾ in. at the curbs. A longitudinal camber of 3 in. will ensure that no water stands on the bridge.

Full details of the composite bridge are shown in Fig. 12.31.

REFERENCES

12.1 "Standard Specifications for Highway Bridges," American Association of State Highway Officials, 1961.

12.2 I. M. Viest, R. S. Fountain, and R. C. Singleton: "Composite Construction in Steel and Concrete," McGraw-Hill Book Company, Inc., New York, 1958.

12.3 ACI-ASCE Committee 333: Tentative Recommendations for Design of Composite Beams and Girders for Buildings, *J. ACI*, p. 623, December, 1960.

12.4 R. S. Fountain and I. M. Viest: Selection of the Cross Section for a Composite T Beam, *J. Struct. Div., ASCE*, p. 1313-1, July, 1957.

appendix **A**

FLAT SLABS WITH SQUARE OR RECTANGULAR PANELS (ACI 1963)

2100 Notation

A = distance in direction of span from center of support to intersection of center line of slab thickness with extreme 45° diagonal line lying wholly within concrete section of slab and column or other support, including drop panel, capital and bracket

b_0 = periphery of critical section for shear

c = effective support size [see Art. 2104(c)]

d = distance from extreme compression fiber to centroid of tension reinforcement

f'_c = compressive strength of concrete (see Art. 301)

h = distance from top of slab to bottom of capital

H = story height of the column or support of flat slab center to center of slabs, ft

K = ratio of moment of inertia of column provided to I_c required by Eq. (21-1)

L = span length of flat-slab panel center to center of supports

M_0 = numerical sum of assumed positive and average negative moments at critical design sections of flat slab panel [see Art. 2104(f)1]

R_n = factor for increasing negative moment [Art. 2104, Eq. (21-2)]
R_p = factor for increasing positive moment [Art. 2104, Eq. (21-3)]
t = thickness of slab at center of panel, in.
t_1 = thickness of slab without drop panels, or through drop panel, if any, in.
t_2 = thickness of slab with drop panels at points beyond the drop panel, in.
w' = uniformly distributed unit dead and live load
W = total dead and live load on panel
W_D = total dead load on panel
W_L = total live load on panel, uniformly distributed

2101 Definitions and Scope

(*a*) ***Flat slab*** A concrete slab reinforced in two or more directions, generally without beams or girders to transfer the loads to supporting members. Slabs with recesses or pockets made by permanent or removable fillers between reinforcing bars may be considered flat slabs. Slabs with paneled ceilings may be considered as flat slabs provided the panel of reduced thickness lies entirely within the area of intersecting middle strips, and is at least two-thirds the thickness of the remainder of the slab, exclusive of the drop panel, and is not less than 4 in. thick.

(*b*) ***Column capital*** An enlargement of the end of a column designed and built to act as an integral unit with the column and flat slab. No portion of the column capital shall be considered for structural purposes which lies outside of the largest right circular cone with 90° vertex angle that can be included within the outlines of the column capital. Where no capital is used, the face of the column shall be considered as the edge of the capital.

(*c*) ***Drop panel*** The structural portion of a flat slab which is thickened throughout an area surrounding the column, column capital, or bracket.

(*d*) ***Panel strips*** A flat slab shall be considered as consisting of strips in each direction as follows:

A middle strip one-half panel in width, symmetrical about panel center line
A column strip consisting of the two adjacent quarter-panels, one each side of the column center line

(*e*) ***Ultimate strength design*** Flat slabs shall be proportioned by Part IV-A only, except that Part IV-B may be used if the following modifications are made in the design:[1]

1. For either empirical or elastic analysis the numerical sum of the positive and negative bending moments in the direction of either side of a rectangular panel shall be assumed as not less than

$$M_0 = 0.10WLF\left(1 - \frac{2c}{3L}\right)^2$$

in which $F = 1.15 - c/L$ but not less than 1.

2. The thickness of slab shall not be less than shown in Table 2101(*e*).

[1] Parts IV-A and IV-B refer to analysis by W.S.D. and U.S.D. methods, respectively.

Table 2101(*e*)

f_y	Minimum slab thickness	
	With drop panels*	Without drop panels
40,000	$L/40$ or 4 in.	$L/36$ or 5 in.
50,000	$L/36$ or 4 in.	$L/33$ or 5 in.
60,000	$L/33$ or 4 in.	$L/30$ or 5 in.

* To be considered effective, the drop panel shall have a length of at least one-third the parallel span length and a projection below the slab of at least one-fourth the slab thickness.

2102 Design Procedures

(*a*) ***Methods of analysis*** All flat slab structures shall be designed in accordance with a recognized elastic analysis subject to the limitations of Arts. 2102 and 2103, except that the empirical method of design given in Art. 2104 may be used for the design of flat slabs conforming with the limitations given therein. Flat slabs within the limitations of Art. 2104, when designed by elastic analysis, may have resulting analytical moments reduced in such proportion that the numerical sum of the positive and average negative bending moments used in design procedure need not exceed the sum of the corresponding values as determined from Table 2104(*f*).

(*b*) ***Critical sections*** The slab shall be proportioned for the bending moments prevailing at every section except that the slab need not be proportioned for a greater negative moment than that prevailing at a distance A from the support center line.

(*c*) ***Size and thickness of slabs and drop panels***

1. Subject to limitations of Art. 2102(*c*)4, the thickness of a flat slab and the size and thickness of the drop panel, where used, shall be such that the compression due to bending at any section, and the shear about the column, column capital, and drop panel shall not exceed those permitted in Part IV-A or Part IV-B. When designed under Art. 2104, three-fourths of the width of the strip shall be used as the width of the section in computing compression due to bending, except that on a section through a drop panel, three-fourths of the width of the drop panel shall be used. Account shall be taken of any recesses which reduce the compressive area.

2. The shear on vertical sections which follow a periphery b_0 at distance $d/2$ beyond the edges of the column, column capital, or drop panel, and concentric with them, shall be computed as required and limited in Chap. 12 or 17.

3. If shear reinforcement is used, the first line shall be not further than $d/2$ from the face of the support.

4. Slabs with drop panels whose length is at least one-third the parallel span length and whose projection below the slab is at least one-fourth the slab thickness shall be not less than $L/40$ nor 4 in. in thickness.

Slabs without drop panels as described above shall be not less than $L/36$ nor 5 in. in thickness.

5. For determining reinforcement, the thickness of the drop panel below the slab shall not be assumed to be more than one-fourth of the distance from the edge of the drop panel to the edge of the column capital.

(*d*) *Arrangement of slab reinforcement*

1. The spacing of the bars at critical sections shall not exceed 2 times the slab thickness, except for those portions of the slab area which may be of cellular or ribbed construction. In the slab over the cellular spaces, reinforcement shall be provided as required by Art. 807.

2. In exterior panels, except for bottom bars adequately anchored in the drop panel, all positive reinforcement perpendicular to the discontinuous edge shall extend to the edge of the slab and have embedment, straight or hooked, of at least 6 in. in spandrel beams, walls, or columns where provided. All negative reinforcement perpendicular to the discontinuous edge shall be bent, hooked, or otherwise anchored in spandrel beams, walls, or columns.

3. The area of reinforcement shall be determined from the bending moments at the critical sections but shall be not less than required by Art. 807.

4. Required splices in bars may be made wherever convenient, but preferably away from points of maximum stress. The length of any such splice shall conform to Art. 805.

5. Bars shall be spaced approximately uniformly across each panel strip, except:

a. At least 25 per cent of required negative reinforcement in the column strip shall cross the periphery located at a distance of d from the column or column capital.

b. At least 50 per cent of the required negative reinforcement in the column strip shall cross the drop panel, if any.

c. The spacing for the remainder of the column strip may vary uniformly from that required for (*a*) or (*b*) to that required for the middle strip.

(*e*) *Openings in flat slabs*

1. Openings of any size may be provided in flat slabs if provision is made for the total positive and negative moments and for shear without exceeding the allowable stresses except that when design is based on Art. 2104, the limitations given therein shall not be exceeded.

2. When openings are provided within the area common to two column strips, that part of the critical section shall be considered ineffective which either passes through an opening, or is covered by a radial projection of any opening to the centroid of the support.

(*f*) *Design of columns*

All columns supporting flat slabs shall be designed as provided in Chap. 14 or 19 with the additional requirements of this chapter.

(*g*) *Transfer of bending moment between column and slab* When unbalanced gravity load, wind, or earthquake cause transfer of bending moment between column and slab, the stresses on the critical section shall be investigated by a rational analysis, and the section proportioned accordingly by the requirements of Part IV-A or IV-B. Concentration of reinforcement over the column head by additional reinforcement or closer spacing may be used to resist the moment of the section. A slab width between lines that are 1.5t each side of the column may be considered effective.

2103 Design by Elastic Analysis

(*a*) ***Assumptions*** In design by elastic analysis the following assumptions may be used and all sections shall be proportioned for the moments and shears thus obtained.

1. The structure may be considered divided into a number of bents, each consisting of a row of columns or supports and strips of supported slabs, each strip bounded laterally by the center line of the panel on either side of the center line of columns or supports. The bents shall be taken longitudinally and transversely of the building.

2. Each such bent may be analyzed in its entirety or each floor thereof and the roof may be analyzed separately with its adjacent columns as they occur above and below, the columns being assumed fixed at their remote ends. Where slabs are thus analyzed separately, it may be assumed in determining the bending at a given support that the slab is fixed at any support two panels distant therefrom provided the slab continues beyond that point.

3. The joints between columns and slabs may be considered rigid, and this rigidity (infinite moment of inertia) may be assumed to extend in the slabs from the center of the column to the edge of the capital, and in the column from the top of slab to the bottom of the capital. The change in length of columns and slabs due to direct stress, and deflections due to shear, may be neglected.

4. Where metal column capitals are used, account may be taken of their contributions to stiffness and resistance to bending and shear.

5. The moment of inertia of the slab or column at any cross section may be assumed to be that of the cross section of the concrete. Variation in the moments of inertia of the slabs and columns along their axes shall be taken into account.

6. Where the load to be supported is definitely known, the structure shall be analyzed for that load. Where the live load is variable but does not exceed three-quarters of the dead load, or the nature of the live load is such that all panels will be loaded simultaneously, the maximum bending may be assumed to occur at all sections under full live load. For other conditions, maximum positive bending near midspan of a panel may be assumed to occur under three-quarters of the full live load in the panel and in alternate panels; and maximum negative bending in the slab at a support may be assumed to occur under three-quarters of the full live load in the adjacent panels only. In no case, shall the design moments be taken as less than those occurring with full live load on all panels.

(*b*) ***Critical sections*** The critical section for negative bending, in both the column strip and middle strip, may be assumed as not more than the distance A from the center of the column or support and the critical negative moment shall be considered as extending over this distance.

(*c*) ***Distribution of panel moments*** Bending at critical sections across the slabs of each bent may be apportioned between the column strip and middle strip, as given in Table 2103(*c*). For design purposes, any of these percentages

Table 2103(*c*) **Distribution between column strips and middle strips in per cent of total moments at critical sections of a panel**

Strip		Moment section			
		Negative moment at interior support	Positive moment	Negative moment at exterior support	
				Slab supported on columns and on beams of total depth equal to the slab thickness*	Slab supported on reinforced-concrete bearing wall or columns with beams of total depth equal or greater than 3 times the slab thickness*
Column strip		76	60	80	60
Middle strip		24	40	20	40
Half column strip adjacent and parallel to marginal beam or wall	Total depth of beam equal to slabt hickness*	38	30	40	30
	Total depth of beam or wall equal or greater than 3 times slab thickness*	19	15	20	15

* Interpolate for intermediate ratios of beam depth to slab thickness.

Note: The total dead and live reaction of a panel adjacent to a marginal beam or wall may be divided between the beam or wall and the parallel half column strip in proportion to their stiffness, but the moment provided in the slab shall not be less than that given in Table 2103(*c*).

may be varied by not more than 10 per cent of its value, but their sum for the full panel width shall not be reduced.

2104 Empirical Method

(*a*) ***General limitations*** Flat slab construction may be designed by the empirical provisions of this section when they conform to all of the limitations on continuity and dimensions given herein.

1. The construction shall consist of at least three continuous panels in each direction.
2. The ratio of length to width of panels shall not exceed 1.33.

3. The grid pattern shall consist of approximately rectangular panels. The successive span lengths in each direction shall differ by not more than 20 per cent of the longer span. Within these limitations, columns may be offset a maximum of 10 per cent of the span, in direction of the offset, from either axis between center lines of successive columns.

4. The calculated lateral force moments from wind or earthquake may be combined with the critical moments as determined by the empirical method, and the lateral force moments shall be distributed between the column and middle strips in the same proportions as specified for the negative moments in the strips for structures not exceeding 125 ft high with maximum story height not exceeding 12 ft 6 in.

(*b*) *Columns*

1. The minimum dimension of any column shall be as determined by (*a*) and (*b*) below, but in no case less than 10 in.

a. For columns or other supports of a flat slab, the required minimum average moment of inertia, I_c, of the gross concrete section of the columns above and below the slab shall be determined from Eq. (21-1) and shall be not less than 1000 in.^{4} If there is no column above the slab, the I_c of the column below shall be $(2 - 2.3h/H)$ times that given by the formula with a minimum of 1000 in.^{4}

$$I_c = \frac{t^3 H}{0.5 + W_D/W_L} \tag{21-1}$$

where t need not be taken greater than t_1 or t_2 as determined in (*d*), H is the average story height of the columns above and below the slab, and W_L is the greater value of any two adjacent spans under consideration.

b. Columns smaller than required by Eq. (21-1) may be used provided the bending moment coefficients given in Table 2104(*f*) are increased in the following ratios:

For negative moments

$$R_n = 1 + \frac{(1 - K)^2}{2.2(1 + 1.4W_D/W_L)} \tag{21-2}$$

For positive moments

$$R_p = 1 + \frac{(1 - K)^2}{1.2(1 + 0.10W_D/W_L)} \tag{21-3}$$

The required slab thickness shall be modified by multiplying w' by R_n in Eq. (21-4) and (21-5).

2. Columns supporting flat slabs designed by the empirical method shall be proportioned for the bending moments developed by unequally loaded panels, or uneven spacing of columns. Such bending moment shall be the maximum value derived from

$$\frac{WL_1 - W_D L_2}{f}$$

***Table* 2104(*f*) Moments in flat slab panels in percentages of M_0**

Strip	Column head	Side support type	End support type	Exterior panel: Exterior negative moment	Exterior panel: Positive moment	Exterior panel: Interior negative moment	Interior panel: Positive moment	Interior panel: Negative moment
Column strip	With drop		*A*	44	24	56	20	50
			B	36				
			C	6	36	72		
	Without drop		*A*	40	28	50	22	46
			B	32				
			C	6	40	66		
Middle strip	With drop		*A*	10	20	17*	15	15*
			B	20				
			C	6	26	22*		
	Without drop		*A*	10	20	18*	16	16*
			B	20				
			C	6	28	24*		
Half-column strip adjacent to marginal beam or wall	With drop	1	*A*	22	12	28	10	25
			B	18				
			C	3	18	36		
		2	*A*	17	9	21	8	19
			B	14				
			C	3	14	27		
		3	*A*	11	6	14	5	13
			B	9				
			C	3	9	18		
	Without drop	1	*A*	20	14	25	11	23
			B	16				
			C	3	20	33		
		2	*A*	15	11	19	9	18
			B	12				
			C	3	15	25		
		3	*A*	10	7	13	6	12
			B	8				
			C	3	10	17		

***Table* 2104(f) (*Continued*)**

Percentage of panel load to be carried by marginal beam or wall in addition to loads directly superimposed thereon	Type of support listed in Table 2104(f)		
	Side support parallel to strip	Side or end edge condition of slabs of depth t	End support at right angles to strip
0	1	Columns with no beams	
20	2	Columns with beams of total depth $1\frac{1}{4}t$	A
		Columns with beams of total depth $3t$ or more	B
40	3	Reinforced concrete bearing walls integral with slab	
		Masonry or other walls providing negligible restraint	C

* Increase negative moments 30 per cent of tabulated values when middle strip is continuous across support of type B or C. No other values need be increased.

Note: For intermediate proportions of total beam depth to slab thicknesses, values for loads and moments may be obtained by interpolation. See also Fig. 2104(f)a and 2104(f)b.

L_1 and L_2 being lengths of the adjacent spans ($L_2 = 0$ when considering an exterior column) and f is 30 for exterior and 40 for interior columns.

This moment shall be divided between the columns immediately above and below the floor or roof line under consideration in direct proportion to their stiffness and shall be applied without further reduction to the critical sections of the columns.

(*c*) ***Determination of "c" (effective support size)***

1. Where column capitals are used, the value of c shall be taken as the diameter of the cone described in Art. 2101(b) measured at the bottom of the slab or drop panel.

2. Where a column is without a concrete capital, the dimension c shall be taken as that of the column in the direction considered.

3. Brackets capable of transmitting the negative bending and the shear in the column strips to the columns without excessive unit stress may be substituted for column capitals at exterior columns. The value of c for the span where a bracket is used shall be taken as twice the distance from the center of the column to a point where the bracket is $1\frac{1}{2}$ in. thick, but not more than the thickness of the column plus twice the depth of the bracket.

4. Where a reinforced concrete beam frames into a column without capital or

bracket on the same side with the beam, for computing bending for strips parallel to the beam, the value of c for the span considered may be taken as the width of the column plus twice the projection of the beam above or below the slab or drop panel.

5. The average of the values of c at the two supports at the ends of a column strip shall be used to evaluate the slab thickness t_1 or t_2 as prescribed in (*d*).

(*d*) *Slab thickness*

1. The slab thickness, span L being the longest side of the panel, shall be at least:

$L/36$ for slab without drop panels conforming with (*e*), or where a drop panel is omitted at any corner of the panel, but not less than 5 in. nor t_1 as given in Eq. (21-4)

$L/40$ for slabs with drop panels conforming to (*e*) at all supports, but not less than 4 in. nor t_2 as given in Eq. (21-5)

2. The total thickness, t_1, in inches, of slabs without drop panels, or through the drop panel if any, shall be at least

$$t_1 = 0.028L\left(1 - \frac{2c}{3L}\right)\sqrt{\frac{w'}{f'_c/2000}} + 1\tfrac{1}{2} \qquad \text{(21-4)*}$$

3. The total thickness t_2, in inches, of slabs with drop panels, at points beyond the drop panel shall be at least

$$t_2 = 0.024L\left(1 - \frac{2c}{3L}\right)\sqrt{\frac{w'}{f'_c/2000}} + 1 \qquad \text{(21-5)*}$$

4. Where the exterior supports provide only negligible restraint to the slab, the values of t_1 and t_2 for the exterior panel shall be increased by at least 15 per cent.

(*e*) *Drop panels*

1. The maximum total thickness at the drop panel used in computing the negative steel area for the column strip shall be $1.5t_2$.

2. The side or diameter of the drop panel shall be at least 0.33 times the span in the parallel direction.

3. The minimum thickness of slabs where drop panels at wall columns are omitted shall equal $(t_1 + t_2)/2$ provided the value of c used in the computations complies with (*c*).

(*f*) *Bending moment coefficients*

1. The numerical sum of the positive and negative bending moments in the direction of either side of a rectangular panel shall be assumed as not less than

$$M_0 = 0.09WLF\left(1 - \frac{2c}{3L}\right)^2 \qquad \text{(21-6)}$$

in which $F = 1.15 - c/L$ but not less than 1.

* In these formulas, t_1 and t_2 are in inches and L and c are in feet, and w' is in lb. per ft^2.

Panel		Interior		Exterior						
Moment		Support	Center of span	1st. interior support	Center of span	Exterior support		1st. interior support	Center of span	Exterior support
End support						B	A			C
Marginal half column strip — Side support	3	−12	+6	−13	+7	−8	−10	−17	+10	−3
	2	−18	+9	−19	+11	−12	−15	−25	+15	−3
	1	−23	+11	−25	+14	−16	−20	−33	+20	−3
Middle strip		−16*	+16	−18*	+20	−20	−10	−24*	+28	−6
Column strip		−46	+22	−50	+28	−32	−40	−66	+40	−6

⟵ Direction of all moments ⟶

Fig. 2104(f)a Moments in flat-slab panels in percentages of M_0, with drops. [See Table 2104(f) for notes and classification of conditions of end supports and side supports.]

* Increase negative moments 30 per cent when middle strip is continuous across a support of type B or C; no other values need be increased.

Panel		Interior		Exterior						
Moment		Support	Center of span	1st. interior support	Center of span	Exterior support		1st. interior support	Center of span	Exterior support
End support						B	A			C
Marginal half column strip — Side support	3	−13	+5	−14	+6	−9	−11	−18	+9	−3
	2	−19	+8	−21	+9	−14	−17	−27	+14	−3
	1	−25	+10	−28	+12	−18	−22	−36	+18	−3
Middle strip		−15*	+15	−17*	+20	−20	−10	−22*	+26	−6
Column strip		−50	+20	−56	+24	−36	−44	−72	+36	−6

⟷ Direction of all moments ⟷

Fig. 2104(f)b Moments in flat-slab panels in percentages of M_0, with drops. [See Table 2104(*f*) for notes and classification of conditions of end supports and side supports.]

* Increase negative moments 30 per cent when middle strip is continuous across a support of type B or C; no other values need be increased.

2. Unless otherwise provided, the bending moments at the critical sections of the column and middle strips shall be at least those given in Table 2104(*f*).

3. The average of the values of c at the two supports at the ends of a column strip shall be used to evaluate M_0 in determining bending in the strip. The average of the values of M_0, as determined for the two parallel half column strips in a panel, shall be used in determining bending in the middle strip.

4. Bending in the middle strips parallel to a discontinuous edge shall be assumed the same as in an interior panel.

5. For design purposes, any of the moments determined from Table 2104(*f*) may be varied by not more than 10 per cent, but the numerical sum of the positive and negative moments in a panel shall be not less than the amount specified.

(*g*) ***Length of reinforcement*** In addition to the requirements of Art. 2102(*d*), reinforcement shall have the minimum lengths given in Tables 2104(*g*)1 and 2104(*g*)2. Where adjacent spans are unequal, the extension of negative reinforcement on each side of the column center line as prescribed in Table 2104(*g*)1 shall be based on the requirements of the longer span.

(*h*) ***Openings in flat slabs***

1. Openings of any size may be provided in a flat slab in the area common to two intersecting middle strips provided the total positive and negative steel areas required in (*f*) are maintained.

2. In the area common to two column strips, not more than one-eighth of the width of strip in any span shall be interrupted by openings. The equivalent of all bars interrupted shall be provided by extra steel on all sides of the openings. The shear stresses given in Art. 2102(*c*)2 shall not be exceeded following the procedure of Art. 920(*b*).

3. In any area common to one column strip and one middle strip, openings may interrupt one-quarter of the bars in either strip. The equivalent of the bars so interrupted shall be provided by extra steel on all sides of the opening.

4. Any opening larger than described above shall be analyzed by accepted engineering principles and shall be completely framed as required to carry the loads to the columns.

***Table* 2104(g)1 Minimum length of negative reinforcement**

Strip	Percentage of required reinforcing steel area to be extended at least as indicated	Minimum distance beyond center line of support to end of straight bar or to bend point of bent bar*			
		Flat slabs without drop panels		Flat slabs with drop panels	
		Straight	Bend point where bars bend down and continue as positive reinforcement	Straight	Bend point where bars bend down and continue as positive reinforcement
Column strip reinforcement	Not less than 33 per cent.	$0.30L$†		$0.33L$‡	
	Not less than an additional 34 per cent. . .	$0.27L$†		$0.30L$‡	
	Remainder†.	$0.25L$ or	$0.20L$	$0.25L$ or	To edge of drop but at least $0.20L$
Middle strip reinforcement	Not less than 50 per cent.	$0.25L$		$0.25L$	
	Remainder§.	$0.25L$ or	$0.15L$	$0.25L$ or	$0.15L$

* At exterior supports where masonry walls or other construction provide only negligible restraint to the slab, the negative reinforcement need not be carried further than $0.20L$ beyond the center line of such support.

† Where no bent bars are used, the $0.27L$ bars may be omitted, provided the $0.30L$ bars are at least 50 per cent of total required.

‡ Where no bent bars are used, the $0.30L$ bars may be omitted provided the $0.33L$ bars provide at least 50 per cent of the total required.

§ Bars may be straight, bent, or any combination of straight and bent bars. All bars are to be considered straight bars for the end under consideration unless bent at that end and continued as positive reinforcement.

Note: See also Fig. 2104(g)a.

Table 2104(*g*)2 **Minimum length of positive reinforcement**

Strip	Percentage of required reinforcing steel area to be extended at least as indicated	Maximum distance from center line of support to end of straight bar or bend point of bent bar			
		Flat slabs without drop panels		Flat slabs with drop panels	
		Straight	Bend point where bars bend up and continue as negative reinforcement	Straight	Bend point where bars bend up and continue as negative reinforcement
Column strip reinforcement	Not less than 33 per cent.	$0.125L$		Minimum embedment in drop panel of 16 bar diameters but at least 10 in.	
	Not less than 50 per cent*.	3 in. or	$0.25L$		
	Remainder*.	$0.125L$ or	$0.25L$	Minimum embedment in drop panel of 16 bar diameters but at least 10 in. or	$0.25L$
Middle strip reinforcement	50 per cent.	$0.15L$		$0.15L$	
	50 per cent*.	3 in. or	$0.25L$	3 in. or	$0.25L$

* Bars may be straight, bent, or any combination of straight and bent bars. All bars are to be considered straight bars for the end under consideration unless bent at that end and continued as negative reinforcement.

Note: See also Fig. 2104(*g*)a.

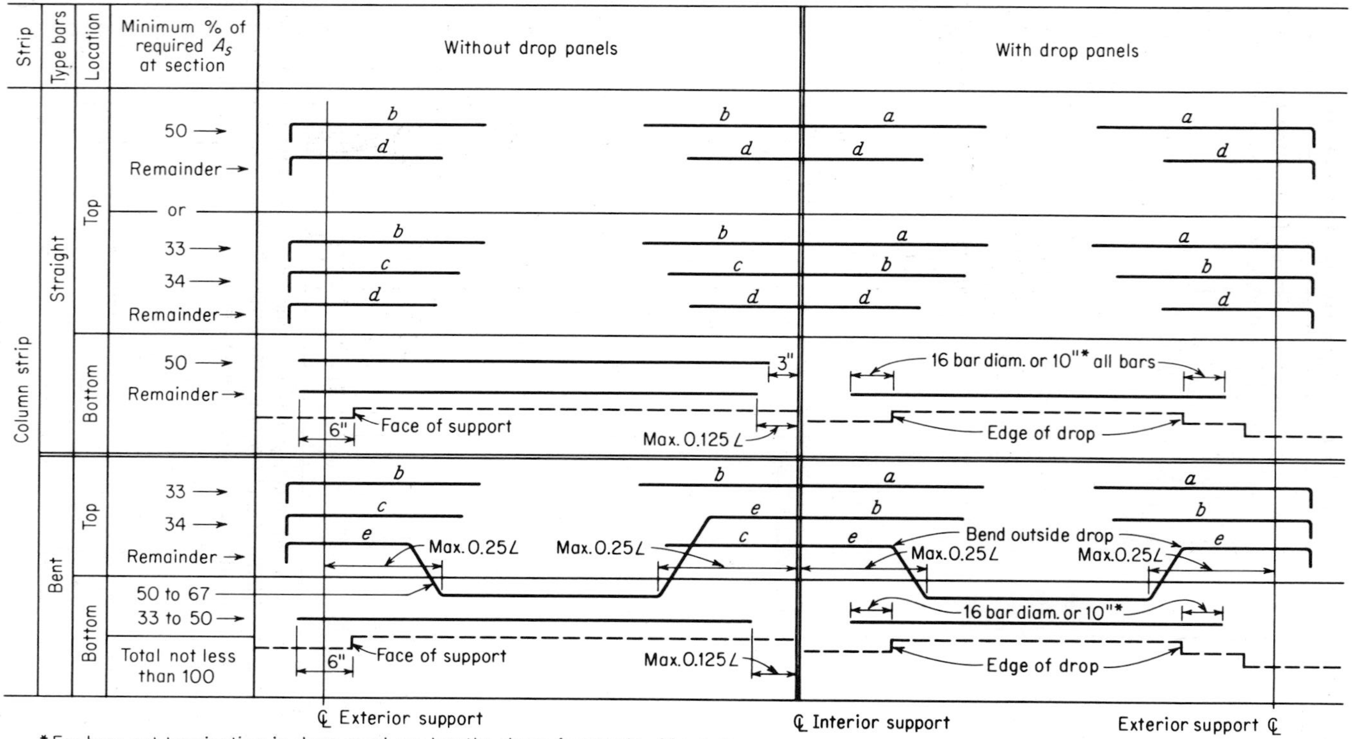

* For bars not terminating in drop panel use lengths shown for panels without drops

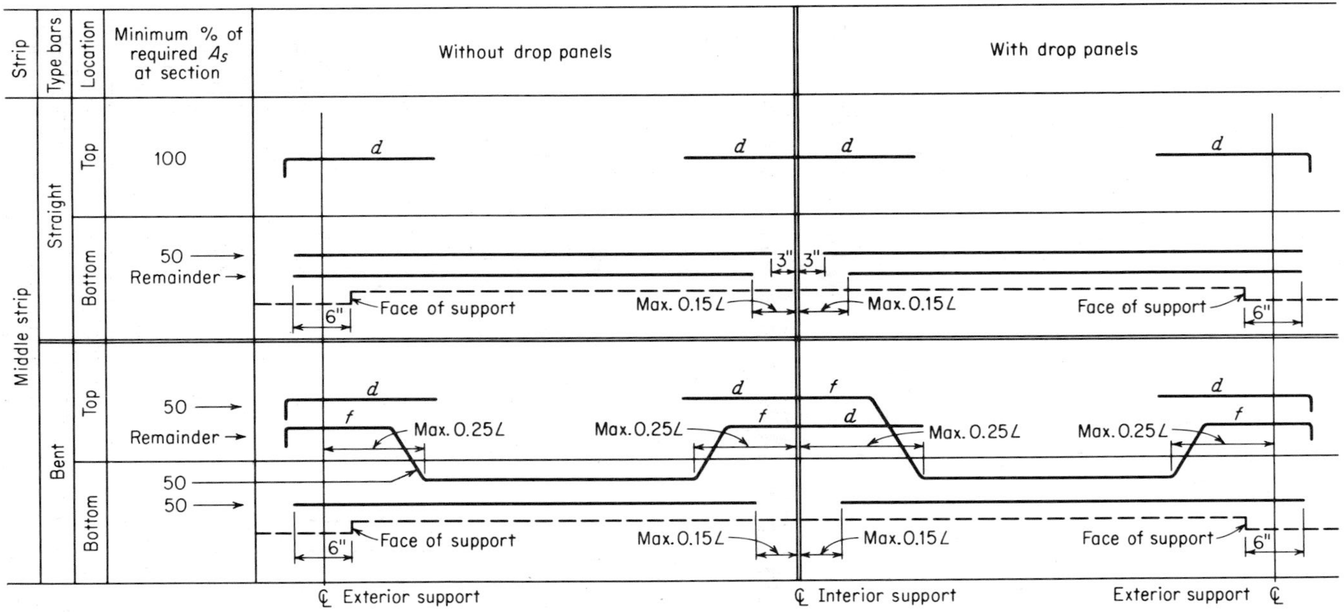

Minimum length of bar from ℄ support

Mark	a	b	c	d	e	f
Length	$0.33L$	$0.30L$	$0.27L$	$0.25L$	$0.20L$	$0.15L$

At interior supports, L is longer of adjacent spans

Fig.* 2104(*g*)*a Minimum length of flat-slab reinforcement. (At exterior supports, where masonry walls or other construction provides only negligible restraint to the slab; the negative reinforcement need not be carried further than $0.20L$ beyond the center line of such support; any combination of straight and bent bars may be used provided minimum requirements are met.)

appendix **B**

TABLES AND DIAGRAMS

***Table* 1 Designations, areas, perimeters, and weights of standard bars**

Bar No.*	Diameter, in.	Cross-sectional area, in.^{2}	Perimeter, in.	Unit weight per foot, lb
2	$\frac{1}{4}$ = 0.250	0.05	0.79	0.167
3	$\frac{3}{8}$ = 0.375	0.11	1.18	0.376
4	$\frac{1}{2}$ = 0.500	0.20	1.57	0.668
5	$\frac{5}{8}$ = 0.625	0.31	1.96	1.043
6	$\frac{3}{4}$ = 0.750	0.44	2.36	1.502
7	$\frac{7}{8}$ = 0.875	0.60	2.75	2.044
8	1 = 1.000	0.79	3.14	2.670
9	$1\frac{1}{8}$ = 1.128†	1.00	3.54	3.400
10	$1\frac{1}{4}$ = 1.270†	1.27	3.99	4.303
11	$1\frac{3}{8}$ = 1.410†	1.56	4.43	5.313
14*S*	$1\frac{3}{4}$ = 1.693†	2.25	5.32	7.650
18*S*	$2\frac{1}{4}$ = 2.257†	4.00	7.09	13.600

* Based on the number of eighths of an inch included in the nominal diameter of the bars. The nominal diameter of a deformed bar is equivalent to the diameter of a plain bar having the same weight per foot as the deformed bar. Bar No. 2 is available in plain rounds only. All others are available in deformed rounds.

† Approximate to the nearest $\frac{1}{8}$ in.

Table 2 Areas of groups of standard bars in square inches

Bar No.	Number of bars												
	2	3	4	5	6	7	8	9	10	11	12	13	14
4	0.39	0.58	0.78	0.98	1.18	1.37	1.57	1.77	1.96	2.16	2.36	2.55	2.75
5	0.61	0.91	1.23	1.53	1.84	2.15	2.45	2.76	3.07	3.37	3.68	3.99	4.30
6	0.88	1.32	1.77	2.21	2.65	3.09	3.53	3.98	4.42	4.86	5.30	5.74	6.19
7	1.20	1.80	2.41	3.01	3.61	4.21	4.81	5.41	6.01	6.61	7.22	7.82	8.42
8	1.57	2.35	3.14	3.93	4.71	5.50	6.28	7.07	7.85	8.64	9.43	10.21	11.00
9	2.00	3.00	4.00	5.00	6.00	7.00	8.00	9.00	10.00	11.00	12.00	13.00	14.00
10	2.53	3.79	5.06	6.33	7.59	8.86	10.12	11.39	12.66	13.92	15.19	16.45	17.72
11	3.12	4.68	6.25	7.81	9.37	10.94	12.50	14.06	15.62	17.19	18.75	20.31	21.87
14*S*	4.50	6.75	9.00	11.25	13.50	15.75	18.00	20.25	22.50	24.75	27.00	29.25	31.50
18*S*	8.00	12.00	16.00	20.00	24.00	28.00	32.00	36.00	40.00	44.00	48.00	52.00	56.00

Table 3 Perimeters of groups of standard bars in inches

Bar No.	Number of bars												
	2	3	4	5	6	7	8	9	10	11	12	13	14
4	3.1	4.7	6.2	7.8	9.4	11.0	12.6	14.1	15.7	17.3	18.8	20.4	22.0
5	3.9	5.9	7.8	9.8	11.8	13.7	15.7	17.7	19.5	21.6	23.6	25.5	27.5
6	4.7	7.1	9.4	11.8	14.1	16.5	18.8	21.2	23.6	25.9	28.3	30.6	33.0
7	5.5	8.2	11.0	12.7	16.5	19.2	22.0	24.7	27.5	30.2	33.0	35.7	38.5
8	6.3	9.4	12.6	15.7	18.9	22.0	25.1	28.3	31.4	34.6	37.7	40.9	44.0
9	7.1	10.6	14.2	17.7	21.3	24.8	28.4	31.9	35.4	39.0	42.5	46.0	49.6
10	8.0	12.0	16.0	20.0	23.9	27.9	31.9	35.9	39.9	43.9	47.9	51.9	55.9
11	8.9	13.3	17.7	22.2	26.6	31.0	35.4	39.9	44.3	48.7	53.2	57.6	62.0
14*S*	10.6	16.0	21.3	26.6	31.9	37.2	42.6	47.9	53.2	58.5	63.8	69.2	74.5
18*S*	14.2	21.3	28.4	35.5	42.5	49.6	56.7	63.8	70.9	78.0	85.1	93.2	100.3

Table 4 Areas of bars in slabs in square inches per foot

Spacing, in.	Bar No.								
	3	4	5	6	7	8	9	10	11
3	0.44	0.78	1.23	1.77	2.40	3.14	4.00	5.06	6.25
3½	0.38	0.67	1.05	1.51	2.06	2.69	3.43	4.34	5.36
4	0.33	0.59	0.92	1.32	1.80	2.36	3.00	3.80	4.68
4½	0.29	0.52	0.82	1.18	1.60	2.09	2.67	3.37	4.17
5	0.26	0.47	0.74	1.06	1.44	1.88	2.40	3.04	3.75
5½	0.24	0.43	0.67	0.96	1.31	1.71	2.18	2.76	3.41
6	0.22	0.39	0.61	0.88	1.20	1.57	2.00	2.53	3.12
6½	0.20	0.36	0.57	0.82	1.11	1.45	1.85	2.34	2.89
7	0.19	0.34	0.53	0.76	1.03	1.35	1.71	2.17	2.68
7½	0.18	0.31	0.49	0.71	0.96	1.26	1.60	2.02	2.50
8	0.17	0.29	0.46	0.66	0.90	1.18	1.50	1.89	2.34
9	0.15	0.26	0.41	0.59	0.80	1.05	1.33	1.69	2.08
10	0.13	0.24	0.37	0.53	0.72	0.94	1.20	1.52	1.87
12	0.11	0.20	0.31	0.44	0.60	0.78	1.00	1.27	1.56

balanced design

Table 5 Design of rectangular beams and slabs

$k = n/(n + r)$; $j = 1 - k/3$; $p_e = n/2r(n + r)$; $K = \frac{1}{2}f_ckj$ or pf_sj

n and f'_c	f_s	f_c	k	j	p_e	K
	18,000	1000 1125	0.357 0.385	0.881 0.872	0.0099 0.0120	157 189
10 (2500)	20,000	1000 1125	0.333 0.360	0.889 0.880	0.0083 0.0101	148 178
	24,000	1000 1125	0.294 0.319	0.902 0.894	0.0061 0.0075	133 160
	18,000	1200 1350	0.375 0.403	0.875 0.866	0.0125 0.0151	197 235
9 (3000)	20,000	1200 1350	0.351 0.377	0.883 0.874	0.0105 0.0128	186 223
	24,000	1200 1350	0.310 0.336	0.897 0.888	0.0078 0.0095	167 201
	18,000	1600 1800	0.416 0.444	0.861 0.852	0.0185 0.0222	286 341
8 (4000)	20,000	1600 1800	0.390 0.419	0.870 0.860	0.0156 0.0188	272 324
	24,000	1600 1800	0.345 0.375	0.884 0.875	0.0116 0.0141	246 295
	18,000	2000 2250	0.438 0.467	0.854 0.844	0.0243 0.0292	374 443
7 (5000)	20,000	2000 2250	0.412 0.441	0.863 0.853	0.0206 0.0248	355 423
	24,000	2000 2250	0.368 0.396	0.877 0.868	0.0154 0.0186	323 387

lower figures for balanced design.

$K = \frac{1}{2} f_c k j = \frac{M}{bd^2}$ $\quad d = \sqrt{\frac{M}{Kb}}$

*

Table 6 **Review of rectangular beams and slabs**

$k = \sqrt{2pn + (pn)^2} - pn;\ j = 1 - \frac{1}{3}k$

p	$n = 7$		$n = 8$		$n = 9$		$n = 10$	
	k	j	k	j	k	j	k	j
0.0010	0.112	0.963	0.119	0.960	0.125	0.958	0.132	0.956
0.0020	0.154	0.949	0.164	0.945	0.173	0.942	0.180	0.940
0.0030	0.185	0.938	0.196	0.935	0.207	0.931	0.217	0.928
0.0040	0.210	0.930	0.223	0.926	0.235	0.922	0.246	0.918
0.0050	0.232	0.923	0.246	0.918	0.258	0.914	0.270	0.910
0.0054	0.240	0.920	0.254	0.915	0.267	0.911	0.279	0.907
0.0058	0.247	0.918	0.262	0.913	0.275	0.908	0.287	0.904
0.0062	0.254	0.915	0.269	0.910	0.283	0.906	0.296	0.901
0.0066	0.261	0.913	0.276	0.908	0.290	0.903	0.303	0.899
0.0070	0.268	0.911	0.283	0.906	0.298	0.901	0.311	0.896
0.0072	0.271	0.910	0.287	0.904	0.301	0.900	0.314	0.895
0.0074	0.274	0.909	0.290	0.903	0.304	0.899	0.318	0.894
0.0076	0.277	0.908	0.293	0.902	0.308	0.897	0.321	0.893
0.0078	0.280	0.907	0.296	0.901	0.311	0.896	0.325	0.892
0.0080	0.283	0.906	0.299	0.900	0.314	0.895	0.328	0.891
0.0082	0.286	0.905	0.303	0.899	0.317	0.894	0.331	0.890
0.0084	0.289	0.904	0.306	0.898	0.321	0.893	0.334	0.889
0.0086	0.292	0.903	0.308	0.897	0.324	0.892	0.338	0.887
0.0088	0.295	0.902	0.311	0.896	0.327	0.891	0.341	0.886
0.0090	0.298	0.901	0.314	0.895	0.330	0.890	0.344	0.885
0.0092	0.300	0.900	0.317	0.894	0.332	0.889	0.347	0.884
0.0094	0.303	0.899	0.320	0.893	0.335	0.888	0.350	0.883
0.0096	0.306	0.898	0.323	0.892	0.338	0.887	0.353	0.882
0.0098	0.308	0.897	0.325	0.892	0.341	0.886	0.355	0.882
0.0100	0.311	0.896	0.328	0.891	0.344	0.885	0.358	0.881
0.0104	0.316	0.895	0.333	0.889	0.349	0.884	0.364	0.879
0.0108	0.321	0.893	0.338	0.887	0.354	0.882	0.369	0.877
0.0112	0.325	0.892	0.343	0.886	0.359	0.880	0.374	0.875
0.0116	0.330	0.890	0.348	0.884	0.364	0.879	0.379	0.874
0.0120	0.334	0.889	0.353	0.882	0.369	0.877	0.384	0.872
0.0124	0.339	0.887	0.357	0.881	0.374	0.875	0.389	0.870
0.0128	0.343	0.886	0.362	0.879	0.378	0.874	0.394	0.867
0.0132	0.347	0.884	0.366	0.878	0.383	0.872	0.398	0.867
0.0136	0.351	0.883	0.370	0.877	0.387	0.871	0.403	0.866
0.0140	0.355	0.882	0.374	0.875	0.392	0.869	0.407	0.864
0.0144	0.359	0.880	0.378	0.874	0.396	0.868	0.412	0.863
0.0148	0.363	0.879	0.382	0.873	0.400	0.867	0.416	0.861
0.0152	0.367	0.878	0.386	0.871	0.404	0.865	0.420	0.860
0.0156	0.371	0.876	0.390	0.870	0.408	0.864	0.424	0.859
0.0160	0.374	0.875	0.394	0.869	0.412	0.863	0.428	0.857
0.0170	0.383	0.872	0.403	0.867	0.421	0.860	0.437	0.854
0.0180	0.392	0.869	0.412	0.863	0.430	0.857	0.446	0.851
0.0190	0.400	0.867	0.420	0.860	9.438	0.854	0.455	0.848
0.0200	0.407	0.864	0.428	0.857	0.446	0.851	0.463	0.846

***Table* 7 Permissible bond-stress values** (Top value of each pair is for top bars, bottom for other bars.)

Bar No.	f'_c									
	W.S.D.					U.S.D.				
	2500	3000	4000	5000	6000	2500	3000	4000	5000	6000
2	160	160	160	160	160	250	250	250	250	250
	160	160	160	160	160	250	250	250	250	250
3	350	350	350	350	350	560	560	560	560	560
	500	500	500	500	500	800	800	800	800	800
4	340	350	350	350	350	560	560	560	560	560
	480	500	500	500	500	800	800	800	800	800
5	272	298	344	350	350	536	560	560	560	560
	384	421	486	500	500	760	800	800	800	800
6	227	248	287	321	350	447	489	560	560	560
	320	351	405	453	496	633	694	800	800	800
7	194	213	246	275	301	383	419	484	541	560
	274	300	347	388	425	543	595	687	768	800
8	170	186	215	240	263	335	367	424	474	519
	240	263	304	339	372	475	520	601	672	736
9	151	165	191	213	233	297	325	376	420	460
	213	233	269	301	330	421	461	533	596	652
10	134	147	169	189	207	264	289	334	373	409
	189	207	239	267	293	374	410	473	529	579
11	121	132	153	171	187	238	260	301	336	368
	170	186	215	241	264	337	369	426	476	522
14*S*	105	115	133	148	163	210	230	266	297	325
	150	164	190	212	232	300	329	379	424	465
18*S*	105	115	133	148	163	210	230	266	297	325
	150	164	190	212	232	300	329	379	424	465
All deformed compression bars	325	356	400	400	400	650	712	800	800	800

***Table* 8 Development lengths* in inches**
$L = A_s f_s / \Sigma_0 \times 0.8 \times u_{all}$ (Top value is for top bars, bottom for other bars.)

Bar No.	W.S.D. f_s		U.S.D. $f_s = f_y$		
	20,000	24,000	40,000	50,000	60,000
$f'_c = 3000$:					
2	9.75 9.76	11.7 11.7	13.2 12.5	15.7 15.6	18.8 18.8
3	6.70 4.69	8.04 5.63	8.37 5.86	10.5 7.32	12.6 8.79
4	8.93 6.25	10.7 7.50	11.2 7.81	14.0 9.77	16.7 11.7
5	13.1 9.29	15.7 11.1	14.0 9.77	17.4 12.2	20.9 14.6
6	18.9 13.4	22.7 16.0	19.2 13.5	24.0 16.9	28.7 20.3
7	25.7 18.2	30.8 21.8	26.1 18.4	32.6 23.0	39.1 27.6
8	33.6 23.8	40.3 28.5	34.1 24.0	42.6 30.0	51.1 36.0
9	42.7 30.2	51.2 36.3	43.3 30.6	54.2 38.2	65.0 45.8
10	54.1 38.3	65.0 46.0	54.9 38.7	68.7 48.4	82.4 58.1
11	66.7 47.3	80.1 56.7	67.7 47.8	84.6 59.7	71.6 101.6
14*S*	92.0 64.4	110.4 77.3	92.0 64.4	115.0 80.5	138.0 96.6
18*S*	122.6 85.8	147.2 103.0	122.6 85.8	153.3 107.3	184.0 128.8

* When the bar stress calculated from the bending moment is smaller than the respective maximum values shown in the table, the necessary development length is obtained by reducing the tabulated length in the ratio of calculated steel stress to tabulated steel stress.

***Table* 8 Development lengths* in inches (*continued*)**
$L = A_s f_s / \Sigma_0 \times 0.8 \times u_{all}$ (Top value is for top bars, bottom for other bars.)

Bar No.	W.S.D. f_s		U.S.D. $f_s = f_y$		
	20,000	24,000	40,000	50,000	60,000
$f'_c = 4000$:					
2	9.75 9.76	11.7 11.7	13.2 12.5	15.7 15.6	18.8 18.8
3	6.70 4.69	8.04 5.63	8.37 5.86	10.5 7.32	12.6 8.79
4	8.93 6.25	10.7 7.50	11.2 7.81	14.0 9.77	16.7 11.7
5	11.4 8.04	13.6 9.65	14.0 9.77	17.4 12.2	20.9 14.6
6	16.3 11.6	19.6 13.9	16.7 11.7	20.9 14.6	25.1 17.6
7	22.3 15.8	26.7 18.9	22.6 15.9	28.2 19.9	33.9 23.9
8	29.1 20.6	34.9 24.7	29.5 20.8	36.9 26.0	44.2 31.2
9	37.0 26.2	44.4 31.4	37.5 26.5	46.9 33.1	56.3 39.7
10	46.9 33.2	56.3 39.8	47.6 33.6	59.5 41.9	71.4 50.3
11	57.8 40.9	69.3 49.1	58.6 41.4	73.3 51.7	88.0 62.0
14*S*	79.7 55.7	95.6 66.9	79.7 55.8	99.6 69.7	119.5 83.7
18*S*	106.2 74.3	127.5 89.2	106.2 74.3	132.8 92.9	159.3 111.5

* When the bar stress calculated from the bending moment is smaller than the respective maximum values shown in the table, the necessary development length is obtained by reducing the tabulated length in the ratio of calculated steel stress to tabulated steel stress.

***Table* 8 Development lengths* in inches (*continued*)**
$L = A_s f_s/\Sigma_0 \times 0.8 \times u_{all}$ (Top value is for top bars, bottom for other bars.)

Bar No.	W.S.D. f_s		U.S.D. $f_s = f_y$		
	20,000	24,000	40,000	50,000	60,000
$f'_c = 5000$:					
2	9.75 9.76	11.7 11.7	13.2 12.5	15.7 15.6	18.8 18.8
3	6.70 4.69	8.04 5.63	8.37 5.86	10.5 7.32	12.6 8.79
4	8.93 6.25	10.7 7.50	11.2 7.81	14.0 9.77	16.7 11.7
5	11.2 7.81	9.38 13.4	14.0 9.77	17.4 12.2	20.9 14.6
6	14.6 10.4	17.5 12.4	16.7 11.7	20.9 14.6	25.1 17.6
7	19.9 14.1	23.9 16.9	20.2 14.2	25.3 17.8	30.3 21.4
8	26.0 18.4	31.2 22.1	26.4 18.6	33.0 23.3	39.6 27.9
9	33.1 23.4	39.7 28.1	33.6 23.7	42.0 29.6	50.4 35.5
10	41.9 29.7	50.3 35.6	42.6 30.0	53.2 37.5	63.8 45.0
11	51.7 36.6	62.0 43.9	52.5 37.0	65.6 46.2	78.7 55.5
14*S*	71.3 49.9	85.5 59.9	71.3 49.9	89.1 62.4	106.9 74.8
18*S*	95.0 66.5	11.4 79.8	95.0 66.5	118.7 83.1	142.5 99.7

* When the bar stress calculated from the bending moment is smaller than the respective maximum values shown in the table, the necessary development length is obtained by reducing the tabulated length in the ratio of calculated steel stress to tabulated steel stress.

Table 9 Weights, areas, moments of inertia of circular columns and moments of inertia of column verticals arranged in a circle 5 in. less than the diameter of column

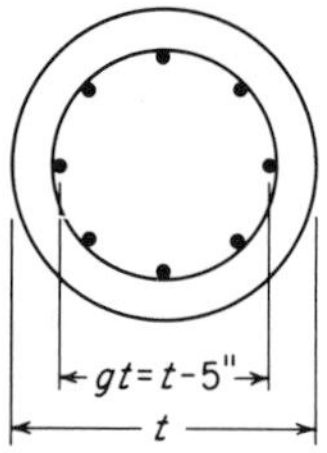

Diameter of column t, in.	Weight per foot, lb	Area, in.^{2}	I, in.^{4}	A_s where $p_g = 0.01$*	I_s, in.^{4}†
12	118	113	1,018	1.13	6.92
13	138	133	1,402	1.33	10.64
14	160	154	1,886	1.54	15.59
15	184	177	2,485	1.77	22.13
16	210	201	3,217	2.01	30.40
17	237	227	4,100	2.27	40.86
18	265	255	5,153	2.55	53.87
19	295	284	6,397	2.84	69.58
20	327	314	7,854	3.14	88.31
21	361	346	9,547	3.46	110.7
22	396	380	11,500	3.80	137.2
23	433	416	13,740	4.16	168.4
24	471	452	16,290	4.52	203.9
25	511	491	19,170	4.91	245.5
26	553	531	22,430	5.31	292.7
27	597	573	26,090	5.73	346.7
28	642	616	30,170	6.16	407.3
29	688	661	34,720	6.61	475.9
30	736	707	39,760	7.07	552.3

* For other values of p_g, multiply the value in the table by $100p_g$.

† The bars are assumed transformed into a thin-walled cylinder having the same sectional area as the bars. Then $I_s = A_s(gt)^2/8$.

***Table* 10 Size and pitch of spirals, ACI Code**

Diameter of column, in.	Out to out of spiral, in.	f'_c			
		2500	3000	4000	5000
f_y = 40,000:					
14, 15	11, 12	3/8–2	3/8–1 3/4	1/2–2 1/2	1/2–1 3/4
16	13	3/8–2	3/8–1 3/4	1/2–2 1/2	1/2–2
17–19	14–16	3/8–2 1/4	3/8–1 3/4	1/2–2 1/2	1/2–2
20–23	17–20	3/8–2 1/4	3/8–1 3/4	1/2–2 1/2	1/2–2
24–30	21–27	3/8–2 1/4	3/8–2	1/2–2 1/2	1/2–2
f_y = 60,000:					
14, 15	11, 12	1/4–1 3/4	3/8–2 3/4	3/8–2	1/2–2 3/4
16–23	13–20	1/4–1 3/4	3/8–2 3/4	3/8–2	1/2–3
24–29	21–26	1/4–1 3/4	3/8–3	3/8–2 1/4	1/2–3
30	27	1/4–1 3/4	3/8–3	3/8–2 1/4	1/2–3 1/4

***Table* 11 Properties of prestressing steel**

A. Uncoated stress-relieved seven-wire strands (*John A. Roebling's Sons Corporation.*)

Nominal diameter, in.	Weight per 1000 ft, lb	Approximate area, in.^{2}	Ultimate strength, lb	Design load, lb	Tensioning load, lb
1/4	122	0.0356	9000	5040	6300
5/16	198	0.0578	14,500	8120	10,150
3/8	274	0.0799	20,000	11,200	14,000
7/6	373	0.1089	27,000	15,120	18,900
1/2	494	0.1438	36,000	20,160	25,200

B. Stress-relieved solid wire

Diameter, in.	Weight per 1000 ft, lb	Area, in.^{2}	Ultimate stress, psi	Ultimate strength, lb
0.192	98	0.0290	251,000	7280
0.196	103	0.0302	250,000	7550
0.250	167	0.0491	240,000	11,800
0.276	203	0.0598	236,000	14,100

C. Alloy-steel bars

Diameter, in.	Weight per foot, lb	Area, in.^{2}	Ultimate strength, lb
3/4	1.50	0.442	64,100
7/8	2.04	0.601	87,100
1	2.67	0.785	113,800
1 1/8	3.38	0.994	144,100
1 1/4	4.17	1.227	177,900

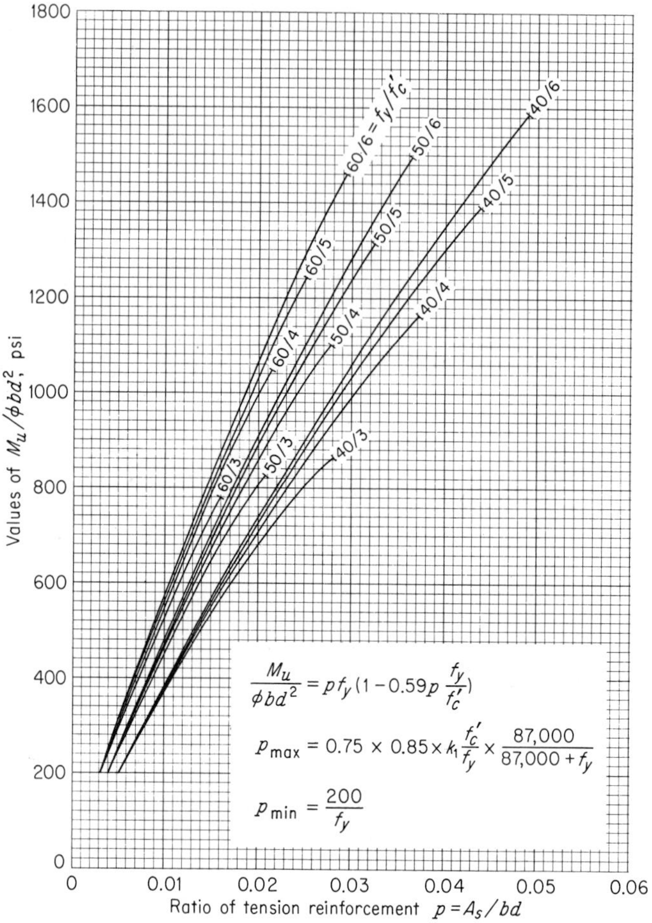

(*a*)

Graph 1a Moment capacity of rectangular sections.

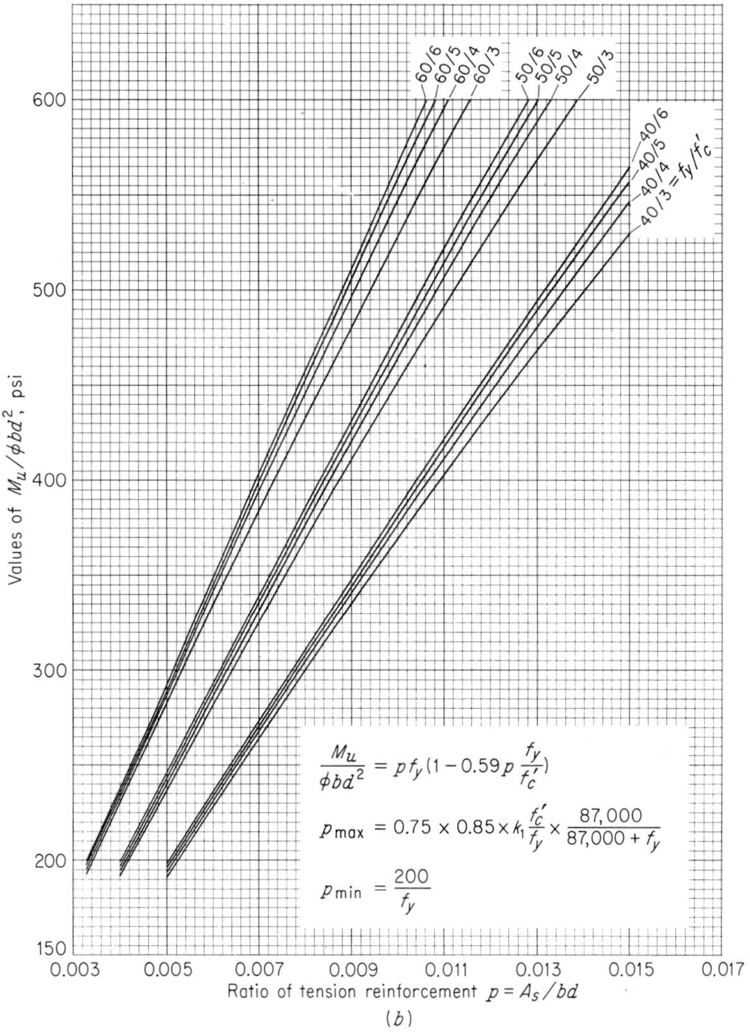

Graph 1b Moment capacity of rectangular sections.

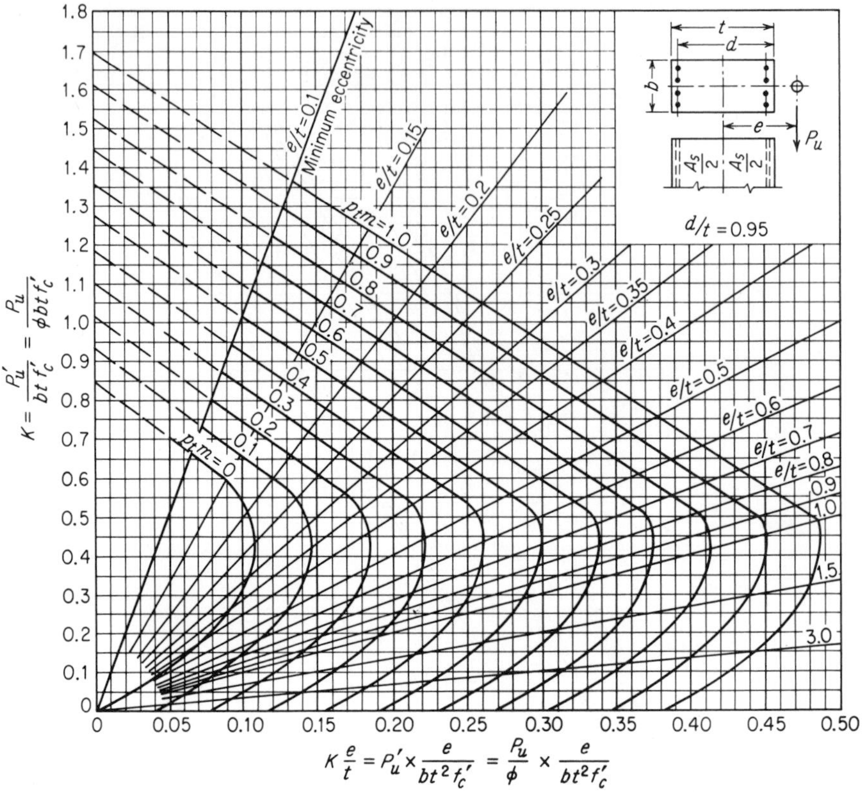

Graph 2 Bending and axial load—rectangular sections. (*Taken, with the authors' and publisher's permission, from C. S. Whitney and Edward Cohen, Guide for Ultimate Strength Design of Reinforced Concrete, J. ACI, vol. 28, no. 5, p. 455, November, 1956.*)

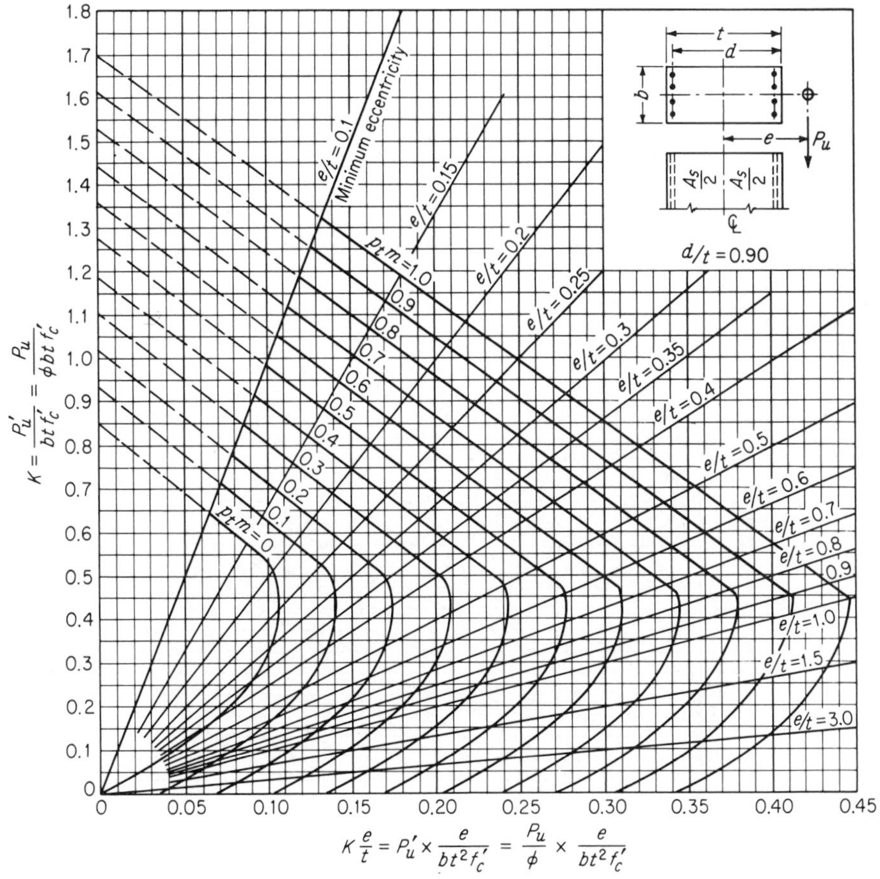

Graph 3 Bending and axial load—rectangular sections. (*Taken, with the authors' and publisher's permission, from C. S. Whitney and Edward Cohen, Guide for Ultimate Strength Design of Reinforced Concrete, J. ACI, vol. 28, no. 5, p. 455, November, 1956.*)

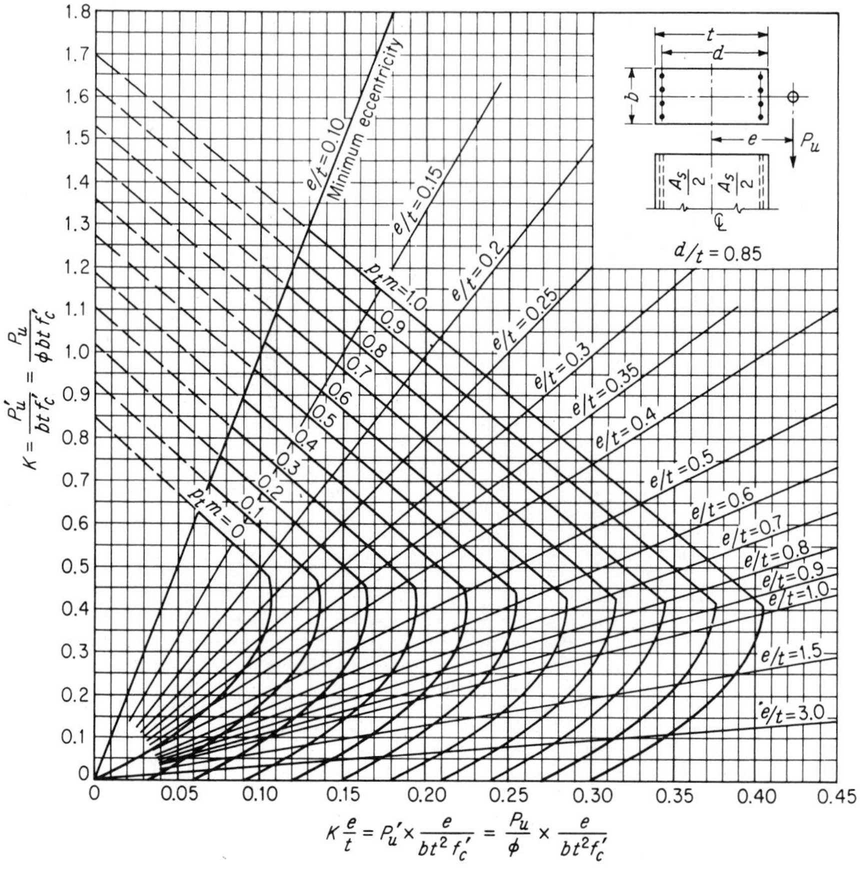

$$K = \frac{P'_u}{btf'_c} = \frac{P_u}{\phi btf'_c}$$

$$K\frac{e}{t} = P'_u \times \frac{e}{bt^2 f'_c} = \frac{P_u}{\phi} \times \frac{e}{bt^2 f'_c}$$

***Graph* 4** Bending and axial load—rectangular sections. (*Taken, with the authors' and publisher's permission, from C. S. Whitney and Edward Cohen, Guide for Ultimate Strength Design of Reinforced Concrete, J. ACI, vol.* 28, *no.* 5, *p.* 455, *November,* 1956.)

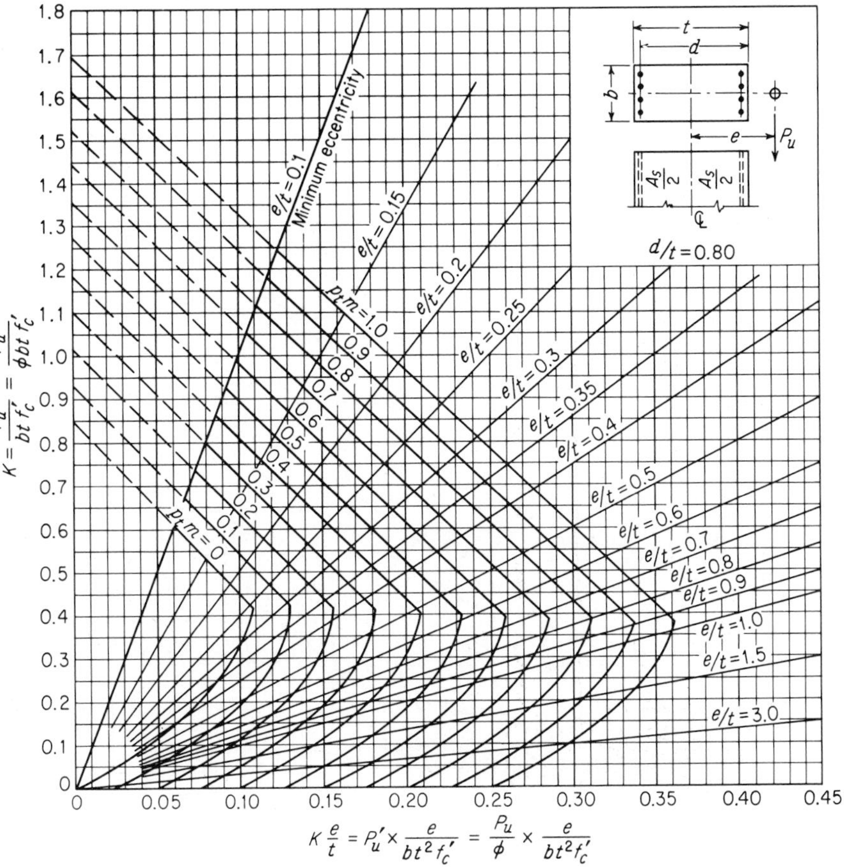

Graph 5 Bending and axial load—rectangular sections. (*Taken, with the authors' and publisher's permission, from C. S. Whitney and Edward Cohen, Guide for Ultimate Strength Design of Reinforced Concrete, J. ACI, vol. 28, no. 5, p. 455, November, 1956.*)

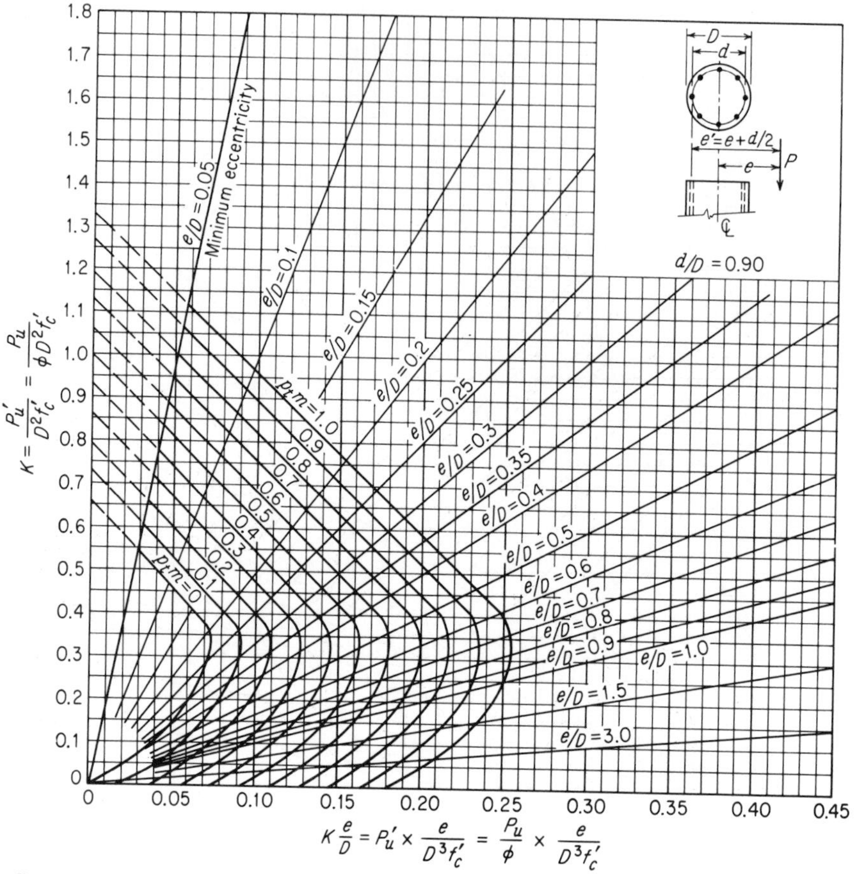

Graph 6 Bending and axial load—circular sections. (*Taken, with the authors' and publisher's permission, from C. S. Whitney and Edward Cohen, Guide for Ultimate Strength Design of Reinforced Concrete, J. ACI, vol. 28, no. 5, p. 455, November, 1956.*)

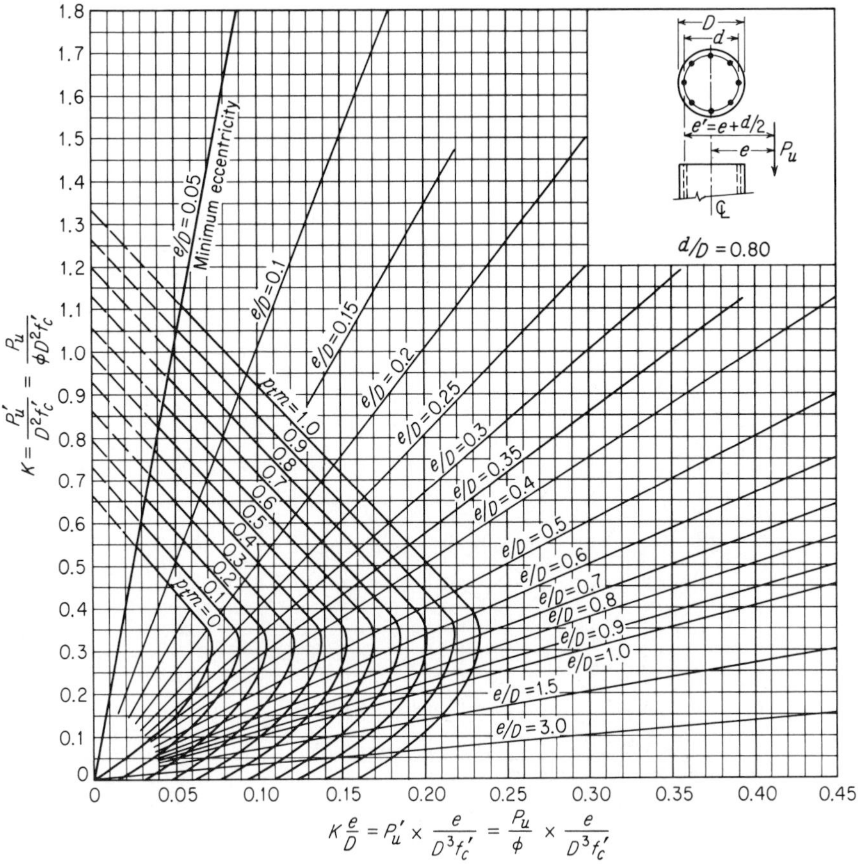

***Graph* 7** Bending and axial load—circular sections with spiral reinforcement. *(Taken, with the authors' and publisher's permission, from C. S. Whitney and Edward Cohen, Guide for Ultimate Strength Design of Reinforced Concrete, J. ACI, vol. 28, no. 5, p. 455, November, 1956.)*

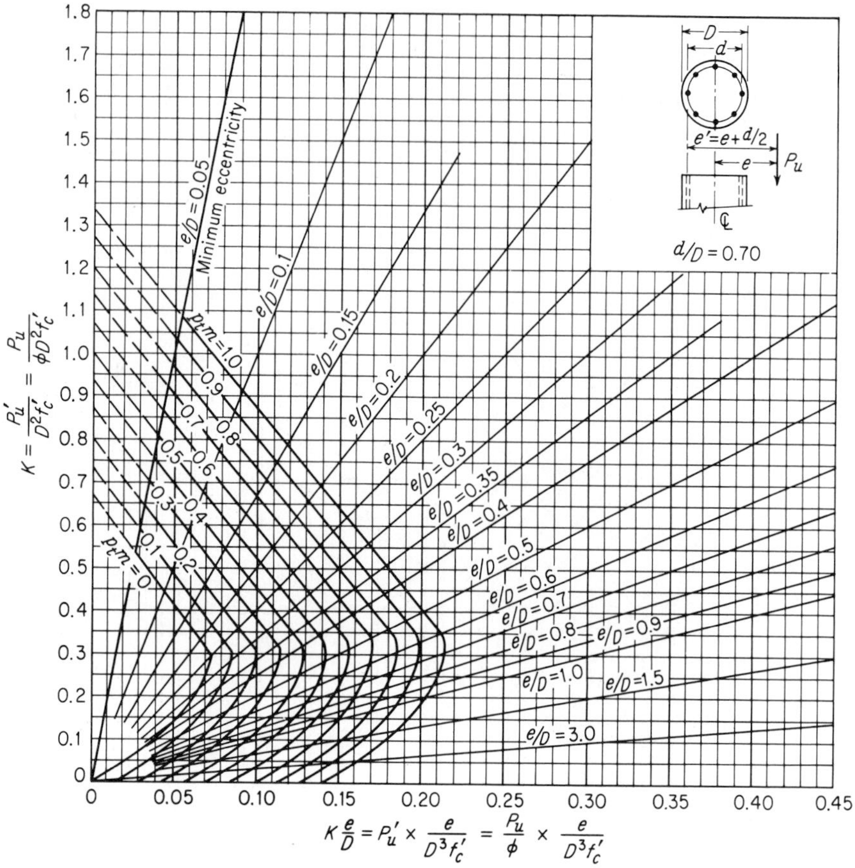

***Graph* 8** Bending and axial load—circular sections with spiral reinforcement. (*Taken, with the authors' and publisher's permission, from C. S. Whitney and Edward Cohen, Guide for Ultimate Strength Design of Reinforced Concrete, J. ACI, vol. 28, no. 5, p. 455, November, 1956.*)

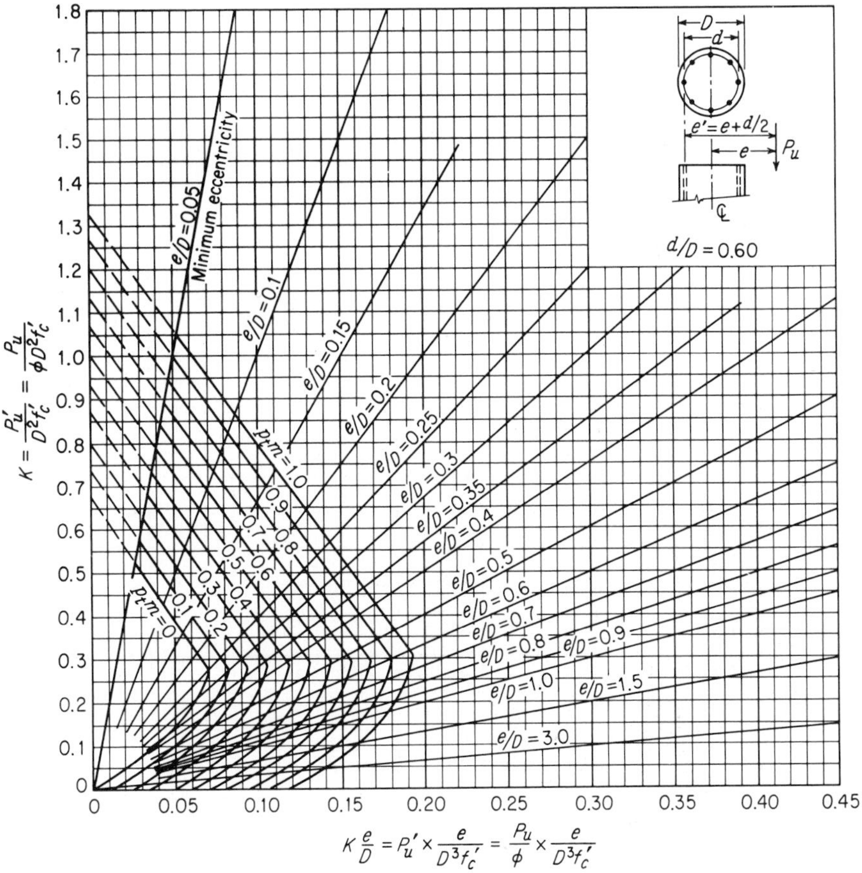

Graph 9 Bending and axial load—circular sections with spiral reinforcement. (*Taken, with the authors' and publisher's permission, from C. S. Whitney and Edward Cohen, Guide for Ultimate Strength Design of Reinforced Concrete, J. ACI, vol. 28, no. 5, p. 455, November, 1956.*)

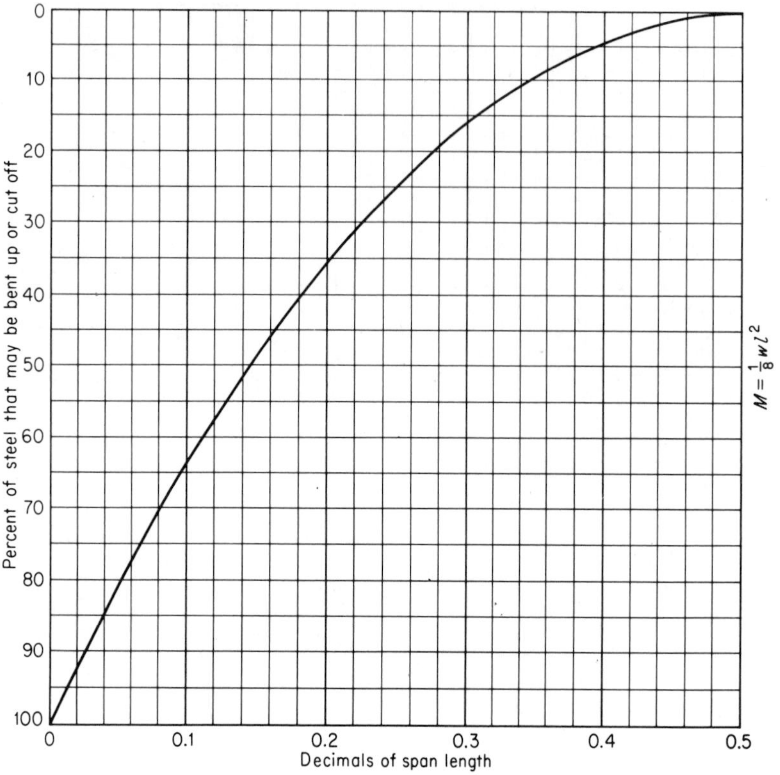

***Graph* 10** Locations of points at which bars may be bent up for simply supported beams uniformly loaded.

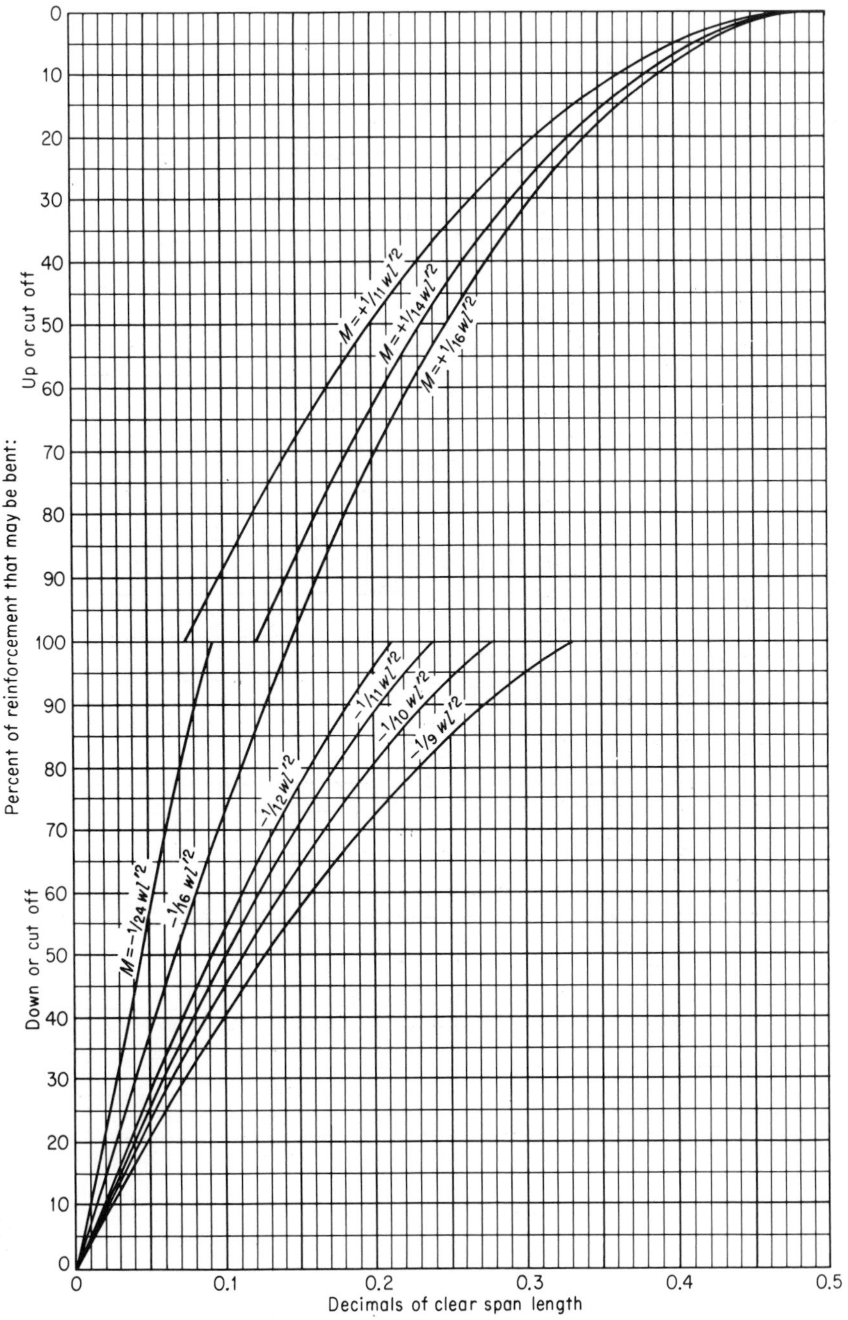

***Graph* 11** Approximate locations of points at which bars may be bent up or down or cut off for continuous beams uniformly loaded and built integrally with their supports according to the coefficients of the ACI Code.

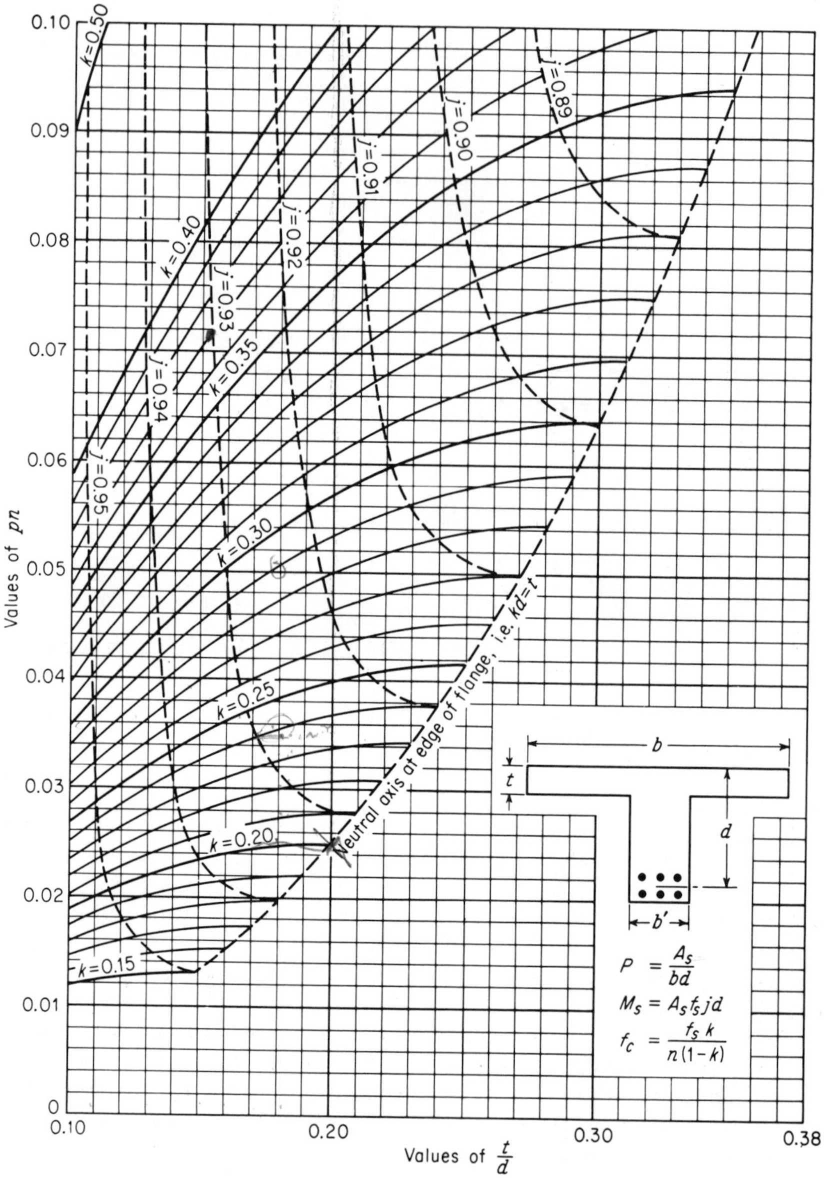

Graph 12 T-beam review.

appendix C

ANALYSIS AND DESIGN OF BEAMS FOR TORSION

C.1 General Considerations In addition to effects considered earlier, concrete beams may be subjected to torsional moments. Torsion rarely occurs alone in reinforced-concrete structures; it is present more often in combination with transverse shear and bending. Torsion may be a primary influence, as in curved beams, but more frequently it is a secondary effect, as in spandrel beams or T beams loaded unsymmetrically. If neglected, torsional stresses can cause distress or failure.

The behavior of concrete members subject to torsion is not completely understood at present, although intensive investigations are in progress in the United States and abroad (Ref. C.1). The present ACI Code mentions torsion only briefly, yet good design practice must account for its effect. In spite of a lack of adequate theoretical and experimental data, foreign code treatment of the subject follows a consistent pattern. These codes focus attention on conditions in the member at working load, and the concrete is presumed to behave elastically. Calculation of torsional stresses is based on the classical theory of Saint-Venant (Ref. C.2).

The Australian Building Code (Ref. C.3) appears to be the most current and reliable guide to the design of members for torsion. The material which follows is patterned after the Australian code, adapted to practice in the United States.

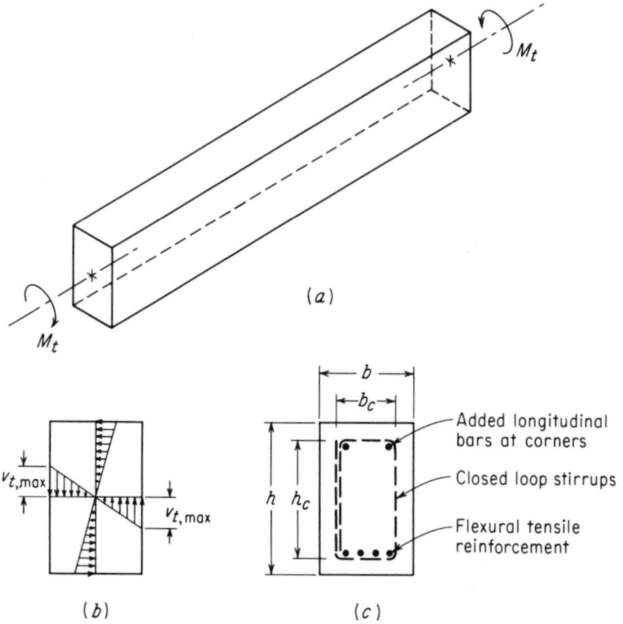

***Fig.* C.1** (*a*) Rectangular beam subject to torsion; (*b*) distribution of torsional shear along horizontal and vertical centerline of section; (*c*) reinforcement for torsion.

It may serve as a guide to design until such time as the ACI Code will include specific recommendations.

C.2 Torsional Stresses The application of twisting moment to a noncircular prismatic member results in (1) relative rotation of the cross sections and (2) warping of the originally plane cross sections. For a rectangular homogeneous member subject to pure torsion, the application of a twisting moment M_t (see Fig. C.1*a*) results in shearing stresses which vary linearly along any radial line with distance from the section centroid (see Fig. C.1*b*). For a rectangular section, the maximum torsional shear stress obtains at the middle of the long sides. If this shear stress is sufficient in magnitude, diagonal cracks of opposite direction will form near the center of the two long faces. If the section is nearly square, cracks will be evident on all four faces, in a spiral pattern.

In a rectangular section, the maximum flexural shear stress occurs at the neutral axis. Thus, at the center of one long face of such a beam, maximum flexural and torsional shear stresses are additive, while on the opposite face they tend to cancel.

In an elastic rectangular member, the maximum torsional shear stress v_t can be calculated from the expression

$$v_t = \frac{\eta M_t}{b^2 h}$$

in which M_t = torsional moment
b = smaller cross-sectional dimension
h = larger cross-sectional dimension
η = a coefficient which depends on the cross-sectional shape

For rectangular cross sections of usual proportions, η varies from about 3.5 to 4.5. According to the Australian code, η is taken equal to 5, so that

$$v_t = \frac{5M_t}{b^2h} \tag{C.1}$$

For T, I, and L sections common to reinforced-concrete construction, torsional shear at the face of the web can be approximated by the expression

$$v_t = \frac{3M_tb'}{\Sigma b^3h} \tag{C.2}$$

in which b' = web width
b = smaller dimension of each component rectangle of the section
h = larger dimension of each component rectangle of the section
Σb^3h = sum of b^3h terms of the component rectangles

This equation is based on the assumption that the torsional rigidity of the section is equal to the sum of the torsional rigidities of the component rectangles. While originally intended for application to sections of rather slender proportions, it appears to be satisfactory for thicker sections as well.

Elastic theory indicates that high shear stress occurs at reentrant corners—i.e., where the flange joins the web in T, I, and L sections—and that fillets at these junctions would be desirable. Such fillets complicate construction, however, and are not common. Their omission may be justified by consideration of conditions within the beam when failure is imminent. At that stage of loading, an inelastic redistribution of stresses occurs which tends to equalize torsional shear over the entire cross section.

A problem facing the designer in dealing with torsion is what portion of the slab should be considered as effective flange. There is no reason to suppose that the effective width for torsion is the same as that for flexure. It has been suggested (Ref. C.4) that the entire overhanging portion of the flange may be disregarded in torsion calculations. For beams in which the web width is substantially larger than the slab thickness, this may be satisfactory; in other cases it seems unduly conservative.

C.3 Allowable Torsional Shear To guard against diagonal cracking of members without web reinforcement, it is necessary that torsional shear stress be kept below certain allowable limits. Since torsion produces shear and diagonal tension, permissible torsional shear stresses may be taken the same as values presently prescribed for flexural shear, that is,

$$\begin{aligned} &\text{For beams:} \quad v_c = 1.1\sqrt{f'_c} \\ &\text{For joists:} \quad v_c = 1.2\sqrt{f'_c} \end{aligned} \tag{C.3}$$

If a member is subjected to combined flexural and torsional shear, as in most cases, some codes permit shear stress substantially higher than would be permitted if either flexural or torsional shear were acting alone (Ref. C.1). However, lack of sufficient experimental evidence is reason to be somewhat conservative in this respect. It seems reasonable that there be no *reduction*, at least, in the allowable shear stress for combined cases and that the allowable shear for combined cases be the same as that used when either type of shear is acting alone.

C.4 Reinforcement for Torsion Failure of a concrete member subject to torsion can be delayed by the inclusion within the member of steel reinforcement arranged to cross potential diagonal cracks. The most efficient form of torsion reinforcement would consist of a pair of 45° spirals, one left hand and the other right hand. Such spirals are not often used, for practical reasons.

Diagonal tensile stresses due to torsion differ from those due to transverse shear in that they exist on all four faces of a rectangular section. It is evident that U-shaped stirrups or bent-up bars are not suitable for torsional reinforcement. Closed loops must be used. These are placed perpendicular to the axis of the member. Additional longitudinal bars are placed at the corners of the stirrups to accommodate the longitudinal component of stress and form a closed cage (see Fig. C.1*c*). Stirrup loops must have a sufficient length of embedment at the ends of the bars to ensure that allowable stresses can be developed. In flanged sections, the ends of the stirrups may project into the slab (see Fig. C.2). It is obvious that all such web reinforcement is in addition to that placed for flexural shear, although there is no reason why the two area requirements can not be combined into one set of stirrups.

If adequate reinforcement is provided, nominal torsional-shear stresses computed by Eqs. C.1 or C.2 may exceed the allowable values of Eqs. C.3. A maximum nominal shear stress equal to that permitted for web-reinforced beams subject to flexural shear is appropriate, that is,

$$v = 5\sqrt{f'_c} \tag{C.4}$$

Shear stress, in such a case, is calculated as if the presence of the reinforcement had no effect on stress distribution.

Experimental evidence indicates that if torsional reinforcement is provided, it need be designed only for the excess shear above that permitted on the plain concrete. In cases where torsional and flexural shear combine, the shear resisted by the concrete should be subtracted only once, either from the torsional- or flexural-shear requirement, but not from both. Australian practice is to proportion the reinforcement separately for shear and torsion, with v_c subtracted only from the larger of the shear stresses.

According to Australian code, the total steel area in the two legs of a transverse stirrup used for torsional reinforcement is

$$A_{st} = \frac{M'_t s}{0.8 b_c h_c f_v} \tag{C.5}$$

while the total area of additional longitudinal bars can be found from the equation

$$A_{sl} = \frac{M'_t(b_c + h_c)}{0.8b_ch_cf_s} \tag{C.6}$$

In the above equations,

M'_t = excess of torsional moment over that resisted by the concrete
s = spacing of stirrups
b_c = smaller dimension of the closed stirrup
h_c = larger dimension of the closed stirrup
f_v = allowable stress for stirrup steel
f_s = allowable stress for longitudinal bars

Present investigations in the United States, as yet incomplete, indicate that the numerical coefficient in the denominator may be taken equal to 0.6 for better agreement with test results.

According to the present ACI Code, at least one longitudinal bar should be placed in each corner of the stirrup cage; these bars are to have a diameter at least equal to that of the stirrup, but in no case less than ½ in.

C.5 Example A reinforced concrete T beam (see Fig. C.2) has an overall depth of 24 in., web width of 12 in., flange width of 36 in., and flange thickness of 5 in. Calculate the amount of torsion reinforcement required if the beam is subject to a twisting moment of 150,000 in.-lb. The concrete strength is $f'_c = 4000$ psi; $f_s = f_v = 20{,}000$ psi.

The allowable torsional shear on the plain concrete may be taken equal to $v_c = 1.1\sqrt{f'_c} = 1.1\sqrt{4000} = 70$ psi. The twisting moment resisted by the concrete alone is found from Eq. C.2:

$$\begin{aligned} M_{tc} &= \frac{v_t}{3b'} \sum b^3h \\ &= \frac{70}{3 \times 12} [(12^3 \times 24) + (5^3 \times 12 \times 2)] = 86{,}300 \text{ in.-lb} \end{aligned}$$

The addition twisting moment for which web reinforcement must be provided is

$$M'_t = M_t - M_{tc} = 150{,}000 - 86{,}300 = 63{,}700 \text{ in.-lb}$$

Assuming 2 in. from the face of concrete to the center of the stirrup steel,

$$\begin{aligned} b_c &= 12 - 4 = 8 \text{ in.} \\ h_c &= 24 - 4 = 20 \text{ in.} \end{aligned}$$

Then, from Eq. C.5,

$$A_{st} = \frac{M'_ts}{0.8b_ch_cf_v} = \frac{63{,}700 \times s}{0.8 \times 8 \times 20 \times 20{,}000} = 0.0248s$$

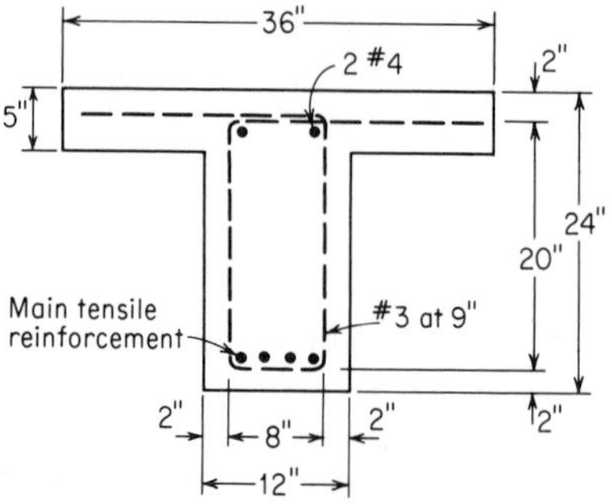

Fig. C.2

For No. 3 stirrups, with two vertical legs per stirrup, $A_{st} = 0.22$ in.² Then, $s = 0.22/0.0248 = 8.88$ in., say 9 in. o.c. From Eq. C.6, the total area of additional longitudinal steel is found:

$$A_{sl} = \frac{M'_t(b_c + h_c)}{0.8 b_c h_c f_s} = \frac{63{,}700 \times 28}{0.8 \times 8 \times 20 \times 20{,}000} = 0.70 \text{ in.}^2$$

Two additional No. 4 bars will be added at the upper stirrup corners; bottom steel will be increased by 0.35 in.² above the requirement for flexural tension. Stirrup legs will be extended into the overhanging flanges. The layout of reinforcement is shown in Fig. C.2.

REFERENCES

C.1 G. P. Fisher and P. Zia: Review of Code Requirements for Torsion Design, *J. ACI*, vol. 61, p. 1, 1964.

C.2 S. Timoshenko and J. N. Goodier: "Theory of Elasticity," chap. 11, McGraw-Hill Book Company, Inc., New York, 1961.

C.3 Australian Standard No. CA. 2, SAA Code for Concrete in Buildings, Standards Association of Australia, Sidney, 1958.

C.4 H. J. Cowan: Design of Beams Subject to Torsion Related to the New Australian Code, *J. ACI*, vol. 56, p. 591, 1960.

INDEX

BIOCHEMISTRY OF CANCER

JESSE P. GREENSTEIN

Chief, Laboratory of Biochemistry
National Cancer Institute, National Institutes of Health
United States Public Health Service
Bethesda, Maryland

SECOND EDITION, *Revised and Enlarged*

ACADEMIC PRESS INC., PUBLISHERS
NEW YORK, N. Y.
1954

ACADEMIC PRESS INC.
125 EAST 23rd STREET
NEW YORK 10. N. Y.

PRINTED IN THE UNITED STATES OF AMERICA

To The Memory of My Parents

and to My Wife

PREFACE TO THE SECOND EDITION

The first edition of this book was written under the shadow of a great war. Since the close of that conflict, it is gratifying to note the resurgence of scientific life among many peoples and a return to the great tradition and heritage of learning which knows no national boundaries. Only the dead who have fallen with their promise do not return, and so much greater is the responsibility of the living.

Although the general outline of the first edition has been retained, the individual chapters have been pruned in some places, and expanded in others. Many new tables and figures have been interpolated into the text. Newer approaches to carcinogenesis and to chemotherapy have been intensively developed in recent times, and these procedures, with their successes and failures, are paid due attention. New and absorbing developments in the chemistry of the tumor-bearing host have made their appearance. As one surveys the field of cancer research from its comparatively recent beginnings, it is difficult to avoid a feeling of optimism. That increasingly secure measures of control must follow the accumulation of so much knowledge is as certain as that day must follow night, and as long as man need contend only with Nature, the ultimate victory is assured.

I am grateful for the generous response to the first edition of this book, and more than a little surprised at its warmth, for my purpose in writing was primarily as a means of self-education. It is no easy responsibility to enter, if even briefly, into the thoughts and aspirations and accomplishments of each of a thousand men, for as old Sam Johnson said long ago, "to play round the text of an author . . . is no very arduous work, but to attend it without deviation, and measure step with step, requires at once vigor and caution." I have tried to avoid "deviation" and to "measure step with step" to the extent of never referring to an author's work without the original before me at the moment; whether I have shown too much "vigor" and too little "caution" can be decided only by others. It is my earnest hope that any shortcomings in the first edition of this work shall be corrected, as far as it is humanly possible, in the present. A considerable measure of gratitude is due my wife and my publisher for their generous patience.

JESSE P. GREENSTEIN

Bethesda, Maryland
May, 1954

PREFACE TO THE FIRST EDITION

Cancer is one of the most complex of medical and biological problems, and research into its causes, development, and control forms one of the most intricate scientific activities of modern times. Cancer research is a focus of many independent scientific disciplines, biological, chemical, and physical, and is most fruitful when ideas, concepts, and techniques in these disciplines are freely exchanged. No single individual is capable of mastering the entire field of cancer research, and no single individual in any one of its component disciplines can work effectively at the modern level without comprehension and appreciation of those disciplines on its boundaries.

The present volume is concerned with the application to the study of cancer of one of these disciplines, namely biochemistry, and a brief presentation is made of those biochemical studies which have yielded results of interest and significance. To this end, the attempt has been made to select fundamental data of this field of cancer research and, on the basis of these data, to assess that which the biochemical approach to the cancer problem has thus far achieved and to illustrate the possibilities of the reciprocal enrichment of the fields of normal and of abnormal physiology. No attempt at inclusiveness is made. Instead, the intention is to stress the development and the rationale of the biochemical approaches to the cancer problem and to indicate the extent to which the value of these approaches is due to advances made in contiguous fields of research. The study of the phenomena of cancer draws sustenance from many sources and is facilitated from various directions.

The material has been divided for presentation into three general categories relating, respectively, to the induction of tumors, to attempts to influence the induction and the growth of tumors, and to a description of the chemical properties of tumors. Many of the topics described in the following pages are not strictly biochemical in nature but have been included because such matters as inbred strains of mice and pathologic criteria of tumors are part of the equipment with which the biochemist works in this field. In few subjects of biochemical interest is the investigator compelled to depend upon so many disciplines foreign to his own.

Above all it is the author's hope that the relative sparseness of the results presented will reveal and emphasize the enormous gaps in our knowledge which only devoted and painstaking labor can fill.

The author is grateful to his colleagues for their kindness in reading parts or all of the manuscript, namely, Drs. Chalkley, Andervont, Shear, J. White, Shimkin, Bryan, Eschenbrenner, Hartwell, Dunn, Algire, Heston, Blum, Burk, and Earle. The responsibility for any errors, whether retained or overlooked, is, of course, the author's own. A considerable debt of gratitude is felt toward these colleagues, not merely in the present instance, but for the opportunity over many years of learning from them. The author also wishes to thank his chief, Dr. R. R. Spencer, for his encouragement in this enterprise, and his wife, Lucy L. Greenstein, for her help in compiling the indexes.

JESSE P. GREENSTEIN

Bethesda, Maryland
1947

CONTENTS

Chapter I

Introduction—The Oncological Sciences

Cancer research, or oncology, is not a science in itself but the simultaneous and frequently coordinated activity of many independent scientific disciplines, viz. clinical medicine, surgery, pathology, radiation physics, genetics, immunology, endocrinology, and biochemistry. All these approaches have been directed toward the common aim of the elucidation and control of the neoplastic transformation and like all applied sciences are nourished, sustained, and invigorated by fundamental advances and discoveries in these and related fields. They did not start from the same chronologic point, but each, as its usefulness became evident, joined the group which may be called the oncological sciences. It is quite possible that the list of the oncological sciences is not yet complete and that some new mode of approach, not envisioned at the present time, will be added in the future.

Cancer as a disease was recognized in antiquity and, indeed, its very name is derived from the ancient description of its frequent clinical course. Until the nineteenth century it was entirely within the therapeutic province of the physician and surgeon. With the development of microscopic techniques, the fine morphological details of tumors became evident to the pathologist, and the foundation for the scientific study of these kinds of abnormal growths was laid. The morphological description of tumors became not only of practical aid to the surgeon but, by classifying these lesions into various categories, was the necessary first step in their understanding. The terminology of the morphological pathologist became the basic language of the field of oncology, for this has always been the privilege of taxonomy.

Cancer research, as an experimental science, began at the close of the nineteenth century with the study of animal tumors and of the transplantability of these tumors into new hosts, and with the establishment by workers of the Imperial Cancer Research Fund and by others that such animal tumors were in all respects comparable with the malignant neoplasms encountered in man. The introduction of animal experimentation into the field of oncology has been of great value, for it enabled the investigator to study various characteristics of neoplastic disease at will, unhampered by the limitations of the human subject. With the discovery of radium emanation and of X-rays at the turn of the century, and with the subsequent observation that these forms of radiation readily affected many kinds of rapidly dividing cells, yet another approach, that of radiation physics, was added to the group of oncological sciences. For the most part, the animals used up to this period, about 1910, were heterozygous in genetic composition, and many of the conflicting results on such animals were gradually attributed to this factor. As a result, the fruitful era of the geneticist ensued, in which the development of inbred strains of mice, each with different neoplastic potentialities, was carried out, through which a tool of great value was placed in the hands of the experimental oncologist. The role of the sex glands in certain forms of cancer was elucidated by classical endocrinological investigations some thirty years ago, and a considerable literature subsequently followed. The triumphs of immunology in other problems stimulated work in oncology, with the production of results yet puzzling and inconclusive. Thus, step by step, new approaches to the understanding of the neoplastic transformation were introduced, some of them waiting until others were achieved (as chemo-analytical studies became rational only when tumors arising from known and available normal tissues were developed), but each was carried on in a more or less orderly fashion by trained and experienced investigators in the particular specialty.

Biochemistry, as a pursuit of professional stature, was added to the oncological sciences only about a decade ago. The delay in the adoption of its full resources by the field of oncology is a matter of regret because so much ground must be made up. Chemistry is not of comparatively recent vintage, as is radiology or endocrinology or immunology, but is an art nearly as ancient as the practice of medicine itself. In view of the fact that Lavoisier, Liebig, Berzelius, and others had established chemistry as a quantitative discipline long before the rise of scientific oncology, it is indeed curious that chemistry, instead of being among the earliest, has been the latest of the oncological sciences. It is possible that long familiarity with the almost universal practice and application of chemistry produced the effects of an underestimation of its value and of the illusion of its ease of mastery. Yet, many decades ago, a few men foresaw the potentialities of the chemical approach to the science of medicine and laid the foundation of sound experimental techniques for their realization.

Over seventy-five years ago, chemical physiologists, led by Hoppe-Seyler, Kossel, Kühne, and others, had hoped that problems in tissue function might be partially explained in terms of the properties of isolated chemical components. From the chemical characterization of normal function to the development of a chemical pathology seemed the next logical step. In a letter to His, date 1890, the great Swiss physiologist, Friedrich Miescher, summed up this feeling and expressed the belief that the study of the chemical phenomena of tissues would clarify many pathological manifestations such as inflammation and degeneration (cancer) which were obscure or incapable of explanation by microscopic examination alone, and he concluded the letter with the oft-quoted, rueful comment, "Das Mikroskop lässt einen . . . gewiss oft im Stich." There is no doubt that well over fifty years ago progressive (if cloistered) medical opinion was seeking a more dynamic and a more quantitative approach to problems in pathology than those afforded by the conventional histological techniques.

However, the development of the science of pathological chemistry, beyond its application to urine analysis, received little subsequent support from either pathology or chemistry, and pathological chemistry became either the drudge or the toy of the clinician as well as an object of indifference to the orthodox biochemist. During the past few years this situation has changed for the better and has become far more encouraging. There is little use in reviewing the errors of the past, or in dwelling on the reasons for the present, except to interpret such reasons on the basis of the growth of enlightened opinion. The hospitality of the medical sciences to chemistry, although still somewhat limited, is now, for the most part, an established fact. There remains one phenomenon, however, which is a legacy from the past and, since it has been particularly operative in oncology, is deserving of consideration.

The art of surgery, the insight of pathology, the mastery of radiology, and the effective practice of clinical medicine, all require a long and arduous apprenticeship. Standards in these fields are jealously guarded by organized professional bodies, by the watchful scrutiny of highly competent and responsible individuals, and by the legal powers of the state. For the most part, these fields are rather watertight compartments, with relatively little overstepping of the boundaries between them, and, as in all guilds, this exclusive character has tended to promote fine workmanship. Relatively few untrained amateurs or dilettantes have ventured to wander into these disciplines.

Yet, for some reason, many of the practitioners of these and other fields, with little or no chemical training, have not hesitated to assume a chemical competence. Some of the work performed under these conditions has been excellent, some of it has been adequate, but much of it, especially in oncology, has been grossly inept. The errors of the chemical amateur in oncology have been due, not to the failure to apprehend properly the value of chemical approaches, but to the failure to realize that chemistry is a field in which considerable training and experience, particularly in the fundamental sciences, are prerequisite. The test tube, no less than the scalpel or the microscope, is the tool of the skilled workman.

But if chemistry has had its amateurs from other fields, oncology has also had its occasional curious and isolated chemists. The most successful foray in this direction has been achieved by Warburg, but it should be noted that Warburg contributed to oncology, as Pasteur did to other fields of pathology, not only genius but many years of intensive labor. More chemists than one have blundered in oncology, not so often on the basis of poor oncology as of bad chemistry. For some odd reason, cancer research has been the graveyard of many a scientific reputation.

The bibliographer in the field of cancer research is confronted with a monstrous and amorphous literature, controversial, often hastily ambitious, and frequently haunted by the ghosts of countless once-hopeful and dazzling hypotheses. To the experienced biochemist, a large part of the chemical work in oncology is a veritable wonderland, in which cancer and biochemistry have been combined in much the same fashion as Mr. Pott's erudite and ingenious friend synthesized Chinese metaphysics. That which is fine and enduring in this literature should be separated and accorded recognition.

This is an era of rapid development in the physical sciences, and all branches of human endeavor have felt the impact of chemical techniques. The admission of biochemistry into the group of the oncological sciences has provided the opportunity for professional chemists to initiate powerful, diverse, and, above all, sustained lines of approach toward the elucidation and control of cancer. Confidence in such lines of approach is indicated by the character of the personnel and the programs of investigation undertaken by the great centers of cancer research. This confidence in the chemist requires, in return, circumspection and grave responsibility. The chemist in the field of oncology is not, and never will be, a free lance. The fundamental definition of the material with which the chemist works is within the province of the morphologist, and a substantial cooperation between the two is essential for work of value.

The goal toward which all oncological disciplines are directed is not yet reached, although progress has undeniably been made. The mystery of cancer, and the human tragedy which it encompasses, have endowed it with an emotional quality and an urgency which open pitfalls to the unwary and innumerable disappointments to scientific and lay public alike. It is well to remember in this connection the wise comment of Woglom, written in 1913, but still pertinent today: "It must be frankly confessed that so far, at least, the study of cancer, instead of affording an understanding of the nature of the disease, has but opened up new problems which were formerly not even conceived. Hence, earnest students have had to content themselves with slowly and laboriously collecting data, in the hope that at some future time these may be combined into a coherent whole. Slow at best, this is nevertheless the only way in which the goal can be surely attained. . . . ." There is still much ground to be covered before the end is in sight, but science admits of no insuperable barricades. With confidence in the scientific method, and with tools of ever-increasing power and subtlety, it is certain that the combined efforts of the oncological sciences will ultimately yield the comprehension and the mastery of the neoplastic transformation.

Chapter II

The General Phenomena and Taxonomy of Cancer

Introduction

The orderly development of the living multicellular organism is probably the most extraordinary and most intricate phenomenon in nature. Starting from the single fertilized egg cell, there gradually emerge through numerous cell divisions, diverging in various directions under the guidance of organization centers, primitive groups of cells with varying distribution, morphological appearance, and functional potentiality. With continued growth of each group of cells their separate characteristics diverge more and more from each other and become increasingly accentuated in each group. Such groups of cells, each developing with continued cell division into morphologically distinguishable entitites (both gross and microscopic), are called tissues. Concurrently with the morphological development of each of the tissues, there occurs a specialization of physiological function. This process of development and the divergence of the morphological and specific functional characteristics of the tissues from each other is referred to as differentiation. As the maximum degree of differentiation is attained, the further growth of the tissues slows down and ultimately ceases and the adult organism is formed.

However, the capacity of the tissues to grow is not lost when the fully differentiated and adult state is reached. For example, when superficial areas of the epidermis are removed, the basal layer produces more epidermal cells, and excision of part of the liver results in an increased assumption of cell division in the residual mass. Under normal circumstances there is always some breakdown of tissues with subsequent regeneration through cell division. In most cases, the regeneration of these tissues reaches the maximum tolerated limit characteristic of the adult organism and then ceases. The growth potentialities of each tissue, therefore, are usually confined within definite limits by controls exerted by the organism. From the very beginning of cell multiplication out of the fertilized egg, the development of each tissue is coordinated with that of all other tissues, and this harmonious integration is apparently maintained by elaborate systems of physiological control throughout the greater part of the life span of the organism. The living form is thus an intricate and highly developed mosaic of varying and individually specific components. With senescence of the adult organism the regenerative capacities of the tissues are gradually diminished at rates which may be different for different tissues.

The normal existence of the multicellular organism is thus attained by the subordination of the capacity of tissues for growth to the maintenance and balance of the organism as a whole, and of the individual parts. Occasionally, a tissue may grow in localized areas a little beyond the usually determined architectural scheme of the organism, but, as long as it remains under the control of the organism, this overgrowth usually occurs relatively slowly, and the affected tissue may ultimately either return to its normal size or at some point of time achieve a balance and stop growing further. These benign, controlled aberrations of tissue growth consist in a localized and limited increase in mass which, under ordinary circumstances, is not lethal to the organism as a whole. If these growths impinge mechanically upon crucial and sensitive structures within a confined and unyielding space, as within the skull, a lethal effect may occur owing to mechanical factors alone. The specific physiological functions as well as the microscopic cell pattern of such limited growths largely resemble those of the tissues from which such growths originally sprang.

There is yet another kind of tissue growth which to some extent is apparently free of the control of the organism. This type of growth is frequently unlimited, continuous, at a rate usually far in excess of the normal, without consideration for neighboring tissues which it progressively invades, destroys, and replaces, independent and heedless of the well-being of, and ultimately lethal to, the organism as a whole. The microscopic appearance of these growths may vary considerably, some resembling in certain features those of the fully developed tissues from which they sprang, others resembling somewhat the embryonic, primitive forms of the tissues of their origin. The pattern of the cells in these growths is frequently disordered, degenerated, and undifferentiated. It would appear as if the orderly and integrated pattern of the affected tissue area was sacrificed to the urgency for unrestrained growth. This abnormal type of growth is the identifying characteristic of the phenomenon known as cancer, and the neoplasms which ensue are known as cancers or tumors.

Definition and Some Characteristics of Tumors

Tumors may be defined as growths of cells which are largely or wholly independent of the organism which supplies their nutrition, which frequently possess an atypical structure, and which reach no definite limit to growth. These aberrations of tissue growth are common to all living multicellular forms, both animals and plants. Clinical observations on cancer are recorded as far back as 1500 B.C.

Tumors arise from the cells of the host by a transformation at present unknown, and once this transformation has occurred it is apparently not reversible. Most adult mammalian tissues cultured *in vitro* fail to grow except during a brief early period, whereas most cancerous tissues under the same conditions exhibit continuous growth over many years. To all indications, the capacity for growth of the tumor lies largely within itself and.

although it may superficially resemble the growth and regenerative capacities of normal tissues, has certain qualities peculiar to itself.

Normal tissue growth occurs in an orderly, generally logarithmic, fashion without injury to surrounding tissues. Cancerous tissue growth, although progressive, is sometimes capricious and may occur at different rates throughout its course. Normal tissues do not apparently affect neighboring tissues whereas cancerous tissues often invade, destroy, and replace neighboring normal tissues. Normal tissues transplanted to other sites in the organism may grow or be maintained briefly for a while, but they ultimately necrose and completely regress. Such a transplantation is incompatible with the harmonious balance of the organism. In many cancerous tissues cell masses may become detached and, by traveling through the circulatory system to distant sites in the organism, set up further growths from these emboli at such sites. These extensions of the original, primary tumor are called metastases. In mice, the lung is a frequent site for metastatic growth, as are also lymph nodes, liver, and bone. In man, as in most animals, the site of metastasis generally depends on the predilection of each tumor. Few metastatic growths have been observed in the spleen, but few primary tumors arise in this organ. According to Ewing, there is often a gradual loss in structural differentiation in metastatic tumors (1). They become more anaplastic, i.e., they resemble to a decreasing degree the normal tissues of origin, so that metastatic growths from primary tumors of different kinds of normal tissues are sometimes indistinguishable. Like the primary tumor, the metastatic growths continue progressively, sometimes at considerably greater rates than that of the primary tumor. The presence of these transplanted cells is also incompatible with the harmonious balance of the organism, but the latter apparently displays little successful protective reaction against the destructive growth.

It is apparent that the capacity for growth exhibited by tumors represents something novel as well as dangerous in the history of the individual organism, and is not due simply to a release of the normal growth potential of the tissue of origin. This normal growth potential is controlled by the organism, and, hence, the growth of a normal tissue is balanced between tissue and organism. Cancerous growth capacity is apparently independent of the organism, and, hence, the growth capacity of the tumor is a nearly unique property of the tumor itself. This property of autonomous, or nearly autonomous, growth is the most striking characteristic of tumors as a class, and within the factors responsible for this property lies the secret of control of this growth.

Classification of Animal Tumors

Tumors arise in certain tissues through the agency of certain factors, some known, some suspected, and many of them unknown. Tumors may, therefore, be classed according to either (a) their known etiology or (b) the normal tissue from which they arise or most resemble. The former, in the absence of general etiological information, has only a limited applicability. The latter, although noncommittal as to causation, is more practical and descriptive. The classification of tumors was originally designed to be applied to human tissues but, with minor modifications known to the experienced judgment of the histologist, may also be applied to tumors arising in the lower animals. Classification by histogenesis is also limited because it does not take into account the possibility that tumors arising from the same kind of tissue may show quite different growth characteristics.

The term *carcinoma* may be applied to tumors which arise from epithelial tissue, whether pavement or glandular. Thus, a tumor of the skin may be termed an epithelioma or epidermoid carcinoma, and a tumor of the gastric or intestinal mucosa would be in either case an adenocarcinoma.

The term *sarcoma* may be applied to tumors arising from connective and muscle tissues. Thus a tumor of fibrous connective tissue would be a fibrosarcoma, that of cartilage a chondrosarcoma, that of bone an osteogenic sarcoma, that of the blood vessels an angiosarcoma, that of lymphatic tissue a lymphosarcoma, that of striated muscle a rhabdomyosarcoma, etc.

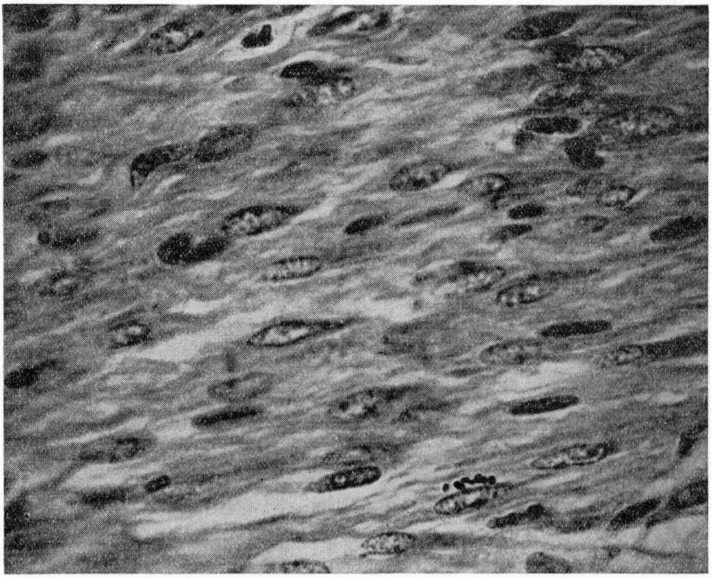

FIG. 1. Normal fibroblasts (×1008), or connective tissue cells from a healing wound. Photograph illustrates cells from which fibrosarcomas are derived. Note regular order of cells and normal complement of collagen between cells. (Courtesy of W. R. Earle.)

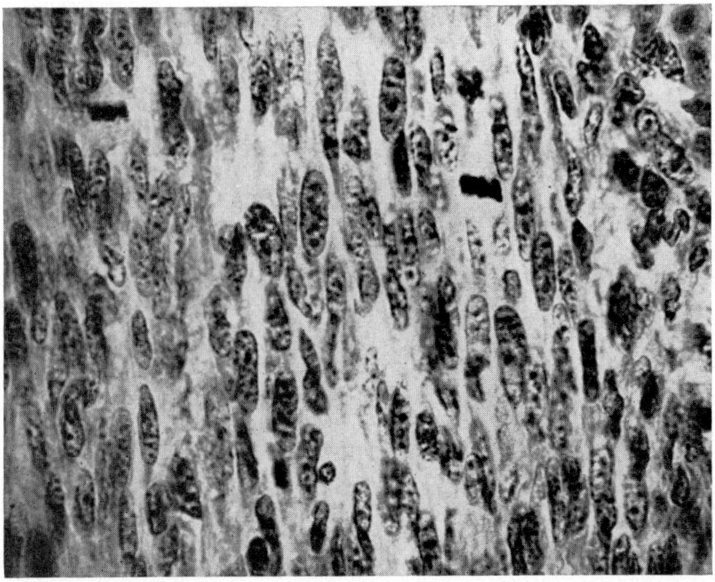

FIG. 2. A fibrosarcoma (×1008) which shows relatively little morphologic alteration in cell type from normal, but which has developed an autonomous and unrestrained growth. Note greater density of cells and loss of collagen. (Courtesy of W. R. Earle.)

Tumors characterized by the terms carcinoma and sarcoma are frequently anaplastic and often bear relatively little resemblance in histological structure to the normal tissues of their origin. Tumors arising in various tissues which resemble more closely the tissues of origin and which appear to have a limited growth are referred to in terms which omit mention of carcinoma or of sarcoma and are called, according to histogenesis, fibroma, osteoma, angioma, rhabdomyoma, adenoma, etc. In clinical practice, the latter terms are presumed to represent relatively benign types of growth. The suffixes carcinoma and sarcoma are, on the other hand, generally applied to what may be called malignant growths. The terms benign and malignant are rather relative in meaning and are applied to neoplasms not only on the basis of histological criteria, i.e., the degree of deviation from the appearance of the normal tissues of origin, but also on the basis of the course of growth of the tumor and the general judgment of the clinical observer. So-called benign growths are generally self-limited and, except in crucial areas, are relatively harmless. So-called malignant growths are frequently invasive in character, destructive to neighboring normal tissues, and prone to give rise to metastatic lesions elsewhere in the host. The dividing line between these categories is often not very sharp. Malignancy may also apparently vary in degree, and systems of subclassification on this

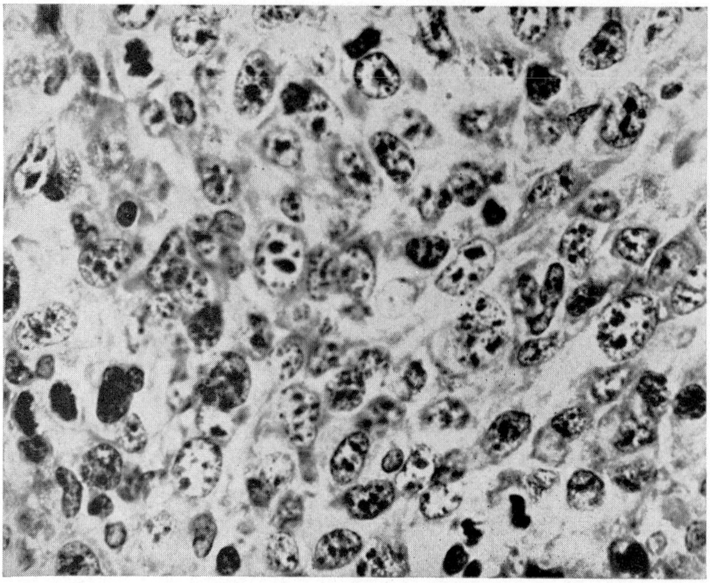

FIG. 3. A fibrosarcoma (×1008) showing a more advanced degree of morphologic alteration than in Fig. 2. Cells bear little if any resemblance to the normal fibroblasts of origin and the tissue pattern is completely disorganized. (Courtesy of W. R. Earle.)

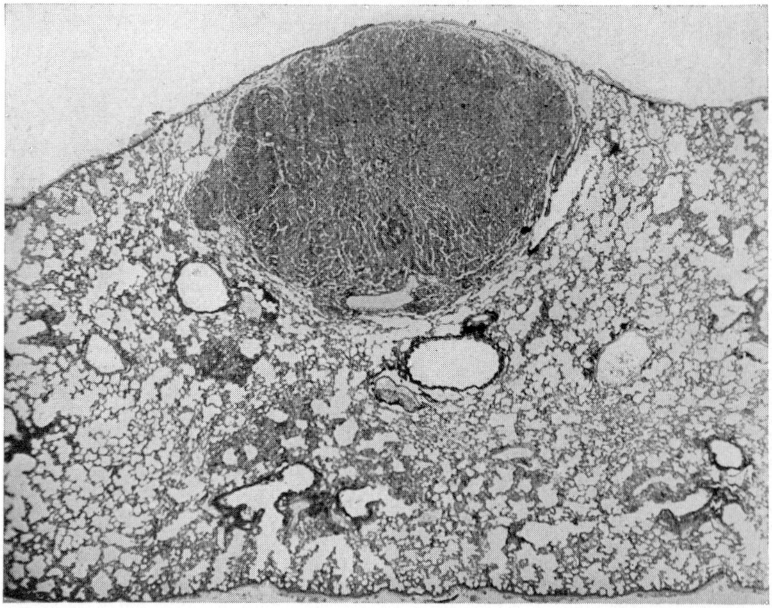

FIG. 4. A pulmonary tumor in a mouse, with gland-like formations, which is replacing and compressing the normal lung tissue (×20). (Courtesy of Dr. T. B. Dunn.)

basis are employed by histopathologists in ways usually suiting their individual predilections.

Other criteria may be based upon the relative capacity of tumors for autonomous growth. Under such criteria, a benign growth would be largely dependent upon the organism and hence not truly autonomous, whereas a malignant growth would be largely autonomous and independent of the organism. Such a distinction might be a value if there were independent applicable evidence. Conflicts with traditional criteria may also arise, as in the case of metastatic prostatic carcinoma, which, because it often readily responds by regression to administration of estrogen, may be considered to be relatively non-autonomous and hence benign, but because it is invasive and metastatic should be considered malignant. However, after such a responsive period the prostatic carcinoma becomes refractory, hence presumably autonomous, and thus malignant. The possibility of consecutively dependent and autonomous, or benign and malignant phases, during the growth of a tumor may not be excluded. There is obviously no precise classification for the relative degrees of tumor growth and characteristics, and the terms generally applied must be used with some discretion. Since tumors of any description represent aberrant forms of growth, it is obvious that such disorderly arrangements may take a multitude of forms. After eons of evolutionary development the tissue in normal growth usually assumes a single and unique pattern. Cancer may be considered to represent a local flight into seeming chaos, and the wonder is not that there are so many forms of cancerous growth but that there are not many more. However, the available permutations and combinations must be limited by the number of cellular components present in a constant environment, and the

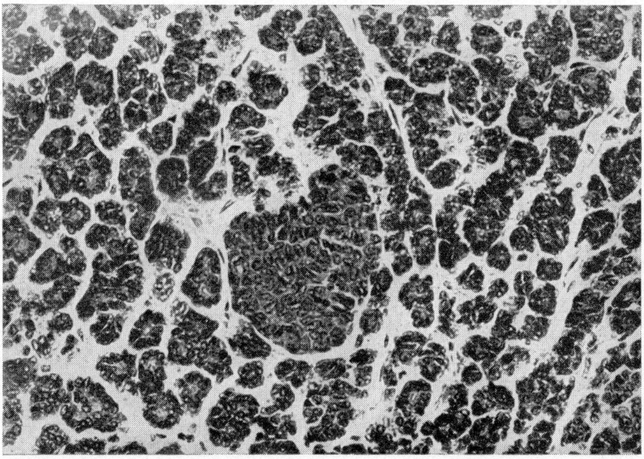

FIG. 5. A mammary tumor in a mouse, adenocarcinomatous in structure (×200). (Courtesy of Dr. T. B. Dunn.)

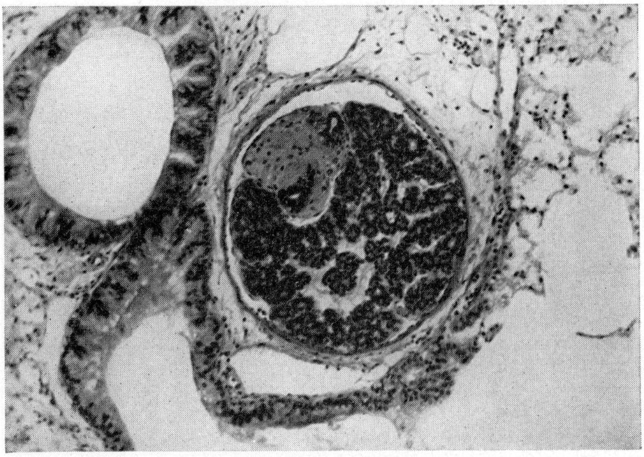

FIG. 6. Metastasis in the lung from the mammary tumor pictured in Fig. 5, showing reproduction of structure similar to that of the primary growth (×200). (Courtesy of Dr. T. B. Dunn.)

nearly uniform chemical pattern which most cancer tissues display suggests that the neoplastic transformation is not haphazard and chanceful but follows a definite sequence of events. The recognition of these events in chemical terms is one of the goals of chemical oncology.

TRANSMISSIBILITY OF TUMORS AND THE EXPERIMENTAL BASIS OF CANCER RESEARCH

The study of cancer in man is for obvious reasons extremely limited, and the experimental study of the disease has been largely conducted with laboratory animals. As in all complex, living forms, tumors arise in rats and in mice, and the relatively short life span of these animals renders it possible to follow the development and course of the tumors throughout the life of the animals. In the early experiments, the investigator was handicapped by the fact that he was limited to the study of the few tumors which arose spontaneously and apparently by chance in a small proportion of his animal colony. If he came across an interesting example of a tumor, it usually died with the host animal. For the extensive study of tumors, it was obviously necessary to be able to carry such tumors along indefinitely, and this could be accomplished only if they could be transferred from one animal to another.

Metastasis of a tumor to a distant site is a mode of autologous transplantation, e.g., transfer within the same organism. A great step forward in the understanding of tumor growth came about at the end of the last century when Hanau, and later Jensen, succeeded in transplanting a tumor from one rat to another. This type of heterologous transfer opened up new avenues of approach in the experimental study of cancer. Jensen, and subsequently Bashford, studying similar heterologous transplants in mice, demonstrated that the tumors which grew from the inoculum were derived exclusively from the cells of the inoculum, and not from the cells of the host. The transfer from animal to animal necessitated the presence of living cells; cell-free extracts were ineffective in transmitting the tumor from one host to another. The success of transplantation of tumors with subsequent continuous growth of these tumors emphasized their essentially autonomous nature and suggested that they grew out of themselves. The success of the heterologous transplant depends, however, upon its ability to elicit continuously from the host a supporting structure of connective tissue (stroma) and an adequate supply of blood vessels.

It should not be assumed that a tumor transplanted serially through several generations must remain immutable in character. There are, in fact, numerous reports in the literature describing the transformation of transplanted epithelial tumors into sarcomas at some stage in the transplantation series. The first observation of this sort was made in 1906 by Ehrlich and Apolant (2), who reported that in the tenth generation of transplantation of their mouse adenocarcinoma a mixed growth developed, containing both carcinomatous and sarcomatous areas, which by the fourteenth generation was purely sarcomatous. A considerable number of confirmatory reports subsequently appeared by other workers who described similar changes in the course of transplantation of epithelial tumors, chiefly of mammary-gland origin, in mice and in rats (cf. 3). More recently, the development of sarcomas at the site of serial transplantation of pulmonary tumors (4) and of hemangioendotheliomas and bone sarcomas at the site of serial transplantation of several types of spontaneous and induced hepatomas has been described (5). It is not improbable that the relatively slow-growing epithelial tumors can induce other forms of tumor in the susceptible host adjacent to it, whether the normal fibroblastic tissue of the stroma (6) or nearby vascular tissue (5). The responsiveness of normal tissues adjacent to a growing tumor is one of the most striking effects induced by the latter type of tissue and may conceivably vary all the way from a benign stimulation in growth, as in the vascular response noted by Algire, or in the increased growth rate of normal tissues contiguous to autonomous tumor tissue in the guinea pig eye (7), to the induction of a malignancy of a different type. In the case of the hepatomas, no internal change in their structure was noted during development of the new, adjacent tumor types, and this, together with the fact that the tumors of the new type were dependent on the genetic character of the host, suggested the action of some carcinogenic (or perhaps more properly sarcomagenic) agent. The determination of the chemical nature and identity of such stimulating substances elaborated by the tumor is one of the great challenges of chemical oncology. It must, however, be emphasized that many epithelial tumor lines can and have been transplanted for many generations without apparent morphologic change, but it does illustrate the need for caution in always maintaining histologic controls on all transplanted tumors used for biochemical and other studies. A survey of available transplanted animal tumors has been made by Dunham and Stewart (8).

Related to these observations is the experience of Earle and his associates, who grew tissues of mouse hepatomas, melanomas, and thyroid tumors in culture, which when subsequently injected into mice of the same strains gave rise at the site of injection not to these tumors but invariably to sarcomas (9). This curious phenomenon suggested that (a) the original tumors were admixed with sarcoma elements, (b) the primary tumor cell type underwent a change in morphology in culture, and (c) the primary tumor cells were overgrown in culture by fibroblasts which were transformed to sarcomas.

The production of antibodies by tumors is most clearly revealed with transmissible leukemic strains in mice. It has been long recognized that serum withdrawn from mice of a foreign strain rendered immune by several injections of leukemic cells is capable of inactivating these cells *in vitro* (10). Similarly, the injection of leukemic mouse cells into a heterologous host produces antibodies, and the resulting antiserum can effect an inactivation of such cells *in vitro* (11, 12). In general, spleen of the same strains has been used as a normal tissue control, and it has been noted that neutralizing antibodies against the leukemic cells can be induced by normal splenic tissue and even by the normal serum of the rabbit alone (13). The difference, however, between these effects can be increased by a prior heating of the serum, whereby the neutralizing antibodies in normal rabbit serum, and those evoked in rabbit serum by injection of normal splenic tissue, are greatly diminished in comparison with those evoked in such serum by the leukemic cells themselves.

The data in Table 1 illustrate these observations (13). These data, although interesting in themselves, do not yet demonstrate that the anti-

TABLE 1

INACTIVATION *in Vitro* OF MOUSE LEUKEMIAS BY HEATED RABBIT ANTISERUM (13)

	With unheated serum % survivals		With heated serum (60° for 30 minutes) % survivals	
Experiment	Myeloid	Lymphatic	Myeloid	Lymphatic
Antileukemic serum	100	93	87	67
Antisplenic serum	66	53	21	13
Normal serum	28	13	12	0
Saline	0	0	—	—

bodies engendered by the leukemic cells are qualitatively different from those evoked by the normal spleen, or even from the naturally occurring inhibitor for mouse leukemic cells present in the normal rabbit serum. It appears more probable that the tumor cells may evoke a quantitatively greater antibody response, and that the differential denaturing effect of heat would be revealed to a greater degree on the antiserum containing the fewer antibodies. The technique of differential heat denaturation in distinguishing the effects of associated, biologically active proteins is a powerful and accepted tool, but it is not usually applicable to single experiments, and it only appears regrettable that the extremely interesting experiments cited in the above table were not carried beyond their apparently arbitrarily set limits. That quantitative rather than qualitative differences in antibody response may be the result of injection of cellular fractions of normal and leukemic mice spleens appears probable from the studies of Dulaney and her associates (14, 15), although here too the possibility of qualitative distinctions cannot be entirely excluded. It is tantalizing to reflect on the possibilities which a clear-cut fractionation of the various immune serums cited into their various protein components would yield in answering the perennial question of whether tumor cells contain unique antigens.

The same may be said of the interesting series of immunological studies carried on in Japan on the Yoshida sarcoma, an ascites tumor. Here the problem is one of affecting the free-living cells in what amounts to a separate culture in the peritoneal cavity, and the effect of the immune sera *in vitro* on the transplantability of the ascites tumor cells is not nearly as clear-cut as in the case of the leukemic cells noted above (16); however, as is usual, the sera contain antibodies in various proportions which may be common both to the tumor and to normal rat cells, and those which may be specific to the tumor (17–19). At the risk of repetition, it is difficult to interpret results derived from a mixture of twentieth-century cancer research and nineteenth-century immunology.

The probable participation of antibodies in the lack of establishment of transmitted tumors is suggested in a negative sense by the successful heterologous transfer of leukemic cells to the newborn of a foreign mice strain (20), or of mouse sarcoma 180 to the newborn rat (21) or the newborn hamster (22), for it is not improbable that in such young animals the antibody response has not yet fully developed.

In 1911 Rous reported the discovery that certain forms of sarcoma in fowl could be transmitted from one animal to the other by means of cell-free extracts of the tumor (23). This finding was confirmed by others and introduced into the field of cancer research the phenomena associated with viruses. The agent responsible for tumor formation could be isolated in concentrated form from the cell-free extracts and, on injection into appropriate fowl, would induce the formation of sarcoma. Analogous procedures were announced for certain forms of fowl leukosis. It is evident, therefore, that the transmissibility of certain kinds of cancer in this species is independent of the presence of living cells.

Later, Shope observed that papillomas could be transmitted from one cottontail rabbit to another by means of cell-free extracts. Introduced into domestic rabbits, the growths altered in character, became highly invasive, and, coincidentally, the transmissibility in cell-free extracts of the tumor disappeared.

Due, to a considerable extent, to the work of Bashford and his colleagues of the Imperial Cancer Research Fund, the use of mice on an extensive scale was introduced in cancer research. In the early work on these animals it was noted that tumors occurred more often in certain cages of the colonies than in others. The immediate response to this observation was the suggestion that the tumors were transmitted by a form of infection, a suggestion strongly advanced by Borrel. Loeb, however, saw in this uneven distribution the transmission of hereditary factors, and this concept was supported by the work of Tyzzer, Bashford, and J. A. Murray. Murray showed in 1911 that female mice in whose ancestors cancer of the breast had occurred were more liable to develop the disease than mice in whose ancestors the disease was more remote. Later work by Loeb and by Slye demonstrated that hereditary factors influenced the formation of tumors. The work was rendered difficult by the necessity for working with mice of heterozygous genetic constitution. Little, and later Strong and others, set about the development of inbred strains of mice with known incidence of cancer, in which the inheritance of cancer from one generation to the next could be accurately predicted. It soon developed that there was no simple inheritance of cancer, such as Slye believed, but the study of such inbred mice did show that genetic factors played a role in cancer development. Furthermore, a very significant finding emerged in experiments on the relation of incidence of mammary tumors to the susceptibility in maternal and paternal strains. It was found that the incidence of such tumors in the offspring followed generally the incidence of the maternal rather than the paternal line and suggested a form of extrachromosomal inheritance. The problem was clarified when it was discovered by Bittner of the Jackson Memorial Laboratory that an inciter for mammary tumor formation was transmitted through the milk of the mother to very young mice. Thus, Borrel was not very far wrong, and a virus-like agent with special and limited properties may be transmitted from one mammal to another under normal conditions of nursing.

The development of inbred mice was of great service to the field of cancer research, for it enabled the investigator to work with animals of reasonably well-known, reproducible, and constant characteristics. At least twenty generations of brother-sister matings are essential before a mouse strain is considered homozygous, and careful selection by geneticists produced some strains in which, for example, virtually all breeding females developed mammary cancer, and other strains in which the incidence was less than 1%. The genealogy of several of the more commonly used strains of mice has been summarized by Strong (24). A partial list of a few of the strains is given as follows (25–27):

Strain *A*—Inbred since 1918 by L. C. Strong. Descended from a stock of albino mice which H. J. Bagg started to inbreed in 1912. High lung tumor incidence, and breeding females show high mammary tumor incidence.
Strain *DBA*—Inbred since 1909, and started by C. C. Little. Dilute brown color. Breeding females have high incidence of spontaneous mammary tumors.
Strain *C3H*—Inbred since 1921 by L. C. Strong. Color of wild house mice. High incidence of mammary tumors and moderate incidence of hepatomas.
Strain *CBA*—Inbred since 1921 by L. C. Strong. Color of wild house mice. Both *C3H* and *CBA* strains are descended from an outcross between the strain *DBA* and strain *A* mice.
Strain *C*—Developed by MacDowell. Relatively high incidence of pulmonary tumors and of lymphatic leukemia.
Strain *I*—Developed by L. C. Strong. Susceptible to adenomatous hyperplastic lesions of stomach.
Strain *C58*—Developed by MacDowell. High incidence of leukemia.
Simpson subline—Developed by Pybus and Miller. Moderate incidence of bone tumors.
Strain *C57 Black*—Developed by C. C. Little. Very low incidence of mammary and pulmonary tumors.

There are at the latest count some eighty inbred strains of mice, many of which are used in research. For this reason alone, a standard system of nomenclature has been introduced (28) by a committee formed for this purpose.

The use of these inbred mice strains has frequently been compared with the use of chemically pure reagents by the chemist. To some extent this is a happy comparison. However, the living animal, no matter how highly inbred, is not a stationary object, and it sometimes happens that an inbred strain with characteristic properties in one laboratory will develop more or less slight variations when it is moved to another laboratory. Furthermore, sublines may develop which are genetically different from one another and from the original line. The sublines so developed nearly always resemble in characteristics the parent strain far more than they do any other strain, and the new variations introduced may be completely inheritable. It is necessary to bear these factors in mind when assaying the results on what appears to be the same strain in two different laboratories, for, as an example, the Andervont *C3H* mice strain and the Jackson Memorial Laboratory *C3H* strain, although very similar, are not identical.

The strains of mice described above were inbred for the purpose of demonstrating the occurrence of one kind of cancer in each strain. Sometimes a strain is developed in which two types of tumors appear. Thus, *A* strain mice are susceptible to lung tumors, and in breeding females also to mammary tumors; these females succumb to mammary tumors before the time at which lung tumors appear in the virgin females of this strain. If the mammary tumors are removed, the animals subsequently develop lung tumors and die therefrom. The inbreeding of mice does not rule out the possibility that more than one tumor may develop. What happens is that the strains chosen for one tumor generally die before other tumors appear; i.e., the latent period for the development of one kind of tumor is very much shorter than for other kinds of tumors. The potentialities for these other tumors are revealed by crossing the strains and noting the variety of tumors in the hybrids. The inheritance of cancer is not due to a single factor but may be linked with many other genetic influences, such as that for longevity, and may frequently be obscured by such extrinsic influences as the nature of diet (cf. Chapter V), the absence of specific inciting agents (cf. Chapter IV), and the mother's age at parturition.

The inheritability of certain characteristics, including susceptibility to spontaneous and experimentally induced cancer, is quite predictable in various highly inbred strains of mice. When mice of one strain are bred with mice of another strain, is it possible to predict the degree of cancer susceptibility of the resultant hybrids? This question has been the subject of a number of interesting studies by Andervont. This investigator used, among others, the following inbred strains of mice: *C3H* (high susceptibility to mammary tumors and low susceptibility to pulmonary tumors), *I* and *Y* (resistant to mammary tumors but susceptible to pulmonary tumors), and *C57 Black* (resistant to mammary tumors). The F_1 hybrids obtained by mating strains *C3H* and *I* were more susceptible to induced lung tumors than either parental strain, whereas those procured by mating strains *C3H* and *Y* were as insusceptible as the more resistant *C3H* maternal strain. The $C3H \times IF_1$ hybrids were not only more susceptible to the formation of spontaneous mammary tumors than the F_1 hybrids $C3H \times Y$ but also more susceptible than the maternal *C3H* strain (29, 30). Outcrossing of strain *C3H* to strains *Y* and *I* produced hybrids that were of intermediate susceptibility to induced subcutaneous tumors when compared with their parents (31).

In these studies, one of the two parental strains possessed a higher degree of susceptibility to certain tumors than the other, and, as observed, the F_1 hybrid may show a smaller or a larger degree of susceptibility than either one of the parents, or else a susceptibility intermediate between the two. When, however, two strains are crossed, each of which is highly resistant to either the development or growth of certain tumors, the F_1 hybrids sometimes show a susceptibility far exceeding that of either parental strain.

Thus, mice of strains *I* and *L* are almost completely resistant to the progressive growth of transplantable sarcoma 37, but of the F_1 hybrids of these strains 87 % showed progressive growth of this tumor (31). Mice of strains *C57 Black* and *I* are each resistant to the development of mammary tumors, but the F_1 hybrids of these strains show a high incidence of such tumors at a relatively early age (30), when appropriately foster-nursed.

The mean of hybrid characteristics cannot be equated to the mean of the parental characteristics, and it is evidently impossible to predict from the properties of even highly inbred strains of animals the properties of resulting hybrids. Not only the inheritance of cancer susceptibility, but that of tuberculosis as well (32), shares this uncertainty. In the face of this obstacle with pure animal strains, the hope at the present time of prediction of cancer incidence and of genetic control of cancer susceptibility in heterozygous stocks, such as man, is not particularly bright. Further work may be more illuminating, for any comprehensive study of cancer must take genetic factors into consideration.

Tissue Immunity Reactions and the Phenomenon of Heterologous Transplantation

If it is assumed that cancer is a potentiality of all living tissues, the problem arises as to why certain tissues are more susceptible to a neoplastic transformation than are others. Furthermore, in the general dissemination of metastatic emboli of tumor cells throughout the host, certain organs frequently escape these secondary growths. The comparative resistance of these tissues cannot be explained on a purely genetic or purely circulatory basis. The presence of a tumor in one tissue does not preclude the possibility of tumors arising in other tissues and in certain cases may even appear to acclerate such a development of multiple tumors.

Different strains of mice may, with the same tumor implant, show different organophilic tendencies in regard to metastases of this tumor. Thus tumor C-198 was shown by Cloudman (33) to metastasize readily to liver, kidneys, and ovaries in certain strains, but not in others. An interesting divergence from this apparent rule was shown by parabiotic union between *B* strain mice which are refractory toward this tumor and *L* strain mice which are susceptible, for in this manner the *B* host became readily susceptible to transplants of the tumor. The tumor in turn became altered in its new *B* host and could subsequently be readily transplanted into free *B* hosts. In this manner the receptivity of the host could be changed, and the host in turn could change the implanted tumor which it nurtured (33).

The organophilic character of metastatic detachment and subsequent growth is a complex affair and is not readily interpretable on the experimental level. Thus, tumors which are implanted in various internal organs of animals will readily take and grow equally well in each site selected, whether spleen, adrenal, liver, kidney, or muscle (34). Indeed, the rabbit spleen appears to be a somewhat better site for growths of transplantable rabbit tumors than the other tissues studied, an observation which might appear surprising in view of this particular tissue's alleged antineoplastic character. The explanation for the comparative scarcity of metastatic lesions in certain organs cannot therefore be attributed to their failure to support growth of such lesions or to provide them with stroma and an adequate blood supply.

That metastatic tumor cells may lurk in ostensibly normal tissues of the tumor-bearing host has been known for many years (cf. 35). Thus, Blumenthal and Auler (36) showed that the subcutaneous inoculation of minced spleen from a tumor-bearing rat into normal animals would produce local tumors. The intraperitoneal inoculation of minced organs or of blood from tumor-bearing mice into normal mice resulted in many instances in peritoneal growth of the original tumor (37): the separate organs employed were liver, kidney, spleen, lungs, and brain, and tumors were derived from each of these tissues, as well as from blood. Control experiments using tissue minces from normal animals revealed no evidence of growth when implanted intraperitoneally into normal mice, although there was an increase in peritoneal fluid. It would appear that the tumors arose from viable tumor cells living in otherwise normally appearing organs, organs in which the further growth of these wandering cells had apparently been inhibited.

On the experimental level, fundamental immunity studies in cancer have been chiefly concerned with the effect of transplanting tumor tissues into animals (cf. 38–43), and a most interesting, if puzzling and inconclusive, scientific literature has emerged from these studies. The conditions necessary for the successful transplantation of a tumorous graft are many and complex and depend upon a number of factors which may be either genetic or environmental, or both. It is an accepted fact that, under normal circumstances, a tumor originating in an inbred mouse can be transplanted to all mice of the same strain, and to none of an unrelated strain of mice (44). Tumors transplanted to the unrelated strain (homoiotransplants) show either no growth, or temporary growth followed by complete regression. The maximum size attained by the graft varies according to the tumor and the host strain employed (45). It would appear that a considerable measure of genetic compatibility is necessary for the successful grafting of a tumor. Yet even in the earlier years of cancer research, before inbred strains of experimental animals had been developed, it was shown that the transplantation of tumors could be enhanced or inhibited by external influences. Thus Flexner and Jobling in 1907 (46) showed that pretreatment of rats with heat-killed tumor tissue enhanced the growth

of subsequently inoculated living tumor, and later Casey (47) prepared tumor tissue for pretreatment of host animals by storing the tissue at freezing temperatures until it no longer caused tumors when inoculated. On the other hand, Bashford in 1908 (48) showed that administration of defibrinated blood would induce a resistance of the host toward the inoculation of a tumor to which it was ordinarily very susceptible. In more recent times, these phenomena have been amplified and extended by Snell (41, 49), Kaliss (50, 51), and Barrett (42), among others, employing inbred strains of mice. Lyophilized preparations of tumors, and in some cases of normal tissues, introduced intraperitoneally into mice, frequently permitted successful growth of inoculated tumors in animals ordinarily resistant to such grafts. Very striking was the observation that, whereas the larger amounts of lyophilized preparations used produced susceptibility of the hosts to the tumor, smaller amounts of the same preparations produced resistance (52). It is well known that growth and regression of a tumor transplant in a foreign strain evokes an immunity such that a second graft usually shows no growth at all (cf. 53). However, Lewis and Lichtenstein (54) showed that repeated grafts from one strain to another finally resulted in successful takes and growth, and it is not improbable that with multiple grafts, as with larger doses of the lyophilized preparations, the normal resistance of the host is diminished or injured. It is of particular interest that normal kidney preparations, like tumor preparations, showed this dosage effect. Similar liver preparations were ineffective. Illustrations in Table 2 are taken from Kaliss (52).

Not only are prior injections of lyophilized tissue successful in abrogating the resistance of mice to tumor grafts from alien strains, but also successful are prior injections of lyophilized spleen and of immune serum evoked by spleen homogenates (51).

The other side of the picture is shown in Barrett's observations on the

TABLE 2

EFFECT OF PRIOR INJECTIONS OF LYOPHILIZED TISSUES ON THE SUBSEQUENT GROWTH OF GRAFTS OF TUMOR E-0771 IN *C3H/KS* MICE (52)

Milligrams of material injected per mouse	Per cent mice dying with tumors after injection of:	
	Kidney	Tumor E-0771
50	94	90
5	100	40
0.5	44	30
0.05	45	30
0.005	25	0
Control	56	40

effect of blood cells on inducing resistance; whereas strain *C* mice injected with the serum of strain *DBA* blood permitted 81% successful takes of sarcoma *DBA49*, under the same conditions—except that the corresponding red cells were injected in place of the serum—the percentage of successful grafts was only 6% (42). The effective part of the red cells was the stromata (55).

The question naturally arises as to the nature of the factor or factors which produce the effects noted. Preliminary attempts to concentrate such activity by differential centrifugation of extracts of the lyophilized material were unsuccessful (49). Extraction with ether, alcohol, or dioxane had no effect on the preparations. Some clue to the chemical nature of an abrogating agent comes from the observation that a combination of ascorbic acid and rutin was effective in enhancing the transplantability of hepatomas in an otherwise resistant *Leaden* strain of mice (56).

That genetic factors alone are not determinant in the grafting of tumors is clear from the foregoing, and many tumors are known which, for example, require for their continued growth the administration of a hormonal agent, e.g., certain testicular and thyroid tumors (see below). Perhaps most dramatic in the effect of environmental agents on the growth of grafts has been the successful implantation of human tumors into rats which were treated either with cortisone (57, 58) or with X-radiation (59–61). The basis for these studies goes back to the early observations of Murphy in 1914 on the role of the lymphocytes of the host in the resistance to heterotransplantation (62). Both cortisone and X-radiation reduce the lymphocyte counts of the treated animals, and presumably less antibodies are available for resistance to the heterologous graft (cf. 63). Whether this is the proper explanation, or whether some disturbance in the general cellular metabolism of the treated animals is responsible, or both, cannot be determined at present. In any event, a not unexpected observation in the cancerous subject treated with cortisone is the notable increase in metastases (cf. 63a).

An extremely clear-cut example of the single and combined effect of cortisone and of X-radiation on the homoiotransplantation of mouse leukemic cells in otherwise completely resistant mouse strains is shown by the work of Werder, Friedman, MacDowell, and Syverton (64), but the most important aspect of this work appears to be the synergistic effect of these agents and their inability to bring about the same homoiotransplantation into mice rendered immune previously. Tables 3 and 4 illustrate these findings.

It will be recalled in this connection that not only radiation but also the administration of trypan blue will depress the host's resistance to the transplanted tumor (65, 66), and it is not improbable that this derangement of the resistance mechanism in a normal host might eventually acti-

TABLE 3

EFFECTS OF CORTISONE AND X-RADIATION EMPLOYED ON THE SUSCEPTIBILITY OF RESISTANT MICE STRAINS TO MOUSE LEUKEMIA, LINE *Ib*[1] (64)

X-Radiation r.	0	200	200	200	0	0
Cortisone, mg.	0	2	0.35	0	2	0.35
Strain of Mice						
BALB	20/20	0/15	0/15	3/15	0/15	9/15
CFW	20/20	0/15	0/20	6/20	10/20	20/20
STOLI	20/20	0/10	0/10	6/10	3/10	10/10

[1] Denominator is number of mice; numerator is number of survivors.

TABLE 4

EFFECTS OF CORTISONE AND X-RADIATION EMPLOYED ON THE SUSCEPTIBILITY OF RESISTANT MICE STRAINS TO MOUSE LEUKEMIA, LINE *Ib*, AFTER IMMUNIZATION[1] (64)

X-Radiation, r.	200	300	0	200	300	0
Cortisone, mg.	0.35	0	0.35	0.35	0	0.35
Strain of Mice	Immunized with Leukemic Spleen			Immunized with Normal Spleen		
BALB	11/15	14/15	13/15	0/15	0/15	1/15
CFW		27/30	20/20		2/15	12/15
A	10/15	8/10	10/10	0/15	0/10	10/10

[1] Denominator is number of mice; numerator is number of survivors.

vate and disseminate latent spontaneous tumors (67). Perhaps related to changes in the susceptibility of the host brought about by X-irradiation is the increased metastasizing capacity of tumor locally treated with X-rays (68, 69).

It would not be proper to diminish the value of purely genetic approaches to the problem of tumor immunity, for these are capable of illuminating many of the basic criteria of this problem. It has been postulated by Gorer (70) that the genes which govern the fate of a transplant also control isoantigenic differences. The name "histocompatibility genes" (*H/h*) has been proposed by Snell (71), perhaps the best known of which is the *H*-2 locus in the strain *A* mouse. *H*-2 and its alleles apparently play a dual role, for they determine erythrocyte antigen II (one of the four known murine blood groups) and susceptibility or resistance to certain transplanted tumors. It is not improbable that all *H*-genes are related to antigens, although serological identification remains to be accomplished.

The successful heterotransplantation of tumor grafts into alien strains or species, and sometimes the successful homotransplantation into the same strain, is effected by suitable alteration of the host as described above. Tumor tissues may, however, also survive in alien environments without prior rearrangement of the environment. These are the classic tissue culture flasks, the chorioallantoic membrane of the developing chick embryo (72–77), the anterior chamber of the eye (78), the brain (79), and the hamster cheek pouch (80, 81). Each of these is essentially a form of pure culture, the host furnishing the supporting structures and nutrition. The capacity of cancer tissue to grow in alien hosts (anterior chamber of the eye) is shared to a nearly equal extent by embryonic tissue. The following tabulation by Greene (82) is illustrative:

Transplantation of Mammalian Tissues (82)

Tissue	Autologous	Homologous	Heterologous
Normal adult	+	+	−
Normal embryonic	+	+	+
Benign tumor	+	−	−
Cancer	+	+	+

The property of heterologous transplantability is thus shared by embryonic and cancerous tissues, and this phenomenon suggests that the tissues possess attributes in common. The chemical relationships between the two types of tissues are discussed in Chapter VIII.

The practical basis of many heterologous transplantation techniques has been to correlate degrees of clinical malignancy in man with the capacity of the tumors involved to grow in alien hosts, on the belief, as expressed by Greene (78), that the more autonomous or malignant phases of tumor growth will be expressed in part by a greater capacity for transference and subsequent growth in an alien host. Greene has stated that in a series of 123 human tumors subjected to heterologous transplantation (in the anterior chamber of the guinea pig eye) 65 grew and 58 failed to grow, and of the successful takes a marked correlation existed between the biological status of the tumor at the time of transfer and the clinical fate of the patient (cf. 78). Attempts to repeat the intraocular transplantation technique with human tumors in other laboratories were reported to be considerably less successful (83–85). A scientific technique which has been developed in a laboratory over a period of years, and which has been ground to a fine precision on the wheel of experience, is not easily undertaken *de novo* in another laboratory. Few such transplants are ever homologous, and the new host is only too often incompatible.

The heterologous transplantation experiments possess many features of theoretical interest. One important question which naturally arises is concerned with the maintenance of identity of the transplant in the foreign host. Transplanted tissues obtain their stroma and vascular supply from the new host, and it might be expected that the growing cells of the transplant should reflect the constitution of the new host. However, the Shope

papilloma and the Rous sarcoma can be readily transplanted to the brains of alien species, and the Shope papilloma can be induced in transplants of embryonic rabbit skin in species resistant to the infecting agent (86). It would appear that the reactions of the transplant are those of the donor species rather than those of the host (86, 87), although the cases cited may be in a special category characteristic of virus-induced cancers (cf. 86). A more pertinent example might be the ready transplantability of the mouse sarcoma 180 into the intraperitoneal cavity of the newborn rat (88) or the newborn hamster (89), its serial passage through several newborn members of these species, and its ready subcutaneous growth after twelve such passages back in the mouse without histologic or biological change. However, it is not always likely that the tumor in heterologous sites remains unchanged, as noted above in the experiment of Cloudman's (33) whereby tumor C-198 became altered when adapted to the previously resistant *B* strain of mice, and indeed Cloudman recognized this possibility to the extent of revising the designation of the tumor to C-198a. An even more striking example, visually, is the series of experiments carried on in Algire's laboratory on the melanotic tumor S-91 (90). This highly pigmented tumor arose in a *DBA* mouse and was carried by this strain, but when it was transplanted to *C* strain mice portions of the tumor became less melanotic. Continued selection of these amelanotic areas and successive transplantation in *C* strain mice ultimately gave rise to a grossly amelanotic melanoma line. When this amelanotic melanoma was transplanted back to the original *DBA* mice strain, it grew with a relatively sudden increase in melanotic pigmentation. However, this pigmentation was never as extensive as that of the original pigmented tumor. Thus, in this case, the tumor transformation may be considered to be partially reversible.

On the basis of the observation that certain animals do not possess the capacity to react immunologically against foreign homologous tissue cells to which they are exposed sufficiently early in fetal life, it has been found that embryos *in utero* in *CBA* female mice when injected with a suspension of adult *A* mice tissues develop into adults with a marked tolerance for skin grafts from *A*, but not from other strains of mice (91). Thus, the exposure of animals to antigens before the development of the ability to respond immunologically leads to tolerance rather than to heightened resistance (cf. 92). The acquired tolerance furthermore appears to be highly specific toward the antigen which evoked it and toward no others. Whether accidental incorporation of maternal cells into the fetus may lead to conditions of adult tolerance later on in life is an interesting possibility. The treatment of prospective hosts with lyophilized tissue preparations to enhance the growth of tumor grafts (cf. 41) may be based on mechanisms unrelated to these.

Experimental Induction of Tumors

The cancer investigator is interested in the origin, the characteristics, the fate, and the control of neoplastic growths. It is evident that the study of only those growths which arise spontaneously might limit the number of avenues of approach. Among heterozygous animals, neoplasms arise more or less irregularly. When, through intensive inbreeding, mice strains were developed, each with a known incidence of cancer at specific sites in the animals, the appearance of spontaneous neoplasms could be accurately predicted. At this point, therefore, two of the above interests of the cancer investigator, namely, the characteristics and the fate of tumors, could be effectively studied. However, the problem of origin still remained to be explained, together with the problem of control, which may be linked with that of the mode of origin. It was necessary to devise methods of inducing tumors experimentally in animals (or in plants) so that some idea of the mode of origin of tumors be gained and the sequence from the normal to the cancerous state be apprehended. If it were known how tumors originated and how various external and internal factors modified or accelerated the inception of tumors, rational methods of prophylactic, and quite possibly of therapeutic, control might be instituted. But in animals in which spontaneous cancer arises at sites where experimentally induced cancer is sought, confusion is averted only if the incidence of the former kind of neoplastic growth is reasonably well known. For this purpose, the development of inbred strains of animals alluded to above has been most useful; in animals heterozygous in genetic composition only a considerable study of necropsy records of a large number of such animals can provide information as to the relative spontaneous incidence of various kinds of tumors.

Many agents have been employed successfully in the experimental induction of tumors in several species of animals. These experimentally induced neoplastic growths are nearly indistinguishable from those which arise spontaneously at the same site and their biological behavior is also nearly identical. Thus, a spontaneous growth arising in one animal is often readily transplanted only in animals of the same strain. Similarly, as Andervont noted, tumors induced in animals of any one of several strains are also transplantable, and these will usually grow successfully only in animals of the same strain (93). The transplantability of tumors thus follows a genetic pattern and is apparently independent of the etiology of the tumors. With few exceptions, donor and recipient must apparently have similar genetic constitutions. A tumor arising in either of two parent inbred strains will usually grow in their F_1 hybrid, since the hybrid has a complete assortment of the genes occurring in each parent strain (sex-linked genes excepted), but the transplantation of a tumor arising in a hybrid animal of the F_1 generation into either parent is seldom successful, since neither parent strain possesses all genes found in the hybrid.

Apart from the purely pragmatic approach of simply inducing tumors for the sake of experimental study, there is the very fundamental question as to whether certain of the inducing agents used by the experimenter are necessarily artificial but actually may be, at least in part, responsible for the origin of spontaneous tumors. To all intents and purposes, a spontaneous tumor is simply a neoplastic growth of relatively unknown origin. The problem, therefore, arises as to whether (a) the inducing agent hastens or precipitates the occurrence of a tumor which would normally arise spontaneously in the same site later in the life of the animal, or (b) the agent is sufficiently powerful to effect the neoplastic transformation at sites which are ordinarily highly resistant to the spontaneous development of such transformation. This problem is considered in the following chapter. The following tabulation illustrates a few of the carcinogenic agents found effective in inducing a considerable proportion of tumors well above and prior to the incidence of such tumors spontaneously in the animals designated. References to the original literature are given in those cases not further considered in later chapters. It is understood that in no sense of the word is the list of agents given in Table 5 complete. Even in this partial list some idea is obtained of the great diversity of the carcinogenic agents.

It will be noted that among the carcinogenic agents listed in the table is a liver parasite, *Cysticercus*, which, when it infests the rat, causes sarcoma (94). The way in which the parasite induces tumors within the liver is still obscure, but there is little doubt that the latent period of sarcoma induction is directly related to the number of parasites in the host's liver. An increase in the number of cysts decreased directly the average time interval before the onset of sarcoma. The active agent exists in the larvae obtained from rats bearing an induced *Cysticercus* sarcoma. It can apparently be extracted from the freshly ground larvae in phosphate buffer at pH 7.2 to 7.4 and, when the suspension is injected intraperitoneally into rats of the same strain, will produce peritoneal sarcomas (94a).

Perhaps the earliest "synthetic" preparation which experimentally induced tumors in laboratory animals was cholesterol which had been heated to 810°. These experiments, reported by Kennaway and Sampson in 1928 (95), involved a temperature considerably higher than that employed in the cooking of foods (200 to 300°). At this temperature range, heated cholesterol induced few if any tumors in experimental animals (cf. 96). Cholesterol heated to 430° yielded a mixture of products which could induce skin tumors in mice (97). The products formed by pyrolysis of cholesterol at 360° have been identified as: cholestenone, dicholesteryl ether, 3,5-cholestadiene, the naphthalene derivative of cholesterol, the phenanthrene derivative of cholesterol, methylcyclopentenophenanthrene, and chrysene (98). Except for cholestenone, all these products are intermediates in the transformation of cholesterol to methylcholanthrene, and the possi-

TABLE 5

PARTIAL LIST OF CARCINOGENIC AGENTS

Extrinsic

Agent	Tumor	Animal Species
Tar	Epithelioma (skin)	Mice, rats, rabbits
Polycyclic hydrocarbons	Sarcoma (subcutaneous)	Fowl
	Epithelioma (skin)	Mice, rats
	Sarcoma (subcutaneous)	Mice, rats, rabbits, guinea pigs, fowl
	Glioma (47, 99)	Mice, rats
	Lung tumors	Mice, rats
	Leukemia	Mice, rats, fowl
	Adenocarcinoma (stomach, intestine)	Mice
β-Naphthylamine	Bladder carcinoma	Dogs
Azo dyes	Hepatoma	Mice, rats
	Sarcoma (subcutaneous)	Mice
	Lung tumors	Mice
	Hemangioendotheliomas	Mice
Halogenated aliphatic hydrocarbons	Hepatoma	Mice
Concentrated hexose solutions (100)	Sarcoma (subcutaneous)	Mice
Bakelite disks (101)	Sarcoma	Rats
Zinc salts	Teratoma (testis)	Fowl
Phthalate buffer in HCl (102)	Sarcoma (subcutaneous)	Mice
Thorium dioxide (103; *cf.* 100)	Sarcoma (subcutaneous)	Mice
Radium salts	Sarcoma (subcutaneous)	Rats, guinea pigs, fowl
Ultraviolet radiation	Sarcoma (subcutaneous)	Mice, rats
X-Radiation	Leukemia	Mice
Cysticercus	Sarcoma (liver)	Rats
Chromium, arsenic, cobalt (104)	Sarcoma	Rabbits
Beryllium (105, 106), nickel (107), uranium (108)	Bone sarcoma	Rats, rabbits

TABLE 5—*Continued*

Intrinsic

Agent	Tumor	Animal Species
Estrogens	Tumors of the mammary and sex tissues	Mice, rats
Viruses	Sarcoma	Fowl
	Mammary tumors	Mice
	Papilloma (skin)	Rabbits
	Carcinoma	Frogs

bility that the latter, powerful carcinogen might be formed under pyrolytic conditions in very small amounts cannot be excluded.

Cancerous Transformation of animal Tissues *in Vitro*

It is not necessary that normal cells undergo a neoplastic transformation solely within the living animal, for apparently this change can also occur in such cells grown in tissue culture.

Earle has carried mouse fibroblasts in culture, grown on a fibrin clot and bathed in a fluid mixture of horse serum and chick embryo juice. When a carcinogenic hydrocarbon, such as methylcholanthrene, is added to such cultures, marked changes in the morphology and growth behavior of the cells occur, and these changes appear to increase with the length of time during which the carcinogenic agent remains in contact with the culture.

Cultures of cells so treated, when inoculated subcutaneously into the same strain of mice from which they were derived, grow progressively and rapidly in the hosts, are transplantable to new hosts, frequently metastasize, and ultimately cause death. Such tumors arising from these altered cell cultures may be considered typical sarcomas (109–111).

Similar morphological alterations in cells grown in the absence of the carcinogenic chemical occurred to a lesser degree, and these cells, on injection into mice, gave rise to tumors which were less anaplastic. Whether this transformation was due to a trace contamination of the carcinogenic agent or whether the cells grown in so heterologous a medium as horse serum and chick embryo juice passed "spontaneously" into a sarcomatous state cannot be answered at the present time. A similar transformation of normal to malignant cells was shown by Firor and Gey (112).

These striking experiments reveal that it is apparently possible to induce a cancerous transformation of animal tissue apart from the natural environment of the host. They further suggest the essentially autonomous nature of cancer cells which apparently need only nutritive sources for their development. How far the heterologous medium substitutes for the natural environment of the tissue cultures remains a moot point. However, there is no question that this heterologous culture fluid used by Earle permits luxuriant and continued growth of the normal cells and of the sarcoma cells derived therefrom.

Growth and the Vascular Reactions of Tumors

Most microscopic studies of tumor growth are performed on fixed, sectioned, and stained material. Such studies, perforce, are limited to discontinuous stages in the growth of cells obtained from different animals killed at various intervals. The disadvantages inherent in this procedure are obvious.

Newer techniques have been developed which permit the cultivation and direct microscopic observation of tumor cells within the living animal, thereby making it possible to carry on continuous or intermittent examination of the same group of cells over a prolonged period of time. The experimental difficulties in the way of such studies are formidable. Lucké and Schlumberger (113) used a method based on slit-lamp microscopy on anterior chamber implants of a carcinoma of the frog. A transparent-chamber technique was developed for the rabbit ear by Sandison (114), Clark et al. (115), Ebert et al. (116), and Williams (117), and was adapted to the mouse by Algire (118). The application of this technique to tumors has been made by Ide et al. (119), who observed the vascularization of the Brown-Pearce rabbit epithelioma, and by Algire (118) and Algire and Chalkley (120), who studied the vascular reactions of transplanted tumors in the mouse. The basis of the method, as adapted to the mouse, rests upon the insertion of a transparent chamber into a skin flap in the animal (118). Under the experimental conditions used, the tumor cells are maintained under normal environmental conditions of growth and nutrition.

Certain of the vascularization studies of Algire and Chalkley are illustrated in Figs. 7 and 8 (120). The results of these investigations indicated (a) that the rapid growth of tumor transplants is dependent upon the development of a rich vascular supply, and (b) that an outstanding characteristic of the tumor cell is its capacity to elicit continuously the growth of new capillary endothelium from the host. The stimulation of vascular proliferation is fundamentally a property shared by traumatized tissues and by transplants of normal tissues as well as by tumors, but this stimulation is only temporary in the case of the former two tissues whereas it is continuous in the case of the last-mentioned tissues. Cancer cells thus seem to be able to provoke a continued vascular proliferation from the surrounding host tissue, and this property may be, in part at least, responsible for their autonomous nature (cf. 121). The identity of the provoking substance elaborated by the tumor is yet to be revealed. Among the many uses to which the transparent-chamber technique may be put in cancer research is the direct visual study of the effect of chemical therapeutic agents on cancer

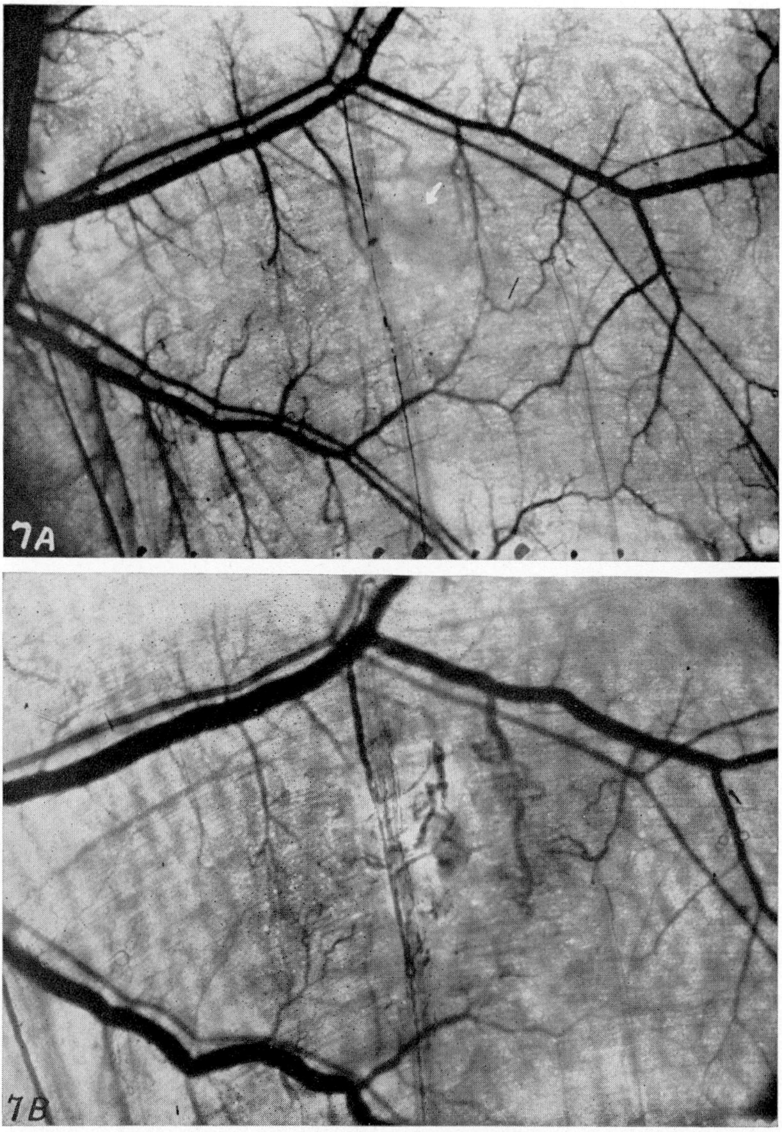

FIG. 7. A, implant of mammary gland carcinoma on the first day after operation. Tumor mass appears as an opaque area at center (arrow) surrounded by normal vascular bed. ×25. B, mammary gland carcinoma on the fifth day after implantation, showing initial vascularization. Vascular level of tumor, 28%; of connective tissue, 27%. ×25. From Algire, G. H., and Chalkley, H. W., *J. Natl. Cancer Inst.* **6,** 73 (1945).

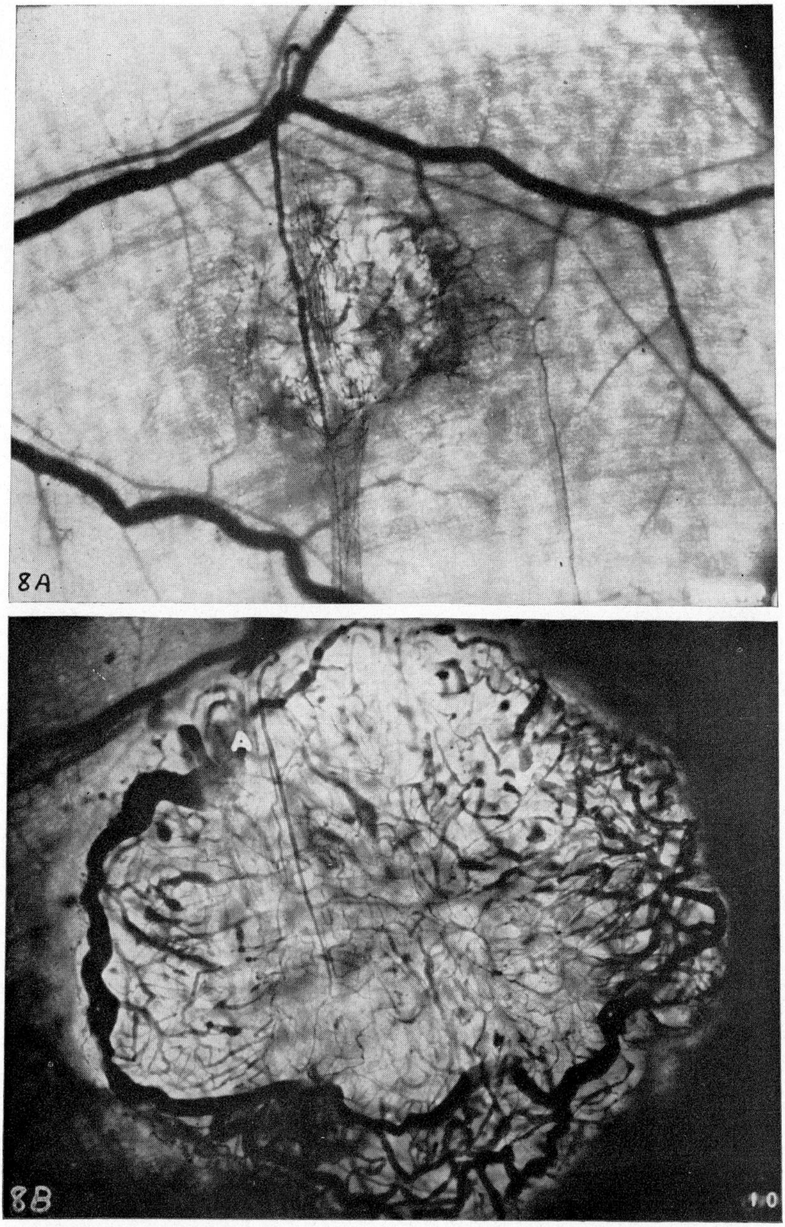

FIG. 8. A, mammary gland carcinoma on the seventh day after implantation, showing completion of initial vascularization. Compare with previous figure. Note dilation of surrounding capillaries, proliferation of new vessels at and about the edge of tumor, also the vessels of overlying nerve trunk, and from vessels of nerve trunk to right of tumor. Vascular level of tumor, 48%; of connective tissue, 24%. ×25. B, fully developed vascular bed of the mouse mammary carcinoma on the seventeenth

cells growing in the living animal (122), as well as of the effects of hypotensive agents (123) and of local X-irradiation (124).

Plant Tumors

Several types of plants, when infected with bacteria of the species *Phytomonas tumefaciens*, develop "crown galls" or tumorous growths at the site of inoculation. These are characterized by rapid, disorganized continuous growth, by invasion of surrounding tissue, and frequently, in certain species of plants, by metastasis. The tumors are transplantable only in the form of living cells from one plant to another. White demonstrated (125) that the metastatic lesions were bacteria-free and possessed properties similar to those of malignant tumors in animals, including the capacity for unlimited growth *in vivo* and, as cultures, *in vitro*. Within the limitations imposed by the structural differences of plants and animals, the autonomous characteristics of the crown gall tumors resemble those of the tumors of animals in very many respects. The presence of metastases in plants is quite puzzling, since these do not contain a circulating and distributing system as do animals and, hence, the metastases cannot conceivably have resulted from a transport of tumor cells in a manner identical with that in animals.

Tissues of bacteria-free crown-galls cultured for many generations *in vitro* have been successfully implanted into sunflower and artichoke. The retention after many years of the tumefacient property in the absence of the original inciting agent is evidence of the fundamental character of this property. This property is also characteristic of plant tumors of genetic origin. Thus, tumors which arose spontaneously in the hybrid *Nicotiana langsdorffi* × *N. glauca*, and which were maintained in tissue culture for five years, could be grafted into healthy plants of *Nicotiana glauca* and grow therein as the original form. This parent species is not naturally subject to tumefaction and never produces spontaneous tumors (125).

This demonstration of relatively independent plant tumor tissues led to three general lines of investigation (126), in which it was shown (a) that tumor inception in plants is dependent on highly thermolabile metabolic systems (127), (b) that normal plant tissue cultures will grow *in vitro* when supplied with various auxins such as indoleacetic acid in the nutrient medium (whereas tumor tissue cultures need little if any of such supplements) (128, 129), suggesting that the plant tumors owe their relative autonomy to an enhanced capacity to synthesize auxins as compared with normal

---

day, showing irregular pattern, and variation in size of vessels. Compare with preceding figures. Note particularly the huge marginal vessels, enveloped artery (A), and blood-filled cul-de-sacs. Vascular level of tumor, 55%; of connective tissue, 26%. ×25. From Algire, G. H., and Chalkley, H. W., *J. Natl. Cancer Inst.* **6,** 73 (1945).

plant tissues, and (c) that certain normal plant tissues, such as that of the carrot, may, after suitable transfer experiments in culture, become independent of the need for auxins and approach a tumefaction stage in which a capacity for autonomous or independent growth is acquired together with the capacity for internal synthesis of the needed auxins (130). This last-mentioned phenomenon is fairly analogous to the *in vitro* transformation of normal animal cells into tumors observed by Earle and by Gey, mentioned above. In both plant and animal cells, a permanent and fundamental change has taken place in the cells of the surviving cultures.

The role of growth substances of the auxin type appears to be intimately associated with many of the cancer phenomena in plants, and further studies on this problem should illuminate several problems common both to plants and to animals. It is regrettable that botany should be so esoteric and relatively unfamiliar a subject to many investigators as to make its resources, scientific advantages, and not least its esthetic values so little conducive to study.

A very important contribution to the problem of the transforming principle in bacteria has been the finding that extracts of bacteria-containing crown-gall tumor tissue, the nucleic acid produced by crown-gall bacteria, and the deoxyribonucleic acid isolated from crown-gall bacteria are each capable of transmitting the property of specific host virulence to avirulent strains (131). The property of virulence, once acquired, appears to be genetically fixed. The relation of this finding to the alteration of normal plant cells into primary crown-gall tumor cells is somewhat obscure. It is possible (a) that the transforming agent is itself the tumor-inducing factor which acts like a virus, and after duplication in the bacterium is transferred to the cells of the host, or (b) that the tumor-inducing factor is a metabolic product of virulent crown-gall bacteria whose production is controlled by genetic factors evoked in deficient forms by the appropriate transforming principle (131).

Tumors in Cold-Blooded Vertebrates

As Lucké and Schlumberger point out (132), all the main varieties of tumors which occur in man and other warm-blooded animals also have been observed in the cold-blooded vertebrates. Indeed, some types of tumors are more common in the latter group, such as tumors of the pigment cells in fishes. The most common of these tumors is the melanoma of the skin, subcutaneous tissue, or eye, but other pigment cell tumors, unique to fishes, are those which arise from the red-pigmented erythrophores, from yellow-pigmented xanthophores, and from guanophores (cells which contain guanine crystals).

Lucké observed a high incidence of a kidney carcinoma of possibly virus origin in the leopard frog (133, 134), which has provided much valuable experimental material (cf. 132). Frequent metastatic growths of this tumor have been observed (135), and it probably constitutes the most readily available tumor known in cold-blood vertebrates. It is readily transplantable into the anterior chamber of the eyes of frogs of alien species (136) and into tadpoles in various sites (137). With increasing environmental temperature, to which the frog naturally responds with a parallel rise in body temperature, the rate of growth of the tumors increases, there is an accompanying greater vascularity, and the opportunities for metastatic emboli to form are correspondingly enlarged (138).

A particularly interesting illustration of the genetic development of tumors is provided by the work of Gordon on melanomas in fish (139). Spontaneous malignant melanomas are produced in the hybrid offspring of the black-spotted platyfish and the albino swordtail. The melanomas are developed genetically in the hybrids by the interaction of the sex-linked, heritable factor for macromelanophores with a series of genetic modifiers of the swordtail (Fig. 9).

Tumors in Invertebrates

Whether true cancerous growths can occur in the class of invertebrates still remains something of a problem. As Scharrer and Lockhead (140) emphasize, the data in this area are difficult to evaluate, and the terminology of cancer in mammals is not quite applicable to the question of analogous tissue growths in a lower phylum. However, it does appear

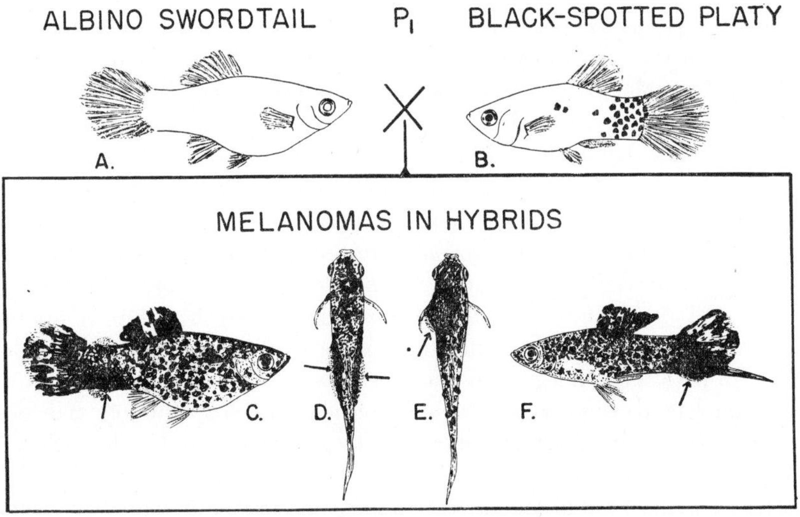

Fig. 9. Origin of melanomas in hybrid fishes. When an albino swordtail without black pigment (upper left) is mated with a macromelanophore-carrying platyfish (upper right) their hybrid offspring (lower line) give rise to melanomas. From Gordon, M., *Cancer Research* **1,** 656 (1941).

probable that under certain conditions invertebrate tissues are capable of some sort of neoplastic transformation, and the clearest evidence on this point has been derived from studies on insects.

It has long been known that certain chromosomal deficiencies cause cytological abnormalities leading to severe morphogenetic disturbances in *Drosophila*, and Stark has noted in such examples the presence of sex-linked tumors (141). These hereditary tumors contain much melanin, proliferate, infiltrate, and metastasize. The deposition of pigment is frequently so rapid in these tumors as to hinder their subsequent histologic study, and such tumors have been homologized with the melanomas of vertebrates (141, 142). Burdette (142) observed that development of the tumor was dependent on a yeast factor (cf. also 143), and subsequent work has confirmed and established the relation between tumor penetrance and nutritive factors (144).

The most striking observation in the field of tumorogenesis in insects was the induction of tumors in the roach (*Leucophaea*) by severance of a recurrent nerve (145). After this severance, tumors develop in organs previously innervated, and these are the foregut and anterior midgut, and the salivary organs. The tumors produced appear to be malignant and are more lethal to the females of this species than to the males. This sex difference disappears after castration, which suggests the presence of sex hormones in this insect.

Ascites Tumors

The occurrence of free tumor cells in certain neoplastic exudates was described in the last century (146), and the term ascites tumor has generally been applied to the exudate accumulation in the peritoneal cavity containing a large proportion of free tumor cells. Such tumors, which may approach the state of a nearly pure culture, obviously offer a great many advantages over the use of solid tumors. For the most part, the ascites tumors have been developed experimentally by implanting solid tumor preparations intraperitoneally into genetically related strains of animals. After a period of time, samples of the abdominal fluid are removed and reinoculated intraperitoneally into a fresh group of animals (147–150). By suitable modifications in procedure it is possible to shift the ratio between solid growth and free cells in the peritoneal fluid (150). A systematic method of producing ascitic from solid tumors has been described by Klein (150) and shown to be applicable to a wide variety of experimental neoplasms.

The existence of individual, free tumor cells makes possible the experimental demonstration of the transmissibility of a single tumor cell. This problem was approached by Ishibashi (151) and by Hosokawa (152), who showed by a careful technique that a single cell of the Yoshida sarcoma was sufficient to transmit the tumor. It will be recalled in this connection that Furth and Kahn (153) had demonstrated the transmissibility of mouse leukemia by but a single leukemic cell.

Single sarcoma 37 cells (ascites) are capable of giving rise to tumors on transplantation to subcutaneous tissue (154), and this observation emphasizes the difficulty in the interpretation of experiments designed to indicate cell-free transmission of tumors. The fact that tumors can be derived from inocula of very small numbers of cells also must be considered in the interpretation of apparent changes in cell type of tumors on transplantation when the original tumor may consist of several cellular types.

References

(1) Ewing, J., Neoplastic Diseases, 4th ed. W. B. Saunders Co., Philadelphia, 1940.
(2) Ehrlich, P., and Apolant, H., *Berlin. klin. Wochschr.* **43,** 37 (1906).
(3) Woglom, W. H., *J. Cancer Research* **2,** 471 (1917).
(4) Stewart, H. L., Grady, H. G., and Andervont, H. B., *J. Natl. Cancer Inst.* **7,** 207 (1947).
(5) Andervont, H. B., and Dunn, T. B., *J. Natl. Cancer Inst.* **13,** 455 (1952).
(6) Ludford, R. J., and Barlow, H., *Cancer Research* **5,** 257 (1945).
(7) Browning, H., *Cancer Research* **12,** 13 (1952).
(8) Dunham, L. J., and Stewart, H. L., *J. Natl. Cancer Inst.* **13,** 1299 (1953).
(9) Sanford, K. K., Likely, G. D., Evans, V. J., Mackey, C. J., and Earle, W. R., *J. Natl. Cancer Inst.* **12,** 1057 (1952).
(10) Gorer, P. A., *J. Pathol. Bacteriol.* **54,** 51 (1942).
(11) Dulaney, A. D., and Arneson, K., *Proc. Soc. Exptl. Biol. Med.* **72,** 665 (1949).
(12) Nettleship, A., *Am. J. Pathol.* **21,** 527 (1945).
(13) Werder, A. A., Kirschbaum, A., MacDowell, E. C., and Syverton, J. T., *Cancer Research* **12,** 886 (1952).
(14) Arneson, K., Goldsmith, Y., and Dulaney, A. D., *Cancer Research* **9,** 669 (1949).
(15) Dulaney, A. D., Goldsmith, Y., Arneson, K., and Buxton, L., *Cancer Research* **9,** 217 (1949).
(16) Nagasawa, B., *Gann* **42,** 19 (1951).
(17) Onoe, T., Honda, H., Okubo, S., Meguro, H., Murayama, F., Akemine, M., and Hagiwara, S., *Gann* **41,** 175 (1950).
(18) Ishikura, H., Itakura, S., Usubuchi, I., Suzuki, K., Aizawa, M., Imamura, T., and Mori, S., *Gann* **41,** 177 (1950).
(19) Takeda, K., Watanabe, S., Ikeda, K., and Sugawara, H., *Gann* **41,** 179 (1950).
(20) Gross, L., *Proc. Soc. Exptl. Biol. Med.* **73,** 246 (1950).
(21) Patti, J., and Moore, A. E., *Cancer Research* **11,** 540 (1951).
(22) Patti, J., and Biesele, J. J., *Cancer Research* **11,** 540 (1951).
(23) Cf. Rous, P., *Am. J. Cancer* **28,** 233 (1936).
(24) Strong, L. C., *Cancer Research* **2,** 531 (1942).
(25) Andervont, H. B., *Public Health Repts.* (*U.S.*) **49,** 60 (1934).
(26) *Mouse Genetic News*, No. **1** (G. D. Snell, ed.). Jackson Memorial Laboratory, 1941.
(27) Biology of the Laboratory Mouse (G. D. Snell, ed.). The Blakiston Co., Philadelphia, 1941.
(28) Committee on Standardized Nomenclature for Inbred Strains of Mice, *Cancer Research* **12,** 602 (1952).

(29) Andervont, H. B., *J. Natl. Cancer Inst.* **1,** 135 (1940).
(30) Andervont, H. B., *J. Natl. Cancer Inst.* **3,** 359 (1943).
(31) Andervont, H. B., *J. Natl. Cancer Inst.* **2,** 1 (1941).
(32) Wright, S., *U. S. Dept. Agr. Bull.* No. **1121** (1922).
(33) Cloudman, A., *Cancer Research* **7,** 585 (1947).
(34) de Long, R. P., and Coman, D. R., *Cancer Research* **10,** 513 (1950).
(35) Woglom, W. H., *Am. J. Cancer* **38,** 328 (1940).
(36) Blumenthal, F., and Auler, H., *Z. Krebsforsch.* **24,** 285 (1927).
(37) Goldie, H., Jeffries, B. R., Jones, A. M., and Walker, M., *Cancer Research* **13,** 566 (1953).
(38) Woglom, W. H., *Cancer Rev.* **4,** 9 (1929).
(39) Spencer, R. R., *J. Natl. Cancer Inst.* **2,** 317 (1942).
(40) Hauschka, T. S., *Cancer Research* **12,** 615 (1952).
(41) Snell, G. D., *Cancer Research* **12,** 543 (1952).
(42) Barrett, M. K., *Cancer Research* **12,** 535 (1952).
(43) Law, L., *Advances in Cancer Research* **2** (in press).
(44) Little, C. C., The genetics of tumor transplantation, *in* Biology of the Laboratory Mouse, p. 279. The Blakiston Co., Philadelphia, 1941.
(45) Snell, G. D., Cloudman, A. M., and Woodworth, E., *Cancer Research* **8,** 429 (1948).
(46) Flexner, S., and Jobling, J. W., *Proc. Soc. Exptl. Biol. Med.* **4,** 156 (1907).
(47) Casey, A. E., *Proc. Soc. Exptl. Biol. Med.* **31,** 663 (1934).
(48) Bashford, E., Murray, J. A., and Cramer, W., *3rd Sci. Rept. Imp. Cancer Research Fund*, p. 315 (1908).
(49) Snell, G. D., *J. Natl. Cancer Inst.* **13,** 719 (1952).
(50) Kaliss, N., and Snell, G. D., *Cancer Research* **11,** 122 (1951).
(51) Kaliss, N., Molomut, N., Harriss, J. L., and Gault, S. D., *J. Natl. Cancer Inst.* **13,** 847 (1953).
(52) Kaliss, N., *Cancer Research* **12,** 379 (1952).
(53) Andervont, H. B., *Public Health Repts.* (*U.S.*) **47,** 1859 (1932).
(54) Lewis, M. R., and Lichtenstein, E. G., *Am. J. Cancer* **28,** 746 (1936).
(55) Barrett, M. K., and Hansen, W. H., *Cancer Research* **13,** 269 (1953).
(56) Leise, E. M., Schwanfelder, A. B., and Harvey, E. K., *Cancer Research* **12,** 643 (1952).
(57) Hoch-Ligeti, C., and Hsii, Y. T., *Science* **117,** 360 (1953).
(58) Toolan, H. W., *Cancer Research* **13,** 389 (1953).
(59) Murphy, J. B., *J. Am. Med. Assoc.* **62,** 1459 (1914).
(60) Toolan, H. W., *Proc. Soc. Exptl. Biol. Med.* **77,** 572 (1951).
(61) Sommers, S. C., Chute, R. N., and Warren, S., *Cancer Research* **12,** 909 (1952).
(62) Murphy, J. B., *J. Am. Med. Assoc.* **62,** 199 (1914).
(63) Green, H. N., and Whiteley, H. J., *Brit. Med. J.* **ii,** 538 (1952).
(63a) Baserga, R., and Shubik, P., *Cancer Research* **14,** 12 (1954).
(64) Werder, A. A., Friedman, J., MacDowell, E. C., and Syverton, J. T., *Cancer Research* **13,** 158 (1953).
(65) Ludford, R. J., *Brit. J. Exptl. Pathol.* **12,** 45, 108 (1931).
(66) Andervont, H. B., *Public Health Repts.* (*U.S.*) **51,** 591 (1936).
(67) Cohen, A., and Cohen, L., *Nature* **167,** 1063 (1951).
(68) von Essen, C. F., and Kaplan, H. S., *J. Natl. Cancer Inst.* **12,** 883 (1952).
(69) Kaae, S., *Cancer Research* **13,** 744 (1953).
(70) Gorer, P. A., *J. Pathol. Bacteriol.* **47,** 231 (1938).
(71) Snell, G. D., *J. Genet.* **49,** 87 (1948).

(72) Murphy, J. B., *J. Exptl. Med.* **17,** 482 (1913).
(73) Taylor, A., Hungate, R. E., and Taylor, D. R., *Cancer Research* **3,** 537 (1943).
(74) Armstrong, M. I., Gray, A. E., and Ham, A. W., *Cancer Research* **12,** 698 (1952).
(75) Kaufman, N., Prieto, L. C., Jr., Mason, E. J., and Kinney, T. D., *Am. J. Pathol.* **28,** 561 (1952).
(76) Sommers, S. C., Sullivan, B. A., and Warren, S., *Cancer Research* **12,** 915 (1952).
(77) Campbell, J. G., *Brit. J. Cancer* **3,** 72 (1949).
(78) Greene, H. S. N., *Cancer Research* **11,** 899 (1951); *Cancer* **5,** 24 (1952).
(79) Greene, H. S. N., *Cancer Research* **11,** 529 (1951); **13,** 422 (1953).
(80) Lemon, H. M., Lutz, B. R., Pope, R., Parsons, L., Handler, A. H., and Patt, D. I., *Science* **115,** 461 (1952).
(81) Chute, R. N., Sommers, S. C., and Warren, S., *Cancer Research* **12,** 912 (1952).
(82) Greene, H. S. N., *Cancer Research* **3,** 809 (1943).
(83) Lushbaugh, C. C., and Steiner, P. E., *Cancer Research* **9,** 299 (1949).
(84) Morris, D. S., McDonald, J. R., and Mann, F. C., *Cancer Research* **10,** 36 (1950).
(85) Towbin, A., *Cancer Research* **9,** 716 (1951).
(86) Greene, H. S. N., *Cancer Research* **13,** 58, 681 (1953).
(87) Albrink, W. S., and Greene, H. S. N., *Cancer Research* **13,** 64 (1953).
(88) Patti, J., and Moore, A. E., *Cancer Research* **10,** 674 (1950).
(89) Patti, J., and Biesele, J. J., *Cancer Research* **11,** 540 (1951).
(90) Loustalot, P., Algire, G. H., Legallais, F. Y., and Anderson, B. F., *J. Natl. Cancer Inst.* **12,** 1079 (1952).
(91) Billingham, R. E., Brent, L., and Medawar, P. B., *Nature* **172,** 603 (1953).
(92) Burnet, F. M., and Fenner, F., The Production of Antibodies. Melbourne, 1949.
(93) Andervont, H. B., *Public Health Repts.* (*U.S.*) **49,** 620 (1934); **50,** 1211 (1935).
(94) Curtis, M. R., Dunning, W. F., and Bullock, F. D., *Am. J. Cancer* **17,** 894 (1933).
(94a) Dunning, W. F., and Curtis, M. R., *Cancer Research* **13,** 838 (1953).
(95) Kennaway, E. L., and Sampson, B., *J. Pathol. Bacteriol.* **31,** 609 (1928).
(96) Beck, S., Kirby, A. H. M., and Peacock, P. R., *Cancer Research* **5,** 135 (1945).
(97) Kirby, A. H. M., *Cancer Research* **5,** 129 (1945).
(98) Falk, H. L., Goldfein, S., and Steiner, P. E., *Cancer Research* **9,** 438 (1949).
(99) Seligman, A. M., and Shear, M. J., *Am. J. Cancer* **37,** 364 (1939).
(100) Cf. Hartwell, J. L., Survey of Compounds Which Have Been Tested for Carcinogenic Activity. U.S. Public Health Service, 1941; 2nd ed., 1951.
(101) Turner, F. C., *J. Natl. Cancer Inst.* **2,** 81 (1941).
(102) Suntzeff, V., Babcock, R. S., and Loeb, L., *Am. J. Cancer* **39,** 56 (1940).
(103) Andervont, H. B., and Shimkin, M. B., *J. Natl. Cancer Inst.* **1,** 349 (1940).
(104) Schinz, H. R., and Uehlinger, E., *Z. Krebsforsch.* **52,** 425 (1942).
(105) Hoagland, M. B., Grier, R. S., and Hood, M. B., *Cancer Research* **10,** 629 (1950).
(106) Barnes, J. M., Denz, P. A., and Sissons, H. A., *Brit. J. Cancer* **4,** 212 (1950).
(107) Hueper, W. C., *Texas Rept. Biol. Med.* **10,** 167 (1952).
(108) Hueper, W. C., Zuefle, J. H., Link, A. M., and Johnson, M. G., *J. Natl. Cancer Inst.* **13,** 291 (1952).
(109) Earle, W. R., *J. Natl. Cancer Inst.* **4,** 165 (1943).
(110) Earle, W. R., and Nettleship, A., *J. Natl. Cancer Inst.* **4,** 213 (1943).
(111) Nettleship, A., and Earle, W. R., *J. Natl. Cancer Inst.* **4,** 229 (1943).
(112) Firor, W. M., and Gey, G. O., *Ann. Surg.* **121,** 700 (1945).
(113) Lucké, B., and Schlumberger, H., *J. Exptl. Med.* **70,** 257 (1939).
(114) Sandison, J. C., *Am. J. Anat.* **41,** 447 (1928).
(115) Clarke, E. R., Kirby-Smith, H. T., Rex, R. O., and Williams, R. G., *Anat. Record* **47,** 187 (1930).

(116) Ebert, R. H., Florey, H. W., and Pullinger, B. D., *J. Pathol. Bacteriol.* **48,** 79 (1939).
(117) Williams, R. G., *Anat. Record* **60,** 493 (1934).
(118) Algire, G. H., *J. Natl. Cancer Inst.* **4,** 1 (1943).
(119) Ide, A. G., Baker, N. H., and Warren, S. L., *Am. J. Roentgenol.* **42,** 891 (1939).
(120) Algire, G. H., and Chalkley, H. W., *J. Natl. Cancer Inst.* **6,** 73 (1945).
(121) Lindgren, A. G. H., *Acta Pathol. et Microbiol. Scand.* **22,** 493 (1945).
(122) Algire, G. H., Legallais, F. Y., and Park, H. D., *J. Natl. Cancer Inst.* **8,** 53 (1947).
(123) Algire, G. H., and Legallais, F. Y., *J. Natl. Cancer Inst.* **12,** 399 (1951).
(124) Merwin, R., Algire, G. H., and Kaplan, H. S., *J. Natl. Cancer Inst.* **11,** 593 (1950).
(125) White, P. R., and Braun, S. C., *Cancer Research* **2,** 597 (1942); cf. White, P. R., *Am. J. Botany* **32,** 237 (1945); *Cancer Research* **4,** 791 (1944).
(126) White, P. R., *Quart. Rev. Biol.* **26,** 1 (1951).
(127) Braun, A. C., and Mandle, R. J., *Growth* **12,** 255 (1948).
(128) Gautheret, R. J., *Compt. rend.* **226,** 270 (1948).
(129) Gautheret, A. J., *Compt. rend. soc. biol.* **142,** 774 (1948).
(130) Camus, G., and Gautheret, R., *Compt. rend. soc. biol.* **142,** 15, 769, 771 (1948).
(131) Klein, D. T., and Klein, R. M., *J. Bacteriol.* **66,** 220 (1953).
(132) Lucké, B., and Schlumberger, H., *Physiol. Revs.* **29,** 91 (1949).
(133) Lucké, B., *Am. J. Cancer* **20,** 352 (1934).
(134) Lucké, B., *J. Exptl. Med.* **68,** 457 (1938).
(135) Lucké, B., *Am. J. Cancer* **34,** 15 (1938).
(136) Schlumberger, H., and Lucké, B., *Cancer Research* **9,** 52 (1949).
(137) Briggs, R. W., and Grant, R., *Cancer Research* **3,** 613 (1943).
(138) Lucké, B., and Schlumberger, H. G., *J. Exptl. Med.* **89,** 269 (1949).
(139) Gordon, M., *Cancer Research* **1,** 656 (1941).
(140) Scharrer, B., and Lockhead, M. S., *Cancer Research* **10,** 403 (1950).
(141) Stark, M. B., *Am. J. Cancer* **31,** 253 (1937).
(142) Burdette, W. J., *Texas Repts. Biol. Med.* **8,** 123 (1950).
(143) Begg, M., and Robertson, F. W., *J. Exptl. Biol.* **26,** 380 (1950).
(144) Mittler, S., *Science* **115,** 271 (1952).
(145) Scharrer, B., *J. Natl. Cancer Inst.* **10,** 375 (1949); *Cancer Research* **13,** 73 (1953).
(146) Lücke, A., and Klebs, E., *Virchow's Arch. pathol. Anat.* **41,** 1 (1867).
(147) Lowenthal, H., and Jahn, G., *Z. Krebsforsch.* **37,** 439 (1932).
(148) Yoshida, T., *Gann* **40,** 1 (1949).
(149) Goldie, H., and Felix, M. D., *Cancer Research* **11,** 73 (1951).
(150) Klein, G., *Exptl. Cell Research* **2,** 518 (1951).
(151) Ishibashi, K., *Gann* **41,** 1 (1950).
(152) Hosokawa, K., *Gann* **41,** 236 (1950).
(153) Furth, J., and Kahn, M. C., *Am. J. Cancer* **31,** 276 (1937).
(154) Hewitt, H. B., *Brit. J. Cancer* **7,** 367 (1953).

THE INDUCTION OF TUMORS

Chapter III

Extrinsic Factors

Introduction

A large number of agents of many kinds—physical, chemical, and biological—are capable of inducing cancerous growths in various tissues of animals. Some of these are agents presumably foreign to the animal (extrinsic); others are produced either by the animal itself or by other living organisms of different species (intrinsic). To the staggering number of agents already known, new ones are added every year. In 1941, Hartwell (1) listed close to 700 chemical substances which had been tested for carcinogenic activity. Some 170 were reported to possess the power to evoke cancer in experimental animals, or roughly one-quarter of the compounds tested. Ten years later, Hartwell (1) published a second compilation, embodying about 600 new compounds tested, of which 150, or again one-quarter, were found to be carcinogenic. It is therefore not improbable that, as the number of compounds studied increases, new ones will be found which are capable of inducing cancer in animals.

It would be obviously impossible, short of writing an encyclopedia, to discuss this phase of cancer research in its entirety. Instead, in this and the succeeding chapter, chiefly those developments of the subject are discussed which have been systematically investigated with particular classes of agents and which may illustrate certain fundamental principles.

Before passing to this discussion it might be advisable at the very beginning to define what is meant by a carcinogenic agent. Obviously, reference is made to an agent which will produce cancer in an animal, but this is far from the whole story, for the animal itself participates in the process. An agent may induce tumors predominantly of connective tissue (sarcomas) in one strain of mice, predominantly epithelial tumors (carcinomas) in another strain, and neither kind of tumor in still a third strain. An agent carcinogenically active in one species of animal may be inactive in another species. An agent may be active under some modes of administration and inactive under others. Thus, these and many other observations indicate that the carcinogenic potency of an agent does not reside in the nature of the agent alone but is a function of the following factors: the dosage, the nature of the vehicle, the mode and length of time of administration of the agent; the strain, the species, the sex, and the age of the test animals; the site of application, the presence of concomitant factors such as the level of essential dietary constituents and the number of animals kept in a cage, and perhaps still other as yet unknown conditions. Therefore, when carcinogenic activity is referred to, it is understood that such activity is exhibited under the limitations of the experimental conditions employed and not necessarily under any others. It will also be noted that the term carcinogenesis is applied to the formation of any tumor, whether carcinoma or sarcoma, etc., and it is also understood that the description of the potency of any given agent refers to the type of tissue upon which it acts.

If it were possible to know and control all the factors responsible for carcinogenesis, other than the agent in hand, these factors could be held at optimum levels and thus make the nature of the carcinogenic agent the limiting and decisive factor. Unfortunately, this is impossible, for many of these factors may themselves change during the course of carcinogenesis. To take two examples at random, (a) the application of a carcinogenic agent may make the animal so sick that it will lower its food intake with consequences affecting the incidence of tumors, or (b) the action of a carcinogen which requires a year to produce a tumor in a mouse consumes a considerable proportion of the life span of the animal. It is just not possible to maintain all carcinogenic factors at a constant level, and, hence, the carcinogenic process may be the resultant of several successive and concurrent reactions. The results described must, therefore, be viewed in the light of this possibility.

Throughout this monograph the terms cancer, tumor, and neoplasm are used interchangeably. This usage may not be strictly accurate, but the alternative, in the light of the interminable and confusing controversies over defining these terms, may be worse. Benignancy and malignancy have clinical connotations and are largely based as much on clinical experience as on histological criteria. It may be considered one of the obligations of the chemist in this area of research to seek a definition of cancer and of its manifestations in chemical terms. The substitution of a chemical for a histological terminology may not be more illuminating, but it may be more precise.

The Carcinogenic Action of Coal Tar

The clinical recognition that workmen in certain occupations were particularly prone to develop certain types of cancer dates back to the eighteenth century, and Sir Percival Potts' description of cancer of the scrotum in chimney sweeps may be said to have been among the earliest observations on the subject. With the development of the coal tar industry during the nineteenth century it was noticed that workers in the tar distillation plants showed an abnormally high incidence of skin cancer. Any causal relation which could be shown to exist between tar or its products to the initiation and development of cancer had more than just significance as far as exposure to industrial hazards was concerned, important as that may be. If it could be definitely established that cancer could be produced by a known chemical substance it would at once sweep away the accumulated hypotheses of centuries, based solely on surmise, and substitute instead the possibility of an exact knowledge of the external agents of cancer genesis and the means of combating the effects of these agents.

The proof of these possibilities could be ascertained only through experiments on laboratory animals, and for many years attempts were made—fruitlessly—to induce cancer by the application of tar to the skin of experimental animals, chiefly rabbits. The relatively long history of failure in this respect raised doubts as to the susceptibility of laboratory animals to the action of coal tar, and from this to the question as to whether man also was susceptible to cancer ostensibly produced by this agent. It seems likely that the major error in most of this early, experimental work was due to the relatively short period of time that the coal tar was applied to the animals under observation. As a result of the long and patient application of coal tar to the ears of rabbits, Yamagiwa and Ichikawa were able to announce in 1915 (2) the first successful production of cancer in an experimental animal. With the production of undoubted epitheliomas by the Japanese workers, the study of chemical carcinogenesis began. Equally as striking as the discovery that a chemical substance could produce cancer was the inference that different species (here man and rabbit) might be susceptible to the same carcinogenic agent or agents. Work performed much later revealed that this inference is not generally true, but in the early studies on several rodent species there was sufficient justification to encourage the notion of universal carcinogenic agents.

After the pioneer investigations establishing the carcinogenic effect of coal tar, the next logical step was concerned with the fractionation of the coal tar and the ultimate isolation of the active material or materials. This task was undertaken by a group of investigators in London, including Kennaway, Cook, Hieger, and many others. In the arduous nature of the task and the success which crowned it, only one analogous and equally dramatic example comes to mind, and that is the isolation of radium from pitchblende by the Curies. The London group actually set itself a dual task, which was namely (a) to isolate from coal tar the substance or substances with carcinogenic properties, and (b) to prepare, by methods of organic chemical synthesis, compounds analogous to these in the hope of finding in some unique chemical structural feature the specific requirement for carcinogenic potency.

The method of fractionation of the coal tar required rapid and specific methods of assay for each fraction. It might have been expected that the carcinogenic activity of these fractions would have been tested on experimental animals. There were several objections to such a procedure. Among these the most important were the lack of a suitable method of bioassay relating carcinogenic activity to amount of material and the long period of time which elapsed before a tumor appeared in the test animals, in this case mice.

The problem of ascertaining the carcinogenic material in coal tar was facilitated from three directions, namely (a) the discovery that the activity resided in the high-boiling, neutral, nitrogen-free fraction (3), (b) the observation that a characteristic fluorescence spectrum was apparently always associated with fractions carrying carcinogenic activity, and (c) the chemical examination and synthesis of compounds with properties simulating those suspected as being present in the active fractions of the tar. Evidence rapidly began to accumulate that the active components might be of the nature of unsaturated polycyclic hydrocarbons, and, indeed, later work proved this to be the case.

The investigations of Cook, Kennaway, Hieger, *et al.* in London began in the 1920's and extended until the early 1940's. In the early 1930's, under the auspices of the U. S. Public Health Service, a group of investigators in Boston, including Shear, Fieser, and Andervont, embarked on a series of investigations on the carcinogenicity of the polycyclic hydrocarbons. This cooperative effort between the Public Health Service and Harvard University lasted for about a decade. Over a period of roughly ten years, therefore, the two major efforts in this field overlapped. It is gratifying to note that where experiments were conducted on identical compounds under similar experimental conditions nearly complete accord was achieved and a state of transatlantic harmony reigned. Of the relatively few discrepancies in findings between the two groups, most were due to differences in the methods of application and bioassay used. These differences were and still are crucial. Where the emphasis of the London group was primarily chemical and the experimental animal was used in much the same fashion as the Curies used an electroscope, namely as a test object, the fundamentally important contributions of the Boston group consisted in an apprehension of and an appreciation for the biological aspects of carcinogenic susceptibility. Both groups of investigators used mice as test objects, and in the discussion of the carcinogenic activity of the polycyclic hydrocarbons in this connection it is understood that it is the susceptibility of mice toward these agents which is under consideration.

The London group was faced with the problem of examining the carcinogenicity of literally hundreds of synthetic polycyclic hydrocarbons and their derivatives. They were, therefore, forced in the interests of economy to adopt an arbitrary technique which involved a biweekly painting of the skin of stock (genetically heterozygous) mice with a 0.3% solution of the test compound in benzene solution. When tumors resulted from this painting, they were examined histologically and ordinarily found to be epitheliomas (skin tumors). Thus, when describing the greater part of the contributions of the London group, the carcinogenicity of the compounds studied relates not only to mice of heterozygous genetic constitution but also to the induction of epitheliomas in such mice. The techniques of administration of the Boston group will be described below.

Because of the fact that the contributions of each group, although complementary, exhibited interesting points of departure, these contributions will be described more or less separately. If emphasis is laid for the most part on the efforts of these two groups, it is because they represented the only systematic approaches over a long period of time by cooperating specialists and thus form not only the bulk of the early contributions in this field but an integrated sequence of events.

The Polycyclic Hydrocarbons

As stated above, the fractionation of coal tar into carcinogenic fractions was facilitated by the discovery that tars and oils known to produce cancer in experimental animals gave characteristic fluorescence spectra, the major bands occurring at 4000, 4180, and 4400 Å. (4). Many known compounds with natural fluorescence were examined, among them anthracene, but only 1,2-benzanthracene was found to give bands near the wavelengths mentioned above. None of these substances was markedly carcinogenic, but the resemblance of the spectrum of 1,2-benzanthracene to those of the carcinogenic tars stimulated work on the synthesis of polycyclic hydrocarbons related to this compound. These substances were synthesized,

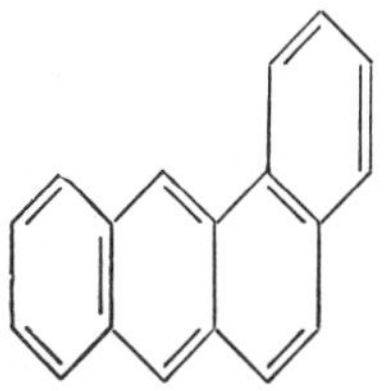

1,2-Benzanthracene

many by new methods, by J. W. Cook (5, 6), and were tested biologically and spectroscopically by Hieger and by Kennaway (4, 7).

Among the compounds related to 1,2-benzanthracene studied was 1,2,5,6-dibenzanthracene, a polycyclic hydrocarbon synthesized sometime earlier by Clar (8). This substance proved to be a highly active carcinogenic substance and was the first representative of this class of substances which, in the pure form, would induce cancer in an experimental animal.

Simultaneously with, and assisted by, the study of the synthetic hydrocarbons went the fractionation of coal tar, and in 1933 Cook *et al.* (9) succeeded in isolating a hitherto unknown hydrocarbon in pure form from

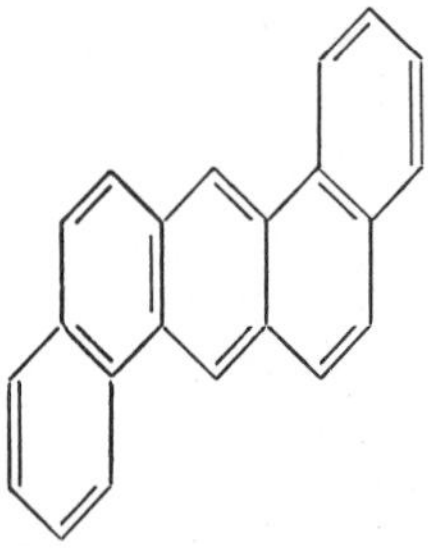

1,2,5,6-Dibenzanthracene

coal tar for which the structure of 3,4-benzpyrene was established by synthesis. This compound possessed a fluorescence spectrum

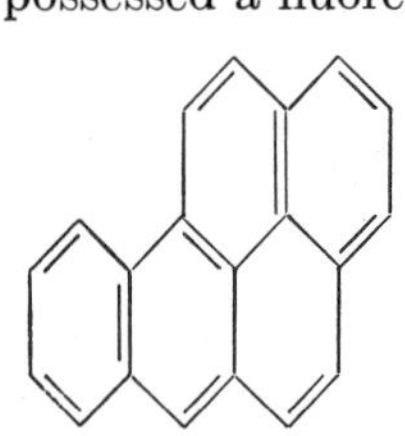

3,4-Benzpyrene

identical with that of the more active fractions of the original tar, was present in the original tar to the extent of at least 0.003 %, and was powerfully carcinogenic. Indeed, its carcinogenicity was found to exceed that of 1,2,5,6-dibenzanthracene. Recent spectrophotometric observations suggest a content of benzpyrene in certain tars of as much as 1.5 % (10), and chromatographic methods have been developed for isolating this hydrocarbon in high yield from tar distillates (75 mg. from 10 g. distillate) (11).

On testing the comparative carcinogenicity of tar with that of 3,4-benzpyrene, it was revealed that the former was still more potent in this respect than was the latter, and the presence of one or more additional carcinogens in the tar appeared likely (12). This additional carcinogen which seems to be a polycyclic aromatic hydrocarbon is a good deal more active on the skin of rabbits than is 3,4-benzpyrene, but the reverse applies to the case of the skin of the mouse. It cannot be emphasized too frequently that the degree of carcinogenicity of an agent is not independent of the test object.

3,4-Benzpyrene is one of the most widely employed carcinogens in experimental cancer research, and it is of considerable further interest because of its wide distribution. It has been identified in the soot of industrial cities and in the exhaust of internal combustion engines (13), in processed rubber (14), in carbon blacks (15) and in the atmosphere (16). In this connection it is noteworthy that the extracts of atmospheric dusts are carcinogenic when injected into mice (17).

Since the carcinogenic activity of 1,2-benzanthracene appeared to be enhanced by alkyl substitution at positions 5 and 6, it was considered desirable to start from this point in the synthesis of more complex derivatives. Almost simultaneously Wieland (18) and Cook (19) undertook the degradation of deoxycholic acid and obtained in final yield an aromatic hydrocarbon which could be considered a derivative of 1,2-benzanthracene with alkyl substituents at 5, 6, and also 10. The need for substituents at these positions was subsequently found to be illusory, but it served its purpose in leading to the preparation of a compound, 20-methylcholanthrene (position 20 in the sterol numbering system), which is one of the most powerful carcinogenic agents known in the class of polycyclic hydrocarbons. Its properties were described in 1934 by Cook and Haslewood (19).

Not only did the considerable carcinogenic activity of methylcholanthrene arouse interest but also the nature of the starting materials for its synthesis. As noted, it was derived by degradation processes from a naturally occurring substance in the animal, namely deoxycholic acid. Fieser subsequently derived the hydrocarbon from cholic acid, which is a still more abundant component of the bile (20). The steps by which the bile acids were converted to methylcholanthrene involved successively oxidation, hydrogenation,

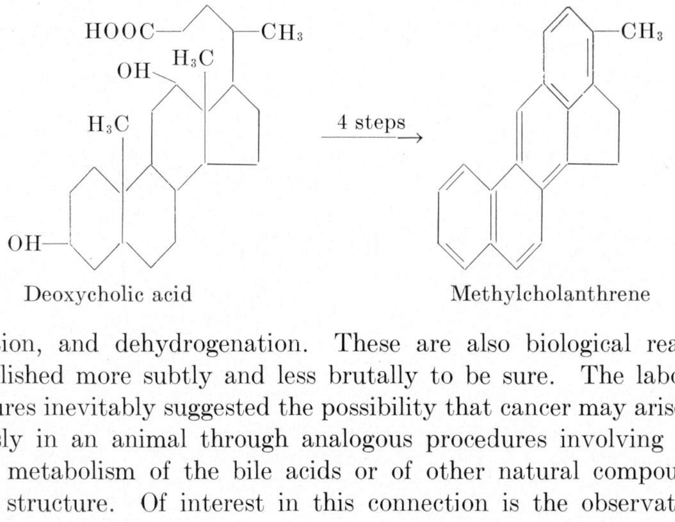

cyclization, and dehydrogenation. These are also biological reactions, accomplished more subtly and less brutally to be sure. The laboratory procedures inevitably suggested the possibility that cancer may arise spontaneously in an animal through analogous procedures involving an abnormal metabolism of the bile acids or of other natural compounds of related structure. Of interest in this connection is the observation by Cook, Kennaway, and Kennaway (21) that subcutaneous injection of deoxycholic acid itself into mice gave rise to sarcomas. Whether the bile acid is intrinsically carcinogenic or whether it gives rise to transformation products which are active remains an open question.

A perhaps closer resemblance of methylcholanthrene to products of biological origin may be drawn from considerations of the adrenocortical steroids (22). Thus, dehydrocorticosterone might conceivably condense with an aldehyde, or estrone with pyruvate, followed by aromatization, ring closure, and further dehydrogenation, to yield the corresponding cholanthrene or its derivatives (22). In this connection, i.e., the possibility that the cortical steroids may be the precursors of carcinogens *in vivo*, the remarkable experiments of Fekete and Little may be cited (23), in which *CE* strain mice castrated shortly after birth develop adrenocortical cancer. This response on the part of the adrenal cortex may be a compensation for the absence of gonadal secretions, for it may be suppressed by administration of sex hormone (24). There still is no proof, however, for the biogenesis of the carcinogenic polycyclic hydrocarbons, and any of the possible relationships mentioned must for the present remain highly conjectural.

Another group of compounds studied by the English workers was that derived from 3,4-benzphenanthrene (7). The parent compound

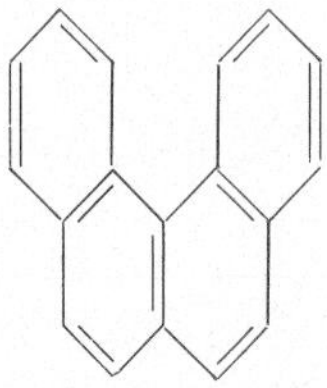

3,4-Benzphenanthrene

is very weakly carcinogenic but the 2-methyl, 2-ethyl, and 1-methyl derivatives were active in producing epitheliomas (7).

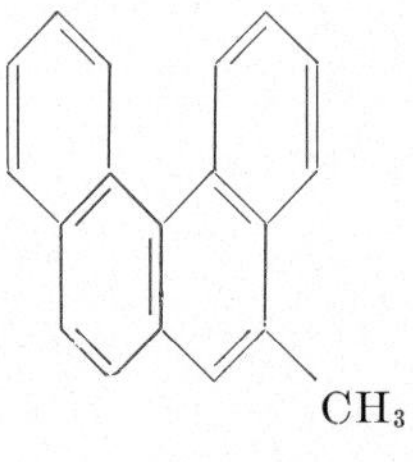

2-Methyl-3,4-benzphenanthrene

If many of the active polycyclic hydrocarbons are considered as derivatives of phenanthrene, then 1,2-benzanthracene may also be viewed as 2,3-benzphenanthrene. 1,2-Benzanthracene, like 1,2-benzphenanthrene (chrysene), is weakly active (25).

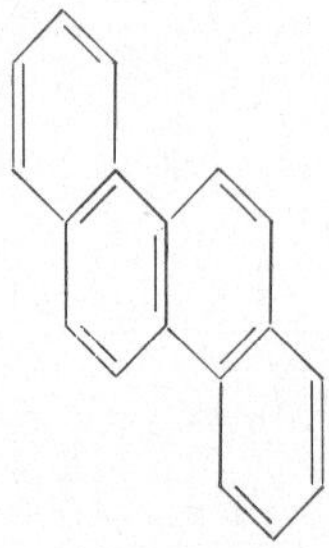

Chrysene

If, however, further substitutions are made in 2,3-benzphenanthrene (= 1,2-benzanthracene) at position 4 (benzpyrene), or at 1 (cholanthrene) or at 1 and 4 (9,10-dimethyl-1,2-benzanthracene = 1,4-dimethyl-2,3-benzphenanthrene), then very active compounds arise.

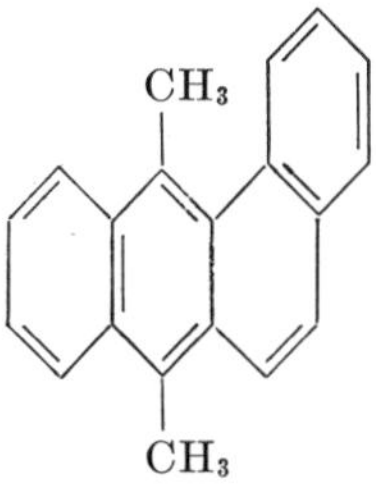

1,4-Dimethyl-2,3-benzphenanthrene
(9,10-Dimethyl-1,2-benzanthracene)

Consideration of the molecular structures of the active hydrocarbons of the 3,4-benzphenanthrene and 1,2-benzanthracene series led to the synthesis of 1,2-dimethylchrysene, which was quite active carcinogenically,

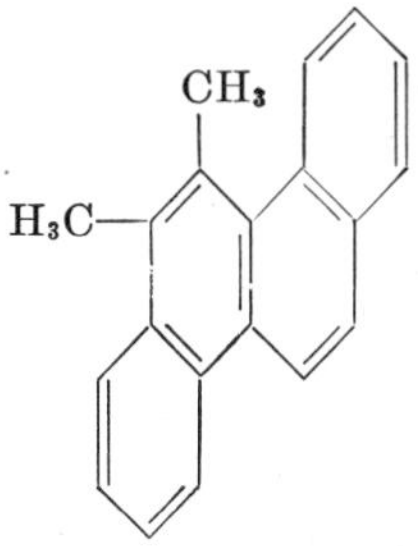

1,2-Dimethylchrysene
(3,4-Dimethyl-1,2-benzphenanthrene)

and also 1,2,3,4-tetramethylphenanthrene, which was weakly active. 5-Methylchrysene was later found to be active, whereas the 4-methyl derivative was practically inactive.

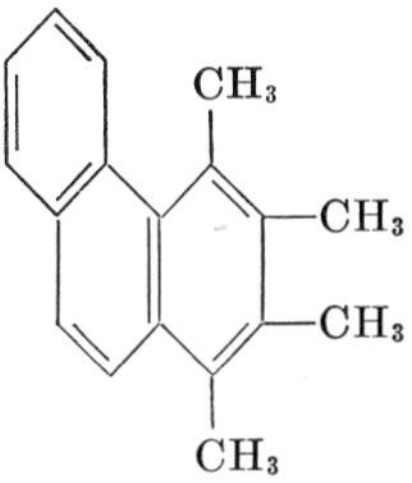

1,2,3,4-Tetramethylphenanthrene

If the middle six-carbon ring in 1,2,5,6-dibenzanthracene is replaced by a five-membered ring, the carcinogenic potency is reduced but not lost. The resulting 1,2,5,6-dibenzfluorene has the following structure.

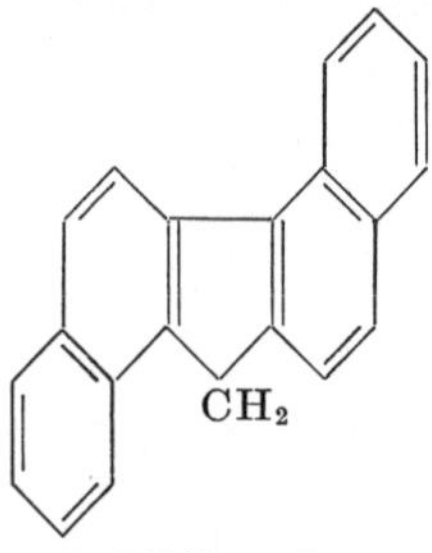

1,2,5,6-Dibenzfluorene

Skin tumors were produced not only with the 1,2,5,6 derivatives of fluorene, but also the 1,2,3,4- and the 1,2,7,8-dibenzfluorenes (7), whereas the 3,4,5,6 derivative was inert.

Compounds related in structure to the dibenzfluorenes are the dibenzcarbazoles. Boyland and Brues (26) noted that 3,4,5,6-, 1,2,5,6-, and

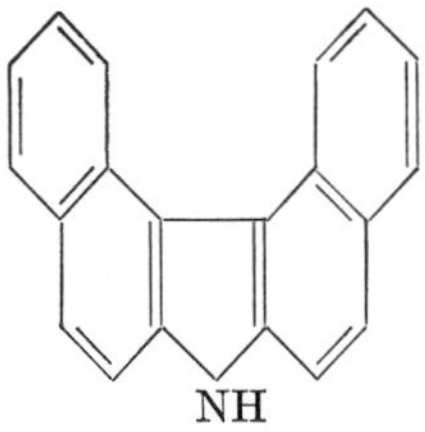

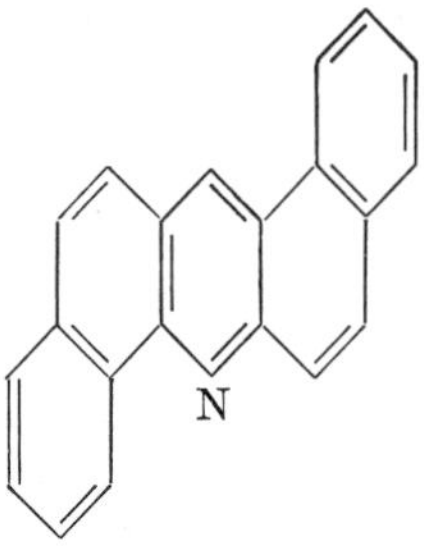

3,4,5,6-Dibenzcarbazole 1,2,5,6-Dibenzacridine

1,2,7,8-dibenzcarbazole had carcinogenic properties, but only the first-mentioned notably affected the livers of the treated animals. 1,2,5,6-Dibenzacridine which contains a central pyridine ring is also carcinogenic, as is the 3,4,5,6 derivative.

The simplest known polycyclic hydrocarbons which are carcinogenic are 1,2,3,4-tetramethylphenanthrene (referred to above) and 9,10-dimethylanthracene, which are tricyclic structures.

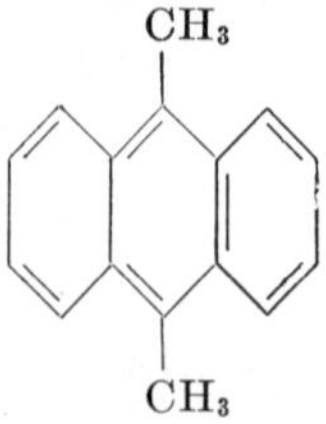

9,10-Dimethylanthracene

It may be of interest to note that the largest polycyclic hydrocarbons which are carcinogenic are the hexacyclic structures 1,2,3,4-dibenzpyrene and 3,4,8,9-dibenzpyrene.

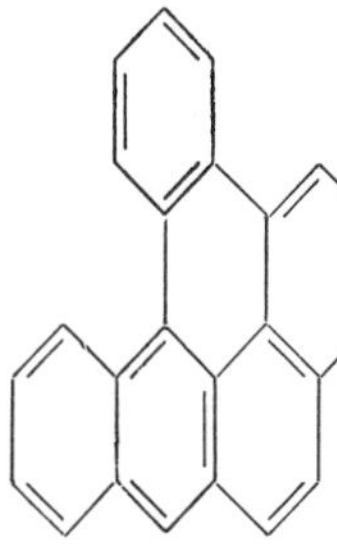

1,2,3,4-Dibenzpyrene

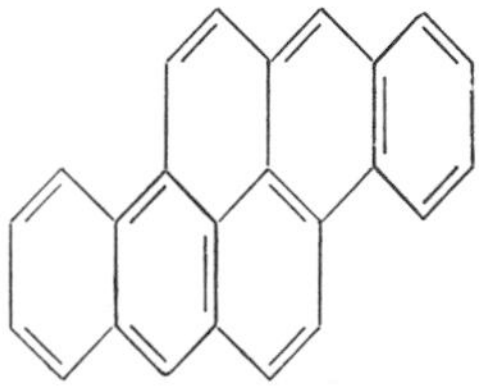

3,4,8,9-Dibenzpyrene

Further illustration of the variations in structure of the polycyclic hydrocarbons would only further emphasize the elegant art of synthetic organic chemistry and the complexities of the carcinogenic process. For a more complete report in this area, the recent reviews by Hartwell (cited above), Haddow (27), Haddow and Kon (28), Badger (29), and Boyland (30) should be consulted. The remainder of this discussion will deal with some of the technical problems involved in the administration of the carcinogens, and in the following section some of the procedures employed in comparing the relative carcinogenic action of the hydrocarbons will be described. A later section of this chapter will deal with certain of the recent attempts to relate on quantum-mechanical principles the structure of the carcinogens to their biological actions.

With the inception of the program undertaken in Boston, Fieser and his colleagues developed improved methods for the synthesis of the more powerful known carcinogenic hydrocarbons and, in addition, prepared new compounds with systematically altered variations in structure. These newer hydrocarbons, tested by Shear for carcinogenicity in mice, added further information on the relation of chemical structure to carcinogenic activity in this species. This information, however, was limited in interest to the chemical nature of the class of compounds studied. Of greater future usefulness was the knowledge which emerged from the use of only a few of these molecules applied to selected biological problems.

As stated above, the London workers consistently tested for carcinogenic potency by painting the skin of stock mice with a benzene solution of the tested hydrocarbon. However, in 1932, Burrows, Hieger, and Kennaway (31) dissolved 1,2,5,6-dibenzanthracene in lard and, on subcutaneous injection into experimental animals, obtained tumors of connective tissue (sarcomas) at the site of injection. This was a significant discovery, for it illustrated the possibility that a chemical, carcinogenic for one kind of tissue, may also, depending upon the site administered, be carcinogenic for another kind of tissue. Furthermore, the relative rate of tumor induction at each site gives some idea of the relative susceptibility of that tissue toward the agent employed. In the case of 1,2,5,6-dibenzanthracene, this substance, applied in benzene solution to the skin, produced epitheliomas in 8 to 9 months whereas, when injected subcutaneously in lard solution, it induced sarcomas in 4 to 5 months. This observation was noted but not carried forward consistently in later experiments on testing by the London workers.

The technique of subcutaneous inoculation of solutions of the hydrocarbons in fatty vehicles was adopted as a more or less consistent practice by Shear and by Andervont in Boston. The tumors which were induced by the active agents at the site of injection were, therefore, sarcomas and, unless where otherwise noted, the term carcinogenicity as applied to the hydrocarbons studied by this group refers to induction of sarcomas. The study of the active hydrocarbons in this way suggested the greater susceptibility of connective tissue toward the carcinogenic effect of these agents and assisted in the explanation of the discrepancies sometimes observed between the London and the Boston workers. Thus, the former reported that by the skin-painting technique 10-methyl-1,2-benzanthracene was relatively noncarcinogenic (32). By the subcutaneous injection route, however, Shear noted that this hydrocarbon readily induced the formation of sarcomas (33). Subsequent repetition with alternate techniques resulted in accord.

Although it would appear that the hydrocarbons derived from 1,2-benzanthracene possessed greater induction power for sarcomas than for epitheliomas, quite the contrary has been claimed by Cook, Kennaway, *et al.* in the case of the hydrocarbons derived from 3,4-dibenzphenanthrene (7). This observation indicates further that the carcinogenicity of any compound or group of compounds depends, among a host of other factors, upon the relative susceptibility of the tissues affected by these agents.

The relatively few discrepancies not yet cleared up between the workers on each side of the Atlantic may not necessarily have been due in the final analysis to the differences in genetic background of the mice used, although this might have been an important factor, but to the use of different kinds of solvents for the hydrocarbons in the injection experiments. In the experiments of Burrows, Hieger, and Kennaway (31) the solvent employed was lard. In later experiments by the London group sesame oil and other complex fatty vehicles were also used as solvents. That lard itself might have carcinogenic properties was recognized by Burrows *et al.* (31, 34), and the possibility that sesame oil might be carcinogenic too was pointed out by Gardner (35). Even if these vehicles were not carcinogenic, such complex fats as lard and sesame oil are rarely reproducible in chemical constitution and in properties from one preparation to another. The question of whether the vehicle, though not carcinogenic itself, yet may affect the carcinogenic potency of a given hydrocarbon was considered by many investigators (36, 37). This problem has wide ramifications and is discussed below in a later section. In order to avoid the use of vehicles of doubtful properties and reproducibility, Shear *et al.* developed several methods of administration based upon the subcutaneous injection of crystals of the hydrocarbons moistened in glycerol (33), or of solutions of the hydrocarbons dissolved in cholesterol (38) or in tricaprylin (36). It is obvious that quantitative methods of bioassay involving the relative activity of a group of active agents can be made only if the possible effect of the vehicle for these agents is either eliminated or accurately known. The use of pellets of the hydrocarbons in cholesterol permitted the relatively easy withdrawal of the carcinogen at any time after its injection, and Andervont and Shear noted that only a brief exposure of subcutaneous tissue to such pellets of methylcholanthrene was necessary to induce the formation of sarcomas in mice; the longer the period of exposure, however, the greater was the subsequent incidence of tumors (39).

The polycyclic hydrocarbons are largely insoluble in water, and it has been usually assumed that they display their activity in the lipid phase of tissues. Their aqueous solubility is, however, considerably increased in the presence of purines which is accompanied by a reversible quenching of the fluorescence of the hydrocarbons (40, 41). The solvent effect of the purines on 3,4-benzpyrene increases (a) with the number of substitutions by oxygen of positions 2, 6, and 8 of the purine ring, and (b) with the number of N-methyl groups. Thus, hypoxanthine with the weakest solvent power stands at one end of the scale, tetramethyl uric acid with the strongest one, at the other. The nucleosides, adenosine and guanosine, also show a solvent effect.

Stable emulsions of the hydrocarbons have been prepared in serum (42) and in the presence of such "association colloids" as sodium cholate, soaps, and soap-like compounds (43). Thus 2% solutions of triton N (alkyl aryl polyether alcohol) or sodium myristyl sulfate dissolved in clear and stable solutions approximately 0.012 and 0.005% 3,4-benzpyrene, respectively (44).

The use by the London workers of stock mice of mixed and unknown genetic characteristics interposed several hazards in the accurate estimation of cancer genesis. These hazards were due to the unavoidable lack of knowledge of (a) the relative degree of resistance or of susceptibility toward the applied agents among the individual mice of any given group, and (b) the incidence of spontaneous tumors in these mice. Furthermore, the heterozygous character of such mice made a check on the autonomous nature of the induced tumors through transplantation of these tumors into new host mice almost impossible. The problem described under (a) above could be partially removed by employing many animals and by using maximal tolerated doses of the agents, but the others defied solution.

The availability of inbred stocks of mice through the enterprise of the Jackson Memorial Laboratory in Maine, of Marsh in Buffalo, and of Strong in New Haven permitted the extension of studies on chemical carcinogenesis to experimental animals of known and reproducible genetic characteristics. Andervont observed that, similar to the experiments of the London workers on stock mice, subcutaneous injection of 1,2,5,6-dibenzanthracene induced the formation of sarcomas in inbred mice of several strains (45). These induced tumors, like spontaneous tumors, were also found to be transplantable to mice of the same strain but not to mice of different strains. With this finding a supplementary testing of the tumors, in addition to that of histologic examination, became feasible.

The studies in chemical carcinogenesis were thus conducted in Boston on inbred strains of mice. These studies, subsequently carried on in Bethesda after dissolution of the cooperative arrangement with Harvard in 1939, may be considered as falling into three general categories, namely: (a) the determination of the carcinogenicity of a large number of polycyclic hydrocarbons using a single inbred strain of mice, (b) the examination of the variation of susceptibility of all available strains of mice toward a limited number of polycyclic hydrocarbons, and (c) the study of the effect of the *menstruum* and dosage on the carcinogenicity of a limited number of hydrocarbons in a few strains of mice. Many investigators in other parts of the world engaged in similar studies, and only general headings are employed in the sections which follow.

Comparative Carcinogenicity of the Hydrocarbons

With a paper published in 1942, Cook, Kennaway, and their collaborators concluded their report of tests on "several hundred" new polycyclic compounds and their derivatives (7). In 1941 (36), Shear concluded his survey of 181 similar and analogous compounds. Of the 181 substances tested, Shear reported that 60 exhibited carcinogenic potency. Confining attention only to derivatives of 1,2-benzanthracene, a partial summation of the data may be given as it refers to sarcomas induced in *A* mice by subcutaneous injection of the compounds tested (Table 6). Complete details of the data amassed on this subject may be found in reviews by Cook and Kennaway (46), by Fieser (47) and by Shear (36), and more recently by Boyland (30) and by Badger (29).

A rough index of the relative potency of the various active hydrocarbons for sarcoma production in *A* strain mice may be one based upon differences in the latent period of induction necessary for about half the number of animals to show tumors. The most active agents thus have the smallest period of induction. This distinction is thus based upon the rate of forma-

TABLE 6

CARCINOGENIC ACTIVITY OF DERIVATIVES OF 1,2-BENZANTHRACENE IN *A* STRAIN MICE

Active (sarcomas at site of subcutaneous injection)	Inactive (no tumors at site of subcutaneous injection)
3-Methyl-1,2-benzanthracene	1,2-Benzanthracene (may be very weakly active)
4-Methyl-1,2-benzanthracene	1'-Methyl-1,2-benzanthracene
9-Methyl-1,2-benzanthracene	3-Hydroxy-1,2-benzanthracene
10-Methyl-1,2-benzanthracene	3-Amino-1,2-benzanthracene
10-Ethyl-1,2-benzanthracene	7-Methyl-1,2-benzanthracene
5-Methyl-1,2-benzanthracene	7-Methyl-8,9-dimethylene-1,2-benzanthracene
4,9-Dimethyl-1,2-benzanthracene	10-Amino-1,2-benzanthracene
9,10-Dimethyl-1,2-benzanthracene	10-Propyl-1,2-benzanthracene
5,9-Dimethyl-1,2-benzanthracene	8-Methyl-1,2-benzanthracene
5,10-Dimethyl-1,2-benzanthracene	3,9-Dimethyl-1,2-benzanthracene
8,9-Dimethylene-1,2-benzanthracene	5-Hydroxy-3,4-benzpyrene
1,2,5,6-Dibenzanthracene	4'-Hydroxy-3,4-benzpyrene
9-Methyl-1,2,5,6-dibenzanthracene	3- or 6-Chloro- and 3- or 6-cyano-20-methylcholanthrene
1',9-Methylene-1,2,5,6-dibenzanthracene	20-*t*-Butylcholanthrene
3,4-Benzpyrene	
5-Methyl-3,4-benzpyrene	
4'-Methyl-3,4-benzpyrene	
20-Methylcholanthrene	
20-Ethylcholanthrene	
20-Isopropylcholanthrene	
16-Hydroxy-20-methylcholanthrene	
15,20-Dimethylcholanthrene	
16,20-Dimethylcholanthrene	
Cholanthrene	

tion of tumors and does not imply that ultimately the same proportion of tumors would not be induced in the test mice by the slower agents at a later date. The index is given in Table 7, in which the compounds studied are divided into three categories depending, respectively, upon whether the latent period of sarcoma induction is (a) low, or less than 4 months, (b) moderately low, or within 4 to 6 months, and (c) high, or longer than 6 months.

Iball suggested a method of estimating the approximate relative potency of the different hydrocarbons by taking into account the proportion of animals showing epithelial tumors after skin painting as well as the average time during which tumors make their appearance (48). The ratio of the proportion of tumors divided by the latent period of induction gives, when multiplied by 100, the approximate carcinogenic index. Iball was aware of the dangers involved in this simplified treatment of the data—e.g., different test groups of stock mice were not invariably uniform in their reactions to the same carcinogen, and considerable differences often

TABLE 7

APPROXIMATE CLASSIFICATION OF HYDROCARBONS ACCORDING TO LATENT PERIOD OF INDUCTION OF SARCOMAS IN *A* STRAIN MICE (47)

Low latent period	Moderate latent period	High latent period
3,4-Benzpyrene	1,2,5,6-Dibenzanthracene	3,4-Benzphenanthrene
20-Methylcholanthrene	9-Methyl-1,2-benzanthracene	6-Methyl-1,2-benzanthracene
5,10-Dimethyl-1,2-benzanthracene	5-Methyl-1,2-benzanthracene	3-Methoxy-1,2-benzanthracene
9,10-Dimethyl-1,2-benzanthracene	20-Ethylcholanthrene	
10-Methyl-1,2-benzanthracene	2-Methylbenzphenanthrene	

existed in the period from the beginning of the experiment to the death of the mice. Nevertheless, the table which he constructed serves as an approximate index of the relative potency of the chemicals tested under the conditions of the experiments. It will be noted that there is a rough parallelism in order of potency of the agents given in Table 7 (relating to sarcoma production) and Table 8 (relating to epithelioma production).

Berenblum (49) has suggested a method for grading carcinogenic potency based upon the following formulae:

$G = 16 - 6.5 (\log W)$, where G = the grade of activity, and W = latent period in weeks (i.e., the time taken for 50% of the surviving animals to develop tumors.

In the case of very weak carcinogens, the formula would be:

$g = 16 - 6.5 (\log 2w)$, where g = the grade of activity, and w represents the time in weeks to develop the first tumor.

The second equation represents an extrapolation of the data, based on the assumption that the time taken for 50% of tumors to develop is roughly twice as long as that taken for the first tumor to appear.

The methods suggested above yield only rough orders of potency of the hydrocarbons under the experimental conditions employed and, for more exact comparisons, the factors of dosage, vehicle used, etc., must be taken into consideration.

The ratio of papillomas to epitheliomas induced by the carcinogens (Table 8) is highly variable and may depend upon many factors such as the relative survival periods of the animals; e.g., the toxicity of a given agent may be so high as to cause the death of many mice before the papillomas developed into epithliomas. This factor may well be responsible for the high proportion of papillomas in the case of the application of 9,10-dimethyl-1,2-benzanthracene.

For a more exact comparison of relative carcinogenic potency it is desir-

TABLE 8

CARCINOGENIC COMPOUNDS ARRANGED IN DESCENDING ORDER OF POTENCY IN INDUCING EPITHELIAL TUMORS BY SKIN PAINTING OF STOCK MICE (48)

Compound	Number of animals alive when first tumor appeared	Number of tumors	Per cent tumors *A*	Papilloma	Epithelioma	Average latent period days	Index *A/B* × 100
9,10-Dimethyl-1,2-benzanthracene	20	13	65	6	7	43	151
20-Methylcholanthrene	18	18	100	1	17	99	101
3,4-Benzpyrene	9	7	78	2	5	109	80
Cholanthrene	49	28	57	5	23	112	51
5,6-Cyclopenteno-1,2-benzanthracene	14	13	93	1	12	194	48
2-Methyl-3,4-benzphenanthrene	16	12	75	5	7	155	48
10-Methyl-1,2-benzanthracene	18	12	67	2	10	147	45
5,6-Dimethyl-1,2-benzanthracene	19	16	84	0	16	220	38
6-Isopropyl-1,2-benzanthracene	15	11	74	1	10	204	36
3,4,5,6-Dibenzcarbazole	19	9	48	4	5	143	33
3,4,8,9-Dibenzpyrene	17	10	59	0	10	205	29
5-Methyl-1,2-benzanthracene	8	7	88	2	5	317	28
5-Ethyl-1,2-benzanthracene	9	7	78	2	5	285	27
1,2,5,6-Dibenzanthracene	65	41	63	8	33	239	26
3,4-Benzphenanthrene	18	12	67	5	7	387	17
1,2,5,6-Dibenzcarbazole	9	4	45	1	3	263	17
5-Propyl-1,2-benzanthracene	20	6	30	3	3	192	16
3,4,5,6-Dibenzacridine	28	11	39	2	9	357	11
3′-Methyl-1,2,5,6-dibenzanthracene	25	7	28	1	6	325	9
1,2,5,6-Dibenzacridine	25	6	24	2	4	350	7

able to know the effect of injecting doses of the compounds up to and including the dose above which no increase in the incidence and no decrease in the latent period can be obtained under otherwise standardized conditions. Such a study was instituted by Shimkin and Andervont (37) and applied to the relative carcinogenic potency in *C3H* mice of 20-methylcholanthrene, 3,4-benzpyrene, and 1,2,5,6-dibenzanthracene. The solvent used was tricaprylin, and the solutions were injected subcutaneously. At each dosage the average latent periods were computed by multiplying the number of tumors appearing each week by the time in weeks after injection

TABLE 9

INDUCTION OF SUBCUTANEOUS TUMORS IN *C3H* MICE WITH SINGLE SUBCUTANEOUS INJECTION OF CARCINOGENIC HYDROCARBONS (50)

Hydrocarbon	Dose, mg.	Number of mice	Number of tumors	Average latent time, weeks	50% latent time, weeks	Carcinogenic index
20-Methylcholanthrene	0.25	20	20	10.1	8.9	140
	0.5	20	20	9.5	8.0	150
	1.0	20	20	9.1	7.8	155
	2.0	20	20	10.1	8.6	140
3,4-Benzpyrene	0.25	20	18	15.4	13.3	90
	0.5	20	19	13.8	11.6	100
	1.0	20	20	12.5	11.1	115
	2.0	20	20	12.1	11.1	120
1,2,5,6-Dibenzanthra-cene	0.25	19	17	24.6	20.6	50
	0.5	20	18	23.4	20.3	55
	1.0	20	19	21.7	18.3	60
	2.0	18	17	17.7	14.8	75
	3.0	16	15	15.9	14.1	85

and dividing the sum by the total number of tumors. The 50%-average latent periods were calculated by the same method, but only the first 50% of the animals which developed tumors in each group were considered. The carcinogenic indices have been described by Iball (48). The results of these experiments are described in Table 9 to illustrate the range of activity and the consistency in the data.

It is clear that, under the conditions used, the relative order of carcinogenic activity in descending order is methylcholanthrene, benzpyrene, and dibenzanthracene. Further observations revealed that single doses of dibenzanthracene were as effective as multiple doses each containing a fractional part of the single dose. That the relative order of potency of the agents tested holds only at the doses used is emphasized in a later table where, with lower doses, the order is changed.

Tables 6–9 describe the hydrocarbons active or inactive in producing sarcomas or epitheliomas in mice. Certain of these tables refer to the relative potency of a few of the active agents. The need for referring precisely to the affected tissue as well as to the mode of alternative administration of the agent for the same tissue is emphasized in the data of Andervont and Shimkin (51). These investigators studied the incidence of lung tumors induced by subcutaneous and by intravenous administration of various hydrocarbons and compared such incidence with each other and with the incidence of sarcomas and epitheliomas evoked by the same agents. Their composite table is given in Table 10.

It is evident from the data of Andervont and Shimkin (51) that, if the

TABLE 10

RELATIVE CARCINOGENIC POTENCY OF HYDROCARBONS FOR THE SKIN, SUBCUTANEOUS TISSUE, AND LUNGS OF MICE (51)

Compound	Subcutaneous injection	Skin painting	Lung tumor induction by: Intravenous injection	Lung tumor induction by: Subcutaneous injection
20-Methylcholanthrene	High	High	High	High
3,4-Benzpyrene	High	High	Medium	Low
3,4,5,6-Dibenzcarbazole	Medium	Medium	Medium	Medium
1,2,5,6-Dibenzanthracene	Medium	Medium	High	High
4′-Methyl-3,4-benzpyrene	Medium	—	Low	Low?
2-Methyl-3,4-benzphenanthrene	Low	Medium	Low	Low
15,16-Benzdehydrocholanthrene	Low	—	Medium	Low
1,2,5,6-Dibenzacridine	Low?	Low	Medium	High
1,2,7,8-Dibenzacridine	Negative?	Low	—	Medium
3-Methoxy-10-propyl-2-benzanthracene	Negative	—	Negative	Negative
1,2-Benzanthracene	Negative?	Negative	Negative	Negative

carcinogenic potency of the hydrocarbons is assayed by the technique of pulmonary tumor induction, a quite different order of potency is obtained from that by induction of either subcutaneous sarcoma or epithelioma. Thus, such compounds as 1,2,7,8-dibenzacridine did not yield sarcomas but readily produced lung tumors. The relative order of potency for three of the hydrocarbons for both skin and subcutaneous tumors is, in descending order, 20-methylcholanthrene, 3,4-benzpyrene, and 1,2,5,6-dibenzanthracene; but for lung tumors it is 1,2,5,6-dibenzanthracene, 20-methylcholanthrene, and 3,4-benzpyrene. The last-mentioned is, indeed, relatively weak in producing lung tumors although highly active in producing subcutaneous tumors and epitheliomas.

Furthermore, there have been a few examples of differences in relative potency reported for the same carcinogen when applied to the skin and to the subcutaneous tissues although, in general, a fair agreement has been observed. Shear reported that 10-methyl-1,2-benzanthracene is highly active when administered subcutaneously but weakly active when painted on the skin (33). On the other hand, 2-methyl-3,4-benzphenanthrene is more potent on the skin than in the subcutaneous tissues (7).

Thus, the results obtained by one method of biological testing will not, *a priori*, agree with those obtained by other methods, and when the carcinogenic potency of a substance is referred to it is necessary to define exactly the conditions under which it is used and to what it is applied. Certain tissues are more susceptible to certain agents than are other tissues. If the tissues of the same animal do not respond equally to the action of the same chemical, the impossibility of applying specific orders of magnitude generally to other chemicals and to other species of animals is evident. Carcinogenicity is a relative term.

These considerations have been illustrated by a number of instances, but it may be of interest to cite two recent and particularly striking examples involving the same compound. 1,2-Benzanthracene has usually been considered non-carcinogenic for, when painted on the skin or injected subcutaneously, neither epitheliomas nor sarcomas were reported to develop. However, if the experiments are allowed to run long enough a decided carcinogenic action of the compound is revealed (25). Furthermore, when it is incorporated into the diet of Osborne-Mendel rats a proportion of the animals develop multiple hepatomas (52). Thus, a chemical reported to be non-carcinogenic may with patience or ingenuity, be shown to possess carcinogenic activity. How many of the negative compounds listed in Hartwell's survey might turn out to be active under conditions other than those described? One final example may be cited in recent experiments on the possible carcinogenicity of crude oils and their fractions which were conducted under exemplary conditions by Hieger and Woodhouse (53). These authors observed extremely slight effects of these fractions on the skin of mice and very high activity on the skin of rabbits. The possibilities opened to the legal profession in compensation cases involving these phenomena must be quite attractive.

The Relative Susceptibility of Mice Strains to the Polycyclic Hydrocarbons

The studies devoted to the effect of chemical structure as related to carcinogenicity involved the use of a very large number of chemicals with either stock mice or with the inbred *A* strain mice. Techniques of skin painting with stock mice induced epitheliomas when active agents were used, whereas subcutaneous injection of active agents induced sarcomas at the site of injection. In general, therefore, when the carcinogenicity of the hundreds of polycyclic hydrocarbons was referred to, it usually meant the possibility of the induction of such tumors in such mice under entirely arbitrary experimental conditions.

Studies involving the carcinogenicity of a few hydrocarbons in a number of inbred strains of mice were undertaken by Andervont (45). Early investigations revealed that, although the subcutaneous injection of 1,2,5,6-dibenzanthracene (in lard solution) gave rise to sarcomas in all the inbred strains tested, the latent period of induction of these tumors varied from strain to strain. There appeared to be, therefore, in mice of the different inbred strains, a different degree of susceptibility toward the carcinogenic agent. Using lard solutions of either 1,2,5,6-dibenzanthracene or 20-methylcholanthrene in doses of 0.8 mg. per mouse, it was observed that strain *C3H* mice were most susceptible to the action of the agents, sarcomas appearing on the average in 17 to 18 weeks after injection, whereas strain I and strain Y mice were least susceptible, the tumors appearing on the average at about 30 weeks after injection of the carcinogen. The difference shown between these strains under the conditions stated was likewise revealed when pellets of methylcholanthrene in cholesterol were employed; the medium in which the cancer-inducing compound was dissolved had little influence upon its relative carcinogenicity for the two strains. Midway in susceptibility toward the carcinogenic agents were mice of strains, *C*, *M*, *C57 Black*, *A*, and *DBA*, in descending order. The wide variations in susceptibility revealed by the strains of mice studied indicate the necessity of using inbred animals when comparing the carcinogenic activity of different substances. It must be emphasized, however, that the order of susceptibility toward the carcinogens named is on the basis of the effects obtained by the subcutaneous injections of lard solutions and that this order might be altered if a different mode of administration were adopted. In this connection it is worthy of note that strain *C57 Black* mice were observed to be more susceptible than those of strain *A* when subjected to skin painting with 1,2,5,6-dibenzanthracene dissolved in benzol (54). Furthermore, Andervont and Lorenz (55) had shown that lard solutions of 1,2,5,6-dibenzanthracene induced sarcomas earlier than did colloidal suspensions or the crystalline material (in *A* mice).

As demonstrated, *C3H* strain mice were found to be more susceptible to sarcoma formation through subcutaneous injection of dibenzanthracene than were mice of the *Y* or *I* strains. When mice of these strains were reciprocally bred, the hybrid mice, regardless of origin, were of intermediate susceptibility, since they were, on the average, more resistant than the parent *C3H* mice and more susceptible than the *Y* or *I* strain parents (45). If susceptibility to the action of the carcinogens has a genetic basis, it is probably due to the influence of multiple factors.

In the consideration of the varying latent periods exhibited by various animals, the possibility arises as to whether the injected carcinogen may not be metabolized or altered by apparently resistant animals in such a way as to minimize or destroy its carcinogenic activity. This question was answered in the negative by experiments which showed that injected carcinogens, under the skin of mice that show no tumors, may be withdrawn from these mice and, on subsequent injection into susceptible mice, produce tumors at the site of injection.

Each of the inbred strains of mice which Andervont studied possessed a different incidence of spontaneous tumors. Thus the *C3H*, *A*, *DBA* strains have a high incidence, the *C57 Black* and the *I* strains have a low incidence, of spontaneous mammary tumors. Similarly, mice of the *A* strain have a high incidence, those of the *DBA* strain have a low incidence, of spontaneous pulmonary tumors. The segregation of genetic characters through long inbreeding thus resulted in strains of mice with different susceptibility toward various forms of cancer. As a result of the evidence pointing to analogous strain differences in susceptibility toward sarcomas induced by the polycyclic hydrocarbons, the question arose as to whether there was any relation between the incidence of spontaneous and of induced tumors. Obviously, to provide a sound basis of comparison, only the incidence of the same kind of tumor could be considered.

The recognition of the incidence of spontaneous tumors of all kinds (and at known ages of the mice) is a relatively simple, if tedious, matter of observation over long periods of time of large numbers of mice of each strain. The recognition of the incidence of induced tumors is, however, limited to those tumors capable of being experimentally produced. Up to this point epitheliomas, through skin painting with hydrocarbons, and sarcomas, through subcutaneous injection of hydrocarbons, were the only tumors consistently induced in mice. In order to broaden the area of investigation to include tumors induced in other sites of the animal, considerable experimentation was needed. The earliest kind of tumor to be produced at a site other than those mentioned was the pulmonary tumor.

In 1925, Murphy and Sturm (56) noted that painting of the skin of mice with tar produced a large proportion of lung tumors in such mice. No lung tumors appeared spontaneously in untreated control mice during the period in which such tumors appeared in the painted mice. Similar results employing tar as the carcinogenic agent were noted by others. In studies involving the subcutaneous injection of lard solutions of 1,2,5,6-dibenzanthracene, Andervont noted that not only were sarcomas induced at the subcutaneous site of injection of the hydrocarbon but lung tumors also appeared in these mice (57). The greatest proportion of such lung tumors, induced at a site far removed from the site of injection, appeared in mice of the *A* strain. The spontaneous incidence of pulmonary tumors in mice of the *A* strain is quite high, but the pulmonary tumors induced in the treated mice of this strain appeared long before the spontaneous tumors were due. Shear also observed the precocious appearance of lung nodules in *A* strain mice after a subcutaneous injection of crystalline 8,9-dimethylene-1,2-benzanthracene (58).

The apparent fact that pulmonary tumors could arise in a susceptible strain through administration of a carcinogen at a distant site suggested that the agent found its way from the site of injection into the general circulation. To test this possibility, intravenous injection of the carcinogen was necessary. In the forms of the carcinogen ordinarily employed, i.e., lard solutions, etc., this was clearly inadequate. The problem was solved by the employment by Andervont and Lorenz (55) of fine and stable emulsions of dibenzanthracene in horse serum. After intravenous injection of such emulsions, a relatively rapid induction of pulmonary tumors was observed. Similar results were noted later when methylcholanthrene was employed in such emulsions (59). The pulmonary tumors arising by the use of these emulsions were transmissible, by transplantation, to other mice of the same strain. The injection of emulsions of these hydrocarbons under the skin gave rise to sarcomas at the site of injection as well as in the same mouse to pulmonary tumors (51). By means of the emulsion technique pulmonary tumors were also obtained in the lungs of *C3H* strain mice. This technique provided a useful tool in the experimental production of lung tumors in mice of susceptible strains. Genetic experiments by Heston on outcrossing susceptible *A* strain mice to resistant strains suggested that susceptibility to induced lung tumors was based on the influence of multiple factors (60).

Pulmonary tumors (alveolar adenomas) were also induced in guinea pigs by intravenous administration of dibenzanthracene and of methylcholanthrene (61). In the case of rats, however, intravenous administration of fat emulsions of 9,10-dimethyl-1,2-benzanthracene led to the curious finding of a high proportion of skin tumors (62).

The successful use of the hydrocarbon emulsions in the production of pulmonary tumors suggested still further extensions of their carcinogenic effect or effects. When such emulsions were included in the drinking water of *A* strain mice, Lorenz and Stewart observed the production of an adenocarcinoma of the small intestine of these mice as well as multiple primary tumors of the lung in the same mouse (63). Similar emulsions of the hydrocarbons implanted in the wall of the pyloric end of the stomach of *C3H* strain mice induced the formation of gastric adenocarcinomas (64). Both kinds of adenocarcinoma were successfully transplanted under the skin of mice of the respective strains.

Intramural injection of methylcholanthrene also produced tumors of the glandular stomach of rats (65) and of mice of several strains. A similar direct implantation of methylcholanthrene into the uterine horn of *CBA* strain mice resulted in the production of endometrial carcinomas, together with some sarcomas at the site of implantation (66).

The direct implantation of carcinogens in viable tissues removed from the host was demonstrated in the induction of tumors in embryonic tissues (67). The fetal tissue enclosing the polycyclic hydrocarbon can be transplanted in various sites; in the case of fetal skin of strain *C* mice transplantation subcutaneously, intramuscularly, and in the liver, spleen, and testis gave rise to both sarcomatous and carcinomatous elements in all sites except the liver, where only squamous cell carcinomas were found (68). Tissues treated in this way need not be embryonic, for Horning showed that adult lung tissue of mice carefully wrapped around crystals of methylcholanthrene and implanted subcutaneously into mice gave rise to bronchogenic carcinomas (69). These tumors were transplantable under the influence of stilbestrol. A similar technique had been employed earlier by the same author in the induction of transplantable glandular carcinomas of the prostate in mice (70). More recently, Pan and Gardner (71) have successfully induced uterine tumors in mice by wrapping excised uterine cervical and horn tissues around crystals of methylcholanthrene and subcutaneously implanting the tissue so treated into litter mates of the animals sacrificed.

Another procedure effective in inducing adenocarcinoma of the small intestine, this time in *C* strain and *C3H* strain mice, was that of White and Stewart (72), who fed a methylcholanthrene-containing diet to these mice. The tumor subsequently metastasized to the regional lymph nodes, pancreas, liver, and lung. At the same time primary pulmonary tumors also developed, with the higher incidence in the *C* strain mice. The hypothesis was adduced that methylcholanthrene was absorbed from the small intestine into the system because of the occurrence of primary hemangioendotheliomas of the mesenteric structures as well as of primary lung tumors in mice fed the hydrocarbon. The former tumors developed from tissues located along the pathway which the methylcholanthrene traversed after absorption from the small intestine.

That the nature of the carcinogenic agent as well as the strain of mouse are important in the development of tumors distant from the site of application is noted from the fact that, although subcutaneous administration of benzpyrene, dibenzanthracene, or methylcholanthrene has little or no effect on the induction of remote tumors in strain *Street* mice, similar administration of 9,10-dimethyl-1,2-benzanthracene accelerated the spontaneous development of leukemia, pulmonary adenoma, and granulosa-cell tumors in this strain (73). The spontaneous incidence of mammary tumors, however, was not affected.

So far, therefore, by appropriate techniques of application of the polycyclic hydrocarbons, the kinds of tumors successfully induced in mice included sarcomas, epitheliomas, pulmonary tumors, hemangioendotheliomas, and adenocarcinomas of the stomach and intestine. Many of these tumors, induced by the same agent, arose concurrently in the same animal. This number of tumors was subsequently increased when Morton and Mider (74) and Engelbreth-Holm (75) noted that painting of the skin of dilute brown mice induced the early appearance of leukemia in these mice, when Murphy induced lymphatic leukemia in rats with 1,2,5,6-dibenzanthracene (76), and when Strong *et al.* induced the formation of mammary tumors in certain strains of mice after the subcutaneous injection of methylcholanthrene in sesame oil solution (77). It is interesting to note Strong's procedure, for it is evident that under ordinary circumstances the route of administration employed would favor the induction of sarcomas. Strong avoided this by genetically selecting two sublines of the *NHO* strain mice which, through inbreeding, had been directed toward resistance against local tumors induced by methylcholanthrene, such as sarcoma and epithelioma.

The experiments of Morton and Mider revealed that the skin painting of mice of several strains with an incidence of spontaneous leukemia (*DBA*, *C*, and *C57 Black*) did not necessarily lead to an increase in incidence of the disease in all these strains nor did it hasten the appearance of the disease in all the strains. Only mice of the *DBA* strain responded with the production of leukemia to the action of the carcinogen applied to the skin. McEndy, Boon, and Furth (78) noted that the types of leukemia induced by the painting of the skin with methylcholanthrene solutions in benzene in mice were chiefly lymphoid or atypical.

All the tumors induced in the ways described in this section resembled, in the respects studied, the corresponding tumors which arise spontaneously in these sites. Before discussing the comparison in incidence between spontaneous and induced tumors within the same strain of mice, it is significant to note that the active polycyclic hydrocarbons, ordinarily so carcinogenic at certain sites in mice, failed almost completely to evoke tumors of the liver (hepatomas) and of the spleen. When the active hydrocarbons, e.g., active at the sites mentioned above, were implanted within the livers or the spleens of mice, little pathological reaction was produced in the former organ and only a few sarcomas were induced in the latter organ (79). The implanted hydrocarbon could be withdrawn unaltered from the livers of these animals. The parenchyma of the liver and the spleen of mice are thus highly resistant to the action of those polycyclic hydrocarbons studied which readily induce tumors in other sites. The production of hepatomas in mice was successfully accomplished by the use of two other types of carcinogenic agents, namely (a) the azo dyes, and (b) the halogenated aliphatic hydrocarbons.

Dosage of and Response to the Carcinogenic Hydrocarbons

In order to evaluate, in quantitative terms, the response of a given animal or group of animals to the action of a carcinogenic agent, the factor of dosage must be taken into consideration. In most of the work in the field of carcinogenesis arbitrary doses have been generally employed at levels high enough to ensure the experimental animals responding to at least the more active carcinogens. The reasons behind the use of maximum effective doses (highest tumor incidence in the shortest time) were naturally compelling and understandable. A group of investigators faced with the problem of studying a large number of hydrocarbons would prefer to complete the test of each compound in the shortest possible time and, hence, doses were stepped up to levels barely short of the toxic. In the case of induction of certain tumors such as the pulmonary, mammary, and lymphatic, it was actually necessary to produce the neoplastic transformation long before the appearance in certain mice strains of similar spontaneous growths. Then again, when working with genetically heterozygous mice, the individual differences between mice were always considerable and, hence, the use of maximal doses assisted in leveling such differences.

It soon became apparent to workers in the field that the use of maximal doses were likely to obscure a number of phenomena which might be readily revealed were minimum or marginal doses employed. Where effects of large order of magnitude are encountered, even with overwhelming doses, there may be little need to experiment with dosages in order to refine such observations. But many biological effects are subtly conducted, whereby relatively small amounts of concomitant materials may force a reaction to proceed in any one of several directions. Hence, for the study of effects which may operate on a delicately adjusted level, it is often advisable to employ the smallest possible amount of material which is effective.

Before such critical experiments can be instituted, it is essential that all conditions be as highly standardized as possible. It may be expected that the complexity of the neoplastic transformation would lead to hazards in comparison. Although inbred strains of mice may be used as test objects in this transformation, it is understood that no one mouse, even from the same litter, is an exact duplicate of another mouse. The purely chemical procedures can be as accurately standardized as the limits of accuracy of gravimetric and volumetric analysis permit, but the biological procedures always possess an inherent uncertainty.

The experiments of Leiter and Shear are instructive in this respect. These investigators performed quantitative experiments on tumor production with about 5000 strain *A* mice injected with marginal doses of 3,4-benzpyrene (80). Such marginal doses were calculated to produce tumors in an appreciable percentage of the mice but were below the dosage required for production of tumors in all the animals. A single injection of benzpyrene was given subcutaneously in the dose range of 0.05 to 0.2 mg. of the carcinogen dissolved in a single specimen of tricaprylin. Experiments with various groups of animals of roughly 50 each were performed repeatedly since, even under conditions as closely standardized as possible, variations in results between groups in successive experiments occurred. Standard reference experiments were set up in this manner in ascertaining the dose-response relationships in the range in which tumors were produced in one-third to two-thirds of the animals. The following average values were obtained for tumor production in 12 months: in three experiments, in which the dose of benzpyrene was 0.05 mg., the tumor incidence was 38 %; in five experiments with a 0.065-mg. dose, the tumor incidence was 45 %; and in four experiments, using 0.1-mg. doses, the tumor incidence was 65 %. The care required in these experiments is stressed by the authors.

TABLE 11

EFFECT OF SEX ON THE PRODUCTION OF SUBCUTANEOUS TUMORS IN *A* STRAIN MICE WITH 3,4-BENZPYRENE IN TRICAPRYLIN (80)

Experiments performed	Dose	Sex of mice	Number of mice	Mice with induced tumors		
				Number	%	Ratio
3	0.2	Male	113	81	72	1.0
		Female	145	101	70	
13	0.1	Male	323	233	72	1.5
		Female	321	152	47	
8	0.08	Male	200	98	49	1.7
		Female	200	57	29	
40	0.065	Male	1,010	328	32	1.7
		Female	1,010	188	19	
3	0.05	Male	62	28	45	1.5
		Female	59	18	31	

The value of using such minimal doses is further revealed in the sex differences noted by Leiter and Shear. At relatively high doses of the carcinogen, both males and females show the same incidence of tumor production. At the marginal doses employed, however, a clear-cut distinction is elicited whereby, at equal dosages, the males show a higher tumor incidence than the females. This is revealed in Table 11.

Some time earlier, Dobrovolskaïa-Zavadskaïa (81) had attempted to find the minimum amount of 1,2,5,6-dibenzanthracene which would produce tumors in mice. Subcutaneous administration in single doses of 0.01 to 0.00125 mg. of the hydrocarbon were given to a large number of mice of unstated hereditary constitution. The data are given in Table 12.

Methods of biomathematical statistics were applied to the available data in the literature and to new data by Bryan and Shimkin (82). The newer data were obtained from a study of the range of dose response with three carcinogens, 20-methylcholanthrene, 3,4-benzpyrene, and 1,2,5,6-dibenzanthracene, injected subcutaneously into over 1000 strain *C3H* male mice. Over 99% of the tumors obtained were spindle-cell sarcomas (83). The results of these authors are given in Table 13.

TABLE 12

SUBCUTANEOUS TUMORS INDUCED IN MICE BY VARIOUS DOSAGES OF 1,2,5,6-DIBENZANTHRACENE (81)

Dose, mg.	Mice injected	Mice with tumors	Tumor incidence
0.01	328	37	11
0.005	364	13	4
0.0025	167	2	1
0.00125	158	0	0

TABLE 13

TUMOR INCIDENCE AND LATENT PERIOD OF TUMOR INDUCTION OF *C3H* MICE INJECTED SUBCUTANEOUSLY WITH HYDROCARBONS (82)

Dose, mg.	20-Methylcholanthrene		3,4-Benzpyrene		1,2,5,6-Dibenzanthracene	
	Tumor incidence, %	Mean latent period, months	Tumor incidence, %	Mean latent period, months	Tumor incidence, %	Mean latent period, months
1.0	100	2.4	90	3.3	100	3.6
0.5	100	2.6	100	3.9	95	3.8
0.25	100	2.8	67	4.4	91	4.0
0.125	100	3.3	78	5.1	91	4.5
0.062	85	3.9	20	5.8	100	5.1
0.031	65	5.2	0	—	80	6.3
0.0156	34	4.6	0	—	32	6.0
0.0078	18	7.0	0	—	15	8.8
0.0039	0	—	—	—	—	—
0.00195	0	—	2	8.4	3	9.5
0.00098	0	—	—	—	—	—
0.00024	0	—	—	—	—	—

It is of interest to note that, at the dosages used, the relative potency of the agents tested was dibenzanthracene, methylcholanthrene, and benzpyrene, with relative ratios of 6:5:1. According to Bryan and Shimkin, the potency difference between dibenzanthracene and methylcholanthrene is not significant, and the two agents may actually be of equal potency in this regard. This order of relative activity was observed by Andervont and Shimkin in the induction of lung tumors (51), with dibenzanthracene well ahead of methylcholanthrene, and with benzpyrene relatively weak.

The results of Bryan and Shimkin on the relative order of potency of the three hydrocarbons are at variance with those usually given in the literature for the induction of subcutaneous sarcomas in mice, (*vide infra*), e.g., methylcholanthrene, benzpyrene, and dibenzanthracene. However, the data of Bryan and Shimkin were obtained at much lower dose levels than those hitherto used. The results emphasize the fact again that the carcinogenicity of a given agent is a relative matter and, among a great many other factors, is dependent upon the dosage administered. Methylcholanthrene acts more quickly than does dibenzanthracene, as the respective latent induction periods show (Table 13). The relative carcinogenicity of the compounds may also be partly due to their solubilities and respective rates of diffusion in the tissues.

Cramer and Stowell (84) studied the effect of skin painting with carcinogens over various time intervals with several interesting results. With equal amounts of 20-methylcholanthrene applied to the skin of mice until 100% of the mice developed tumors, the total dose of carcinogen required was found to depend upon the intervals between painting. One group of

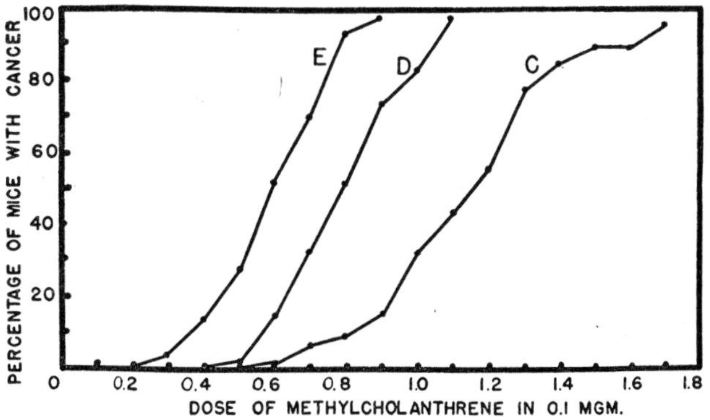

FIG. 10. Incidence of skin cancer in mice relative to dosage of methylcholanthrene after discontinuous exposure at intervals of 2 (C), 3 (D), and 4 (E) weeks. From Cramer, W., and Stowell, R. E., *Cancer Research* **3,** 668 (1943).

mice (C) was painted once every 2 weeks, another (D) was painted once every 3 weeks, and still a third group (E) was painted once every 4 weeks. The single dose was approximately 0.1 mg. of methylcholanthrene, and about 45 mice were used in each group. The results are portrayed in Fig. 10. The data reveal that the total dose necessary to induce cancer in 100 % of the animals diminishes as the exposure of the skin to the carcinogen becomes increasingly discontinuous. If the painting is performed thrice weekly, it was observed that the amounts of carcinogen necessary to produce the first tumor in a group of animals were as large as, or larger than, those required in the discontinuous method of exposure to produce tumors in all of the mice of a similar group.

Experiments by Lavik *et al.* are interesting in this connection (85). Painting of the skin of mice with 0.2 to 0.3 % solutions of methylcholanthrene twice weekly for 2 months resulted in a skin cancer incidence 3 months after the last painting of about 15 %. At this point either methylcholanthrene or benzpyrene was reapplied twice weekly for a month to the animals which had failed to develop tumors. Three months from the final painting these repainted animals revealed a tumor incidence of 50 %, whereas animals without the repainting (only the initial period of painting) had an incidence of only 20 %. It seems likely that the original treatment of the skin with methylcholanthrene had produced changes which persisted for several months and were exacerbated by the second application of the carcinogen with subsequent production of tumors. It is possible that the first period of application of the carcinogen gave rise to subcancerous or dormant cancer cells in the skin which were only evoked to development and further growth by the second period of application. The data of Lavik *et al.* are portrayed in Fig. 11.

The concept that methylcholanthrene in subactive form may yet "sensi-

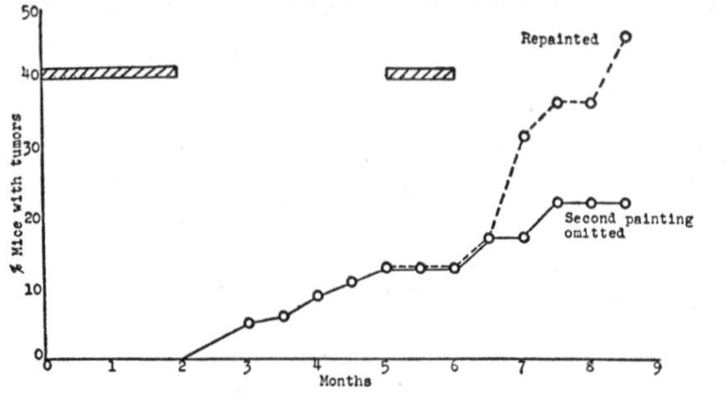

FIG. 11. Increased skin tumor formation in mice due to a renewed painting of hydrocarbon after a 3-month interval. The cross-hatched areas represent the periods of application of methylcholanthrene. From Lavik, P. S., Moore, P. R., Rusch, H. P., and Baumann, C. A., *Cancer Research* **2,** 189 (1942).

tize" tissues to subsequent applications of the carcinogen in active form was suggested again by Simpson and Cramer (86). Solutions of methylcholanthrene in anhydrous lanolin appear to be inactive in producing tumors when applied to the skin of mice. When, however, such application is followed by painting with a solution of methylcholanthrene in benzene (active form), tumors appear in greater incidence and in a considerably shorter period than when this preliminary sensitizing process is omitted.

Influence of the Solvent

The carcinogenic polycyclic hydrocarbons are very nearly insoluble in water, and if homogeneous solutions of fairly adequate concentration are to be applied to experimental animals, it is obvious that fat solvents must be employed. Various solvents have been used for this purpose, among them benzene, chloroform, ether, acetone, sesame oil, olive oil, lanolin, and tricaprylin. It soon became evident, even in the early work on carcinogenesis, that the nature of the solvent played an important role in the results obtained. The volatile solvents, such as chloroform and ether, were satisfactory as pure liquids with reproducible properties and with little if any chemical interaction with the hydrocarbon, but when applied to the skin they sometimes produced untoward pathological symptoms on this tissue and, in the case of benzene, also caused changes in the blood picture of the host; for subcutaneous, intravenous, or oral administration, they were of course out of the question. Under otherwise similar conditions, moreover, the carcinogenic effect of a given hydrocarbon might be greater in one volatile solvent than in another. Thus, Stowell and Cramer observed that epidermal carcinogenesis was obtained more rapidly with acetone than with benzene as a solvent for methylcholanthrene (87). On the whole, however, the problem of employing a satisfactory solvent among the volatile group in the area of experimental skin carcinogenesis is not a difficult one. When a non-volatile type of solvent is considered for this purpose, several at present inexplicable phenomena emerge. Thus, when lanolin (sheep sebum) was employed as a solvent for methylcholanthrene, no skin tumors in mice were induced (86). This observation appeared at first to be due to the persistence of the carcinogen in its initial, low concentration in the non-volatile solvent as contrasted with deposition of the same amount of carcinogen in more concentrated form after evaporation of a volatile solvent such as ether (88). However, the fact that solutions of methylcholanthrene in human sebum were quite effective in producing skin cancers in mice (89) takes this particular problem out of the realm of simple solubilities and into the sorry area of species differences. For quantitative studies in skin carcinogenesis, for which a constant effective concentration of carcinogen is obviously desirable, a non-volatile solvent containing a high concentration of the carcinogen may often be of value, and refined mineral oil has been recently recommended for this purpose by Berenblum and Shubik (90).

For subcutaneous administration, where solutions of the agents were desired, higher-boiling fats were essential. The use of these materials provided a number of complications, which have been listed by Berenblum as follows (91): (a) the solvent serving merely as a diluent, determining the intensity of action of the carcinogen, (b) the solvent influencing the rate of absorption of the carcinogen into the neighboring cells, (c) the solvent influencing the rate of diffusion of the carcinogen away from the site of action, (d) changes in the effective concentration of the carcinogen through a more rapid absorption of the solvent than of the carcinogen, (e) the solvent acting on the carcinogen itself, destroying it, or, by virtue of antioxidant properties, preserving it from rapid destruction *in situ*, and (f) the solvent being itself carcinogenic, or influencing the responding tissues through cocarcinogenic or anticarcinogenic action.

The earlier used media for subcutaneous administration of the carcinogenic polycyclic hydrocarbons were vegetable oils, lards, and other animal fats. Not only were the results obtained with such highly variable natural materials discordant and non-reproducible (37, 80), but it was shown that lard and olive oil, under certain conditions, could be active carcinogens themselves (34, 92). In order to avoid the uncertainties inherent in the use of such materials as solvents, Leiter and Shear (80) and Shimkin and Andervont (37) recommended the employment of tricaprylin, a solvent of known composition, of favorable physical properties, and of readily available purity. This solvent, however, has recently been reported to be very weakly carcinogenic itself in *C57 Black* mice, producing something like 1.3% tumor incidence with an average induction time of 343 days (25). In reports of this kind, where such marginal effects appear, it is often desirable to purify the agent and repeat the experiment. The experience of Hieger

(93) comes to mind in this connection, in which various samples of commercial cholesterol were found to be weakly carcinogenic when injected into mice, but these same samples, when purified, failed to elicit tumors.

An ingenious use of natural fats as solvents was the employment of the animal's own fat for such purposes (94–96). Here, however, the action of the carcinogen was found to be minimal or absent, and, as shown by Peacock, the carcinogen disappears very rapidly (along with the homologous fat) from the site of injection (97). In such cases when olive oil or tricaprylin is used as the solvent and remains encapsulated at the site of injection for a long period, the carcinogen persists at this site and a number of sarcomas subsequently develop in the animals. It was therefore considered that a slower rate of elimination of the carcinogen from the site of injection was associated with a higher incidence of tumors at that site (97), a conclusion also reached by Strait *et al.* (98) on the basis of their partition studies of hydrocarbons distributed between lipid solvents and serum.

With the hypothesis that part of the failure of carcinogens to be effective in homologous fats was due to some specific anticarcinogenic constituent in it, Dickens and Weil-Malherbe (99) carried out comparative tests on various fractions of the fats as solvents and noted that inhibitory effects appeared to be associated with the phospholipid fractions. However, although phospholipids in 50% solution proved to be inhibitory (100), the effect of weaker solutions of about the same concentration as that of phospholipids in mouse fat (i.e., tricaprylin containing 1.5% cephalin and 1.5% lecithin) was merely to delay but not to prevent the ultimate appearance of the same

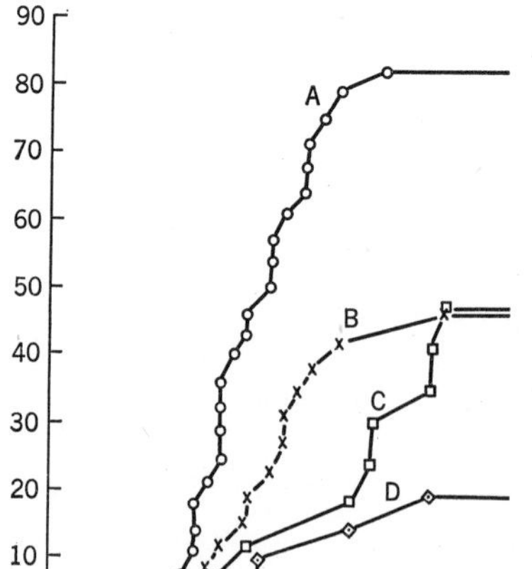

FIG. 12. Incidence of local tumors after injection into mice of 0.3 mg. 3,4-benzpyrene in 0.3 ml. of the following solvents: A, tricaprylin containing 3% cholesterol; B, tricaprylin alone; C, tricaprylin containing cephalin and lecithin; and D, fresh mouse fat. Abscissa: weeks after injection; ordinate: % tumors. From Weil-Malherbe, H., and Dickens, F., *Cancer Research* **6**, 171 (1946).

proportion of tumors as in tricaprylin alone (99) (Fig. 12). The accelerating influence of cholesterol on tumor production is dramatic (Fig. 12).

A possible explanation for the results with inhomogeneous preparations of the natural fats may be noted in the results of Mueller, Miller, and Rusch (101). When the carcinogenic hydrocarbons are dissolved in various lipids and the latter allowed to autoxidize, a considerable destruction of the agents occurs with the formation of non-carcinogenic oxidation products. Thus, benzpyrene and methylcholanthrene were rapidly destroyed in autoxidizing linoleic acid with losses of 35 and 84% noted, respectively, after only 1 week. 3,4-Benzpyrene-5,8-quinone and 3,4-benzpyrene-5,10-quinone were isolated from such mixtures. It is obvious from these results that a laboratory procedure which involved the dissolution of a carcinogen in a crude fat and which permitted such a solution to stand for varying lengths of time on the shelf or exposed occasionally to the air might give results which would be highly variable and often reveal a striking loss in activity of the agent. It should be noted that tocopherol added to such mixtures inhibits both autoxidation and destruction of the carcinogen. The stability of dibenzanthracene in autoxidizing lipids is noteworthy (Table 14).

Photo-oxidation of the hydrocarbons reduces their carcinogenic properties (102); on the other hand, the polycyclic hydrocarbons have been found to inhibit the autoxidation of certain aldehydes (103). The light sensitivity of the hydrocarbons is particularly noteworthy, for marked changes in the physicochemical properties of methylcholanthrene have been observed in aqueous suspensions exposed to diffuse daylight (104).

The use of serum (42), purine solutions (40, 41), and soap solutions (44)

TABLE 14

THE DISAPPEARANCE OF CARCINOGENIC HYDROCARBONS IN AUTOXIDIZING LIPIDS[1] (101)

Hydrocarbon, 50 γ	Lipid, 5 mg.	Tocopherol, 200 γ	Per cent hydrocarbon destroyed: 1 week	4 weeks	8 weeks
3,4-Benzpyrene	Linoleic acid	−	35	66	74
3,4-Benzpyrene	Linoleic acid	+	0.6	1	67
3,4-Benzpyrene	Ethyl linoleate	−	7	46	72
3,4-Benzpyrene	Ethyl linoleate	+	0	37	72
3,4-Benzpyrene	Ethyl oleate	−	0	11	16
3,4-Benzpyrene	Ethyl oleate	+	0	8	10
3,4-Benzpyrene	Tricaprylin	−	0	4	5
20-Methylcholanthrene	Linoleic acid	−	84	92	94
1,2,5,6-Dibenzanthracene	Linoleic acid	−	0	0	0.7

[1] By fluoroscopy.

as aqueous media for the carcinogenic hydrocarbons has been referred to. The last-mentioned has been particularly employed in efforts to break through the mucin barrier of the glandular stomach in rodents and induce adenocarcinoma. Penetration was observed, but no malignant tumors developed, perhaps because of the very low concentrations of the carcinogen.

Cocarcinogenesis and Anticarcinogenesis

The response of an animal to a carcinogenic agent may be profoundly modified by extraneous factors, both chemical and physical, when administered simultaneously with or subsequent to the agent. If the result of the modification leads to an augmentation in tumor production (i.e., a higher yield of tumors or a diminution in the latent period), it is called *cocarcinogenesis*; when the result leads to an inhibition of tumor production, it is called *anticarcinogenesis*. Actually these terms are indefinite unless applied to a particular standard of reference, which necessarily must be arbitrary. Such a reference standard must obviously not consist of conditions under which maximal tumor production is obtained, or nothing will be found to be cocarcinogenic; and similarly, it must not provide conditions in which too few tumors are obtained, or very few factors will be found to be anticarcinogenic. The standard must therefore provide conditions of a medium response to the carcinogenic agent, permitting the possibilities of an increase or a decrease in response to the agent.

Cocarcinogenesis. The ideal cocarcinogen is a chemical or physical agent which itself is non-carcinogenic but which augments the production of tumors by a carcinogenic agent. An even more dramatic example of such a cocarcinogen is one which, when applied in conjunction with a dosage of carcinogen administered at too low a level to produce tumors, will cause the production of such tumors. In the course of chemical carcinogenesis, it is not improbable that many more cells become cancer cells than ever develop into tumors unless they receive a further stimulus to make them multiply. This stimulus may be non-specific in the sense that, acting alone, it never produces tumors. In the early work on this subject, various irritating devices were employed to augment the production of tumors, such as scarification, wounding, heat and freezing, and trauma (cf. 91). Among the earliest applications of chemicals to this phenomenon was the observation by Sall and Shear that the basic fraction of creosote oil accelerated the production of skin tumors by various hydrocarbons (105), and by Berenblum on the use of croton oil for the same purpose (106). Experiments on the cocarcinogenic effect of croton oil have occupied much of the recent attention in this area of research, and a great deal of the quantitative studies have been performed by Berenblum and his colleagues (cf. 107).

A single application of 3,4-benzpyrene to the skin of a mouse may not induce cancer, but, if the single application is followed by repeated treatment with croton oil, tumors will develop (108). Croton oil by itself has no carcinogenic action, and if applied prior to the application of benzpyrene it has no effect (107). These experiments suggest that carcinogenic agents may have two actions, an initiating effect and a precipitating effect, on the second of which the cocarcinogen is catalytic. The experiments of Simpson and Cramer (86) may be alluded to again (p. 72), in which solutions of methylcholanthrene in lanolin gave rise to no skin tumors in mice but apparently "sensitized" the animals, since subsequent application of the same carcinogen in benzene caused the production of tumors in greater incidence and in a shorter period of time than when this preliminary sensitizing process was omitted. The possibility is not excluded that a carcinogen may under some conditions be a cocarcinogen for itself, although by strict definition it may not properly belong to this category.

According to Berenblum and Shubik (109), the latent period of carcinogenesis is dependent on the cocarcinogenic efficacy, whereas the actual tumor yield is predetermined by the initiating action of the carcinogen itself. Their experiments were based on four groups of 100 mice each, each group treated with a single but varying amount of 9,10-dimethyl-1,2-benzanthracene, and subsequently treated 4 weeks later on the same area of skin with croton oil applied twice weekly for 25 weeks. The results are described in Table 15. Thus, with increase in the concentration of initiator (carcinogen) there is a progressive increase in the tumor yield, although the average latent periods show no difference. It is possible that the initiating process is sudden and irreversible, not unlike a mutation. The action of the promoting or cocarcinogenic agent may, however, be a gradual one. Salaman (110) showed that a single application of croton oil to the skin of mice previously treated once with 9,10-dimethyl-1,2-benzanthracene produced no tumors. With weekly applications of croton oil, tumor production began after a latent period of 68 days and continued for 2 to 3 weeks after the croton oil treatment was stopped. When the applications were resumed after a 9-week interval, new tumors appeared, again after a latent period of 58 (or a nearly equal number of) days. Klein's recent studies

TABLE 15

PROMOTING ACTION OF CROTON OIL (109)

Concentration of carcinogen, %	Latent period, weeks	Number of mice with tumors	Total number of tumors	Average number of tumors per tumor-bearing animal
0.06	14.4	9	10	1.1
0.17	12.1	25	61	2.4
0.5	10.6	43	118	2.7
1.5	11.8	63	248	3.9

are in agreement, for they demonstrate that in intermittent treatment with croton oil each period of administration is relatively independent of the preceding in promoting the production of tumors (111). Thus the change produced by croton oil is a gradual one, requiring repeated treatment for progression toward tumor formation. In accord with such a concept are comparative experiments on the development of carcinogenesis in mice by a single application of 9,10-dimethyl-1,2-benzanthracene followed by repeated applications of either croton oil or the carcinogen itself (112). In the former case all kinds of tumor, from benign to malignant, develop, whereas in the latter practically only malignant tumors develop. It is not impossible to conceive of the carcinogen being a more effective cocarcinogen for itself than is croton oil. Further application of croton oil is unnecessary once a certain stage in tumor promotion has been reached (111).

The effect of such an agent as croton oil on the skin of mice previously treated with a carcinogen has been of great value in assisting and directing quantitative studies on carcinogenesis, particularly that of the skin. It is, however, limited to mice among the available laboratory animals, for croton oil possesses no apparent promoting action on carcinogens applied to the skin of rats, rabbits, or guinea pigs (113). For rabbits, wound-healing and applications of turpentine have been shown to be effective promoters of carcinogenesis by tar (114). After a single application of 9,10-dimethyl-1,2-benzanthracene, wound-healing alone was found to be an effective stimulus in rabbits (113). Relatively few studies on cocarcinogenesis in subcutaneously induced tumors have been made, and among these the effect of cholesterol in accelerating the rate of sarcoma induction by 3,4-benzpyrene is noteworthy (99) (see Fig. 12, p. 74).

The phenomena of cocarcinogenesis have been considered by Berenblum (91) as possible examples of irritation effects, involving a hyperplastic response at the site of irritation. However, if the effective promoting agents are merely irritants, it is difficult to see why so many irritating agents are ineffective in this respect. Moreover, among those quite different effective agents, it is not clear as to what they might possess in common (91). The most valuable result of these studies has been the indication of at least two independent steps in carcinogenesis.

The carcinogenic agent administered in subthreshold amounts need not be a hydrocarbon but can also be a source of radiation. Thus, a single exposure of the skin of mice to the moderately energetic β-rays of thallium^{204}, followed by application of croton oil, results in the formation of skin tumors with an average latent period of 3.5 months (115); animals receiving the same dose of radiation but not treated with croton oil, do not develop tumors.

The applications of cocarcinogens, and of the anticarcinogens to be subsequently described, have been more or less topical. The effect of such remote factors as the nature of the diet affecting carcinogenesis *pro* or *contra* will be described in Chapter V.

Anticarcinogenesis. The inhibitory effects of certain solvents on carcinogenesis have been described above, and the specific phenomena referred to the inclusion of phospholipids in inert solvents have been noted (Fig. 12). Complex formation between purines and the aromatic carcinogens in aqueous solutions has been suggested as one reason for the diminished activity of the latter (40, 41). These effects were induced by the carcinogen and the inhibitor administered, as it were, in juxtaposition.

The local application of bromobenzene (116), of unsaturated dibasic acids such as maleic and citraconic acids (117), and of heptaldehyde (118) markedly retards the effect of the carcinogenic polycyclic hydrocarbons. The halogenated benzene apparently interferes with the sulfur metabolism of the skin, for the glutathione and ascorbic acid levels are lowered after treatment, and the bromobenzene is detoxified as the mercapturate. It may be assumed that the local sulfur depletion in the skin lowers the potentiality for the neoplastic transformation. Analogous inhibitory effects by mustard gas on the induction of tar tumors may be explicable on the same grounds (119). Naphthalene, anthracene, and phenanthrene applied to the skin of mice caused urinary mercapturate excretion, and each of these compounds applied to the skin effectively checked the carcinogenic action of 3,4-benzpyrene and 1,2,5,6-dibenzanthracene (120). The carcinogens themselves did not produce mercapturate excretion. It is not improbable that the carcinogenic process may require combination between carcinogen and some SH-containing cell constituent (121, 122) and that the inhibitors cited are effective in competing more successfully than are the carcinogens with such constituents.

Synergistic Effect of Carcinogens. When a mixture of two hydrocarbons of nearly similar molecular configuration, one of which is actively carcinogenic and the other weakly carcinogenic, is applied to the skin of mice, the carcinogenic effect is apparently weaker than when the stronger agent is applied alone (123). Thus, mixtures of 20-methylcholanthrene and dibenzfluorene, or 1,2,5,6-dibenzanthracene and 1,2,5,6-dibenzacridine, are weaker, respectively, than methylcholanthrene or dibenzanthracene. It would appear that the weaker agent, acting in competition at critical physiological sites within the animal with the stronger agent in the mixture, reduces the effect of the latter.

This type of competitive inhibition experiment, first performed by Lacassagne and his coworkers (123), has been extended in a number of interesting directions. Riegel and his colleagues noted that the simultaneous painting of 20-methylcholanthrene and 1,2,5,6-dibenzfluorene delayed skin carcinogenesis in mice beyond the period characteristic of methylcholanthrene alone, but chrysene, fluorene, and 1,2,7,8-dibenzfluorene

TABLE 16

Carcinogenicity and Combination Effects[1] (25)

Compound(s)	Amount, mg.	Tumor yield, %	Average induction time, days
Chrysene	5.0	16.6	401
1,2-Benzanthracene	5.0	18.2	285
1,2,5,6-Dibenzanthracene	0.02	58.3	329
20-Methylcholanthrene	0.02	58.1	246
Chrysene plus 1,2-benzanthracene	2.5 each	44.1	346
1,2-Benzanthracene plus 1,2,5,6-dibenzanthracene	5.0 + 0.02	36.6	324
1,2,5,6-Dibenzanthracene plus 20-methylcholanthrene	0.02 each	78.5	180
Tricaprylin control	0.2–2.0 ml.	1.3	343
Uninjected controls	None	0	

[1] Compounds injected subcutaneously into *C57 Black* mice, 50 mice in each test.

had no effect when mixed with the more active carcinogen (methylcholanthrene) (124). One of the most thorough studies in this connection is that of Steiner and Falk (25), illustrated in Table 16. Again, when a weak and a strong carcinogen were simultaneously administered, the result was not summation but apparent inhibition. However, when two weak carcinogens (1,2-benzanthracene and chrysene) were simultaneously administered, the result was a definite summation if not actually a synergistic action. The tumor yield was greater than the sum of their individual tumor yields, despite the fact that half of the dose of each compound had been injected (Table 16). Subsequent studies showed that the original dose of 5.0 mg. of 1,2-benzanthracene was considerably above the saturation level, for as little as 0.05 mg. per mouse still produced tumors (125). The effects observed in Table 16 may therefore be considered additive in this case rather than synergistic. Finally, when two strong carcinogens (dibenzanthracene and methylcholanthrene) were simultaneously injected, the effect was additive although imperfectly so.

Other observations in this area anticipate later discussion in this volume, but they may be summarized as follows. The simultaneous administration of 20-methylcholanthrene and 3′-methyl-dimethylaminoazobenzene resulted in a lower induction of liver tumors than that produced by the azo dye alone (126) and very significantly prolonged the lives of the animals (127). Liver cirrhosis was either delayed or prevented. In these experiments the methylcholanthrene was administered in various ways, i.e., in the diet, subcutaneously, intraperitoneally, or by vaginal lavage. When the methylcholanthrene was administered orally or intraperitoneally nearly complete inhibition of the liver tumors occurred, but when given intravaginally or even subcutaneously the inhibition of liver tumor formation was only partial. Even though the production of liver tumors was inhibited, fibrous tumors due to the methylcholanthrene made their usual appearance in animals receiving the carcinogen subcutaneously and intraperitoneally. Thus, methylcholanthrene under these conditions may be considered an anticarcinogen for 3′-methyl-dimethylaminoazobenzene. The negative results noted with methylcholanthrene and dimethylaminoazobenzene (128) may be attributed to the use of too little of the former compound. Nitrogen mustard [methylbis(β-chloroethyl)amine], i.e., HN_2, injected at the time of feeding 3′-methyl-dimethylaminoazobenzene also gives rise to much less liver tumors than does the azo dye alone (129). However, when two hepatic carcinogens are fed simultaneously, there results an actual synergism, for mixtures of 2-acetylaminofluorene with 3′-methyl-dimethylaminoazobenzene, or of dimethylaminoazobenzene with 4′-methyl-dimethylaminoazobenzene, resulted in a higher incidence of liver tumors than the sum of the incidences obtained when the same levels of each of the compounds were fed singly (130).

Certain mice strains respond to either methylcholanthrene administration or to X-irradiation by the development of leukemia, and under certain conditions these agents may act synergistically (131–133). Under a variety of conditions the administration of hormones, or alterations in the diet, affect the incidence of tumors, both spontaneous and induced, but a consideration of these effects does not properly belong under the present heading and will be discussed below.

Distribution and Metabolism of Administered Hydrocarbons

In the endeavor to obtain some information as to how the carcinogenic hydrocarbons may effect the production of tumors, solutions or suspensions of these agents were injected or otherwise applied by a number of investigators in several species of animals and the fate of the agents followed. These studies generally took two forms, namely (a) observations on the distribution and persistence of the agents in the tissues, and (b) the isolation from the urine and feces of the treated animals of substances which might conceivably represent metabolic products of these agents.

Studies on the distribution of the hydrocarbons are facilitated by their known fluorescence spectra in the ultraviolet. By following this fluorescence after application of the agent some concept of its early fate may be ascertained. After one application of 3,4-benzpyrene to the skin, Beck and Peacock reported that the carcinogen disappeared from this site in 4 days (134). Hieger observed that, no matter how long mice were painted with 1,2,5,6-dibenzanthracene, the fluorescence of the compound was not detected more than 3 weeks after the last application (135). Simpson and Cramer (136) found that the painting of mouse skin with a benzene solution of methylcholanthrene resulted in a selective distribution of the agent. Immediately after application the bulk of the carcinogen was observed in the epidermis at two special sites: in the sebaceous glands and in the keratin layer. At these sites the carcinogen was dissolved, respectively, in the sebum and in the free lipids of the keratinized epithelium. There was no evidence that the unchanged carcinogen was taken up directly by the epithelial cells of the normal epidermis. After 10 days, the fluorescence due to the carcinogen disappeared from all parts of the skin. That most of the applied hydrocarbons may disappear relatively quickly from the sites of application was also noted by Chalmers (137) and by Berenblum and Kendal (138). However, not all the hydrocarbon disappears from the site of application, for, by an improved technique, Lorenz and Shear observed the presence of 1,2,5,6-dibenzanthracene within tumors induced by lard solutions of this agent (139). Transplants of the tumors, however, showed no evidence for the presence of the agent. The difficulty in interpreting the results in this approach is due to the fact that the carcinogenic transformation may not necessarily be due to the hydrocarbon originally applied but to some alteration product thereof. The disappearance of properties associated with the original hydrocarbons may mean either that it is disappearing as such through the general circulation or that it is being rapidly converted into products with new, and as yet unrecognized, characteristics. Hydrogenation of the double bonds would produce loss in fluorescence. The difficulty alluded to above is further exemplified in the experiments of Lorenz and Shimkin (140).

The relative susceptibility of certain strains of mice to the same carcinogenic agent is by now an accepted fact. Thus in *A* strain mice, intravenous injection of emulsions of methylcholanthrene produces multiple lung tumors with a high incidence within a short period of time; under the same conditions lung tumors appear in *C57 Black* strain mice with a low incidence only after a period roughly five times as long as that required for *A* strain mice. If the lower susceptibility of the *C57 Black* strain mice is due to a more rapid disappearance of the carcinogen from these mice than from *A* strain mice, it should be possible to detect this difference readily by absorption spectrum analysis both of the lungs and of the entire carcasses of mice of both strains. Lorenz and Shimkin, however, noted that the rate of disappearance of the carcinogen was the same for both strains and, hence, this rate does not explain the considerable difference in susceptibility to induced primary lung tumors of the two strains of mice.

This is further exemplified by the data of Weil-Malherbe and Dickens (cf. Fig. 12, p. 74) on the elimination rates of 3,4-benzpyrene dissolved in tricaprylin alone, tricaprylin containing 3 % cholesterol, or tricaprylin containing 1.5 % cephalin and 1.5 % lecithin. These rates were shown to be of the same order as the carcinogenic activity of the mixtures, and the results suggest that the more rapid rates of disappearance of the carcinogen may simply mean not that the latter is being lost to the host animal but that it is being correspondingly rapidly transformed by metabolic reactions into products which are themselves the true carcinogenic agent or agents. Results obtained by the use of C^{14}-labeled carcinogens are consistent with these observations, for under more or less standardized conditions, i.e., same injected dose in tricaprylin as solvent, dibenzanthracene-9,10-C^{14} (141), methylcholanthrene-11-C^{14} (142), and benzpyrene-5-C^{14} (143) were eliminated from mice (through the feces) at quite different rates, benzpyrene and methylcholanthrene, which are the more active carcinogens, being eliminated the faster. The more active carcinogens may be those which are most readily metabolized.

The fate of the carcinogenic polycyclic hydrocarbons has generally been followed by fluorescence and light absorption methods, and more recently by the use of tracer studies using C^{14} (cf. 144), and sometimes by a combination of both optical and radioactive tracer techniques (145). If radioactivity alone is measured in the various tissues of animals administered the labeled carcinogen, the results show just the distribution of the radioactive element which may be associated with (a) the unaltered carcinogen, (b) some detoxication product of the carcinogen, or (c) some metabolic degradation product of the carcinogen. Such studies are therefore usually supplemented by the so-called carrier technique in which unlabeled carcinogen or metabolic product thereof is added, and the mixture is subsequently recrystallized from several solvents to constant radioactivity or, if the amounts involved are very small, chromatographed on paper and the resulting spot fractions radioautographed. In the absence of these supplementary procedures, distribution studies in various tissues of radioactivity just by itself have little meaning.

Individual Carcinogens. If carcinogenic effectiveness in an animal was due not to the carcinogen itself but to one or more specific metabolic products thereof, it might be expected that the original compound, introduced into animals of two species, for one of which it is carcinogenic and for the other of which it is not carcinogenic, would be metabolized differently in each. This approach has been intensively cultivated by Boyland (146–148), and many interesting and suggestive phenomena have emerged. It has long been known that phenolic derivatives can be isolated from the urine of animals given aromatic hydrocarbons. These phenolic derivatives may have been produced in part at least from labile precursors during the collection or chemical manipulation of the urine. In any event, it is probable that the animal body has the capacity to add the elements of hydrogen peroxide to aromatic hydrocarbons in such a way as to form neutral, water-soluble compounds (perhydroxylation—Fieser, 22).

Administration of naphthalene or anthracene (149) to animals yields several water-soluble derivatives in the urine, among the most abundant of which are the diols, or 1,2-dihydroxy-1,2-dihydronaphthalenes and 1,2-dihydroxy-1,2-dihydroanthracenes. Analogous diols have been obtained from the urine of animals given phenanthrene (149). On treatment with acid the diols readily give up water and are converted into the corresponding phenols. The hydroxyl groups possess the *trans* configura-

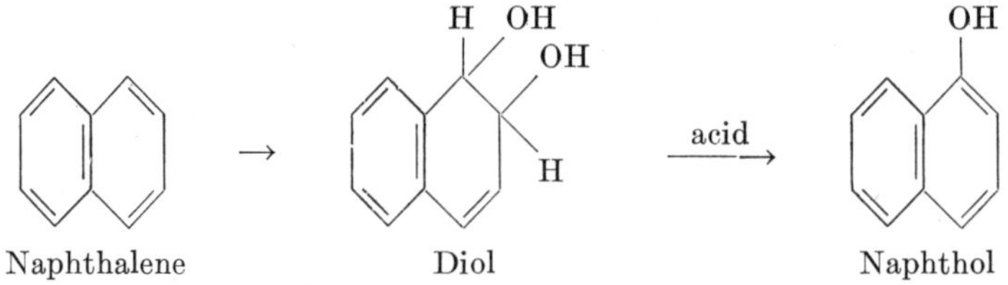

d- and *dl*- forms from rabbits
l- and *dl*- forms from rats

tion (146). With rats, the diol compounds are mainly levorotatory; with rabbits they are mainly dextrorotatory. The formation of the diols in the two species is obviously governed by a different optical specificity. To extrapolate these findings to the carcinogenicity of 1,2,5,6-dibenzanthracene in the former species, and its lack of carcinogenicity in the latter species, would not be warranted, but such findings do suggest future areas of investigation and provide some basic knowledge of what is meant by that vague and all-too-often convenient expression "species difference."

3,4-Benzpyrene is excreted from the animal only in small amounts as such; the greater part of the administered material is excreted mainly (in the feces) as metabolites. Berenblum and his colleagues identified one of the metabolites as 8-hydroxy-3,4-benzpyrene (150, 151). Both rats and rabbits excrete 8- and also 10-hydroxy-3,4-benzpyrene, the former species excreting relatively less of the 10-compound in relation to the 8-isomer than do rabbits. Oxidation of these phenols leads to 5,8- and 5,10-quinones (101, 152). Other metabolites of benzpyrene have been more difficult to identify (153). Thus, intravenous administration of benzpyrene leads to the excretion of blue fluorescent material in the bile, which is different from that of benzpyrene itself. This material was called "BPX" by Peacock (154). When the bile reaches the ileocecal valve, the fluorescence changes to green-blue, and it is this green-blue fluorescent constituent of the feces which was identified as 8-hydroxy-3,4-benzpyrene. "BPX" is thus a precursor of the phenol, and it is found not only in the digestive tract but in a variety of tissues after administration of 3,4-benzpyrene to the animal, whether by painting on the skin or by subcutaneous injection. Four apparently different compounds have been separated from extracts of the various blue-fluorescent tissues of benzpyrene-treated animals (155, 156). Two were called X_1 and X_2, and the others, separated from extracts of the large intestine and feces, were termed F_1 and F_2. The four compounds are distinguishable from each other spectroscopically and chemically. Their relations have been described as follows (147):

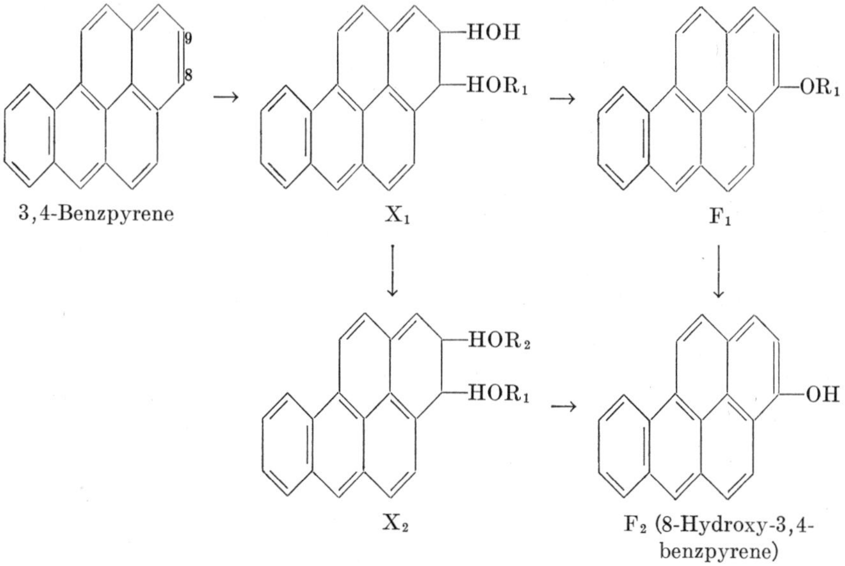

It is possible that X_1 and X_2 correspond to the dihydroxydihydroanthracenes and are convertible to the phenolic end product. The chemical nature of R_1 and R_2 is not yet known, nor is it known whether X_1, X_2, and F_1 are carcinogenic on administration to animals. It was formerly believed that F_2 or 8-hydroxy-3,4-benzpyrene, like all hydroxylated hydrocarbons, possessed no carcinogenic activity. However, Cook and Schoental tested synthetic 8-hydroxy-, 8-methoxy-, and also 8-methyl-3,4-benzpyrene by skin painting or by subcutaneous injection in *CBA* strain mice (157) and noted the following: (a) the 8-hydroxy compound was inactive on injection but on painting produced skin tumors in 50% of the animals in 113 weeks; although the compound was obviously very weakly carcinogenic, it is the first example of an active phenolic metabolite of a carcinogenic hydrocarbon; (b) the 8-methoxy compound was extremely active by both routes of administration not only in the mouse strain cited but in rats as well; and (c) the 8-methyl compound was at least as potent a carcinogen as the parent substance. The 8-position is apparently crucial in this connection, for the high activity of 8-methoxy-3,4-benzpyrene stands in contrast with that of the ineffective 4′-methoxy- and 5-methoxy-3,4-benzpyrenes (158).

After intraperitoneal injection of 3,4-benzpyrene into *A* strain mice, the unchanged carcinogen is found in the mitochondrial and nuclear fractions of the livers of these animals (159). The hydrocarbon is detected in the former fraction during the interval of 4 hours to 5 days after the original injection, whereas it persists in the nuclear fraction for as long as 21 weeks. No trace of the hydrocarbon is found in the supernatant fluid fraction, and none of the primary oxidation products.

1,2-Benzanthracene, a weak carcinogen, yields as an excretion product the 4′-hydroxy derivative (160, 161), 9,10-dimethyl-1,2-benzanthracene, gives the 4⁷-hydroxy derivative (162), whereas 1,2,5,6-dibenzanthracene yields the 4′,8′-dihydroxy derivative (163, 164). The phenolic products of these compounds seem to suggest a similar pattern of metabolism, no matter what their degree of carcinogenicity may be among themselves or between susceptible species like the mouse and rat or resistant species like the rabbit. Such a suggestion might prove misleading, however, since, as noted above in the simpler hydrocarbons studied by Boyland, the end products as phenols may be the same, but the relatively unstable precursors, which somewhere down the line may include the active carcinogenic agent or agents, may be clearly different. In contrast with the high carcinogenic potency of 8-methoxy-3,4-benzpyrene is the lack of any carcinogenic effectiveness of 4′-methoxy-9,10-dimethyl-1,2-benzanthracene (165).

That the hydroxyl derivative of the intact polycyclic structure of the parent hydrocarbon need not be the end product of the metabolism was shown in a masterly performance of the isotope carrier technique by Heidelberger and Wiest (166). These authors prepared 1,2,5,6-dibenzanthracene-9,10-C^{14} and, after administration to albino mice, isolated 5-hydroxy-1,2-naphthalic acid. The probable sequence of the metabolism of 1,2,5,6-dibenzanthracene is given on the following page (144). The hydroxynaphthalic acid has no apparent carcinogenicity in mice, nor does it affect the growth of established tumors, and it is clearly a detoxication product. The demonstration that dibenzanthracene-3,4-quinone is a metabolite (167) is of some interest in that it is the first instance known in which a product of a carcinogenic hydrocarbon has been found with substituents on the phenanthrene double bond (the so-called K-region—see below). However, there is another phenanthrene double bond in dibenzanthracene, and the symmetrical compound, dibenzanthracene-3,4,7,8-quinone, has been shown not to be a metabolite (167).

It must be reluctantly concluded that, despite many interesting approaches, few if any decisive facts have emerged regarding the modes whereby the carcinogenic agent effects its mission. Of the total amount of hydrocarbon administered to an animal, only a very small fraction can be isolated as metabolites of recognizable identity (168). It may be wondered whether a full accounting of all the possible metabolites is desirable or possible and whether new experimental approaches based upon biochemical mechanisms involving tissue components would not be of greater value. In an area which has been almost exclusively dominated by synthetic organic chemistry and pathology, the biochemist has had little opportunity until

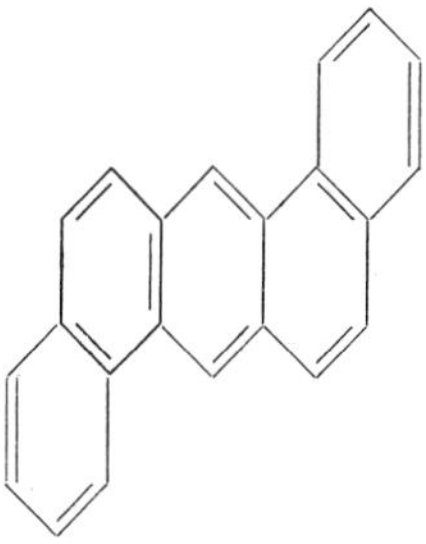

1,2,5,6-Dibenzanthracene

↙ ↘

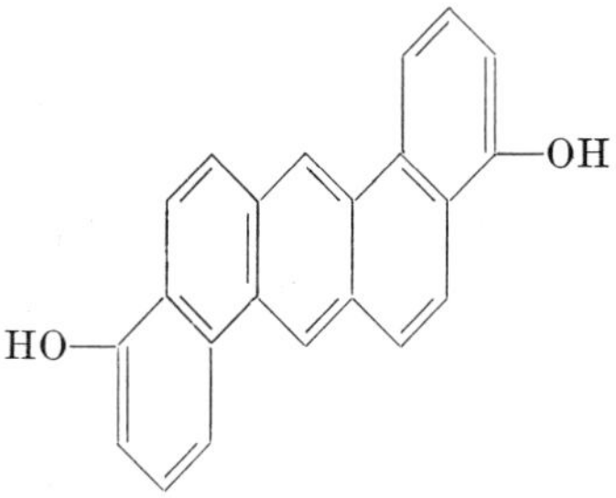

4′,8′-Dihydroxy-1,2,5,6-dibenzanthracene

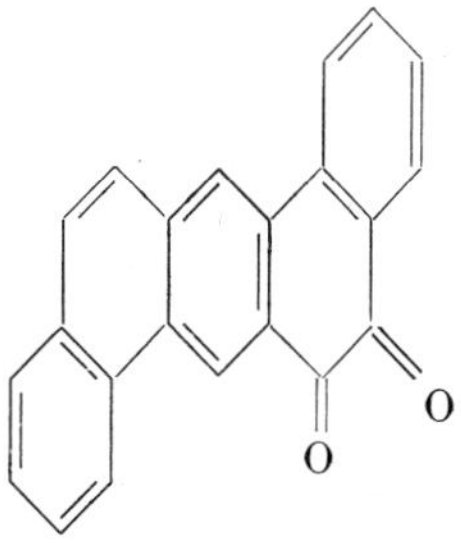

1,2,5,6-Dibenzanthracene-3,4-quinone

↓

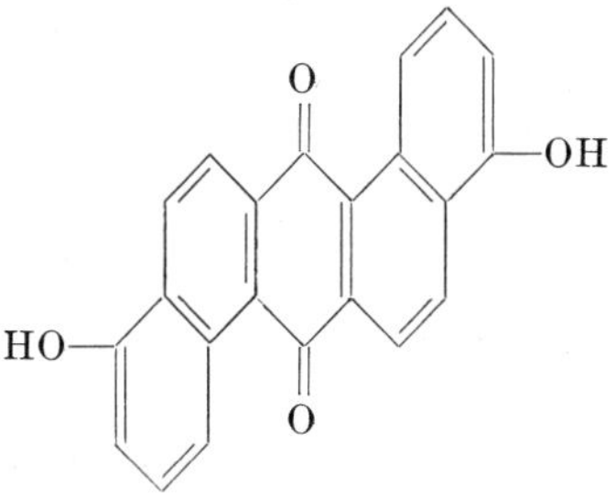

4′,8′-Dihydroxy-1,2,5,6-dibenzanthracene-9,10-quinone

↓

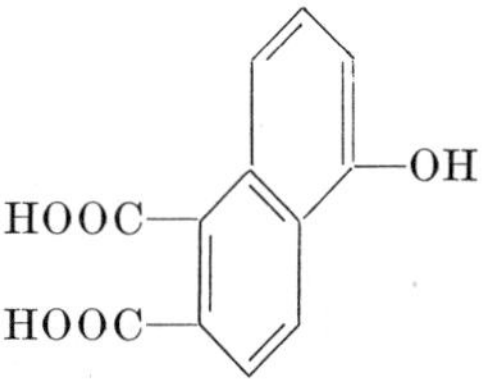

5-Hydroxy-1,2-naphthalic acid

recently to show his wares. It is not improbable that a further development of the newer approaches will provide the rationale that this very important field needs.

The Azo Dyes

With few exceptions, the polycyclic hydrocarbons produce tumors at the site of application. The effect of the nitrogen-containing compounds is more generally to produce tumors at sites distant from that of application. Among this class of compound are the azo dyes, the aminofluorenes, the aminostilbenes, etc. Whereas the aminofluorenes and the aminostilbenes induce tumors in a wide variety of tissues, the azo dyes are carcinogenic almost exclusively for the liver. Like the polycyclic hydrocarbons, the carcinogenic properties of the azo dyes are strongly influenced by their chemical structure. The history of the use of the azo dyes has been described by Shear (169), Kinosita (170), Kirby (171), J. A. and E. C. Miller (172), and Badger (29).

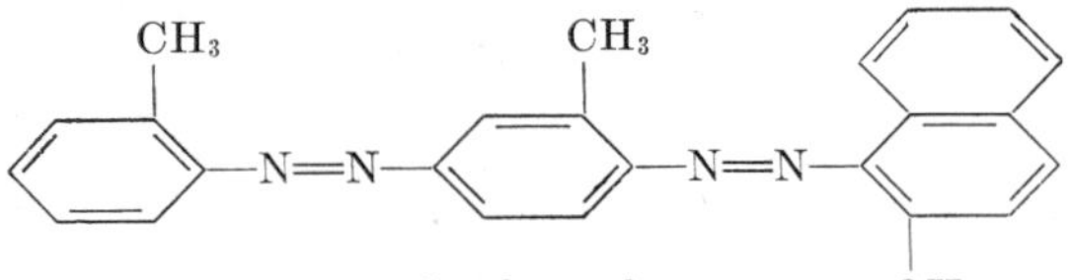

Scarlet red

The earliest work on the proliferative properties of the azo dyes dates back to 1906 when B. Fischer (173) injected solutions of scarlet red into the ears of rabbits. An atypical epithelial proliferation resulted which eventually regressed. The resemblance of such proliferation to a cancerous growth impressed Fischer and the numerous investigators who subsequently repeated, confirmed and extended his work on scarlet red (174, 175).

The proliferative properties of scarlet red were employed by clinicians in the early years of this century in the healing of epithelial wounds (176). In the course of studies designed to avoid the use of the highly colored dye, it was noted that *o*-aminoazotoluene was the active part of the scarlet red molecule. The use of *o*-aminoazotoluene revealed its capacity to produce a rapid proliferation of epithelial tissue when externally applied. These

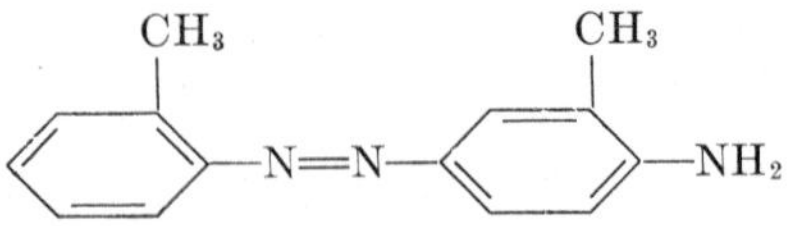

o-Aminoazotoluene

properties might have led to further intensive study on this class of chemical substances, but, with the publication in 1915 of Yamagiwa and Ichikawa which announced the first successful induction of epithelial cancer through the use of tar, interest in the topic of carcinogenesis shifted from the azo compounds to coal tar and its derivatives.

The use of azo dyes as possible carcinogenic agents was taken up later by Yoshida in Japan. Yoshida noted that, on subcutaneous injection of a solution of *o*-aminoazotoluene into guinea pigs, the thyroids of these animals showed degenerative atrophy followed by atypical epithelial regeneration. When aminoazobenzene was used, however, only epithelial damage without regeneration was produced. When solutions of these compounds were administered subcutaneously to mice, the aminoazotoluene induced a considerable proliferation of hepatic tissue (177, 178). Further studies by Yoshida in 1934 revealed that the subcutaneous injection of *o*-aminoazotoluene in olive oil into rats and mice—or its feeding, together with a rice diet—produced, after many months, the development of hepatomas in these animals. The hepatomas which appeared in rats could be subsequently transplanted into other rats of a similar line. The *p*-isomer of aminoazotoluene was non-carcinogenic.

These observations of Yoshida were of great interest, for they represented the first successful attempt to induce a tumor of a parenchymous tissue, other than that of lung, at a site considerably removed from the site of application. In 1937 Kinosita announced that 4-dimethylaminoazobenzene when incorporated in the diet of rats produced hepatomas in these animals after many months of feeding (179). In mice, no hepatomas were invoked by this chemical substance.

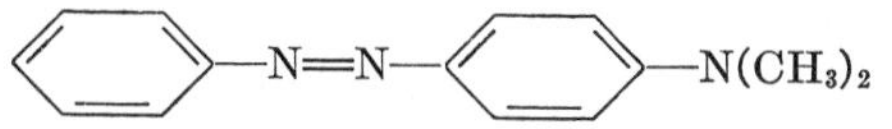

4-Dimethylaminoazobenzene

Intensive investigation in this class of molecules followed, both in Japan by Kinosita, and in the United States by Shear, Andervont, J. White, and Baumann. In 1937, Shear injected inbred *A* strain mice subcutaneously with *o*-aminoazotoluene and obtained multiple primary hepatomas which could be transplanted into new hosts of the same strain (180).

Administration of 4-dimethylaminoazobenzene causes degenerative changes in liver cells accompanied by chromatolysis of cytoplasmic structures that stain with basic dyes. These structures contain ribonucleic acid. Chromatolysis is succeeded by focal regeneration with reaccumulation of ribonucleic acid in the cytoplasm. Hepatomas appear to arise from these foci of basophile hyperplasia (181).

The multiple carcinogenic effects of *o*-aminoazotoluene were revealed by Andervont *et al.* (182–184), who showed that subcutaneous administration of the substance induced in mice of various inbred strains not only hepatomas but also hemangioendotheliomas, pulmonary tumors, and, particularly in *C57 Black* mice, subcutaneous sarcomas. In general, females were more susceptible to the development of hepatic lesions than were males. This sex difference is apparently quite pronounced in mice of all the strains studied, e.g., *A*, *C*, and *C57 Black*, because a 10-mg. dose of the carcinogen evoked hepatic lesions in all the females of these strains, whereas 100-mg. doses failed to evoke these lesions in most males of these strains. Andervont and Edwards noted that the response of *A* strain female mice to *o*-aminoazotoluene was roughly proportional to the amount of carcinogen employed, the percentage incidence of hepatomas rising from 30% with a 10-mg. dose to 65% with a 60-mg. dose.

The fact that *o*-aminoazotoluene possesses a rather wide range of carcinogenic effects was also demonstrated by Law (185), Morosenskaya (186), and Turner and Mulliken (187). This agent apparently can produce neoplasms simultaneously in the liver, lung, blood vessel endothelium, and subcutaneous fibrous tissue. The hemangioendotheliomas may occur in the lung, ovary, liver, adrenal cortex, and fat depots throughout the body of the mouse (182). These effects are not limited to subcutaneous injections of solutions of the carcinogen but may also be evoked by incorporating it in the diet of susceptible strain *C* mice, as shown by Andervont, White, and Edwards (188).

o-Aminoazotoluene is, therefore, a highly potent carcinogenic agent in mice. It appears from the pioneer work of Yoshida and Iikubo that it is also quite active in inducing hepatomas in rats, but it has not received in this species anything like the attention which has been paid to its effect in mice. The compound is also carcinogenic in dogs, for, when fed at a rate of 5 mg. per kilo per day for 30 to 60 months, tumors developed in the liver, the urinary bladder, and the gall bladder (189). It is of interest to note that the deaminated compound, azotoluene, is non-carcinogenic to the rat liver but does produce papillomas of the urinary bladder in this species (190). Dogs fed 4-dimethylaminoazobenzene at the rate of 20 mg. per kilo per day for 16 months developed tumors of the urinary bladder (189). The capacity for several of the amino-substituted aromatic compounds to induce tumors of the bladder is noteworthy, and their suspected implication in problems of industrial cancer in regard to human beings will be discussed below.

The other representative of this class of substances which has received much attention is 4-dimethylaminoazobenzene. As noted, this compound, when incorporated into the diet of rats, readily produces hepatomas. Administered subcutaneously in olive oil solution to mice of several inbred strains (*A*, *C*, and *C57 Black*), or incorporated in the diet of *C* strain mice, this compound induced only very few and scanty hepatic lesions. Thus, in rats, 4-dimethylaminoazobenzene and *o*-aminoazotoluene are both active in inducing hepatomas, but in mice the former compound has relatively little carcinogenic activity whatever as compared with the latter compound.

With the inclusion of 4-dimethylaminoazobenzene in the diet of experimental animals, it was noted by the Japanese workers (cf. 191) that the incidence of the hepatomas which resulted could be markedly affected by the kind of diet used. The early diets employed were made up largely of rice and carrots, and the incidence of the tumors, as well as the mortality of the animals prior to the appearance of tumors, was high. When liver was fed to such animals simultaneously with the dye, the incidence of tumors decreased. These findings led to much subsequent work, with the observation that the inclusion of riboflavin in experimental diets containing the carcinogen retarded the appearance of hepatomas (192, 193) (cf. Chapter V).

In the description of the effect of chemical structure on the carcinogenic action of this class of compounds, a numbering system for substituents is employed as follows:

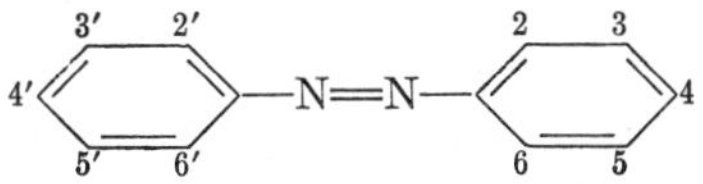

Thus *o*-aminoazotoluene is 4-amino-2′,3-azotoluene, and *p*-dimethylaminoazobenzene is 4-dimethylaminoazobenzene. The parent compound, 4-aminoazobenzene, induces a few liver tumors in the rat after a very long period of feeding (194). However, even the amino group is not essential for activity in this class of compounds, for Cook, Hewett, Kennaway, and Kennaway (195) found that some of the azonaphthalenes were carcinogenic in mice. Thus, by different modes of administration many liver tumors of the cholangioma type were obtained with 2,2′-azonaphthalene, and a few with 1,1′-azonaphthalene.

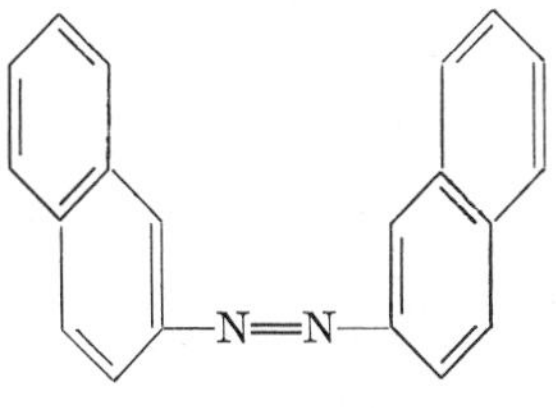

2,2′-Azonaphthalene

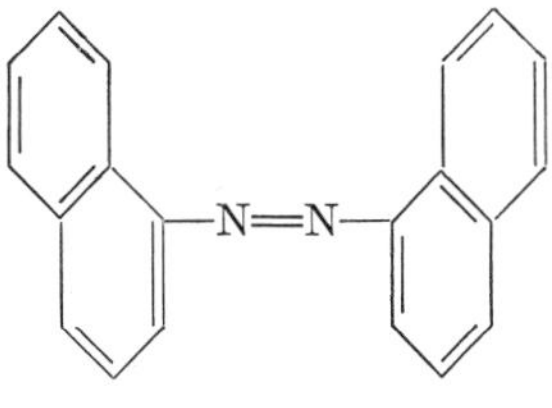

1,1′-Azonaphthalene

These authors (195) made the interesting suggestion that the active azo compound might be reduced *in vivo* to the hydrazo derivative and subsequently undergo a benzidine transformation with loss of ammonia to form the corresponding carbazole derivative, thus:

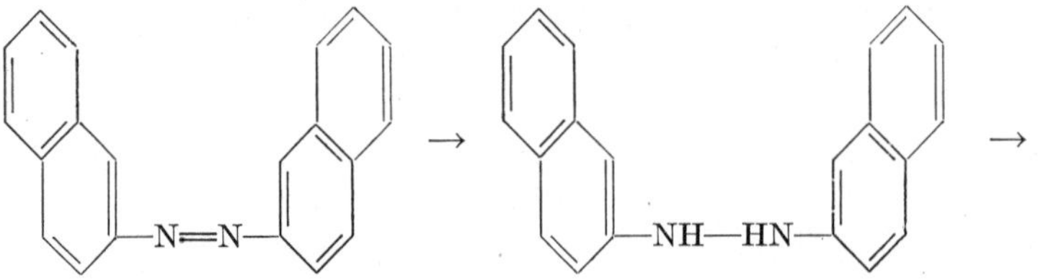

2,2′-Azonaphthalene

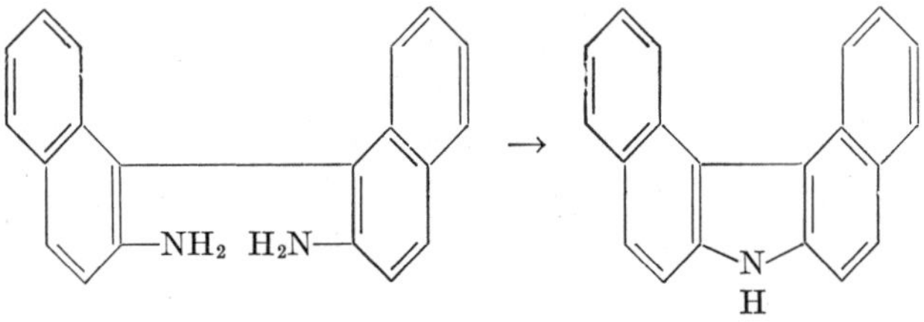

3,4,5,6-Dibenzcarbazole

These transformations can occur *in vitro*, but whether they occur *in vivo* remains conjectural. The 1,2′-azonaphthalene which is not carcinogenic yields by the same transformation the non-carcinogenic 1,2,5,6-dibenzcarbazole. The carcinogenic 2,2′-azonaphthalene, on the other hand, yields the carcinogenic (liver) 3,4,5,6-dibenzcarbazole (196). In the case of the 4-dimethylaminoazobenzenes, however, benzidine rearrangement of the corresponding hydrazo compound yields inactive 2,4′-diamino-5-dimethylaminodiphenyl (197). However, 4-dimethylaminodiphenyl induces

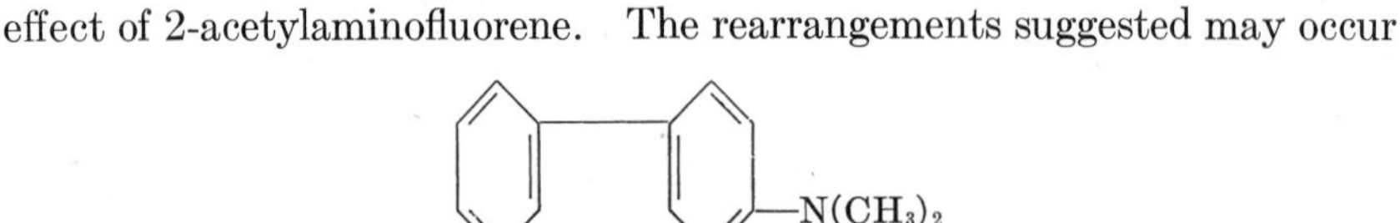

2,4′-Diamino-5-dimethylaminodiphenyl

cancer in a wide variety of tissues in the male rat (198), much like the effect of 2-acetylaminofluorene. The rearrangements suggested may occur

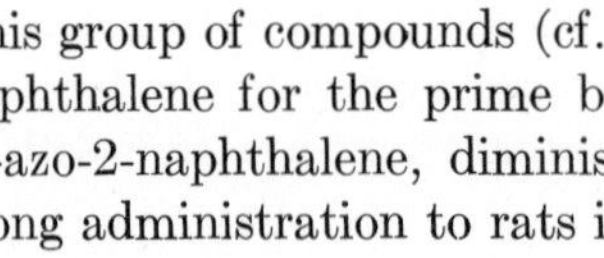

4-Dimethylaminodiphenyl

in certain of the azo dyes, but doubt has been expressed as to their more general occurrence in this group of compounds (cf. 199).

Substitution of a naphthalene for the prime benzene ring, as in 4-dimethylaminobenzene-1-azo-2-naphthalene, diminishes the activity of the compound. On very long administration to rats it induced the formation of liver tumors (200), and in mice it induced the formation of hepatomas and hemangioendotheliomas (201). Substitution of one of the benzene rings by pyridine, as in pyridine-1-oxide-4-azo-*p*-dimethylaniline, results in a very active compound in producing hepatomas in rats (201a).

Replacement of the nitrogen atoms of the azo linkage by CH, one at a time, leads to inactive compounds. Thus, where one N has been replaced by a CH, as in N,N-dimethyl-N′-benzal-*p*-phenylenediamine or as in 4-dimethylaminobenzalaniline, no activity in rats was noted. When both nitrogens were replaced, however, as in 4-dimethylaminostilbene, a potent carcinogen was produced. This carcinogen produces a variety of tumors in the rat (202), and it would appear that the replacement of the azo linkage in 4-dimethylaminoazobenzene thus produces a carcinogen of less specialized activity. However, replacement of the azo linkage in the very active 2,2′-azonaphthalene by the same CH═CH linkage, as in 2,2′-dinaphthylethylene, leads to an inactive compound (7).

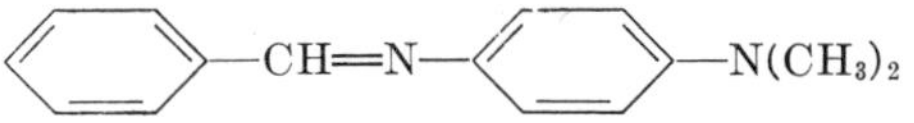

N,N-Dimethyl-N′-benzal-*p*-phenylenediamine

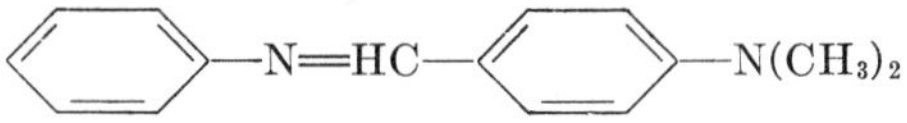

4-Dimethylaminobenzalaniline

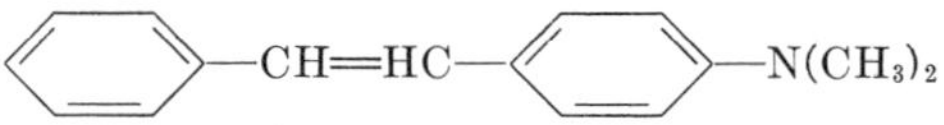

4-Dimethylaminostilbene

The six structural isomers of aminoazotoluene were examined for their carcinogenicity under comparable conditions by Crabtree (203); the results are shown in Table 17. The diet employed was deliberately inadequate in protein and in certain of the B vitamins. The results demonstrate the importance of the position of the substituents in this type of molecule, and the greater effect on mice than on rats.

TABLE 17

Carcinogenic Activity of the Isomeric Aminoazotoluenes (203)

Compound	Carcinogenic activity in: Mice	Rats
4-Amino-2′,3-azotoluene	++	+
2-Amino-2′,5-azotoluene	++	+
4-Amino-4′,2-azotoluene	++	0
4-Amino-3′,2-azotoluene	±	0
4-Amino-4′,3-azotoluene	±	0
2-Amino-4′,5-azotoluene	0	0

Among the substituted azobenzenes, active carcinogens for the liver of rats have been noted for the 4-amino (relatively weak), 4-methylamino (++), 4-methylethylamino (++), 4′-methyl-4-amino (+), 2′-methyl-4-methylamino (+), 3′-methyl-4-methylamino (+++), and 4′-methyl-4 methylamino (+) derivatives (cf. 204). The use of higher alkyl substituents, i.e., diethyl, dipropyl, dibutyl, in place of methyl as substituents in the 4-amino group led to inactive compounds (205). The 2′- and 4′-methyl derivatives are less effective than the parent 4-methylaminoazobenzene, but the 3′-derivative is a very active carcinogen. The same feature holds in the case of the substituted 4-dimethylaminoazobenzenes.

The effect of substitution on this class of hepatic carcinogens has been intensively studied by Baumann and the Millers (cf. 172). They have used a somewhat arbitrary scale in comparing the potency of the various derivatives, in which the unsubstituted 4-dimethylaminoazobenzene is given the value of 6 (206). The various compounds were fed to rats in equivalent amounts (equivalent to 0.06% of 4-dimethylaminoazobenzene which, under the conditions employed, gave a liver tumor incidence of 70 to 92% in 4 months and 100% in 6 months). The formula employed was:

$$\text{Relative activity} = \frac{6 \times \text{months of feeding 4-dimethyl-aminobenzene} \times \text{per cent tumors with test compound}}{\text{Months of feeding test compound} \times \text{per cent tumors with 4-dimethylaminoazobenzene}}$$

Table 18 describes the collected data reported by Miller *et al.* (207). The extraordinary effect of the fluorine atom substituent in enhancing the activity of the parent compound, no matter where substituted, is noteworthy. Of all the methyl substituents, only the 3′-derivative enhances

TABLE 18

CARCINOGENESIS (LIVER) OF VARIOUS RING-SUBSTITUTED DERIVATIVES OF 4-DIMETHYLAMINOAZOBENZENE[1] (207)

Position	Substituent						
	F	CH_3	Cl	Br	NO_2	CF_3	OH
4′	10–12	<1	1–2		0	0	0
3′	10–12	10–12	5–6	0	5	0	0
2′	7	2–3	2		3	0	0
2	>10	0					0
3		0					
2′,4′	>10	0					
2′,5′	>10	0	0				
3′,5′	>10	0					
2′,4′,6′	>10		0	0			

[1] Parent compound = activity of 6.

activity. It may be pointed out here that the 7-fluoro derivative of 2-aminofluorene is also more active in inducing tumors in rats than is the parent compound (208). The inhibitory action of the trifluoromethyl group, even in the 3′-position, is rather curious (Table 18).

The activity of the 4′-fluoro derivative, like that of the parent dye, can be inhibited by high levels of riboflavin in the diet (209). On the other hand, the activity of the 3′-methyl derivative, another example of a carcinogen more potent than the parent dye, is not appreciably affected by dietary supplements of this vitamin. Another interesting point of difference among these derivatives is the fact that, although the parent dye produces hepatic tumors nearly equally well in males and in females, the 3′-methyl and 4′-fluoro derivatives are much more active in males than in females (210). It is stated that primary hepatomas in human beings occur much more frequently among males than among females (211). It may be that other physiological factors are influenced by the structure of the dyes, which in turn affect the carcinogenic process. Liver slices derived from animals of both sexes cleaved the 3′-methyl and 4′-fluoro derivatives at the same rate, and thus the differences in incidence of tumors in the two sexes may very likely be due to influences other than those involved in the hepatic metabolism of these compounds (210).

The simultaneous administration of 4-dimethylaminoazobenzene and 4′-methyl-4-dimethylaminoazobenzene, or of 2-acetylaminofluorene and 3′-methyl-4-dimethylaminoazobenzene, resulted in a higher incidence of liver tumors than the sum of the incidences obtained when the same levels of each of the compounds were fed singly (212). When 20-methylcholanthrene (213) or nitrogen mustard (214), were administered together with 3′-methyl-4-dimethylaminoazobenzene, however, the liver tumor incidence was sharply reduced.

Many compounds in the category herein considered fall among the class of dyes used at times for the coloration of foods and for other purposes. The example of scarlet red has already been cited, while 4-dimethylaminoazobenzene for some time was employed under the name of "butter yellow." 1-Benzeneazo-2-naphthol was used as a coloring matter for foods and was found by Kirby and Peacock to be a powerful liver carcinogen for mice (215). Other dyes such as methyl red (2′-carboxy-4-dimethylaminoazo-

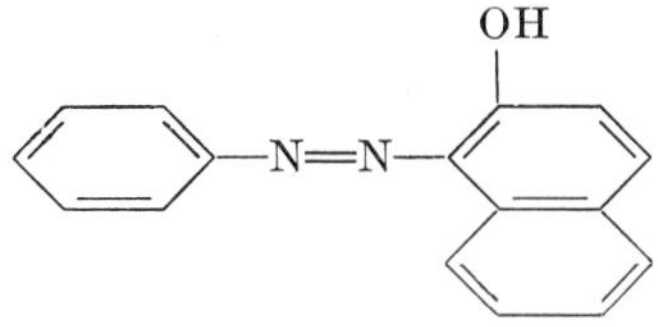

1-Benzeneazo-2-naphthol

benzene), methyl orange (4′-sodium sulfonate-4-dimethylaminoazobenzene), and sudan I, II, and III are all non-carcinogenic in rats (cf. 204).

It should be mentioned that many of the azo compounds, both active and inactive in producing true cancers of the liver, nevertheless may produce a spectrum of pathological conditions of the liver, including such phenomena as multiple areas of perilobular necrosis and irregularities of pattern and size of nuclei. In few areas of chemical carcinogenesis is it so necessary to rely upon strict histologic criteria. Gross inspection of what appears to be cancerous nodules is never sufficient.

Metabolism of the Azo Dyes

Tumors of the liver parenchyma of rats are produced when *o*-aminoazotoluene or 4-dimethylaminoazobenzene is incorporated into the diets of these animals. The pioneer observations of the Japanese workers were noted with animals fed an inadequate diet in addition to the carcinogen. Further work in Japan showed that the appearance of hepatomas could be retarded by fortifying the diet with such products as liver extract. Subsequent investigations revealed that the so-called protective effect of liver extract might be due to its high riboflavin content (192, 193). However, hepatomas appear in animals fed a diet adequate for maintenance and growth; lowering of the cystine content of such a diet retards the appearance of hepatomas and reduces their number (216). It would appear, therefore, that the incidence of hepatomas produced in rats by the ingestion of the azo dye was quite responsive to the character of the diet simultaneously fed. This suggested the possibility that the carcinogenicity of the dye itself was closely linked with its metabolism and with the effects of the resulting metabolic products on the host.

Kensler, Suguira, and Rhoads (217) noted that the content of diphosphopyridine nucleotide in the livers of rats fed 4-dimethylaminoazobenzene decreased considerably and reached a low and constant level in the hepatoma which ultimately formed. This observation led Rhoads and his co-workers to consider the possibility that the dye, or its metabolic products, may in part effect the neoplastic transformation in the liver by affecting certain enzyme systems therein whose activity depends on diphosphopyridine nucleotide. It was first necessary to know what the possible metabolic products of the dye could be.

By a process of fractionation of the urine of rats fed 4-dimethylaminoazobenzene, Stevenson, Dobriner, and Rhoads (218) isolated *p*-phenylenediamine, *p*-aminophenol, and the acetylated forms of these substances. The presence of such derivatives in the urine of the experimental animals led to the suggestion that the primary metabolic step in the degradation of the dye was a splitting at the azo linkage, followed by demethylation of the resulting dimethylphenylenediamine to yield phenylenediamine, the form actually isolated from the urine. That a reduction of the azo to a hydrazo linkage must take place is suggested by the isolation of benzidine and aniline from the urine of rats fed azobenzene (219). The former is formed as a result of mild acid treatment of an unknown precursor.

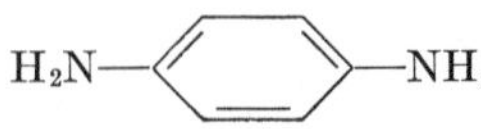

p-Phenylenediamine

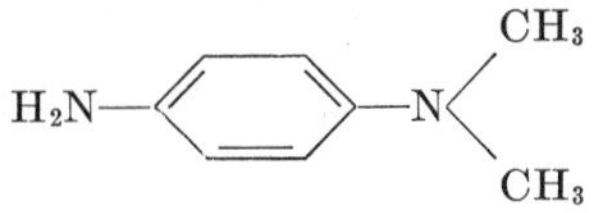

N,N-Dimethyl-*p*-phenylenediamine

The effect of *p*-phenylenediamine (isolated from urine) and of its possible precursor, N,N-dimethyl-*p*-phenylenediamine (hypothetical metabolite not isolated from urine), was tested on a fermenting yeast system in which diphosphopyridine nucleotide was the limiting factor, and it was found that these substances in low concentrations, when in the oxidized form, were toxic to this system. The fact that the aromatic diamines were toxic only in the oxidized, not in the reduced, forms makes the non-toxicity of the stable acetylated forms understandable (220).

The possible mode of action of the oxidized aromatic diamines on biological systems might be expected to be effected through oxidation of enzymes whose activity depends upon their being in the reduced state. Among such enzymes are those apparently dependent upon the presence of intact sulfhydryl groups in their molecular structure, e.g., urease, succinic dehydrogenase, etc. Oxidized *p*-phenylenediamine, N-methyl-*p*-phenylenediamine, and N,N-dimethyl-*p*-phenylenediamine were, indeed, found to be inhibitory *in vitro* to urease and to succinic dehydrogenase (221), as well as to transaminase (222). These compounds, however, did not affect the activity of D-amino acid oxidase or alkaline phosphatase; the former is reduced, the latter considerably increased, in the neoplastic transformation of rat liver by 4-dimethylaminoazobenzene.

Tissue culture studies revealed that the normal glandular epithelium of the rat liver was sensitive to extremely low concentrations of N,N-dimethyl-*p*-phenylenediamine under autoxidizing conditions (223). The toxic action of the compound could be prevented by sulfite. It is of interest to note that the fully oxidized form of the aromatic diamine is non-toxic to the liver cells, and hence the toxic action observed may be confined to intermediate levels of oxidation. It will be remembered in this connection that, on oxidation, the aromatic diamines pass into polymerized quinonoid products of various colorations. The intermediate levels consist in free radical semiquinones of varying stability. The oxidized aromatic diamines (cf 224) (free radical semiquinones → polymerized quinones) are inhibitory *in vitro* to certain enzyme systems, but there is no evidence that these products are present in liver or that they are concerned with the cancerous transformation of this tissue.

None of the products isolated from urine (*p*-phenylenediamine, *p*-aminophenol, and their respective acetylated forms) nor the possible but hypothetical precursors (N,N-dimethyl-*p*-phenylenediamine) produced hepatomas when fed to rats. Information is lacking on the quantitative relation between the amount of dye fed and the amount of urinary products found.

The problem of the fate of 4-dimethylaminoazobenzene in the body of the rat was taken up by Baumann and his collaborators and described in a series of noteworthy papers (225, 226). These investigators had noted that when the dye was fed together with a choline-free diet it prevented the renal symptoms of choline deficiency. This result could not be duplicated with aminoazotoluene (as another liver carcinogen), and hence it seemed likely that the 4-dimethylaminoazobenzene functioned as a methyl group donor and suggested the lability of such groups in the dye. It therefore seemed profitable to search the tissues of rats fed the dye for the presence of partially methylated and completely demethylated derivatives. The first task that Baumann and his colleagues assumed was the establishment of accurate methods of detecting small amounts of the parent dye, of 4-methylaminoazobenzene, and of 4-aminoazobenzene in tissues. These were effected by removal of the desired substances from the non-saponifiable fraction of tissues by petroleum ether extraction followed by fractional chromatographic adsorption on alumina. Normal tissues contain none of these materials. Analysis of the tissues of rats fed 4-dimethylaminoazobenzene revealed the presence of the parent dye and of its demethylated derivatives, 4-methylaminoazobenzene and 4-aminoazobenzene. Most of the dye was observed in the red blood cells in the form of 4-aminoazobenzene. Essentially similar results were noted for ingested 4-diethylaminoazobenzene (227), which is non-carcinogenic.

On feeding 4-methylaminoazobenzene, the liver was found to contain both 4-aminoazobenzene and 4-dimethylaminoazobenzene in addition to the substance fed, whereas the blood contained only 4-aminoazobenzene. Evidently the liver can both methylate and demethylate the monomethyl derivative of the dye. When 4-aminoazobenzene was fed to rats, however, the only form of dye found in the tissues was 4-aminoazobenzene itself.

These findings of Baumann *et al.* strongly suggested that 4-dimethylaminoazobenzene is demethylated *in vivo* prior to any reduction at the azo linkage. The 4-dimethylaminoazobenzene and 4-methylaminoazobenzene have nearly equal hepatoma-inducing potency; 4-aminoazobenzene is completely inactive. In the course of these experiments, the highly carcinogenic 3′-methyl-4-dimethylaminoazobenzene was discovered (228) (*vide infra*).

Attempts to influence the carcinogenic activity of 4-monomethylaminoazobenzene by feeding simultaneously methyl acceptors (guanidoacetic acid or nicotinamide) or methyl donors (choline) (228) were unsuccessful because the treated rats developed the same number of tumors as the untreated. Although N-methylation of aminoazobenzene increases activity, the N-methylation of 3,4,5,6-dibenzcarbazole, another hepatoma-producing agent, decreases activity (171).

The experiments concerned with the search for metabolic pathways in the breakdown of the azo dyes, in the hope of correlating such mechanisms with that of carcinogenesis, have been of great interest but, like all analogous attempts with the polycyclic hydrocarbons, have yielded little, if any, decisive information in this respect. It is possible that the chemical reactivity of the azo dyes and their split products, actual or conjectured, may be deceptive and may suggest carcinogenic mechanisms more illusory than real. That carcinogenesis may be due to an enzyme derangement has long been a favorite hypothesis, but more enzymes than one are different in hepatoma than in normal liver and whether these differences are cause or effect in the neoplastic transformation awaits further study.

The danger in a too-facile correlation of metabolic data with possible carcogenic mechanisms is illustrated by the data of Miller and Baumann (228) on the 2′-, 3′-, and 4′-methyl derivatives of dimethylaminoazobenzene. By fission at the azo linkage these three compounds would all yield N,N-dimethyl-*p*-phenylenediamine, yet the 2′-compound has a carcinogenic activity for rat liver about one-third that of the parent dye and the 4′-compound is about as weak as 4-aminoazobenzene, whereas the 3′-compound is much more active than the parent dye. On the other hand, if demethylation occurs prior to reductive fission of the azo linkage, then *p*-aminoazobenzene and the dimethylated dye with greatly different carcinogenic potency would both yield the same product, namely *p*-phenylenediamine. In either event, no clear-cut relation between the comparative carcinogenic activity of the parent dyes and the enzyme-inhibitory power of the aromatic diamines is apparent at the present time.

The experiments of Crabtree employing the isomeric aminoazotoluenes cited above (203) may also be considered pertinent in this connection. Fission at the azo linkage of these compounds leads to an aromatic amine and an aromatic diamine. If the nature of the diamine moiety were crucial in determining carcinogenesis, and since 4-amino-2′,3-azotoluene is carcinogenic to rats and mice, whereas 2-amino-4′,5-azotoluene is inactive, it might be expected that 2,5-toluylene diamine would be an active, and 3,4-toluylene diamine an inactive, moiety. However, reference to Crabtree's table, cited above (Table 17, p. 93), shows that 2,5-toluylene diamine would be furnished by azo linkage splitting from the noncarcinogenic 4-amino-4′,3-azotoluene, whereas 3,4-toluylene diamine would arise by the same mechanism from the carcinogenic 2-amino-2′,5-azotoluene.

By contrast, as Crabtree pointed out, the two carcinogenic compounds yield *o*-toluidine, whereas the two inactive isomers yield *p*-toluidine, and he

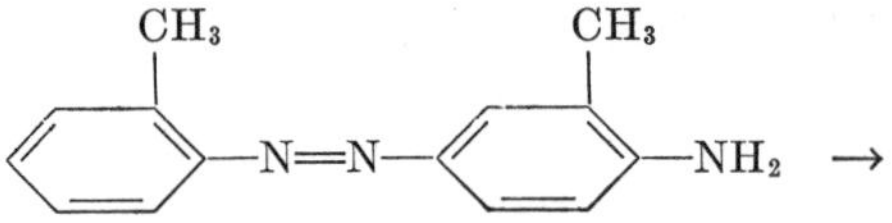

4-Amino-2′,3-azotoluene

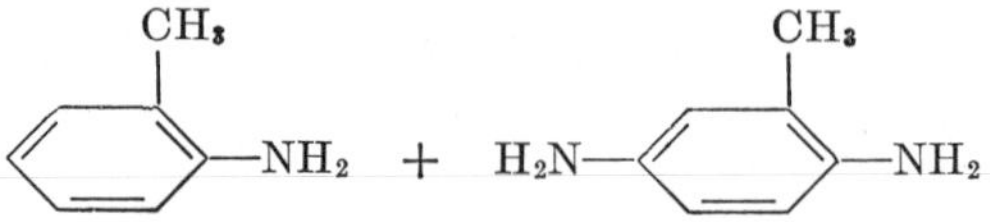

o-Toluidine 2,5-Toluylene diamine

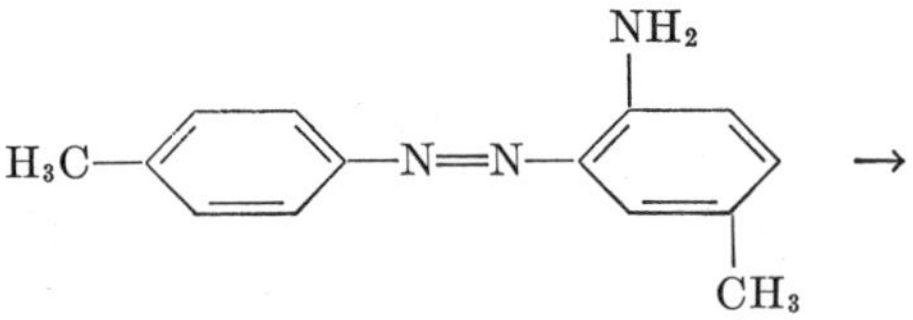

2-Amino-4′,5-azotoluene

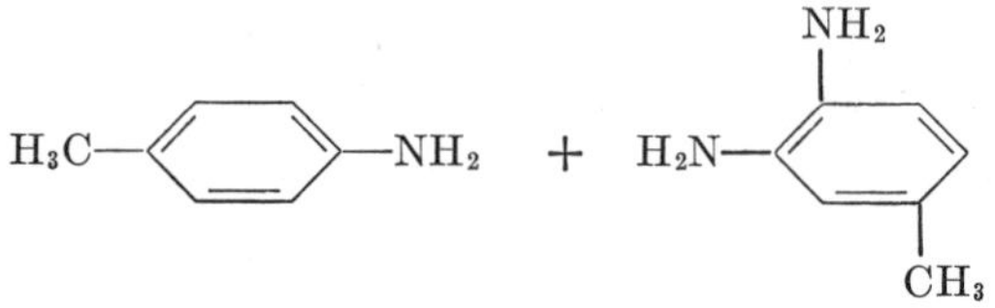

p-Toluidine 3,4-Toluylene diamine

suggested that, if carcinogenic activity is to be ascribed to either of the split products, it should more properly be associated with the amine moiety (203). The enhancing effect of a methyl group *meta* to the azo linkage as in 3′-methyl-4-dimethylaminoazobenzene, and the weakening effect of methyl groups *ortho* or *para* to this linkage, has long been recognized from the work of Miller and Baumann (228) (cf. Table 18, p. 94), and by Sugiura (229).

o-Toluidine fed to growing rats had no effect on their growth rate, but *p*-toluidine fed at the same level acted as a growth stimulant (203). The two aminoazotoluenes which acted as carcinogens in this species, and which would be expected to yield *o*-toluidine on reductive fission of the azo linkage (cf. the primed numbers in the formulae in Table 17, p. 93), did not affect the growth rate. However, the four aminoazotoluenes which were not carcinogenic, three of which would by the same mechanism yield *p*-toluidine, all acted as growth stimulants, the most effective being the weakest carcinogen even for mice, namely 2-amino-4′,5-azotoluene. *o*-Acetotoluidine is metabolized to an aminophenol, whereas *p*-acetotoluidine is metabolized to the corresponding acetylated *p*-aminobenzoic acid (230). On the basis of these observations, Crabtree suggested that the *p*-toluidine presumably formed from the growth-stimulating, non-carcinogenic aminoazotoluene isomers was converted to one or more of the folic acids by way of *p*-aminobenzoic acid. The possible relation between the metabolism of folic acid and the mechanism of cancer induction is, however, not clear at the present time.

The N-dimethyl and N-monomethyl substituted 4-aminoazobenzenes have essentially the same capacity to induce liver tumors in rats, whereas the 4-aminoazobenzene may owe its slight degree of carcinogenicity to a small amount of N-methylation *in vivo* (231). The nearly equal activities of the 4-dimethylamino and 4-methylamino derivatives may be due to a readily reversible demethylation of the 4-dimethylamino dye; demethylation of the 4-methylamino derivative also occurs readily but is only slightly reversible (231).

The hepatic system responsible for the demethylation reaction or reactions involves the presence of oxygen, diphosphopyridine nucleotide, triphosphopyridine nucleotide, and hexosediphosphate for optimal activity (232). Since the products of the reaction are the primary amine and formaldehyde, it would appear that this reaction was oxidative in character, rather than a transmethylation or hydrolysis. An interesting point in this connection is the effect of added glutathione in conjugating with one of the reaction intermediates to form a water-soluble azo dye complex, which liberates the free primary aminoazo dye on acid treatment. The course of the reactions as it involves 3-methyl-4-methylaminoazobenzene in fortified rat liver homogenates is as follows (232):

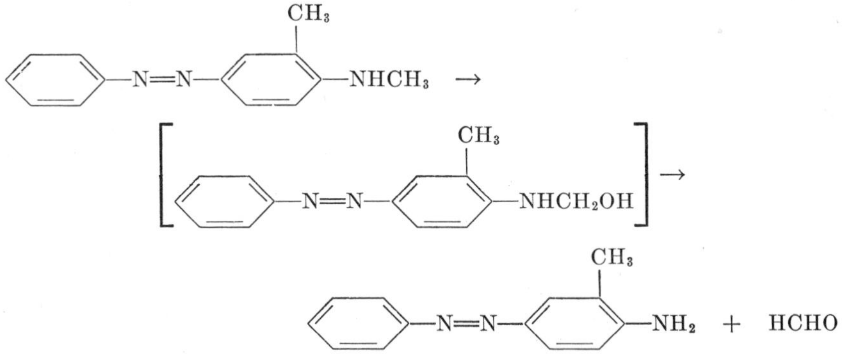

The enzyme system responsible for the demethylation reaction apparently requires the complete homogenate, since neither the particulate nor the soluble fraction is active by itself (232).

Several derivatives of 4-aminoazobenzene with widely different carcinogenic activities, such as the 4-dimethylamino-, the 4-methylamino-, the 3′-methyl-4-dimethylamino-, the 4′-methyl-4-dimethylamino-, the 4′-

methyl-4-methylamino-, and the 3-methyl-4-methylamino-, were labeled with C^{14} in the N-methyl groups, fed to male rats, and the fate of the label followed (233, 234). In all cases, by 48 hours 50 to 70% of the C^{14} had been expired as $C^{14}O_2$, 10 to 30% had been excreted in the urine, and 4 to 9% in the feces. Radioactivity was also found at the same specific activity in the β-carbon of serine, regardless of the dye fed, and, similarly, in the N-methyl groups of choline. The general metabolism of the methyl groups of the dyes, as measured by these criteria, was the same whether the dye was strongly or weakly carcinogenic. Perhaps this is further evidence in favor of the contention that the diamine moiety of the aminoazobenzenes is relatively unimportant in comparison with the nature of the amine moiety. Yet it is known that the presence of one or two methyl groups on the amino group greatly activates the molecule, and *in vivo* the activity of both types of substituents is nearly equal. However, the liver demethylase system attacks N-monomethyl dyes much faster than the corresponding N-dimethyl dyes, and, although liver homogenates from normal rats demethylate the N-methyl groups from 3′-methyl-4-dimethylaminoazobenzene about three times as fast as liver homogenates from rats prefed this active carcinogen, both groups of rats, when given a single dose of the compound labeled with C^{14} in the N-methyl position, expired $C^{14}O_2$ at the same rate. Apparently the liver demethylation system is not the rate-limiting factor *in vivo* (234). That other factors enter even the distribution of the label is shown by the observation that deprivation of vitamin B_{12} resulted in a diminished incorporation of C^{14} into choline but no change in the incorporation into serine. Rats deficient in this vitamin are much less responsive to the carcinogenic effect of the dye (233, 235).

Not only demethylation is accomplished by the hepatic enzyme system, but also reductive fission at the azo linkage. Kensler (236) showed that the capacity of liver preparations to destroy the azo dyes is dependent upon the level of riboflavin in the hepatic tissue, and Mueller and Miller (237) subsequently demonstrated that the reductive cleavage of 4-dimethylaminoazobenzene to N,N-dimethyl-*p*-phenylenediamine and aniline by fortified homogenates was inhibited by treatment with carbon dioxide and reactivated by the specific addition of riboflavin adenine dinucleotide. The cleavage products have no carcinogenic action, and it is not unlikely that the long-known protective effect of riboflavin in the diet of animals fed 4-dimethylaminoazobenzene might be due to its effective participation in the enzymatic cleavage of the carcinogen to innocuous amines. The demethylation reaction and the reductive cleavage reaction apparently occur independently, for, when a series of 4-methylamino dyes with various ring methyl substitutions were compared, it was found that the 3-methyl- and the 2-methyl-4-methylaminoazobenzenes were not cleaved or hydroxylated at the 4′-positions (238) to any significant extent, although they were appreciably demethylated (232). The cleavage reaction, like the demethylation reaction, takes place in fortified hepatic homogenates, an important component of which is triphosphopyridine nucleotide (239).

The role that reductive cleavage, or, for that matter, demethylation, plays in the carcinogenesis of liver induced by the azo dyes is not known. It may simply be a detoxication mechanism, or it may be simply a case of cross-specificity whereby the enzymatic systems involved are normally used for naturally occurring substrates arising in the course of normal hepatic metabolism. Thus, the kidney which is not susceptible to the carcinogenic action of the dye can nevertheless metabolize it (239), and oxidative demethylations in the liver for substrates of a more natural origin are not unknown (cf. 240).

The role which each of the three nitrogen atoms plays in the carcinogenesis by 4-dimethylaminoazobenzene is yet unknown. Berenbom and White (241) have studied the distribution of three preparations of this compound, each containing N^{15} in a different position, and noted that the N^{15} in which the dimethyl group was substituted was retained by the liver to a greater extent than was the other two.

Much attention was devoted to the polycyclic hydrocarbons when it was felt that these were the sole, or at least the principal, agents in the production of epitheliomas and sarcomas and, in some enthusiastic quarters, of induced neoplasia in general. This emphasis was shaken when the study of the azo dyes was resumed and it was discovered that certain of these compounds, besides inducing hepatomas, also induced pulmonary tumors as well as sarcomas at the site of injection. Now, in turn, it is to be noted that the capacity of the azo dyes to produce hepatomas in mice must be shared with such entirely dissimilar agents as carbon tetrachloride and chloroform, and in rats hepatomas are induced not only by the azo dyes but by 1,2-benzanthracene (52) as well.

This does not imply, however, that the carcinogenic mechanism is not a relatively specific process. Indeed, no reaction of any kind occurs unless the reactants bear some specific relation to each other. Many workers, impressed and perhaps discouraged by the wide variety of carcinogenic agents, have often fallen back upon such vague terms as "non-specific irritation" or "injury" to describe the mechanism of carcinogenesis. Yet to describe a reaction as non-specific is a contradiction in terms and has no scientific meaning. The mere fact that not all chemicals, but only a few, will produce cancer, even though these few may be apparently unrelated, is sufficient to establish the carcinogenic process as being due to relatively unique chemical reactions. The nature of these reactions is simply not known at the present time.

Halogenated Aliphatic Hydrocarbons

An interesting series of hepatoxic agents which induce hepatomas in mice are the halogenated aliphatic hydrocarbons. Edwards (242) noted that mice fed a solution of carbon tetrachloride in olive oil over a period of several months showed a high incidence of neoplasms of the liver. Repeated oral administration in doses of 0.04 ml. in olive oil induced the formation of hepatomas in *C3H*, *A*, *C*, and *Y* strain mice (243, 244). The method of dosage is quite important, for single or limited amounts of administered carbon tetrachloride in concentrations sufficient to cause hepatic necrosis failed to induce tumors. When, however, the same total amount of carbon tetrachloride was given in divided doses over a longer period of time, hepatomas developed in high incidence. Thus, although three large doses of carbon tetrachloride, totaling 0.12 ml., produced no hepatomas, this quantity divided into twenty-five or thirty doses and given 2 to 3 days apart produced hepatomas in 41 out of 58 mice.

The question of dosage and interval between dosages was critically examined by Eschenbrenner (245), who studied hepatoma incidence under the following conditions: among a series of *A* strain mice, the total number of doses of carbon tetrachloride and the time elapsing between the first dose

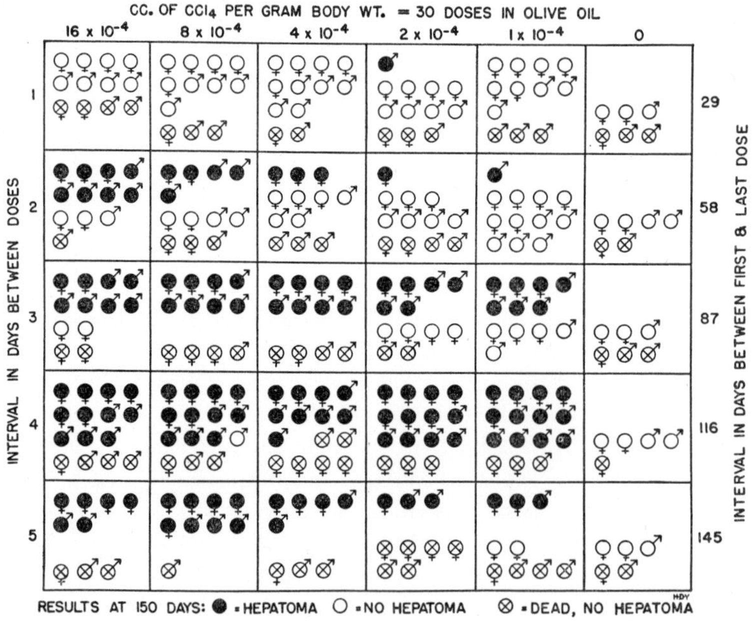

Fig. 13. Incidence of hepatomas induced in strain *A* mice by thirty doses of carbon tetrachloride in olive oil. Effect of variations in size of dose and in the interval between doses. From Eschenbrenner, A. B., *J. Natl. Cancer Inst.* **4**, 385 (1944).

and final examination for hepatoma production was kept constant, whereas the size of individual doses and the interval in days between successive doses were varied. Under these conditions Eschenbrenner noted (a) that the incidence of hepatoma increases with increase of total time during which a given amount of carbon tetrachloride is administered, and (b) that with a given constant total time during which the agent is administered the incidence of hepatomas increases with the total amount administered. The technique involved thousands of individual gastric tube feedings of measured quantities of the agent. The data are shown in Fig. 13.

Further experiments indicated that hepatoma formation can take place under non-necrotizing doses of carbon tetrachloride, and thus necrosis through the action of the agent followed by regeneration is not a *sine qua non* for hepatoma induction. Thus, chronic regeneration may be associated with hepatoma formation but no causal relation need be present.

Eschenbrenner (246) noted that oral administration of chloroform also induced hepatomas histologically indistinguishable from those induced by carbon tetrachloride in *A* strain mice. An interesting side-light developed in the course of this investigation when it was noted that males of this strain showed severe and fatal renal necrosis, and only females lived long enough to show hepatomas. This demonstrates a striking sex difference in renal susceptibility to chloroform and is analogous to other findings suggesting a sex difference in renal morphology in mice (cf. 246).

The carcinogenic action of the agents appears to have no relation to their anesthetic properties, for the minimum necrotizing and minimum tumor induction doses for carbon tetrachloride are roughly eight times those for chloroform (245). However, the relative narcotic activity of the two chemicals is of the reverse order, a far smaller quantity of chloroform than of carbon tetrachloride being required to produce a given depth of anesthesia. Another point of interest is the relatively brief period of time (no longer than 24 hours) during which the agents remain in the body.

The hepatomas developed by Eschenbrenner in mice possess many interesting chemical properties, for even in the transplants of these tumors they resemble those of normal liver in certain respects and are quite unlike those of normal liver in other respects (see Chapter VIII).

So far as is known, the halogenated aliphatic hydrocarbons induce in mice only hepatoma and no other kind of tumor. Administration of carbon tetrachloride to rats results in pronounced hepatic cirrhosis but no cancer (247).

Amino Compounds—Carcinogenic Action and Metabolism

The azo dyes might properly be considered amino compounds, but they have been separately described (a) because they are almost exclusively active on the liver, (b) because they induce tumors of the liver almost exclusively on prolonged feeding, rather than by injection or by painting, and (c) because their capacity to induce tumors of the liver is frequently dependent upon the nature of the diet simultaneously given the animals. The amino compounds considered in this section include such compounds as aminofluorene, aminodiphenyl, aminostilbene, naphthylamine, urethane, and the nitrogen mustards. With the exception of urethane, which induces tumors only of the lungs, and of naphthylamine, which induces tumors only of the bladder, these compounds are capable by a single administration of inducing a variety of tumors in the same animal.

In the course of investigating the effectiveness and toxicity of the insecticide, 2-acetylaminofluorene, Wilson, De Eds, and Cox (248) observed that this compound, when incorporated into the diet of rats in concentrations of 0.03 % or more produced multiple tumors in 3 to 4 months. The tumors included those of the liver, bladder, breast, and auditory canal. Occurring even more frequently, and probably preceding these malignant developments, was an irregular epithelial hyperplasia of the bladder, renal pelvis, liver, pancreas, and lung.

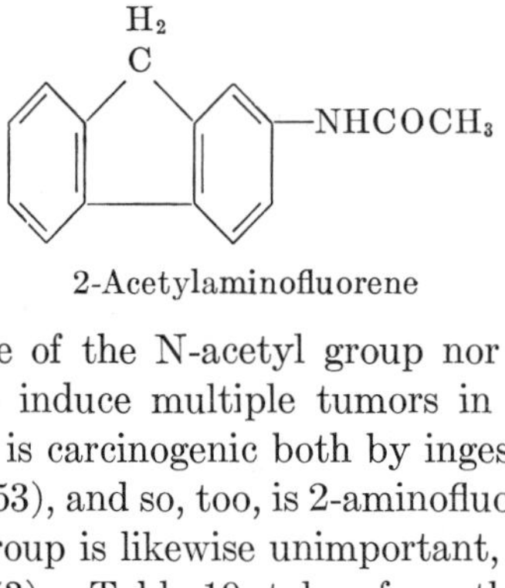

2-Acetylaminofluorene

Neither the presence of the N-acetyl group nor ingestion of the compound is necessary to induce multiple tumors in experimental animals. 2-Acetylaminofluorene is carcinogenic both by ingestion (249–252) and by painting on the skin (253), and so, too, is 2-aminofluorene (253). The basic nature of the amino group is likewise unimportant, for the 2-nitrofluorene is also carcinogenic (253). Table 19, taken from the work of Morris *et al.* (253), illustrates the tumor incidence noted by a series of fluorene derivatives administered either orally or by skin painting. The tumors noted in the group of rats studied include those of the liver, mammary gland, auditory canal, skin, pituitary gland, adrenal gland, lung, fibrous tissue, salivary gland, thymus, kidney pelvis, bladder, and intestine. The distribution of these tumors is not uniform from one derivative to the other but varies according to the nature of the derivative. Thus, aminofluorene induced liver tumors mainly of the cholangioma type, whereas acetylaminofluorene and diacetylaminofluorene induced mainly hepatomas, and nitrofluorene had no apparent effect upon the liver. Mammary tumors were induced in male rats by acetylaminofluorene but not by aminofluorene or by diacetylaminofluorene. Tumors were induced at ten sites by acetylaminofluorene, at eight sites by nitrofluorene, at five sites by aminofluorene, and

TABLE 19

TOTAL AND MULTIPLE TUMOR INCIDENCE (253)

	Fluorene Derivative								Control	
	2-Nitro		2-Amino		2-Acetyl-amino		2-Diacetyl-amino			
	Painting	Oral	Painting	Oral	Painting	Oral	Painting	Oral	Painting	Oral
Total number: tumor-bearing rats	6	2	7	5	7	12	9	12	0	0
Total number: non-tumor-bearing rats	4	7	4	6	2	8	2	0	6	6
Total number of rats	10	9	11	11	9	20	11	12	6	6
Total number of tumors	8	2	9	9	15	23	15	12	0	0
Average number of tumors in tumor-bearing rats	1.3	1.0	1.3	1.8	2.1	1.9	1.7	1.0	0	0
Per cent rats developing tumors	60	22	64	45	78	60	82	100	0	0
Number of rats with multiple tumors	2	0	2	3	5	7	4	—	—	—
Average number of tumors per rat in multiple tumor-bearing rats	2	—	2	2.3	2.6	2.9	2.25	[1]	—	—

[1] Only hepatomas were induced, which were always multiple, but they have been counted as one tumor per rat.

at four sites by diacetylaminofluorene. It would be of interest to know if nitrofluorene was reduced to aminofluorene in the course of its metabolism.

The distribution of the carcinogen or some metabolite(s) thereof throughout the tissues of the rat in concentrations sufficiently high to induce cancer must be one explanation for the production of so many distant tumors. No carcinogen known is as versatile. The differences in the types and locations of the distant tumors among the compounds described in Table 19 suggest some fundamental carcinogenic property which is altered by the nature of the substituent chemical group on the fluorene molecule (253). This is also strikingly illustrated in recent experiments of Bielschowsky and Bielschowsky (254), who noted that acetylaminofluorene induced many more hepatomas in rats than did either N-methylaminofluorene or N-dimethylaminofluorene, although the incidence of cancer induced in other organs was nearly the same for all three compounds. That the genetic constitution of the host animal also plays a role in this distribution has been noted (251–253) both for rats and for mice.

The wide distribution of the effects elicited by the fluorene derivatives made it desirable to see whether a correlation could not be found between the level of the derivative in the various tissues and the degree of neoplastic response to the presence of the derivative. The first attempt in this direction was undertaken by Westfall, who found that aminofluorene after diazotization would couple with R-salt to form a dye which could be estimated colorimetrically (255) and by which Morris and Westfall followed the distribution and excretion of acetylaminofluorene administered to animals (256). They could, however, account for only about one-third of the administered dose of carcinogen, which suggested that an appreciable amount of the compound was transformed into metabolites which did not possess the aromatic, diazotizable amino group or in which this group was firmly bound in linkage either with some normal tissue metabolite like pyruvic acid (257) or with protein (cf. 258). Another possibility to account for the apparent loss in diazotizable nitrogen has been suggested by Gutmann *et al.* (259), who found that one of the known metabolites of aminofluorene, namely, 2-amino-7-hydroxyfluorene, can, like the parent compound, be diazotized and coupled with R-salt to form sodium 7-hydroxyfluorenyl-2-azo-2′-naphthol-3′,6′-disulfonate, which absorbs maximally at the same wavelength as the corresponding derivative of 2-aminofluorene but whose extinction is only a fraction of the latter. The discrepancy frequently noted between the amounts of diazotizable material and of N^{15} recovered after administration of acetylaminofluorene-N^{15} can in part be accounted for by the presence of the 7-hydroxy metabolite (260).

The use of C^{14}-labeled acetylaminofluorene was introduced by Morris, Weisburger, and Weisburger (261), who employed the 9-C^{14} and ω-C^{14} labels to follow the metabolism of this compound. Both labels were widely distributed, but, whereas the ω-C^{14} appeared quickly in the expired air, no 9-C^{14} appeared. Evidently the acetyl group was hydrolyzed rapidly and after incorporation into the body acetate pool was metabolized to carbon dioxide. The 9-C^{14} label appeared to reach a maximum after the first few hours of administration and thereafter declined. The relatively rapid elimination of the carcinogen is one reason why so much of it has to be administered to develop cancer at any site. This is essentially the problem with all so-called systemic carcinogens which have to find their own way to susceptible sites. Only the insoluble, subcutaneously administered carcinogens remain sufficiently long at the site of injection to induce a tumor with but a single dose.

That the acetyl group is split off from the amino group of the fluorene molecule during the metabolism of the compound appears to be substantiated by the failure of *p*-toluenesulfonylaminofluorene to be carcinogenic, as well as by the very weakly carcinogenic activity of benzoylaminofluorene (262). The tosyl group is not hydrolyzed at all, and the benzoyl group only with difficulty.

A close similarity has been observed both qualitatively and quantitatively between the distribution and excretion of acetylaminofluorene-9-C^{14} and of acetylaminofluorene-N^{15}, which suggests that the molecule remains intact during metabolism as far as these two atoms are concerned (263).

The earliest known metabolite of 2-acetylaminofluorene was 2-acetylamino-7-hydroxyfluorene (264). This compound is not carcinogenic (265), but it is of interest that 2-acetylamino-7-fluorofluorene is more active in inducing hepatomas than is the parent compound (208). The enhancing effect of fluoro substitution is evident here as it is in the azo dyes.

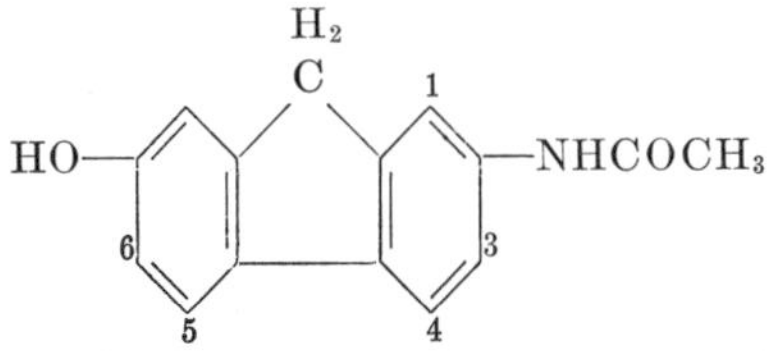

2-Acetylamine-7-hydroxyfluorene

Weisburger, Weisburger, and Morris (265a) have found that in addition to the known metabolites of orally administered 2-acetylaminofluorene—2-aminofluorene, 2-amino-7-hydroxyfluorene, and 2-acetylamino-7-hydroxyfluorene, and their glucuronides—there is also 2-acetylamino-1-hydroxyfluorene and 2-acetylamino-3-hydroxyfluorene, as well as their glucuronides.

Of interest in this connection is the observation by Morris and Dubnik (266) that 2,7-diacetylaminofluorene is more carcinogenic than is 2-acetylaminofluorene. Evidently the 7-position is not an "unfavorable" position, but it needs the right substituent. The 4-acetylaminofluorene is non-carcinogenic (267).

With the object of determining whether the CH_2 bridge in the fluorene molecule is essential to activity, Miller *et al.* (268) tested three analogues, in which the bridge consisted of —S— as in 3-acetylaminodibenzothiophene, S(=O)— as in 3-acetylaminodibenzothiophene-5-oxide, and —O— as in 3-acetylaminodibenzofuran. The acetylamino group in these compounds is in the same position as it is in 2-acetylaminofluorene, but owing to the numbering system in heterocyclic compounds they are described as in the 3-position. Also tested was 4-dimethylaminodiphenyl in which the bridge was absent. The analogue with the —S— substituent had the same carcinogenicity for mammary and ear duct tissue as 2-acetylaminofluorene, whereas the analogues with —S(=O)— and —O— substituents had less carcinogenic activity. Interestingly enough, none of these three analogues induced any liver tumors, in contrast with the effect of 2-acetylaminofluorene. 4-Dimethylaminodiphenyl induced tumors of the mammary gland, the liver, and the ear duct in male rats. The sites attacked by this compound are more similar to those affected by the aminofluorenes than by the azo dyes which induce only liver tumors when fed to rats.

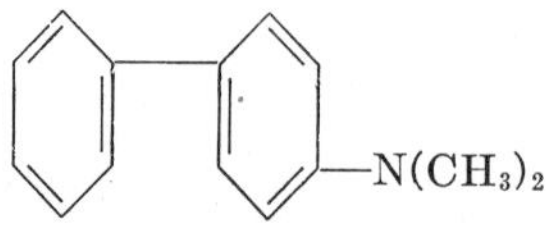

4-Dimethylaminodiphenyl

Tumors of the bladder in dyestuff workers have been attributed in part to the presence of benzidine, i.e., 4,4′-diaminodiphenyl, and administration of this compound to rats has led to the induction of tumors of the ear canal, the liver, and the intestine (269). Walpole *et al.* (270) induced a variety

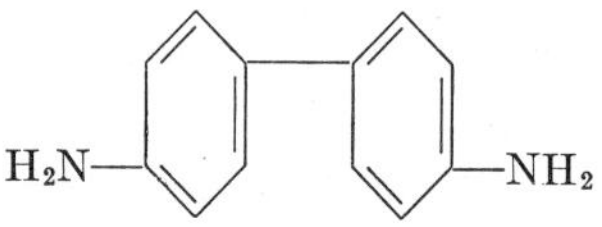

4,4′-Diaminodiphenyl (benzidine)

of tumors with 4,4′-diaminodiphenyl and an even greater number with 3,2′-dimethyl-4-aminodiphenyl (270). In this connection it will be recalled that 2,3′-azotoluene yields bladder papillomas in rats, whereas

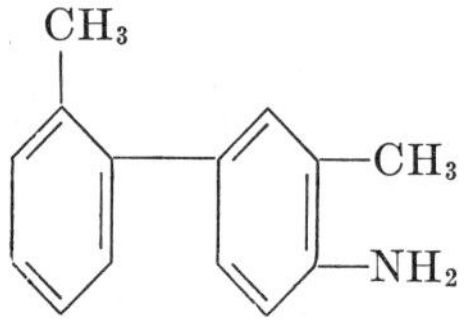

3,2′-Dimethyl-4-aminodiphenyl

azobenzene is inactive (271). The activating influence of methyl groups in favorable locations has been alluded to above.

The requirement for a planar arrangement of a carcinogenic hydrocarbon is well illustrated by the studies on 4-aminostilbene and its derivatives (202); one of the features necessary for activity in this series of compounds is an unbroken conjugation of the amino group with both nuclei whereby the compound assumes a resonating quinonoid structure. A similar explanation is possible for the greater carcinogenic activity of derivatives of fluorene over that of biphenyl derivatives (268), thus:

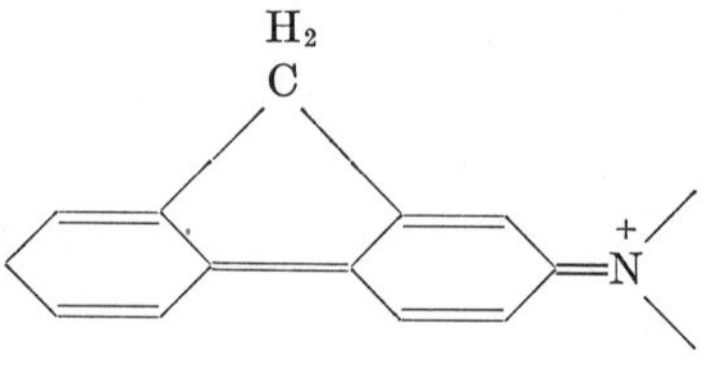

TABLE 20

CARCINOGENIC ACTION AND ULTRAVIOLET ABSORPTION OF CERTAIN FLUORENE AND BIPHENYL DERIVATIVES (272)

Compound	Sex	Per cent incidence of tumors in: Liver	Mammary gland	Ear duct	Small intestine	Absorption maxima in angstroms at	Extinction
2-Acetylaminofluorene	M	85	0	38	50	2880	4.46
2-Acetylaminofluorene	F	0	84	80	20		
4-Acetylaminobiphenyl	M	0	0	0	0	2740	4.42
4-Acetylaminobiphenyl	F	0	73	13	0		
2-Methyl-4-acetylaminobiphenyl	M	0	0	0	0	2600	4.34
2-Methyl-4-acetylaminobiphenyl	F	0	0	0	0		
2′-Methyl-4-acetylaminobiphenyl	M	0	0	0	0	2600	4.35
2′-Methyl-4-acetylaminobiphenyl	F	0	0	0	0		

The presence of the methylene bridge between the two aromatic rings induces a significant shift of the ultraviolet absorption by the compounds to longer wavelengths, and this phenomenon suggests that the principal effect of this bridge is to increase charge transfer between the two rings as a consequence of the greater planarity of the ring system (272). On this basis it would be expected that the more carcinogenic compounds of this series would absorb ultraviolet radiation maximally at longer wave lengths. That there is such a correlation is revealed in Table 20 (272).

A suspected metabolite of benzidine is 3,3′-dihydroxybenzidine, and Baker has found that this compound fed to rats induced a variety of tumors such as hepatomas, squamous carcinomas of the stomach, and neoplasms of the auditory canal and bladder (273). The similarity between results of tumor production by this compound and 2-acetylaminofluorene suggests that the metabolism of these compounds follows a parallel course, and subsequent studies on the distribution of benzidine expressed as diazotizable amino groups showed this to be indeed the case (274).

2-Acetylaminofluorene induces tumors not only in rats and in mice but also in dogs (tumors of the liver and of the bladder) after 7 to 9 years of ingestion (275).

Similar in their versatility as induction agents for tumors in a wide variety of tissues after administration are the aminostilbenes, as pointed out by Haddow *et al.* (202). Structurally, this class of compounds resembles the azo dyes (see above), but in their cancer-induction action they resemble the aminofluorenes. In particular, the carcinomatous development of the external acoustic duct is an odd sort of tumor and was never reported in rats until Bielschowsky described it as a consequence of the administration of 2-acetylaminofluorene and 2-anthramine (276). This tumor is now also induced by 4-dimethylaminodiphenyl and by the aminostilbenes. 4-Aminostilbene, 4-dimethylaminostilbene, and 4-dimethylamino-2′-methylstilbene induced a variety of tumors, whether by subcutaneous administration or by feeding, and the carcinogenic activity of these compounds was considerably greater for rats than for mice (202). The tumors included those of the mammary glands, the liver, the auditory canal, and the subcutaneous fibrous tissue at the site of injection.

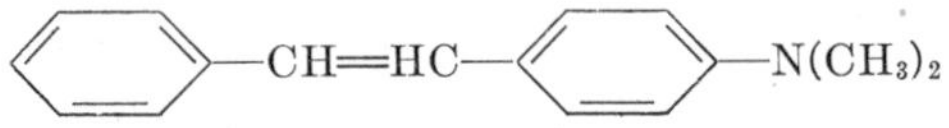

4-Dimethylaminostilbene

This brilliant report by Haddow and his colleagues on the aminostilbenes (202) is a classic example of scientific correlation, for, starting with the assumption that this class of compounds might well be inhibitory toward the growth of established tumors, and finding it to be the case, they predicted that these compounds in turn should also be carcinogenic. Further discussion of Haddow's stimulating concept of a possible relation between cancer-inhibiting and cancer-inducing properties of chemicals will be deferred to Chapter VII.

2-Anthramine, unlike its isomers, is also carcinogenic when administered to rats and induces a variety of tumors (276). Its similarity in structure to 2-aminofluorene is apparent.

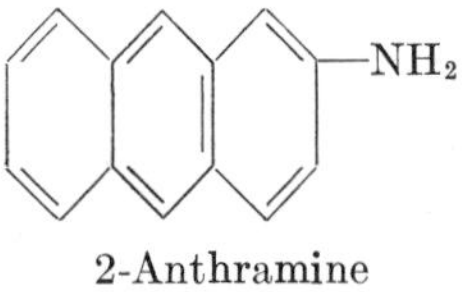

2-Anthramine

The study of the amino compounds as causative agents probably started with the observation of the high prevalence of bladder cancer among workers in dyestuff factories. The possible implication of benzidine has been mentioned above. Equally, suspicion has fallen on 2-naphthylamine, which experimentally has induced bladder tumors when fed to dogs, rats, and rabbits over long periods of time; in mice, this compound induces liver tumors (277). Bonser and her colleagues (277) have suggested that it is not 2-naphthylamine which is the active carcinogen, but rather its metabolic product, 2-amino-1-naphthol. Thus, the dog, which is very susceptible to

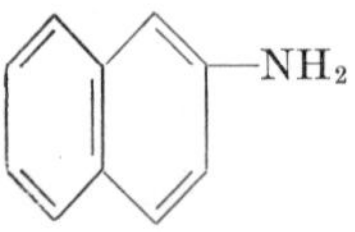

2-Naphthylamine

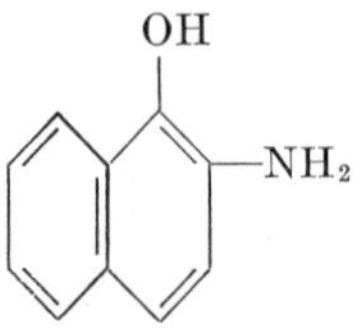

2-Amino-1-naphthol

the action of 2-naphthylamine, excretes 55 to 70 % of the administered dose as the naphthol, whereas the rat, rabbit, and mouse, which are much less susceptible, excrete much less of the naphthol. When surgically introduced into the lumen of the bladder of the mouse, 2-amino-1-naphthol, but not 2-naphthylamine, induced cancer of the bladder. It would appear that it is the metabolite which is the active carcinogen at the site of action. It is possible that aromatic amines are carcinogenic because of their conversion to *ortho*-hydroxy amines (277a).

$C_2H_5OCONH_2$
Urethane

Ethylcarbamate (urethane) is a rather unique carcinogen, in that it acts specifically on the lungs. When administered orally or intraperitoneally in subanesthetic doses, it hastened the appearance and raised the incidence of lung tumors in *A* and in *C3H* strain mice (278). Its effect in mice is generally proportional to the spontaneous incidence of lung tumors (278, 279). Of all the alkyl derivatives, only the ethyl is active (280). The compound is also effective in inducing lung tumors in rats (281–283) but is ineffective in other species (279).

Urethane is hydrolyzed in the host to carbon dioxide, ethanol, and ammonia (284). Administration of C^{14}-labeled urethane in the carbonyl group to mice showed complete conversion in 24 hours to respiratory carbon dioxide, and no evidence prior to that for any selective localization.

Yet there must be a localization of action of urethane (or some metabolic product thereof) in the lung, for this is the only target tissue in mice for this carcinogen. Experiments of interest in this connection were carried out simultaneously by Shapiro and Kirschbaum (285) and by Heston and Dunn (286). The former investigators crossed *Bagg albinos* (susceptible) with *DBA* (resistant) and implanted lung tissue from 1-day-old mice of each of the parent strains into the ears of the F_1 hybrids. On administering urethane to the F_1 hosts, those with the lung graft from the *Bagg albinos* showed cancerous changes, whereas those from the *DBA* strain were practically cancer-free. The latter investigators crossed *A* strain mice (susceptible) with *L* strain (resistant) and implanted lung tissue from each of the parent strains into the F_1 hybrids; on intravenous administration of 1,2,5,6-dibenzanthracene into the latter, 39 % of the *A* strain grafts were cancerous, and only 3 % of the *L* strain grafts were cancerous. Susceptibility to lung tumors by these carcinogens is thus less a systemic than a localized property of the target tissue, although some genic influence through a general systemic mechanism is evident since the LAF_1 host reduced the tumor incidence of *A* strain lung grafts from 100 %, which it should have been, and increased the susceptibility of the *L* strain lung grafts from 0 %, which it should have been. Figure 14 illustrates this type of experiment.

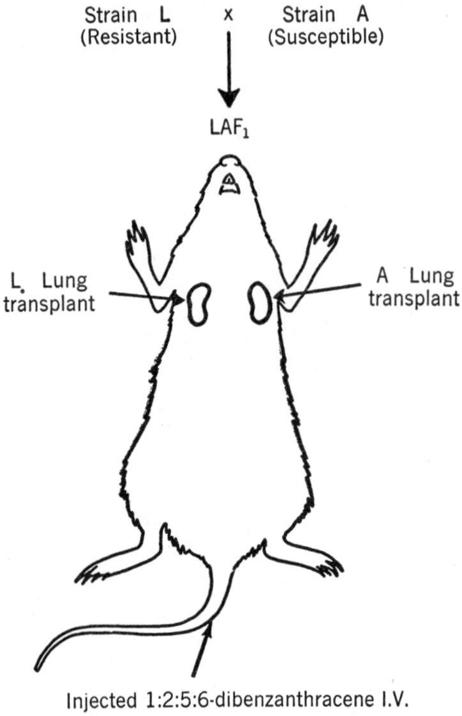

FIG. 14. Experiment on transplantation of lung tissue. From Heston, W. E., and Dunn, T. B., *J. Natl. Cancer Inst.*, **11**, 1057 (1951).

CH_3-$N(CH_2CH_2Cl)_2$	$N(CH_2CH_2Cl)_3$
Methyldi(2-chloroethyl)amine	Tri(2-chloroethyl)amine

The vesicants (nitrogen mustards)—methyldi(2-chloroethyl)amine, i.e., HN_2, and tri(2-chloroethyl)amine, i.e. HN_3—induce mutations and act generally as radiomimetic agents (cf. Boyland, 287). Acting on the assumption that such potentially anticarcinogenic agents should also induce cancer, Boyland and Horning (288) gave mice weekly subcutaneous injections of these compounds and induced various tumors, particularly of the lungs. Heston (289) subsequently demonstrated that on intravenous administration of methyldi(2-chloroethyl)amine·HCl, lung tumors were induced in *A* strain mice with a response of about the same order as that brought about by urethane; i.e., a 0.1-mg. dose resulted in 100% of the animals developing lung tumors 16 weeks or less after injection, with eight or ten nodules per animal. Like urethane, the nitrogen mustard not only hastens the induction of lung tumors in a susceptible strain but also is palliative in certain leukemias, as will be noted in Chapter VII.

Methyldi(2-chloroethyl)amine·HCl, administered as an aerosol to a tumor strain of *Drosophila*, increased the tumor incidence and also the lethal mutation rate (290). The dual effect is of interest, but it is conjectural as to whether tumors in insects and in mammals are the same thing.

It is probable that the nitrogen mustards exert their action by cyclization to the ethyleneiminonium cation, which is a powerful alkylating agent (cf. 291). A proof of this was furnished by Seligman and his associates (292), who administered diethyl-β-iodoethylamine-I^{131}, which on cyclization releases the halogen as inorganic iodide and forms the cyclic salt. The

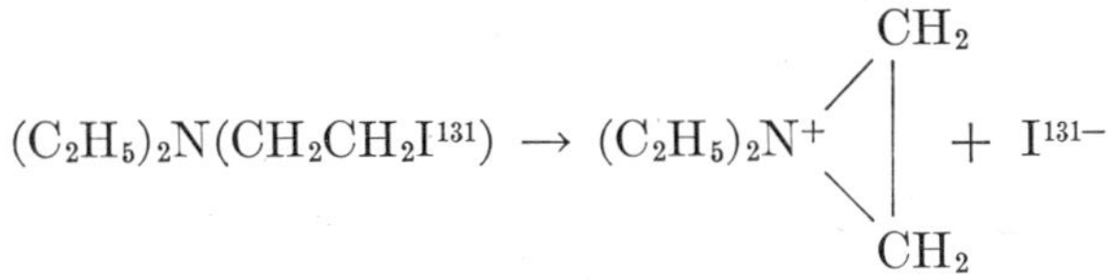

radioactivity pattern in most organs was almost identical with that shown for radioactive sodium iodide, indicating that cyclization does take place to a considerable extent in the intact animal.

Not only the aliphatic but also the aromatic nitrogen mustards are carcinogenic, the di(chloroethyl) derivative of 2-naphthylamine being particularly active in this respect. They induce a variety of tumors, including sarcomas at the site of injection.

Consideration of the possible mechanisms and chemical reactivity of the mustards led to the simultaneous observation by workers at the Royal Cancer Hospital in London under Haddow (293–295) and at the laboratories of the Imperial Chemical Industries, Ltd. (296–298), that other types of alkylating agents might also have the cytotoxic properties associated with the mustards. One of these considerations was based upon the higher degree of activity exhibited by the bifunctional nitrogen mustards, i.e., two 2-haloalkyl groups (299), followed by the hypothesis offered by Haddow (300), Goldacre *et al.* (301), and Loveless and Revell (302) that the chromosomal abnormalities noted after treatment with mustards (303) might be due to an alkyl attachment to each of two adjacent chains of nucleic acids (304) or proteins whereby cross-linking would occur. Cross-linking agents for textile fibers had been known for years, and the textile auxiliaries section of the Imperial Chemical Industries laboratories furnished a wide variety of such polyalkylating agents which were subsequently tested in experimental animals for their cytotoxic and cancer-therapeutic activities (cf. 296–298). Among these compounds were the epoxides and ethyleneimines, to which another type, namely the methanesulfonates (305), was later added. The essential chemical groupings of this class of alkylating agents is as follows:

Sulfur mustards —SCH_2CH_2Cl

Nitrogen mustards =NCH_2CH_2Cl

Epoxides

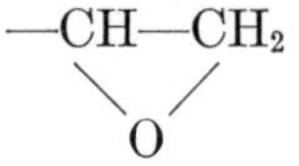

Ethyleneimines

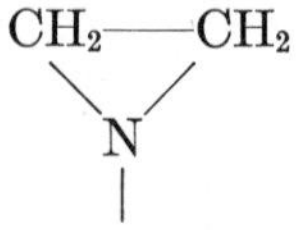

Methanesulfonates —CH_2SO_2O—

As stated, the principal interest in these compounds lay in their cancer therapeutic possibilities (see later section), but on the basis of Haddow's concept of a relation between cancer therapy and cancer induction (306) a few compounds in this category were tested for carcinogenic action. An active carcinogenic agent in both rats and mice was found in the strongly cytotoxic bis-epoxide vinylcyclohexene dioxide, which induced sarcoma at the site of injection and skin tumors in mice after painting (297). Butadiene dioxide was an apparently weaker carcinogen (297) but an active

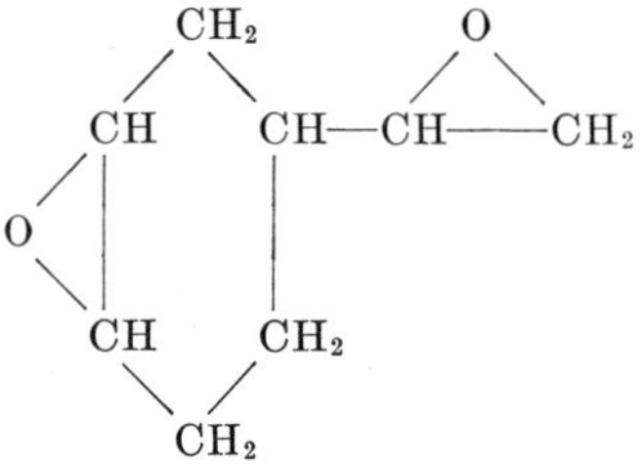

4-Vinylcyclohexene dioxide

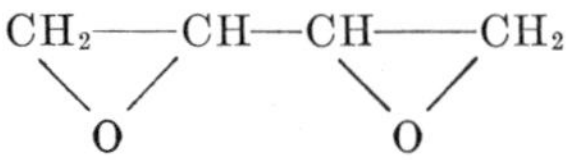

Butadiene dioxide

mutagen. Among the cytotoxic ethyleneimines (298), stearoyl ethyleneimine was found to be strongly, and tris-ethyleneimino-1,3,5-triazine very weakly, carcinogenic.

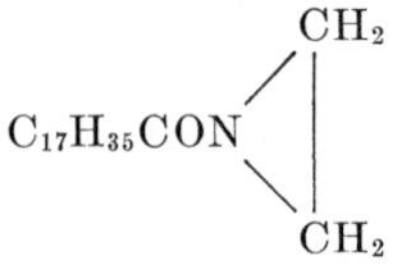

Stearoyl ethyleneimine

The cytotoxic studies on the alkylating, cross-linking agents had begun at Manchester with a series of polymethylolamides derived from amides by condensation with formaldehyde (296). Among these was an active alkylating agent, namely, the polymer of trimethylolmelamine:

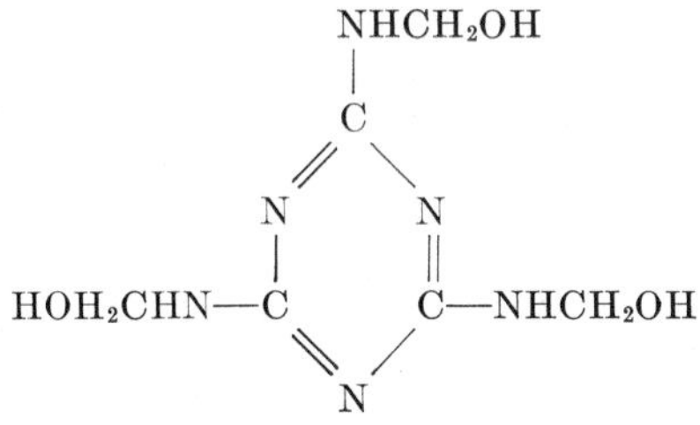

Trimethylolmelamine

Maximum activity is attained with the trisubstituted melamine, and it is possible that two of the methylol groups participate in the polymerization, while the third is available for reaction. This polymeric substance was inhibitory toward established tumors, but its carcinogenicity appeared to be equivocal.

However, several polymeric types of compounds have been found to be strongly carcinogenic in experimental animals, i.e., Bakelite (307), Cellophane (308), and certain polyamides resembling Nylon (309). These materials are relatively inert chemically, and their mechanism of action is obscure. Since the embedding of plastics into rodents leads to the production of a variety of malignant tumors at the site, perhaps the increasing use of such materials in surgical procedures should be carefully considered (310). The possibility that free radicals, or free radical-yielding substances (310a), are involved in the action of the high polymer carcinogens is of interest in view of polymerization techniques using radical-delivering catalysts (310b).

At this time, the carcinogenic activities of the alkylating agents have not been systematically reported, for as a rule such studies have been only incidental to the more important problem of cancer therapy. Nevertheless, the results of the former type of study are awaited with interest, for the compounds involved not only represent a new class of biologically active agents, but their chemical modes of action *in vivo* may be strongly inferred from their known reactions *in vitro*. That such compounds should stem first from considerations of the behavior of the vesicant war gases and then of the cross-linking agents of the textile industry, as the polycyclic hydrocarbons stemmed from the coal tar industry and the azo dyes from an antiseptic, only illustrates the wide scope of the field of cancer research and the origin of significant observations from frequently quite unexpected sources.

Synthetic Combinations of Proteins and Carcinogens

The development of this interesting area in the field of cancer research began in 1939 with the report by Fieser and Creech (311) on the conjugation of amino acids with the isocyanates of certain polycyclic hydrocarbons.

Phenylisocyanate derivatives of proteins had been prepared by Hopkins and Wormall (312) and shown to possess immunological properties. The difficult problem of conjugating the isocyanates of several polycyclic hydrocarbons with proteins was undertaken by Creech and his associates and described in a notable series of publications (313–323). This conjugation was successfully effected after preparing the isocyanates of various carcinogenic hydrocarbons by coupling them in aqueous dioxane at low temperatures and at a pH between 8 and 10 with crystalline serum albumin preparations from different species. From the earlier observations of Landsteiner (324), it might be expected that such conjugates on injection into animals would elicit antibodies which would react not only with the conjugate or with its protein component but also with the prosthetic group alone or conjugated with a non-antigenic substance such as an amino acid or peptide. The purpose of this approach, therefore, was to produce such synthetic antigens which upon injection into animals would cause the production of antisera capable of preventing carcinogenesis by the hydrocarbons alone.

1,2-Benzanthracene-3- and 10-isocyanate (313), 3,4-benzpyrene-5-isocyanate and 10-methyl-1,2-benzanthracene-3-isocyanate (314), 1,2,5,6-dibenzanthracene-9-isocyanate (315), 9-methyl- and 9,10-dimethyl-1,2-benzanthracene-3-isocyanate (318), and the 4′-isocyanates of 4-dimethylaminostilbene and of 2′-methyl-4-dimethylaminostilbene, and the 7-isocyanate of 2-acetylaminofluorene (319, 320, 323) were prepared and conjugated with various serum albumins, and in some cases with ε-aminocaproic acid and other amino acids and peptides (316). The reaction involved the isocyanate with the primary amino group, thus:

$$ArNCO + H_2NR \rightarrow ArNHCONH—R$$

In the case of the proteins, the reactive groups were almost entirely due to the free ε-amino groups of the lysine components, and the amount of carcinogen prosthetic group introduced into the protein could be varied at will up to a maximum value. On the basis of the lysine content of serum albumin, it should be possible to introduce something like 66 groups into the molecule, and by suitably increasing the amount of reactive isocyanate, pH, and dioxane concentration, about 62 molecules of 2′-methyl-4-dimethylaminostilbene have been added in the conjugate (319). The maximum amount of 1,2-benzanthracene introduced was 38 groups, 3,4-benzpyrene 19 groups, and 1,2,5,6-dibenzanthracene 21 groups. The extent of conjugation in the proteins was determined by ultraviolet spectrophotometry at wavelengths greater than 325 mμ, on the basis of comparison of the absorption of similar conjugates with ε-aminocaproic acid (cf. 313, 321). The conjugates yielded clear solutions at 1 to 2 % in water and were nearly homogeneous by electrophoretic criteria (323). Their sedimentation diagrams, however, revealed considerable aggregation.

Another type of conjugation has involved combination of the stilbene molecule through an azo linkage with the tyrosine components of the protein, thus (323):

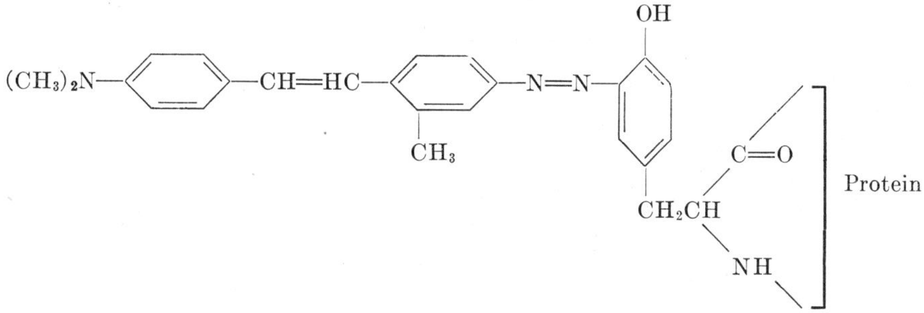

None of the protein conjugates with the carcinogens produced tumors, although the combination of 1,2,5,6-dibenzanthracene with glycine was capable of producing tumors in mice (314, 325). Indeed, the 9-isocyanate of 1,2,5,6-dibenzanthracene by itself appeared to be more carcinogenic by subcutaneous administration than the parent compound. On the other hand, the isocyanates and amino acid conjugates located at the 3- or 10-position of 1,2-benzanthracene, at the 3-position of 10-methyl- and 9,10-dimethyl-1,2-benzanthracene, or at the 5-position of 3,4-benzpyrene were found to be either inactive or very weakly carcinogenic. Conjugates involving 9,10-dimethyl-1,2-benzanthracene had the effect of arresting the development of frog's eggs and of producing certain chromosomal abnormalities (326).

Conjugates of the hydrocarbons with albumin moieties derived from human, bovine, and equine sources were injected into rabbits, and antibodies were elicited which reacted specifically with the protein moiety, but definite evidence of cross prosthetic group reactivity was obtained when the test conjugate contained a different protein from that used in the immunizing antigen (321). Thus, antisera toward 1,2-benzanthracene conjugated with horse serum albumin reacted with bovine serum albumin conjugated not only with this hydrocarbon but also with 3,4-benzpyrene. The antisera also reacted with carcinogen conjugates with amino acids or peptides, for, after such a mixture was produced, subsequent addition of a test antigen composed of the homologous carcinogen-heterologous protein led to little or no precipitation (inhibition technique) (311, 316, 327).

Up to the present time, the efforts in this area have been directed toward ascertaining conditions needed for maximum immunizing capacity of the conjugates. Thus, the introduction of too few or too many carcinogen groups into the protein may mean less haptenic activity than that displayed by some intermediate value, as shown in the aminostilbene series (321), and the interpretation of the immunological results might sometimes depend on whether the conjugates had ever been exposed to light, as in those involving 9,10-dimethyl-1,2-benzanthracene, or the aminostilbene series (*trans-cis* shift) (321). The future development of this area in the application of immunological techniques to problems in carcinogenesis is awaited with interest.

Effect of Carcinogens on the Chemistry of the Host

It would be expected that the sequence of events leading from the initial administration of a carcinogen to the development of a cancer would involve a series of integrated chemical alterations on the part of the host, and particularly in the tissue specifically affected by the carcinogen. It is clear from previous discussion how relatively little is known of the metabolic fate of the carcinogens themselves, and still less of what the actual form may be in which these compounds exert their specific effects. However, a considerable literature has developed over many years on the histological changes which these agents induce, and only relatively recently has a comparable literature begun to accumulate on the chemical interactions with the host in which these agents presumably participate.

In the evaluation of what might loosely be termed the pharmacology of these agents, it is necessary to determine what reaction, of the many that might be observed, may be correlated with the carcinogenic process. In view of the general ignorance of the latter process, such a criterion can be adhered to only with some difficulty and uncertainty. Nevertheless, considerable progress has been made in this area, a pin-pointing of knowledge upon at least one sure mechanism of action of the carcinogenic agents, namely upon the initial binding of the agent with one or more tissue proteins of the host. Evidence for this binding, without specification of the nature of the binding forces involved, has come about through three more or less independent sets of evidence: (a) the effect of the polycyclic hydrocarbons on protein sulfhydryl levels or upon physiological mechanisms governed by these levels; (b) the actual isolation of proteins to which the carcinogenic agents are firmly bound; and (c) the effect of alkylating agents derived by intramolecular rearrangements, as in the mustard or 1,2-epoxide series, on reactions with proteins and nucleic acids. It might be fairly said that the initial reaction of any active physiological agent is to combine with the catalytically specific protein which alters it, and the entire theory of enzyme reactions is based upon the initial formation of the enzyme-substrate complex. In this sense, the complexing of the carcinogenic agent with one or more proteins is only the first step in the understanding of the mechanism of carcinogenesis, for if it be assumed that this complex involves only specific proteins, it will be necessary ultimately to know their nature. Perhaps as secondary evidence of the effect of carcinogenic agents upon the host are the numerous examples of changes in enzyme levels and other specific tissue components. These examples, *per se*, have little meaning except as compared with similar properties of the cancer which finally develops, and hence their discussion is deferred to Chapter VIII.

Sulfhydryl Levels. The studies of Crabtree on the anticarcinogenic action of such sulfhydryl-binding compounds as bromobenzene and the unsaturated maleic and citraconic acids has been alluded to above (p. 79). There is no direct evidence that sulfur plays any part in the detoxication of the aromatic polycyclic carcinogens, for, although the administration of such active compounds as 3,4-benzpyrene or 1,2,5,6-dibenzanthracene produces profound inhibition of growth of young animals (328, 329), this growth inhibition could not be accounted for in terms of the urinary excretion of mercapturic acids involving these carcinogens (120, 330). In fact, there is no evidence that any such mercapturic acids are ever excreted (331, 332), even when sulfur-containing proteins are fed to the animals in large amounts or when radioactive sulfur-labeled cystine (333) or methionine (334) is simultaneously administered with the carcinogen. Nevertheless, the fact that interference with some aspect of intracellular sulfur metabolism tends to oppose the action of the carcinogenic agents has led to the inference that sulfur groups are involved in the mechanism of action of these agents, and Crabtree has suggested that the carcinogenic agents, probably in the oxidized state, become fixed to SH-containing cellular constituents, and that inhibitors of S-metabolism antagonize this process by preferential combination (122). Among the SH-containing cellular entities may be included proteins, both catalytic and non-catalytic. If these concepts are correct, the provision of more SH-groups for the carcinogen to attach itself to should result in an anticarcinogenic action, and it has been shown that the simultaneous administration of 2,3-dimercaptopropanol (BAL) with 3,4-benzpyrene very markedly reduced the proportion of skin tumors in mice which were treated with these agents (335).

More direct proof of the action of 3,4-benzpyrene has been obtained from the significant decrease in SH-content of the serum of rabbits and dogs given intravenous injections of aqueous colloidal dispersions of the carcinogen (336); a similar effect was not obtained on injection of anthracene in the same manner. It is of interest that this effect was obtained only after *in vivo* administration of 3,4-benzpyrene, for the *in vitro* incubation of rabbit or dog serum with the compound produced no change in the sulfhydryl content. Of interest in this connection are the numerous observations of the generally low sulfhydryl levels in the plasma of cancer patients (337–339).

The direct inhibition of the nitroprusside reaction of mercaptans by addition of colloidal dispersions of 3,4-benzpyrene was demonstrated by Calcutt (340), who also showed that this inhibition appeared to run parallel with a change in fluoresence color of the benzpyrene from yellow-green to pale blue. In caffeine solutions, the inhibition was accelerated. Rondoni (341) showed by means of the Prussian blue reaction that both benzpyrene and acetylaminofluorene bind the SH-group of cysteine rather strongly, anthracene binds even more strongly, and 20-methylcholanthrene little if any. He has concluded that there is no regular association *in vitro* between SH-binding and carcinogenesis *in vivo*.

Indirect evidence for combination of the carcinogens with sulfhydryl groups has been derived from the extended series of studies by Rondoni and his collaborators (341, 342) on the inhibition of several intracellular proteolytic enzyme systems which require the presence of these intact groups for their maximal activity, and by Wood on the inhibition of the sulfhydryl enzyme urease (cf. 336). It may be that these inhibitory reactions are due to the oxidation of the sensitive and exposed sulfhydryl groups by oxidation products of the carcinogens, which might thus function as oxidative catalysts. Non-carcinogenic hydrocarbons do not produce the inhibitions noted (342). Table 21 describes the results noted by Rondoni and Barbieri (342).

Isolation of Carcinogen-Bound Proteins. The implication of tissue proteins in the initial stages of the reaction of the animal with carcinogenic agents has been a theme of many authors (see above). The most direct evidence for the combination *in vivo* between tissue proteins and carcinogens has come from the work of E. C. and J. A. Miller, and the larger bulk of the data dealing with this phenomenon has been derived from the study of aminoazo dye carcinogenesis.

The oral administration of 4-dimethylaminoazobenzene to rats is followed by the metabolism of the compound through (a) reductive cleavage of the azo linkage, (b) hydroxylation of the ring in the 4′-position, and (c) oxidative demethylation. In addition, a small percentage of the administered dye is metabolized to a derivative or series of derivatives which become chemically bound to certain of the liver proteins. This phenomenon was first described by the Millers in 1947 (343) and thoroughly explored in this initial, remarkable report. Briefly summed up, their findings were: (a) the bound dyes were not removable by boiling organic solvents or by hot trichloroacetic acid, but only by prolonged tryptic or alkaline hydrolysis; (b) the alkali-liberated dyes could be fractionated by solvent extraction into non-polar and polar dyes, the former, in lesser

TABLE 21

EFFECT ON AUTOLYSIS OF LIVER EXTRACTS BY POLYCYLIC HYDROCARBONS (342)

Compounds	Inhibition of autolysis	Carcinogenicity of compounds
Pyrene	None	Negative
Anthracene	None	Negative
Phenanthrene	None	Negative
Perylene	None	Negative
3,4,5,6-Dibenzphenanthrene	None	Negative
1,2,5,6-Dibenzacridine	None	Slight
1,2-Dimethylchrysene	Slight	Slight
3,4-Benzpyrene	Definite	Positive
20-Methylcholanthrene	Definite	Positive
1,2,5,6-Dibenzanthracene	Definite	Positive
2-Acetylaminofluorene	Definite	Positive
1,2,5,6-Dibenzfluorene	Inhibits cysteine activation	Positive
9,10-Dimethyl-1,2-benzanthracene	Inhibits cysteine activation	Positive
o-Aminoazotoluene	Inhibits cysteine activation	Positive

amount, being composed of the 4-methylamino and the 4-amino derivatives of the parent dye, and the latter, in greater amount, being still unidentified; (c) the same amount of bound dyes appears in the livers of rats fed the equally potent carcinogens 4-dimethylaminoazobenzene and 4-monomethylaminoazobenzene, whereas only bound 4-aminoazobenzene and very low levels of an apparently non-methylated polar bound dye are found in the livers of rats fed the non-carcinogenic 4-aminoazobenzene; (d) the level of bound dye (or dyes) in the liver reaches a maximum after about 4 to 6 weeks of feeding and thereafter slowly decreases, the level being lower in the animals fed a protective diet high in riboflavin than in those fed a non-protective diet low in riboflavin; (e) no bound dye is found in rat tissues in which 4-dimethylaminoazobenzene does not induce tumors, i.e., small intestine, kidney, spleen, lung, heart, and skeletal muscle, but low levels of bound dye are found in the blood plasma proteins; (f) low levels of bound dye are found in the livers of mice, in which tumors develop slowly, but no bound dye is found at all in the livers of resistant species, namely, guinea pigs, rabbits, cotton rats, or chickens; and (g) no bound dyes are found in the tumors arising in livers which contain considerable levels of these dyes. The Millers concluded from these observations that the correlations noted between the bound dyes and carcinogenesis of the liver indicated that the process of binding must be concerned with the carcinogenic action of 4-dimethylaminoazobenzene, and they suggested that perhaps the autonomous tumor could be the result of an alteration or loss of proteins essential for the control of growth but not for the maintenance of life.

The shape of the curves of bound dye with feeding various of the substituted aminoazo dyes is described in Fig. 15 (344). The initial rates of increase and maximum levels of bound dye correlate directly with the carcinogenic activities of the dye fed (numbers in parentheses), but the times at which the maximum levels of bound dye are reached are inversely related to the carcinogenic activities. An interesting example of the inhibition of the action of an azo dye by the administration of another carcinogen has been described by Richardson and Cunningham (126) in the case of the inhibitory action of 20-methylcholanthrene on the action of 3′-methyl-4-dimethylaminoazobenzene. That this treatment results in an alteration in the shape of the bound dye curve so that it resembles that of weak carcinogen is shown in Fig. 16 (172). Similarly, the inhibition of the action of 3′-methyl-4-dimethylaminoazobenzene by prior treatment of rats with alloxan so as to induce diabetes resulted in a decrease in the bound dye level (345).

More than one-half of the bound dye in the livers of rats fed the active azo dyes is found associated with the soluble proteins of this tissue (346). The electrophoretic pattern of the water-soluble proteins of normal liver

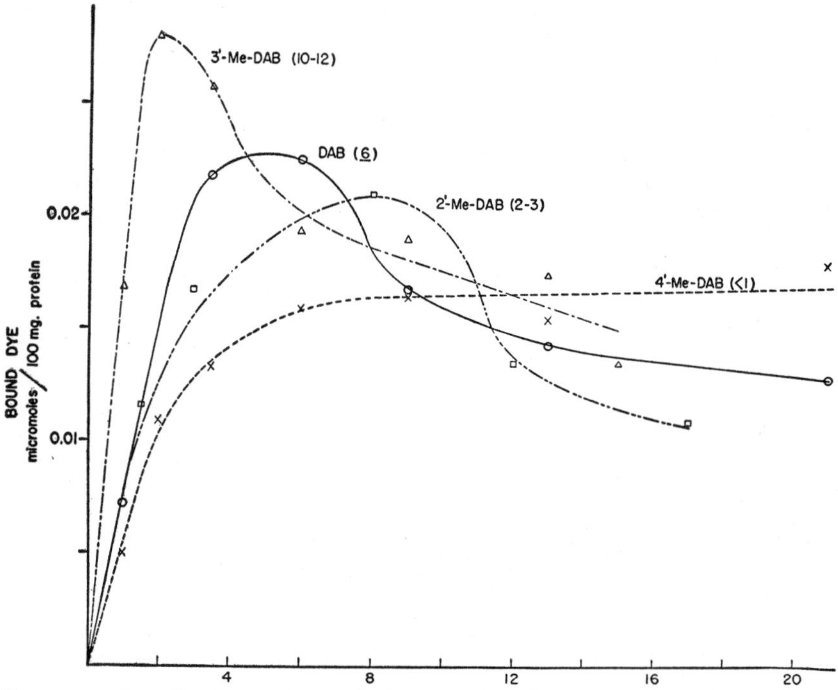

FIG. 15. Levels of protein-bound dye in livers of rats fed 4-dimethylaminoazobenzene or certain of its ring methyl derivatives. From Miller, E. C., Miller, J. A., Sapp, R. W., and Weber, G. M., *Cancer Research* **9**, 336 (1949).

and of the livers of rats fed an active azo dye are very nearly alike (347, 348), and indeed the proteins combined with dye derived from 3′-methyl-4-dimethylaminoazobenzene have the same electrophoretic mobility as those combined with much weaker carcinogens of this class, i.e., 4′-methyl- or 2-methyl-4-dimethylaminoazobenzene (349). This is of interest in view of the fact that differences in rate of accumulation of the protein-bound dyes exist *in vivo*, differences which can be correlated with the carcinogenic activities of the parent dyes (172). However, it was shown by Sorof and Cohen (347) that normal liver soluble protein (as well as the livers of rats fed the azo dyes) contains a group of relatively slowly migrating components which they called *h* components and which are very markedly reduced in the soluble components of the actual hepatic tumor. The major portion of the bound dyes among the soluble portion of the liver proteins migrated with these *h* components (349), suggesting that the metabolic derivatives of the azo dyes bind specific proteins which are subsequently lost in the cancerous transformation. About 80 % of the bound dye appears to be associated with a fraction comprising only 8 to 15 % of the soluble proteins (347).

The same type of approach has been applied to carcinogenesis by other types of agents. Thus E. C. Miller noted that after mice were painted with 3,4-benzpyrene the epidermal protein bound chemical derivatives of the hydrocarbon, which were detected by their strong blue fluorescence (350). When the mice were treated in the dark, the epidermal protein contained more of these derivatives than when the mice had been kept in bright light, a correlation with the observation that more skin tumors develop in mice

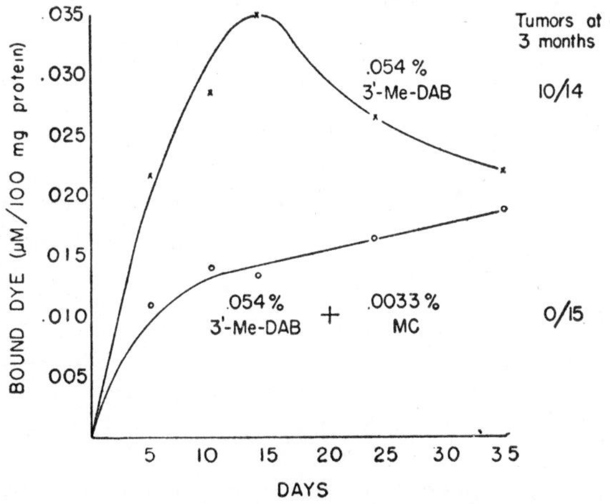

FIG. 16. Levels of protein-bound dye in livers of rats fed diets containing 3′-methyl-4-dimethylaminoazobenzene with and without 20-methylcholanthrene. From Miller, J. A., and Miller, E. C., *Advances in Cancer Research* **1**, 339 (1953).

maintained in the absence of light (351, 352). After a single application of benzpyrene, the maximum level of protein-bound fluorescence occurred in less than 2 days and then decreased until barely detectable at 2 weeks (350).

Essentially similar results were noted by Wiest and Heidelberger (353), who used 1,2,5,6-dibenzanthracene-9,10-C^{14}. The maximum protein-bound radioactive material in the skin also reaches its level within 2 days and sharply decreases thereafter. The apparently irreversible binding occurs between the carcinogen or its metabolite and the nucleoproteins, particulate or soluble proteins, but not with nucleic acids. In the case of administration of the radioactive-labeled carcinogen to the submaxillary gland of mice, less satisfactory results were obtained, for the distribution of the total radioactivity is dependent on the nature of the vehicle employed for the carcinogen, i.e., tricaprylin or sucrose. However, the presence of protein-bound radioactivity is associated with all cell fractions of the gland, only the C^{14} in the soluble protein fraction showing significant changes with time. Figure 17 represents data on the epidermis-bound radioactivity after a single painting with 1,2,5,6-dibenzanthracene-9,10-C^{14} (353).

Rats fed 2-acetylaminofluorene-9-C^{14} bind C^{14} in their livers (354, 355),

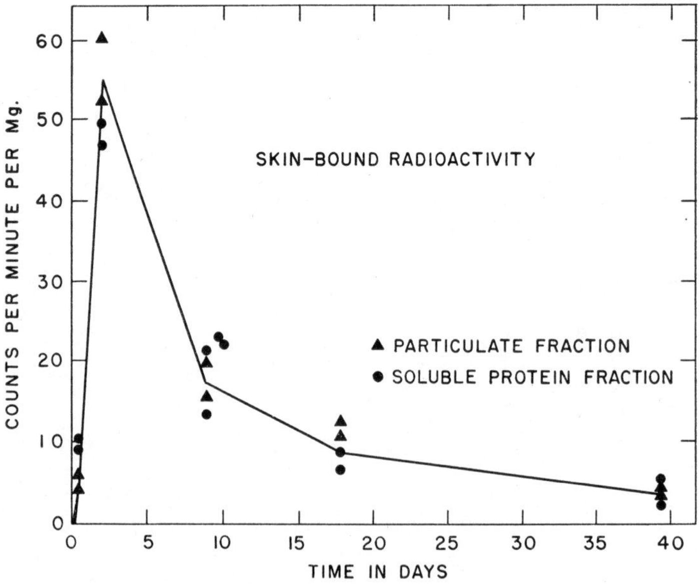

FIG. 17. Levels of protein-bound C^{14} in the particulate and soluble protein fractions from the epidermis of mice given a single topical application of 1,2,5,6-dibenzanthracene-9,10-C^{14} at zero time. From Wiest, W. G., and Heidelberger, C., *Cancer Research* **12,** 308 (1952).

TABLE 22

Distribution of Radioactivity 3 Hours after Feeding 5.05 Mg. (21 × 10^6 Counts) of 2-Acetylaminofluorene-9-C^{14} (355)

Fraction	Liver: Total counts/min. × 10^{-3}	Liver: Per cent counts	Liver: Counts/ mg. N	Kidney: Total counts/min. × 10^{-3}	Kidney: Per cent counts	Kidney: Counts/ mg. N
Homogenate	315	100	2420	91	100	3210
Nuclei	40.5	12.8	1520	7.6	8.4	962
Mitochondria	42.4	13.5	2640	2.9	3.2	1930
Microsomes	37.9	2.0	3200	6.4	7.0	2560
Supernatant	118	37.5	4280	43.5	47.8	6210
Washings	61.1	19.4	2470	20.7	22.7	4200

and, as in the case of the azo dyes, the greater proportion of the protein-bound C^{14} is found in the soluble fraction not only of the liver but of the kidneys as well. Table 22 gives a picture of the events in the two tissues (355).

Hydrolysis of the radioactive proteins in alcoholic KOH, followed by ether extraction, revealed that the organic phase contained 18 % of the counts, and 82 % of the activity remained in the aqueous layer (355). This suggests that the compounds carrying the activity are of the water-soluble type. Their nature remains to be revealed.

It would appear that, with all the observations mentioned, a new concept of the initial stage of carcinogenesis has emerged with enough experimental evidence to take it out of the realm of the purely speculative. The carcinogen apparently has the capacity to bind tightly with several intracellular proteins, perhaps among them key proteins specifically concerned with the control over cellular growth (172). When an active azo dye is removed from the diet, the level of bound dye diminishes at the same rate no matter at what stage of administration of the dye, the half-life for the bound dye being about 3½ days (354), or about the same for the average liver protein of normal rats (356). The tumor proteins contain no bound dye and are deficient in protein components characteristic of the normal or dye-bound liver. The concept that the loss of key proteins leads to the permanent transformation known as cancer has received notable support from these observations. There remains, however, always the perennial question whenever a theory of induced carcinogenesis emerges, no matter how attractive, and that is—how does it explain the so-called spontaneous origin of cancer, whether of the liver or any other tissue?

Effect of Alkylating Agents. The mustards, the epoxides, the ethylene imines, and others of this category of agents (see p. 116) all possess the ability to alkylate certain types of chemical groups in aqueous solutions at nearly neutral reactions. They react with the exposed groups of proteins, i.e., the carboxylate anion $—COO^-$, the uncharged amino group $—NH_2$, and the ionized sulfhydryl group —SH. Obviously the reactions will be favored the more alkaline are the conditions, for the ionized nitrogenous groups are relatively unreactive. These agents also react with the primary and secondary phosphate groups and the amino groups of purine and pyrimidine components (pK 3 to 4), of the nucleic acids. In all cases, the corresponding alkyl esters or N-alkyl derivatives are formed, and the biological changes presumably induced by the alterations of proteins and nucleic acids *in vivo* by these agents may be assumed to be the prelude to their cytotoxic or their carcinogenic action. That the immunological characteristics of a protein treated with nitrogen mustard are different from the original protein has been shown by Watkins and Wormall (357). Table 23 describes some of the data by Alexander on the decrease of amino and carboxyl groups of two proteins after treatment with a series

TABLE 23

REACTION OF ALKYLATING AGENTS WITH PROTEINS (299)

Substance	Reduction in per cent of			
	Amino groups		Carboxyl groups	
	Serum albumin	Wool	Serum albumin	Wool
$CH_3·N·(CH_2CH_2Cl)_2$	45			
p-$CH_3O·C_6H_4N(CH_2CH_2Cl)_2$		21		
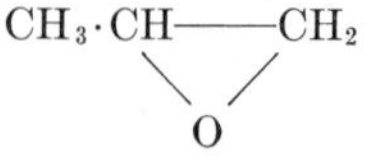		16		7
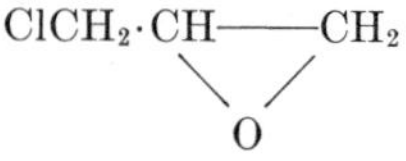		47		25
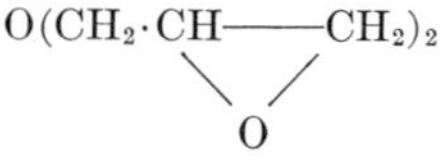	49	47	15	6
$CH_3·SO_2·O(CH_2)_4·OSO_2·CH_3$	31	3	0	4
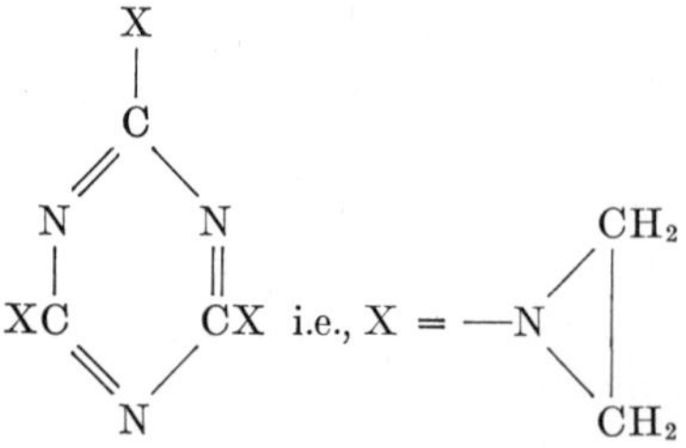	23	16	0	

of alkylating agents (299), which also illustrates the markedly different degrees of effectiveness of the agents.

Although alkylation appears to be a necessary condition for the biological activity of these compounds, there is no distinct correlation between the biological effectiveness of the compounds and their alkylating effectiveness *in vitro* (299).

The description of the mechanisms whereby these agents alkylate to susceptible chemical groupings is beyond the scope of this monograph and has been adequately treated in recent reviews on the subject (299, 291). Speculation has been active in regard to the possible fate of the alkylated macromolecules *in vivo* and in certain instances has been more fruitful than is customary with this form of indulgence. Thus, Haddow and his colleagues suggested that the activity of the nitrogen mustards may be due to their reaction with two centers of the protein or nucleic acid. If these points of attachment were on the same chain, changes in shape of the molecule might ensue. On the other hand, each alkyl attachment might be on different chains, whereby cross-linking of the chains might take place. Such cross-linking might serve to explain observed chromosomal abnormalities. However, it is not yet possible to test such reactions with chromosomes *in vitro*, and the use of model systems leaves something to be desired. Nevertheless, such considerations have led to the discovery of the active epoxides and ethyleneimines, which had been known for some time in the textile industry to cross-link wool and cellulose textile fibers.

The carcinogenic activity of these agents has been announced but at this time not fully described. Most of the work done with them has involved their cytotoxic properties, and presumably their initial reactions in the therapy and in the genesis of cancer may be considered indistinguishable by present criteria. In this connection it is of interest that Boyland drew attention to the similarities between the biological actions of X-irradiation and of the mustards and used the expression radiomimetic to describe the effects of the chemical agents. Although there are some points of undoubted similarity between the action of radiation and that of certain of the alkylating agents, there are others, such as the sensitivity of SH-enzymes toward the former and their inertness toward the latter, which are markedly different.

The radiomimetic compounds, such as the mustards, the epoxides, the ethyleneimines, and the sulfonic acid esters, may be considered as alkylating agents which readily esterify anions (358). Under conditions in which such interaction can take place, it would be expected that chemical reactions at such susceptible anionic groups would be hindered. Thus, the interaction between nucleic acid and protamine is interfered with by the various alkylating agents, and this inhibition can be reversed by subjecting the nucleic acid derivative to a mild alkaline hydrolysis which brings about saponification of the phosphate ester groups (358). On prolonged standing with nitrogen mustard, deoxyribonucleic acid desaggregates into particles with increasingly smaller sedimentation constants (359). It is difficult to ascertain therefore whether the effect of the mustards in reducing the physical property of viscosity is due to the partial neutralization of the charges on the molecule through alkylation or to some early degradative reaction. X-Radiation, too, has an effect on the physical properties of the nucleate when given at relatively low dosages, and only at high dosage levels does the molecule appear to break down chemically.

Chemical Structure and Carcinogenesis

The wealth of observations derived from the study of literally hundreds of synthetic organic compounds led inevitably to attempts to find some correlation between their structure and their cancer-inducing potency. Up to about 1940 surveys of this subject appeared to stress its empirical aspects, i.e., the blunt facts that a substituent placed here or there in the molecule either enhanced or diminished its carcinogenic effectiveness. Perhaps a tendency at that time to look not much further than the facts was based on the general impression of the relative chemical inertness of the polycyclic hydrocarbons, together with the growing awareness that the experimental induction of cancer in an animal was the result of a large number of factors of which the chemical structure of the carcinogen was only one. With the observations that a wide variety of apparently unrelated agents such as metal salts, viruses, and radiation could also induce cancer, a rational explanation of the action of the synthetic hydrocarbons based purely on structure appeared nearly hopeless. Yet the most empirical biologist, deviled by all the complexities inherent in the experimental induction of tumors in laboratory animals, must at times have been grateful for the use of methylcholanthrene and perhaps wondered, not why methylcholanthrene was more or less effective under various circumstances, but why cholanthrene was rarely effective at all.

With increasing recognition that the polycyclic carcinogens were not chemically unreactive but possessed the ability to interact with a number of reagents at specific reactive sites which in many cases were predictable, there emerged during the past decade a remarkable series of attempts to relate carcinogenic activity to specific electronic configurations of the hydrocarbon carcinogens. These investigations were carried out by the Pullmans and by Daudel in France, and subsequently extended by Badger in Australia and by Coulson and Boyland in England. At first glance, the theoretical considerations involved, and the emphasis placed exclusively on the chemical compounds involved, might appear to have little connection with the realities daily faced by the empirical biologist mentioned above. Since these correlations have for the most part dealt largely with mice, the critic may captiously wonder what would have happened to such correlations if mice had not been invented and carcinogenesis had only been studied with rabbits or guinea pigs. Nevertheless, it is true that mice are the most susceptible of all known experimental animals, and it is quite proper to employ—as a first approximation, at the least—the most favorable subject to test an hypothesis. Unsuitable subjects may be so for reasons other than those which the hypothesis must take for granted. Thus, methylcholanthrene is a good skin tumor-inducing agent in the mouse but a very poor one for the rat. On the other hand, 9,10-dimethyl-1,2-benzanthracene is a good induction agent for skin tumors in both species. The latter agent causes a destruction of the sebaceous glands in both species, but the former agent causes such destruction only in the skin of the mouse, and it has been suggested that this difference in response of the sebaceous glands may be responsible for the relative susceptibility of the mouse and rat to these compounds (360). It must be assumed that a subject will respond in kind if not in degree, and the order of carcinogenic effectiveness of two chemicals cannot be compared in two species if in each species the two chemicals are handled in different ways (cf. 361). The considerations illustrated in this section will therefore, unless otherwise stated, apply only to mice.

Bergmann pointed out in 1942 that the active, aromatic hydrocarbons possess a flat, planar configuration and that whatever causes a departure from this configuration is accompanied by a loss in carcinogenic activity (362). The surmise was advanced that the active molecules function by virtue of a special size and shape, as well as by their inherent molecular constitution, and that these molecules may combine as complexes with specific tissue components in degrees of stability which are governed by the mutual configuration of agent and receptor. The fact that the active compounds cannot be less than tricyclic or larger than hexacyclic has been mentioned (p. 52). There is little doubt that any distortion from planarity of the molecule, whether by partial hydrogenation (363), by higher alkyl substitution (364), or by changing from a *trans* configuration as in the aminostilbenes to the corresponding *cis* (28), produces a loss in carcinogenic activity. There is equally little doubt that the active carcinogens react in a specific way with various tissue components to form a relatively tight binding (see previous section). Consistent with such complex formation are the observations (a) that the carcinogenic hydrocarbons are metabolized to phenolic derivatives in which the hydroxy groups occupy comparable positions, i.e., the 4′-position in 1,2-benzanthracene and 9,10-dimethyl-1,2-benzanthracene, the 3-position in chrysene, and the 8-position in 3,4-benzpyrene, and (b) that competitive inhibition is exerted by one carcinogen on another (p. 79). It is possible that the compounds are all fixed in the tissue at some more or less common grouping and that the metabolic hydroxylation takes place at an exposed position (29). Similarly, a weak carcinogen may successfully compete with a strong one for a specific binding site in the tissues and thereby inhibit its action.

It is possible, as Boyland suggests, that the complex of hydrocarbon with the tissue constituent, or of the metabolite with the tissue constituent, may be the proximate carcinogenic agent (365). Thus, in the case of 1,2,5,6-dibenzanthracene, the sequence of events might be:

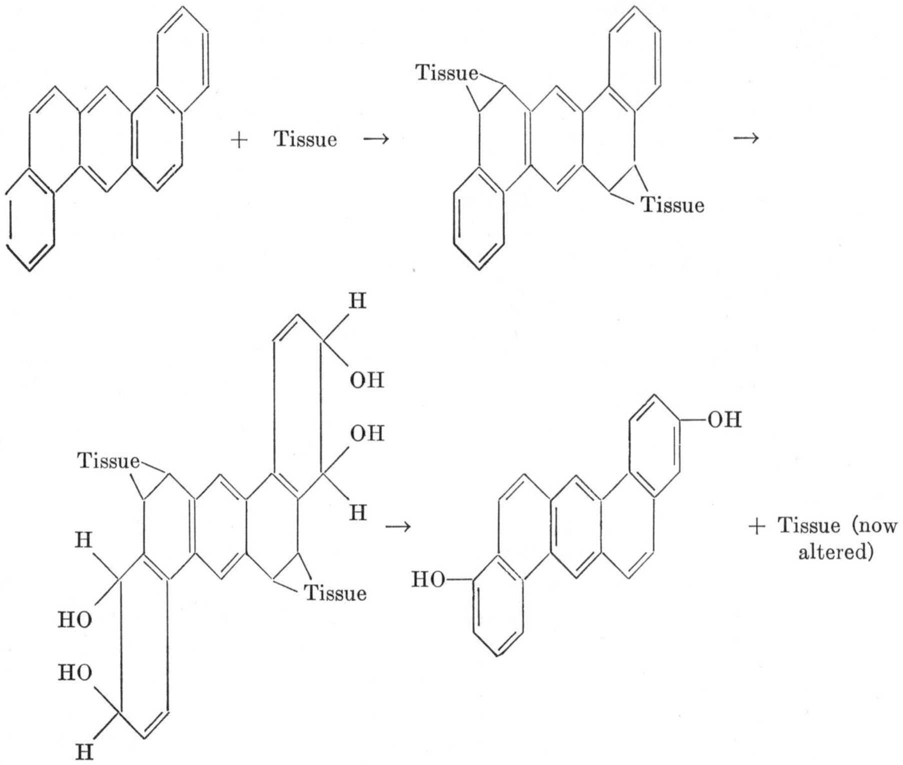

Since substitution at a position ordinarily hydroxylated during metabolism results in an inactive compound, it would appear that such metabolism is part of the carcinogenic process.

It has long been known that the aromatic compounds form complexes with such reagents as picric acid, aluminum chloride, stannic chloride, and antimony pentachloride, with varying degrees of stability (cf. 366). Thus, anthracene and benzanthracene form more stable picrates than those formed from benzene or naphthalene, and methyl substitution, which generally increases carcinogenic activity in such molecules, also enhances the ease of formation and stability of the picrate complexes. The stronger carcinogens, such as 3,4-benzpyrene and 20-methylcholanthrene, form very stable picrates. Any substituent which destroys the planarity of the molecule (and presumably also the carcinogenicity) hinders the ease of picrate complex formation. Thus, *trans*-, but not *cis*-, stilbene forms a picrate complex.

With the suggestion that the melting point of the picrate complex be taken as a measure of its stability, it was noted that as a general rule the methyl derivatives of 1,2-benzanthracene had melting points higher than that of the parent hydrocarbon, the carcinogenic 10-methyl and 5-methyl derivatives yielding picrate complexes with quite high melting points (366). An exception to this observation occurs in the case of the highly carcinogenic 9-methyl-1,2-benzanthracene in which steric interference between the 9-methyl and 1′-hydrogen is possible, and whose picrate consequently has a very low melting point (366). Picrate complexes with the hydrocarbons, however, are not protein complexes with the hydrocarbons, and observations that involve stability and crystal lattice energy are not readily extrapolated to carcinogenicity. Thus, the melting point values of the 1,1-derivatives of trinitrofluorenone with the methylated 1,2-benzanthracenes were relatively close together, and, although the value for the 9-methyl derivative was again the lowest for the entire series of complexes studied, there was little evidence for a correlation of melting point of the complex with carcinogenicity of the hydrocarbon (367). Nevertheless, the fact that the polycyclic hydrocarbons possess the ability to form such complexes offers many possibilities of interpreting their modes of biological action.

In 1946, Robinson made the important suggestion that the essential feature of the carcinogen hydrocarbon is the possession of a phenanthrene-type bridge, which may be activated by suitable substitution or by additional benzene rings (368). Isomeric dimethylthiophanthrene derivatives were prepared to test this hypothesis, and it was found that those which had phenanthrene structures were carcinogenic whereas that which did not was inactive (the asterisk refers to the phenanthrene bond). In this connection it should be pointed out that such hydrocarbons as 1,2,3,4-dibenzanthracene, 9,10-dimethyl-1,2,3,4-dibenzanthracene, 4,7-dimethyl-2,3,5,6-dibenzthionaphthene (in which a sulfur atom replaces the phenanthrene-type double bond in 9,10-dimethyl-1,2-benzanthracene), and 6,7-dihydro-20-methylcholanthrene (in which the phenanthrene-type double bond is reduced) are all inactive or nearly so, and none possesses the phenanthrene bond (29).

Benzene possesses a hexagonal structure. Since each carbon atom contributes four valency electrons and each hydrogen one, there are altogether thirty valency electrons. Twelve of these are involved in the six carbon-carbon bonds, and another twelve in the six carbon-hydrogen bonds. This leaves six electrons, the so-called π-electrons, unaccounted for. The

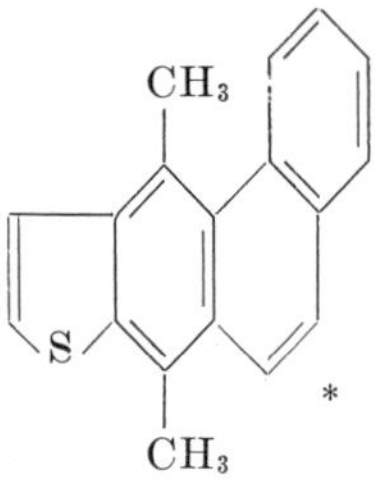

Active

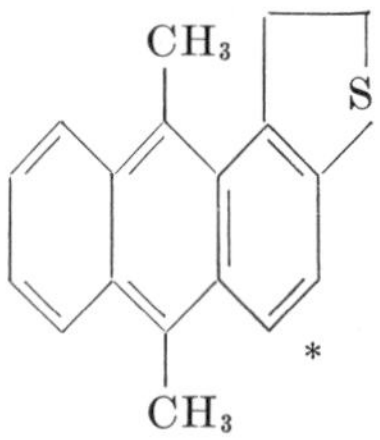

Active

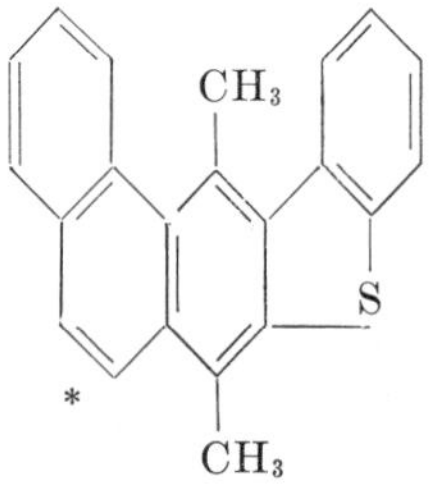

Active

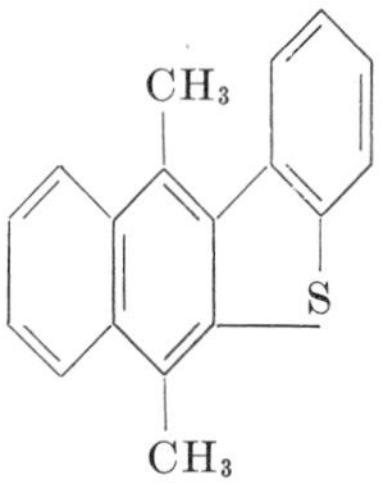

Inactive

disposition of these "mobile" electrons has been solved on quantum-mechanical grounds (cf. review by Coulson, 369). Emerging from the quantum calculations has been the assignment of so-called free valence numbers to the various carbon atoms of the cyclic compounds, which numbers may be considered as relative measures of the unused bonding capacity of the carbon atoms. Since in benzene all the carbon atoms are identical, all have the same free valence number. In the condensed ring structures this will obviously not be so. Also emerging from the quantum calculations has been the concept of so-called bond order, or relative double-bond character. For example, in 1,2-benzanthracene, the 10-position has the greatest free valence number, and the 3,4-bond has the greatest bond order. In 3,4-benzphenanthrene, the 2-position has the greatest free valence number, and the 1,2-bond has the greatest bond order. Similarly, the 2-position in chrysene has the greatest free valence number and the 1,2-bond has the greatest order (29). Those positions having the greatest free valence numbers are most readily attacked in substitution reactions, and the presence of a phenanthrene-type bond of high order may be considered a prerequisite for carcinogenic activity in this class of compounds. The more readily substituted positions, i.e., the "favorable" positions, those with the greatest free valence numbers, may yield the most active carcinogens, as shown by Table 24 of methyl-substituted derivatives of benzanthracene (cf. Badger, 29).

Thus the 5-, 9-, and 10-positions in 1,2-benzanthracene have the greatest conjugating capacities, and methyl substitution at these positions yields the most active carcinogens. Newman and Kosak (370) have pointed

TABLE 24

Conjugating Abilities of Various Methyl Substitution Positions in 1,2-Benzanthracene and Carcinogenic Capacity[1] (29)

Position	Free valence number (molecular-orbital method)	Free valence number (valence-bond method)	Carcinogenic activity for: Skin	Subcutaneous tissue
6	0.089	0.168	+	
7	0.090	0.168	+	+
4	0.137	0.200	+	++
8	0.138	0.196	+	0
3	0.138	0.204	+	++
5	0.140	0.198	++	++
9	0.180	0.241	++	+++
10	0.196	0.255	+++	++++

[1] This and succeeding tables in this section which have been taken from Badger's papers (cf. 29) employ his values of + signs, which in turn are based upon Iball's index (Table 8, p. 59) thus: 75–151 is ++++, 45–48 is +++, 26–28 is ++, and 7–17 is + (see also 364).

out that carcinogenic activity appears when a methyl group is substituted at a position of high chemical reactivity, and Badger (29) mentions that all the possible dimethylbenzanthracenes involving the 5-, 9-, and 10-positions are active carcinogens, and 5,9,10-trimethyl-1,2-benzanthracene is one of the most potent carcinogens known for the skin of mice. However, methyl substitution *per se* does not necessarily lead to enhancement of carcinogenicity, for such substitution at any prime position in the benz ring of 1,2-benzanthracene leads to inactive compounds. In 3,4-benzphenanthrene, the 2-position has the greatest free valence number, and of all the methyl-substituted benzphenanthrenes the 2-methyl derivative is the most carcinogenic (29). It is of interest in this connection to point out that Jones suggested that there might be an approximate correlation between the carcinogenic activities of a series of substituted benzanthracenes and the position of the most intense absorption band in the ultraviolet region (371), an observation which Badger and his colleagues later interpreted and extended to a relation between the magnitude of the bathochromic shift and the conjugating ability of the substitution position (372). Thus, of the monomethyl derivatives, the largest such shifts were noted for the 9-methyl- and 10-methyl-1,2-benzanthracenes.

It would appear that there may well be some correlation between favorable or reactive positions in potentially carcinogenic polycyclic systems and what may be called the induction of carcinogenic activity by conjugation at these positions. Methyl substituents, which are electron donors, contribute a higher electron charge to the ring system at such positions than in positions having lower conjugating capacities and produce simultaneously a greater carcinogenic capacity. It therefore is reasonable to suppose that the capacity of a compound to function as a carcinogen is in some way connected with its electron configuration and electron density, although this by far is not the whole story.

The work of the French theoretical chemists, the Pullmans (373–378), and the Daudels (379–381) has led to calculations which indicate that potentially carcinogenic ring systems, such as 1,2-benzanthracene, 3,4-benzphenanthrene, and chrysene, all have a phenanthrene-type bond with a particularly high electron density or bond order, whereas other ring systems not potentially carcinogenic, such as triphenylene or naphthacene, do not possess such a region. The electron density at the phenanthrene bond would be expected to be increased by methyl substitution, by an amount which depended on the site of substitution. This phenanthrene-type bond was called the K-region by Schmidt (382), and it was suggested that this K-region (K for Krebs) was associated with carcinogenesis, an optimum charge of π-electrons above a critical value being needed to induce cancer by the compound. The calculations indeed revealed that the total charge of π-electrons at the K-region for non-carcinogenic polycyclic hydrocarbons was relatively lower than for the carcinogenic compounds. Thus, anthracene, naphthacene, and triphenylene have bonds with electron densities, respectively, of 1.259*e*, 1.258*e*, and 1.260*e*, whereas 3,4-benzphenanthrene has a K-region with a charge of 1.293*e*, 1,2-benzanthracene of 1.283*e*, and chrysene of 1.272*e*. The critical charge on the bond, below which the compounds are not carcinogenic, was assumed to be about 1.290*e*. Methyl substitution of course increased the charge—thus, 10-methyl substitution in 1,2-benzanthracene was estimated to increase the charge to 1.306*e*, and in dimethyl substitution the charge increased proportionately together with enhanced carcinogenicity. The carcinogenicity was further assumed to reach an optimal value with increase of electron charge at the K-region, and increasing substitution with increase in charge would lead only to a diminution in the carcinogenicity.

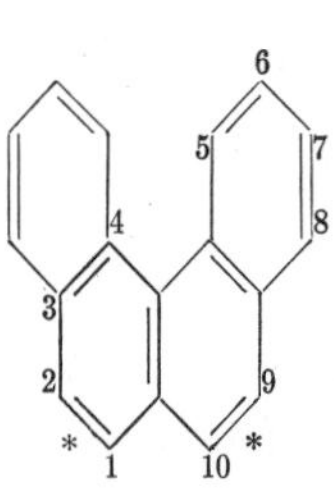

3,4-Benzphen-
anthrene

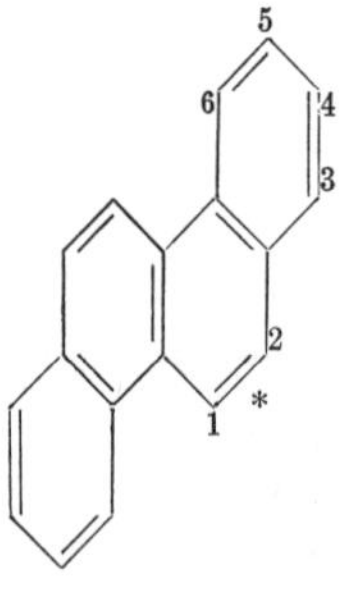

Chrysene

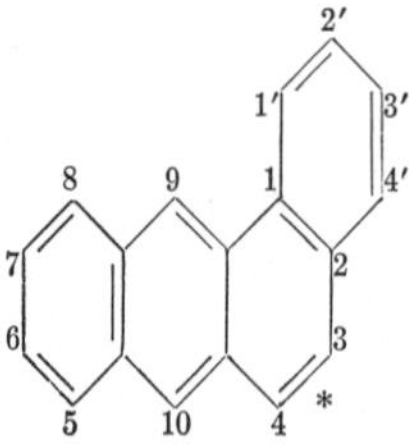

1,2-Benzanthracene

* represents K-region

TABLE 25

RELATION BETWEEN CARCINOGENICITY AND DENSITY OF K-REGION ELECTRONS (π) IN 1,2-BENZANTHRACENE SERIES (29)

Compound	Electron density at K-region (Pullman)	Carcinogenicity in skin
1,2-Benzanthracene	1.283	Very weak
6-Methyl-1,2-benzanthracene	1.294	+
3-Methyl-1,2-benzanthracene	1.298	+
5-Methyl-1,2-benzanthracene	1.296	++
9-Methyl-1,2-benzanthracene	1.296	++
10-Methyl-1,2-benzanthracene	1.306	+++
5,6-Dimethyl-1,2-benzanthracene	1.307	+++
9,10-Dimethyl-1,2-benzanthracene	1.319	++++
6,9,10-Trimethyl-1,2-benzanthracene	1.330	++++
5,9,10-Trimethyl-1,2-benzanthracene	1.332	++++
5,6,9,10-Tetramethyl-1,2-benzanthracene	1.343	+++

There may be more than one K-region in some of the compounds in this category. Thus, 3,4-benzphenanthrene has two K-regions, at the 1,2- and 9,10-bonds, and 1,2,5,6-dibenzanthracene has two K-regions, at the 3,4- and 7,8-bonds. Table 25 reveals some of the data on substituted benzanthracenes (29).

As Badger points out, there are several exceptions to the theory, most notable of which is the fact that both electron-attracting and electron-donating substituents transform 1,2-benzanthracene into an active carcinogen. Thus, 10-cyano- and 10-formyl-1,2-benzanthracenes, like the 10-methyl derivative, are also carcinogenic (29). The dibenzfluorenes must also constitute an exception to the theory, for these substances cannot have a markedly high density of electrons at the K-region (29). In view of these difficulties it was proposed (380) to compare the carcinogenic activity of the various compounds with the "excess charge" on the K-region caused by the methyl substitution. By these calculations, a fair correlation was observed between the excess charge on the K-region brought about by substitution of methyl groups at various positions in benzanthracene and benzacridine and the carcinogenicity of the compounds (29). In such calculations, the effect of an annular nitrogen atom (as in benzacridine) on decreasing the electron charge on the K-region was taken into consideration, as was also the compensatory effect due to the presence of methyl substituents at favorable positions in the molecule.

Greenwood (383) similarly calculated by another procedure the increased charge on the K-region by various methyl substituents, as well as by the annular nitrogen atom, and his data together with those of Badger (29) are given in Table 26.

Perbenzoic acid is a reagent which appears to react with carcinogenic

TABLE 26

Excess Charge on the K-Region and Carcinogenic Activity (364, 383)

Compound	Excess charge on K-region (383)	Carcinogenic activity (364)	
		Skin	Subcutaneous tissue
7-Methyl-3,4-benzacridine	−0.0393	0	
3,4-Benzacridine	−0.0387	0	
5,7-Dimethyl-3,4-benzacridine	−0.0366	0	
5-Methyl-3,4-benzacridine	−0.0360	0	
5,7,9-Trimethyl-3,4-benzacridine	−0.0335	+++	0
5,9-Dimethyl-3,4-benzacridine	−0.0329	0	+
5,8-Dimethyl-3,4-benzacridine	−0.0233	+	0
1,2-Benzacridine	−0.0027	0	
1,2-Benzanthracene	0	0	+
7-Methyl-1,2-benzacridine	0.0004	0	
9-Methyl-1,2-benzanthracene	0.0027	++	+++
6-Methyl-1,2-benzanthracene	0.0031	+	
5,6-Dimethyl-1,2-benzanthracene	0.0122	+++	
5,9-Dimethyl-1,2-benzacridine	0.0354	+++	+++
5-Methyl-1,2-benzacridine	0.0360	+++	
5,7,9-Trimethyl-1,2-benzacridine	0.0385	+++	++
10-Methyl-1,2-benzanthracene	0.0387	+++	++++
5,7-Dimethyl-1,2-benzacridine	0.0391	++++	+++
9,10-Dimethyl-1,2-benzanthracene	0.0414	++++	+++
5,8-Dimethyl-1,2-benzacridine	0.0487	++++	+++
5,6,9,10-Tetramethyl-1,2-benzanthracene	0.0536	+++	+

hydrocarbons at rates roughly proportional to their biological activity (384). The data obtained by Boyland are described in Table 27.

Another strong reagent for the double-bond K-region of the various polycyclic hydrocarbons has been found to be osmium tetroxide (385). Thus, with 1,2-benzanthracene it adds exclusively at the 3,4-bond, at the 1,2-bond of chrysene, and at the 6,7-bond of 3,4-benzpyrene. These

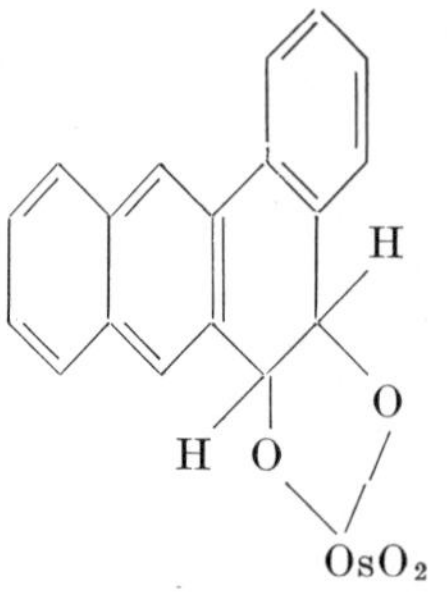

1,2-Benzanthracene-osmium oxide complex

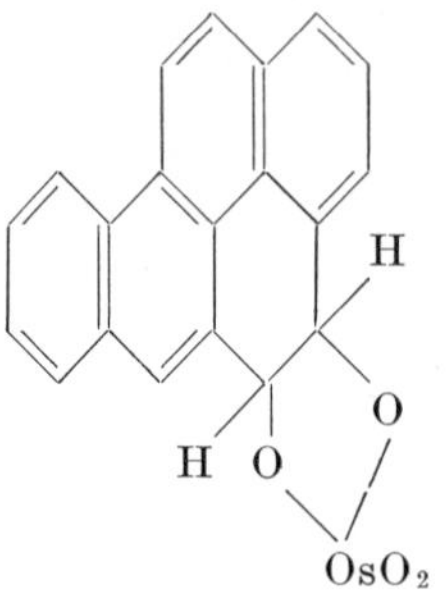

3,4-Benzpyrene-osmium oxide complex

TABLE 27

REACTIONS OF HYDROCARBONS WITH PERBENZOIC ACID (384)

Compound	Millimoles reagent used per mole substrate in 48 hours at 25°	Carcinogenic activity
9,10-Anthraquinone	0	Negative
Naphthalene	20	Negative
Phenanthrene	20	Negative
9,10-Phenanthraquinone	25	Negative
Anthracene	60	Negative
1,2-Benzanthracene	70	Weak
1,2,5,6-Dibenzanthracene	35	Positive
5-Methyl-1,2-benzanthracene	40	Positive
4-Aminostilbene	120	Positive
2-Acetylaminofluorene	100	Positive
3,4-Benzpyrene	130	Positive
3,4-Benzphenanthrene	145	Positive
Stilbene	110	?
3,4,5,6-Dibenzcarbazole	265	Positive
20-Methylcholanthrene	340	Positive
2′-Methyl-4-dimethylaminostilbene	465	Positive
4-Dimethylaminoazobenzene	615	Positive

adducts are easily hydrolyzed to yield *cis*-dihydroxy-dihydro derivatives. Substituents were shown by Badger and his colleagues (386, 387) to influence the rate of addition of osmium tetroxide to the K-region, methyl and other alkyl groups increasing this rate, depending upon the position of the substitution. Thus, in the alkyl-1,2-benzanthracenes, the most rapid rates occurred with groups in the *meso* positions, i.e., 9-methyl, 10-methyl, and 9,10-dimethyl, whereas methyl substitutions at the 6- or 5,6-positions resulted in lesser effects on the rates. 1,2-Dimethylchrysene reacted more rapidly with the reagent than did the parent compound.

It would therefore appear that there should be some correlation between the relative reactivity of the polycylic hydrocarbons toward osmium tetroxide and their carcinogenic activity, since both bear a relation to the electronic charge on the phenanthrene-type double bond or K-region. The results described by Badger (386, 387) are given in Table 28. Since the osmium tetroxide reaction is accelerated by *meso* substitution, the high rate of reaction with 9,10-diphenyl-1,2-benzanthracene is explicable, even though the substituents are at right angles to the plane of the rings and hence completely inhibit the carcinogenic potentiality. The peculiar effect of the cyano substituent, which markedly causes a diminution in the rate of reaction of osmium tetroxide but which apparently does not hinder but even accelerates carcinogenic activity over and beyond that of the parent hydrocarbon, is more difficult to explain. Perhaps, as Badger suggests,

TABLE 28

REACTIVITY TOWARD OsO_4 AND CARCINOGENIC ACTIVITY (386, 387)

Compound	Relative reactivity toward OsO_4	Carcinogenic activity
9,10-Dimethyl-1,2-benzanthracene	5.6	++++
9,10-Diethyl-1,2-benzanthracene	4.4	+++
9-Methyl-1,2-benzanthracene	2.0	+++
10-Methyl-1,2-benzanthracene	1.90	++++
9,10-Diphenyl-1,2-benzanthracene	1.46	0
10-Acetoxymethyl-1,2-benzanthracene	1.27	+
1,2-Benzanthracene	1.00	±
10-Cyano-9-methyl-1,2-benzanthracene	0.83	++++
10-Bromo-1,2-benzanthracene	0.56	0
9,10-Diacetoxy-1,2-benzanthracene	0.44	0
10-Cyano-1,2-benzanthracene	Slow	+

the cyano group may itself possess a peculiar affinity for the receptor groups in the tissues with which it presumably complexes, perhaps through hydrogen bonding (29). The larger substituents, such as the phenyl or acetoxy, even though at "favorable" positions, by destroying the planarity of the compounds may inhibit by such steric effects the necessary complex formation with tissue receptors which is the prelude to carcinogenesis.

Thus, it seems very likely that the carcinogenic activity of the polycyclic hydrocarbons is associated with (a) a planar configuration and (b) a reactive double bond, and that methyl substitution at positions favorable to further activation of this double bond leads to enhanced carcinogenicity. These requirements are explicable in terms of a complexing arrangement of the carcinogen with some tissue components, in which steric factors and hydrogen-bonding characteristics likewise play a role. Boyland has made an interesting analogy of the effects of enhancement by methyl substitution of the actual or latent carcinogenicity of a hydrocarbon to the action of the auxochrome group on a potential colored molecule which enhances or brings out the latent color of the chromophoric group in this molecule (388). Thus in azo benzene the azo group is the chromophore and the 4-amino group is the auxochrome. Similarly in 1,2-benzanthracene the 3,4-bond or K-region might be termed the carcinogenophore and favorably situated methyl groups might be termed the auxocarcinogens. In typical aromatic compounds, the carcinogenophoric groups might include the phenanthrene and stilbene double bonds, the *meso* positions of anthracene or tetramethyl phenanthrene, the azo linkage, the heterocyclic nitrogen, the amino nitrogen, or the sulfide link.

Reports by A. and B. Pullman (388a) suggest that the carcinogenic activity of compounds containing four or five fused benzene rings may be related to the presence of a second region (L-region) of low activity in such molecules. For carcinogenic activity the sum of the free valences of the two carbon atoms constituting this region must be less than unity.

This L-region is typified by the C_9-C_{10} section of anthracene, or by the C_6-C_{11} section of naphthacene.

The mechanisms by which the complexing arrangement between carcinogen and tissue protein may be effected are little known. It is clear from the Millers' work (see above) that in general the complexing of the azo dyes with hepatic protein is proportional to the carcinogenicity of the dye. The reactive K-region of the carcinogenic hydrocarbons, the "exposed bond" (369), is very probably involved in the formation of any complex with tissue protein. What happens to the protein after such complexing occurs is largely unknown. Perhaps, as Schmidt suggested (382), the hydrocarbon serves as a catalyst in tautomeric changes within the protein chains, which, persisted in for any length of time, lead to further rearrangements which are more difficult to terminate and reverse to the normal situation (cf. 381).

The other class of carcinogenic compounds whose structure has been studied in an analogous manner is the azo compounds. Each nitrogen atom in the —N═N— bond has a lone pair of electrons, which to some extent are shared with the aromatic rings to which the azo bond is attached. Since substituents have a considerable effect on the electron density of the two nitrogen atoms, it was suggested by the Pullmans (377) that the essential requirement for carcinogenic activity was a certain critical charge at this —N═N— bond or so-called K′-region. Relatively little work has been done in evaluating the relative electron densities at the K′-region of the azo compounds, and the hypotheses advanced by the Pullmans to distinguish the relative carcinogenicity of the various azo dyes have not been very satisfactory (cf. 29). Nevertheless, owing to the work of the Millers, the binding of this class of substances to the liver proteins has been so clearly delineated that a full understanding of the reactive groupings in these substances becomes a necessary task.

Information on the reactivity of the K′-region through the addition of electrophilic reagents has been carried on in two ways. One has been by estimating the ionization constants in acid of a series of 4′-substituted 4-dimethylaminoazobenzenes (389), and the other by studying the rate of oxidation by perbenzoic acid of a number of substituted azobenzenes (29, 390). In the former method, a proton is added to one of the azo-nitrogen atoms of the K′-region in 50% ethanol at a pH range of 1.96 to 3.58, and a second proton is added to the dimethylamino group in aqueous sulfuric acid at a pH range of −1.13 to −7.61, thus:

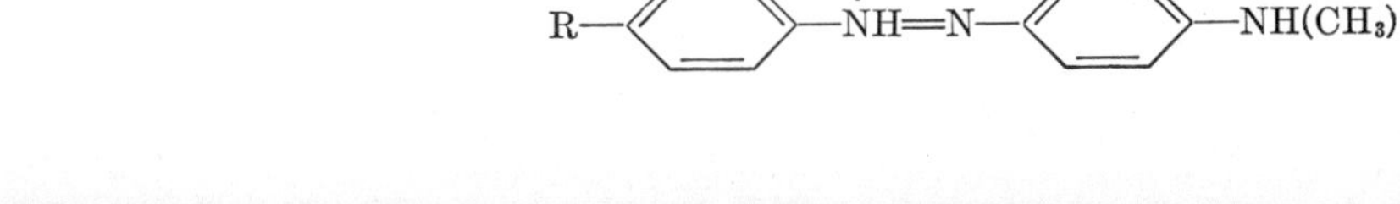

The respective constants, pK_1 and $-pK_2$, were determined spectrophotometrically. The effect of the 4′-substitution on the proton affinity of each of the nitrogen atoms was noted to be in the same order (linear) as the net electron affinities of the group as measured by the Hammett substituent constants (391) (using values for the *para* substituents in the benzene ring). The slopes of the lines relating pK to the Hammett constants were negative, for pK_1 the value was 0.55, compared with 4.35 for $-pK_2$. The 4′-nitro group with high positive Hammett constant and the 4′-methyl group with high negative Hammett constant have, respectively, the smallest pK_1, namely 1.81, and the largest pK_1, namely 2.31. They represent therefore extreme effects, and neither compound is appreciably carcinogenic in rats. Among the substituents with intermediate values of Hammett constant and pK_1 are some active carcinogens, but not all the substituted azo dyes in this category are carcinogenic.

In the latter method, reaction with perbenzoic acid and the azo dye leads to the corresponding azoxy derivatives, thus:

$$Ar\text{—}N\text{=}N\text{—}Ar \;+\; Ph\cdot CO_3H \;\rightarrow\; Ar\text{—}\underset{\substack{\downarrow\\ O}}{N}\text{=}N\text{—}Ar \;+\; Ph\cdot CO_2H$$

The active carcinogens, whether polycyclic hydrocarbons, aminostilbene derivatives, or azo dyes, all seem to react vigorously with perbenzoic acid, the last-mentioned reacting most rapidly of all (30, 384). Whether they react at the same or analogous bonds remains to be seen. The rate of oxidation by perbenzoic acid of the carcinogenic 2,2′-azonaphthalene is nearly equal to that of the non-carcinogenic azobenzene and 1,2′-azonaphthalene (392), and therefore the electron density around the nitrogen atoms (K′-region) must be nearly the same for the three compounds. The oxidation rate of these compounds is, however, far below that of the carcinogenic aminoazo dyes (392). It may well be that 2,2′-azonaphthalene is not active *per se*, but, as Cook *et al.* have suggested, is transformed *in vivo* to the carcinogenic 3,4,5,6-dibenzcarbazole. The aminoazo dyes probably do not undergo this type of transformation and may require the presence of the amino group. Comparison of the azonaphthalenes and the aminoazobenzene compounds purely on the basis of electron density at the respective azo linkages is undoubtedly an oversimplification, and the lack of consistency noted may be both a warning and an impetus to further metabolic research.

These theoretical considerations may well be valid, but attempts to correlate the carcinogenic activity of the azo dyes with the Hammett constants, considering that the latter bear some relation to the charge on the K′-region, have not led to any striking or consistent conclusions. There is probably no question that among the prerequisites for carcinogenicity of the azo dyes an optimal electron charge on the K′-region must be present, but this may play a relatively minor role compared with (a) steric effects, and (b) hydrogen bonding through electron-attracting substituents, which are involved in the relatively tightly bound complexes of this class of substances with the tissue receptors (proteins).

When all the theoretical factors, with their many approximations and assumptions, are assayed, in what way do they assist in the interpretation of the carcinogenic induction by such agents as arsenic or radiation? It is not improbable that such agents may bring about the production by the host of organic chemicals similar perhaps in certain details of structure and potency to those considered in this section. If the carcinogenic process actually consists in two consecutive actions, namely an induction or preneoplasia whereby one or more cells become potentially malignant, plus a promoting effect which precipitates such latent cells into the frankly malignant state, it is possible to conceive of almost any foreign agent capable of performing the second of these functions. At the present state of our knowledge any such argument is bound to be weak. Perhaps a better answer, although no more illuminating, is the fact that many roads lead to Rome, and no two travelers need journey in the same manner.

The Effect of Carcinogenic Agents in Various Species

To a very considerable extent, the impetus given to the study of chemical (and radiation) carcinogenesis arose from the long-recognized higher incidence of certain occupational cancers among individuals practicing certain vocations as compared with that of the general population. Coal tar, suspected as an etiological agent in man, was found to be carcinogenic to the skin of rabbits. The fractionation of coal tar followed, and the isolation of 3,4-benzpyrene was achieved (*vide infra*). This compound proved to be highly carcinogenic on the skin or under the skin of mice. Subsequent work by Dunning *et al.* (393) and others revealed that 3,4-benzpyrene and 20-methylcholanthrene were also powerfully carcinogenic in rats.

However, when 3,4-benzpyrene was administered to rabbits the unexpected result was noted that this species of animal was highly refractory to the agent at concentrations in excess of that found in tar. This finding inevitably suggested the hypothesis that there might be some other material in tar which, acting alone or in conjunction with 3,4-benzpyrene, is responsible for the production of skin tumors in rabbits. Whatever the merits of this hypothesis may be, the interesting fact emerges that a hydrocarbon strongly carcinogenic in two species, mice and rats, is relatively non-carcinogenic in at least a third species, the domestic rabbit. Another active carcinogenic agent for rats and mice, 1,2,5,6-dibenzanthracene, was likewise found to be very weakly carcinogenic for rabbits (394). On the other hand, the very powerful agent, 20-methylcholanthrene, is highly carcinogenic not only for mice and rats but also for the cottontail rabbit (395). This agent readily produced sarcomas at the subcutaneous site of injection. Thus, the rabbit is not necessarily refractory toward all hydrocarbons carcinogenic for mice and rats, but apparently only for some of them. This fact emphasizes the desirability of always referring the degree of carcinogenicity of a given agent to, among other factors, the species of animal studied. The susceptibility of the rabbit to formation of tumors by tar has been alluded to above. The promoting action of a virus on the carcinogenic action of the polycyclic hydrocarbons will be discussed in Chapter IV.

Attempts to induce cancer in monkeys by means of hydrocarbons or estrogens have thus far been fruitless.

The guinea pig is susceptible to the carcinogenic action of 1,2,5,6-dibenzanthracene, 3,4-benzpyrene, and 20-methylcholanthrene but to no such extent as are mice and rats. Subcutaneous sarcomas and some liposarcomas (396) are induced when these agents are administered under the skin. Tissues of the transplanted guina pig embryo are more susceptible to the carcinogenic action of methylcholanthrene than are adult tissues —as are also the embryonic tissues of mice (397, cf. 398).

High carcinogenicity in the rat refers to subcutaneous administration, for on skin painting the rat is somewhat less susceptible than the mouse to 20-methylcholanthrene. Toward 9,10-dimethyl-1,2-benzanthracene both species respond nearly equally on skin painting (360). The feeding of 20-methylcholanthrene to rats resulted in a moderate proportion of the animals developing leukemia (399), but mice under the same conditions were unresponsive (400).

9,10-Dimethyl-1,2-benzanthracene is still another carcinogen which shows different potency in different species. Thus, Berenblum has shown that on skin painting the carcinogenic response to this compound is very high and in the following descending order: rabbit, mouse, rat, guinea pig (401). On subcutaneous injection an equal response from mice, rats, and guinea pigs was achieved when the dosages were, respectively, 0.35 mg., 1.0 mg., and 20 mg.; rabbits, however, were completely unresponsive to the compound even at high levels.

Tumors may be induced not only in mammals but also in fowl and apparently even in fruit flies (402). Peacock (403, 404) and Murphy *et al.* (405, 406) noted that tumors in chickens arose at the site of subcutaneous injection of tar or of 1,2,5,6-dibenzanthracene dissolved in either lard or benzene. McIntosh also noted the same phenomena with lard solutions of tar (407). This author, as well as Murphy and Sturm, observed that solutions of tar or of dibenzanthracene in fat produced not only tumors at the site of injection but also at distant sites, resulting in such effects as leukemia and tumors of the ovary. Solutions of dibenzanthracene in benzene, which reduce the possibility of systemic dissemination, gave rise to no such distant effects. An interesting side-light which emerged from these studies was the observation of a seasonal variation in the susceptibility to induced tumors, a variation which corresponded closely to that in susceptibility to transplantation of tumors. Thus, there is a high susceptibility in the spring months and a low susceptibility in the fall months. Pigeons and guinea fowls readily yield sarcomas at the sites of injection of 20-methylcholanthrene (408) but ducks and turkeys are refractory to this agent. Although carcinogenic hydrocarbons induce sarcomas in fowl, they have so far failed to induce epithelial tumors (409).

It is sufficiently clear that even closely related species, such as rats and mice or guinea fowl and turkeys, may vary considerably in their response to a given carcinogenic agent. The difference in the response of rats and of mice to 4-dimethylaminoazobenzene has been mentioned. Table 29 summarizes in brief outline certain of the phenomena described.

Finally, to return to man, whose possible susceptibility to the assumed carcinogenic effect of coal tar precipitated so much of this study on carcinogenesis, it is sufficiently obvious that few experimental studies of the effect of the hydrocarbons have been deliberately made in this species. A few observations have been made of nodules which appeared on the skin of individuals handling polycyclic hydrocarbons, but these are hardly to be taken seriously. Cottini and Mazzone (411) applied 3,4-benzpyrene in benzene daily to the skin of twenty-six patients in their clinic and obtained the following sequence of phenomena: (a) a generally slight erythema, (b) pigmentation due to increase in melanin in the basal layer of the epidermis, (c) slight desquamation, (d) consistent formation of verrucae, and (d) in a few patients, evidence of infiltration. The treatment was ended after 4 months, and after another 2 to 3 months all manifestations described completely regressed. It may be presumed, by analogy with results on mice, that the final phenomena of this heroic experiment will not be known until 1968—provided that the subjects are continually available for observation.

Relation Between Induced and Spontaneous Tumors

Spontaneous tumors may be defined as neoplasms induced by extrinsic or intrinsic factors, unknown or suspected. Each inbred strain of mice may be characterized by a known incidence of spontaneous tumors at various sites. Each strain may also show for different tissues a greater susceptibility than others to cancer induced by known agents. The question that arises is whether there is any relation in the susceptibility of a particular tissue in a given mouse strain to spontaneous and to induced tumors. As stated in Chapter II, one of the fundamental problems of induced carcinogenesis is whether (a) the inducing agent hastens or precipitates the occurrence of a tumor which would normally arise spontaneously in the same site later in

TABLE 29

RELATIVE SUSCEPTIBILITY OF VARIOUS SPECIES TO CARCINOGENIC AGENTS[1]

Carcinogenic agent	Species	Kind of tumor	Relative tumor incidence[2]
20-Methylcholanthrene	Mouse	Sarcoma or epithelioma	High
20-Methylcholanthrene	Rat[3]	Sarcoma or epithelioma	High
20-Methylcholanthrene	Rabbit	Sarcoma or epithelioma	Moderate
20-Methylcholanthrene	Guinea pig	Sarcoma or epithelioma	Moderate
20-Methylcholanthrene	Pigeon	Sarcoma	Moderate
20-Methylcholanthrene	Guinea fowl	Sarcoma	Moderate
20-Methylcholanthrene	Duck	Sarcoma	Low
20-Methylcholanthrene	Turkey	Sarcoma	Low
3,4-Benzpyrene	Mouse	Sarcoma or epithelioma	High
3,4-Benzpyrene	Rat	Sarcoma or epithelioma	High
3,4-Benzpyrene	Rabbit	Sarcoma or epithelioma	Low
3,4-Benzpyrene	Guinea pig	Sarcoma	Moderate
1,2,5,6-Dibenzanthracene	Mouse	Sarcoma or epithelioma	Moderate
1,2,5,6-Dibenzanthracene	Rat	Sarcoma or epithelioma	Moderate
1,2,5,6-Dibenzanthracene	Rabbit	Sarcoma or epithelioma	Low
1,2,5,6-Dibenzanthracene	Guinea pig	Sarcoma	Moderate
1,2,5,6-Dibenzanthracene	Chicken[4]	Sarcoma	Moderate
β-Naphthylamine[5]	Rat	Bladder carcinoma	Low
β-Naphthylamine[5]	Rabbit	Bladder carcinoma	Low
β-Naphthylamine[5]	Dog	Bladder carcinoma	High
4-Dimethylaminoazobenzene	Mouse	Hepatoma	Low
4-Dimethylaminoazobenzene	Rat	Hepatoma	High
o-Aminoazotoluene	Mouse	Hepatoma	Moderate
o-Aminoazotoluene	Rat	Hepatoma	Moderate
Bakelite disks	Mouse	Sarcoma	Very low
Bakelite disks	Rat	Sarcoma	Moderate
Ultraviolet radiation	Mouse	Sarcoma	High
Ultraviolet radiation	Rat	Sarcoma	High
Ultraviolet radiation	Rabbit	Sarcoma	Low
Ultraviolet radiation	Guinea pig	Sarcoma	Low
Carbon tetrachloride	Mouse	Hepatoma	High
Carbon tetrachloride	Rat	Hepatoma	Low

[1] Low spontaneous incidence of all tumors mentioned.

[2] Also based on latent period of induction.

[3] The latent period of induction of rats to this and the other active polycyclic hydrocarbons is somewhat greater than that of mice, but it doubtful whether, in the former species, the maximum effective dose was employed.

[4] Zinc salts injected intratesticularly induce teratomas in thie species (410).

[5] 2-Acetylaminofluorene is an agent found effective in producing bladder carcinoma in mice and in rats.

TABLE 30

INCIDENCE OF CERTAIN SPONTANEOUS TUMORS IN VARIOUS MICE STRAINS[1, 2]

Strain	Pulmonary	Hepatic	Leukemia	Mammary	Subcutaneous sarcoma
A (F)	Very high	Very low	Low	Very high[3]	Very low
A (M)	Very high	Very low	Low	—	Very low
C3H (F)	Low	Very low	Low	Very high[4]	Very low
C3H (M)	Low	Medium	Low	—	Very low
C (F)	Medium	Very low	High	Very low	Very low
C (M)	Medium	Very low	High	—	Very low
C57 Black (F)	Very low	Low	High	Very low	Very low
C57 Black (M)	Very low	Low	High	—	Very low
I (F)	Medium	Low	—	Very low	Very low
I (M)	Medium	Low	—	—	Very low
Y (F)	Medium	Very low	—	Very low	Very low
Y (M)	Medium	Very low	—	—	Very low
DBA (F)	Low	—	High[5]	Medium	Very low
DBA (M)	Low	—	High[5]	—	Very low
Ak	Low	—	High	Low	Very low
Rf	Medium	—	Low	Low	Very low
NHO (F)	—	—	—	Low	Very low

[1] Very high = 80–100%; high = 60–80%; medium = 40–60%; low = 20–40%; very low = 0–20%. F = females, M = males.

[2] Time of observation above 15 months' survival.

[3] Very high only in breeding animals; virgins have low incidence.

[4] Very high in both virgins and bred animals.

[5] Subline 212.

the life of the animal, or (b) the agent is sufficiently powerful to effect the neoplastic transformation at sites which are ordinarily highly resistant to the spontaneous development of such transformation. Has every tissue a threshold for carcinogenic susceptibility which is lowered by the presence of the carcinogen?

The problems posed cannot be answered fully until the role which intrinsic carcinogenic agents play can be considered (Chapter IV). Nevertheless, a comparison of the spontaneous (Table 30) and the induced incidence (Table 31) of the same kind of tumor in each strain of mice may be informative. The descriptions of incidence in these tables have been taken from cited papers by Andervont *et al.*, Furth, Morton and Mider, Engelbreth-Holm, Law, Strong, and Shear.

Very few agents are carcinogenic for a single tissue. Most agents, as exemplified in perhaps extreme form by acetaminofluorene, produce any number of tumors at various sites, depending on the strain, sex, or species of animal. So far it would appear that only urethane and the halogenated aliphatic hydrocarbons are unique in inducing one kind of tumor, pulmonary tumors and hepatomas, respectively.

TABLE 31

INCIDENCE OF CERTAIN INDUCED TUMORS IN VARIOUS MICE STRAINS[1]

Strain	Pulmonary induced by:		Hepatic induced by:	Leukemia induced by:	Mammary induced by:	Subcutaneous induced by:		
	DBA, MCA[2]	AAT[3]	AAT[4]	MCA	MCA	DBA, MCA	BP[5]	AAT
A (F)[6]	Very high	Very high	Very high	Low	—	High	Medium	Very low
A (M)	Very high	Very high	Medium	Low	—	High	High	Very low
C3H (F)[6]	Medium	Very low	Medium	Medium	—	Very high	—	—
C3H (M)	Medium	Very low	Low	Medium	—	Very high	—	—
C (F)	High	Medium	Very high	Very low	—	High	—	Very low
C (M)	High	Medium	Low	Very low	—	High	—	—
C67 Black (F)	Low	Very low	Very high	Very low[7]	—	Medium	—	—
C57 Black (M)	Low	Very low	Very low	Very low	—	Medium	—	Medium
I (F)	Medium	—	High	—	—	Low	—	—
I (M)	Medium	—	Medium	—	—	Low	—	—
Y (F)	Medium	—	Medium	—	—	Low	—	—
Y (M)	Medium	—	Low	—	—	Low	—	—
DBA (F)	—	—	—	High	High	—	—	Very low
DBA (M)	—	—	—	High	—	—	—	Very low
Ak	—	—	—	High[5]	—	—	—	—
Rf	—	—	—	Medium	—	—	—	—
NHO (F)	—	—	—	—	Medium	—	—	—

[1] Very high = 80–100%; high = 60–80%: medium = 40–60%; low = 20–40%; very low = 0–20%. F = females, M = males.

[2] DBA = 1,2,5,6-dibenzanthracene, MCA = 20-methylcholanthrene.

[3] AAT = *o*-aminoazotoluene.

[4] Hemangioendotheliomas were also induced in several sites in all of the strains studied. The females in each strain invariably showed a considerably higher incidence than did the males.

[5] BP = 3,4-benzpyrene.

[6] Intraperitoneal or oral administration of ethyl urethane resulted in induction of pulmonary tumors in female *A* strain and *C3H* strain mice, the incidence being higher in the former strain.

[7] 9,10-Dimethyl-1,2-benzanthracene.

Pulmonary Tumors. Lynch (412) studied the effect of tar painting and of dibenzanthracene administration on several strains of mice and noted the difference in response of these strains to the induction of pulmonary tumors. Andervont, however, was the first to make a systematic investigation of (a) the relative incidence of different tumors induced in different inbred mice strains by various pure carcinogenic agents, (b) the genetic inheritance of cancer susceptibility toward various agents, and (c) the possible correlation of spontaneous and induced tumor incidence. He demonstrated the high susceptibility of the *C3H* strain to the induction of sarcomas and the low susceptibility of the *Y* and *I* strains to induction of this tumor. The development of procedures for the induction of pulmonary tumors are largely due to Andervont, Lorenz, and Shimkin. On extending these procedures to a number of inbred strains, and by using several carcinogenic agents, Andervont was able to indicate the rather good correlation between the incidence of spontaneous lung tumors and the degree of carcinogenic response to the administration of these agents (Tables 30 and 31). Thus, in strains with a high spontaneous pulmonary tumor incidence (*A* and *C*), administration of carcinogens precipitates the appearance of these tumors in high yield. Conversely, in strains with a low spontaneous pulmonary tumor incidence (*L* and *C57 Black*), administration of the carcinogens elicits little or no response in the lungs. The apparent role of the carcinogen in the high pulmonary tumor strains is simply to hasten the appearance of the tumors which would naturally appear later in the life of the animals. The extrinsic agents merely accelerate a reaction already inherent in the animal. The similar effect of dibenzanthracene and methylcholanthrene in inducing lung tumors is not altogether surprising, although benzpyrene has a somewhat weaker effect, but the general similarity in effect of so dissimilar a substance as aminoazotoluene is somewhat surprising. It will be noted that there is no apparent sex difference in either spontaneous or induced pulmonary tumors.

Nettleship and Henshaw (413) noted that urethane administered intraperitoneally or orally in subanesthetic doses hastened the appearance and raised the incidence of lung tumors in *A* and in *C3H* strain mice. The tumor incidence was greater in the former strain. Urethane is one of the very few active carcinogens which are readily soluble in water.

Hepatomas. These tumors, as demonstrated by Andervont *et al.*, do not show a consistent correlation between induced and spontaneous incidence. Moreover, there is a striking sex difference for the induced hepatomas, the females of the *A*, *C3H*, *C*, and *C57 Black* strains being considerably more susceptible than the males of these strains. The spontaneous incidence of this tumor is generally low (Table 30), and hence the effect of the carcinogen is to increase considerably the incidence of the tumor in females of the above strains. Administration of the carcinogen to the males of these strains produces, therefore, little if any response. The azo dyes injected into mice produce other neoplasms in addition to hepatoma, whereas carbon tetrachloride produces only hepatoma.

Leukemia. There is still less correlation in this disease between spontaneous and induced incidence. Although the administration of carcinogen to animals of a high spontaneous incidence (*DBA* and *Ak* strains) results in an earlier appearance in high yield of the disease, and administration of carcinogen to animals of low spontaneous incidence may either yield no response (*A* strain) or else precipitate the disease (*C3H* and *Rf* strains), there is, in addition, the surprising finding that administration of the same carcinogen to animals with a high spontaneous incidence (*C* and *C57 Black*) results in no apparent response. Like the hepatic tumors, the development of this disease must require several factors.

Mammary Tumors. Many investigators have shown that the administration of methylcholanthrene is capable of inducing mammary tumors in animals of a low spontaneous incidence and of hastening the appearance of these tumors in high yield in animals of high spontaneous incidence (cf. 414). The example of a strain genetically selected by Strong (*NHO*) for low susceptibility to spontaneous mammary and induced connective tissue tumors is cited in Tables 30 and 31, but examples of mice strains of low spontaneous incidence which respond to carcinogens with a high induced incidence are cited in the above references.

Subcutaneous Connective Tissue Tumors. Little data exist on the incidence of sarcomas of spontaneous origin. The very few reports available (415, 416), suggest that the incidence of tumors of subcutaneous fibrous tissue is rather low. In several strains (*C3H*, *A*, and *C*) the susceptibility of connective tissue toward certain of the carcinogenic agents is relatively high, in others (*Y* and *I*) this susceptibility is relatively low (45). By using marginal doses of 3,4-benzpyrene in *A* strain mice, Leiter and Shear (80) observed a sex difference in reaction toward the agent, the males being more susceptible. It will be noted that this susceptibility is quite opposite to that found in the induction of hepatomas by aminoazotoluene in several strains of mice (Table 31). Of the strains studied, only the *C57 Black* is relatively susceptible to the induction of subcutaneous sarcoma at the site of injection of *o*-aminoazotoluene.

It is evident that, with the exception of pulmonary tumors, little correlation can be noted between the incidence of spontaneous and of induced tumors. Yet a rationalization of the phenomena may be ventured.

It is probable that each tissue possesses a threshold for neoplasia, which, at a certain period in the life span of the animal, is sufficiently lowered to permit the development and appearance of a tumor (spontaneous incidence). The factors responsible for establishing this threshold are primarily genetic in character and, through the influence of specific genic mechanisms, give rise to a type of metabolism which, like a clockwork, is set to go off at a certain period of time. As the genic mechanism varies from strain to strain, it would be expected that the metabolic factors which it creates would also tend to vary, in certain particulars at least, from strain to strain. To carry the analogy further, the clockwork made of different parts in each strain responds differently to external influences and strikes at different times.

The threshold for mammary tumors in all strains, and the threshold for hepatic tumors in females of the strains, and the threshold for leukemia in the *DBA*, *C3H*, *Ak*, and *Rf* strains are held strongly in check by the normal controlling forces of the body. The administration of carcinogen, nevertheless, is able to overcome these controlling forces and to precipitate the neoplastic transformation. Similarly, the controlling forces over the development of pulmonary tumors in the *A* and *C* strains and over the development of mammary tumors in the *A* and other high incidence strains are weak and are readily destroyed by the carcinogen to precipitate the neoplastic transformation. On the other hand, the threshold forces for pulmonary tumors in the *C57 Black* strain, for hepatic tumors in males of the various strains, and for leukemia in the *C* and *C57 Black* strain are strongly held and resistant to the action of the carcinogenic agents used. In the last-mentioned case, leukemia develops spontaneously within mice of the strains mentioned, but only at the order of the normal controlling mechanism.

If the susceptibility toward induced carcinogenesis be placed on the basis of threshold forces as above, it is immediately obvious that genetic mechanisms alone are unable to account for these assumed differences in frailty or strength of the thresholds. Different tissues within the same strain, which should have the same threshold toward the same agent, show striking differences (e.g., pulmonary and hepatic tumors induced by aminoazotoluene, Table 31). Furthermore, different tissues within animals of the same strain (lung and liver), as well as the same kind of tissue in animals of different strains (liver), may show striking sex differences (Table 31). Purely genetic differences are insufficient to account for these phenomena. Carcinogenesis through extrinsic agents may be profoundly influenced by such intrinsic controlling factors as hormones, and the consideration of these intrinsic factors forms the subject of the next chapter.

The incidence of so-called spontaneous neoplasms in the various strains of mice (Table 30), which is primarily genetically determined, demonstrates that all tumors cannot be grouped as a single character controlled by the same gene or complex of genes. If this were the case, it might be expected that an inbred strain would either develop all types of tumors or be resistant to all types. None of the mouse strains develops a high percentage of all tumors, and none is completely resistant to all types. Furthermore, when specific types of tumor are considered, the gradation of incidences shown by the various strains rules out the possibility of a single-factor inheritance of cancer and suggests instead a multiple-factor type of inheritance (417). This point has been brought out in hybridization studies, an example of which has been the inheritance of induced lung tumors (418). This type of tumor has also been shown to be linked with genes (wave-2, shaker-2, flexed-tail, and lethal yellow) which are borne on at least three pairs of chromosomes (419, 420). Susceptibility to leukemia in *DBA* mice has likewise been shown to be associated with the chromosome carrying the flexed-tail gene (*f*) (421).

If the inheritance of cancer in inbred strains depends upon the action of multiple genetic factors, the difficulty in predicting such inheritance in any individual in a heterozygous population is evident and has been alluded to above. Furthermore, the effect of non-genetic factors on tumor incidence, such as the carcinogenic agents described in this chapter which produce induced tumors at sites which rarely show spontaneous tumors (*viz.*, subcutaneous fibrous tissue), shows that genetic insusceptibility may be overcome. Environmental non-genetic factors influence the direction of the chain of events which lead to cancer production and, under certain conditions, may be decisive. Thus, a strain of mice with an incidence of spontaneous mammary carcinoma of close to 100% may, under otherwise constant and normal genetic status and environmental conditions, have such incidence reduced to nearly zero by the device of reducing the dietary intake of calories at the time of weaning. Genetic factors thus appear to be reproducibly operative only in the presence of a constant and known environment. Since cancer arises relatively late in life, the period of time is extended during which environmental influences may enter and affect physiological directions originally genetically determined. The importance of genetic approaches to the study of cancer cannot be minimized, even if, at the present time, these approaches are limited largely to homozygous strains. The use of such strains has shown that cancer is inheritable, and the incidence of cancer in such strains has shown that this inheritance is due to more than one genetic factor.

The problems of the geneticist are not entirely foreign to the experience of the chemist, for the properties of chemical compounds are, like the evidences of the gene, modified by environmental circumstances, and, although the properties of the elements in a chemical compound may be exactly known, it is at present impossible to predict the properties of all compounds from the known properties of their elemental constituents. These points are increasingly emphasized as more complex and heterogeneous types of biologically important compounds, like the proteins, are considered. The phenomena associated with the gene may be considered to be fundamentally chemical in nature, and, although physiological genetics at the moment is concerned with simple organisms, it is to be anticipated that within the near future, in conjunction with purely chemical studies on nucleic acids and proteins, it will be applied with equal success to the problem of genetic mechanisms in tumors.

Radiation as a Carcinogenic Agent

A great many forms of radiation are capable of inducing the formation of tumors. The tragic experience of the pioneer workers on X-radiation and on radium attest to the fact that radiation of very short wavelength may be a potent carcinogenic agent. The incidence of cancer in certain industrial and professional occupations demonstrates that the problems of adequate protective devices are not yet fully mastered. With the development of sources of atomic power, these problems are likely to be emphasized.

Exposure to radiation of very short wavelengths may in most cases, short of the phenomena of war, be a matter of choice. There is, however, a form of radiation to which most living matter is exposed to greater or lesser degree, and that is sunlight. The accumulated experience of many dermatologists over the past fifty years has led them to suspect that sunlight might be an etiologic agent in the production of skin cancers in man. Subject to the usual limitations of the epidemiologic method, it would appear from statistical observations that individuals engaged in occupations requiring constant exposure to the sun had a higher incidence of skin cancer than individuals practicing more protected avocations. Since the former individuals invariably develop sunburn, and since the effective wavelengths of sunlight which produce this effect lie in the ultraviolet region of the spectrum, it was suggested that ultraviolet light might be the causative agent which induced those skin cancers attributable to sunlight. This idea remained largely hypothetical until it received some measure of support in 1928 when Findlay succeeded in inducing skin cancer in mice through the use of radiation from the mercury arc (422). Since Findlay's observation, many other workers have confirmed and extended the studies on the carcinogenic effect of ultraviolet irradiation in laboratory animals.

So far it would appear that rats and mice are the only laboratory animals susceptible to the carcinogenic action of ultraviolet radiation, and, of these, albino types are more susceptible than pigmented types. The tumors which develop in these animals are chiefly in the dermis (sarcomas), whereas those in man arise chiefly in the epidermis (carcinomas). This difference has been shown to be due to the relative penetrating power of the effective light through the tissues of the two species. Figure 18 illustrates this difference (423). In mice, carcinomas sometimes occur with the more frequent sarcomas, the ratios of the former to the latter increasing with frequency of exposure to the radiation (424).

The wavelength range for maximum tumor production is from 2600 to

3400 Å. (425, 426). However, light at wavelengths above and below this range may influence the carcinogenic response (427). Some tumor production may occur in regions as low as 2537 Å, but more energy is required at this wavelength. It is possible that the screening effect of the outer layers of the skin is responsible for the weak carcinogenic effect of wavelengths lower than 2800 Å. Estimates of the energy required for tumor induction in mice are necessarily approximate, and the smallest value observed was 6.3×10^6 ergs per square centimeter per day for 42 days, or a total of 2.6×10^8 ergs per square centimeter of the tumor-producing wavelengths (energy calculated incident on a flat surface normal to the light rays at the approximate distance of the animals from the source) (426). Tumor induction in mice of the *A* strain is virtually independent of intensity above a certain critical intensity value; below this critical intensity carcinogenesis falls off rapidly.

The induction time of radiation-produced tumors is shorter when the same total dose of radiation is given in smaller, more frequent exposures. This phenomenon is similar to that encountered in the application of carcinogenic chemicals (*vide infra*).

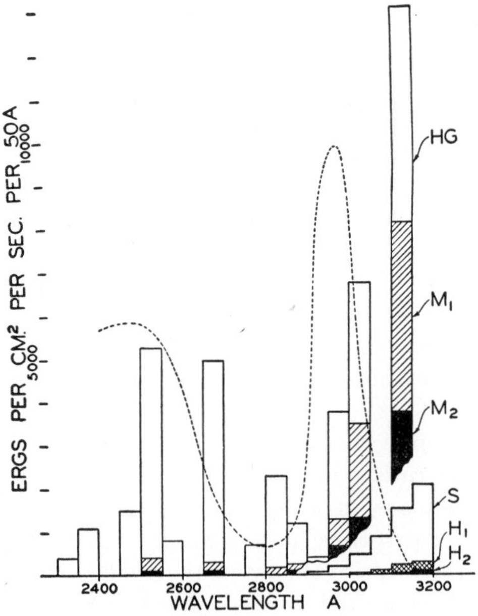

FIG. 18. Spectral distribution and intensity of sunlight within the tumor-inducing region compared with those of the mercury arc. HG, energy of the mercury arc; M_1 and M_2, respectively, transmissions of normal and irradiated mouse epidermis; S, energy of sunlight at maximum exposure; H_1 and H_2, respectively, transmissions of untanned and tanned human epidermis; the dotted line is the action spectrum for the erythema of sunburn. From Kirby-Smith, J. S., Blum, H. F., and Grady, H. G., *J. Natl. Cancer Inst.* **2,** 403 (1942).

The photoprocesses which occur in normal human skin, and which are known to be brought about by wavelengths included in sunlight, have been enumerated by Blum as follows (426): (a) sunburn mechanism, (b) antirachitic action, and (c) darkening of previously colorless pigment. The last-mentioned effect occurs at wavelengths much higher than that known to occur in tumor production and may be omitted from consideration.

The sunburn mechanism consists in an erythema followed by appearance of melanin in the epidermis of the affected area. Both are apparently sequels to injury to the prickle cells. The action spectrum for cancer production does not agree with that for erythema in mice, for few tumors are ordinarily produced at 2537 Å., which wavelength is quite effective in producing erythema. However, in mice the primary change resulting in erythema occurs in the epidermis, whereas for cancer production it may be necessary to affect deeper layers also, i.e., the corium. The epidermis thus probably acts as a filter, allowing only wavelengths longer than 2800 Å. to penetrate and induce sarcomas in the lower layers. For mice, it is possible that cancer production is the result of photochemical changes similar to those causing the erythema of sunburn, but occurring in cells at a deeper layer.

Excessive insolation and irradiation by ultraviolet lamps induce skin cancer in test animals, but this treatment apparently reduces the incidence of spontaneous mammary and other tumors in mice. The irradiated mice have a lower food intake, lower body weight, and higher mortality rate than control mice, and it is probable that these evidences of toxicity combined with hormonal imbalance account for the lower mammary cancer rate in the irradiated animals (Chapter V).

The antirachitic action of ultraviolet radiation consists in part, at least, of the conversion in the skin of 7-dehydrocholesterol to vitamin D. Irradiation of skin results in an augmentation of cholesterol, but neither the precursors nor the analogues of vitamin D, nor irradiated cholesterol, nor extracts of irradiated skin, is carcinogenic. In fact, skin painting with methylcholanthrene results in a decrease in cholesterol. It seems likely that any idea that sterols in the skin may be changed to chemical carcinogens by ultraviolet radiation has little evidence to support it. Indeed, there is some evidence to refute such a concept. Rusch *et al.* (428) observed that ultraviolet irradiation failed to augment the weak carcinogenicity of suboptimal application of carcinogenic hydrocarbons. Blum (429) noted that irradiation did not cause an earlier induction of lung tumors in susceptible *A* strain mice, a phenomenon which regularly occurs when carcinogenic hydrocarbons or azo dyes are applied. Irradiation products of skin surface fats painted on the ears of white mice for 15 to 18 months failed to produce any precancerous or cancerous changes (430), nor was any extractable carcinogen observed in the skin of human beings with multiple precancerous keratoses (431). Thus, it does not appear probable

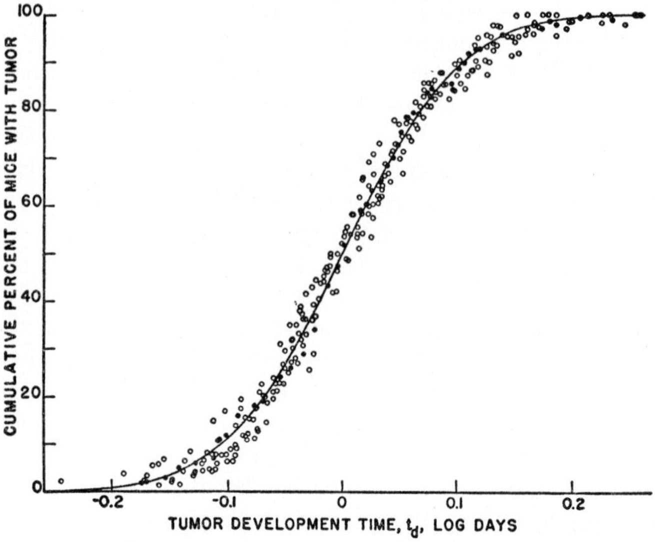

FIG. 19. Distribution of the logarithm of the tumor development time, t_d, for a population of genetically homogeneous strain *A* mice exposed to ultraviolet radiation, the exposure being placed at regular intervals up to the time of tumor appearance. From Blum, H. F., *J. Natl. Cancer Inst.* **11,** 463 (1950).

that as a result of the irradiation a carcinogenic agent is formed in the skin which resembles any carcinogen known at the present time.

Blum has suggested that successive doses of radiation progressively accelerate the relative rate of cell proliferation whereby each dose brings about an increase in rate (432). The cells peculiarly affected originally constitute a small fraction of the total cell population of the normal tissue and ultimately, by their abnormally rapid growth, constitute the tumor. Figure 19, based upon the tumor development in mice after ultraviolet radiation, represents one of the most careful and complete studies encountered in experimental carcinogenesis, regardless of the merits of the theory drawn therefrom.

As with chemical carcinogens (84, 433), a plot of the percentage incidence of tumors against the log of the latent period results in a normal distribution curve, and, in both chemical and ultraviolet carcinogenesis, increasing the dosage above a certain value does not decrease the latent period any further (432).

Radiation of Shorter Wavelengths. Whole-body X-irradiation of mice leads most frequently to the development of a variety of ovarian tumors (434, 435) and to an increase in the incidence of leukemia and lymphatic disease (434–438). After irradiation of 4- to 6-week-old mice, ovarian tumors (which were subsequently transplantable) began to appear when the mice were about 11 months of age (439). Three histologic types were evident, namely, granulosa cell tumors, luteomas, and tubular adenomas. Very few of the mice developed ovarian tumors when painted on the skin with 20-methylcholanthrene, but such painted mice when irradiated in addition showed a higher incidence of ovarian tumors than when the painting was omitted. An interesting observation is that contact irradiation of one ovary by 200 r will not result in tumor development if the other ovary is untreated and functional (440), thus:

Method of irradiation with 200 r	Per cent tumors in irradiated ovaries
Local to each ovary	100
Local to one ovary, second ovary removed	100
Local to one ovary, second ovary untreated	0
Whole body	100

Ovarian tumors have also been induced by very low (0.11 r) dosages given daily over a long period to mice, together with a high incidence of mammary tumors attributable perhaps to the ovarian tumors (441, 442). Similar long-term irradiation with low doses of γ-irradiation to guinea pigs and rabbits resulted in a diminished life span and increase in disease, including the neoplastic. Similar effects have been noted with neutrons administered to rats (443).

Virgin *C3Hb* mice chronically irradiated over the total body with 8.8 r daily develop mammary tumors in a considerable proportion of the animals (444).

The mouse is a species peculiarly sensitive to the development of lymphatic disease, and experiments designed to develop this disease find it a very susceptible subject. Virtually all radiation-induced lymphomas appear to originate in the thymus, and thus young animals are still more susceptible to lymphatic disease induced by this agent (cf. 445). Furth (446) reduced the incidence of spontaneous leukemia in susceptible *AK* strain mice by thymectomy, and a similar resistance (447) to the action of carcinogens (448) and to the action of X-rays (449) was also noted after this operation on young mice.

There is now ample evidence that whole-body X-irradiation of mice leads to the induction of lymphoid tumors and that in some way the thymus is involved. The question which arises is whether the incident radiation is a local or a generalized effect. Kaplan (450) sharply localized X-irradiation of strains *A* and *C57 Black* mice and consistently failed to obtain lymphoid tumors at the rate noted after whole-body exposure. When the thymus of strain *A* mice was shielded, whole-body irradiation still yielded lymphomas, suggesting that the role of the thymus was indirect. When thymectomized mice after X-irradiation were treated with thymic grafts, they showed a higher incidence of lymphoid tumors than did their litter mates similarly irradiated but not implanted with thymic tissue (451). The cancer-promoting effect of the thymus is thus reversible. On the other hand, when other areas of the body of *C57 Black* mice were shielded during exposure of the whole animal to X-rays, the incidence of leukemia was very considerably reduced (452). These important observations suggest that the induction of mouse lymphoid tumors by irradiation is the result not of a direct but of a systemic response, and that non-irradiated tissue may in some way inactivate a humoral agent emanating from the radiated portion of the body. These observations are thus in accord with the induction of ovarian tumors described in the table above.

The dramatic effect of partial shielding of the body during X-irradiation on reducing the incidence of induced lymphomas is probably to be ascribed to the presence of intact bone marrow in the shielded area (453–455), although shielding only the spleens of irradiated animals produces the same effect (456). Injection of cell suspensions of homologous bone marrow into irradiated mice accelerates regeneration of the radiation-involuted thymus and lymph nodes and inhibits the development of thymic lymphoid tumors (457). The chemical nature of the apparently radiosensitive agent in the marrow is not yet known, and its neutralizing reactions with the products of radiation injury which lead to tumor formation cannot even be conjectured. Hormonal influences also play a role in the control of lymphatic tumors (458, 459).

As is often the case in carcinogenesis by whatever agent, graded fractionated doses of X-irradiation are more efficient in tumor production than a single larger dose (460, 461).

X-Irradiation of the skin in human beings has frequently led to epidermal carcinoma and sometimes to tumors of subcutaneous tissue (cf. 462). The classic studies of Martland and others have shown that ingestion of radium produces osteogenic sarcomas (463, 464) in human beings and in experimental animals (465, 466). It is of interest that in order to induce bone tumors in animals a much higher proportion of radiation (per unit weight) must be used than, tragically, in human beings—indeed, some 150 times (467).

Other sources of strong ionizing radiations have been found to induce bone tumors in animals, namely plutonium, Sr^{89} (468) and P^{32} (469, 470). The last-mentioned element also induces lymphomas in mice in much the same way that total-body irradiation will. Neoplasms to an incidence of some 40% were induced in rats receiving a single LD_{50} dose of P^{32} with an average latent period of 290 days and repeated doses of 1.5 μc. per gram of P^{32} with an average latent period of 165 days (470). Most of the tumors were osteogenic sarcomas. The LD_{50} dose of 4.5 mc. per gram in the rat corresponds to 300 mc. for a 70-kg. human being, e.g., about twenty times the usual therapeutic dose. Although C^{14} travels to the bone after administration, Skipper and his colleagues noted (470) that in mice it also rapidly leaves this site, i.e., from a concentration of 44.8 millimicrocuries 24 hours after injection to 4.9 at 12 weeks after the injection.

The latent period for the development of radiation tumors is generally long, and even under the most intense stimulation it generally cannot be shortened to the few weeks characteristic of some of the more active chemical carcinogens. It is difficult to explain this by direct formation by radiation of malignant cells. It seems more likely that some intermediate factors must exist between the onset of the radiation dose and the induction of the tumor, some conversion perhaps of tissue components into carcinogenic agents. The general carcinogenic effect of whole-body irradiation is apparently correlated with a reduction in the life span of the affected animals, and it may be wondered whether radiations may not act through an acceleration of the aging process (471).

Synergistic Effects. An interesting example of the synergistic effect of ultraviolet radiation on the spontaneous incidence of mammary tumors in *C3H* strain mice (which this form of radiation does not by itself induce) is shown by the data in Table 32 (472). The mean latent periods for the groups listed were: exposed to ultraviolet 299 days, dark 369 days, light (no ultraviolet) 391 days (472).

X-Rays may also accelerate the induction of leukemia by 20-methylcholanthrene in some strains of mice (473, 474), whereas in others there is no effect (475). Rats fed 4-dimethylaminoazobenzene and simultaneously irradiated with soft X-rays have been reported either to fail to develop liver tumors or to develop them much later than usual (476). When *A* strain mice were irradiated with 900 r (shielded spleen) and then treated with nitrogen mustard, the incidence of lung tumors was about that of mice which were only irradiated and was less than that of mice given the nitrogen mustard alone (477). Like many such experiments involving the use of two or more carcinogens in the same animal, the reason for the results obtained is not clear at present.

Possible Mechanisms of Radiation Effects. Penetrating radiations produce ionization either directly in their passage through matter, as β-rays, α-rays, and protons, or indirectly through X-rays, γ-rays, or neutrons. In the process of ionization, a negative electron is removed from the atom, leaving it positively charged, the negative electron itself becoming attached to a molecule and conferring upon it a negative charge. The ion pair so formed may further dissociate, form radicals, or lead to more stable compounds. Besides ionization, the passage of radiation may also produce excitation; i.e., the orbital electrons may absorb energy and become elevated

TABLE 32

SYNERGISTIC EFFECT OF RADIATION (472)

Experiment	Frequency in per cent of mammary tumors in animals exposed to:		
	Ultraviolet	Dark	Light (no ultraviolet)
1	90	60	59
2	74	57	46
3	62	25	20

to an excited state, the residual atom then dissociating, emitting light quanta, or colliding with other atoms to release the excitation energy through vibrational and rotational energy. Radiation dosage may thus be defined as the energy absorbed in the form of ionization and excitation per gram of tissue.

The direct effect of radiation on tissues may be expressed in the form of the splitting or fragmentation of their macromolecular components. In the indirect action of radiation, whereby the primary ionization or excitation takes place at some distance from the affected molecules, the liquid medium appears to be partially converted into radicals and intermediate compounds which then react with the affected biological macromolecules. Thus, water on ionization decomposes into H and OH radicals which, depending on conditions, can interact to form hydrogen gas and hydrogen peroxide. The latter can react with exposed mercaptan groups on protein molecules or can be partially prevented from so reacting by the presence of glutathione or catalase.

When the total body is irradiated there occur not only direct radiation effects on the cells of each exposed tissue but indirect effects as well, owing to the circulation of humoral agents. On the other hand, partial irradiation apparently leaves certain areas of the body intact, thereby affording a measure of protection against the radiation effect. The protective agents are therefore also bloodborne. The nature of these biological protective agents, derivable from spleen, bone marrow, and other tissues, is not yet known. Simpler and known compounds, such as cyanide, azide, thiourea, and certain amines, are protective and may function by removing perhydroxyl (HO_2) radicals formed by radiation in the presence of oxygen. A lowered oxygen tension acts similarly.

Visible injury to the chromosomes by radiation have long been known, and the genetic effects which ensue have frequently been studied (cf. 478). Chemical studies in this area have tended to concentrate on the effect of radiation in changing the molecular properties of proteins and of nucleic acids, and of inhibition of certain types of intracellular enzymes.

When a complex system of proteins such as in serum is irradiated with ultraviolet light for a period of several days, the individual electrophoretically distinct components coalesce into a single large and homogeneous peak (479), which, although electrophoretically homogeneous, consists of a wide variety of molecular aggregates. This curious phenomenon is apparently a special case of the more general and obscure phenomenon of protein denaturation. A similar desaggregation appears to occur also when deoxyribonucleate solutions are irradiated with ultraviolet light, for the high structural viscosity and streaming birefringence of the compound are both sharply reduced (480).

Mitchell (481) and Stowell (482) have noted relatively slight changes involving nucleic acids in tissues exposed to X-rays, and Mitchell (481) and others (483) have interpreted the effect of X-irradiation on tissues as leading to a depression of the metabolism of deoxyribonucleic acid (a generalized systemic effect), and to an increase in ribonucleotides in the cytoplasm. Consistent with these observations is the inhibition by X-rays of the incorporation of C^{14}-labeled acetate (484), bicarbonate, or formate (485) into the purine carbons of deoxyribonucleate, although $C^{14}O_2$ fixation into the viscera was not depressed. The enzymes concerned with nucleic acid formation must be readily inhibited.

Of quite active interest has been the effect of X-rays on the viscosity and streaming birefringence of deoxyribonucleate in aqueous solutions. Sparrow and Rosenfeld (486) showed that X-irradiation of such solutions resulted in a decrease in viscosity. Taylor, Greenstein, and Hollaender noted that (a) there is a parallel loss in the structural viscosity and streaming birefringence, (b) there is a decrease in the particle weight, (c) there are no subsidiary chemical changes, such as splitting off of ammonia or inorganic phosphate, and (d), there occurs a continuous and progressive diminution in viscosity after the irradiation had ceased (487). The last-mentioned phenomenon, to which the designation "after-effect" has been given, was also demonstrated by other workers subsequently (488, 489) and may provide part of the explanation of the effect of radiation on biological systems.

It is not likely that the effects of radiation on susceptible bio-organic compounds in aqueous solutions are direct but more probably are mediated by the initial formation of short-lived radicals such as H or OH which react with the compounds. It has been suggested (490) that the after-effect may be due to (a) a chain reaction initiated by these radicals which are produced by the initial action of the X-rays, (b) reaction of the radicals with nucleic acid to form an unstable intermediate which slowly and spontaneously breaks down to the non-viscous product, or (c) transformation of the radicals to a peroxide. In connection with the last point, it is known that hydrogen peroxide is formed on X-irradiation of oxygen-containing water. Hydrogen peroxide in turn is readily decomposed by ultraviolet light to yield OH radicals, and deoxyribonucleate is rapidly degraded in solutions containing hydrogen peroxide by relatively short periods of exposure to ultraviolet radiation (489). Hydroxyl radicals formed by the dark reaction between peroxide and ferrous ions are also effective in degrading deoxyribonucleate (489). In water carefully freed of oxygen, no after-effect is noted in solutions of deoxyribonucleate irradiated with X-rays (489). It is apparent that the depolymerization of this important chromosomal component is brought about in some as yet unknown fashion by the free radicals formed by the incident radiation.

The fact that the nitrogen mustards degrade deoxyribonucleate in much the same way as X-rays, producing a molecular breakdown and a decrease in viscosity with time like the after-effect of X-radiation (490, 491), has lent support to the "radiomimetic" designation of this class of carcinogens, although this apparent parallel action does not seemingly hold for all phenomena studied (cf. 492). The reaction of polyfunctional nitrogen mustards might be to change the shape of the elongated deoxyribonucleate molecule, which would assist in the explanation of the interference by the mustards of the formation of a nucleoprotein complex with protamine (493). Esterification by the mustards of the phosphate ester groups might also contribute to the changes in physical properties observed, for this esterification appears to be reversible (492). The perhydroxyl radical, HO_2, formed by X-rays in oxygen-containing water, is probably the agent responsible for the radiation degradation. At very high X-radiation dosages, not only are the macromolecules of nucleic acid degraded into smaller fragments, but the nitrogen rings and ester groups are also chemically attacked, and ammonia and inorganic phosphate appear in the aqueous solutions (494).

These physical changes in the absorbing components of cells are of intellectual interest in the consideration of the mechanisms of carcinogenesis, but they are obviously a long way from providing more than an uncertain clue to the many effects which radiation exerts on living tissues. That these changes may occur *in vivo* is suggested by the work of Limperos (495), who extracted deoxyribonucleate from the thymus of rats 24 hours after X-irradiation, and who showed that the diminution in structural viscosity and streaming birefringence was directly proportional to doses of 250 to 1000 r. Furthermore, placing the animals under low oxygen tensions was found to inhibit the depolymerization of the nucleate by radiation, which would be expected on the basis of the free radical effect mentioned above. It is obvious that the understanding of the mechanisms of radiation carcinogens can only be secured by acquiring one fact at a time.

The remaining phenomenon to be considered in this connection is the inhibiting effect of X-irradiation on enzyme systems *in vitro* known to be dependent upon the presence of intact —SH groups (496) and, as a corollary, the failure of such inhibition by the presence of glutathione or catalase.

It is likely that the explanation for these phenomena lies in the production of hydrogen peroxide in the course of the radiation. The known effect of administration of sulfhydryl compounds in significantly increasing the survival of animals subjected to whole-body X-irradiation may also rest upon this basis (497). However, whole-body X-irradiation appears to have a selective action in inhibiting only certain —SH enzymes such as spleen succinoxidase, and not others such as liver and kidney succinoxidase, or adenosine triphosphatase (498). Cytochrome oxidase and lactic dehydrogenase, which do not fall within the —SH enzyme category, were not at all affected. The *in vivo* inhibition of spleen succinoxidase by X-rays could be prevented by either pre- or post-irradiation injection of cysteine. The radiomimetic nitrogen mustards do not inhibit the so-called —SH enzymes, yet their toxicity can be considerably reduced by the prior injection of cysteine (499); this effect of cysteine, which is not shared by other sulfhydryl compounds including glutathione or BAL, is apparently not due to any combination of the mustard with the cysteine but rather to some sort of systemic effect. It may well be that any induced physiologic state in which the oxygen tension is reduced, thus inhibiting the formation of free radicals by action of the radiation, will protect against the toxic action of X-irradiation. Thus, even anesthesia, which reduces oxygen consumption, results in experimental animals in a decrease in mortality from X-rays (500).

Environmental Factors as Carcinogenic Agents

Man, like all other living forms, lives in an environment predominantly hostile, and only by virtue of a powerful capacity for adaptability has some measure of precarious equilibrium with this environment been achieved. The universe, as it is apparently constructed, is neither friendly nor helpful to the maintenance of life. Survival is attained only by the exercise of superior intelligence or instinct in the course of perpetual conflict with inanimate forces of nature and with other living forms. Complex organisms have found some measure of safety and of survival value in the integration of separate moieties within communal societies and in the subordination of the individual capacities and potentialities of such separate moieties to the purpose of survival of the whole. Such societies may exist at any level, from single-cell forms, through multicellular organisms, to elaborate and interrelated combinations of multicellular organisms as in hives, ant-hills, and nations. The advantages of the communal society are many, but its essential weakness lies in its dependence upon the normal and uninterrupted functioning of each separate part. The degeneration of, and loss of control over, any one moiety jeopardizes the existence of the entire organism or society, and this degeneration can be caused by factors either from within or from without. It is evident that this description can apply equally to the phenomenon known as cancer, a physical disease of internal disequilibrium within all complex living forms, and to the social ills of human communities which have been given many names but, like cancer, few rational explanations or solutions. In both instances it is easier to look for external causes than for those arising internally, although it appears probable that these causes in each instance may well be synergistic.

Among the hazards with which the life of man is surrounded are those external agents which may be concerned with the induction of cancer. Barring direct experimentation on man, there are two methods, indirect and imperfect at best, which have been employed in the attempt to recognize such agents. These are (a) comparative epidemiological and statistical surveys of cancer in workers in selected occupations and in the general population, and (b) the testing of such agents on laboratory animals.

The weaknesses of the epidemiologic method are due to many causes, among them the variations in systems of recording vital statistics in different areas of any country, the variations in histologic diagnosis by any two or three pathologists, the difficulties in correlating statistics over a wide population area on the basis of similar age groups, sex, occupational variations, and different standards of medical care, and finally, since the terminal stages of cancer are frequently complicated by other pathologic states, the assignment of the cause of death on medical certificates may occasionally be a matter of choice. Despite these handicaps, epidemiologic surveys have definitely correlated exposure to certain forms of environmental influences with a cancer incidence in the exposed human population higher than that of protected populations. Among these influences are chemicals of various kinds and radiation of relatively short wavelengths.

Chemicals. It had been noticed early in the present century that workers in certain occupations using tar, tar products, and mineral oils had a relatively high incidence of skin cancer, and in England the Home Office in 1925 created a special committee of inquiry. The conclusion was reached that the incidence of certain forms of cancer among workers in certain occupations, such as spinners in textile mills, was so very much greater than among those in the general population as to lead inevitably to the acceptance of a causal relation between the implements of these occupations and the incidence of cancer. In the case of the textile workers, the high incidence of cancer of the scrotum was related to the constant spray of mineral oil used as lubricant over the affected workmen. The interest aroused in these observations led to the work on the fractionation of coal tar and opened up the field of experimental chemical carcinogenesis described in this chapter.

An example of the epidemiologic method is as follows; the data on cancer of the scrotum are drawn from the General Register Office for

England and Wales as given in an article by Kennaway and Kennaway (501):

CANCER OF SCROTUM (ENGLAND AND WALES 1911–1940)

Occupation	Population	Deaths from cancer of scrotum
Cotton mule spinners	32,448	415
Chimney sweeps	5,274	118
Gas, tar, pitch, and creosote workers	157,102	114
Fishermen, boatmen, fishing-net makers	139,313	49
Engine and crane drivers, firemen	167,235	27
Total	501,372	723

The total number of deaths in this period from cancer of the scrotum was 1752 from a population of 13,893,848 males aged 14 and over. The adjusted proportion of deaths from this form of cancer was 144 per 100,000 in workers in the above occupations as compared with 7 per 100,000 in the remainder of the population. The causative agents in the first instance were noted to be tar, tar products, and mineral oils, and, in particular, the unsaturated fractions thereof.

Another reasonably well-authenticated case of chemical carcinogenic hazard is provided in the unusually high incidence of bladder carcinoma among workers in factories handling dyes derived from coal tar products (502). Statistical surveys in Basel revealed that such tumors were thirty-three times as frequent among workers in the dye factories as among the remainder of the male population (503). This is the so-called "aniline cancer," or neoplasms presumed to be induced by aromatic amines. In contrast with the majority of occupational cancers, the aniline tumors develop at a site (bladder) remote from the primary contact with the suspected agent. According to Hueper (502), β-naphthylamine is definitely incriminated. Whatever the agent or agents may be, they act specifically on the bladder and induce, in many cases, multiple tumors which may co-exist side by side in benign and in malignant forms within the same organ.

Occupational cancers from chemicals in other kinds of industry have been suspected, viz., arsenic in cobalt smelting and mining (cf. 504, 505).

One of the major difficulties in correlating cancer with occupational hazard is the latent period which may be involved between the time of exposure and the time when the neoplasm is apparent. Hueper has listed (506) certain latent periods for various types of cancer (see Table 33). These wide ranges in latent periods in Table 33 indicate that not only individual susceptibility must play a role but also irregularities in the intensity of exposure to the environmental carcinogens (506). To explore

TABLE 33

Latent Periods of Environmental and Occupational Cancers (506)

Organ	Agent	Average latent period, years	Range of latent period, years
Skin	Arsenic: medicinal	18	3–40
	occupational	25	4–46
	Tar	20–24	1–50
	Creosote oil	25	15–40
	Mineral oil	50–54	4–75
	Crude paraffin oil	15–18	3–35
	Solar radiation	20–30	15–40
	X-Radiation	7	1–12
Lung	Asbestos	18	15–21
	Chromates	15	5–47
	Nickel	22	6–30
	Tar fumes	16	9–23
	Ionizing radiation	15–35	7–50
Bladder	Aromatic amines	11–15	2–40

thoroughly the personal history of every individual with a suspected industrial cancer must be something of a major task for any physician (cf. 507).

Morbidity data on cancer of the respiratory tract have shown an increase in incidence during the past thirty years, particularly in regard to pulmonary neoplasms, and the possible etiological relation of this fact to the smoking of tobacco has been advanced (508). This emphasis on the predominance of a single etiologic environmental factor has been a matter of some controversy (cf. 509), which is not yet settled. The essential weakness in the arguments *pro* is due to the lack of any sound experimental evidence that tobacco smoke is carcinogenic.

Cigarette tar condensates are carcinogenic to the skin of CAF_1 mice (509a). This does not prove that this tar produces bronchogenic cancer in human beings, but it does furnish a tool for study and possibly for the subsequent removal by technological means of the substance from tobacco responsible for this effect. It may be that this strain of mice is peculiarly sensitive to the tobacco tar, and it would be desirable to study other strains of mice in this connection. In any event, even with this strain it required an exposure of roughly 71 weeks, or half the life span of the animals, for the tar to produce epidermoid carcinoma.

The best that epidemiology can do under the circumstances is to draw some correlation between an increase in cancer incidence and a parallel increase in some suspected etiologic factor. In the absence of evidence for the cancerogenic nature of that factor, the argument may approach the absurd, for more things than cigarettes have been manufactured at an accelerated rate over the past thirty years. The striking difference in lung cancer morbidity rates in different cities of this country (510) makes it further difficult to assign the increase in lung cancer incidence to any single factor. At this time, the etiological significance of the apparent association of lung cancer and smoking remains unestablished (509).

Radiation. Early in the history of roentgen and γ-rays it was noted that excessive exposure of the hands or other parts to high-energy radiation resulted in a dermatitis which, in some cases, developed into carcinoma (511). The first case of radiation carcinoma was reported in 1902. Somewhat later, injury to blood and hematopoietic tissues was noted, with occasional reports of leukemia in connection therewith. Workers in industries using luminous paints involving radium and mesothorium demonstrated a relatively high incidence of bone destruction and osteogenic sarcoma, resulting in part from the ingestion of these paints (512). Radium belongs to the same chemical grouping as calcium and tends to accumulate in the bones after ingestion (or inhalation). There is a definite but slow rate of excretion of radioactive materials from the body, which may be increased slightly by parathormone therapy and (513), but it has not thus far been possible to remove such materials before considerable body damage has been accomplished.

There are at least two examples of epidemiological studies in this field, which purport to show (a) that the incidence of leukemia among radiologists is roughly ten times as great as among medical practitioners in other fields (514), and (b) that the incidence of leukemia among physicians of all kinds is 1.7 times as great as that noted in the general population (511). These studies suggest that exposure to radiation may be an occupational hazard in medical practice, but it is always possible that other factors may also be operative. It would have been interesting to possess data on a somewhat equivalent group of professional men who are not generally exposed to radiation of very short wavelength.

With the prospect of increasing and widespread use of sources of short-wave radiation (*vide* possible future uses of nuclear energy), the problem of personnel exposed to these sources is becoming more and more acute. Much time and attention has been devoted by engineers and others to protective shielding devices around X-ray units, cyclotrons, betatrons, etc. (cf. 515–519) as well as to the establishment of minimal tolerated doses of ingested radium in nostrums, etc. (520, 521). In the last-mentioned connection the National Bureau of Standards has considered 0.1 γ of radium to be the tolerance value for human beings. About 55% of the body radium in man is usually exhibited as γ-rays.

Exposure to excessive solar radiation produces in sailors and in farmers a relatively high incidence of skin cancer in exposed sites (522). That ultraviolet wavelengths may be responsible has been alluded to above (p. 153).

It is therefore highly probable that exposure to radiation of wavelengths shorter than those in the visible spectrum, such as 3000 to 2000 Å. in the ultraviolet, 1.0 to 0.01 Å. in the roentgen region, and still shorter in the γ-ray region, can produce in man carcinoma of the skin, leukemia, and osteogenic sarcoma. It is interesting to note that the wavelengths in the roentgen- and γ-ray regions are also used therapeutically to alleviate and arrest cancerous growth. There is therefore the rather paradoxical situation that the same agents, when acting on normal tissues, may induce a neoplastic transformation, and, when acting on tissues already neoplastic, produce destruction and regression. The experimental conditions whereby each effect is induced is, of course, somewhat different. The basis of the therapeutic action on cancer tissue was stated in 1904 in the generalization of Bergonie and Tribondeau (523) to the effect that "immature cells and cells in active stages of division are more sensitive to radiation than are cells which have already acquired their adult morphological and physiological characters." It is difficult not to be sadly impressed by the contrast between the magnificent engineering and technical developments in radiation procedures—such as the construction of super-high-voltage X-ray equipment capable of deep penetration through many layers of tissues, cyclotrons capable of generating neutrons of great penetrating power and ionizing potentialities within tissues, and betatrons which accelerate electrons with energy in excess of a half million volts—and the very meager information available on the biochemical mechanisms affected by these extraordinary machines. It is little wonder that their use in cancer therapy and induction has been entirely empirical and, as far as the more recent machines, such as the cyclotron, have been concerned, of a relatively trivial nature.

Animal Experimentation. As noted throughout the present chapter, those chemicals and radiations suspected of producing cancer in man will also produce cancer in one or more species of laboratory animals. The lubricating oils implicated in the production of cancer in cotton mule spinners induced skin tumors in mice (524). Tar and tar products caused tumors in rabbits, rats, and mice (*vide infra*). β-Naphthylamine produced bladder tumors in dogs (502). Exposure to excessive insolation produced skin tumors in a large proportion of rats so exposed (525), and ultraviolet irradiation readily induced tumors in both mice and rats (*vide infra*). Osteogenic sarcoma could be produced in rabbits (526) and in rats (512) by the intravenous injection of radium salts, and leukemia has been induced in susceptible strains of mice by X-radiation (439, 527).

It might appear that man, like other animals, is generally responsive to the same carcinogenic stimuli. Some care and discretion in comparing effects on man and on the lower animals must, however, be exercised. The fact that the mouse will produce a cancer through an agent suspected as carcinogenic in man is no proof of the latter possibility but only a strong inference. If the rat or the rabbit fails to respond to an agent active in the mouse, a not uncommon observation, this inference is correspondingly weakened. On the other hand, if the mouse or other laboratory animal fails to respond carcinogenically to a given agent, this failure is still no unequivocal proof that the agent is not carcinogenic in man. Evidence from both epidemiological and animal experimental sources is required to establish the possibility of a carcinogenic agent for man.

Other suspected sources of carcinogenic agents for man may be the dusts of industrial cities (possibly related to incidence of pulmonary cancer) or products of cooking at high temperatures (possibly related to incidence of gastric cancer). However, concentrated tarry extracts of city dusts, injected subcutaneously into mice, gave rise to 7 to 8% incidence of sarcomas at the site of injection, although dusts from such cities as Pittsburgh were no more carcinogenic than from less highly industrialized centers (528). Heated fats fed to laboratory animals produced at the most only benign gastric papillomas (529, 530, 531); earlier claims of the production of gastric adenocarcinomas by Roffo (532) have not been confirmed.

In conclusion, it is interesting to note that, although workers exposed to certain active carcinogenic agents show a relatively high incidence of cancer, compared to the unexposed population, this incidence is astonishingly low compared to the total number of workers so exposed. Thus, in the above table of data from the General Register Office some half million workers are constantly in contact with external agents presumed to be more highly carcinogenic than those to which most of the remainder of the population is exposed. Yet of this half million workers only 723 or a little more than 0.1% develop scrotal cancer. An experimental oncologist working with chemical carcinogens on laboratory animals would probably pay little attention to a carcinogen which gave no higher percentage incidence than this. Whether the amounts of tars and tarry products under industrial conditions ever attain the proportions used in experimental animals, or whether there is a constitutional resistance among a large proportion of the population toward these agents, cannot be answered at the present time. Since constitutional resistance, if it exists, cannot be predicted *a priori*, every conceivable effort should be made to prevent and avoid exposure to external hazards potentially carcinogenic.

References

(1) Hartwell, J. L., "Survey of Compounds Which Have Been Tested for Carcinogenic Activity." *U. S. Public Health Service*, **1941**, 2nd ed., **1951.**

(2) Yamagiwa, K., and Ichikawa, K., *Tokyo Igakkai Zassi* **15,** 295 (1915); *J. Cancer Research* **3,** 1 (1918).

(3) Bloch, B., and Dreifuss, H., *Schweiz. med. Wochschr.* **2,** 1033 (1921).
(4) Hieger, I., *Biochem. J.* **24,** 505 (1930).
(5) Cook, J. W., *J. Chem. Soc.* **1930,** 1087; **1931,** 487, 489, 499, 2012, 2524, 2529, 3273; **1932,** 456, 1472.
(6) Cook, J. W., and Hewett, C. L., *J. Chem. Soc.* **1933,** 1408.
(7) Badger, G. M., Cook, J. W., Hewett, C. L., Kennaway, E. L., Kennaway, N. M., and Martin, R. H., *Proc. Roy. Soc. (London)* **B 131,** 170 (1942).
(8) Clar, J., *Ber.* **62,** 350, 1378 (1939).
(9) Cook, J. W., Hewett, C. L., and Hieger, I., *J. Chem. Soc.* **1933,** 395.
(10) Berenblum, I., and Schoental, R., *Brit. J. Exptl. Pathol.* **24,** 232 (1943).
(11) Berenblum, I., *Nature* **156,** 601 (1945).
(12) Berenblum, I., and Schoental, R., *Brit. J. Cancer* **1,** 157 (1947).
(13) Goulden, F., and Tipler, M. M., *Brit. J. Cancer* **3,** 157 (1949).
(14) Falk, H. L., Steiner, P. E., Goldfein, S., Breslow, A., and Hyks, R., *Cancer Research* **11,** 318 (1951).
(15) Falk, H. L., and Steiner, P. E., *Cancer Research* **12,** 30 (1952).
(16) Waller, R. E., *Brit. J. Cancer* **6,** 8 (1952).
(17) Leiter, J., and Shear, M. J., *J. Natl. Cancer Inst.* **3,** 167 (1942).
(18) Wieland, C., and Dane, E., *Z. physiol. Chem.* **219,** 240 (1933).
(19) Cook, J. W., and Haslewood, D., *J. Chem. Soc.* **1934,** 248.
(20) Fieser, L. F., "Chemistry of Natural Products Related to Phenanthrene." Reinhold Publishing Corp., New York, 1936.
(21) Cook, J. W., Kennaway, E. L., and Kennaway, N. M., *Nature* **145,** 627 (1940).
(22) Fieser, L. F., "Production of Cancer by Polynuclear Hydrocarbons." University of Pennsylvania Bicentennial Conference, Philadelphia, 1941.
(23) Fekete, E., and Little, C. C., *Cancer Research* **5,** 220 (1945).
(24) Woolley, G. W., and Little, C. C., *Proc. Natl. Acad. Sci. U.S.* **32,** 239 (1946).
(25) Steiner, P. E., and Falk, H. L., *Cancer Research* **11,** 56 (1951).
(26) Boyland, E., and Brues, A. M., *Proc. Roy. Soc. (London)* **B 122,** 429 (1937).
(27) Haddow, A., *Brit. Med. Bull.* **4,** 331 (1947).
(28) Haddow, A., and Kon, G. A. R., *Brit. Med. Bull.* **4,** 314 (1947).
(29) Badger, G. M., *Advances in Cancer Research* **2,** 73 (1954).
(30) Boyland, E., *Cancer Research* **12,** 77 (1952).
(31) Burrows, H., Hieger, I., and Kennaway, E. L., *Am. J. Cancer* **16,** 57 (1932).
(32) Cook, J. W., Robinson, A. M., and Goulden, F., *J. Chem. Soc.* **1937,** 393.
(33) Shear, M. J., *Am. J. Cancer* **33,** 499 (1938).
(34) Burrows, H., Hieger, I., and Kennaway, E. L., *J. Pathol. Bacteriol.* **43,** 419 (1936).
(35) Gardner, W. U., *Arch. Pathol.* **27,** 138 (1939).
(36) Shear, M. J., and Leiter, J., *J. Natl. Cancer Inst.* **2,** 241 (1941).
(37) Shimkin, M. B., and Andervont, H. B., *Public Health Repts. (U. S.)* **55,** 537 (1940).
(38) Shear, M. J., and Lorenz, E., *Am. J. Cancer* **36,** 201 (1939).
(39) Andervont, H. B., and Shear, M. J., *J. Natl. Cancer Inst.* **2,** 333 (1942).
(40) Weil-Malherbe, H., *Biochem. J.,* **40,** 351, 363 (1946).
(41) Neish, W. J. P., *Rec. trav. chim.* **67,** 361 (1948).
(42) Andervont, H. B., and Lorenz, E., *Public Health Repts. (U. S.)* **52,** 637 (1937).
(43) Ekwall, P., Setälä, K., and Sjöblom, L., *Acta Chem. Scand.* **5,** 175 (1951).
(44) Ekwall, P., Ermala, P., Setälä, K., and Sjöblom, L., *Cancer Research* **11,** 758 (1951).
(45) Andervont, H. B., *Public Health Repts. (U. S.)* **49,** 620 (1934); **53,** 1647 (1938).
(46) Cook, J. W., and Kennaway, E. L., *Am. J. Cancer* **39,** 521 (1940).

(47) Fieser, L. F., *Am. J. Cancer* **34,** 37 (1938).
(48) Iball, J., *Am. J. Cancer* **35,** 188 (1939).
(49) Berenblum, I., *Cancer Research* **5,** 561 (1945).
(50) Shimkin, M. B., and Andervont, H. B., *J. Natl. Cancer Inst.* **1,** 57 (1940).
(51) Andervont, H. B., and Shimkin, M. B., *J. Natl. Cancer Inst.* **1,** 225 (1940).
(52) White, F. R., and Eschenbrenner, A. B., *J. Natl. Cancer Inst.* **6,** 19 (1945).
(53) Hieger, I., and Woodhouse, D. L., *Brit. J. Cancer* **6,** 293 (1952).
(54) Branch, C. F., *Am. J. Cancer* **26,** 110 (1936).
(55) Andervont, H. B., and Lorenz, E., *Public Health Repts.* (*U. S.*) **52,** 637 (1937).
(56) Murphy, J. B., and Sturm, E., *J. Exptl. Med.* **42,** 693 (1925).
(57) Andervont, H. B., *Public Health Repts.* (*U. S.*) **52,** 212 (1937).
(58) Shear, M. J., and Leiter, J., *J. Natl. Cancer Inst.* **1,** 303 (1940).
(59) Shimkin, M. B., *Arch. Pathol.* **29,** 229, 239 (1940).
(60) Heston, W. E., *J. Natl. Cancer Inst.* **2,** 127 (1941).
(61) Heston, W. E., and Deringer, M. K., *J. Natl. Cancer Inst.* **13,** 705 (1952).
(62) Geyer, R. P., Bleisch, V. R., Bryant, J. E., Robbins, A. N., Saslaw, I. M., and Stare, F. J., *Cancer Research* **11,** 474 (1951).
(63) Lorenz, E., and Stewart, H. L., *J. Natl. Cancer Inst.* **1,** 17 (1940).
(64) Stewart, H. L., and Lorenz, E., *J. Natl. Cancer Inst.* **3,** 175 (1942).
(65) Hare, W. V., Stewart, H. L., Bennett, J. G., and Lorenz, E., *J. Natl. Cancer Inst.* **12,** 1019 (1952); Stewart, H. L., Hare, W. V., and Bennett, J. G., *J. Natl. Cancer Inst.* **14,** 105 (1953).
(66) Bonser, G. M., and Robson, J. M., *Brit. J. Cancer* **4,** 196 (1950).
(67) Rous, P., and Smith, W. E., *J. Exptl. Med.* **81,** 597 (1945).
(68) Klein, M., *J. Natl. Cancer Inst.* **11,** 985 (1951).
(69) Horning, E. S., *Lancet* **ii,** 207 (1947).
(70) Horning, E. S., *Lancet* **i,** 829 (1946).
(71) Pan, S. C., and Gardner, W. U., *Cancer Research* **8,** 613 (1948).
(72) White, J., and Stewart, H. L., *J. Natl. Cancer Inst.* **3,** 331 (1942).
(73) Rask-Nielson, R., *Brit. J. Cancer* **4,** 124 (1950).
(74) Morton, J. J., and Mider, G. B., *Cancer Research* **1,** 95 (1941).
(75) Engelbreth-Holm, J., and Lefevre, H., *Cancer Research* **1,** 102 (1941).
(76) Murphy, J. B., and Sturm, E., *Cancer Research* **1,** 379 (1941).
(77) Strong, L. C., *Proc. Soc. Exptl. Biol. Med.* **59,** 217 (1945).
(78) McEndy, D. P., Boon, M. C., and Furth, J., *J. Natl. Cancer Inst.* **3,** 227 (1942).
(79) Shear, M. J., Stewart, H. L., and Seligman, A. M., *J. Natl. Cancer Inst.* **1,** 291 (1940).
(80) Leiter, J., and Shear, M. J., *J. Natl. Cancer Inst.* **3,** 455 (1943).
(81) Dobrovolskaïa-Zavadskaïa, N., *Compt. rend. soc. biol.* **129,** 1055 (1938).
(82) Bryan, W. R., and Shimkin, M. B., *J. Natl. Cancer Inst.* **1,** 807 (1941); **3,** 503 (1943).
(83) Shimkin, M. B., and Bryan, W. R., *J. Natl. Cancer Inst.* **4,** 25 (1943).
(84) Cramer, W., and Stowell, R. E., *Cancer Research* **3,** 668 (1943).
(85) Lavik, P. S., Moore, P. R., Rusch, H. P., and Baumann, C. A., *Cancer Research* **2,** 189 (1942).
(86) Simpson, W. L., and Cramer, W., *Cancer Research* **5,** 5 (1945).
(87) Stowell, R. E., and Cramer, W., *Cancer Research* **2,** 193 (1942).
(88) Berenblum, I., and Schoental, R., *Cancer Research* **7,** 390 (1947).
(89) Plaut, A., and Sobel, H., *Cancer Research* **9,** 294 (1949).
(90) Berenblum, I., and Shubik, P., *Brit. J. Cancer* **1,** 379, 383 (1947).
(91) Berenblum, I., *Advances in Cancer Research* **2,** 129 (1954).
(92) Peacock, P. R., *J. Pathol. Bacteriol.* **36,** 141 (1933).

(93) Hieger, I., *Brit. J. Cancer* **3,** 123 (1949).
(94) Watson, A. F., *Am. J. Cancer* **25,** 753 (1935).
(95) Peacock, P. R., and Beck, S., *Brit. J. Exptl. Pathol.* **19,** 315 (1938).
(96) Morton, J. J., and Mider, G. B., *Proc. Soc. Exptl. Biol. Med.* **41,** 357 (1939).
(97) Peacock, P. R., Beck, S., and Anderson, W., *Brit. J. Cancer* **3,** 296 (1949).
(98) Strait, L. A., Hrenoff, M. K., and DeOme, K. B., *Cancer Research* **8,** 231 (1948).
(99) Dickens, F., and Weil-Malherbe, H., *Cancer Research* **2,** 560 (1942); **6,** 161 (1946).
(100) Weil-Malherbe, H., and Dickens, F., *Cancer Research* **4,** 425 (1944); **6,** 171 (1946).
(101) Mueller, G. C., Miller, J. A., and Rusch, H. P., *Cancer Research* **5,** 401 (1945).
(102) Engelbreth-Holme, J., and Iverson, S., *Cancer Research* **7,** 372 (1947).
(103) Lisle, E. B., *Cancer Research* **11,** 153 (1951).
(104) Daniel, G. E., and May, G. H., *Brit. J. Cancer* **4,** 139 (1950).
(105) Sall, R. D., and Shear, M. J., *J. Natl. Cancer Inst.* **1,** 45 (1940).
(106) Berenblum, I., *Arch. Pathol.* **38,** 233 (1944).
(107) Berenblum, I., and Shubik, P., *Brit. J. Cancer* **1,** 379, 383 (1947).
(108) Mottram, J. C., *J. Pathol. Bacteriol.* **56,** 181, 391 (1944).
(109) Berenblum, I., and Shubik, P., *Brit. J. Cancer* **3,** 109 (1949).
(110) Salaman, M. H., *Brit. J. Cancer* **6,** 155 (1952).
(111) Klein, M., *Cancer Research* **13,** 427 (1953); *J. Natl. Cancer Inst.* **14,** 83 (1953).
(112) Shubik, P., *Cancer Research* **10,** 713 (1950).
(113) Shubik, P., *Cancer Research* **10,** 13 (1950).
(114) Friedewald, W. F., and Rous, P., *J. Exptl. Med.* **80,** 101 (1944).
(115) Shubik, P., Goldfarb, A. R., Ritchie, A. C., and Lisco, H., *Nature* **171,** 934 (1953).
(116) Crabtree, H. G., *Cancer Research* **4,** 688 (1944).
(117) Crabtree, H. G., *Cancer Research* **5,** 346 (1945).
(118) Carruthers, C., *Arch. Pathol.* **30,** 1184 (1940).
(119) Berenblum, I., *J. Pathol. Bacteriol.* **40,** 549 (1935).
(120) Crabtree, H. G., *Cancer Research* **6,** 553 (1946).
(121) Wood, J. L., and Fieser, L. F., *J. Am. Chem. Soc.* **62,** 2674 (1940).
(122) Crabtree, A. G., *Brit. Med. Bull.* **4,** 345 (1947).
(123) Lacassagne, A., Buu-Hoï, and Rudali, G., *Brit. J. Exptl. Pathol.* **26,** 5 (1945).
(124) Riegel, B., Wartman, W. B., Hill, W. T., Reeb, B. B., Shubik, P., and Stanger, D. W., *Cancer Research* **11,** 301 (1951).
(125) Steiner, P., and Edgcomb, J. H., *Cancer Research* **12,** 657 (1952).
(126) Richardson, H. L., and Cunningham, L., *Cancer Research* **11,** 274 (1951).
(127) Richardson, H. L., Stier, A. R., and Borsos-Nachtnebel, E., *Cancer Research* **12,** 356 (1952).
(128) Jaffé, W. G., *Cancer Research* **7,** 529 (1947).
(129) Griffin, A. C., Brandt, E. L., and Setter, V., *Cancer Research* **11,** 868 (1951).
(130) MacDonald, J. C., Miller, E. C., Miller, J. A., and Rusch, H. P., *Cancer Research* **12,** 50 (1952).
(131) Furth, J., and Boon, M. C., *Science* **98,** 138 (1943).
(132) Mixer, H. W., and Kirschbaum, A., *Radiology* **50,** 476 (1948).
(133) Kirschbaum, A., Shapiro, J. R., and Mixer, H. W., *Cancer Research* **13,** 262 (1953).
(134) Beck, S., and Peacock, P. R., *Brit. J. Exptl. Pathol.* **21,** 227 (1940).
(135) Hieger, I., *Am. J. Cancer* **28,** 522 (1936).
(136) Simpson, W. L., and Cramer, W., *Cancer Research* **3,** 362 (1943); **5,** 449 (1945).
(137) Chalmers, J. G., *Biochem. J.* **28,** 1214 (1934).
(138) Berenblum, I., and Kendal, L. P., *Brit. J. Exptl. Pathol.* **15,** 366 (1934).
(139) Lorenz, E., and Shear, M. J., *Am. J. Cancer* **26,** 333 (1936).

(140) Lorenz, E., and Shimkin, M. B., *J. Natl. Cancer Inst.* **2,** 491 (1942).
(141) Heidelberger, C., and Jones, H. B., *Cancer* **1,** 252 (1948).
(142) Dauben, W. G., and Mabee, D., *Cancer Research* **11,** 216 (1951).
(143) Heidelberger, C., and Weiss, S. M., *Cancer Research* **11,** 885 (1951).
(144) Heidelberger, C., *Advances in Cancer Research* **1,** 273 (1953).
(145) Shay, H., Friedmann, B., Greenstein, M., and Weinhouse, S., *Cancer Research* **10,** 797 (1950).
(146) Booth, J., and Boyland, E., *Biochem. J.* **44,** 1948 (1949).
(147) Boyland, E., and Weigert, F., *Brit. Med. Bull.* **4,** 968 (1947).
(148) Boyland, E., *Biochem. Soc. Symposia (Cambridge, Engl.)*, No. **5,** 40 (1950).
(149) Boyland, E., and Wolf, G., *Biochem. J.* **47,** 65 (1950).
(150) Berenblum, I., and Schoental, R., *Cancer Research* **3,** 145 (1943).
(151) Berenblum, I., Crowfoot, D., Holiday, E. R., and Schoental, R., *Cancer Research* **3,** 151 (1943).
(152) Berenblum, I., Schoental, R., Holiday, E. R., and Jope, E. M., *Cancer Research* **6,** 669 (1946).
(153) Berenblum, I., and Schoental, R., *Cancer Research* **6,** 699 (1946).
(154) Peacock, P. R., *Brit. J. Exptl. Pathol.* **17,** 164 (1936).
(155) Weigert, F., and Mottram, J. C., *Biochem. J.* **37,** 479 (1943).
(156) Weigert, F., and Mottram, J. C., *Cancer Research* **6,** 97, 109 (1946).
(157) Cook, J. W., and Schoental, R., *Brit. J. Cancer* **6,** 400 (1952).
(158) Berenblum, I., and Schoental, R., *Ann. Rept. Brit. Empire Cancer Campaign* **21,** 56 (1944).
(159) Calcutt, G., and Payne, S., *Brit. J. Cancer* **7,** 279 (1953).
(160) Berenblum, I., and Schoental, R., *Cancer Research* **3,** 683 (1943).
(161) Holiday, E. R., *Cancer Research* **3,** 689 (1943).
(162) Dickens, F., and Weil-Malherbe, H., *Ann. Rept. Brit. Empire Cancer Campaign* **22,** 53 (1945).
(163) Boyland, E., Levi, A. A., Mawson, E. H., and Roe, E., *Biochem. J.* **35,** 184 (1941).
(164) Dobriner, K., Rhoads, C. P., and Lavin, G. I., *Cancer Research* **2,** 95 (1942).
(165) Dickens, F., *Ann. Rept. Brit. Empire Cancer Campaign* **23,** 98 (1946).
(166) Heidelberger, C., and Wiest, W. G., *Cancer Research* **11,** 511 (1951).
(167) Wolf, G., and Heidelberger, C., *Cancer Research* **11,** 290 (1951).
(168) Hieger, I., *Brit. J. Ind. Med.* **6,** 1 (1949).
(169) Shear, M. J., *Am. J. Cancer* **29,** 269 (1937).
(170) Kinosita, R., *Yale J. Biol. and Med.* **12,** 287 (1940).
(171) Kirby, A. H. M., *Cancer Research* **5,** 673, 683 (1945).
(172) Miller, J. A., and Miller, E. C., *Advances in Cancer Research* **1,** 340 (1953).
(173) Fischer, B., *Münch. med. Wochschr.* **53,** 2041 (1906).
(174) Beuthin, W., *Z. Krebsforsch.* **10,** 227 (1911).
(175) Haga, I., *Z. Krebsforsch.* **12,** 525 (1913).
(176) Schmieden, V., and Hayward, E., *Deut. Z. Chir.* **112,** 467 (1911).
(177) Yoshida, T., *Trans. Soc. Pathol. Japon.* **22,** 193, 934 (1932); **23,** 636, (1933); **24,** 523 (1934).
(178) Yoshida, T., *Gann* **28,** 441 (1934); **29,** 213, 295, 302 (1935).
(179) Kinosita, R., *Trans. Soc. Pathol. Japon.* **27,** 665 (1937).
(180) Shear, M. J., *Am. J. Cancer*, **29,** 269 (1937).
(181) Opie, E. L., *J. Exptl. Med.*, **84,** 91 (1946).
(182) Andervont, H. B., *Public Health Repts. (U.S.)* **54,** 1529, 1986 (1939).
(183) Andervont, H. B., Grady, H. G., and Edwards, J. E., *J. Natl. Cancer Inst.* **3,** 131 (1942).

(184) Andervont, H. B., and Edwards, J. E., *J. Natl. Cancer Inst.* **3,** 349, 355 (1943); **2,** 139 (1941).
(185) Law, L. W., *Cancer Research* **1,** 397 (1941).
(186) Morosenskaya, L. S., *Arch. sci. biol.* (*U.S.S.R.*) **56,** 53 (1939).
(187) Turner, J. C., and Mulliken, B., *Proc. Soc. Exptl. Biol. Med.* **49,** 317 (1942).
(188) Andervont, H. B., White, J., and Edwards, J. E., *J. Natl. Cancer Inst.* **4,** 583 (1944).
(189) Nelson, A. A., and Woodard, G., *J. Natl. Cancer Inst.* **13,** 1497 (1953).
(190) Otsuka, L., and Nagao, N., *Gann* **30,** 561 (1936).
(191) Kinosita, R., *Yale J. Biol. and Med.* **12,** 287 (1940).
(192) Kensler, C. J., Sugiura, K., Young, N. F., Halter, C. R., and Rhoads, C. P., *Science* **93,** 308 (1941).
(193) Miner, D. L., Miller, J. A., Baumann, C. A., and Rusch, H. P., *Cancer Research* **3,** 296 (1943).
(194) Kirby, A. H. M., and Peacock, P. R., *J. Pathol. Bacteriol.* **59,** 1 (1947).
(195) Cook, J. W., Hewett, C. L., Kennaway, E. L., and Kennaway, N. M., *Am. J. Cancer* **40,** 62 (1940).
(196) Boyland, E., and Brues, A. M., *Proc. Roy. Soc.* (*London*) **B 122,** 429 (1937).
(197) Jacobsen, P., *Ann.* **428,** 76 (1922).
(198) Miller, E. C., Miller, J. A., Sandin, R. B., and Brown, R. K., *Cancer Research* **9,** 504 (1949).
(199) Miller, J. A., Miller, E. C., and Sapp, R. W., *Cancer Research* **11,** 269 (1951).
(200) Mulay, A. S., and Firminger, H. I., *J. Natl. Cancer Inst.* **13,** 35 (1952).
(201) Mulay, A. S., and Saxen, E. A., *J. Natl. Cancer Inst.* **13,** 1259 (1953).
(201a) Brown, E. V., Faessinger, R., Malloy, P., Travers, J. J., McCarthy, P., and Cerecedo, L. R., *Cancer Research* **14,** 22 (1954).
(202) Haddow, A., Harris, R. J. C., Kon, G. A. R., and Roe, E. M. F., *Trans. Roy. Soc.* (*London*) **241,** 147 (1948).
(203) Crabtree, H. G., *Brit. J. Cancer* **3,** 387 (1949).
(204) Badger, G. M., and Lewis, G. E., *Brit. J. Cancer* **6,** 270 (1952).
(205) Suguira, K., Halter, C. R., Kensler, C. J., and Rhoads, C. P., *Cancer Research* **5,** 235 (1945).
(206) Miller, J. A., and Miller, E. C., *J. Exptl. Med.* **87,** 139 (1948).
(207) Miller, J. A., Miller, E. C., and Finger, G. C., *Cancer Research* **13,** 93 (1953).
(208) Miller, J. A., Miller, E. C., Sandin, R. B., and Rusch, H. P., *Cancer Research* **12,** 283 (1952).
(209) Giese, J. E., Clayton, C. C., Miller, E. C., and Baumann, C. A., *Cancer Research* **6,** 679 (1946).
(210) Rumsfeld, H. W., Jr., Miller, Jr., W. L., and Baumann, C. A., *Cancer Research* **11,** 814 (1951).
(211) Spatt, S. D., and Grayzel, D. M., *Am. J. Med.* **5,** 570 (1948).
(212) MacDonald, J. C., Miller, E. C., Miller, J. A., and Rusch, H. P., *Cancer Research* **12,** 50 (1952).
(213) Richardson, H. L., Stier, A. R., and Borsos-Nachtnebel, E., *Cancer Research* **12,** 356 (1952).
(214) Griffin, A. C., Brandt, E. L., and Setter, V., *Cancer Research* **11,** 868 (1951).
(215) Kirby, A. H. M., and Peacock, P. R., *Glasgow. Med. J.* **30,** 364 (1949).
(216) White, J., and Edwards, J. E., *J. Natl. Cancer Inst.* **2,** 535 (1942).
(217) Kensler, C. J., Suguira, K., and Rhoads, C. P., *Science* **91,** 623 (1940).
(218) Stevenson, E. S., Dobriner, K., and Rhoads, C. P., *Cancer Research* **2,** 160 (1942).
(219) Elson, L. A., and Warren, F. L., *Biochem. J.* **38,** 217 (1944).

(220) Kensler, C. J., Dexter, S. O., and Rhoads, C. P., *Cancer Research* **2,** 1 (1942).
(221) Potter, V. R., *Cancer Research* **2,** 688 (1942).
(222) Cohen, P. P., Hekhuis, G. L., and Sober, E. K., *Cancer Research* **2,** 405 (1942).
(223) Kopac, M. J., Cameron, G., and Chambers, R., *Cancer Research* **3,** 290 (1943).
(224) Kuhn, R., and Beinert, H., *Ber.* **76,** 904 (1943).
(225) Miller, J. A., and Baumann, C. A., *Cancer Research* **5,** 157 (1945).
(226) Miller, J. A., Miller, E. C., and Baumann, C. C., *Cancer Research* **5,** 162 (1945).
(227) Kensler, C. J., Magill, J. W., Sugiura, K., and Rhoads, C. P., *Arch. Biochem.* **11,** 376 (1946).
(228) Miller, J. A., and Baumann, C. A., *Cancer Research* **5,** 227 (1945); **6,** 289 (1946).
(229) Suguira, K., *Cancer Research* **8,** 141 (1948).
(230) Jaffe, M., and Hilbert, P., *Z. physiol. Chem.* **12,** 295 (1888).
(231) Miller, J. A., and Baumann, C. A., *Cancer Research* **12,** 283 (1952).
(232) Mueller, G. C., and Miller, J. A., *J. Biol. Chem.* **202,** 579 (1953).
(233) Miller, E. C., Plescia, A. M., Miller, J. A., and Heidelberger, C., *J. Biol. Chem.* **196,** 863 (1952).
(234) MacDonald, J. C., Plescia, A. M., Miller, E. C., and Miller, J. A., *Cancer Research* **13,** 292 (1953).
(235) Day, P. L., Payne, L. D., and Dinning, J. S., *Proc. Exptl. Biol. Med.* **74,** 854 (1950).
(236) Kensler, C. J., *J. Biol. Chem.* **179,** 1079 (1949).
(237) Mueller, G. C., and Miller, J. A., *J. Biol. Chem.* **185,** 145 (1950).
(238) Mueller, G. C., and Miller, J. A., *J. Biol. Chem.* **176,** 535 (1948).
(239) Mueller, G. C., and Miller, J. A., *J. Biol. Chem.* **180,** 1125 (1949).
(240) Mackenzie, C. G., Johnston, J. M., and Frisell, W. R., *Federation Proc.* **11,** 252 (1952).
(241) Berenbom, M., and White, J., *J. Natl. Cancer Inst.* **12,** 583 (1951).
(242) Edwards, J. E., *J. Natl. Cancer Inst.* **2,** 197 (1941).
(243) Edwards, J. E., and Dalton, A. J., *J. Natl. Cancer Inst.* **3,** 19 (1942).
(244) Edwards, J. E., Heston, W. E., and Dalton, A. J., *J. Natl. Cancer Inst.* **3,** 297 (1942).
(245) Eschenbrenner, A. B., *J. Natl. Cancer Inst.* **4,** 385 (1944).
(246) Eschenbrenner, A. B., *J. Natl. Cancer Inst.* **5,** 251 (1945); *Science* **102,** 302 (1945).
(247) Cameron, G.., and Karunaratne, W. A. E., *J. Pathol. Bacteriol.* **42,** 1 (1936).
(248) Wilson, R. H., De Eds, F., and Cox, A. J., *Cancer Research* **1,** 595 (1941).
(249) Bielschowsky, F., *Brit. J. Exptl. Pathol.* **25,** 1 (1944); **27,** 54 (1946).
(250) Armstrong, E. C., and Bonser, G. M., *J. Pathol. Bacteriol.* **56,** 507 (1944).
(251) Dunning, W. F., Curtis, M. R., and Madsen, M. E., *Cancer Research* **7,** 134 (1947).
(252) Kirby, A. H. M., *Brit. J. Cancer* **2,** 294 (1948).
(253) Morris, H. P., Dubnik, C. S., and Johnson, J. M., *J. Natl. Cancer Inst.* **10,** 1201 (1950).
(254) Bielschowsky, F., and Bielschowsky, M., *Brit. J. Cancer* **6,** 89 (1952).
(255) Westfall, B. B., *J. Natl. Cancer Inst.* **6,** 23 (1945).
(256) Morris, H. P., and Westfall, B. B., *Cancer Research* **10,** 506 (1950).
(257) Neish, W. J. P., *Rec. trav. chim.* **67,** 349 (1948).
(258) Dyer, H. M., Ross, H. E., and Morris, H. P., *Cancer Research* **11,** 307 (1951).
(259) Gutmann, H. R., Kiely, G. E., and Klein, M., *Cancer Research* **12,** 350 (1952).
(260) Damron, C. M., and Dyer, H. M., *J. Natl. Cancer Inst.* **14,** 279 (1953).
(261) Morris, H. P., Weisburger, J. H., and Weisburger, E. K., *Cancer Research* **10,** 620 (1950).
(262) Ray, F. E., and Argus, M. F., *Cancer Research* **11,** 783 (1951).

(263) Dyer, A. M., Damron, C. M., and Morris, H. P., *J. Natl. Cancer Inst.* **14,** 93 (1953).
(264) Bielschowsky, F., *Biochem. J.* **39,** 287 (1945).
(265) Hoch-Ligeti, C., *Brit. J. Cancer* **1,** 391 (1947).
(265a) Weisburger, J. H., Weisburger, E. K., and Morris, H. P. (in press).
(266) Morris, H. P., and Dubnik, C., *Cancer Research* **10,** 233 (1950).
(267) Weisburger, J. H., Weisburger, E. K., and Morris, H. P., *J. Am. Chem. Soc.* **74,** 4540 (1952).
(268) Miller, E. C., Miller, J. A., Sandin, R. B., and Brown, R. K., *Cancer Research* **9,** 504 (1949).
(269) Spitz, S., Maguigan, W. H., and Dobriner, K., *Cancer* **3,** 789 (1950).
(270) Walpole, A. L., Williams, M. H. C., and Roberts, D. C., *Brit. J. Ind. Med.* **9,** 255 (1952).
(271) Otsuka, I., and Nagao, N., *Gann* **30,** 561 (1936).
(272) Sandin, R. B., Melby, R., Hay, A. S., Jones, R. N., Miller, E. C., and Miller, J. A., *J. Am. Chem. Soc.* **74,** 5073 (1952).
(273) Baker, R. K., *Cancer Research* **13,** 137 (1953).
(274) Baker, R. K., and Deighton, J. G., *Cancer Research* **13,** 529 (1953).
(275) Morris, H. P., and Eyestone, W. H., *J. Natl. Cancer Inst.* **13,** 1139 (1953).
(276) Bielschowsky, F., *Brit. Med. Bull.* **4,** 382 (1947).
(277) Bonser, G. M., Clayson, D. B., Jull, J. W., and Pyrak, L. N., *Brit. J. Cancer* **6,** 412 (1952).
(277a) Clayson, D. B., *Brit. J. Cancer* **7,** 460 (1953).
(278) Nettleship, A., and Henshaw, P. S., *J. Natl. Cancer Inst.* **4,** 309 (1943).
(279) Cowen, P. N., *Brit. J. Cancer* **4,** 245 (1950).
(280) Larsen, C. D., *J. Natl. Cancer Inst.* **7,** 12 (1946).
(281) Jaffe, W. G., *Cancer Research* **7,** 107 (1947).
(282) Guyer, M. F., and Claus, P. E., *Cancer Research* **7,** 342 (1947).
(283) Klein, M., *J. Natl. Cancer Inst.* **12,** 1003 (1952).
(284) Bryan, C. E., Skipper, H. E., and White, L., Jr., *J. Biol. Chem.* **177,** 941 (1949).
(285) Shapiro, J. R., and Kirschbaum, A., *Cancer Research* **11,** 644 (1951).
(286) Heston, W. E., and Dunn, T. B., *J. Natl. Cancer Inst.* **11,** 1057 (1951).
(287) Boyland, E., *Biochem. Soc. Symposia (Cambridge, Engl.)* **2,** 61 (1948).
(288) Boyland, E., and Horning, E. S., *Brit. J. Cancer* **3,** 118 (1949).
(289) Heston, W. E., *J. Natl. Cancer Inst.* **10,** 125 (1949); **13,** 415 (1953).
(290) Burdette, W. J., *Cancer Research* **12,** 366 (1952).
(291) Ross, W. C. J., *Advances in Cancer Research* **1,** 397 (1953).
(292) Seligman, A. M., Rutenberg, A. M., and Friedman, O. M., *J. Natl. Cancer Inst.* **9,** 261 (1949).
(293) Everett, J. L., and Kon, G. A. R., *J. Chem. Soc.* **1950,** 3131.
(294) Ross, W. C. J., *J. Chem. Soc.* **1950,** 2257.
(295) Haddow, A., *Proc. Roy. Soc. Med.* **44,** 263 (1951).
(296) Hendry, J. A., Rose, F. L., and Walpole, A. L., *Brit. J. Pharmacol.* **6,** 201 (1951).
(297) Hendry, J. A., Homer, R. F., Rose, F. L., and Walpole, A. L., *Brit. J. Pharmacol.* **6,** 235 (1951).
(298) Hendry, J. A., Homer, R. F., Rose, F. L., and Walpole, A. L., *Brit. J. Pharmacol.* **6,** 357 (1951).
(299) Alexander, P., *Advances in Cancer Research* **2,** 1 (1954).
(300) Haddow, A., *Proc. 1st Natl. Cancer Conf.*, p. 88 (1949).
(301) Goldacre, R. J., Loveless, A., and Ross, W. C. J., *Nature* **163,** 667 (1949).
(302) Loveless, A., and Revell, S., *Nature* **164,** 938 (1949).

(303) Haddow, A., Kon, G. A. R., and Ross, W. C. J., *Nature* **162,** 824 (1948).
(304) Elmore, D. T., Gulland, J. M., Jordan, D. O., and Taylor, H. F. W., *Biochem. J.* **42,** 308 (1948).
(305) Haddow, A., and Timmis, G. M., *Acta Unio. Intern. contra Cancrum* **7** (3), 469 (1951).
(306) Haddow, A., *Nature* **136,** 868 (1935).
(307) Turner, F. C., *J. Natl. Cancer Inst.* **2,** 81 (1941).
(308) Oppenheimer, B. S., Oppenheimer, E. T., and Stout, A. P., *Proc. Soc. Exptl. Biol. Med.* **79,** 366 (1952).
(309) Druckrey, H., Schmähl. D., and Danneberg, P., *Naturwissenschaften* **39,** 393 (1952).
(310) Oppenheimer, B. S., Oppenheimer, E. T., Stout, A. P., and Danishefsky, I., *Science* **118,** 305 (1953).
(310a) Park, H. F., *J. Phys. and Colloid Chem.* **54,** 1383 (1950).
(310b) Fitzhugh, A. F., *Science* **118,** 783 (1953).
(311) Fieser, L. F., and Creech, H. J., *J. Am. Chem. Soc.* **61,** 3502 (1939).
(312) Hopkins, S. J., and Wormall, A., *Biochem. J.* **27,** 740 (1933).
(313) Creech, H. J., and Jones, R. N., *J. Am. Chem. Soc.* **62,** 1970 (1940).
(314) Creech, H. J., *J. Am. Chem. Soc.* **63,** 576 (1941).
(315) Creech, H. J., and Jones, R. N., *J. Am. Chem. Soc.* **63,** 1661, 1670 (1941).
(316) Green, L. Q., and Creech, H. J., *J. Am. Chem. Soc.* **68,** 2401 (1946).
(317) Creech, H. J., Oginsky, E. L., and Cheever, F. S., *Cancer Research* **7,** 290 (1947).
(318) Smith, W. M., Jr., Pratt, E. F., and Creech, H. J., *J. Am. Chem. Soc.* **73,** 319 (1951).
(319) Creech, H. J., and Peck, R. M., *J. Am. Chem. Soc.* **74,** 463 (1952).
(320) Peck, R. M., and Creech, H. J., *J. Am. Chem. Soc.* **74,** 468 (1952).
(321) Creech, H. J., *Cancer Research* **12,** 557 (1952).
(322) Creech, H. J., Havas, H. F., and Andre, J., *Cancer Research* **13,** 335 (1953).
(323) Peck, R. M., Miller, G. L., and Creech, H. J., *J. Am. Chem. Soc.* **75,** 2364 (1953).
(324) Landsteiner, K., "The Specificity of Serological Reactions," Rev. ed. Harvard University Press, Cambridge, 1945.
(325) Dunlap, C. E., and Warren, S., *Cancer Research* **6,** 454 (1946).
(326) Green, E. U., and Creech, E. M. H., *Cancer Research* **11,** 252 (1951).
(327) Creech, H. J., Oginsky, E. L., and Tryon, M., *Cancer Research* **7,** 301 (1947).
(328) Haddow, A., Scott, C. M., and Scott, J. D., *Proc. Roy. Soc.* (*London*) **B 122,** 477 (1937).
(329) White, J., and White, A., *J. Biol. Chem.* **131,** 149 (1939).
(330) Elson, L. A., Goulden, F., and Warren, F. L., *Biochem. J.* **39,** 301 (1945).
(331) Elson, L. A., Goulden, F., and Warren, F. L., *Brit. J. Cancer* **1,** 80 (1947).
(332) Elson, L. A., and Warren, F. L., *Brit. J. Cancer* **1,** 86 (1947).
(333) Gutmann, H. R., and Wood, J. L., *Cancer Research* **10,** 8 (1950).
(334) Gutmann, H. R., and Wood, J. L., *Cancer Research* **10,** 701 (1950).
(335) Lusky, L. M., Braun, H. A., and Woodard, G., *Cancer Research* **7,** 667 (1947).
(336) Wood, J. L., and Kraynak, M. E., *Cancer Research* **13,** 358 (1953).
(337) Black, M. M., *Cancer Research* **7,** 592 (1947).
(338) Schoenbach, E. B., Weissman, N., and Armistead, E. B., *J. Clin. Invest.* **30,** 762 (1951).
(339) Shacter, B., and Shimkin, M. B., *Cancer Research* **10,** 240 (1950).
(340) Calcutt, G., *Brit. J. Cancer* **3,** 306 (1949).
(341) Rondoni, P., *Pontif. Acad. Sci. Script. Var.* No. **7,** 251 (1949).
(342) Rondoni, P., and Barbieri, G. P., *Enzymologia* **14,** 10 (1950).
(343) Miller, E. C., and Miller, J. A., *Cancer Research* **7,** 468 (1947).

(344) Miller, E. C., Miller, J. A., Sapp, R. W., and Weber, G. M., *Cancer Research* **9,** 336 (1949).
(345) Salzberg, D. A., and Griffin, A. C., *Cancer Research* **12,** 294 (1952).
(346) Price, J. M., Miller, E. C., Miller, J. A., and Weber, G. M., *Cancer Research* **10,** 18 (1950).
(347) Sorof, S., and Cohen, P. P., *Cancer Research* **11,** 376 (1951).
(348) Eldredge, N. T., and Luck, J. M., *Cancer Research* **12,** 801 (1952).
(349) Sorof, S., Cohen, P. P., Miller, E. C., and Miller, J. A., *Cancer Research* **11,** 383 (1951).
(350) Miller, E. C., *Cancer Research* **11,** 100 (1951).
(351) Doniach, I., and Mottram, J. C., *Am. J. Cancer* **39,** 234 (1940).
(352) Morton, J. J., Mider, G. B., Luce-Clausen, E. M., and Mahoney, E. B., *Cancer Research* **11,** 559 (1951).
(353) Wiest, W. G., and Heidelberger, C., *Cancer Research* **13,** 246, 250, 255 (1953).
(354) Miller, E. C., and Miller, J. A., *Cancer Research* **12,** 547 (1952).
(355) Weisburger, E. K., Weisburger, J. H., and Morris, H. P., *Arch. Biochem. and Biophys.* **43,** 474 (1953).
(356) Tarver, H., *in* "Amino Acids and Proteins," p. 769. Charles C Thomas, Springfield, 1951.
(357) Watkins, W. M., and Wormall, A., *Biochem. J.* **52,** 365 (1952).
(358) Alexander, P., *Nature* **169,** 226 (1952).
(359) Butler, J. A. V., Gilbert, L., James, D. W. F., and Ross, W. C. J., *Nature* **168,** 985 (1951).
(360) Cambel, P., *Cancer Research* **11,** 370 (1951).
(361) Berenblum, I., *J. Natl. Cancer Inst.* **10,** 167 (1949).
(362) Bergmann, F., *Cancer Research* **2,** 660 (1942).
(363) Shear, M. J., and Leiter, J., *J. Natl. Cancer Inst.* **2,** 241 (1941).
(364) Badger, G. M., *Brit. J. Cancer* **2,** 309 (1948).
(365) Boyland, E., *Biochem. Soc. Symposia* (*Cambridge, Engl.*) No. **5,** 40 (1950).
(366) Orchin, M., *J. Org. Chem.* **16,** 1165 (1951).
(367) Takemura, K. H., Cameron, M. D., and Newman, M. S., *J. Am. Chem. Soc.* **75,** 3280 (1953).
(368) Robinson, R., *Brit. Med. J.* **i,** 945 (1946).
(369) Coulson, C. A., *Advances in Cancer Research* **1,** 1 (1953).
(370) Newman, M. S., and Kosak, A. I., *J. Org. Chem.* **14,** 375 (1949).
(371) Jones, R. N., *J. Am. Chem. Soc.* **62,** 148 (1940).
(372) Badger, G. M., Pearce, R. S., and Pettit, R., *J. Chem. Soc.* **1952,** 1112.
(373) Pullman, A., *Ann. chim.* (*Paris*) **2,** 5 (1947).
(374) Pullman, A., *Compt. rend.* **226,** 486 (1948).
(375) Pullman, B., *Compt. rend.* **222,** 1396 (1946).
(376) Pullman, B., *Bull soc. chim.* **15,** 533 (1948).
(377) Pullman, A., and Pullman, B., *Rev. sci.* **84,** 145 (1946).
(378) Pullman, A., and Pullman. B., *Acta Unio-Intern. contra Cancrum* **6,** 57 (1948).
(379) Daudel, P., *Compt. rend.* **230,** 99 (1950).
(380) Daudel, R., *Bull. cancer* **35,** 110 (1948).
(381) Daudel, P., and Daudel, R., *Biol. méd.* (*Paris*) **39** (4), 201 (1950).
(382) Schmidt, O., *Z. physik. Chem.* **42,** 83; **43,** 185; **44,** 193 (1939).
(383) Greenwood, H. H., *Brit. J. Cancer* **5,** 441 (1951).
(384) Boyland, E., *Biochem. et Biophys. Acta* **4,** 293 (1950).
(385) Cook, J. W., and Schoental, R., *J. Chem. Soc.* **1950,** 170.
(386) Badger, G. M., *J. Chem. Soc.* **1949,** 456; **1950,** 1809.
(387) Badger, G. M., and Lynn, K. R., *J. Chem. Soc.* **1950,** 1726.

(388) Boyland, E., *J. chim. phys.* **47,** 942 (1950).
(388a) Pullman, A., and Pullman, B., *J. chim. phys.* **50,** 548 (1953).
(389) Rogers, M. T., Campbell, T. W., and Maatman, R. W., *J. Am. Chem. Soc.* **73,** 5122 (1951).
(390) Badger, G. M., and Lewis, G. E., *Nature* **167,** 403 (1951).
(391) Hammett, L. P., "Physical Organic Chemistry." McGraw-Hill Publishing Co., New York, 1940.
(392) Badger, G. M., and Lewis, G. E., *J. Chem. Soc.* **1953,** 2151.
(393) Dunning, W. F., Curtis, M. R., and Eisen, M. J., *Am. J. Cancer* **40,** 85 (1940).
(394) Burrows, H., and Boyland, E., *Am. J. Cancer* **32,** 367 (1938).
(395) Syverton, J. T., Berry, G. P., and Dascomb, H. E., *Cancer Research* **2,** 436 (1942).
(396) Shimkin, M. B., and Mider, G. B., *J. Natl. Cancer Inst.* **1,** 707 (1941).
(397) Greene, H. S. N., *Science* **101,** 644 (1945).
(398) Rous, P., and Smith, W. E., *J. Exptl. Med.* **81,** 597, 621 (1945).
(399) Shay, H., Gruenstein, M., Marx, H. E., and Glazer, L., *Cancer Research* **11,** 29 (1951).
(400) Stewart, H. L., and Lorenz, E., *J. Natl. Cancer Inst.* **2,** 193 (1941).
(401) Berenblum, I., *J. Natl. Cancer Inst.* **10,** 167 (1949).
(402) Hartung, E. W., *Cancer Research* **2,** 837 (1942).
(403) Peacock, P. R., *J. Pathol. Bacteriol.* **36,** 141 (1933).
(404) Peacock, P. R., *Am. J. Cancer* **25,** 37 (1935).
(405) Murphy, J. B., and Landsteiner, K., *J. Exptl. Med.* **41,** 807 (1925).
(406) Murphy, J. B., and Sturm, E., *Cancer Research* **1,** 477 (1941).
(407) McIntosh, J., and Selbie, F. R., *Brit. J. Exptl. Pathol.* **20,** 49 (1939).
(408) Duran-Reynals, F., Shrigley, E. W., and de Hostos, E., *Cancer Research* **5,** 11 (1945).
(409) Peacock, A., and Peacock, P. K., *Brit. J. Cancer* **3,** 289 (1949).
(410) Falin, L. I., and Gromzewa, K. E., *Am. J. Cancer* **36,** 233 (1939).
(411) Cottini, G. B., and Mazzone, G. B., *Am. J. Cancer* **37,** 186 (1939).
(412) Lynch, C. J., *Proc. Soc. Exptl. Biol. Med.* **31,** 215 (1933); **33,** 401 (1935).
(413) Nettleship, A., and Henshaw, P. S., *J. Natl. Cancer Inst.* **4,** 309 (1943).
(414) Shimkin, M. B., *in* "Mammary Tumors in Mice." *American Association for the Advancement of Science*, Washington, D. C., 1945 .
(415) Edwards, J. E., Dalton, A. J., White, J., and White, T. N., *J. Natl. Cancer Inst.* **3,** 191 (1942).
(416) Lippincott, S. W., Edwards, J. E., Grady, H. G., and Stewart, H. L., *J. Natl. Cancer Inst.* **3,** 199 (1942).
(417) Heston, W. E., *J. Natl. Cancer Inst.* **5,** 161 (1944).
(418) Heston, W. E., *J. Natl. Cancer Inst.* **3,** 69 (1942).
(419) Heston, W. E., *J. Natl. Cancer Inst.* **7,** 463 (1947).
(420) Heston, W. E., Deringer, M. K., Hughes, I. K., and Cornfield, J., *J. Natl. Cancer Inst.* **12,** 1141 (1952).
(421) Law, L. W., *J. Natl. Cancer Inst.* **12,** 1119 (1952).
(422) Findlay, G. M., *Lancet* **215,** 1070 (1928).
(423) Kirby-Smith, J. S., Blum, H. F., and Grady, H. G., *J. Natl. Cancer Inst.* **2,** 403 (1942).
(424) Grady, H. G., Blum, H. F., and Kirby-Smith, J. S., *J. Natl. Cancer Inst.* **3,** 371 (1943).
(425) Rusch, H. P., Kline, B. E., and Baumann, C. A., *Arch. Pathol.* **31,** 135 (1941).
(426) Blum, H. F., *J. Natl. Cancer Inst.* **3,** 533, 539 (1943).
(427) Bain, J. A., and Rusch, H. P., *Cancer Research* **3,** 425 (1943).
(428) Rusch, H. P., Kline, B. E., and Baumann, C. A., *Cancer Research* **2,** 183 (1942).

(429) Blum, H. F., *J. Natl. Cancer Inst.* **5**, 89 (1944).
(430) Snapp, R. H., Niederman, D. J., and Rothman, S., *Cancer Research* **10**, 73 (1950).
(431) Moks, F. E., *Cancer Research* **8**, 371 (1948).
(432) Blum, H. F., *J. Natl. Cancer Inst.* **11**, 463 (1950).
(433) Crabtree, H. G., *Cancer Research* **4**, 688 (1944).
(434) Furth, J., and Furth, O. B., *Am. J. Cancer* **28**, 54 (1936).
(435) Bali, T., and Furth, J., *Cancer Research* **9**, 449 (1949).
(436) Henshaw, P. S., *Radiology* **43**, 279 (1944).
(437) Kirschbaum, A., and Kaplan, H. S., *Science* **100**, 360 (1944).
(438) Lorenz, E., Heston, W. E., Eschenbrenner, A. B., and Deringer, M. K., *Radiology* **49**, 274 (1947).
(439) Furth, J., and Boon, M. C., *Cancer Research* **7**, 241 (1947).
(440) Lick, L., Kirschbaum, A., and Mixer, H., *Cancer Research* **9**, 532 (1949).
(441) Lorenz, E., Heston, W. E., Jacobson, L. O., Eschenbrenner, A. B., Shimkin, M., Deringer, M., and Doniger, J., Atomic Energy Commission Declassified Document, CH-3698 (1946); *J. Natl. Cancer Inst.* **6**, 349 (1946).
(442) Spargo, B., Bloomfield, J. R., Glotzer, D. J., Gordon, E. L., and Nichols, O., *J. Natl. Cancer Inst.* **12**, 615 (1951).
(443) McDonald, E., and staff of the Biochemical Research Foundation, *in* "Neutron Effects on Animals." Williams & Wilkins Co., Baltimore, 1947.
(444) Lorenz, E., Eschenbrenner, A. B., Heston, W. E., and Uphoff, D., *J. Natl. Cancer Inst.* **11**, 947 (1951).
(445) Shelton, E., *J. Natl. Cancer Inst.* **12**, 1203 (1952).
(446) Furth, J., *J. Gerontol.* **1**, 46 (1946).
(447) Law, L. W., and Miller, J. H., *J. Natl. Cancer Inst.* **11**, 253 (1950).
(448) Law, L. W., and Miller, J. H., *J. Natl. Cancer Inst.* **11**, 425 (1950).
(449) Kaplan, H. S., *J. Natl. Cancer Inst.* **11**, 83 (1950).
(450) Kaplan, H. S., *J. Natl. Cancer Inst.* **10**, 267 (1949).
(451) Kaplan, H. S., Brown, M. B., and Paull, J., *Cancer Research* **13**, 677 (1953).
(452) Kaplan, H. S., and Brown, M. B., *Cancer Research* **12**, 441 (1952).
(453) Jacobson, L. O., Marks, E. K., Robson, M. J., Gaston, E. O., and Zirkle, R. E., *J. Lab. Clin. Med.* **34**, 1538 (1949).
(454) Congdon, C. C., Uphoff, D., and Lorenz, E., *J. Natl. Cancer Inst.* **13**, 73 (1952).
(455) Kaplan, H. S., and Brown, M. B., *J. Natl. Cancer Inst.* **12**, 427 (1951).
(456) Lorenz, E., Congdon, C. C., and Uphoff, D., *J. Natl. Cancer Inst.* **14**, 291 (1953).
(457) Kaplan, H. S., Brown, M. B., and Paull, J., *J. Natl. Cancer Inst.* **14**, 303 (1953).
(458) Kaplan, H. S., Marder, S. N., and Brown, M. B., *Cancer Research* **11**, 629 (1951).
(459) Kaplan, H. S., and Brown, M. B., *Cancer Research* **12**, 445 (1952).
(460) Sacher, G. A., and Brues, A. M., *Cancer Research* **9**, 620 (1949).
(461) Kaplan, H. S., and Brown, M. B., *J. Natl. Cancer Inst.* **13**, 185 (1952).
(462) Hueper, W. C., "Occupational Tumors and Allied Diseases." Charles C Thomas, Springfield, 1942
(463) Martland, H. S., *Am. J. Cancer* **15**, 2435 (1931).
(464) Martland, H. S., and Humphries, R. E., *Arch. Pathol.* **7**, 406 (1929).
(465) Sabin, F. R., Doan, C. A., and Forkner, C. E., *J. Exptl. Med.* **56**, 267 (1932).
(466) Dunlap, C. E., Aub, J. C., Evans, R. D., and Harris, R. S., *Am. J. Pathol.* **20**, 1 (1944).
(467) Evans, R. D., Harris, R. S., and Bunker, J. W., *Am. J. Roentgenol.* **52**, 353 (1944).
(468) Brues, A. M., Lisco, H., and Finkel, M. P., Atomic Energy Commission Document, MDDC-145 (1946), quoted in Brues, A. M., *Advances in Biol. and Med. Physics* **2**, 171 (1951).

(469) Koletsky, S., Boute, F. J., and Friedell, H. L., *Cancer Research* **10,** 129 (1950).
(470) Skipper, H. E., White, L., Jr., and Bryan, C. E., *J. Biol. Chem.* **180,** 1187 (1949).
(471) Brues, A. M., *Advances in Cancer Research* **2,** 177 (1954).
(472) Clark, J. H., Luce-Clausen, E. M., and Mider, G. B., *Cancer Research* **12,** 451 (1952).
(473) Furth, J., and Boon, M. C., *Science* **98,** 138 (1943).
(474) Mixer, H. W., and Kirschbaum, A., *Radiology* **50,** 476 (1948).
(475) Kirschbaum, A., Shapiro, J. R., and Mixer, H. W., *Cancer Research* **13,** 262 (1953).
(476) Hoch-Ligeti, C., *Brit. J. Cancer* **3,** 562 (1949).
(477) Heston, W. E., Lorenz, E., and Deringer, M. K., *Cancer Research* **13,** 573 (1953).
(478) Lea, D. E., "Actions of Radiations on Living Cells." Macmillan & Co., London, 1947.
(479) Davis, B. D., Hollaender, A., and Greenstein, J. P., *J. Biol. Chem.* **146,** 663 (1942).
(480) Hollaender, A., Greenstein, J. P., and Jenrette, W. V., *J. Natl. Cancer Inst.* **2,** 23 (1941).
(481) Mitchell, J. S., *Brit. J. Exptl. Pathol.* **23,** 285, 296, 309 (1942).
(482) Stowell, R. E., *Cancer Research* **5,** 169 (1945).
(483) Ohlström, L., Euler, H. von, and Hevesy, G. von, *Arkiv. Kemi, Mineral., Geol.*, **19A** (9 and 13), (1944).
(484) Hevesy, G., von, *Nature* **163,** 869 (1949).
(485) Skipper, H. E., and Mitchell, J. H., Jr., *Cancer* **4,** 363 (1951).
(486) Sparrow, A. H., and Rosenfeld, F. M., *Science* **104,** 245 (1946).
(487) Taylor, B., Greenstein, J. P., and Hollaender, A., *Arch. Biochem.* **16,** 19 (1948).
(488) Butler, G. C., *Can. J. Research* **27,** 972 (1949).
(489) Butler, J. A. V., and Smith, K. A., *Nature* **165,** 847 (1950).
(490) Butler, J. A. V., Gilbert, L. A., and Smith, K. A., *Nature* **165,** 714 (1950).
(491) Butler, J. A. V., Gilbert, L., James, D. W. F., and Ross, W. C. J., *Nature* **168,** 985 (1951).
(492) Alexander, P., and Fox, M., *Nature* **169,** 572 (1952).
(493) Alexander, P., *Nature* **169,** 226 (1952).
(494) Scholes, G., and Weiss, J., *Nature* **171,** 920 (1953).
(495) Limperos, G., *Cancer Research* **11,** 325 (1951).
(496) Barron, E. S. G., Dickman, S., Muntz, J. A., and Singer, T. P., *J. Gen. Physiol.* **32,** 537 (1949).
(497) Straube, R. L., Patt, H. M., Smith, D. E., and Tyree, E. B., *Cancer Research* **10,** 243 (1950).
(498) Fischer, M. A., Coulter, E. P., and Costello, M. J., *Proc. Soc. Exptl. Biol. Med.* **83,** 266 (1953).
(499) Brandt, E. L., and Griffin, A. C., *Cancer* **4,** 1030 (1951).
(500) Mack, H. P., and Figge, F. H. J., *Science* **115,** 547 (1952).
(501) Kennaway, E. L., and Kennaway, N. M., *Cancer Research* **6,** 49 (1946).
(502) Hueper, W. C., *Arch. Pathol.* **25,** 856 (1938); *J. Am. Med. Assoc* **131,** 738 (1946).
(503) Mueller, A., *Z. Urol. Chir.* **36,** 139 (1933).
(504) Hueper, W. C., *in* "Occupational Tumors and Allied Diseases." Charles C Thomas, Springfield, 1942.
(505) Currie, A. N., *Brit. Med. Bull.* **4,** 977 (1947).
(506) Hueper, W. C., *Cancer Research* **12,** 691 (1952).
(507) Henry, S. A., *Brit. Med. Bull.* **4,** 389 (1947).
(508) Wynder, E. L., and Graham, E. A., *J. Am. Med. Assoc.* **143,** 329 (1950).
(509) Sadowsky, D. A., Gilliam, A. G., and Cornfield, J., *J. Natl. Cancer Inst.* **13,** 1237 (1953).

(509a) Wynder, E. L., Graham, E. A., and Croninger, A. B., *Cancer Research* **13,** 855 (1953).
(510) Hueper, W. C., *Cancer Research* **12,** 691 (1952).
(511) Henshaw, P. S., and Hawkins, J. W., *J. Natl. Cancer Inst.* **4,** 339 (1944).
(512) Evans, R. D., Harris, R. S., and Bunker, J. W. M., *Am. J. Roentgenol. Radium Therapy* **52,** 353 (1944).
(513) Aub, J. C., Evans, R. D., Gallagher, D. M., and Tibbetts, D. M., *Ann. Internal Med.* **11,** 1443 (1938).
(514) March, H. C., *Radiology* **43,** 275 (1944).
(515) Pohle, E. A., "Theoretical Principles of Roentgen Therapy." Lea & Febiger, Philadelphia, 1938.
(516) Report of the Royal Commission on the Use of Radium and X-Rays in the Treatment of the Sick etc., Toronto, 1932.
(517) Owen, E. A., *Brit. J. Radiol.* **18,** 369 (1945).
(518) Quimby, E. H., and Pool, J., *Radiol.* **41,** 272 (1943).
(519) Braestrop, C. B., *Radiology* **43,** 286 (1944).
(520) "Safe Handling of Radioactive Luminous Compounds," Handbook H 27. *Natl. Bureau of Standards*, 1941.
(521) Protection against X-Rays and Gamma Rays. Combined report of the Standardization Committees of the American Roentgen Ray Society and the Radiological Society of North American. *Radiology* **46,** 57 (1946).
(522) Blum, H. F., "Photodynamic Action and Diseases Caused by Light." Reinhold Publishing Corp., New York, 1941.
(523) Bergonie, J., and Tribondeau, L., *Compt. rend. soc. biol.* **57,** 400 (1904).
(524) Twort, C. C., and Fulton, J. D., *J. Pathol. Bacteriol.* **32,** 149 (1929).
(525) Roffo, A. H., *Bull. assoc. franç. étude cancer* **23,** 590 (1934).
(526) Sabin, F. R., Doan, C. A., and Forkner, C. E., *J. Exptl. Med.* **56,** 267 (1932).
(527) Henshaw, P. S., *Radiology* **43,** 279 (1944).
(528) Leiter, J., Shimkin, M. B., and Shear, M. J., *J. Natl. Cancer Inst.* **3,** 155 (1942).
(529) Morris, H. P., Larsen, C. D., and Lippincott, S. W., *J. Natl. Cancer Inst.* **4,** 285 (1943).
(530) Kirby, A. H. M., *Cancer Research* **5,** 129 (1945).
(531) Peacock, P. R., *Brit. Med. Bull.* **4,** 364 (1947).
(532) Roffo, A. H., *Bol. inst. med. exptl. estud. cancer* **18,** 929 (1941).

Chapter IV

Intrinsic Factors

Introduction

An intrinsic carcinogenic agent may be tentatively defined as one which possesses a biogenic origin and, in the present instance, has been confined to hormones and viruses. A distinction in many cases between extrinsic and intrinsic agents may be somewhat arbitrary and a considerable flexibility in definition of these agents must be taken for granted. Thus, although a polycyclic hydrocarbon such as methylcholanthrene has been considered as an extrinsic agent, it is possible to conceive of this substance as arising by a process of abnormal metabolism from the bile acids and, hence, under such conditions to be classed as an endogenous agent. Furthermore, an externally administered agent, ordinarily quite foreign to the body economy, and which is not carcinogenic itself, may be altered and degraded by the normal processes of metabolism into a product which is carcinogenic. On the other hand, such agents as viruses induce tumors in new hosts by transmission from previous hosts, e.g., the virus did not originate within the new host. Somewhere, of course, in the earliest history of the virus the latter must have originated endogenously in some kind of host. Thus, it is possible to classify the virus as being of endogenous origin even though it arrives extrinsically to the most recently affected host.

The carcinogenic viruses, however, possess one unique feature which delimits them from other cancer-producing agents in that they possess remarkable specificity; i.e., they transmit and invariably induce the same tumor. Whereas, as noted in Table 31, one and the same carcinogenic chemical can induce several types of cancer in different sites within the treated animal, the viruses generally give rise in each host to only one kind of tumor. An attempt to separate extrinsic from intrinsic carcinogenic agents on the basis of the specificity of the latter breaks down when such a distinction is applied to the other great class of agents usually classed as intrinsic, namely, the sex hormones. It might have been expected that the sex hormones would be specifically concerned only with the carcinogenesis of sex, or perhaps accessory sex, tissues. In fact, however, as already demonstrated in Table 31, sex plays a role in the neoplastic transformation of such non-sex tissues as liver and subcutaneous fibroblasts, and, as will be described in the present chapter, the application of sex hormones induces tumors not only of sex but of certain non-sex tissues as well. Intrinsic agents need not necessarily be specific for any one tissue but may affect several quite different tissues within the same host.

The fact, however, that the administration to an animal of an agent such as a sex hormone presumed to be intrinsic, or of a synthetic imitation or analogue of the sex hormone, results in the production of a tumor in any tissue does not necessarily imply that it acted upon the tissue as such. Hormones undergo continual metabolism in the body which produces or harbors them, and there is no assurance that they or their metabolites act in the same form or manner to induce neoplasia as to carry out their normal influences on their specific target organs. Much of the work in this area of investigation has consisted in the direct administration of various sorts of hormones by different routes into intact or castrated animals, at rest or undergoing some form of external stress. More subtle techniques of hormonal imbalance have been introduced in recent years, by which overcompensatory responses on the part of the animal to artificial stresses have led to the development of neoplasia elsewhere in the animal. By these means the animals' own hormones become the cancer-inducing agent or agents.

Carcinogenesis of Sex and Accessory Sex Tissues

The normal development and function of the sex tissues of animals are regulated and controlled by certain products of glands of internal secretion. These products, which may be referred to collectively as estrogens if they primarily affect female sex tissues and as androgens if they primarily affect male sex tissues, are diverse in origin and in chemical composition. They have one property in common at least, which is that, sometimes alone and sometimes in unison, they are capable of stimulating proliferation of immature sex tissues and of mature sex tissues after periods of regression (1, 2). Sex function is an integrated activity of many hormonal secretions under the limitations of body control. (For leading reviews, cf. 3–8).

The relatively high incidence of cancer of the sex or accessory sex tissues in women and the recognition of changes in the breast with changes in ovarian function, together with the known capacity of the sex hormones to stimulate proliferation, soon led to studies on the possible relation of the ovary to mammary carcinogenesis. The first attempts were clinical and involved ovariectomy in a few cases of breast cancer in women (cf. Chapter VI). The results were not satisfactory, and further surgical efforts in this direction have generally been held in abeyance.

The first experimental demonstration of the influence of hormonal factors on the development of cancer of the breast was made by Lathrop and Loeb in 1916 (9). These authors observed that the incidence of mammary cancer in mice was lower and the average cancer age was higher in animals prevented from breeding than in breeding females of the same stocks. Furthermore, the incidence of mammary tumors appeared to be highest in stocks in which breeding mice developed tumors most frequently. These observations, performed with more or less heterozygous stocks of mice,

TABLE 34

INCIDENCE OF MAMMARY TUMORS IN BREEDING AND NON-BREEDING FEMALE MICE FOR FOUR INBRED STRAINS (CF. 13)

Strain	Non-breeding		Breeding	
	Per cent with tumors	Average tumor age, months	Per cent with tumors	Average tumor age, months
C3H	97	10.4	91	8.6
DBA	12	15.8	77	10.5
A	5	18.5	84	11.1
C57 Black	0	—	0.5	18–29

were confirmed later when inbred strains of mice became available (Table 34).

The apparent influence of breeding on the incidence of mammary tumors in females, plus the fact that these tumors were largely absent in male mice, led Lathrop and Loeb to study the effect of removal of the ovaries. When this procedure was effected at an early age, it completely inhibited or greatly delayed the appearance of mammary tumors, whereas when it was instituted much later in the life span of the animals (after the seventh month), it had little or no effect in suppressing tumor incidence. Cori (10) and subsequently Murray (11), confirmed and extended these findings, the latter by showing that ovarian grafts in castrated male mice produced mammary cancer.

The next step was to isolate the active estrogenic materials from the ovary. This was accomplished by Allen and Doisy in 1923 (12) after the vaginal-smear reaction for the detection of estrogenic substances was established. The material separated by Allen and Doisy was still crude, but, in 1929, at the International Physiological Congress in Boston, Doisy announced the preparation of the first pure, crystalline sex hormone from the ovary, namely, estrone. With the discovery that the urine of several species, especially that of the horse, contained several sex hormones, the isolation of many types of this material was facilitated. Determination of the chemical structure of the crystalline substances from the ovary and from the urine revealed them to be of a condensed ring structure related to the bile acids and cholesterol.

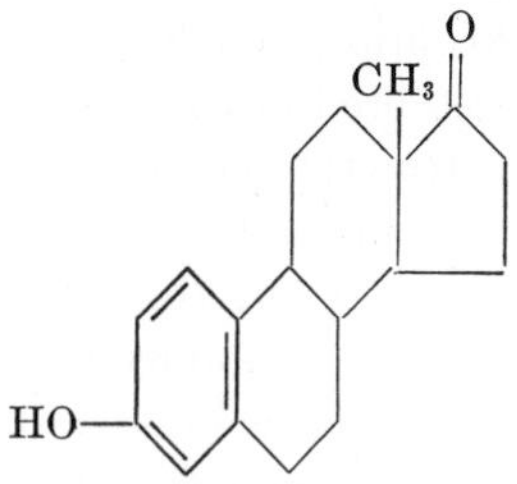

Estrone

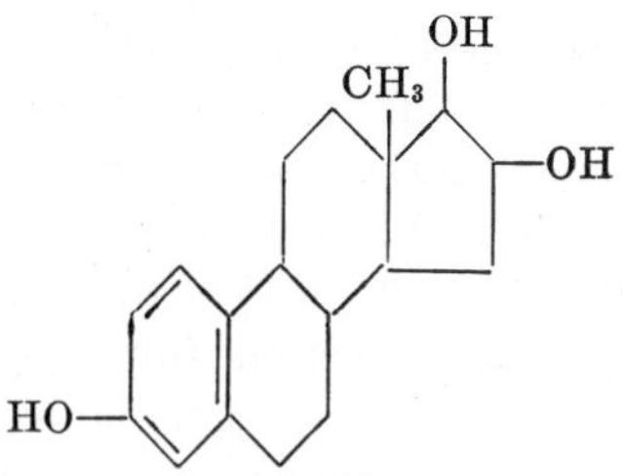

Estriol

As a result of the work of Dodds in England, many synthetic compounds with estrogenic activity soon made their appearance (14; cf. 15). These were derivatives of normal hexane, such as stilbestrol, or of ethylene, such as triphenylethylene. The former group of synthetic estrogens is usually much more active, the latter group generally less active, than the natural sex hormones. A further distinction of synthetic from natural estrogens lies in the fact that such synthetic substances as stilbestrol are highly active perorally (16).

Although diethylstilbestrol in large doses over long periods of time is known to induce cancer of the breast in rats and mice, and fibromas of the uterus, testicular tumors, and lymphoid tumors in mice, its fate in the animal body is still relatively unknown. Twombly and Schoenewaldt (17) injected diethylstilbestrol labeled with C^{14} in the β-ethyl position to mice and noted no selective absorption in uterus, pituitary, or breast, whereas the highest concentration of the label was in the liver.

It is interesting to note that the development of the synthetic estrogens and of the elucidation of the structure of the natural sex hormones occurred during the same period (ca. 1930–1940) when the synthesis of carcinogenic

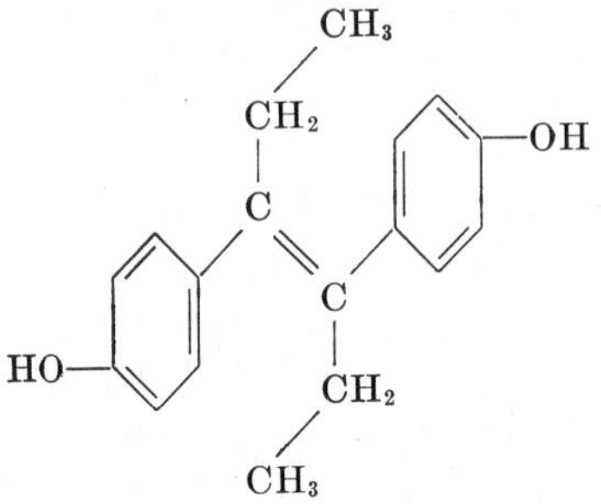

Diethylstilbestrol

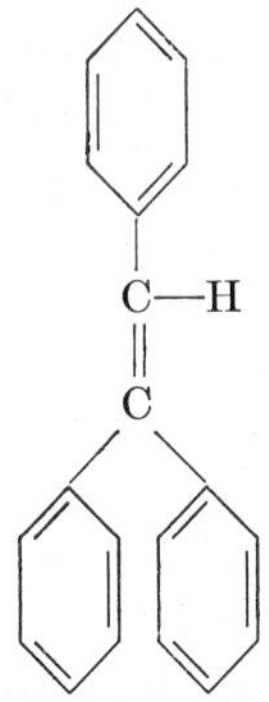

Triphenylethylene

polycyclic hydrocarbons was being intensively developed. The somewhat analogous condensed ring structure of the two classes of compounds inevitably raised the questions (a) whether the carcinogenic hydrocarbons were also estrogenic and (b) whether the estrogenic agents were carcinogenic. The former question, with a few dubious exceptions, could be answered in the negative. The latter question can be answered in the affirmative only under certain experimental conditions. It is true that early experiments on painting mouse skin with the natural sex hormones did not, unlike methylcholanthrene, result in skin tumors. When, however, the estrogens were administered by injection, tumors of the breast were induced.

Lacassagne was the first to induce mammary tumors in mice through the use of pure sex hormones (1932), and, despite the fact that he sometimes worked with as few as two or three mice in a group, he made important and fundamental observations. Lacassagne injected a mixture of estrone, equilin, and equilenin (preparation from pregnant mare urine) into castrated male mice and obtained mammary cancer in a few of them (18). In subsequent experiments he used two groups of castrated male mice, one composed of animals of a strain in which the females had a low incidence of mammary tumors, the other consisting of animals of a strain in which the females had a high incidence of mammary tumors. Injection of estrogens into the animals of the former group resulted in the induction of mammary tumors in a relatively small proportion after a long period of time, whereas injection of estrogens into animals of the latter group resulted in all of them developing mammary cancer within a short period of time (19). Lacassagne then concluded that the ability to induce mammary tumors in males depended upon the incidence of spontaneous mammary tumors in females of the same strain and that a hereditary influence was predominant (20).

Lacassagne made other observations in this connection which were of interest, namely that the administration of estrogens into mice induced the formation not only of mammary tumors but of uterine tumors and lymphosarcomas as well (20).

Several investigators, among them Bonser (21), Cramer (22), Gardner (2), Suntzeff *et al.* (23), and Shimkin and Andervont (24), extended these observations and reached the general conclusion that estrogen administration in males or in non-breeding females induces mammary tumors to the same degree as these tumors spontaneously appear in breeding females of the same strain. Table 35 illustrates data by Shimkin and Andervont (24), by Haagenson and Randall (25) and by Suntzeff *et al.* (23).

It is difficult to state at the present time whether breeding is more effective than estrogen administration in raising the incidence of mammary

TABLE 35

EFFECT OF ESTROGENS ON MAMMARY TUMOR INCIDENCE IN MALE AND FEMALE MICE OF DIFFERENT STRAINS[1] (CF. 13)

Strain	Incidence in normal female mice, %		Incidence in estrogen-treated mice, %	
	Non-breeders	Breeders	Female	Males
C3H	97	91	93	64
C	0	1	2	0
C57 Black	0	0.5	0	0
R3	52	74	76	88[2]
DBA	24	66	55	30
A	3	43	31	44

[1] With the exception noted, none of the males was castrated.

[2] Gonadectomized.

tumors in female mice. As a rule, the incidence of mammary tumors in males and in non-breeding females treated with estrogens is not higher than in breeding females. Furthermore, this incidence appears to be nearly the same in males and in females injected with estrogens. The estrus-producing hormones raise the incidence or cause the earlier production of mammary tumors in mice from strains showing a moderate or high incidence in the untreated controls; mice in which spontaneous mammary tumors rarely appear (*C57 Black*) rarely develop such tumors when estrogens are administered. Castrated *A* strain male mice bearing subcutaneous ovarian grafts develop mammary cancer at a rate in excess of that of virgin females of this strain, but still less than that of breeding females (26).

Mice of strains in which the breeding females have the highest tumor incidence usually develop the tumors earlier. Apparently this relationship also holds for estrogen-treated mice. Depending upon the type and dose of estrogen, the tumors in estrogen-treated mice may develop somewhat earlier than in breeding females of the same strain. In this connection, it is of interest to point out the experiments of Strong *et al.* (27), described in Chapter III, and of others (28–32), on inducing the early appearance of mammary tumors in mice through injection of methylcholanthrene. The hydrocarbon thus serves as an estrogen does in more susceptible strains of mice. Methylcholanthrene, however, induces breast tumors in males only if estrogens are administered simultaneously. Thus, the combined administration of estrone and 20-methylcholanthrene induces mammary cancer in males of the *C3H* strain (high incidence of mammary cancer in the females) and in males of the *C57BL* strain (low incidence of mammary cancer in the females (33), although estrone by itself is sufficient to induce cancer of the breast in males of the former strain. 20-Methylcholanthrene also induces mammary cancer in adult female mice of the ordinarily low spontaneous incidence *C57BL* strain, whether these mice are breeders or virgin. This in itself is an interesting observation, for these adult female mice are completely resistant to the action of the mammary tumor agent (see below) yet respond to a different, and unnatural, agent. It may be wondered whether the methylcholanthrene activates a dormant agent in these mice.

Studies on the relative potency of the various estrogens in inducing mammary tumors in male mice of lines of high incidence in the females (*R3* and *C3H*), revealed that there was little significant difference at equal dosages of diethylstilbestrol and of the natural estrogens, namely estrone, estradiol, equilin, and equilenin, but that of the synthetic estrogen, triphenylethylene, was relatively extremely weak (34–38).

Whereas the natural estrogens lose most of their estrogenic potency when administered by mouth, diethylstilbestrol is effective orally. When the latter was fed to male mice of the susceptible C*3H* strain, mammary tumors developed within 20 weeks after the initial administration (39). The effects of diethylstilbestrol, either orally introduced or injected, are somewhat toxic, resulting in a loss of body weight, atrophy of the viscera, particularly of the spleen, and decreased spermatogenesis in the testes. No hepatic lesions are observed even with lethal doses.

Interestingly enough, estrogen administration in various mice strains may also induce the formation of testicular tumors of the interstitial type. Bonser and Robson (38), Hooker *et al.* (40), and Hooker and Pfeiffer (41) described the induction of such tumors in *A* strain mice by massive estrogen administration over a long period of time. This strain is also susceptible to the formation of mammary tumors when similarly treated and, in Hooker and Pfeiffers' experiments, these tumors appeared in 50% of their mice well before the appearance of testicular tumors. To permit the animals to live long enough to show testicular tumors, the mammary tumors as they appear must be surgically excised. That tumors of the testis can also be evoked in mice of a strain resistant to the mammary tumor-inducing effect of estrogens was shown by Shimkin *et al.* (42). These investigators implanted diethylstilbestrol pellets in cholesterol in mice of the *C* strain and obtained testicular tumors in a considerable proportion of these animals. Gardner (36) injected mice of several strains with the weak estrogen, triphenylethylene, and obtained testicular tumors in mice of the *JK* and *A* strains but not of the *C3H* strain.

It is of further interest to note that the testicular tumors induced as described above failed to grow when transplanted into new hosts of the same strain. When these hosts were treated continually with estrogen, however, the transplanted tumor began to grow. That the tumor "takes" but does not grow in untreated animals was demonstrated by the fact that when estrogen administration was initiated long after the transplantation was performed the tumor began to grow (43). In the experiments of Shimkin *et al.*, several of the primary testicular tumors metastasized to the region above the kidneys, but this form of metastatic transplantation within the same host was very likely successful because the mice, inplanted with stilbestrol pellets, were continuously exposed to estrogen stimulation.

To see whether there was any relation between the incidence of spontaneous and of induced testicular tumors, Gardner (43) compared the potentiality for testicular neoplasia in different strains and in their hybrid generations. The spontaneous incidence of testicular tumors among all strains studied is extremely low (44). Administration of estrogen to *A* strain mice results in a high proportion of testicular tumors; to *C3H* mice such administration results in few, or no, testicular tumors. Mating of *A* strain mice with *C3H* mice results in an F_1 generation which showed a spontaneous incidence of testicular tumors in 3 out of 61 untreated mice. These hybridization experiments reveal a tendency toward development of testicular tumors in the *A* parent strain, at least, which is not realized in the life span of the non-estrinized animals.

Just as intrasplenic grafts of the ovary into castrated animals lead to the development of ovarian tumors in the grafts, so too intrasplenic testicular grafts in gonadectomized male and female rats develop into interstitial tumors (45). The appearance of the latter tumors may rest upon the same basis of pituitary stimulation as has been postulated for the appearance of the former tumors. The testicular tumors produce androgenic effects in the hosts and thus are still functioning testes.

Certain tumors of the testis in the dog and in man contain considerable quantities of estrogen (46). The estrogen appears to be produced by the Sertoli cells in the testicular tubules and results in a pronounced feminization of the host.

It is evident that, for the development of tumors of the mammary gland, the following conditions are necessary: (a) genetic or strain susceptibility and (b) hormonal stimulation. As a result of numerous genetic experiments, it became obvious that these requirements were not entirely sufficient and that some extrachromosomal factor was also needed. This third factor, the so-called milk influence, is described below. It is only necessary here to stress the fact that, by hormonal stimulation, only estrogens are meant, although the technique of intensive or "forced" breeding sometimes has the same effect (cf. 47). Progesterone and the androgenic hormones have little or no capacity, in themselves, to induce mammary tumors. They do possess the ability, when administered simultaneously with estrogens, of nullifying the effect of the latter in many connections (cf. Chapter VI). Testosterone apparently has little or no potency by itself in experimentally inducing any kind of tumor, although it may promote the growth of certain established prostatic carcinomas in man (cf. Chapters VI and IX). This powerful androgen, however, when administered to animals, produces nitrogen retention (48–50), and thus has physiological properties other than sexual. Testosteronized female mice have a lowered mammary cancer incidence (51); cf. Chapter VI.

The need for estrogen, in part, in the initiation of mammary cancer is to fully develop the mammary tissue. The underdeveloped breast, whether undeveloped by castration or by testosterone administration, does not yield mammary carcinoma. For this development, however, an adequate nutritional status is also necessary (cf. Chapter V), as well as a functional pituitary gland.

The entire foregoing discussion opened with the classic investigations of Loeb, of Cori, and of Murray on reducing or inhibiting mammary tumor development through the castration of female mice of heterozygous genetic constitution at a sufficiently early age. More recently, the work by Wooley and Little (52) on certain inbred strains of mice at the Jackson Memorial

Laboratory has demonstrated in striking fashion how these classic results may be evaded even though gonadectomy be similarly employed. When *C3H* strain mice and *DBA* mice were gonadectomized shortly after birth, their mammary and other accessory sex tissues nevertheless developed normally, and the usually high proportion of mammary tumors appeared later on in these animals. Mice of these strains normally have a high incidence of spontaneous mammary tumors. When mice of the *C57 Black* strain and of the *CE* strain, both of which have a very low incidence of spontaneous mammary tumors, were gonadectomized shortly after birth, the mammary tissue of the former strain failed to develop and no tumors subsequently appeared, whereas in the latter strain the mammary tissue not only developed normally but yielded mammary tumors later in the life span of the animals. Essentially similar results were obtained by Gardner who castrated animals much later in life (53).

The explanation for these findings came about through observation of the development of the adrenal cortex in the gonadectomized animals of each strain. After castration, the adrenal cortex in mice of the *DBA* and *C3H* strains undergoes progressive and considerable hyperplasia, in mice of the *C57 Black* strain it undergoes a very mild form of hyperplasia, and in mice of the *CE* strain it not only undergoes a considerable hyperplasia but this overgrowth rapidly goes over into adrenocortical carcinoma. Mammary development and carcinogenesis in the cases cited are probably best explained by the extragenital production of estrogens in the hyperplastic adrenal cortex (cf. 54, 55). The pathologic changes in the adrenals of these mice after castration can be prevented by administration of deoxycorticosterone (56), by massive doses of estrogen (57), and by hypophysectomy (58). In connection with the last-mentioned finding, it is of interest that dietary restriction of castrated and sham-hypophysectomized mice to maintain the same body weight as that of castrated and hypophysectomized animals does not prevent the customary adrenal cortical hyperplasia but does prevent evidence of estrogen secretion from the adrenal; thus some important pituitary functions persist in the face of severe dietary restriction (so-called pseudohypophysectomy—see following chapter).

The effect of inheritance on response of the adrenals of hybrid mice to gonadectomy was unexpected in some instances. Thus, although the F_1 hybrids of *CE* strain mice with *A*, *C3H*, *DBA*, and *C57BL* strains yielded adrenal cortical tumors subsequent to castration shortly after birth, and although it might have been anticipated that such F_1 hybrids would exhibit the characteristics of the *CE* parent, it was found that the F_1 hybrids of *DBA* × *C57BL* and of *A* × *C3H* mice also revealed adrenal cortical tumors under the same conditions even though neither parent showed such response (59). To quote the authors, "it is quite reasonable to assume that. . . . . hybridization itself can produce additive or new changes in internal imbalance that have not been found in the parental strains" (59). It must be pointed out, however, that the adrenal tumors are larger in F_1 hybrid mice which had a *CE* parent, and, furthermore, tumors of the pituitary occur much more frequently in such hybrids as *CE* × *DBA* or *C57BL* × *CE* mice, i.e., those with a *CE* parent. In all cases, the adrenal tumors so induced secreted various hormones.

Medullary tumors of the adrenals of mice may also develop subsequent to castration, for *BRS* strain mice so treated at 4 to 8 weeks of age developed pheochromocytomas (60).

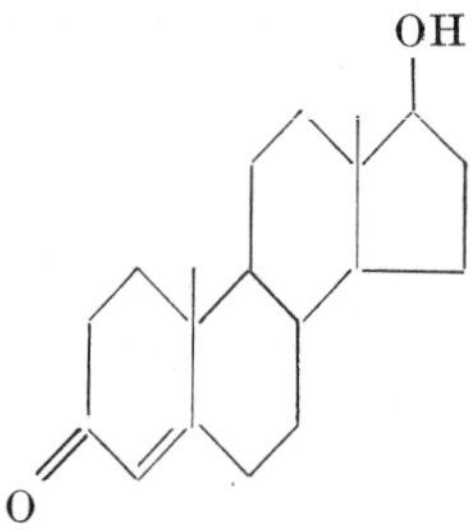

Testosterone

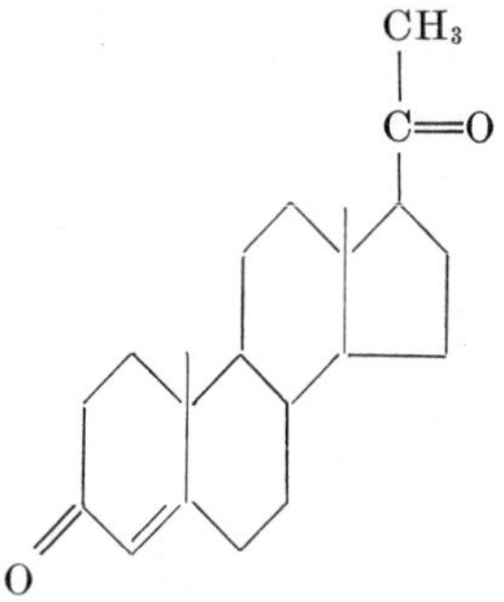

Progesterone

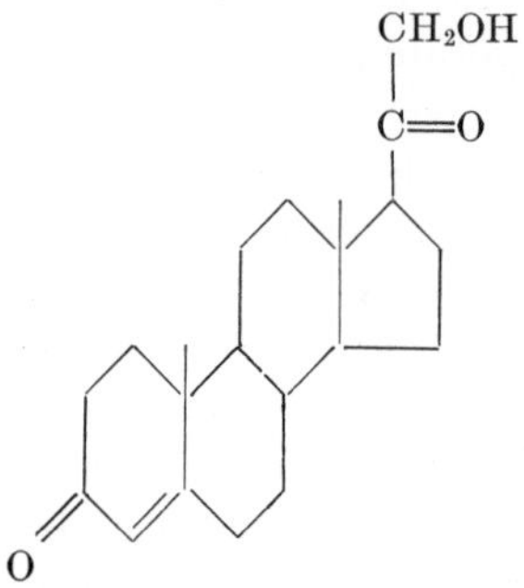

Deoxycorticosterone

The normal activity of the adrenal cortex leads to the production of 17-α-hydroxy-20-ketosteroids, which are known to undergo ready conversion *in vitro* to derivatives of 17-α-methyl-D-homoandrostane. If the latter derivatives undergo biological dehydrogenation (cf. 61), the carcinogenic 3-methylchrysene would result (62). Whether this sequence actually occurs or not, there is enough evidence that the adrenal cortex is in some way involved in carcinogenesis.

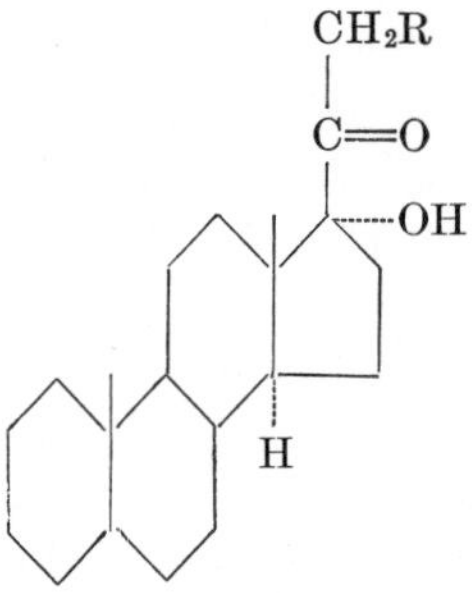

17-α-Hydroxy-20-ketosteroids

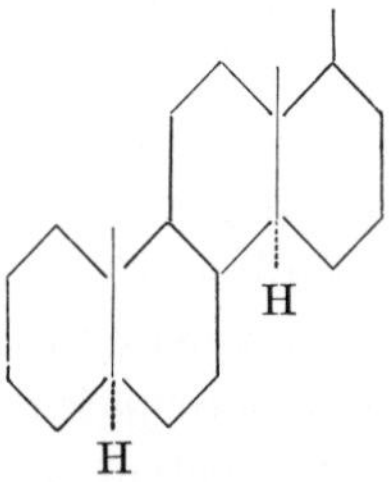

17-α-Methyl-D-homoandrostane

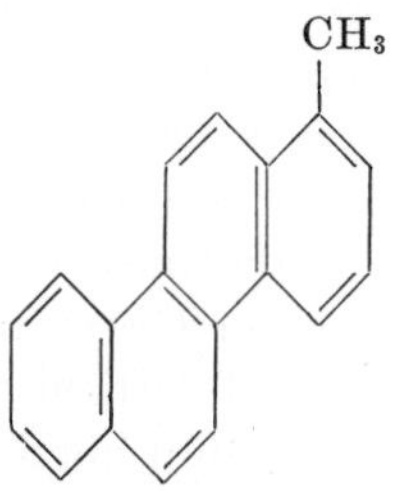

3-Methylchrysene

The adrenocortical transformations in these strains are accomplished only by castration and occur equally well in female and male mice. The incidence of adrenocortical carcinoma in such castrated *CE* strain mice is 100 %, although the females demonstrate this tumor earlier than males. In this connection, Wooley and Little point out that adrenal tumors are reported to occur more often in female than in male children. The hyperplasia and cancerous transformation of the adrenal cortex in mice, as experimentally demonstrated by castration, indicate how such neoplasia may ordinarily be held in check by the normal supply of gonadal components and emphasize the sensitive balance and compensatory devices which must exist among the glands of internal secretion.

Attempts to find some systemic properties which might explain the high mammary tumor incidence in certain mice strains and not in others have not been successful. Aub *et al.* compared the urinary excretion of estrogens and 17-ketosteroids in mice of strains *C3H* and *C57 Black* (63). No significant differences were noted, and no marked changes occurred after pregnancy, or increase in age, or the appearance of tumors in the *C3H* strain mice. Mammalian liver contains an enzymatic system capable of inactivating estradiol, and it might be anticipated that, if this hormone were in part responsible for the induction of mammary tumors, the estradiol-inactivating hepatic system would be more active in mice of low than of high mammary tumor incidence. Investigation by Twombly and Taylor (64) of liver slices of four strains of mice differing in their predisposition to mammary tumors (e.g., *C57*, *A*, *DBA*, and *D*) demonstrated no significant difference in their ability to destroy estradiol *in vitro*. Enzymatic studies on the tissues of mice of various strains are described in later chapters (VIII and IX). There is no correlation yet apparent between biochemical constitution and cancer predisposition, not only toward mammary tumors, but toward any kind of tumor.

In contrast with mice of certain strains, rats of all stocks studied have a relatively low spontaneous mammary tumor incidence. Administration of estrogens, even in high dosage to rats, frequently results in the development only of benign mammary lesions (65). In the more susceptible stocks of rats, prolonged exposure to estrogens through implantation of appropriate pellets results in the appearance of mammary carcinoma in some of the animals (66; cf. 67). It may be that rats need more of the estrogen than do mice for induction of mammary tumors.

Administration of diethylstilbestrol to susceptible rats induces not only mammary but also adrenal (68) and bladder tumors (69). Gastric instillation of 20-methylcholanthrene can induce mammary tumors in female Wistar rats, and also in males, provided that estradiol is simultaneously administered (70). All the breast tumors developed in this experiment were varieties of mixed cancers, including a glandular tumor which predominated in females or in males given estradiol, a spindle-cell and collagenous tumor predominating in females or males given testosterone, and fibroadenomas which predominated in castrated animals. It is usual to refer to breast tumors as such without specification as to the histological pattern or patterns, and much of interest may thereby be missed. This point will be referred to again in later discussion. Another type of carcinogen can also induce breast tumors in rats, for 9,10-dimethyl-1,2-benzanthracene administered intravenously as an oil emulsion induced such tumors in female rats and a few in male rats (71); the latter incidence was considerably increased when estradiol was simultaneously administered.

In a long series of papers, Lipschütz and his collaborators have reported the induction in castrated guinea pigs of benign fibromyomas of the uterus and of the peritoneum through continuous administration (by injection or pellet implantation) of various estrogens (72–80). When, in such animals, progesterone or deoxycorticosterone acetate is simultaneously administered with the estrogen, the development of these benign fibromyomas is very considerably retarded, thus demonstrating the antagonistic, or anti-fibromatogenic, property of the former hormones (cf. Chapter VI). The fact that the fibroid tumors of the uterus and peritoneum were maintained only through continuous administration of estrogen and regressed after its withdrawal, plus the fact that, even in the presence of estrogen, progesterone could inhibit the development of these tumors, all point to the essentially benign, non-autonomous nature of the growths. The initiation of abdominal fibroid growths can be accomplished, even in the absence of uterine tissue, for guinea pigs which were both ovariectomized and hysterectomized gave, as a result of subcutaneous administration of estradiol pellets, 100% incidence of abdominal fibromas (81). In castrated male guinea pigs, continuous administration of estrogen results in the production of fibromyoepitheliomas in the region of the prostate (80).

Administration of large amounts of estrogens to monkeys, rabbits, and dogs has furnished no evidence that mammary tumors are thereby induced in those species (3). In monkeys and in dogs, however, daily injection of massive doses of estrogen resulted in a considerable increase in size of the prostate. Small doses of estrogen (stilbestrol) reduced the size of the functional or hyperplastic prostate, and larger doses produced an enlargement. The hyperplastic prostates decreased in size following castration. Injection of estrone in immature male monkeys caused a marked hypertrophy of the seminal vesicles. The role of endocrine secretions in the development of certain tumors in the dog has been reviewed by Mulligan (82).

The possibility of realizing the experimental induction of carcinoma of the uterus was not attained in guinea pigs, but was in mice. Carcinoma of the uterine cervix, unlike mammary tumors, does not appear spontaneously in many strains of mice. After prolonged treatment with estrogens, a low incidence of cervical lesions in mice has been noted (2). One reason for such low incidence is that formation of mammary tumors precedes that of the cervical tumors, and the animals die from the effects of the former before the latter appear. Surgical extirpation of the mammary tumors often enables the animals to live until cervical tumors appear, but this procedure is rather drastic and may have to be performed more than once. The questions may be raised as to why mice of strains susceptible to the spontaneous appearance of mammary tumors should be used for this purpose, and why mice strains of low spontaneous incidence of mammary tumors were not used. The reason for the choice of the former was that mice of strains susceptible to mammary tumors tolerated estrogen treatment much better than mice of low incidence to these tumors. Although cervical cancer develops in all strains of mice when treated with estrogens, regardless of their resistance or susceptibility to mammary cancer, it is obvious that the incidence of the former disease will depend on the tolerance of the animals to estrogenic treatment.

With the hope of inducing cervical cancer more readily and in greater proportion by averting the difficulties mentioned above, Allen and Gardner (83) utilized hybridization of two different inbred mice strains. The parent strains were as follows:

CBA	*C57 Black*
Medium spontaneous mammary cancer incidence (70%)	Resistant to development of mammary tumors (0%)
No pituitary tumors on estrogenic treatment (0%)	Medium induction of pituitary tumors (40%)
Good tolerance of estrogenic treatment	Poor tolerance of estrogenic treatment

Through hybridization of these mice strains it was expected that the F_1 generation would tolerate estrogenic treatment well, and that the incidence of mammary tumors might be determinable. The two crosses of the F_1 generation, injected with estradiol benzoate, gave results as follows:

C57 Black females × *CBA males*	*CBA females* × *C57 Black males*
No mammary tumors developed (0%)	Several animals died with mammary tumors before a year elapsed (62%)
Medium incidence of cervical cancer (62%)	Medium incidence of cervical cancer (50%)
Good tolerance of estrogenic treatment	Good tolerance of estrogenic treatment

The tumors of the cervix which appeared in these hybrid mice were frequently invasive into non-genital tissue. None of the tumors appeared in less than one year. It is clear that the genetic factors and the transmissible milk factor involved in mammary carcinogenesis play only a small role in determining cancer of the cervix in mice. Only the incidence may be somewhat affected, since animals receiving the milk influence from mothers of susceptible mammary cancer strains (*CBA*) may die of this form of cancer before the age at which cervical cancer appears.

These experiments of Allen and Gardner have been described at some relative length because they illustrate rather clearly the skillful use of different experimental approaches, genetics and endocrinology, to attain a particular goal in experimental carcinogenesis and, thereby, illuminate possible mechanisms in the natural production of certain types of tumors.

Other hybrid mice in which carcinoma of the uterine cervix and vagina has been developed by estrogen and by androgen are *C3H* × *PM* and *PM* × *C3H* (84). The *PM* strain itself has some tendency toward the spontaneous incidence of these tumors. Smooth muscle tumors of the uterus in young female rats have been induced after grafting testis fragments in the neck region (85); an obvious hormonal imbalance was thereby established, for the rats were in constant estrus at the time of sexual maturity. Uterine tumors appear with great frequency in certain stocks of rabbits (86), and indeed this appears to be the most common type of tumor in this species (cf. 87).

An excellent example of carcinogenesis by hormonal imbalance is the work of Biskind *et al.* (88), which demonstrated the induction of tumors in an ovary transplanted into the spleen of castrated rats. This finding is apparently based upon two principles: (a) the capacity of the liver to inactivate ovarian hormones circulating through the hepatic portal systems, and (b) the increase in pituitary gonadotrophin subsequent to castration (89). The ovary is thereby released from estrogenic inhibition, and the uninhibited pituitary stimulation produces a tumor in the graft. Thus, administration of exogenous gonadotrophin results in an acceleration of development of both luteomas and granulosa cell tumors in an ovary transplanted to the spleen of castrated rats (90). If one ovary is left *in situ*, the intrasplenic ovary fails to show growth, even with exogenous gonadotrophin (90), nor will growth occur in grafts with vascularized adhesions which permit drainage through any other path than the hepatic portal systems. Neither will growth occur in castrated mice receiving exogenous estradiol or testosterone, but it will occur in such mice if progesterone is administered (89). Granulosa-cell tumors of an ovary transplanted into the spleen have also been induced in castrated female rabbits (91). Luetomas have also been induced in ovarian autografts in castrated female guinea pigs (92).

Evidence for the augmentation of pituitary gonadotrophin in a castrated animal has accumulated chiefly from studies of parabiotic pairs of animals, one of which is castrated and the other intact (93). The genital tissue of the latter member under these conditions is considerably stimulated. The amount of estrogen sufficient to inhibit this production of pituitary hormone is quite low. An illustration of the course of events in such a parabiotic union is shown in Fig. 20, taken from Gardner (7).

Ovarian grafts have been made not only in the spleen but in the pancreas as well (89). Many of the ovarian tumors formed under the conditions cited are transplantable to new hosts. Differences in the histological structure of the ovarian tumors are observed, depending upon whether the host is a castrated male or spayed female mouse, for in the former granulosa-cell tumors predominate, whereas in the latter either mixed granulosa-cell tumors and luteomas, or pure luteomas, are found (94).

It has been suggested that ovarian tumors arising as a consequence of X-irradiation may also be due, in part, to an endocrine imbalance (cf. 7). Thus, irradiated ovaries implanted in irradiated or non-irradiated spayed mice became cancerous, whereas non-irradiated ovarian grafts in irradiated spayed mice, or irradiated grafts in non-irradiated, intact hosts, did not develop into cancers (95).

If the assumption made above is correct, namely that an excess of pituitary gonadotrophin leads to ovarian tumor development, it might be expected that exogenous administration of this hormone in large doses to an animal would lead to this result. Attempts to do this have not been successful, partly because purified rodent pituitary gonadotrophin is not available, and partly because it is difficult if not impossible to reproduce the internal milieu by external application.

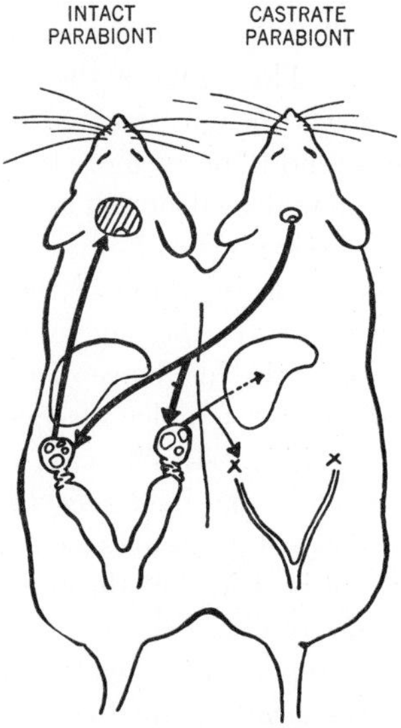

FIG. 20. Endocrine imbalance produced by parabiosis. From Gardner, W. U., *Advances in Cancer Research* **1,** 173 (1953).

The injection of carcinogens into the rodent prostate *in situ* leads generally to the development of squamous or sarcomatous growths. By an ingenious method, Horning (96) has produced prostatic glandular carcinoma in mice arising from subcutaneous grafts of prostatic epithelium impregnated with 20-methylcholanthrene. The carcinogen apparently acts preferentially on relatively non-secreting cells of the gland, rather than on those at the height of their secretory activity. The development of this technique permits a comparison of results in an experimental animal species with the wealth of analogous clinical material (see Chapter VI), a comparison not very often possible. Thus, glandular carcinomas so induced when transplanted into mice castrated before puberty show complete inhibition of secretion followed by squamous differentiation. If the squamous change is not too far advanced, administration of androgens will, in a few cases, cause some of the tumors to grow. A few of the glandular tumors failed to regress when transplanted into castrated hosts but grew at the same rate as in intact male mice, a phenomenon which might have been caused by an androgenic stimulation by the adrenals. Administration of estrogen to intact male mice bearing the prostatic carcinoma grafts produced variable retardation of growth but no regression as occurred in the majority of castrated hosts alone. A parallelism between the experimental animal and man is thus at least partially evident.

Rats treated with pituitary growth hormone over long periods of time developed neoplasms of the lungs, lymphatic tissues, adrenals, and reproductive organs (97). This hormone preparation may be the so-called "diabetogenic factor" (98). The value of the findings noted is uncertain, since no tumors were observed in mice treated in the same way (99).

Spontaneous hepatomas tend to occur more frequently in males of certain strains of mice than in the females, although castration among the males, as well as administration of estrogen result in a lowering of such incidence (100, 101). On the other hand, injection of the females with testosterone seemed to increase susceptibility to the development of spontaneous hepatomas. The sex difference in the incidence of induced hepatomas in mice with azo dyes is the reverse, for females of several strains are more susceptible than males (see p. 148). In the case of rats, induction of liver cancer by certain azo dyes (102) and by 2-acetylaminofluorene (103) occurs more readily in males. Testosterone acts synergistically with the latter carcinogen (104). It cannot be said that the effect of the hormonal environment is very clear in the case of liver cancer.

Male hamsters have been reported to develop bilateral renal tumors after prolonged treatment with large quantities of diethylstilbestrol (105). Females treated the same way prior to their first ovulation also develop such tumors. Cancer of the bladder in rats, associated with urinary calculi, occurs in rats bearing subcutaneous pellets of diethylstilbestrol

(106). The late appearance of sarcomas at the site of injection of several kinds of hormones has been described by Lacassagne (20) and by Gardner (2).

The induction of pituitary tumors in mice subsequent to the development of adrenal cortical tumors after castration has been described above (cf. 107). Basophilic tumors of the pituitary in gonadectomized young mice followed the development of adrenal tumors in *DBA* × *CE* or *CE* × *DBA* F_1 hybrids, probably as a result of hormonal secretion from the adrenals. Chromophobe adenomas of the pituitary in rats and in mice have been induced by prolonged estrogen treatment (108–113). The tumors in mice are transplantable into hosts given estrogens.

A rather dramatic example of hormonal imbalance leading to neoplasia is the development of pituitary tumors in mice made thyroid deficient by injection of large doses of I^{131} ("radiothyroidectomy") (114). Destruction of the thyroid gland is followed by development of TSH (thyroid-stimulating hormone)-secreting pituitary tumors, which can be readily transplanted into mice pretreated in the same way with I^{131} (115). At autopsy of such tumor-bearing animals (116), the most notable findings were (a) a stimulation of the gonads and accessory sex tissues, similar to that observed after administration of large doses of gonad-stimulating hormones, and (b) cystic dilation of the extrahepatic biliary tract. If the tumors are transplanted to mice not pretreated with I^{131}, a marked thyroid hyperplasia is noted and the presence of TSH from the graft can be established (115). In the course of several passages of the pituitary tumors through I^{131}-pretreated mice, the tumors increase in autonomy and finally can be propagated through intact hosts. When they have reached this autonomous stage, they still apparently secrete some TSH, but they have lost the capacity to affect the biliary tract of the host animal, implying that some other secretion than TSH is responsible for the latter effect (115). An analogous effect on the biliary tract had been noted in mice after long-term estrogen administration (117). When I^{131} was added to the tumor-bearing hosts, stimulation of the growth of the grafts was noted; i.e., depression of thyroid function by high I^{131} administration resulted in better growth of the graft. Since there is a reciprocal relation between the thyroid hormone (TH) and TSH, a deficiency in TH causes a stimulation or loss of restraint of the pituitary. Conversely, thyroid grafts or administration of thyroid hormone (TH) prevents the induction of pituitary tumors by I^{131} (118, 119). A possible connecting link between the induction of pituitary tumors by estrogen administration and by I^{131} administration or radiothyroidectomy is the fact that the most susceptible strain of mice, the *C57BL* to the former method of induction is also the most susceptible to the latter.

I^{131}, with a half-life of 8 days, gives off β- and γ-rays, the energy absorbed being largely due to the former radiation. The destructive effect of the radiation on the thyroid gland would be expected to result in a decrease in thyroxin production and thereby a corresponding increase in the secretion of TSH. Indeed, as Purves *et al.* (120) showed, a TH deficiency, no matter how produced, leads to increased TSH secretion, and thus chronic dietary iodine deficiency in rats (121), and I^{131} alone or combined with methylthiouracil (122), lead to the development of thyroid adenomas in rats.

The considerations noted between pituitary and thyroid raise at least two questions, namely (a) whether surgical thyroidectomy would result in the induction of pituitary tumors, and (b) why the goitrogenic drugs do not develop pituitary but only thyroid tumors. The answer to the first of these questions is not yet available. The answer to the second as yet can be only hypothetical. In 1944, Bielschowsky (123) reported that tumors of the thyroid in rats were induced by the simultaneous administration of 2-acetylaminofluorene and allyl-thiourea, and later he showed, with others (124, 125), that such tumors would arise with methylthiouracil alone and could be transplanted readily into animals treated with methylthiouracil or else surgically thyroidectomized (cf. also 126). Morris and his coworkers, beginning with the observation that thiouracil administration to mice of a high spontaneous mammary cancer incidence produced a diminution in estrogen secretion and failure of mammary development with a consequent drop in mammary tumor incidence (Table 36) (127, 128), noted that the thyroids of such mice were markedly hyperplastic. With continued administration of thiouracil, metastatic lesions of thyroid tissue appeared in the lungs (129), which could be transplanted and grown in mice of the same strain given thiouracil. With continued transplantation into new hosts with these and with hyperplastic thyroid tissue from thiouracil-treated mice, the tumors became relatively autonomous, and the hosts no longer needed administration of thiouracil to keep the tumor grafts growing (130). Table 37 shows the effect of thiouracil administration on the organ weights of animals with and without thiouracil (131).

It would appear that chronic stimulation by the thyrotrophic hormone (TSH) is essential for the induction of experimental tumors of the rat thyroid (132). The MacKenzies have shown that thyroid hyperplasia with goitrogenic drugs occurs only in the presence of the pituitary (133).

TABLE 36

EFFECT OF THIOURACIL ON APPEARANCE OF MAMMARY TUMORS IN *C3H* MICE (127)

Diet	Tumor incidence, %	Age when tumors appeared, days
Stock	92	187–529
Thiouracil	19	189–609

TABLE 37

EFFECT OF THIOURACIL FEEDING ON ORGAN WEIGHTS IN MICE (131)

Organ	Average weight, in milligrams, of organs of animals on: Stock diet	Thiouracil
Thyroid	4.5	59.3
Ovary	7.4	4.7
Ovary plus uterus	116.5	36.3
Adrenals	7.2	4.1

Deficiency in gonadotrophic secretion occurs simultaneously with TSH increase, for administration of gonadotrophin in addition to thiouracil did produce tumors in mice (127), together with normal estrus. A schematic diagram taken from Morris (134) (Fig. 21) is illustrative of these observations. The various thyroid tumors developed in mice by Morris and his colleagues differed in their degree of autonomy as judged by their growth rate in transplants and in histologic appearance, and parallel with such biological criteria was the physiological capacity of the various tumor lines to concentrate I^{131} (135, 136). Thus, of four tumor lines, three could be transplanted into hosts without simultaneous administration of thiouracil. The I^{131}-concentrating power of these three tumor lines relative to that of the thyroid was 1/1300, 1/164, and 1/10.3, respectively. The fourth, dependent tumor, showed a similar ratio of 1/2. Radioautograph studies indicated that the same I^{131}-containing intermediates occurred in normal thyroid and in the thyroid tumors during the metabolic conversions to thyroxin, no matter what the degree of autonomy of the tumor.

Thyroidectomy in rats prior to administration of 2-acetylaminofluorene prevented the development of hepatomas but not that of other tumors in these animals (136a). These experiments are essentially analogous to

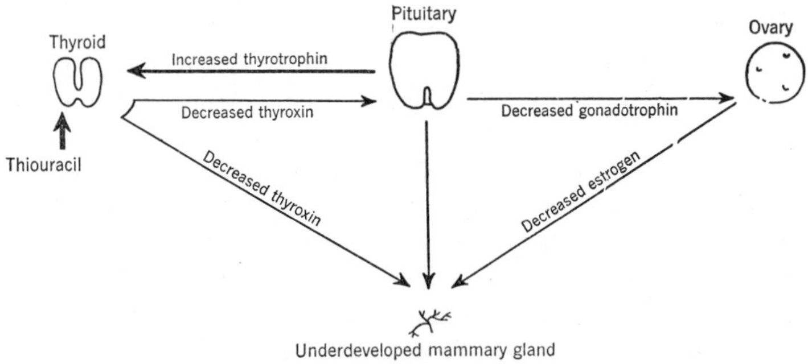

FIG. 21. Schematic diagram to illustrate syndrome produced by prolonged feeding of thiouracil to *C3H* female mice. From Morris, H. P., *Texas Repts. Biol. and Med.* **10,** 1028 (1952).

those of Paschkis, Cantarow, and Stasney (104), who reported that thiouracil protected the liver against the carcinogenic action of acetylaminofluorene.

An interesting demonstration of the systemic effect which the presence of a tumor produces is the diminished concentration of administered I^{131} in the thyroid of rats bearing the Walker 256 tumor (137) and in mice bearing the 15091a tumor (138), compared with that in the thyroids of normal, control animals. The blood levels of I^{131} in the normal and in the tumor-bearing mice are about the same, and the decreased capacity of the thyroid glands of the tumor-bearing animals is probably related to some change in the physiology of the glands themselves. The failure of the spleens of tumor-bearing animals to take up colchicine (139) comes to mind in this connection. The tumors of the rats and mice injected with I^{131} contained on the average 40 to 50% as high a concentration as in the blood serum, exceeding that in the muscle and liver, and lower than that in the kidneys, lungs, thymus, and thyroid (138).

Carcinogenesis of Non-Sex Tissues

The data given in Tables 32 and 33 in the preceding chapter strongly suggest that the sex of the animal plays a role in the incidence of certain types of cancer, whether spontaneous or experimentally induced, in ostensibly non-sex organs and tissues of mice. A similar suggestion may be derived from available statistics of cancer incidence in man, but this species is exposed to a number of hazards in each sex, occupational and otherwise, and a comparison of cancer incidence of the same non-sex site in man and in woman might be open to several objections. Such comparison is better made among experimental animals maintained under identical conditions, even though extrapolation of the results obtained to the problem in human beings may not as yet be proper.

The relation of the sex organs to leukemia or lymphoid tumors in mice is indicated by the greater frequency of the disease in female animals of certain strains (reverse in human beings) and by the experimental production of such growths by estrogen administration. Many investigators have noted that the incidence of leukemia or of lymphoid tumors is greatly enhanced in most strains of mice through estrogen administration (140–143). The most extended work on this subject is that of Gardner *et al.* (144), and the data given below are based on their findings. These investigators studied the separate effects of estrogens and of testosterone and the combined effect of both kinds of hormones on the incidence of lymphoid tumors in several inbred strains of mice (Tables 38 and 39).

In all the strains of mice studied, with the exception of the *C57 Black*, the incidence of lymphoid tumors was higher among the estrogen-treated than among the control (spontaneous incidence) group. The relative num-

TABLE 38

PERCENTAGE OF MICE OF DIFFERENT STRAINS WITH LYMPHOID TUMORS (144)

Strain	Spontaneous incidence, %	Estrogen treated, %	Estrogen plus testosterone, %
C3H	1	14	3
CBA	3	15	0
PM	0	15	13
A	0	2	0
C57 Black	5	2	0
JK	3	5	—
C121	0	6	0

TABLE 39

INCIDENCE OF LYMPHOID TUMORS AMONG ESTROGEN-TREATED MALE AND FEMALE MICE (144)

Strain	Males, %	Females, %
C3H	13	21
CBA	14	25
PM	17	13
C121	7	5

ber of lymphoid tumors was about twice as high among the female *CBA* and *C3H* mice as among the males of these strains. In the other strains, a nearly equal incidence between sexes is observed. Testosterone administered alone neither accelerates nor retards the development of lymphoid tumors. When it is administered together with estrogens, however, it acts antagonistically to the tumor-accelerating effect of the estrogens.

However, when testosterone is administered to irradiated female mice, it diminishes the incidence of induced lymphomas, whereas in irradiated male mice the injection of estradiol enhances the incidence of induced lymphomas (7). In irradiated male mice, testosterone administration produces a marked inhibition of radiation-induced lymphoid tumors (145; cf. 146).

The tendency to develop lymphoid tumors varies among the strains of estrogen-treated mice, being greatest for the *C3H*, *CBA*, and *PM* strains and lowest for the *A* and *C57 Black* strains. The tendency to develop other kinds of tumors varies from strain to strain, and there is little association between these tumors for any one strain (Table 40). Hypophyseal tumors also appear in rats receiving large amounts of estrogen (147). Such tumors may occur spontaneously. These tumors appear to be transplantable only into older rats which, on autopsy, were found to have tumors in their own pituitary glands, a phenomenon which suggests that these tumors are dependent for their origin and continued growth on a particular environment which may be associated with advanced age.

TABLE 40

Relative Incidence of Tumors among Estrogen-Treated Mice (144)

Strain	Lymphoid	Mammary	Testicular	Pituitary
C3H	+++	++++	−	−
CBA	+++	+++	−	−
PM	+++	−	−	+
C121	+	++	−	−
JK	+	−	+	−
A	−	+++	+++	−
C57 Black	−	−	−	+++

It is apparent that estrogens, like several of the polycyclic hydrocarbons, can induce leukemia and lymphatic tumors in mice which ordinarily show a low spontaneous incidence of the disease, and, furthermore, this induction occurs at an earlier age. Although the relation of both kinds of agents to the neoplastic transformation in lymphatic (as in any other) tissue is quite unknown, there is a significant difference in the results achieved. Administration of the active polycyclic hydrocarbons gives rise to a number of neoplastic manifestations which may include myelogenous, monocytic, and lymphosarcomatous leukoses (148). On the other hand, few or no myelogenous or monocytic leukemias occur after estrogen treatment, but only locally invasive lymphatic tumors or generalized lymphatic leukemia.

Recent experiments have revealed that the lymph nodes regress rapidly in animals given adrenal cortical extracts or pituitary adrenotropic hormone (149, 150). The number of circulating lymphocytes also diminishes under these conditions. Thus the lymphoid tissues of the estrogen-treated mice in the experiments of Gardner *et al.* might have been affected through the pituitary and the adrenal.

Removal of the adrenals renders rats very susceptible to a transplantable lymphatic leukemia (151). In agreement with this observation, it has been noted that bilateral adrenalectomy enhances the susceptibility of *C57BL* mice to the development of lymphoid tumors after total-body X-irradiation (152). Cortisone administration inhibits the development of these radiation-induced tumors (152), as do extracts of the adrenal cortex the susceptibility to transmissible leukemia (153) (Fig. 22).

The influence of thymectomy in reducing the incidence of spontaneous (154, 155) carcinogen-induced (156), and X-ray-induced (157) leukemia has been noted above (Table 41). It is of interest to consider in this connection the leukemogenic potentiality of the thymus as skilfully studied by Law (158). In these experiments thymus tissue removed from the *RIL* high leukemic strain was transplanted to $(C3Hb \times RIL)$ F_1 hybrids, the *C3Hb* parent of which had a low leukemic incidence, the hosts subsequently becoming leukemic. If the cells of the *RIL* thymus are potentially leukemic,

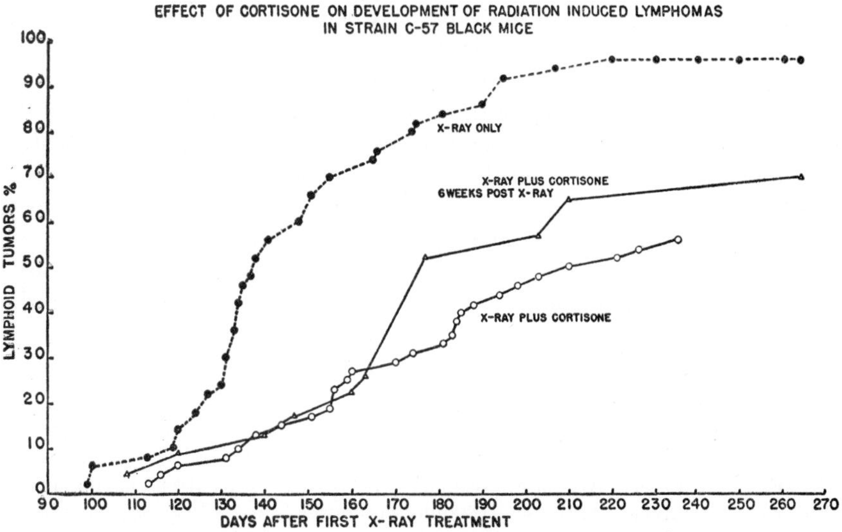

FIG. 22. Effect of cortisone on radiation-induced lymphomas. From Kaplan, H. S., Marder, S. N., and Brown, M. B., *Cancer Research* **11,** 629 (1951).

the leukemia that arises in the F_1 hybrid should be genetically *RIL* in origin, i.e., the resultant leukemia tisses should grow progressively in both *RIL* and in the hybrid *C3Hb* × *RIL* hosts. If, on the other hand, the transplanted *RIL* thymic tissue merely induces leukemia in the F_1 host, the resultant leukemic tissue should be genetically host or *C3Hb* × *RIL* tissue and should grow only in such hybrids and not in *RIL* animals. The second of these alternatives was found to be true, and it must therefore be assumed that the *RIL* thymus is in some way responsible for inducing leukemia in the hybrid host.

Completely adrenalectomized male rats, or intact rats treated with sufficient deoxycorticosterone to produce adrenal atrophy, develop no hepatic tumors within a period when their intact controls readily show such tumors (158a). These findings are consistent with earlier observations on the failure to develop hepatomas in hypophysectomized rats fed azo

TABLE 41

EFFECT OF THYMECTOMY ON REDUCTION OF LEUKEMIA INCIDENCE

Type	Mice strain	Reference	Incidence in: Normal, %	Incidence in: Thymectomized, %
Spontaneous	*RIL*	(155)	83.1	14.6
Methylcholanthrene-induced	*DBA*	(156)	69.7	22.0
X-Ray-induced	*C57BL*	(157)	48.0	4.0

dyes, and the restoration of this capacity when such rats were given adrenocorticotrophin (158b). It appears that the adrenal cortical hormones may be essential for the induction of liver tumors by azo dyes.

The hematopoietic tissues of the estrogen-treated mice are altered by the considerable replacement of bone marrow by osseous tissue (144). Estrogens may thus affect reticular tissues of the bone marrow. Administration of estrone increased the incidence of bone tumors in male mice of a strain in which the females showed a high spontaneous incidence (159).

Before the effect of the sex hormones on the neoplastic transformation of non-sex tissues can be known, it is necessary to possess information on the

TABLE 42

HORMONAL INFLUENCE ON ARGINASE IN NON-SEX TISSUES[1]

Animal	Tissue	Enzyme	Treatment	Results in tissue[2]
Rat (F)	Liver	Arginase	Normal	1900 enzyme units
Rat (F)	Liver	Arginase	Hypophysectomy	930 enzyme units
Rat (F)	Liver	Arginase	Adrenalectomy	580 enzyme units
Rat (F)	Liver	Arginase	Hypophysectomized and treated with: 17-Hydroxycorticosterone	1600 enzyme units
			Deoxycorticosterone	1000 enzyme units
			Estradiol propionate	No change
			Progesterone	No change
			Testosterone propionate	Slight increase?
Rat (F)	Liver	Arginase	Adrenalectomized and treated with: 17-Hydroxydehydrocorticosterone	1090 enzyme units
			Deoxycorticosterone	730 enzyme units
DBA mice (M)	Liver	Arginase	Normal	11,200 enzyme units
DBA mice (M)	Liver	Arginase	Castration	11,200 enzyme units
DBA mice (M)	Liver	Arginase	Castration and treated with testosterone	11,200 enzyme units
DBA mice (M)	Kidney	Arginase	Normal	13 enzyme units
DBA mice (M)	Kidney	Arginase	Castration	13 enzyme units
DBA mice (M)	Kidney	Arginase	Castration and treated with testosterone	182 enzyme units
DBA mice (M)	Kidney	Arginase	Castration and treated with estradiol	28 enzyme units
DBA mice (M)	Kidney	Arginase	Castration and treated with progesterone	12 enzyme units

[1] Data on the rat by Fraenkel-Conrat *et al.* (160). Data on the mouse by Kochakian (161). F = female, M = male.

[2] In arbitrary units.

effect of these agents on the normal function of such tissues. Very little work has been done until recently at this subject. It has been observed by several groups of workers (48–50) that administration of urinary and androgen extracts and of certain steroid hormones produces marked retention of nitrogen in dogs and in humans. These findings suggest that the hormones might affect enzymatic systems concerned with protein metabolism. Studies on this point were initiated, and a few results are given in Table 42. The data on the rat are those of Fraenkel-Conrat *et al.* (160); those on the mouse are by Kochakian (161).

The data obtained so far are only fragmentary but highly promising. It would appear that there are significant differences in response to hormone administration in rats and in mice for the same enzyme. The large order of magnitude in response under certain circumstances, as in the case of administration of corticosterone to hypophysectomized rats or testosterone administration to castrated mice, reveals the considerable ability of the affected tissues to react by changes in enzyme concentration when hormonal administration is instituted. The recent striking work of Cori and coworkers demonstrated that hormones can interfere with enzymatic reactions *in vitro* as well as *in vivo* (162). Thus, the hexokinase reaction concerned with the phosphorylation of glucose can be inhibited by preparations of the anterior pituitary and of the adrenal cortex, and this inhibition can be overcome by the addition of crystalline insulin to the reaction mixture. These reactions demonstrate further the dependence of specific and fixed metabolic factors upon the level of circulating hormones. Whether such factors within tumors respond to similar circulating influences remains for future investigation. Inasmuch as malignant tumors are characterized by a considerable measure of autonomy (a vague phrase implying lack of body control), it might be expected that at some crucial points or points certain specific metabolic catalysts no longer are amenable or subject to hormonal control. The investigation of these possibilities would be highly desirable.

The Mammary Tumor Inciter for Mice

The occurrence of mammary gland cancer in mice was known for a long time to depend upon genetic and endocrine factors. The genetic influences were revealed by the readily observable fact that certain stocks or strains of mice developed a higher incidence of mammary tumors than did other stocks or strains under identical conditions. The hormonal influences were revealed by (a) the effect of breeding in raising the tumor incidence in certain strains, (b) the effect of estrogen injection in hastening the appearance and raising the incidence in certain strains, and (c) the induction of mammary gland cancer in male mice of strains showing a high incidence in the females.

The possibility that still a third factor might be involved was suggested in 1918 by Lathrop and Loeb (163). These investigators observed that the incidence of mammary tumors in hybrid mice was more often dependent upon the tumor rate of the mother strain than the father strain. This observation could not be carried further until highly inbred strains of mice were established, each capable of satisfying the requirements of controlled genetic investigations. The establishment of such strains and the hybridization experiments were performed by the staff of the Jackson Memorial Laboratory and the results of the experiments pertaining to the present problem were published in 1933 (164).

Reciprocal breeding between inbred strains of mice with high and low mammary tumor incidence revealed that the offspring born to mothers of a high tumor strain had a high incidence of tumors whereas the offspring of mothers of a low tumor strain had a low incidence of mammary tumors (Table 43). Thus, the incidence of tumors in the first hybrid generation approximated that of the maternal strain, and it was evident that the transmission of this influence on tumor genesis was not chromosomal in nature. The same differences between reciprocal F_1 hybrids were shown in the F_2 generation as well, and, again, the maternal effect was also apparent in several backcross generations.

Similar findings were independently reported by Korteweg (166), who suggested three possibilities to explain the transmission of the maternal influence on mammary tumor development, namely (a) through the cytoplasm of the ovum, (b) through the placenta during intra-uterine development, and (c) through the milk during nursing. No evidence for either of the first two possibilities has yet been found. The evidence that an inciting agent or agents may be transmitted through the milk is one of the most striking developments in experimental cancer research of the last two decades.

TABLE 43

OCCURRENCE OF MAMMARY TUMORS IN F_1 HYBRID MICE (CF. 165)

Strain of mother	Tumor incidence	Strain of father	Tumor incidence	Tumor incidence in F_1 hybrids
C57Black	Low	*DBA*	High	Low
C57 Black	Low	*A*	High	Low
C57 Black	Low	*C3H*	High	Low
DBA	High	*C57 Black*	Low	High
DBA	High	*Y*	Low	High
A	High	*C57 Black*	Low	High
C3H	High	*I*	Low	High
C3H	High	*C57 Black*	Low	High
I	Low	*C3H*	High	Low

TABLE 44

INFLUENCE OF FOSTER NURSING UPON INCIDENCE OF MAMMARY TUMORS IN INBRED STRAINS OF MICE AND ON F_1 HYBRIDS (165)

Strain or derivative of fostered mice		Strain of foster mother		Effect on tumor incidence of fostered mice
Designation	Tumor incidence	Designation	Tumor incidence	
C57 Black	Low	*C3H*	High	Increased
C57 Black	Low	*A*	High	Increased
C57 Black	Low	*DBA*	High	Increased
C57 Black × *I*	Low	*C3H*	High	Increased
C57 Black × *A*	Low	*A*	High	Increased
C57 Black × *DBA*	Low	*DBA*	High	Increased
C57 Black × *C3H*	Low	*C3H*	High	Increased
DBA	High	*C57 Black*	Low	Decreased
DBA × *C57 Black*	High	*C57 Black*	Low	Decreased
A	High	*C57 Black*	Low	Decreased
C3H	High	*C*	Low	Decreased
C	Low	*C3H*	High	Increased
I	Low	*C3H*	High	Increased
I × *C3H*	Low	*C3H*	High	Increased

In 1936, Bittner demonstrated that, when the offspring of a high tumor strain were suckled by foster mothers belonging to low mammary tumor strains, the foster-nursed animals showed a low tumor rate (167–171). Similar experiments were performed in a number of laboratories (172–175), and there was general agreement that, when the newborn of high tumor mice were foster-nursed by low tumor mice, or *vice versa*, the mammary tumor incidence of the fostered mice approached that of the strain of the foster mother (Table 44). It is evident that there may be present in the milk of high mammary tumor strains an inciting agent for mammary tumor production largely absent from the milk of the low tumor strains. In the absence of this factor, few mammary tumors would arise in a strain ordinarily susceptible to the spontaneous development of these tumors. Since the inciter for this "spontaneous" development is recognized, the adjective in quotation marks may well be superfluous. The essentially artificial distinction between "spontaneous" and "induced" tumors is nowhere better illustrated than in the present instance. "Spontaneity" in biological phenomena is really a problem in semantics.

Foster nursing is best effected as soon as is possible after birth of the litter, for even brief periods of opportunity for the offspring to suckle their own mother show their effect in the later incidence of tumors (176). Thus, in many cases, the offspring of *C3H* strain mothers removed 3 to 24 hours after birth and then nursed by *C57 Black* strain mothers, instead of showing, when grown, the incidence of the latter, namely about zero, gave an incidence definitely above zero. In order to deprive the young of any opportunity to obtain their mother's milk, Andervont devised two procedures: (a) the removal of high tumor strain mice by surgical procedures from the uteri of their mothers, and (b) the searing of the nipples of pregnant high tumor strain mothers (177). When applied to the young of *C3H* strain mothers which were foster-nursed by *C57 Black* strain mice, the mammary tumor incidence of these young when they became adult was zero. In connection with these experiments, Andervont *et al.* (165) used the interesting control experiment of placing the *C57 Black* strain foster mother in the same cage with the *C3H* offspring and the latter's own mothers which were prevented by nipple damage from nursing. Thus, the young were always in close contact with their own mothers while obtaining only *C57 Black* milk. As mentioned, none of these foster-nursed mice developed mammary tumors although their mothers did in high yield. Fekete and Little (178) transferred fertilized ova from high tumor strain *DBA* mice into the uteri of strain *C57* black mice. When the mice were born, they suckled the latter and showed no incidence of mammary tumors.

Not all low tumor strain mice when foster-nursed by high tumor strain milk respond to the same degree. Occasionally, as Bittner pointed out, low tumor strain females fostered by high tumor strain mice could transmit the influence in their milk (as shown by the new generation) although they did not develop breast tumors (170). Andervont studied the fate of the *C3H* strain milk in mice of two low tumor strains, namely, *C* and *C57 Black* (179). The mammary cancer incidence in the three strains was as follows: *C3H*, 94%; *C*, 1%; and *C57 Black*, <1%. When litters of the last two strains were foster-nursed by *C3H* females, every female of the fostered *C* strain transmitted the inciter for mammary cancer to her offspring, which, in the females, produced a high incidence of mammary tumors (about 75%). Thus, a single exposure of *C* strain mice to *C3H* milk influence transformed strain *C* from a very low to a high mammary tumor strain. So far, the inbred mice of the exposed *C* strain show the high incidence as far as the inbred fortieth generation. On the other hand, the *C3H* milk influence was not transferred to successive generations of *C57 Black* strain mice. These important experiments suggest that the alteration of a strain of mice from a low to a high mammary tumor strain needs not only the milk influence but also a particular genetic constitution. Similar experiments by Miller and Pybus revealed that the low tumor *CBA* strain could be converted to a high tumor strain after a single foster nursing on *Simpson* strain dams (180).

The problem of whether the agent is propagated along with the tumor in successive generation transplants has generally depended for its solution on the patience of the experimenter. Thus Dmochowski (181) employed a mammary tumor originating in a *C57BL* low tumor strain after foster nursing an *RIII* high incident dam. After forty-two successive transfers in *C57BL* mice lacking the agent, the tumors still showed the presence of the agent as shown by the tumorous response of $(C57BL \times A)\ F_1$ hybrid mice on injection of the tumor. However, by the eighty-sixth passage the agent was apparently lost, for the hybrid test mice, which are very sensitive to the agent, no longer gave a tumorous response.

The milk agent for mammary tumors appears to be very nearly the same in each of two high tumors strains (*C3H* and *A*), for reciprocal foster nursing did not alter significantly the tumor incidence in later life of the mice (181a). On a dry weight basis, however, the tumor-producing capacity of *C3H* strain tumor tissue is higher than that of *A* strain tumor tissue (182).

As little as 0.1 ml. of milk at a dilution of 1:10,000 from a high tumor strain mouse administered to an animal sufficiently young can produce mammary tumors 8 to 12 months later.

The milk of a high tumor strain mother can be introduced into the young either orally or intraperitoneally, the latter being the more efficacious route (177). It is not even necessary to introduce milk *per se* into young test objects, for, as Bittner and others have shown, the mammary tumor inciter is widely distributed in the body of the mouse. Mammary tumors may be produced in susceptible mice after subcutaneous implantation of spleen (183), thymus (183), whole blood (184), lactating mammary gland (177), and extracts of mammary tumors (177, 185). Materials of high activity could be sedimented from saline extracts of the tumor (185, 186) and it seemed likely that the tumor-inciting activity was associated with particles having sedimentation constants between 25 and 200 *S*. It is of considerable interest that the inciting agent, from whatever source, could produce tumors when fed to mice sufficiently young, and this fact suggests that the material may be either resistant to the action of the digestive enzymes or else dependent upon them for degradation into active fractions. The inciting agent in milk is destroyed by heating at 65° for 30 minutes, which suggests that it may be protein in nature. It is not found in the ether-soluble fraction of milk. The agent is filterable through Seitz or Birkefeld filters.

The agent is associated with microsomes and is centrifugable at $23{,}000 \times g$ (187). The chemical composition of the lactating glands of mice with or without the agent is practically the same (Table 45).

The milk agent is present to approximately the same concentration in the milk as in the secreting gland cells, and since in mid-lactation the mammae of mice produce about double their weight in milk, the agent duplication must proceed at a relatively rapid rate (188). Mice were injected with 10^{-6} g. equivalents of mammary gland microsomes (2.32 mγ of nitrogen), and 43% of the animals developed mammary tumors. Graff *et al.* (189) de-

TABLE 45

COMPOSITION OF MICROSOME FRACTION OF LACTATING GLANDS OF MICE WITH AND WITHOUT THE AGENT (187)

Strain	N[1]	P[1]	Pentose[1]	N/P	N/Pentose
A and *Z* (agent)	2.35	0.49	1.48	4.87	1.61
Ax and *Zb* (no agent)	2.69	0.57	1.63	4.71	1.66

[1] In terms of milligrams per gram wet tissue.

veloped mammary cancer in mice with about the same magnitude of material, *i.e.*, 8 mγ of nitrogen.

The chemical fractionation of the inciting influence has been quite difficult owing largely to the lack of a sufficiently rapid method of bioassay of the fractions. It is necessary to wait at least 9 months before tumors may be expected to appear in the susceptible young animals employed as test objects. As effective test objects, the mice must not only be young but must be of strains which do not themselves contain the milk influence but respond with a high proportion of tumors when treated with the milk influence. Andervont has recently found *C* strain mice suitable for this purpose; earlier he had used $(I \times C3H)F_1$ hybrids (179). High dilutions of the agent can apparently infect mice without producing tumors in them (190), subsequent generations developing tumors containing the agent. This fact obviously would tend to further complicate the bioassay for the agent.

Adult mice are more difficult to infect with the milk agent than are young mice. When the former are infected, they usually do not show tumors but their progeny may. Indeed, the evidence for infection of mice of a non-milk agent strain with the milk agent is very simply confirmed when the progeny show mammary tumors (176). As an example, an extract of mammary tumor of a *C3H* mouse was injected intraperitoneally as well as subcutaneously into $(I \times C3H)F_1$ hybrid female adult mice (176, 191). The potency of the extract was assured by testing with young *C* strain female mice. Eight days after the injection, the $(I \times C3H)F_1$ hybrids were mated with *C3H* males and yielded the $(IC3H \times C3H)$ *BC* generation. Out of twenty-five of the F_1 mothers, only two developed mammary tumors, but roughly one-third of these F_1 mothers yielded a back-cross progeny which showed a high incidence of mammary tumors. Thus, about one-third of the $(I \times C3H)F_1$ adults became infected with the mammary tumor agent and transmitted it in their milk. When adult *I* strain mice were similarly treated, i.e., injected with extract of mammary tumor and then crossed with *C3H* males, neither the injected, adult *I* mothers nor the uninjected, $(I \times C3H)F_1$ progeny revealed tumors. It would appear that the milk agent did not infect the mammary gland tissue of adult strain *I* mice but did infect that of the $(I \times C3H)F_1$ hybrids.

The widespread occurrence of the tumor-inciting agent throughout the body of the mouse, its ready transmissibility in cell-free extracts to susceptible subjects, its propagation through successive generations, all suggest the action of a material bearing some resemblance to the viruses. The tentative classification of the mammary tumor inciter in this category is not unreasonable in view of the fact that similar transmissible chemical agents have been known for some time to produce cancer in fowl. The mouse mammary tumor inciter, however, differs from the known fowl tumor viruses in the relatively long latent period of the former. Furthermore, tumor development is not necessary for transmission of the influence from mother or foster mother to offspring, and in this respect the inciting influence acts as a latent virus infection. The mammary tumor inciter, as the name implies and in common with other viruses, possesses a specificity for a particular tissue. It is not involved in the genesis of spontaneous pulmonary, hepatic, uterine, pituitary, or subcutaneous tissue tumors (cf. 165).

There are, therefore, at least three factors involved in the natural genesis of mammary cancer in many inbred strains of mice, namely (a) the genetic constitution, (b) hormonal stimulation, and (c) the milk agent. Thus, unless the milk influence is introduced into *C* strain mice, genetic susceptibility of the animals and large doses of estrogen do not lead to development of mammary tumors (192). Male mice do not develop mammary tumors in spite of the presence of genetic susceptibility and the milk influence unless the hormonal factor (estrogen) is supplied.

In any one strain, the balance among these three factors may be quite different from that of any other strain and the equilibrium among the factors may be shifted in the direction of tumor production by sufficiently increasing any one of the factors. Thus, the *C57 Black* strain, which has a very low genetic susceptibility to these tumors, will, nevertheless, produce them when the milk factor and massive estrogen stimulation are present (193). Again, F_1 hybrids of maternal lines with a low mammary tumor incidence may, nevertheless, show a relatively high tumor incidence if they give birth to a large number of litters in rapid succession (194–196). In this case the excessive hormonal stimulation compensates for relative lack of genetic susceptibility and the milk factor.

Mammary tumors lacking the inciting agent have also been found in breeding (but not virgin) females in strain *C3Hb* mice derived by Caesarian section from *C3H* mothers and foster-nursed on *C57BL* mice (197). The use of "forced breeding," i.e., several litters in succession, has also been successful in causing the production of mammary tumors in otherwise resistant mice (198). On the other hand, where genetic susceptibility and

TABLE 46

CORRELATIONS OF OBSERVATIONS ON *A* AND *C3H* STRAIN MICE AND THEIR HYBRIDS WITH AND WITHOUT THE AGENT (200)

Factors	*A* strain	*C3H* strain	High mammary tumor hybrids (fostered)	Low mammary tumor hybrids (fostered)
Genetic susceptibility to mammary cancer	Present	Present	Present	Present
Milk factor	Present	Present	Present	Absent
Inherited hormonal influence	Absent	Present	Present	Present
Adrenal cortical changes after castration	27.1%	96.7%	91.7%	91.7%
Uterine stimulation	Absent	Present	Present	Present
Estrus activity	Absent	Present	Present	Present
Mammary tumor incidence	4.3%	54.7%	55.0%	0%

the milk factor coexist, as in *A* strain mice which lack the so-called dominantly inherited hormonal influence (199), i.e., the factor modifying hormonal activity in virgin and breeding mice, crossing with strains which possess this "influence" will result in hybrids with a high incidence of mammary tumors (200). This is illustrated in Table 46.

The equilibrium among the three factors mentioned may also be dependent upon genetic constitution as well as the degree of hormonal stimulation. Thus, the susceptibility to mammary tumor formation of F_1 hybrid generation mice with isogenic mothers is a function of the paternal strain. This is illustrated by data obtained by Andervont (201) (Table 47). It is clear that genetic factors may modify tumor susceptibility in the presence of the same milk influence and approximately the same hormonal stimulation. Thus, of the three outcrossings in Table 47, the *C3H* × *I* was the most susceptible and the *C3H* × *Y* the least susceptible.

TABLE 47

ILLUSTRATION OF THE PATERNAL INFLUENCE ON MAMMARY TUMOR SUSCEPTIBILITY (ISOGENIC MATERNAL STRAIN) (201)

Mice[1]	Group	Tumor incidence, %	Average tumor age, months
C3H (F) × *I* (M)	Virgins	100	10.3
C3H (F) × *I* (M)	Breeders	100	7.7
C3H (F) × *Y* (M)	Virgins	80	15.0
C3H (F) × *Y* (M)	Breeders	71	14.4
C3H (F) × *C57 Black* (M)	Breeders	96	11.9

[1] The mammary tumor incidence in females of the paternal strains is practically zero; that in females of the *C3H* strain is nearly 100%. Hybrids were nursed by their own mothers.

There is little doubt that most, if not all, high mammary tumor mice strains possess the milk influence and that the role of this agent in the natural genesis of mammary tumors in these strains is well established. Indeed, it was only through the use of highly inbred strains that the presence of the milk influence was made clear. Nevertheless, there is some reason to believe that the milk influence, striking as its manifestations may be, may not necessarily be the *sine qua non* for mammary tumor genesis in hybrid mice, or, under certain circumstances, even in certain inbred strains of mice. The evidence upon which this is based consists in the following: (a) it is possible to induce the formation of mammary tumors in mice of very low spontaneous incidence by the subcutaneous injection or percutaneous painting of methylcholanthrene (cf. 202); thus, the carcinogen may, in a sense, be considered as replacing the milk factor; (b) the observations by Bittner (203) and by Murray and Little (204) that low tumor strain females mated with high tumor strain males yielded hybrids which showed a slightly higher incidence of mammary tumors than did the maternal strain; and (c) the observation by Andervont (191) that outcrosses of *C* strain females (low incidence) with *C3H* strain males yielded an F_1 hybrid generation with a high incidence of mammary tumors.

A *DBA* strain which possessed a mammary tumor incidence of 43% in breeding females was made agent-free by foster nursing agent-free dams. When painted with 20-methylcholanthrene, they developed mammary tumors which lacked the agent (205). It is interesting to note in this connection that the mammary tumors induced by the carcinogen showed a variety of histologic types, whereas those developing under the influence of the agent were more uniform. Indeed, as a rule, the morphology of the mammary tumors is likely to be affected by the strain in which the tumor is growing, as well as by the age of the host (206). The susceptibility of a mouse strain to the development of mammary tumors by carcinogens varies from strain to strain and is apparently independent of the normal, spontaneous incidence of the strain (207).

The experiments of Andervont reveal that the offspring of a low tumor maternal strain and of a high tumor paternal strain may, in successive generations, possess a tumor incidence considerably higher than that of the maternal strain. The tumors of the F_1 generation hybrids showed no evidence of the presence of the milk factor. This was demonstrated in the following manner. The F_1 generation hybrids of *I* strain mothers and of *C3H* strain fathers [$(I \times C3H)F_1$] show an extremely low spontaneous incidence of mammary tumors but readily respond to the milk influence. When to such hybrid mice extracts of the tumors of F_1 generation hybrids of $C \times C3H$ mice were fed, no tumors in the test mice arose. When strain *C* females ingested *C3H* strain milk, the milk agent was propagated through successive generations (179) and each of these generations showed a high incidence of mammary tumors. In the case of the *C* × *C3H* hybrid mice, no such agent was evident and yet mammary tumors were present.

The possibility that the higher incidence of mammary tumors in crosses involving the paternal parent of a high tumor line may be due to some infection by the male has occupied the attention of several workers. It is clear that the various tissues of such male mice possess the agent (208), among them the seminal vesicles (209) and the sperm (210). Mühlbock (210) observed that sperm removed from the epididymis of *DBA* males and injected intraperitoneally into ($C57BL \times DBA)F_1$ females induced the formation of mammary tumors to the extent characteristic of *DBA* females, whereas sperm similarly removed from *C57BL* males yielded under the same conditions no tumors at all. Those hybrid females receiving *DBA* strain sperm and which do not develop tumors nevertheless frequently transmit the agent through the milk, for their daughters develop tumors. It is therefore possible that the agent may be transmitted during copulation. The fact that the tumors are relatively few in such crosses where the recipient female is of a low tumor line may be due to several causes. One of these is obviously derived from the fact that the infection must naturally take place when the female is relatively mature, and hence correspondingly less sensitive to the tumor-evoking power of the agent (cf. 211).

It is possible that a higher tumor incidence among hybrids than among mice of the inbred maternal line may be due to the longer life span accompanying hybrid vigor, but this can only be part of the full explanation. It may be that the hybrid possesses a mammary gland tissue more sensitive and more susceptible to the carcinogenic effect of amounts of milk influence and of hormones which would otherwise be subthreshold for the inbred maternal line. Both *I* × *C3H* and *C* × *C3H* hybrids are isogenic in the paternal line, but the former show no tumors whereas the latter show many tumors in the absence of the milk influence; both maternal lines are individually susceptible to the milk influence (Table 48).

It may be wondered, therefore, whether the milk influence is not a phenomenon peculiar to the inbred strain of mouse, and perhaps less of a factor, if one at all, in the genesis of mammary tumors in several forms of hybrid mice. In any event, the phenomena based upon skilful and controlled hybridization experiments reveal how complex the mammary tumorogenic process may be and how closely the possible contribution of each factor in this process must be scrutinized.

The milk agent is highly antigenic and stimulates the formation of antibodies in rabbits and rats (212, 213). The antiserum neutralizes the agent and renders it ineffective. The finding that the antiserum against normal mouse tissue has no effect on the milk agent suggests that the latter is of

TABLE 48

MAMMARY TUMOR SUSCEPTIBILITY IN HYBRID (F_1) MICE PATERNALLY ISOGENIC (191)

Mice[1]	Tumor incidence, %
C (F) × *C3H* (M)	52[2]
I (F) × *C3H* (M)	<1
I (F) × *C3H* (M)[3]	3[4]
C57 Black (F) × *C3H* (M)	<1

[1] The mammary tumor incidence in females of the paternal strain is 94%, that in the females of the maternal strains is practically zero. The *C* strain is more susceptible to the milk influence than is either the *I* or *C57 Black*.

[2] Average tumor age 22 months.

[3] Foster-nursed by strain *C* mice.

[4] Average tumor age 28 months.

exogenous derivation. No neutralizing antibodies to the milk agent in mice have yet been found (214, 215).

Finally, the milk of inbred strains of mice may contain active factors for other kinds of neoplasia. Law (216) observed that an influence was transmitted in the milk of the female mice which was effective in promoting the growth of transplanted leukemia in normally refractive mice. This susceptibility influence was present in the milk throughout the period of lactation. After transfer of this influence to refractory mice by foster nursing, the influence was maintained through three generations of breeding mice of the normally refractory strain. Saline extracts of liver, spleen, and mammary gland contained the influence, the properties of which (dialyzability through parchment, resistance to digestion, etc.) are somewhat different from those of the mammary tumor inciter. The possibility therefore exists that more than one agent effective on the initiation, maintenance, and growth of various kinds of tumors may be transmitted from one generation to the next by extrachromosomal pathways. Foster nursing by low leukemia dams reduces the incidence of the disease in high leukemic strains, but mice of a low leukemia strain nursed with high leukemia strain dams do not develop the disease (217; cf. 218).

The presence of a milk factor for mammary carcinogenesis has not been established for any species of animal beyond the mouse, and any recommendations of complete interruption of breast feeding as a prophylactic measure against cancer in man would be unwarranted at the present time.

VIRUSES AS CAUSATIVE AGENTS

The Rous Chicken Tumor Agent. In 1911 Peyton Rous discovered that cell-free extracts of a spontaneous chicken sarcoma when injected intramuscularly into other chickens gave rise to sarcoma in the new hosts (219). This was an observation of considerable importance, and it lent support to that theory of cancer etiology based on the possibility of transmission by infectious agents from cancerous to susceptible host. The topic has occasioned a lively literature which has frequently yielded more heat than light. In 1933, Shope (220) noted that cell-free extracts of the spontaneous papillomas of cottontail rabbits would transmit these benign growths to other cottontail rabbits. When, in 1936, Bittner demonstrated that mammary tumors could arise in mice of low tumor strains when fed the milk or tissue extracts of mice of high tumor strains, it appeared that still another cell-free material might be a causative agent for cancer in an animal. That cell-free transmissible agents may also exist in an amphibian species was shown by Lucké in the case of carcinoma in the frog (cf. 221). No chemical characterization of the agent which specifically induces the malignant renal tumors in the leopard frog has as yet been made (222). That the Lucké agent can be adapted to and will undergo variation in the cells of the young salamander has recently been shown (223).

It is difficult at this late date to completely understand the resistance that was offered to the acceptance of a cellular component as a carcinogenic agent. In view of the fact that purely chemical agents, such as tar, were known or suspected to produce cancer, there seemed to be little reason to regard as heretical anything less than the intact cell as a transmissible agent. There is no evidence that all tumors are caused by viruses, but only that a few of them are. It may be that carcinogenesis is simply a history of specific injury followed by chance infection in susceptible hosts by ubiquitous cancer viruses. At the moment, however, it is best to view the known cancer viruses as simply another example of carcinogenic agents, like tar and the azo dyes, although much more interesting and suggestive.

Cell-free agents which are transmissible from one host to another, and which multiply in the latter, have received the designation of viruses. The essential property of this remarkable class of substances lies in their capacity for infecting the host in some manner so as to cause the host to multiply such substances at its own expense. The term virus has been principally confined to agents residing in multicellular organisms. When free-living individual cells such as the bacteria are the hosts, these agents are referred to as bacteriophage. In nearly all cases the specific biological property of infectiousness, or obligate parasitism, has been found to be associated with certain nucleoproteins of high particle weight which bear little or no resemblance to the normal nucleoproteins of the host either chemically or serologically, and which themselves vary considerably from virus to virus in chemical composition, particle size and shape, and molecular stability. The only common ground, apart from the property of infectiveness, which the viruses and bacteriophage possess, is the fact that they are all nucleoproteins, or at least proteins associated with nucleic acid. In addition, some of the more complex viruses may contain lipoid and other protoplasmic constituents, suggestive of their being of the nature of incomplete or retrograded microorganisms (cf. 224).

With the establishment of a causative agent for cancer in chickens in cell-free extracts of spontaneous chicken tumor, the separation of the suspected active agent in such extracts could be begun. The biological assay accompanying such fractionation could be readily performed, for young chickens inoculated with the extract develop tumors at the site of injection in about 10 days. The tumors grow rapidly and generally metastasize. The amount of active agent extracted from the tumors is usually inversely proportional to the duration of growth in the host (225).

The activity of the tumor extracts decreases on standing, even at 0°. The extracts absorb ultraviolet radiation with a maximum at about 2600 Å, which is the characteristic band for nucleic acid. Prolonged ultraviolet irradiation results in an inactivation of the extract, and this has suggested that the active agent in the extract is associated with nucleic acid. Heating the extract at 50° for 30 minutes also inactivates the responsible agent or agents and simultaneously, the absorption band at 2600 Å increases. This suggests that disintegration of some nucleoprotein in the extract, yielding nucleic acid, is an accompaniment of biological inactivation and further suggests, although it does not prove, that such nucleoprotein may be the active tumor agent.

The separation from the tumor of a nucleoprotein complex by methods involving differential high-speed centrifugation has been accomplished by several investigators (227–228). The partially purified sedimented material yielded tumors when injected into susceptible fowl at doses as low as 4×10^{-13} g. dry weight (226). It appeared to be a somewhat loosely bound complex of three essential components, namely, nucleic acid, protein, and lipid. Attempts to remove the lipid result in loss of activity of the material, although the lipid itself is non-carcinogenic.

The same methods, involving high-speed centrifugation, were applied by Claude (226) and by Pollard (227) to other animal tissues with the interesting result that the cellular components of high particle weight thus sedimented had rather similar chemical composition (Table 49).

The similarity in composition and in physicochemical properties of the macromolecular particles from different sources suggests that such components are common to animal tissues. Such macromolecular particles are not pure nucleoproteins, but are complex structures of nucleic acid, protein, and lipid such as may be expected to be encountered in an analysis of protoplasm. To the table cited, apparently, could be added the similar chemical composition of the small granules of the filterable chicken sarcoma

TABLE 49

Composition of Particulate Components of Normal and Tumor Cells Sedimented at High Centrifugal Speeds (226)

Source	N, %	P, %	Total lipoids, %	N on fat-free basis, %	P on fat-free basis, %	Ribonucleic acid, %	Sedimentation constant,[1] S	Diameter of particle mμ
Chicken tumor I	8.60	1.54	36.5	12.74	1.16	10–15	500	70
Chick embryo	8.22	2.10	51.0	13.80	1.21	10–15	500	70
Mouse embryo	8.54	2.07	46.0	14.30	1.37	—	—	—
Mouse sarcoma 180	8.00	1.52	49.1	14.51	1.21	—	—	—
Mouse sarcoma 1549	9.26	1.88	42.4	14.90	1.24	—	—	—

[1] On the basis of a spherical particle and a sedimentation constant of 500 S, the average molecular weight is roughly 140,000,000.

(infective) and of the non-filterable, carcinogen-induced chicken sarcoma (229).

The implications of the data in Table 49 are profound and far-reaching, for they reveal that components externally and superficially similar may exist in animal tissues. Yet only one of the materials listed in Table 49 possesses infective power. It would be of great value to carry the purification and chemical analysis of these materials very much further, for it is likely that such analysis might reveal wherein the chicken tumor agent departed in chemical composition from that, say, of the chick embryo component, and thereby suggest the crucial structure responsible for infectivity. Are the analogous components in normal tissues potentially carcinogenic, awaiting only the proper stimulus to effect the necessary alteration?

The evidence for a rather similar composition for the proteins of homologous tissues in several different species is not new and has been adduced by several investigators. Bailey (230) pointed out that the myosins of the rabbit, dog, ox, chicken, fish, and lobster all had very nearly the same values of nitrogen, sulfur, amide N, cystine-cysteine, methionine, tyrosine, and tryptophan. Block (231) observed that the neuroproteins of man, monkey, cow, sheep, rat, and guinea pig had very nearly the same values of nitrogen, histidine, lysine, arginine, cystine-cysteine, tyrosine, and tryptophan. Greenstein and Jenrette (232) noted that the liver nucleoproteins of the rabbit, rat, and cow, and the hepatoma nucleoprotein of the rat all had very nearly the same content of nitrogen, sulfur, phosphorus, amide N, cystine-cysteine, methionine, tyrosine, and tryptophan.

It was noted, however, that such homologous proteins could be distinguished in various species by the relative amounts of cystine and cysteine. Although the sum of these two amino acids may be the same in a group of homologous proteins from different species, Greenstein and Jenrette (232; cf. 233) and Greenstein and Leuthardt (234) noted that the relative amounts of cystine and of cysteine may be quite different in each species. Thus, although the cystine plus cysteine content of the liver proteins of the rat and of the rabbit may be very nearly the same, the ratio of cystine to cysteine in the former species is 3.1, that in the latter species is 0.7 (234). These data are cited to indicate the possibilities which a further analysis of the uniform particulate components described in Table 49 may be expected to reveal.

Such analyses in turn must await unequivocal methods of purification of the virus. The most successful to date has been that of Carr and Harris (235), who used a combination of centrifugation and enzyme technology to concentrate the agent. The tumor extracts were treated with fresh rat testes hyaluronidase to destroy the viscous mucopolysaccharide present in these tumors, then centrifuged, and the pellet digested with crystalline trypsin which removed over 60% of the non-virus protein. The final product contained only 2% of the nitrogen of the original clarified extract but had almost all the virus activity. Assayed on day-old chicks, the minimum infective dose was of the order of 1×10^{-8} mg. nitrogen. The virus agent appears to be associated with the microsomal fraction of the extracts with a size range of some 50 to 150 mμ and is appreciably free of deoxyribonucleic acid.

There is little doubt but that increasingly finer methods of analysis of the cytoplasmic particulate fractions, both infective and non-infective, will be of great interest and probable value. The possible origin of the former as a result of a plasmagene mutation (see Haddow, 236) and its relation to the cytoplasmic type of inheritance described by Sonneborn for races of *Paramecia* offer areas of fascinating speculation. However, dynamic studies of the infective process are so far lacking, i.e., metabolic studies of the changes, for example, in enzyme pattern and direction of protein synthesis which occur when the virus intrudes into the normal cell. Perhaps such changes are only partial, and the normal and neoplastic pathways coexist in the beginning of the infective process, and one finally triumphs and excludes the other. Only a considerable volume of chemical measurements of an almost infinite variety can supply the information needed.

Tumors resembling the Rous sarcoma have been induced in chickens by intramuscular injections of tar solutions in lard (cf. 237). McIntosh (238) reported the successful transmission of such tumors to other fowl through cell-free extracts, but many other workers have failed to confirm this finding (239; cf. 240). However, the existence of a close immunological relationship between the Rous sarcoma agent (spontaneous) and constituents of chemically induced tumors was indicated by neutralization experiments (238). In any event, the transmission of induced fowl tumors by cell-free agents appears to be considerably more difficult than the transmission of spontaneous tumors (cf. 241). (Inasmuch as the virus tumors are propagated by cell-free extracts or purified agents they must be considered as arising *de novo* at each serial passage from the cells of the host.) Another difference, according to Peacock, between the spontaneous (virus-induced) and the chemically (tar) induced sarcomas in fowl lies in the occasional spontaneous regression of the former kind of growth (242). Intramuscular injection of methylcholanthrene into fowl infected by the Rous agent resulted in a regression of the established tumors (*vide* Haddow, 243), with subsequent development of a Rous tumor at the site of injection of the hydrocarbon (244). It has been shown that the Rous virus will infect another, non-filterable tumor growing in the same bird (245). The virus is apparently disseminated by the blood system of the host (244). The transplants of chemically induced sarcoma in fowl to other hosts apparently depends as much upon the season of the year as upon the tissue compatibility between graft and host (246), suggesting the influence of hormonal tides.

Duran-Reynals (247) has described some remarkable experiments involving a chemical carcinogen and a non-neoplastic fowl virus which suggests that viruses not usually associated with tumors may become adapted to cells conditioned by carcinogens and thus play a role in the etiology (and perhaps the therapy?) of cancer. Fowl carrying the pox virus were subjected to skin painting with methylcholanthrene and developed malignant epitheliomas thereby. The filtrates of these tumors did not transmit cancer but only fowl pox.

Leukosis can also be transmitted in fowl by cell-free plasma. Furth (248) has shown that such an agent can produce sarcomas as well as endotheliomas and myeloleukosis. This agent has been shown to be related immunologically with a non-infectious component in a fowl sarcoma induced by methylcholanthrene (249). The readiness with which the fowl viruses induce the formation of antibodies raises the problem as to whether the failure of analogous components in induced tumors to show infective power may be due to the presence of neutralizing antibodies in such tumors. The leukosis agent has an average particle diameter of 72 mμ (250) and is infectious to the extent of 8.6×10^{-8} mg. nitrogen (251). A filterable agent which produces lymphoid tumors and osteopetrosis in chickens has been reported (252). The etiology of fowl tumors has been summarized in an excellent review by Peacock (253).

Chicken tumor virus when injected in large amounts into ducks (254), turkeys, and guinea fowl (255) produces tumors in these species. In order to obtain these tumors, the injection must occur shortly after hatching. Two sorts of tumors arise in ducks, which Duran-Reynals has termed *immediate* and *late*. The immediate tumors occurred from 9 to 30 days after the virus injection and showed the same characteristics as the original chicken tumor; they could be propagated through adult chickens but not through adult ducks. The late tumors arose 40 to 215 days after injection and could be easily propagated through adult ducks but not through adult chickens. In this way, the late tumors yielded duck variants of the original Rous chicken agent. When Duran-Reynals reversed the procedure, and chicks were injected with duck tumor viruses, the same phenomena were encountered. The altered Rous virus, now homologous for ducks, produced tumors localized in the periosteum and endostium, sites never affected by the original Rous chicken tumor agent. The development of periosteal tumors in the chicken is thus an indication of virus variation. Shrigley *et al.* (256) succeeded in growing the Rous chicken sarcoma in the anterior chamber of the guinea pig eye and noted that the tumor agent was altered during this passage, since it produced periosteal tumors in injected chickens. The duck-adapted virus, unlike the original chicken virus, can be transmitted to pigeons regardless of age, and subsequently from one pigeon to another (257). That an antigenic change takes place in the virus as a result of the variation is seen in the observation that the immune bodies that develop in aging chickens neutralize the viruses of both the chicken tumor (Rous sarcoma) and its duck variants, but comparable immune bodies from aging ducks neutralize only duck tumor virus (258).

The virus frequently seems to disappear from tumors in aging chickens, and even the transplantability of the tumors by cells and the induction of metastases are impaired (259). Aggression of the tumor in the aged chicken is generally followed by resistance to further inoculation, thus showing an immune reaction linked with age. The change in the virus with age, however, is probably a masked phenomenon, for it can be reversed by the simple device of transplanting tumor cells from the old chicken into young chicks, and filterable virus can again be readily recovered from the tumor in the young host (259).

The possible relation between the Rous sarcoma and the lymphomatosis avian viruses was studied by rearing chickens in two environments, one with high incidence and the other with low incidence of lymphomatosis. Those subjects in the former environment showed the presence of Rous sarcoma antibodies, whereas those in the latter environment were devoid of these antibodies (260). It is not improbable that if there are two avian viruses, one for the sarcoma and the other for lymphomatosis, both may possess a common antigen, or perhaps the Rous virus may be a mutant of the lymphomatosis virus.

The Shope Rabbit Papilloma Agent. Cell-free extracts of spontaneous papillomas of the wild cottontail rabbit, when injected into other cottontails, induce papillomas in the new hosts. These induced growths (which occur in about 70 % of injected animals) usually regress after some time and rarely undergo a malignant change (261). The papilloma agent and the wild rabbit are evidently long habituated to each other. Such rabbits are not necessarily resistant to cancer, since tarring of the skin readily produces carcinoma. The activity of the cell-free extract is greatest in the natural papilloma growth. With successive inoculation, an extract of diminishing potency is usually obtained (262–267). Not infrequently cancers develop from virus-induced tumors in the natural host, the cottontail rabbit (268). No virus is apparent in these eventual cancers (269). Transfer of the cancerous growths from western cottontail rabbits to eastern cottontails did not result in an increase in resistance to subsequent infection of the latter animals by the papilloma virus, nor did their sera acquire any neutralizing capacity for the papilloma virus. The virus is more of a provocative than a cancerogenic agent.

When the extract of papilloma from the cottontail rabbit is injected into the domestic rabbit, papillomas are induced from which extracts of little or no activity can be obtained. After several months the papillomas become malignant. The period during which the malignant growth develops can be considerably shortened by treating the skin of the domestic rabbit with tar or with methylcholanthrene before injecting with the extract. The injected agent, intravenously administered, readily induces both carcinomas and papillomas at the site of tarring. The carcinomas are transplantable to other domestic rabbits only as intact cells. It is quite striking that the papilloma agent introduced humorally finds its way to the site of injured and benignly neoplastic tissue and there induces malignant growth.

The presence of papillomas in the domestic rabbit induces neutralizing bodies for the papilloma agent, but these bodies have no effect on the course of established papillomas although they act to prevent successful reinoculation. This is of interest because the papillomas of domestic rabbits fail, in most instances, to yield evidence of the presence of a transmissible agent. The latter is thus masked in pathogenicity; occasionally, on rendering the skin hyperplastic before injection of the papilloma extract, virus in small amount can be demonstrated (266). However, a similar condition sometimes prevails in the papillomas produced in wild rabbits by transmission. Little or no masking apparently occurs in the *naturally occurring* papillomas of the wild rabbits. Parallel with the pathogenicity of the papillomas is the level of antibody titer in the serum of animals with these growths. It is curious indeed that vigorous malignant growths can develop in the skin while being nourished by blood with increasing antibody titer; in such a case the agent must be protected or masked in some manner. The serological evidence of the presence of the agent in the tumors of the domestic rabbit, in the absence of direct evidence of its extractability and infectiousness, is similar to that in the case of the non-filterable induced fowl tumors. In any event, it is probable that the lesion in the domestic rabbit is produced with much less multiplication of virus than is the case in the cottontail (270).

Rabbit skin can be rendered abnormally susceptible to papilloma virus infection by prior painting with methylcholanthrene (271). The interrelationship of papilloma agent and tar or methylcholanthrene in the induction of malignant growth in the rabbit has suggested some explanations of the mechanism of carcinogenesis. The fact that methylcholanthrene by itself and the papilloma agent by itself each induces only benign growths in the domestic rabbit in a limited period of time, whereas both acting together within this period produce malignant growths, suggests a complementary action (272–274). According to Rous and Friedewald (272), agents may reside in harmless form for some time in tissues and induce pathological changes only when carcinogens such as tar are introduced. Thus the carcinogenicity of a given material may be markedly affected by the introduction into the host of substances which are themselves either very weakly carcinogenic or non-carcinogenic, which need bear little or no chemical relation to the specific agent, and which may be applied subsequent to the application of the agent and at a site far removed from it.

Beard and his collaborators isolated, from extracts of the rabbit papilloma of cottontail rabbits, an infectious agent in yields proportional to the activity of the extracts from which it was derived (275–278). This agent was in the form of a complex nucleoprotein which was infective in amounts as small as 1×10^{-9} g. of the protein. The nucleic acid associated with the protein was of the thymus (deoxyribose) type. The properties of this agent are described in Table 50. On the basis of a molecular weight of 47,000,000 the infectious dose of 1×10^{-9} g. of protein corresponds with 56,800,000 molecules of the agent. This rather low infective titer has been recently increased by improved methods of administration of the agent (274). These consisted in the following: (a) rendering the skin hyperplastic by painting with equal parts of turpentine and acetone, and (b) covering the inoculated area immediately with paraffined gauze. The combination of inflamed skin and paraffined gauze pad apparently increased the efficacy of a given dose of the rabbit papilloma virus from 100 to 10,000 times.

As Harris has pointed out (279), those viruses which contain deoxyribonucleic acid also contain much less lipoid material (i.e., T_2 bacteriophage, vaccinia, and rabbit papilloma, with lipids about 1.5 to 5.7 %) than do those viruses which contain ribonucleic acid (i.e., chicken tumor and the eastern strain of equine encephalomyelitis, with lipids at about 50 %).

TABLE 50

PROPERTIES OF THE RABBIT PAPILLOMA AGENT (275–278)

N, %	P, %	S, %	Lipoid, %	Deoxyribonucleic acid, %	Sedimentation constant, *S*
15	0.9	2.2	1.46	8.7	280[1]

[1] Molecular weight approximately 47,000,000.

The horny excrescence formed in the Shope papilloma appears to be pseudokeratin (cf. 280) in nature, for on analysis the ratio of histidine: lysine:arginine is 1:2.3:2.5 (281). In the carcinomas arising from these growths, the corresponding ratios are 1:3.3:3.1.

An increased phospholipid turnover has been noted in the rabbit papilloma as compared with skin (281a).

The establishment of the transmissibility of the rabbit papilloma virus raised the question whether papillomas in other species might not contain a similar transmissible agent. Careful studies by Woglom (282) of the mouse papilloma induced by methylcholanthrene painting revealed that of 131 mice of the *RIII* strain inoculated with extracts of the papilloma and observed over a period of many months not one developed a tumor. It cannot be concluded that these papillomas do not contain a virus-like principle but only that, under conditions whereby rabbit and avian tumor viruses are revealed, nothing of the sort is suggested in mouse tumors. Indeed, with the exception of the principle for mammary tumors, no clear-cut evidence has yet been brought forward to show the presence of a virus-like agent in tumors of the mouse. If such agents in fact exist, it may be that the mouse holds on more tenaciously to some of its tumor viruses or that some of them are more labile than certain avian or rabbit viruses.

The problem of the possible existence of transmissible tumor viruses for mammalian tumors (other than the mouse mammary) is one which exerts a continuous fascination. The use of low-temperature preservation of tumors as an alternative to their maintenance by serial transplantation has been in some cases a valuable and economical adjunct to experimental work and in the case of the fowl virus tumors, such as the Rous, has been quite efficient (283–285). A review of many of the procedures has been published by Craigie (286). Gye and his colleagues (287–290) have observed that several mammalian tumors frozen at −79°, or frozen and dried, appeared to retain the capacity to induce tumors in host animals and, since it was believed that all cellular structure had been destroyed by the freezing-desiccation technique, that the transmittal of the neoplastic character was due to the transfer of some form of activated virus. The absence of living cells from such inocula was based on microscopic evidence, since filtration techniques have too often been equivocal and offer too many technical difficulties in the case of viruses of low titer and high lability. The virus concept of Gye and his colleagues was challenged by a number of investigators (291–297), the most important of whose findings were that (a) frozen and lyophilized mouse sarcoma cells would subsequently grow *in vitro* after reconstitution in glucose (292), (b) tumors frozen at −79° would produce growth only in mice that were genetically susceptible to fresh tissue grafts of the tumor tested (295), and (c) since tumors which arise in an inbred strain of mouse grow progressively only in individuals of that strain or in their F_1 hybrids, whereas tumors arising in F_1 hybrid mice will grow progressively only in such F_1 hybrids and in neither of the parental strains, if an activated virus were responsible for the induction of tumors, such tumors should be of the same genetic constitution as that of the host animal; the inoculation of frozen tissue (at $-79°$) from tumors of pure mouse strains into F_1 hybrid mice yielded tumors which progressively grew on transplantation into animals of both the pure strain and of the F_1 hybrid cross, an observation which shows that the tumor was derived from the pure strain donor and clearly was transmitted by the transfer of living cells from that donor (296).

A similar problem arises in the experiments reported by Stasney, Cantarow, and Paschkis (298) on the production of neoplasms in rats by the injection of fractions, histologically cell-free, from these tumors. Klein (299) used the same criteria as did Law (296) in evaluating such observations and, employing two transplantable mouse lymphosarcomas that had originated and been grown in genetically controlled animals, found that the tumors which resulted after subcutaneous inoculation of chromatin fractions of the tumor did not possess the genetic constitution of the host in which they arose, but that of the original donor tumor (cf. 300). It would appear that at the present time there is no evidence, other than the limited mammary tumor inciter in certain strains of mice, for the presence of cancer-inducing viruses in mammals. The occasional association of non-neoplastic viruses with tumors (cf. 301–303) may be adventitious.

The Possibility of Relatively Non-Specific Endogenous Carcinogens

The presence of specific inciting agents for tumors, such as the mammary tumor factor in the tissues of mice, and the viruses for sarcoma and papilloma in the tumors, respectively, of the chicken and of the rabbit, has been well established. The influence of the sex hormones on tumor development has frequently been alluded to (*vide infra*). Do tissues contain other possible carcinogenic agents produced endogenously from normal constituents by some as yet unknown mechanism? Several investigators have been concerned with this question and have tested the possibility by injecting non-aqueous extracts of human and animal tissues into mice of known spontaneous tumor incidence (304–306). In most cases a rise in tumor incidence of 3 to 25% has been noted in such mice after the injection of extracts of the liver, bile, and lung of cancerous and non-cancerous human beings and of certain animal tissues. The tumors so induced have been in various sites. A recent careful investigation of the problem by Hieger (307) has shown a total of 69 sarcomas at the site of injection of lipoid substances in approximately 2000 mice with an average latent period of 18 months; of these tumors, 63 were produced by unsaponifiable fractions derived from human subjects (cancerous or non-cancerous), an incidence of about 3 %. The observation that commercial cholesterol was carcinogenic in 25 out of 436 mice suggested that the carcinogenic factor in the non-saponifiable fractions of the fats may be either cholesterol itself or cholesterol associated with something else. The conclusion that has been reached from all these studies is that human tissues may contain carcinogens (for mice), but the presence of such materials is unrelated to whether the human source was cancerous or non-cancerous.

There are, however, several points in this sort of approach which require clarification. The extraction procedures applied to complex tissues have frequently been brutal, the vehicles employed for the administration have invariably been heterogeneous in nature and untested independently, and the doses used have been relatively huge. The tissues studied have been, in nearly all cases, derived from species foreign to the test animal, and the carcinogenicity of the tissue extract refers not to the species from which the extract was obtained but to the susceptibility of the laboratory mouse to such material. The question therefore arises as to how far such carcinogenicity in the mouse is due to the injection of materials from a foreign species. The presence of denatured and altered proteins cannot be excluded, even in non-aqueous extracts. In this connection it may be wondered why extensive control experiments on extracts of mouse tissues injected into mice were not instituted. Another curious finding is not so much concerned with the fact that the tissues of non-cancerous human beings yielded extracts which produced—in mice—the same tumor incidence as did extracts of the tissues of cancerous human beings, but that extracts of cancers of any species, including the mouse, demonstrated—again in mice—very little carcinogenic potency. The relatively low increase in tumor incidence given by the most active extracts shows in any event that the carcinogenic agent or agents in such extracts are quite weak. Although there is no doubt that the tumor incidence in mice is increased by injection of non-aqueous extracts of human tissues, it is difficult to avoid the impression at the present time that the results merely demonstrate the relative susceptibility of mice to carcinogenic agents of most any and all sorts (*vide infra*) and that such agents may possibly be artifacts, products of uncontrolled methods of preparation, and not necessarily present naturally in the original tissue. The problem of whether intrinsic carcinogenic agents exist within tissues is important, but the methods appropriate to its solution require considerable care.

References

(1) Loeb, L., *J. Natl. Cancer Inst.* **1,** 169 (1940).
(2) Gardner, W. U., *Arch. Pathol.* **27,** 138 (1939).

(3) Gardner, W. U., *Surgery* **16,** 8 (1944).
(4) Nathanson, I. T., *New Engl. J. Med.* **231,** 764, 795 (1944).
(5) Burrows, H., and Horning, E. S., *Brit. Med. Bull.* **4,** 367 (1947).
(6) Hertz, R., *Cancer Research* **11,** 393 (1951).
(7) Gardner, W. U., *Advances in Cancer Research* **1,** 173 (1953).
(8) Furth, J., *Cancer Research* **13,** 477 (1953).
(9) Lathrop, A. E. C., and Loeb, L., *J. Cancer Research* **1,** 1 (1916).
(10) Cori, C. F., *J. Exptl. Med.* **45,** 983 (1927).
(11) Murray, W. S., *J. Cancer Research* **14,** 602 (1930).
(12) Allen, E., and Doisy, E. A., *J. Am. Med. Assoc.* **81,** 819 (1923).
(13) Shimkin, M. B., *in* "Mammary Tumors in Mice." American Association for the Advancement of Science, Washington, D. C., 1945.
(14) Dodds, E. C., Goldberg, L., Lawson, W., and Robinson, R., *Nature* **141,** 247 (1938).
(15) Doisy, E. A., *Cold Spring Harbor Symposia Quant. Biol.* **9,** 21 (1942).
(16) Dodds, E. C., *Biochem. J.* **39,** i (1945).
(17) Twombly, G. H., and Schoenewaldt, E. F., *Cancer* **4,** 296 (1951).
(18) Lacassagne, A., *Compt. rend.* **195,** 630 (1932).
(19) Lacassagne, A., *Compt. rend. soc. biol.* **114,** 427 (1933); **115,** 937 (1934); **122,** 183, 1060 (1936).
(20) Lacassagne, A., *Am. J. Cancer* **37,** 414 (1939).
(21) Bonser, G. M., *J. Pathol. Bacteriol.* **42,** 169 (1936); **56,** 15 (1944).
(22) Cramer, W., *Am. J. Cancer* **38,** 463 (1940).
(23) Suntzeff, V., Kirtz, M. M., Blumenthal, H. T., and Loeb, L., *Cancer Research* **1,** 446 (1941).
(24) Shimkin, M. B., and Andervont, H. B., *J. Natl. Cancer Inst.* **2,** 611 (1942).
(25) Haagensen, C. D., and Randall, H. T., *Arch. Pathol.* **33,** 411 (1942).
(26) Huseby, R. A., and Bittner, J. J., *Cancer Research* **11,** 450 (1951).
(27) Strong, L. C., *Proc. Soc. Exptl. Biol. Med.* **59,** 217 (1945).
(28) Bonser, G. M., and Orr, J. W., *J. Pathol. Bacteriol.* **49,** 171 (1939).
(29) Mider, G. B., and Morton, J. J., *Proc. Soc. Exptl. Biol. Med.* **42,** 583 (1939).
(30) Engelbreth-Holm, J., *Cancer Research* **1,** 109 (1941).
(31) Orr, J. W., *J. Pathol. Bacteriol.* **55,** 483 (1943).
(32) Kirschbaum, A., Lawrason, F. D., Kaplan, H. S., and Bittner, J. J., *Proc. Soc. Exptl. Biol. Med.* **55,** 141 (1944).
(33) Dmochowski, L., and Orr, J. W., *Brit. J. Cancer* **3,** 376 (1949).
(34) Lacassagne, A., *Compt. rend. soc. biol.* **129,** 641 (1938).
(35) Lacassagne, A., *Bull. assoc. franç étude cancer* **27,** 96 (1938).
(36) Gardner, W. U., *Cancer Research* **3,** 92 (1943).
(37) Shimkin, M. B., and Grady, H. G., *J. Natl. Cancer Inst.* **1,** 119 (1940).
(38) Bonser, G. M., and Robson, J. M., *J. Pathol Bacteriol.* **51,** 9 (1940).
(39) Shimkin, M. B., and Grady, H. G., *Proc. Soc. Exptl. Biol. Med.* **45,** 246 (1940).
(40) Hooker, C. W., Gardner, W. U., and Pfeiffer, C. A., *J. Am. Med. Assoc.* **115,** 443 (1940).
(41) Hooker, C. W., and Pfeiffer, C. A., *Cancer Research* **2,** 759 (1942).
(42) Shimkin, M. B., Grady, H. G., and Andervont, H. B., *J. Natl. Cancer Inst.* **2,** 65 (1941).
(43) Gardner, W. U., *Cancer Research* **5,** 497 (1945).
(44) Gardner, W. U., *Cancer Research* **3,** 757 (1943).
(45) Twombly, G. H., Meisel, D., and Stout, A. P., *Cancer* **2,** 884 (1949).
(46) Huggins, C., and Moulder, P. V., *Cancer Research* **5,** 510 (1945).
(47) Gardner, W. U., *Cancer Research* **1,** 345 (1941).

(48) Kochakian, C. D., and Murlin, J. R., *J. Nutrition* **10**, 437 (1935).
(49) Thorn, G. W., and Engel, L. L., *J. Exptl. Med.* **68**, 299 (1938).
(50) Albright, F., *Harvey Lectures* **38**, 123 (1942–43).
(51) Heiman, J., *Cancer Research* **4**, 31 (1944).
(52) Wooley, G. W., and Little, C. C., *Cancer Research* **5**, 193, 203, 211 (1945).
(53) Gardner, W. U., *Cancer Research* **1**, 632 (1941).
(54) Atkinson, W. B., and Dickie, M. M., *Cancer Research* **13**, 165 (1953).
(55) Frantz, M. J., and Kirschbaum, A., *Cancer Research* **9**, 257 (1949).
(56) Houssay, A., Higgins, G. M., and Bennett, W. A., *Cancer Research* **11**, 297 (1951).
(57) Wooley, G. W., and Little, C. C., *Proc. Natl. Acad. Sci.* **32**, 239 (1946).
(58) Ferguson, D. J., and Visscher, M. B., *Cancer Research* **13**, 405 (1953).
(59) Wooley, G. W., Dickie, M. M., and Little, C. C., *Cancer Research* **13**, 231 (1953).
(60) Smith, F. W., Gardner, W. U., Li, M. H., and Kaplan, H., *Cancer Research* **9**, 193 (1949).
(61) Dickens, F., *Nature* **159**, 839 (1947).
(62) Gough, N., and Shoppee, C. W., *Biochem. J.* **54**, 630 (1953).
(63) Karnofsky, D. A., Nathanson, I. T., and Aub, J. C., *Cancer Research* **4**, 772 (1944).
(64) Twombly, G. H., and Taylor, H. C., Jr., *Cancer Research* **2**, 811 (1942).
(65) Eisen, M. J., *Cancer Research* **2**, 632 (1942).
(66) Nelson, W. O., *Yale J. Biol. and Med.* **17**, 217 (1944).
(67) Geschickter, C. F., *Radiology* **33**, 439 (1939).
(68) Dunning, W. F., and Curtis, M. R., *Cancer Research* **12**, 702 (1952).
(69) Dunning, W. F., Curtis, M. R., and Segaloff, A., *Cancer Research* **7**, 511 (1947).
(70) Shay, H., Harris, C., and Gruenstein, M., *J. Natl. Cancer Inst.* **13**, 307 (1952).
(71) Geyer, R. P., Bryant, J. E., Bleisch, V. R., Peirce, E. M., and Stare, F. J., *Cancer Research* **13**, 503 (1953).
(72) Lipschütz, A., Thibaut, R., and Vargas, L., Jr., *Cancer Research* **2**, 45 (1942).
(73) Lipschütz, A., Luco, J. V., and Zanartu, J., *Cancer Research* **2**, 200 (1942).
(74) Lipschütz, A., Vera, O., and Gonzales, S., *Cancer Reseach* **2**, 204 (1942).
(75) Vargas, L., Jr., *Cancer Research* **3**, 309 (1943).
(76) Lipschütz, A., and Maas, M., *Cancer Research* **4**, 18 (1944).
(77) Lipschütz, A., and Schwartz, J., *Cancer Research* **4**, 24 (1944).
(78) Lipschütz, A., Bruzzone, S., and Fuenzalida, F., *Cancer Research* **4**, 179 (1944).
(79) Lipschütz, A., *Rev. Canad. Biol.* **10**, 341, 1951.
(80) Lipschütz, A., Yanine, D., Schwarz, J., Bruzzone, S., Acuna, J., and Silberman, S., *Cancer Research* **5**, 515 (1945).
(81) Woodruff, L. M., *Cancer Research* **1**, 367 (1941).
(82) Mulligan, R. M., *Arch. Pathol.* **39**, 162 (1945).
(83) Allen, E., and Gardner, W. U., *Cancer Research* **1**, 359 (1941).
(84) Pan, S. C., and Gardner, W. U., *Cancer Research* **8**, 337 (1948).
(85) Pfeiffer, C. A., *Cancer Research* **9**, 277 (1949).
(86) Burrows, H., *J. Pathol. Bacteriol.* **51**, 385 (1940).
(87) Greene, H. S. N., and Newton, B. L., *Cancer* **1**, 82 (1948).
(88) Biskind, G. R., Kordan, B., and Biskind, M. S., *Cancer Research* **10**, 309 (1950).
(89) Li, M. H., and Gardner, W. U., *Cancer Research* **9**, 35 (1949).
(90) Biskind, G. R., Bernstein, D. E., and Gospe, S. M., *Cancer Research* **13**, 216 (1953).
(91) Peckham, B. M., and Greene, R. R., *Cancer Research* **12**, 654 (1952).
(92) Iglesias, R., Mardones, E., and Lipschütz, A., *Brit. J. Cancer* **7**, 221 (1953).

(93) Gardner, W. U., *Cancer Research* **8,** 397 (1948).
(94) Furth, J., *Cancer Research* **13,** 477 (1953).
(95) Kaplan, H. S., *J. Natl. Cancer Inst.* **11,** 125 (1950).
(96) Horning, E. S., *Brit. J. Cancer* **3,** 211 (1949).
(97) Moon, H. D., Simpson, M. E., Li, C. H., and Evans, H. M., *Cancer Research* **10,** 297, 364, 549 (1950).
(98) Davidson, W. F., Snair, W. D., and Lei, H. P., *Endocrinology* **46,** 273 (1950).
(99) Moon, H. D., Simpson, M. E., Li, C. H., and Evans, H. M., *Cancer Research* **12,** 448 (1952).
(100) Andervont, H. B., *J. Natl. Cancer Inst.* **11,** 581 (1950).
(101) Agnew, L. R. C., and Gardner, W. U., *Cancer Research* **12,** 757 (1952).
(102) Rumsfeld, H. W., Jr., Miller, W. L., Jr., and Baumann, C. A., *Cancer Research* **11,** 814 (1951).
(103) Bielschowsky, F., *Brit. J. Exptl. Pathol.* **25,** 1 (1944).
(104) Paschkis, K. E., Cantarow, A., and Stasney, J., *Cancer Research* **8,** 257 (1948).
(105) Kirkman, H., and Bacon, R. L., *J. Natl. Cancer Inst.* **13,** 745, 757 (1952).
(106) Dunning, W. F., Curtis, M. R., and Segaloff, A., *Cancer Research* **7,** 511 (1947).
(107) Dickie, M. M., and Wooley, G. W., *Cancer Research* **9,** 372 (1949).
(108) Cramer, W., and Horning, E. S., *Lancet* **230,** 247 (1936).
(109) Burrows, H., *Am. J. Cancer* **28,** 741 (1936).
(110) Gardner, W. U., and Strong, L. C., *Yale J. Biol. and Med.* **12,** 543 (1940).
(111) Zondek, B., *Am. J. Cancer* **33,** 555 (1938).
(112) Nelson, W. O., *Am. J. Physiol.* **133,** 398 (1941).
(113) Segaloff, A., and Dunning, W. F., *Endocrinology* **36,** 238 (1945).
(114) Gorbman, A., *Proc. Soc. Exptl. Biol. Med.* **71,** 237 (1949).
(115) Furth, J., Gadsden, E. L., and Upton, A. C., *Cancer Research* **12,** 739 (1952).
(116) Furth, J., Burnett, W. T., Jr., and Gadsden, E. L., *Cancer Research* **13,** 298 (1953).
(117) Gardner, W. U., Allen, E., and Smith, G. E., *Proc. Soc. Exptl. Biol. Med.* **46,** 511 (1941).
(118) Goldberg, R. C., and Chaikoff, I. L., *Proc. Soc. Exptl. Biol. Med.* **76,** 563 (1951).
(119) Gorbman, A., *Proc. Soc. Exptl. Biol. Med.* **80,** 538 (1952).
(120) Purves, H. D., Griesbach, W. E., and Kennedy, T. H., *Brit. J. Cancer* **5,** 301 (1951).
(121) Bielschowsky, F., *Brit. J. Cancer* **7,** 203 (1953).
(122) Doniach, I., *Brit. J. Cancer* **7,** 181 (1953).
(123) Bielschowsky, F., *Brit. J. Exptl. Pathol.* **25,** 90 (1944); **26,** 270 (1945).
(124) Hall, W. H., and Bielschowsky, F., *Brit. J. Cancer* **3,** 534 (1949).
(125) Bielschowsky, F., Griesbach, W. E., Hall, W. H., Kennedy, T. H., and Purves, H. D., *Brit. J. Cancer* **3,** 541 (1949).
(126) Money, W. L., and Rawson, R. W., *Cancer* **3,** 321 (1950).
(127) Dubnik, C. S., Morris, H. P., and Dalton, A. J., *J. Natl. Cancer Inst.* **10,** 815 (1950).
(128) Morris, H. P., Dubnik Green, C. S., and Dalton, A. J., *J. Natl. Cancer Inst.* **11,** 805 (1951).
(129) Morris, H. P., Dalton, A. J., and Dubnik Green, C. S., *J. Clin. Endocrinol.* **11,** 1281 (1951).
(130) Morris, H. P., and Green, C. S., *Science* **114,** 44 (1951).
(131) Dalton, A. J., Morris, H. P., and Dubnik, C. S., *J. Natl. Cancer Inst.* **9,** 201 (1948).
(132) Bielschowsky, F., *Brit. J. Cancer* **3,** 547 (1949).

(133) MacKenzie, C. G., and MacKenzie, J. B., *Endocrinology* **32,** 185 (1943).
(134) Morris, H. P., *Texas Repts. Biol. and Med.* **10,** 1028 (1952).
(135) Wollman, S. H., Morris, H. P., and Green, C. S., *J. Natl. Cancer Inst.* **12,** 27 (1951).
(136) Wollman, S. H., Scow, R. O., Wagner, B., and Morris, H. P., *J. Natl. Cancer Inst.* **13,** 785 (1953).
(136a) Bielschowsky, F., and Hall, W. H., *Brit. J. Cancer* **7,** 358 (1953).
(137) Stevens, C. D., Stewart, P. H., Quinlin, P. M., and Meinken, M. A., *Cancer Research* **9,** 488 (1949).
(138) Stevens, C. D., Meinken, M. A., Quinlin, P. M., and Stewart, P. H., *Cancer Research* **10,** 155 (1950).
(139) Back, A., and Walaszek, E. J., *Cancer Research* **13,** 552 (1953).
(140) Gardner, W. U., *Publ. Am. Assoc. Advancement Sci.* No. **4,** 67 (1937).
(141) Lacassagne, A., *Compt. rend. soc. biol.* **126,** 193 (1937).
(142) Gardner, W. U., Kirschbaum, A., and Strong, L. C., *Arch. Pathol.* **29,** 1 (1940).
(143) Murphy, J. B., and Sturm, E., *Cancer Research* **9,** 88 (1949).
(144) Gardner, W. U., Dougherty, T. F., and Williams, W. L., *Cancer Research* **4,** 73 (1944).
(145) Kaplan, H. S., and Brown, M. B., *Cancer Research* **11,** 706 (1951); **12,** 445 (1952).
(146) Gardner, W. U., *Proc. Soc. Exptl. Biol. Med.* **75,** 434 (1950).
(147) Zondek, B., *Am. J. Cancer* **33,** 555 (1938).
(148) McEndy, D. P., Boon, M. C., and Furth, J., *J. Natl. Cancer Inst.* **3,** 227 (1942).
(149) White, A., and Dougherty, T. F., *Proc. Soc. Exptl. Biol. Med.* **56,** 26 (1944); *Endocrinology* **36,** 16 (1945).
(150) Dougherty, T. F., and White, A., *Proc. Soc. Exptl. Biol. Med.* **53,** 132 (1943); *Endocrinology* **35,** 1 (1944).
(151) Murphy, J. B., and Sturm, E., *Cancer Research* **10,** 191 (1950).
(152) Kaplan, H. S., Marder, S. N., and Brown, M. B., *Cancer Research* **11,** 629 (1951).
(153) Sturm, E., and Murphy, J. B., *Cancer Research* **4,** 384 (1944).
(154) Law, L. W., and Miller, J. H., *J. Natl. Cancer Inst.* **11,** 253 (1950).
(155) McEndy, D. P., Boon, M. C., and Furth, J., *Cancer Research* **4,** 377 (1944).
(156) Law, L. W., and Miller, J. H., *J. Natl. Cancer Inst.* **11,** 425 (1950).
(157) Kaplan, H. S., *J. Natl. Cancer Inst.* **11,** 83 (1950).
(158) Law, L. W., *J. Natl. Cancer Inst.* **12,** 789 (1952).
(158a) Symeonidis, A., Mulay, A. S., and Burgoyne, F. H., *J. Natl. Cancer Inst.* **14,** 805 (1954).
(158b) Griffin, A. C., Rinfret, A. P., and Corsigilia, V. F., *Cancer Research* **13,** 77 (1953).
(159) Pybus, F. C., and Miller, E. W., *Nature* **142,** 872 (1938); Miller, E. W., Orr, J. W., and Pybus, F. C., *J. Pathol. Bacteriol.* **55,** 137 (1943).
(160) Fraenkel-Conrat, H., Simpson, M. E., and Evans, H. M., *J. Biol. Chem.* **147,** 99 (1943).
(161) Kochakian, C. D., *J. Biol. Chem.* **155,** 579 (1944).
(162) Price, W. H., Cori, C. F., and Colowick, S. P., *J. Biol. Chem.* **160,** 633 (1945); Price, W. H., Slein, M. W., Colowick, S. P., and Cori, G. T., *Federation Proc.* **5,** 150 (1946).
(163) Lathrop, A. E. C., and Loeb, L., *J. Exptl. Med.* **28,** 475 (1918).
(164) Staff of the Roscoe B. Jackson Memorial Laboratory, *Science* **78,** 465 (1933).
(165) Andervont, H. B., *in* "Mammary Tumors in Mice." American Association for the Advancement of Science, Washington, D. C., 1945.
(166) Korteweg, R., *Genetics* **18,** 350 (1936).

(167) Bittner, J. J., *Science* **84,** 162 (1936).
(168) Bittner, J. J., *Am. J. Cancer* **30,** 530 (1937); **36,** 44 (1939).
(169) Bittner, J. J., *Trans. Coll. Physicians Phila.* (4) **9** (3), 129 (1941).
(170) Bittner, J. J., *Cancer Research* **2,** 710 (1942).
(171) Bittner, J. J., Research Conference on Cancer, American Association for the Advancement of Science, Washington, D. C., 1945.
(172) Andervont, H. B., *J. Natl. Cancer Inst.* **1,** 147 (1940); **2,** 7, 13, 307 (1941); **3,** 359 (1943).
(173) De Ome, K. B., *Am. J. Cancer* **40,** 231 (1940).
(174) Dmochowski, L., and Gye, W. E., *Brit. J. Exptl. Pathol.* **24,** 223 (1943).
(175) Miller, E. W., and Pybus, F. C., *Cancer Research* **4,** 94 (1945).
(176) Andervont, H. B., *J. Natl. Cancer Inst.* **5,** 397 (1945).
(177) Andervont, H. B., Shimkin, M. B., and Bryan, W. R., *J. Natl. Cancer Inst.* **3,** 309 (1942).
(178) Fekete, E., and Little, C. C., *Cancer Research* **2,** 525 (1942).
(179) Andervont, H. B., *J. Natl. Cancer Inst.* **5,** 383 (1945).
(180) Miller, E. W., and Pybus, F. C., *Cancer Research* **5,** 94 (1945).
(181) Dmochowski, L., *Brit. J. Cancer* **6,** 249 (1952).
(181a) Heston, W. E., and Andervont, H. B., *J. Natl. Cancer Inst.* **4,** 403 (1944).
(182) Dmochowski, L., *Brit. J. Exptl. Pathol.* **26,** 267 (1945).
(183) Bittner, J. J., *Public Health Repts.* (*U.S.*) **54,** 1827 (1939).
(184) Woolley, G. W., Law, L. W., and Little, C. C., *Cancer Research* **1,** 955 (1941).
(185) Visscher, M. B., Green, R. G., and Bittner, J. J., *Proc. Soc. Exptl. Biol. Med.* **49,** 94 (1942).
(186) Kahler, H., Bryan, W. R., and Sipe, H. M., *J. Natl. Cancer Inst.* **4,** 38 (1943).
(187) Barnum, C. P., and Huseby, R. A., *Cancer Research* **10,** 523 (1950).
(188) Huseby, R. A., and Barnum, C. P., and Bittner, J. J., *Cancer Research* **10,** 516 (1950).
(189) Graff, S., Moore, D. H., Stanley, W. M., Randall, H. T., and Haagensen, C. D., *Cancer* **2,** 755 (1949).
(190) Andervont, H. B., *J. Natl. Cancer Inst.* **11,** 545 (1950).
(191) Andervont, H. B., *J. Natl. Cancer Inst.* **5,** 391 (1945).
(192) Shimkin, H. B., and Andervont, H. B., *J. Natl. Cancer Inst.* **1,** 599 (1941).
(193) Twombly, G. H., *Proc. Soc. Exptl. Biol. Med.* **44,** 617 (1940).
(194) Bagg, H. J., and Jackson, J., *Am. J. Cancer* **30,** 539 (1937).
(195) Strong, L. C., *Proc. Soc. Exptl. Biol. Med.* **53,** 257 (1943).
(196) Andervont, H. B., *J. Natl. Cancer Inst.* **11,** 73 (1950).
(197) Heston, W. E., Deringer, M. K., Dunn, T. B., and Levillain, W. D., *J. Natl. Cancer Inst.* **10,** 1139 (1950).
(198) Dmochowski, L., *Brit. J. Cancer* **7,** 73 (1953).
(199) Bittner, J. J., *Cancer Research* **8,** 625 (1948).
(200) Smith, F. W., *Cancer Research* **8,** 641 (1948).
(201) Andervont, H. B., and McEleny, W. J., *J. Natl. Cancer Inst.* **2,** 7 (1941).
(202) Kirschbaum, A., Williams, W. L., and Bittner, J. J., *Cancer Research* **6,** 354 (1946).
(203) Bittner, J. J., *Public Health Repts.* (*U.S.*) **54,** 1113 (1939).
(204) Murray, W. S., and Little, C. C., *Am. J. Cancer* **37,** 536 (1939).
(205) Andervont, H. B., and Dunn, T. B., *J. Natl. Cancer Inst.* **10,** 895 (1950).
(206) Andervont, H. B., *J. Natl. Cancer Inst.* **10,** 1157 (1950).
(207) Dmochowski, L., and Orr, J. W., *Brit. J. Cancer* **3,** 520 (1949).
(208) Dmochowski, L., *Brit. J. Cancer* **3,** 525 (1949).

(209) Andervont, H. B., and Dunn, T. B., *J. Natl. Cancer Inst.* **8,** 227 (1948).
(210) Mühlbock, O., *J. Natl. Cancer Inst.* **10,** 861 (1950); **12,** 819 (1952).
(211) Bittner, J. J., *Cancer Research* **12,** 387 (1952).
(212) Andervont, H. B., and Bryan, W. R., *J. Natl. Cancer Inst* **5,** 143 (1944).
(213) Green, R. G., Moosey, M. M., and Bittner, J. J., *Proc. Soc. Exptl. Biol. Med.* **61,** 115 (1946).
(214) Gorer, P. A., and Law, L. W., *Brit. J. Cancer* **3,** 90 (1949).
(215) Law, L. W., and Malmgren, R. A., *J. Natl. Cancer Inst.* **11,** 1259 (1951).
(216) Law, L. W., *Cancer Research* **4,** 257 (1944).
(217) Furth, J., *Physiol. Revs.* **26,** 47 (1946).
(218) Gross, L., *Ann. N. Y. Acad. Sci.* **54,** 1184 (1952).
(219) Rous, P., *Am. J. Cancer* **28,** 233 (1936).
(220) Shope, R. E., *J. Exptl. Med.* **58,** 607 (1933).
(221) Lucké, B., and Schlumberger, H., *J. Exptl. Med.* **70,** 257 (1939).
(222) Lucké, B., *Ann. N. Y. Acad. Sci.* **54,** 1093 (1952).
(223) Meryl Rose, S., and Rose, F. C., *Cancer Research* **12,** 1 (1952).
(224) Burnet, F. M., "Virus as Organism." Harvard University Press, Cambridge, 1945.
(225) Carr, J. G., *Brit. J. Exptl. Pathol.* **24,** 133 (1943).
(226) Claude, A., *Science* **91,** 77 (1940).
(227) Pollard, A., *Brit. J. Exptl. Pathol.* **20,** 429 (1939).
(228) McIntosh, J., *Biochem. J.* **39,** vii (1945).
(229) Harris, R. J. C., Roe, E. M. F., and Beale, R. N., *Acta Unio Intern. contre Cancrum* **7,** 372 (1951).
(230) Bailey, K., *Biochem. J.* **31,** 1406 (1937).
(231) Block, R. J., *J. Biol. Chem.* **119,** 765; **120,** 467 (1937).
(232) Greenstein, J. P., and Jenrette, W. V., *J. Natl. Cancer Inst.* **1,** 91 (1940).
(233) Greenstein, J. P., *Advances in Protein Chem.* **1,** 210 (1944).
(234) Greenstein, J. P., and Leuthardt, F. M., *J. Natl. Cancer Inst.* **5,** 111 (1940).
(235) Carr, J. G., and Harris, R. J. C., *Brit. J. Cancer* **5,** 83 (1951).
(236) Haddow, A., *Growth* **11,** 339 (1947).
(237) Murphy, J. B., and Sturm, E., *Cancer Research* **1,** 609 (1941).
(238) McIntosh, J., and Selbie, F. R., *Brit. J. Exptl. Pathol.* **20,** 49 (1939).
(239) Peacock, P. R., *Am. J. Cancer* **25,** 49 (1935).
(240) Murphy, J. B., and Sturm, E., *Cancer Research* **6,** 11 (1946).
(241) Peacock, P. R., and Peacock, A., *Brit. J. Cancer* **7,** 120 (1953).
(242) Peacock, P. R., *Biochem. J.* **39,** ix (1945).
(243) Haddow, A., *J. Pathol Bacteriol.* **47,** 567 (1938).
(244) Carr, J. G., *Brit. J. Exptl. Pathol.* **23,** 221 (1942); **27,** 1 (1946).
(245) Mellanby, E., *J. Pathol. Bacteriol.* **47,** 47 (1938).
(246) Carr, J. G., *Brit. J. Cancer* **7,** 131 (1953).
(247) Duran-Reynals, F., *Ann. N. Y. Acad. Sci,* **54,** 977 (1952).
(248) Stubbs, E. L., and Furth, J., *J. Exptl. Med.* **61,** 593 (1935).
(249) Gottschalk, R. G., *Cancer Research* **3,** 649 (1943).
(250) Stern, K. G., and Kirschbaum, A., *Science* **89,** 610 (1939).
(251) Gottschalk, R. G., *Cancer Research* **6,** 270 (1946).
(252) Burmester, B. R., Prickett, C. D., and Belding, T. C. *Cancer Research* **6,** 189 (1946).
(253) Peacock, P. R., *Cancer Research* **6,** 311 (1946).
(254) Duran-Reynals, F., *Cancer Research* **2,** 343 (1942).
(255) Duran-Reynals, F., *Cancer Research* **3,** 569 (1943).

(256) Shrigley, E. W., Greene, H. S. N., and Duran-Reynals, F., *Cancer Research* **5,** 356 (1945).
(257) Duran-Reynals, F., *Cancer Research* **7,** 103 (1947).
(258) Duran-Reynals, F., and King, J. W., *Cancer Research* **7,** 21 (1947).
(259) Duran-Reynals, F., and Freire, P. M., *Cancer Research* **13,** 376 (1953).
(260) Duran-Reynals, F., Burmester, B. R., Cottral, G. E., and Bryan, E., *Cancer Research* **13,** 408 (1953).
(261) Rous, P., Kidd, J. G., and Beard, J. W., *J. Exptl. Med.* **64,** 385 (1936).
(262) Rous, P., Beard, J. W., and Kidd, J. G., *J. Exptl. Med.* **64,** 401 (1936).
(263) Rous, P., and Kidd, J. G., *J. Exptl. Med.* **67,** 399 (1938).
(264) Kidd, J. G., *J. Exptl. Med.* **67,** 551 (1938); **68,** 703 (1938); **70,** 583 (1939).
(265) Rous, P., and Kidd, J. G., *J. Exptl. Med.* **69,** 399 (1939); **71,** 787 (1940).
(266) Friedewald, W. F., and Kidd, J. G., *J. Exptl. Med.* **79,** 591 (1944).
(267) Kidd, J. G., and Rous, P., *J. Exptl. Med.* **71,** 469, 813 (1940).
(268) Syverton, J. T., Dascomb, H. E., Wells, E. B., Koomen, J., Jr., and Berry, G. P., *Cancer Research* **10,** 440 (1950).
(269) Syverton, J. T., Wells, E. B., Koomen, J., Jr., Dascomb, H. E., and Berry, G. P., *Cancer Research* **10,** 474 (1950).
(270) Selbie, F. R., Robinson, R. H. M., and Shope, R. E., *Brit. J. Cancer* **2,** 375 (1948).
(271) Friedewald, W. F., *J. Exptl. Med.* **75,** 197 (1942).
(272) Rous, P., and Friedewald, W. F., *J. Exptl. Med.* **79,** 511 (1944).
(273) Friedewald, W. F., and Rous, P., *J. Exptl. Med.* **80,** 127 (1944).
(274) Friedewald, W. F., *J. Exptl. Med.* **80,** 65 (1944).
(275) Beard, J. W., Bryan, W. R., and Wyckoff, R. W. G., *J. Infectious Diseases* **65,** 43 (1939).
(276) Bryan, W. R., and Beard, J. W., *J. Infectious Diseases* **65,** 306 (1939).
(277) Taylor, A. R., Beard, D., Sharp, D. G., and Beard, J. W., *J. Infectious Diseases,* **71,** 110 (1942).
(278) Neurath, H., Cooper, G. R., Sharp, D. G., Taylor, A. R., Beard, D., and Beard, J. W., *J. Biol. Chem.* **140,** 293 (1941).
(279) Harris, R. J. C., *Advances in Cancer Research* **1,** 233 (1953).
(280) Block, R. J., *J. Biol. Chem.* **121,** 761 (1937).
(281) Sherp, H. W., and Syverton, J. T., *Cancer Research* **9,** 12 (1949).
(281a) Cornatzer, W. E., Gallo, D. G., Davidson, J. P., and Fischer, R. G., *Cancer Research* **13,** 795 (1953).
(282) Woglom, W. H., *Cancer Research* **5,** 420 (1945).
(283) Carr, J. G., and Harris, R. J. C., *Brit. J. Cancer* **5,** 95 (1951).
(284) Harris, R. J. C., *Vacuum* **1,** 1 (1951).
(285) Burmester, B. R., *Cancer Research* **10,** 708 (1950).
(286) Craigie, J., *Advances in Cancer Research* **2,** 197 (1954).
(287) Gye, W. E., *Brit. Med. J.* **i,** 511 (1949).
(288) Gye, W. E., Begg, A. M., Mann, I., and Craigie, J., *Brit. J. Cancer* **3,** 259 (1949).
(289) Mann, I., *Brit. Med. J.* **ii,** 251, 253 (1949).
(290) Mann, I., and Dunn, W. J., *Brit. Med. J.* **ii,** 255 (1949).
(291) Passey, R. D., and Dmochowski, L., *Brit. Med. J.* **ii,** 1129 (1950).
(292) Passey, R. D., Dmochowski, L., Lasnitzki, I., and Millard, A., *Brit. Med. J.* **ii,** 1134 (1950).
(293) Dmochowski, L., and Millard, A., *Brit. Med. J.* **ii,** 1136 (1950).
(294) Hirschberg, E., and Rusch, H. P., *Cancer Research* **10,** 335 (1950).
(295) Bittner, J. J., and Imagawa, D. T., *Cancer Research* **10,** 739 (1950).

(296) Law, L. W., *Cancer Research* **11,** 795 (1951).
(297) Walsh, L. B., Greiff, D., and Blumenthal, H. T., *Cancer Research* **10,** 726 (1950).
(298) Stasney, J., Cantarow, A., and Paschkis, K. E., *Ann. N. Y. Acad. Sci.* **54,** 1177 (1952).
(299) Klein, G., *Cancer Research* **12,** 589 (1952).
(300) Tourtellotte, W. W., and Storer, J. B., *Cancer Research* **10,** 783 (1950).
(301) Rivers, T. M., and Pearce, L., *J. Exptl. Med.* **42,** 523 (1925).
(302) Law, L. W., and Dunn, T. B., *J. Natl. Cancer Inst.* **11,** 1037 (1951).
(303) Duran-Reynals, F., *Ann. N. Y. Acad. Sci.* **54,** 977 (1952).
(304) Shabad, L. M., *Cancer Research* **5,** 405 (1945); this article contains an extensive bibliography.
(305) Steiner, P. E., *Cancer Research* **2,** 425 (1942).
(306) Wachtel, H., *Science* **103,** 556 (1946); *Nature* **158,** 98 (1946).
(307) Hieger, I., *Brit. J. Cancer* **3,** 123 (1949).

ATTEMPTS AT CONTROL OF TUMOR INDUCTION AND OF TUMOR GROWTH

Chapter V

Nutrition

Introduction

A tumor is a living entity with a usual growth rate to varying degree in excess of that of surrounding host tissues. It might, therefore, be expected that, compared with the nutritional needs of the host, the nutritional needs of the tumor would differ in magnitude and possibly in kind. It is obvious, however, that the dietary materials reach the tumor only after passing through the alimentary system of the host, and any attempt to influence the course of development of a tumor must take, necessarily, the following possibilities into account: (a) that the dietary materials reach the tumor in an unaltered state, (b) that an excess of any dietary component may be excreted, detoxified, or stored in inaccessible tissues by the host before it reaches the tumor, and (c) that the materials essential for initiation and development of the tumor are actually supplied by the tissues of the host which, in turn, utilizes the dietary materials for replenishment of its own stores. Despite the tremendous progress made within the past decade, the full nutritional requirements for any species of animal are not yet known. Still less is known about the nutritional requirements of any kind of tumor. In the absence of completely adequate synthetic diets composed of accurately measured and known constituents, experiments in this field have had to be conducted along more or less empirical lines. The frequently unknown contribution to the nutrition of the host by the metabolic activity of bacterial flora in the intestine provides another source of uncertainty in the employment of a standardized diet.

Under otherwise controlled conditions, the nutritive requirements of an animal are set by the limits of growth, maintenance, and energy for specific function of the tissues of the animal and constitute, together with the gases of the atmosphere and perhaps still other as yet unknown environmental influences, the exogenous factors necessary for its survival. The regulation of growth and maintenance, as well as of specific physiological function, is, however, in large measure a property of endogenous factors within the animal, produced and controlled by glands of internal secretion. The normal existence of the animal is thus the result of the integrated and harmonious blending of exogenous and endogenous factors such that, until the unknown processes of senescence intervene, a state of approximate physiological equilibrium is maintained. The presence of an abnormally developing tissue within the animal may be expected to affect this normal equilibrium with the result that, for a time at least, a new point of equilibrium is maintained. Is it possible by variation in the amount or kind of exogenous factors alone to so alter the physiological equilibrium of the normal animal prior to the appearance of tumors, or of the metastable equilibrium of the cancerous animal, that in the former case tumors will not appear and in the latter case tumors will disappear without affecting irreversibly the natural processes of the host? This is the question which forms the basis of this approach to the problem of the control of cancer.

The application of nutritional techniques to this problem has, in general, followed two lines of attack, namely (a) alterations in dietary status of animals prior to what would be the appearance of tumors, whether spontaneous or deliberately induced, and (b) alterations in dietary status of animals already bearing tumors. In each case the effect of over- as well as of under-alimentation has been studied. There seems to be little doubt from the modern work of Baumann, Rusch, *et al.* (1, 2) and of Tannenbaum (3) that high supplements of certain kinds of fat in the diet tend to promote certain kinds of tumor growth and development. Obesity in human beings is a bad risk from the standpoint of susceptibility to many kinds of degenerative diseases, whether cancer incidence is included directly in this susceptibility or not. It seems more probable that it is in the direction of underfeeding that retardation of pathological manifestaions must be sought, and McCay's now classic experiments on the prolongation of life and on the relative lack of degenerative changes in underfed animals (4–6; cf. Tannenbaum and Silverstone, 7) readily come to mind in this connection. Great effort and skill have been expended on this approach toward the control of tumor incidence, and there is no doubt that in many cases the induction period of tumors has been delayed—and the growth rate of established tumors retarded—by various forms of dietary depletion. But how drastic must the dietary regimens be in order to effect such changes, and what is the cost in terms of the natural processes of the animal?

Induction of Mammary Tumors in Mice

Mammary tumorogenesis in mice as influenced by diet has been more extensively studied than any other tumor of spontaneous origin, and the results obtained by these studies aptly illustrate many of the problems confronting workers in this field. It has long been recognized that the latent period of induction of the spontaneous mammary carcinoma, as well as that of other kinds of tumors in mice, could be prolonged by various forms of dietary restriction. These restrictions in an otherwise adequate diet involved caloric intake (7, 8–11), certain vitamins of the B group (12, 13) and certain essential amino acids (14–16). An apparent exception to this rule appears to exist in the case of nerve tissue, for the removal of thiamine and riboflavin from the diets of rats with intracerebral pellets of methylcholanthrene nearly halved the average latent period of induction of tumors derived from this type of tissue (17); the total incidence was unaffected by the deficiency. When the gamut of B vitamins (thiamine, riboflavin, pyridoxine, panthothenate, niacin, and choline) are administered to young female *C3H* mice in minimal, moderate, and very high levels, the incidence of spontaneous mammary tumors which subsequently develop normally in this strain is the same on each regimen (18). So too is the incidence of induced skin tumors brought about by painting with 3,4-benzpyrene (18, 19). The survival periods of the tumor-bearing animals are also independent of the vitamin intake, which is consistent with the generally held viewpoint that above a minimal level variations in dietary vitamin content have little or no effect on the growth of tumors. As Tannenbaum and Silverstone suggest (18), however, wide ranges of dietary vitamins may result in tissue differences too small to modify carcinogenesis. Variations in the content or nature of the salt components of the diet affect neither the genesis nor the growth of spontaneous mammary tumors or of carcinogen-induced tumors in mice (20).

With increasing levels of dietary fat, the rate of formation of spontaneous mammary tumors in *C3H* mice (21) and of induced mammary tumors by diethylstilbestrol administration to rats (22) appeared to increase, but the survival periods of the animals were little affected. However, a high level of dietary fat does not *per se* have any appreciable effect upon the induction of subcutaneous tumors, spontaneous lung tumors, or induced or spontaneous leukemia (23, 24). Virgin *C3H* mice made obese experimentally with toxic doses of gold thioglucose develop mammary tumors earlier (average time, 246 days) than do their normal litter mates or animals injected with gold which did not show the obesity syndrome (303 days average) (25). The fact that the inclusion of several forms of fat in the diet results in the promotion of the induction of various types of tumors had been recognized for some time (26–29), but there still remain several puzzling and unanswered questions in connection with this phenomenon, apart from the fact that some types of tumors develop apparently independently of this dietary component. One of the most interesting of these questions relates to the effect of different levels of dietary fat on the incidence of tumors. Thus, an increase of 2 to 8 % of dietary fat accelerates the mammary tumor incidence in mice to the same extent as an increase from 8 to about 26 % (21), and a diet containing 27 % fat has stimulated the formation of induced skin tumors to about the same degree as one containing 61 % fat (30). An increase in the content of dietary fat should result in an increased efficiency of energy utilization, and this sparing of net body energy might be regarded as equivalent to an increase in caloric intake (30). If this were so, it might be expected that augmentation of dietary fat would more or less equally influence all types of tumor responsive to the level of caloric intake (7), but this is not the case, as mentioned above, since such neoplasms as lung tumors and the leukemias are unresponsive to dietary fat. A possible source of error in estimating the effect of dietary fat on skin carcinogenesis by chemicals (26) and even by ultraviolet radiation (31) is the oiliness of the skin which might develop by external contact and which might facilitate the solubility and absorption of the carcinogens involved. The dietary fat would thus appear to influence the *initiation* stage of skin carcinogenesis by means obviously non-nutritional. The *developmental* stage of the skin tumors is little affected by ingested fats (28, 32).

Different levels of casein in the diet appear to have little effect on the incidence or time of appearance of spontaneous mammary tumors or induced epithelial or subcutaneous tumors (33). This is in contrast with the effect of such levels on hepatoma development, whether in the rat or the mouse (see below). It is probable that the liver is more responsive than more distant organs to the levels of dietary protein.

Until very recently, little or no attention was apparently paid to possible mechanisms underlying the effect of the inadequate diets and, with few exceptions, the unfavorable *sequelae* attendant upon undernutrition were largely ignored. That such *sequelae* may indeed be crucial was first demonstrated by the experiments of the Whites and coworkers (10, 34, 35). Visscher *et al.*, in studies of female mice on a calorie-restricted diet, had noted that there was not only a decrease in the incidence of spontaneous mammary tumors in these mice but also an irregularity of estrus (11). Similar findings were observed by White and Andervont in mice maintained on a diet low in cystine (16). The essential clue to the problem of the relation of the restricted diet to the induction of mammary tumors in mice was furnished by subsequent decisive experiments of the Whites (34, 35), illustrated in Table 51.

TABLE 51

EFFECT OF A LOW-CYSTINE DIET AND OF SUBCUTANEOUSLY IMPLANTED PELLETS OF DIETHYLSTILBESTROL ON SPONTANEOUS MAMMARY TUMORS IN C3H VIRGIN FEMALE MICE[1]

Mice and diet	Tumor incidence, %	Average tumor age, months
Mice without pellets:		
Chow	97	10.4
High cystine[2]	98	8.4
Low cystine[2]	0	—
Mice with pellets:[3]		
Chow	96	9.1
High cystine	92	8.4
Low cystine	45	11.2

[1] From White and White (34).

[2] Basal experimental diet composed of 4% casein, 22% Crisco, 3% cod liver oil, 6% salts, 5% ryzamin B, and 5% liver extract. The high cystine diet contained in addition 54.6% starch and 0.5% cystine, the low cystine diet contained 55.1% starch and no added cystine.

[3] Pellets composed of 25% diethylstilbestrol in cholesterol and weighing, on the average, 1.5 mg.

Weanling mice maintained at nearly constant, if stunted, weight by a diet deficient in cystine showed no mammary tumors within a period of 22 months, as contrasted with an incidence of nearly 100% in the full-fed, full-grown controls. When, however, the mice on the restricted diet were treated with stilbestrol, the mammary tumor incidence rose to 45%. Further studies, both nutritional and histological, revealed that the mice on diets deficient either in calories or in essential amino acids were anestrous and their mammary tissue failed to grow in the virgin and atrophied in the breeding females (Fig. 23). Implantation of stilbestrol pellets in such mice resulted in growth of the mammary tissue and initiation of continuous estrus and, as noted, a considerable rise in tumor incidence. Failure to obtain 100% incidence after treatment with stilbestrol may be due to the need for other than estrogenic factors or perhaps to the fact that stilbestrol in this case is not a completely adequate estrogen. These experiments of the Whites (34, 35) settled one question based on the weight problem of the experimental animals and raised a host of others. The fact that tumors appeared in stunted mice after treatment with the synthetic estrogen indicated that the arrest in body growth of young animals fed the inadequate diet is not *per se* the explanation of why such animals develop fewer tumors and at a later time than do their full-fed, full-grown controls. Rather the issue is raised as to whether the dietary deficiency does not reduce tumor incidence by affecting the glands of internal secretion directly and the tumor incidence, thereby, only indirectly. The later work of Huseby *et al.* (36), based upon histological examination of the genitalia of female mice on a calorie-restricted diet, revealed marked atrophy of these organs and is thus consistent with the above concept.

Table 52 is a partial summary of the work on this subject and has been taken from a review by Morris on nutritional factors in carcinogenesis (37).

Dietary Deficiency and Hormone Inhibition

Many investigators have demonstrated that caloric restriction leads to atrophic changes in glands of internal secretion (38–42) and that diets deficient in certain essential amino acids cause failures of pregnancy (43). Loeb observed that, when guinea pigs were fed an adequate diet in amounts sufficiently restricted to cause weight loss, the follicles of the ovary did not mature and frequently regressed (38). Evans and Bishop (39), and Asdell and Crowell (40) noted that female rats restricted to such diets that their body weight reached an average of 40 g. became anestrus. Resumption of normal estrus occurred on refeeding until the weight loss was approximately overcome. Trentin and Turner observed that the amount of estradiol benzoate required to produce minimum duct-growth response of the mammary glands of mice was increased as the food-intake level was decreased, and these authors suggested that during partial inanition the pituitary gland responds to estrogen with a much smaller output of the mammogenic factor

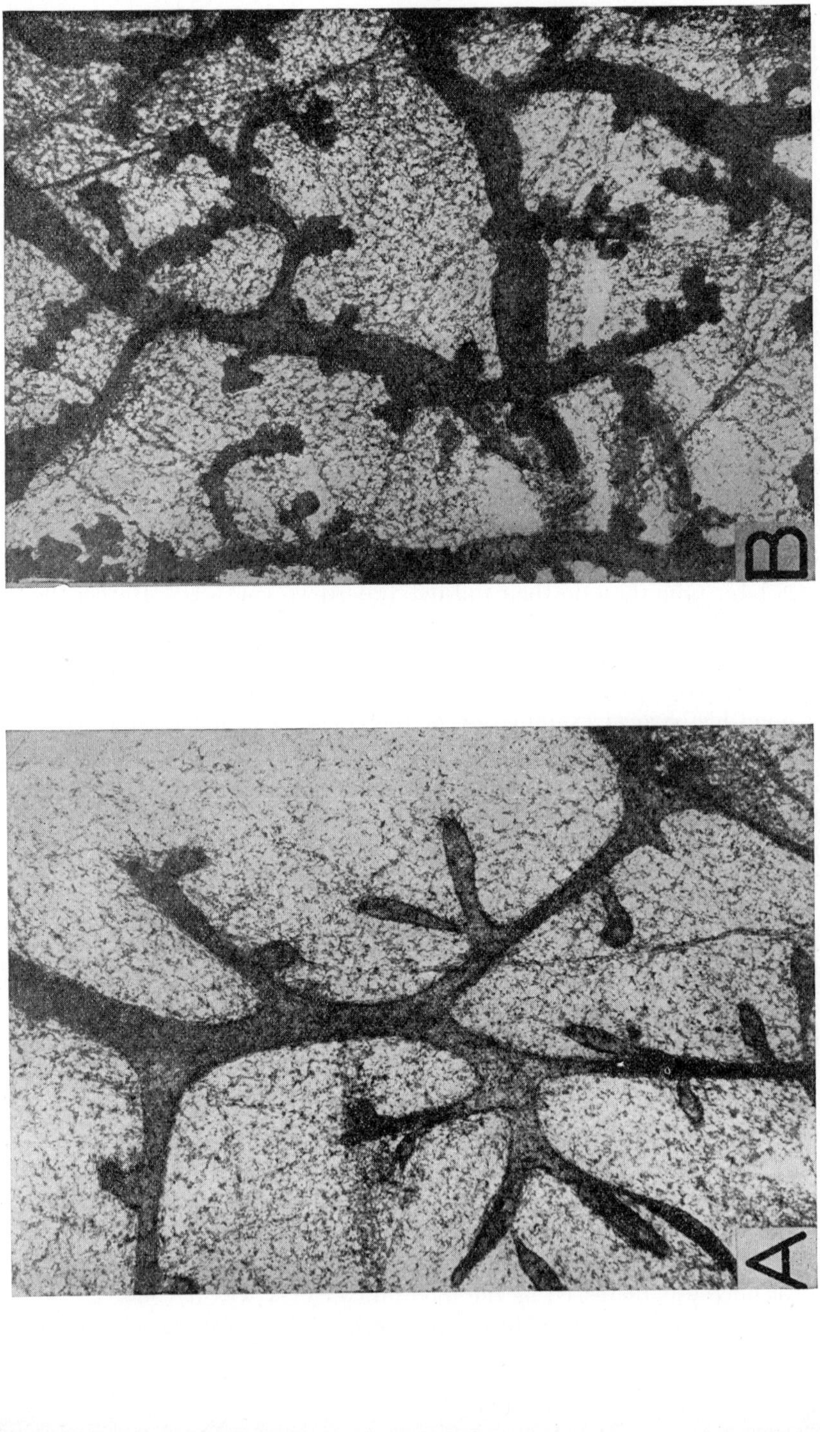

Fig. 23. Gross preparations of mammary glands from virgin female *C3H* mice. A, from mouse 11 months old fed a low cystine diet. B, from a mouse fed a low cystine diet, with subcutaneous stilbestrol pellet. Note undeveloped (A) and developing (B) tissue. From F. R. White, *J. Natl. Cancer Inst.* **5**, 49 (1944).

TABLE 52

Dietary Measures Found Effective in Decreasing the Incidence of Spontaneous Mammary Cancer and Other Observed Effects Such Regimens Have on Female Mice[1]

Reference	Strain	Age, months		Breeding	Regimen	Amount of restriction	Body weight change, %		Breast development test	Effect on		
										Estrus	Tumor incidence, %	
		Started	Ended				Control	Test			Conrol	Test
(7)	*DBA*	2.5	20	Nullipar.	Calorie restriction	½	+50	−10	—	—	38	0
(8)	*DBA*	5.5	18	Nullipar.	Underfeeding	⅓–½	+30	−<25	—	—	40	2
(8)	*DBA*	9.0	24	27% nullipar. 73% par.	Underfeeding	⅓–½	+7	−<30	—	—	30	7
(11)	*C3H*	1	18	Nullipar.	Calorie restriction	⅓	+170	+10	—	—	67	0
(10, 35)	*C3H*	1	22	Nullipar.	Calorie restriction	½	+106	−8	Infantile	Absent	100	13
(10, 35)	*C3H*	4	22	Parous	Calorie restriction	½	+33	−44	Atrophy	—	100	18
(34, 35)	*C3H*	1	28	Nullipar.	Lysine deficient	—	+100	+>20	Infantile Moderate	Occasional	98	25
(16, 35)	*C3H*	1	22	Nullipar.	Cystine deficient	—	+100	0	Infantile	Absent	98	0
(34, 35)	*C3H*	1	17	Nullipar.	Cystine deficient, stilbestrol	—	+100	0	Extensive	Continuous	92	45

[1] *Cf.* Morris, H. P., *Science* **101,** 457 (1945).

(41). Mulinos and Pomerantz coined the term "pseudohypophysectomy" for the effects noted on chronically underfed animals, since these effects closely resembled those elicited on the endocrine organs by hypophysectomy (42).

The observations described above are only a few of those noted relating dietary restrictions with endocrine dysfunction. It is, therefore, to be expected that dietary regimes which inhibit growth of an animal or cause appreciable loss in body weight of the mature animal would produce, among other disturbances, alteration of hormonal secretions. Because of the balance maintained among the various kinds of such secretions, an inhibition, even in any one of them, would presumably affect many, if not all, the others.

The dietary regimes devised to date which effectively prevent the appearance of tumors in experimental animals are for the most part those which likewise abolish estrus and the capacity for breeding. Among the most drastic of these regimes is that involving a 50% reduction in calories from that of the minimum adequate level. At what level above this restriction normal breeding capacity could be resumed is not precisely known, but it is likely that with higher caloric intake the incidence of tumors would similarly increase.

The hormone-producing centers are probably early casualties of dietary deficiencies, and it would appear that the effect of diets sufficiently drastic to inhibit the appearance of tumors is somewhat equivalent to a "reversible" hypophysectomy or castration. Ovariectomized *C3H* mice given diethylstilbestrol yield a high incidence of mammary tumors regardless of dietary status, although the average cancer age is greatly increased by caloric restriction (44). The fact that caloric restriction does not prevent estrogen-induced mammary tumors suggests that this type of dietary restriction causes a suppression of endogenous estrogen production. The lowering of the basal metabolic rate is a familiar sequel to inanition and thus, with a pseudohypophysectomy due to chronic inanition, there might be expected to be simultaneously produced a condition similar to thyroidectomy, whole or in part. Animals in this condition would lower their metabolic needs in order to survive, but this could only be accomplished at the expense, in the female at least, of sexual activity. With resumption of an adequate dietary level, function returns, body growth occurs, and tumors appear.

In Chapter IV it was stated that susceptibility to spontaneous mammary tumor formation in mice was governed by at least three factors, namely, genetic constitution, the availability of the milk factor, and hormonal stimulation. In animals possessing the former two factors such tumors still will not appear when hormonal stimulation is absent. The possible interrelationship of milk factor and of estrogen, described in Chapter IV, comes to mind.

Where retarded general growth is attained, as by low temperature or the feeding of sodium fluoride, even though the dietary intake be unchanged or even augmented, the incidence of spontaneous mammary tumors is significantly inhibited (45). These interesting control experiments suggest that the inhibition of mammary tumor induction is simply associated again with a general inhibition of body growth and body function. An increase in metabolism and food intake, associated with some decrease in body weight incident to the administration of thyroid extract, had little or no effect on the induction of benzpyrene-induced skin tumors in mice (46). A very appreciable decrease in body weight, probably with associated hormone-production damage or depletion, is necessary before an effect on tumor induction can be noted.

Induction of Tumors Other Than Mammary

The effect of diet on the induction of liver tumors in rats by the feeding of 4-dimethylaminoazobenzene is one of the classic subjects in this area of cancer research. Nakahara and his colleagues (47) first showed that the inclusion of whole liver powder in the diet would greatly retard the development of liver tumors in rats fed this dye, an observation further developed by Kensler and his colleagues (48) in their findings that a similar protective effect could be attained by the inclusion of high riboflavin and casein levels in the diet. The induction of such tumors is thus favored by relatively inadequate diets in protein and riboflavin (cf. 49), a rice-carrot diet being particularly favored by some investigators for producing high incidences of tumors with this dye (cf. 48). The ingestion of this and related dyes appears to be correlated with a diminution in the level of hepatic riboflavin, and there may be a rough parallelism between the carcinogenicity of the various azo dyes and their ability to lower hepatic riboflavin. Thus Griffin and Baumann (50) noted that the very active liver carcinogen 3′-methyl-4-dimethylaminoazobenzene produced a much more pronounced reduction in liver riboflavin than did the weak 4′-methyl isomer; the mediumly active dyes such as 4-dimethylaminoazobenzene produced an intermediate drop, whereas the non-carcinogenic azo dyes produced little or no drop in the liver riboflavin. Subsequent observations have further confirmed the inverse relation between hepatic carcinogenesis and hepatic riboflavin. Diets containing hydrogenated coconut oil are known to markedly retard liver tumor induction by 4-dimethylaminoazobenzene (51, 52), and the livers of rats fed a diet containing both the dye and this oil have much more riboflavin than when corn oil is substituted for the hydrogenated coconut oil (53). However, the latter oil does not retard liver carcinogenesis by

3′-methyl-4-dimethylaminoazobenzene, and, when this dye is fed with either of the two oils mentioned, the resulting level of hepatic riboflavin is equally low in both cases, and the tumor incidence equally high (53). This leads to the curious fact that, whereas dietary riboflavin protects the rat against liver carcinogenesis by 4-dimethylaminoazobenzene, it has no apparent protective action against the 3′-methyl homologue of this azo dye (54). There seems to be no available interpretation as yet for this discrepancy. High casein diets are protective against liver carcinogenesis by 4-dimethylaminoazobenzene, possibly by virtue of helping the liver retain its riboflavin (55). Thus, rats fed the azo dyes had more hepatic tumors on a 12% casein diet than on a 24% casein diet or when the 12% casein was supplemented with methionine (55). Diets low in cystine (56) or pyridoxine (57, 58) have been noted to retard the onset of liver tumors induced by the azo dyes, but in these cases a relatively severe deficiency accompanied by appreciable weight loss is necessary to observe their effects. The apparent protective effects of high riboflavin, of hydrogenated coconut oil or its component acids, of lauric acid, and of low fat diets are accompanied by a gain in weight, and often by a consumption of excess food and hence more dye (59). It has been stated that the feeding of biotin results in an appearance of hepatic tumors when rats are given an otherwise protective diet (60). A second group of investigators has confirmed this observation but noted that biotin does not accelerate the onset of liver tumors in a diet favorable to carcinogenesis (61), and a third group has noted no procarcinogenic action of biotin at all (62). Regardless of the merits of this disputed area, it is interesting that the addition of biotin to the diet raises the biotin content of both liver and liver tumors, the latter to a greater degree than the former. Thus, the biotin content of rat liver in terms of micrograms per gram wet weight is 1.3, and of rat liver tumor it is 0.09; on a biotin-supplemented diet, these values become, respectively, 2.4 and 0.38 (16). An interesting sequel to the prolonged feeding of 4-dimethylaminoazobenzene in a diet made protective by supplementation with fresh milk was the development in rats not of hepatic but of malignant pancreatic tumors (63).

The occurrence of fatty infiltration as well as cirrhosis of the liver is influenced by certain dietary constituents. Best *et al.* (64) observed that fatty livers in rats could be prevented by feeding choline. The addition of cystine to a diet low in choline causes a marked increase in liver fat which can be offset by feeding additional casein (65). The component in the casein evidently responsible for this lipotrophic effect is methionine, since methionine can furnish the methyl group for the synthesis of choline. Cirrhosis of the liver can be induced in rats by a low protein, high fat, high cystine diet (66), and this cirrhosis can be largely reduced by feeding choline or methionine (67). György *et al.* (68, 69) reported that the addition of cystine and choline markedly retarded the induction of hepatomas (as well as other forms of liver injury, i.e., necrosis, etc.) in rats fed 4-dimethylaminoazobenzene. The implication was that, if liver injury could be prevented, so too would hepatoma formation. White and Edwards (14) found, however, that no protection against hepatoma formation could be produced by the feeding of either cystine plus choline or methionine in addition to the basal diet and carcinogen, even though no evidence of cirrhosis in the liver adjacent to the tumor was observed. The incidence of hepatomas under these conditions was as high as 90 % up to 8 to 11 months. In the absence of added carcinogen, a severe, choline-restricted diet in rats apparently results in hepatic cirrhosis followed by the development of tumors in the liver and other tissues (70). The inclusion of 50 % bentonite in an otherwise adequate diet for mice produces severe symptoms of choline deficiency, including fatty livers, and hepatomas develop in high incidence in these animals (71); bentonite as a cation-exchange silicate probably removes choline from the intestinal contents, together with other factors, inasmuch as addition of choline by itself does not restore normal growth.

It is of considerable interest that a diet high in riboflavin prevents the appearance of these choline-deficiency tumors (72). Thus, riboflavin exerts the same protective effect in this case as it does in carcinogenesis by 4-dimethylaminoazobenzene. Choline in excess, however, and choline-deficient diets have no effect on established tumors (73) or on the induction of chemically induced sarcomas (74), nor does the addition of choline to the diet prevent the development of azo dye-induced liver tumors (72). A curious observation is the induction of mixed hepatic tumors in female rats by the incorporation in the diet of 0.2 % ethionine (75); it may be wondered whether the presence of this material causes a neoplastic development by interference with the protective action of dietary methionine against some as yet unrecognized liver carcinogen. In the case of certain established tumors, addition of ethionine to the diet produces a regressive effect on the tumor (76).

Like the azo dyes, 4-dimethylaminostilbene is more powerfully carcinogenic when administered together with an inadequate diet (77). Thus, a low protein diet hastens the appearance of cholangiomas when the former carcinogen is administered. Like 2-acetylaminofluorene, 4-dimethylaminostilbene induces a variety of tumors in the same animal, but only the appearance of the liver tumors is accelerated by the low protein diet. However, this type of diet had no effect upon the rate of induction of any sort of tumor by 2′-chloro-4-dimethylaminostilbene (77), which is remindful of the indifference of 3′-methyl-4-dimethylaminoazobenzene to the dietary level of riboflavin contrasted with the sensitivity of the parent dye to this level (see above).

When a carcinogen produces multiple tumors, the appearance of any one of them is apparently a function of the diet (78). Thus, those dietary conditions, such as a high caloric intake, which appear to favor the early appearance of mammary tumors by 2-acetylaminofluorene seem to decrease the incidence of ear-duct tumors, while the relatively rare tumor of the Harderian glands appears to be favored by low fat diets inclusive of the carcinogen (78). The effect of high protein diets is much less clear in the case of 2-acetylaminofluorene carcinogenesis than in the induction of liver cancer by the azo dyes where such diets are definitely protective. Morris and his colleagues (79) noted that rats developed more tumors when a purified diet containing 18 to 24 % casein was used with 2-acetylaminofluorene than when the casein content was 12 %. On a purified diet containing 9 to 27 % casein, weanling rats have developed an 86 % incidence of mammary tumors with this carcinogen, whereas with the same intake of carcinogen (1.8 to 2.1 mg. per rat per day) in diets containing 40 to 60 % of casein the mammary tumor incidence dropped to 12 % (80). Still another investigator (81) has shown that the induction of liver tumors by 2-acetylaminofluorene is independent of the level of dietary protein. Since no two groups of investigators ever seem to employ identical diets, a possible explanation for the several discrepancies which have arisen may be derived from the observations that rats on so-called semipurified diets were more susceptible to carcinogenesis by 2-acetylaminofluorene than they were on stock or crude diets (82). The ingredients of the crude diets which are protective, except possibly riboflavin (83), are yet unknown, and a different proportion of these ingredients in the diet employed by each group of investigators might possibly be responsible in part for their divergent observations.

The discussion so far has involved rats as experimental animals. In mice there are some points of similarity and some of difference. Thus the incidence of spontaneous hepatomas is enhanced by semisynthetic diets not only in *C3H* males in which strain a moderate incidence is normal, but also in *DBA* strain males and females in which this incidence is normally very low (84). Again, the problem is what ordinarily protective factors exist in the crude diet. On the other hand, the incidence of spontaneous hepatomas in mice is lower on a 9 % than on a 18 % casein diet (85), which is remindful of the results of Morris *et al.* (79). A *lower* incidence of induced liver tumors occurs on a rice diet with *o*-aminoazotoluene (86), and the liver response is independent of the level of dietary riboflavin (87). It is clear that dietary status may have taken a different course in the genesis of tumors in different species. However, even within the same species, and in mice even within the same strain, different tumors may differ profoundly in their induction requirements and characteristics. Thus, fat enrichment of the diet enhances the rate of formation of spontaneous hepatomas (87) and of spontaneous mammary tumors (23) but has no effect on spontaneous lung tumors or induced sarcomas, and only a very small effect, if any, on induced skin tumors. Furthermore, mammary tumors and induced skin tumors develop equally well on crude and semisynthetic diets (83) and on low and high casein levels (33). The only observation consistent with all previous phenomena is that chronic caloric restriction results in a marked inhibition of spontaneous hepatomas in the mouse (88).

The use of the azo dyes for the induction of hepatic and pulmonary tumors (89–91) and of benzpyrene in marginal doses for the induction of sarcomas (92), applied to inbred strains of mice, revealed marked differences between males and females of these strains in their response to these carcinogenic agents. These and many other similar experiments suggest the influence of sex (in susceptible strains) on cancer susceptibility in non-sex tissues, as liver, lung, and subcutaneous fibroblasts. Such findings, furthermore, suggest the influence of the sex hormones on the integration of normal tissue function as well as on the malignant transformation of non-sex and sex tissues (cf. Chapter IV).

On the basis of the data so far available, it would appear that the malignant transformation of sex tissues is more generally achieved by a wider variety of deficient diets than is the transformation of certain non-sex tissues. Thus, although the incidence of mammary tumors in mice is reduced by calorie restriction and by cystine deficiency (*vide infra*), the incidence of spontaneous pulmonary tumors is reduced by the former (7) but not by the latter dietary regime (93). Cystine restriction in the diet of mice of susceptible strain (*DBA*) results in a decreased incidence of induced leukemia with methylcholanthrene, with many of the mice on this inadequate diet developing sclerotic lesions of the aorta (15, 94). Weanling mice placed either on a cystine-deficient or on a lysine-deficient diet are equally stunted in growth, but, whereas subsequent painting with methylcholanthrene resulted in a low incidence of leukemia on the former diet, the incidence of this induced disease in the mice on the latter diet was nearly as high as in the controls (15). However, there are some degrees of response too in the case of mammary tumors in the presence of different dietary deficiencies. Thus, although a lysine-deficient diet markedly lowered the incidence of this tumor in mice, the lowering was in no way as complete as when a cystine-deficient diet was used, and estrus was not as regularly inhibited (34). The reduced incidence of nearly all kinds of tumors, derived from either sex or non-sex tissues, is apparently more readily achieved by caloric restriction than by individual essential-factor deficiencies. However, in the absence of adequate caloric intake, the amino acids of the host's tissues may be utilized for fuel, and thus a calorie-restricted diet could indirectly produce multiple amino acid deficiencies.

So far, diets deficient only in cystine and in lysine have been employed in studies of tumor incidence, and further studies of deficiencies of other amino acids, especially of tryptophan and perhaps of arginine and histidine, are greatly to be anticipated.

It is clear from the preceding paragraph that the effect of nutritive deficiencies on the genesis of various kinds of tumors may depend, among other factors, upon the kind of deficiency as well as the kind of tumor studied. The inadequate diets employed probably produce various sorts of hormonal disturbances, but not every kind of inadequate diet produces the same inhibition of appearance of all tumors. It is possible that in the case of each type of tumor a specific combination of hormonal elements is involved. This combination may in turn be apprehended only by the investigation of the effect of a large number of single dietary restrictions accompanied by extensive endocrinological investigations. The success of calorie restriction in suppressing tumor incidence in general may be due to a blanketing effect on one or more specific normal functions or elements the absence of which is, thus, only indirectly brought to bear. Although a decrease in tumors incidence occurs when a calorie-restricted diet is instituted at any time in the life span of the animals prior to the appearance of tumors, it is not surprising that, the earlier such a deficient diet is instituted, the lower is the subsequent incidence of tumors (7).

Table 53 summarizes certain data relating to the effect of various dietary deficiencies on tumor incidence in mice (cf. Fig. 24).

Diet and Different Stages of Carcinogenesis

It is known that tumors may arise long after exposure to the carcinogenic stimulus has ceased (cf. Chapter III). Dietary studies described above have indicated that various forms of restriction lower the incidence of tumors. These observations suggested to Tannenbaum the following novel experiment (7). Four groups of mice were painted with a solution of benzpyrene for a period of 10 weeks. During this period, referred to as the period of skin tumor *initiation*, no tumors appeared. At the end of this 10-week period, the paintings were stopped and the mice were observed for 52 succeeding weeks. During this latter period, referred to as the period of skin tumor *development*, tumors made their appearance. Of the four groups of mice studied, two were given a high calorie diet during the first 10-week painting period (initiation), and two were given a diet restricted in calories. At the end of this period, one of the two groups on the high calorie diet was changed to a low calorie diet, and one of the two groups on the low calorie diet was changed to a high calorie diet. The percentage of incidence of skin tumors was then noted during the subsequent 52-week period (develop-

TABLE 53

EFFECT OF DIETARY RESTRICTIONS ON THE INCIDENCE OF VARIOUS TUMORS IN MICE

Diet	Incidence of tumors: Spontaneous mammary,[1] %	Spontaneous mammary,[2] %	Induced leukemia,[3] %	Spontaneous pulmonary, %	Induced epithelioma,[4] %
Chow	97 (34)	—	90 (15)	58 (93)[5]	—
High cystine	98 (34)	—	90 (15)	32 (93)[5]	—
Low cystine	0 (34)	—	10 (15)	30 (93)[5]	—
High lysine	98 (35)	—	78 (15)	—	—
Low lysine	25 (35)	—	72 (15)	—	—
High calorie	100 (35)	38 (7)	96 (10)	55 (7)[6]	64 (7)
Low calorie	18 (35)	0 (7)	35 (10)	27 (7)[6]	22 (7)
High calorie	67 (11)	—	—	—	—
Low calorie	0 (11)	—	—	—	—

[1] Strain *C3H* virgin mice.
[2] Strain *DBA* virgin mice.
[3] Induced in *DBA* mice by methylcholanthrene painting.
[4] Strain *DBA* mice by benzpyrene painting.
[5] Strain *A* mice.
[6] Strain *ABC* mice.

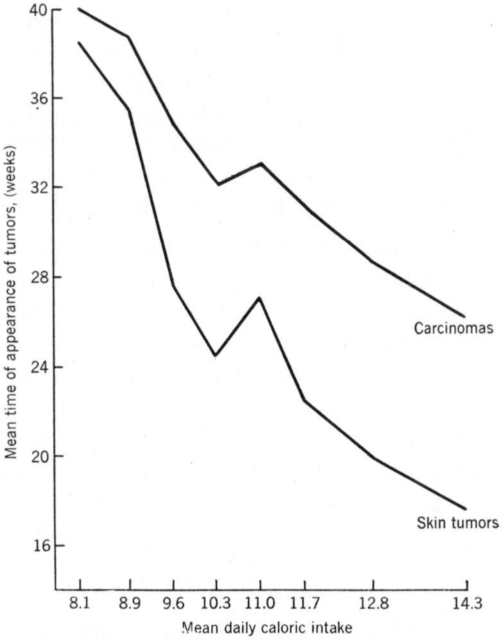

FIG. 24. Relationship between degree of caloric restriction and the mean time of appearance of benzpyrene-induced neoplasms of the skin. From Tannenbaum, A., Cancer Research **5**, 609 (1945).

ment). The results are noted in the following tabulation:

Group	Diet in period of painting (10 weeks)	Diet in period of tumor formation (52 weeks)	Tumor incidence, %
I	High calorie	High calorie	69
II	High calorie	Low calorie	34
III	Low calorie	High calorie	55
IV	Low calorie	Low calorie	24

The relative tumor incidence in groups I and IV is familiar from earlier experiments (*vide infra*). It is the incidence in groups II and III that is of particular interest. According to Tannenbaum these data indicate that the crucial period of dietary restriction does not occur during the initiation phase when the carcinogen is applied but in the developmental phase when tumors are formed and make their appearance. In other words, the initiation phase of the skin tumors is independent of the adequacy of the diet; it is the development phase of the tumors which is a function of dietary adequacy.

These are interesting concepts and the approach employed is ingenious. It should be noted, however, that the differences in tumor incidence between groups I and IV are definite, those between II and III much less so. Coincidentally with the change in diet, the animals in Group II take a precipitate drop in weight and approach that of the animals in Group IV, while the animals in group III show a precipitate rise in weight and approach that of the animals in group I. These changes in body weight between the two phases, with whatever other and unknown accompanying phenomena, present a new set of variables.

Diet and the Established Tumor

From present indications, the effect of dietary alterations on a tumor already established is relatively small. In mice kept for some time on diets deficient in calories and in biotin, the tumors which ultimately appear grow at the same rate as do tumors in the control group (7, 8, 95). Tumors which are transplanted into mice adjusted to a diet restricted in cystine frequently grow as rapidly as in control mice on an adequate diet (96). Tumors may be established and will grow in mice fed a diet negligible in protein, the animals remaining in a state of continuous negative nitrogen balance (97, 98). The last mentioned experiments by F. R. White merit further discussion, for they illustrate in dramatic fashion the essential autonomy of the tumor.

Of two groups of mice of both sexes, one group received an adequate 18 % casein diet and the other group received a diet completely lacking casein. Each group received a supplement of 5 % of liver extract, which, although composed partially of protein split products, was nevertheless too low to supply adequate amounts of lysine, histidine, isoleucine, threonine, and, possibly, tryptophan and other essential amino acids. After a week of adaptation to the respective diets, the mice in each group were simultaneously inoculated with uniform pieces of a transplanted mammary adenocarcinoma. The tumor became established in nearly all the mice in each group and grew at very nearly the same rate, the tumors in the mice on the low nitrogen diet growing slightly slower than those on the adequate high nitrogen diet. Yet, throughout the experiment, the mice on the inadequate diet lost body weight and were in a state of continuous negative nitrogen balance. This state of negative nitrogen balance implied that the proteins of the tissues of the host animal were being broken down not only to supply the nitrogenous factors necessary for its an existence but for that of the growing tumor as well. It is, indeed, astonishing that a tumor can thus attach itself to an organism already running downhill in negative nitrogen balance and subsequently grow at the host's further expense, thus illustrating how little effect dietary restrictions, even of this magnitude, exert on a tumor once it is established.

It is of interest that the genius of Pasteur, in touching briefly on the problem of cancer, selected the preferential utilization by the cancer of the nutriments available to the host as the most characteristic feature of malignancy (98a). His suggested solution was "to feed them (the cancers) . . . by external foods . . . so as to wean them in some way from their mode of life," a suggestion not unknown in ancient folklore, and in modern terms implying the possible formation of adaptive catalytic systems.

There appears to be a decrease in the growth rate of tumors established in well-fed animals when severe restriction of calories (99), of riboflavin (100), or of pantothenic acid (101, 93) (102) is imposed, but, with the initiation of the restriction, the body weight of the animals also falls off and pathological changes intervene. Little differential effect on tumor weight and body weight is attained. The riboflavin content of the tumor under these conditions is not so rapidly depleted as that of liver and muscle (100). Deprivation of thiamine in originally well-fed tumor-bearing animals produces no decrease in size of the tumors (spontaneous mammary) (37). Supplementation of the diet by riboflavin and biotin accelerates the growth of transplanted hepatomas in rats (103).

Conflicting results have been obtained in the case of pyridoxine deficiency, for in mice with spontaneous mammary tumors no effect on the growth rate of the tumors was observed (104), whereas in mice and in rats bearing transplanted sarcomas a general retardation in the growth of the tumors was reported (105, 106). It may be that the difference in these results may be due in part to essential differences between the status and mode of development of spontaneous and transplanted tumors.

The rate of mammary tumor growth can be slightly inhibited for short periods of time during the early stages of growth of the tumor, roughly 40 days, when the mice are fed a diet deficient in lysine (107–109). When the dietary deficiency in lysine is continued for a still longer period of time, however, the growth of the tumors resumes, equaling that of the tumors of animals on a lysine-adequate diet. It would seem as if, under these conditions, either lysine is obtained independently of the diet, i.e., from the host, or else growth of the tumor is capable of proceeding without lysine. The loss in body weight of the animals appears to make the former alternative the more probable. On the basis of the work of F. R. White (98) it is likely that the tissues of the host break down to supply the need of the tumor for lysine. In accord with this is the finding that lysine-deprivation of animals with tumors in an advanced stage of growth has no apparent effect on the tumors (109).

Underfeeding of mice with transmitted leukemia results in a slight prolongation of life which is less than that noted after application of X-radiation, benzene, or arsenicals (9).

Still further evidence that growing tumors utilize the resources of the host is based on studies of vitamin C depletion in guinea pigs bearing tumors (110). This species cannot synthesize the vitamin and placing the animals on a scorbutic diet, therefore, resulted in a loss of vitamin C in both normal and neoplastic tissues. The vitamin reserves were more rapidly exhausted in the animals bearing tumors than in normal animals, and the survival of scorbutic tumor-bearing guinea pigs was considerably briefer than that of the scorbutic non-tumorous animals. Analogous studies on the daily utilization of vitamin C by human beings with extensive neoplastic metastases revealed that the amount of the vitamin utilized was nearly double that observed in normal individuals (111).

Deletion from the diet of any one essential component often causes the experimental animals to reject the entire diet and, thus, short of forced feeding, a state of calorie insufficiency is superimposed above that due to the lack of the essential dietary component. If certain unnatural materials are added to the diet, a condition of inanition may also result. When control animals are used with a calorie intake or total food intake equal to that of the experimental animals, it is obvious that these control animals are not "normal" either. The problem of proper controls in the nutritional approaches in this field is complex and difficult. At the present time the paired-feeding method of H. H. Mitchell represents the most adequate procedure for the use of control or normal animals.

The major effect of dietary deficiencies is on the induction rather than on the growth of tumors. As long as the host is alive, its body tissues are a potential source of nourishment for the tumor and, thus, paradoxically, the host strips itself to feed that which will eventually destroy it.

Although it is often unwise to apply results obtained on one species of animal to another species, numerous recommendations for the control of human cancer based upon studies of dietary restriction in the lower animals have been advanced. These recommendations, advanced without consideration for the possible unfavorable hormonal and metabolic *sequelae*, should be treated with great reserve. Dietary moderation, not necessarily restriction, beyond the period of fertility in human beings is probably of health and cosmetic value. When the vagaries of human nature, the possible carcinogenic hazards to which the individual is exposed, and the demands of modern human civilization are all taken into consideration, it would be impracticable, not to say absurd, to suggest the prolonged abjuration of the few pleasures which life grants in the hope of avoiding cancer at some unknown and distant future. It can be assumed that no specific diet for the cancer patient is yet known, and many of those suggested are not far from the realm of pure fantasy. More intensive work on experimental animals by teams of nutritionists and endocrinologists, plus similar studies on selected cases of human cancer patients, are needed before the potential value of the dietary approach to the control of cancer can be considered adequately explored.

References

(1) Lavick, P. S., and Baumann, C. A., *Cancer Research* **3,** 749 (1943); cf, Rusch, H. P., Kline, B. E., and Baumann, C. A., *Cancer Research* **5,** 431 (1945).

(2) Miller, J. A., Kline, B. E., Rusch, H. P., and Baumann, C. A., *Cancer Research* **4,** 756 (1944); cf. Kline, B. E., Miller, J. A., Rusch, H. P., and Baumann, C. A., *Cancer Research* **6,** 5 (1946).

(3) Tannenbaum, A., *Cancer Research* **2,** 468 (1942); **4,** 683 (1944).

(4) McCay, C. M., *Trans. & Studies Coll. Physicians Phila.* **10,** 1 (1942).

(5) McCay, C. M., Sperling, G., and Barnes, L. L., *Arch. Biochem.* **2,** 469 (1943).

(6) Will, L. C., and McCay, C. M., *Arch. Biochem.* **2,** 481 (1943).

(7) Tannenbaum, A., and Silverstone, H., *Advances in Cancer Research* **1,** 452 (1953).

(8) Tannenbaum, A., *Am. J. Cancer* **38,** 335 (1940).

(9) Saxton, J. A., Boon, M. C., and Furth, J., *Cancer Research* **4,** 401 (1944).

(10) White, F. R., White, J., Mider, G. B., Kelly, M. G., and Heston, W. E., *J. Natl. Cancer Inst.* **5,** 43 (1944).

(11) Visscher, M. B., Ball, Z. B., Barnes, R. H., and Sivertson, I., *Surgery* **11,** 48 (1942).

(12) Miner, D. L., Miller, J. A., Baumann, C. A., and Rusch, H. P., *Cancer Research* **3,** 296 (1943).

(13) du Vigneaud, V., Spangler, J. M., Burk, D., Kensler, C. J., Sugiura, K., and Rhoads, C. P., *Science* **95,** 174 (1942).

(14) White, J., and Edwards, J. E., *J. Natl. Cancer Inst.* **3,** 43 (1942).

(15) White, J., Mider, G. B., and Heston, W. E., *J. Natl. Cancer Inst.* **4,** 409 (1944).

(16) White, J., and Andervont, H. B., *J. Natl. Cancer Inst.* **3,** 449 (1943).

(17) Russell, W. O., *Cancer Research* **5,** 152 (1945).

(18) Tannenbaum, A., and Silverstone, H., *Cancer Research* **12,** 744 (1952).

(19) Boutwell, R. K., Brush, M. K., and Rusch, H. P., *Cancer Research* **9,** 747 (1949).

(20) Tannenbaum, A., and Silverstone, H., *Cancer Research* **13,** 460 (1953).

(21) Silverstone, H., and Tannenbaum, A., *Cancer Research* **10,** 448 (1950).

(22) Dunning, W. F., Curtis, M. R., and Mann, M. E., *Cancer Research* **9,** 354 (1949).

(23) Tannenbaum, A., *Cancer Research* **2,** 468 (1942).
(24) Lawrason, F. D., and Kirschbaum, A., *Proc. Soc. Exptl. Biol. Med.* **56,** 6 (1944).
(25) Waxler, S. H., Tabar, P., and Melcher, L. R., *Cancer Research* **13,** 276 (1953).
(26) Watson, A. F., and Mellanby, E., *Brit. J. Exptl. Pathol.* **11,** 311 (1930).
(27) Lavik, P. S., and Baumann, C. A., *Cancer Research* **3,** 749 (1943).
(28) Tannenbaum, A., *Cancer Research* **4,** 683 (1944).
(29) Rusch, H. P., Kline, B. E., and Baumann, C. A., *Cancer Research* **5,** 431 (1945).
(30) Boutwell, R. K., Brush, M. K., and Rusch, H. P., *Cancer Research* **9,** 741 (1949).
(31) Rusch, H. P., Baumann, C. A., and Kline, B. E., *Proc. Soc. Exptl. Biol. Med.* **42,** 508 (1939).
(32) Lavik, P. S., and Baumann, C. A., *Cancer Research* **3,** 749 (1943).
(33) Tannenbaum, A., and Silverstone, H., *Cancer Research* **9,** 162 (1949).
(34) White, F. R., and White, J., *J. Natl. Cancer Inst.* **4,** 413 (1944); **5,** 41 (1944).
(35) White, F. R., *J. Natl. Cancer Inst.* **5,** 49 (1944).
(36) Huseby, R. A., Ball, Z. B., and Visscher, M. B., *Cancer Research* **5,** 40 (1945).
(37) Morris, H. P., *J. Natl. Cancer Inst.* **6,** 1 (1945).
(38)Loeb, L., *J. Am. Med. Assoc.* **77,** 1646 (1921).
(39) Evans, H. M., and Bishop, K. S., *J. Metabolic Research* **1,** 335 (1922).
(40) Asdell, S. A., and Crowell, M. F., *J. Nutrition* **10,** 13 (1935).
(41) Trentin, J. J., and Turner, C. W., *Endocrinology* **29,** 984 (1941).
(42) Mulinos, M. G., and Pomerantz, L., *Endocrinology* **29,** 558 (1941).
(43) Albanese, A. A., Randall, R. M., and Holt, L. E., Jr., *Science* **97,** 312 (1943).
(44) King, J. T., Casas, C. B., and Visscher, M. B., *Cancer Research* **9,** 436 (1949).
(45) Tannenbaum, A., and Silverstone, H., *Cancer Research* **9,** 403 (1949).
(46) Silverstone, H., and Tannenbaum, A., *Cancer Research* **9,** 684 (1949).
(47) Nakahara, W., Mori, K., and Fugiwara, T., *Gann* **33,** 406 (1939).
(48) Kensler, C. J., Sugiura, K., Young, N. F., Halter, C. R., and Rhoads, C. P., *Science* **93,** 308 (1941).
(49) Harris, P. N., Krahl, M. E., and Clowes, G. H. A., *Cancer Research* **7,** 162 (1947).
(50) Griffin, A. C., and Baumann, C. A., *Arch. Biochem.* **11,** 467 (1946).
(51) Kline, B. E., Miller, J. A., Rusch, H. P., and Baumann, C. A., *Cancer Research* **6,** 1 (1946).
(52) Miller, J. A., Kline, B. E., Rusch, H. P., and Baumann, C. A., *Cancer Research* **4,** 153, 756 (1944).
(53) Griffin, A. C., and Baumann, C. A., *Cancer Research* **8,** 279 (1948).
(54) Giese, J. E., Clayton, C. C., Miller, E. C., and Baumann, C. A., *Cancer Research* **6,** 679 (1946).
(55) Griffin, A. C., Clayton, C. C., and Baumann, C. A., *Cancer Research* **9,** 82 (1949).
(56) White, J., and Edwards, J. E., *J. Natl. Cancer Inst.* **2,** 535 (1942).
(57) Miller, J. A., Miner, D. L., Rusch, H. P., and Baumann, C. A., *Cancer Research* **1,** 699 (1941).
(58) Miller, E. C., Baumann, C. A., and Rusch, H. P., *Cancer Research* **5,** 713 (1945).
(59) Miller, J. A., *Ann. N. Y. Acad. Sci.* **39,** 19 (1947).
(60) duVigneaud, V., Spangler, J. M., Burk, D., Kensler, C. J., Sugiura, K., and Rhoads, C. P., *Science* **95,** 174 (1942).
(61) Harris, P. N., Krahl, M. E., and Clowes, G. H. A., *Cancer Research* **7,** 176 (1947).
(62) Axelrod, A. E., and Hofmann, K., *Cancer Research* **13,** 442 (1953).

(63) Hoch-Ligeti, C., *Brit. J. Cancer* **3,** 285 (1949).
(64) Best, C. H., Hershey, J. M., and Huntsman, M. E., *Am. J. Physiol.* **101,** 7 (1932).
(65) Beeston, A. W., and Channon, H. J., *Biochem. J.* **30,** 280 (1936).
(66) György, P., and Goldblatt, H., *J. Exptl. Med.* **79,** 355 (1942).
(67) Lowry, J. V., Daft, F. S., Sebrell, W. H., Ashburn, L. L., and Lillie, R. D., *Public Health Repts.* (*U. S.*) **56,** 2216 (1941).
(68) György, P., Poling, E. C., and Goldblatt, H., *Proc. Soc. Exptl. Biol. Med.* **47,** 41 (1941).
(69) György, P., and Goldblatt, H., *J. Exptl. Med.* **70,** 185 (1939).
(70) Copeland, D. H., and Salmon, W. D., *Am. J. Pathol.* **22,** 1059 (1946).
(71) Wilson, J. W., *J. Natl. Cancer Inst.* **14,** 57, 65 (1953).
(72) Schaefer, A. E., Copeland, D. H., Salmon, W. D., and Hale, O. M., *Cancer Research* **10,** 786 (1950).
(73) Jacobi, H. P., and Baumann, C. A., *Cancer Research* **2,** 175 (1942).
(74) Cook, J. W., and Schoental, R., *Brit. J. Cancer* **3,** 557 (1949).
(75) Popper, H., de la Huerga, J., and Yesinick, C., *Science* **118,** 80 (1953).
(76) Levy, H. M., Montanez, G., Murphy, E. A., and Dunn, M. S., *Cancer Research* **13,** 507 (1953).
(77) Elson, L. A., *Brit. J. Cancer* **6,** 392 (1952).
(78) Engel, R. W., and Copeland, D. H., *Cancer Research* **11,** 180 (1951).
(79) Morris, H. P., Westfall, B. B., Dubnik, C. S., and Dunn, T. B., *Cancer Research* **8,** 390 (1948).
(80) Engel, R. W., and Copeland, D. H., *Cancer Research* **12,** 905 (1952).
(81) Harris, P. N., *Cancer Research* **7,** 88 (1947).
(82) Engel, R. W., and Copeland, D. H., *Cancer Research* **12,** 211 (1952).
(83) Allison, J. B., and Wase, A. W., *Cancer Research* **12,** 647 (1952).
(84) Silverstone, H., Solomon, R. D., and Tannenbaum, A., *Cancer Research* **12,** 750 (1952).
(85) Silverstone, H., and Tannenbaum, A., *Cancer Research* **11,** 442 (1951).
(86) Silverstone, H., *Cancer Research* **8,** 309 (1948).
(87) Silverstone, H., and Tannenbaum, A., *Cancer Research* **11,** 200 (1951).
(88) Tannenbaum, A., and Silverstone, H., *Cancer Research* **9,** 724 (1949).
(89) Andervont, H. B., Grady, H. G., and Edwards, J. E., *J. Natl. Cancer Inst.* **3,** 131 (1942).
(90) Andervont, H. B., and Edwards, J. E., *J. Natl. Cancer Inst.* **3,** 349 (1943).
(91) Andervont, H. B., White, J., and Edwards, J. E., *J. Natl. Cancer Inst.* **4,** 583 (1944).
(92) Leiter, J., and Shear, M. J., *J. Natl. Cancer Inst.* **3,** 455 (1943).
(93) Larsen, C. D., and Heston, W. E., *J. Natl. Cancer Inst.* **6,** 32 (1945).
(94) White, J., Mider, G. B., and Heston, W. E., *J. Natl. Cancer Inst.* **3,** 453 (1943).
(95) West, P. M., and Woglom, W. H., *Cancer Research* **2,** 324 (1942).
(96) Larsen, C. D., and Andervont, H. B., personal communication.
(97) White, F. R., and Belkin, M., *J. Natl. Cancer Inst.* **5,** 261 (1945).
(98) White, F. R., *J. Natl. Cancer Inst.* **5,** 265 (1945).
(98a) Pasteur, L., *Compt. rend.* **80,** 87 (1875).
(99) Bischoff, F. Long, M. L., and Maxwell, L. C., *Am. J. Cancer* **24,** 549 (1935).
(100) Morris, H. P., and Robertson, W. van B., *J. Natl. Cancer Inst.* **3,** 479 (1943).
(101) Morris, H. P., and Lippincott, S. W., *J. Natl. Cancer Inst.* **2,** 47 (1941).
(102) Montanez, G., Murphy, E. A., and Dunn, M. S., *Cancer Research* **11,** 834 (1951).
(103) Voegtlin, C., and Thompson, J. W., *J. Natl. Cancer Inst.* **10,** 29 (1949).

(104) Morris, H. P., *in* Mammary Tumors in Mice. American Association for the Advancement of Science, Washington, D. C., 1945.
(105) Bischoff, F., Ingraham, L. P., and Rupp, J. J., *Arch. Pathol.* **35,** 713 (1943).
(106) Kline, B. E., Rusch, H. P., Baumann, C. A., and Lavik, P. S., *Cancer Research* **3,** 825 (1943).
(107) Voegtlin, C., and Maver, M. E., *Public Health Repts.* (*U. S.*) **51,** 1436 (1936).
(108) Voegtlin, C., and Thompson, J. W., *Public Health Repts.* (*U. S.*) **51,** 1429 (1936).
(109) Kocher, R. A., *Cancer Research* **4,** 251 (1944).
(110) Watson, A. F., *Brit. J. Exptl. Pathol.* **17,** 124 (1936).
(111) Minor, A. H., and Ramirez, M. A., *Cancer Research* **2,** 509 (1942).

CHAPTER VI

Endocrinology

INTRODUCTION

In Chapter IV the influence which the sex hormones exerted on the initiation and development of various kinds of tumors was described. The present chapter is concerned with the few attempts which have been made, by injection and by ablation techniques, to inhibit the initiation and growth of tumors. The operative procedures involved in the extirpation of any endocrine organ are bound to be drastic, and relatively few observations have been made of the body weights of experimental animals subsequent to such operations, or, in the event of ablation of non-sex tissues, whether the breeding capacities of the animals were maintained. Just as in much of the nutritional studies on cancer the endocrinological aspects have frequently been neglected, so also, in the endocrinological literature on this subject, the reader may often search in vain for information regarding the nutritional status of the animals employed.

Much of the information in the endocrine approach to the study of neoplastic disease has been obtained by the study of the influence of the sex hormones on the inititation and development of tumors not only of sex but of non-sex tissues as well. This has not been necessarily due to the supposition that these hormones play a predominant, if not decisive, role in the neoplastic process, but to the fact that these hormones (derived from or similar in action to those derived from the gonads) have been available in pure form. To these hormonal weapons have now been added a number of pure crystalline compounds derived from or related to the secretions of the adrenal cortex. Of these sterol-like compounds, the most actively studied in many pathologic states has been Kendall's compound E, or cortisone. Together with the purified adrenocorticotrophic hormone of the pituitary, abbreviated to ACTH, which appears to be polypeptide in nature, a new means of approach to the endocrine control of cancer has been started. Yet even these newer preparations appear to be best used in conjunction with at least one of the sex hormones, which illustrates again the delicate balance which is required in equilibrating the needs of therapy with the needs of the organism to survive. It may be that such hormonal attempts are doomed to be nothing better than a temporary alleviation, for agents of this nature act not only upon the parasitic growth, the cancer, but upon the host as well. They are not exclusively target-seekers, or directed missiles, but probably act on the differential basis that their effect may be more intense upon the tumor than upon the host. If they lack the advantages of more specific, organism-foreign drugs, they should also lack their frequent disadvantages in inducing resistance after repeated administration, for it would not be expected that intrinsic agents would induce an immunity to their action on the part of the host to whom they are natural components. That sometimes they appear to do so brings up the sorry distinction between autonomous, non-responsive tissues and dependent, responsive tissues, for which there is, at the present time, no explanation whatever.

Mammary Tumors in Mice

The relation of the ovary to carcinoma of the breast was suggested by clinical observations at the close of the last century. The obvious dependence of the mammary gland on ovarian function led a few surgeons to use ovariectomy as a palliative treatment for cancer of the breast. The results were not particularly successful, and, with the development of radical surgical methods for the removal of the breast and adjacent lymph nodes, ovariectomy fell into disfavor.

The experimental study of the influence of ovarian secretions on mammary tumors began with the classic investigations on mice by Leo Loeb and his associates (1) (cf. Chapter IV). The extremely low incidence of mammary tumors in male mice, as well as the influence of breeding on the incidence of mammary tumors in females, led Lathrop and Loeb in 1916 to study the effect of the removal of the ovaries. Ovariectomy at an early age of female mice of a high mammary tumor line either completely inhibited or greatly delayed the appearance of mammary tumors, whereas castration after the seventh month of age yielded little significant effect. Similar results were obtained by Cori (2, 3), and by Murray (4). Damage of the ovaries by X-radiation also caused a significant decrease of mammary cancer in mice (5).

Since estrogens are necessary for the development of mammary cancer, it might be expected that androgens would repress this development. In parabiotic experiments, Murray joined female to male mice both of the same high tumor strain (*DBA*) and noted that neither the males nor the

TABLE 54

Effect of Ovariectomy on the Incidence of Mammary[1] Tumors in Mice (1)

Description of Mice	Incidence, %
Breeding females	67
Non-breeding females	55
Females spayed at 3–5 months	2
Females spayed at 4–7 months	30
Females spayed at 7–10.5 months	60

[1] Murray performed the crucial control experiment by obtaining mammary tumors in castrated males into which ovarian tissue was subcutaneously implanted (4).

females developed tumors of the breast (6). Wooley (7) confirmed this experiment, but also observed that the mammary glands of female mice in parabiosis with other females showed decreased development, so that it would appear that some factor other than the male hormone might have played a role in the original Murray experiment. This is a case where knowledge of the nutritional status of the parabiotic mice would be of importance. Lacassagne and Raynaud (8) administered testosterone propionate in biweekly injections to young female mice of a highly susceptible strain, beginning a few days after birth and continuing throughout the life of the animals, and noted that none developed mammary carcinoma. However, histological examination revealed that the mammary glands of these mice were completely undeveloped. Lacassagne developed the thesis further (9) that androgen would have no influence in inhibiting the appearance of mammary tumors in adult female mice, but Nathanson and Andervont (10), Jones (11), and Heiman (12) showed that such incidence actually was lowered in adult female mice, whether virgin or bred. Testosterone, however, apparently has no effect on the growth of a mammary tumor once established in a mouse (9, 10), nor does progesterone (9). The androgen may, however, affect benign adenomatous lesions in the rat (*vide ultra*).

Other hormone preparations, with little or no effect on mammary tumors in mice, have been crude extracts of the suprarenal gland and of the pituitary (13), thyrotropic hormone (14), and prolactin (15). Gardner (16) investigated the effect of hypophysectomy, performed either during or immediately after pregnancy, on the growth of spontaneous mammary tumors in first-generation hybrid mice. No effect was found, although the non-cancerous portions of the mammary-gland tissue became atrophic. Adenomatous nodules did not regress either, thus indicating that this stage of growth was also independent of hormonal control. Further evidence of the independence of the growth, if not the origin, of mammary tumors from pituitary control was demonstrated by Korteweg and Thomas (17), who found that mammary tumors could be transplanted to, and would grow in, hypophysectomized mice.

Although progesterone exerts little if any effect upon the development of mammary tumors in mice, it may be mentioned briefly here that this hormone exerts in guinea pigs a decidedly antagonistic action toward the development of abdominal fibroids otherwise elicited by estradiol (18, 19). In large doses, and over a long period of time, progesterone inhibits the growth of the adenomatous portion of spontaneous mammary fibroadenoma in the rat, the large dose being necessary to neutralize (as does testosterone) the stimulating effect of estrogen on this benign growth (20). On the basis partly of these and of other findings (21), Hertz and his colleagues undertook studies of the effect of progesterone on the clinical course of cancer of the cervix with results largely negative in character (22).

The use of estrogens in the treatment of cancer of the breast might at first appear paradoxical, and yet Zondek advanced such a practice on the basis that it would bring about an inhibition in pituitary function and thereby a diminution in the growth of the tumor (23). Studies on mice have shown that the administration of pituitary growth hormone (somatotrophin) to mammary cancer-bearing animals leads to an increase in growth rate of the tumor over and above that of the host (24). By using carefully standardized dietary conditions and forced feeding, it has been shown that hypophysectomy inhibits the growth of intramuscular Walker tumor in rats (25). There is little doubt that the pituitary is concerned in some way with the growth of experimental tumors, and its role in the induction of tumors has been demonstrated by the following. Prolonged administration of growth hormone to rats results in the induction of a variety of neoplasms (26), whereas administration of the same pituitary hormone (27), of methylcholanthrene (28), or of 3′-methyl-4-dimethylaminoazobenzene (29) to hypophysectomized rats results in few if any tumors, compared with intact controls. That pituitary X-irradiation is generally ineffective in clinical cases of cancer may be ascribed in part to too-low doses of radiation, a result of justifiable caution.

However, no matter what the theory of the action of the estrogens may be, these pure compounds have proved decidedly palliative in many cases of advanced breast cancer in patients at least 5 years past the menopause (30–32). Table 55 describes some of the recent observations.

TABLE 55

EFFECT OF ESTROGENS ON SOFT TISSUE LESIONS OF BREAST CANCER (31)

Compound	Number of cases	Average daily dose, mg.	Regressions, %
Diethylstilbestrol[1]	145	15	41
Diethylstilbestrol dimethyl ether	21	20–30	48
Diethylstilbestrol methyl ether	15	20–30	47
Dienestrol, low dose[2]	7	1–3	14
Dienestrol, high dose	9	30	44
Hexestrol[3]	7	24	57
Benzestrol	7	30	30
Ethinyl estradiol	28	3–4.5	54
Sodium estrone sulfate	21	20–30	48
Methyl bisdehydrodoisynolic acid	13	20–30	23
Allenolic acid	4	7.5–15	25
Tripara-anisylchloroethylene	6	24–48	17

[1] ($HO \cdot C_6H_4 \cdot CEt{:}CEt \cdot C_6H_4 \cdot OH$)

[2] ($HO \cdot C_6H_4 \cdot C({:}CHMe) \cdot C({:}CHMe) \cdot C_6H_4 \cdot OH$)

[3] ($HO \cdot C_6H_4 \cdot CHEt \cdot CHEt \cdot C_6H_4 \cdot OH$)

Conflicting reports have appeared on the distribution of radioactive isotope-labeled estrogens. These vary from reports of a definite concentration of the label in breast (33, 34), ovary, thyroid, adrenal, and pituitary (35) to those which report no apparent selective localization in any tissue (36–38). The cause of so complete a discrepancy is not apparent. Yet these hormones exert a definite regressive influence in many cases on mammary tumors and on bone. In this connection, it is important to lay stress on the hypercalcemia which frequently accompanies estrogen treatment of advanced breast cancer in the presence of osteolytic skeletal metastases (39).

The use of testosterone (31, 32, 40, 41), or of weaker androgens such as methylandrostenediol (42), appears to be less efficacious on objective evidence than the estrogens but does appear to have considerable subjective benefit, particularly where osseus metastatic growth exists. This effect may be due to increased protein anabolism (43). In any event the course of steroid therapy in cases of advanced mammary cancer is still unpredictable in too many cases, and even in those responsive initially to such treatment a resistant state ultimately is acquired. Alternating androgenic and estrogenic therapy sooner or later has its limits. Whether the host or the tumor separately assumes this final intransigence, or both together, is not known, but in mice it is known that a mammary tumor originally responsive to estrogen becomes on serial transplantation less and less responsive until finally completely resistant; each new host is itself responsive, it is the tumor which changes (44).

Finally, it is of interest to note an experiment by Andervont on the effect of isolation and of crowding on the incidence of mammary tumors among female *C3H* mice (45). Such mice maintained in individual cages developed tumors at an earlier age than did their litter mates kept eight to a cage. The difference in incidence was much greater among virgin than among breeding mice. Investigation of vaginal smears revealed that estrus cycles started at an earlier age among the segregated virgin mice than among the non-segregated mice. This observation of Andervont's also emphasizes the need for careful consideration of environmental factors in the studies of effects related to the appearance of mammary and perhaps of other tumors in experimental animals. These environmental factors include temperature, and quality and intensity of light, which are known in some species to affect the regularity of the estrus cycle, and possibly the level of thyroid secretion, which have thus far received inadequate study as applied to problems in cancer. Experimental interference with thyroid gland function, as exemplified by thiouracil administration, results in arrest of mammary gland development and a marked diminution in the incidence of mammary tumors (46).

Lymphatic Disease

In both human and mouse leukemia there is a pronounced sex difference in incidence, but the ratio is reversed in each species. In man, with several types of the disease, 60 to 80 % of the cases are in males (47). In the majority of high leukemia strains of mice the reverse holds, with females showing a much higher incidence than males. In a study of the *RI* strain of mice, Murphy (48) observed that the incidence in intact females was 88 %, in ovariectomized females 90 %, and in castrated males 97 %. These figures were significantly different from the incidence in intact males, which was 54 %, and in ovariectomized females treated with testosterone propionate, namely, 58 %. On the basis of these findings it was suggested that sex difference in susceptibility to leukemia in the mouse strain studied was due to the inhibitory effect in males of androgenic factors. The effect of estrogen on the induction of lymphoid tumors in mice has been previously noted, as well as the inhibitory effect of testosterone when administered with estrogen (49) (cf. Chapter IV).

Quite striking observations were made by Furth and his colleagues (50) on the effect of thymectomy on the incidence of spontaneous leukemia in *Ak* mice. Removal of the thymus from mice 31 to 71 days of age resulted in a reduction of incidence of spontaneous leukemia from 77 to 8 % in females, and from 61 to 11 % in males. The thymectomized mice retained the capacity to breed and possessed a longer survival period. It had been noted earlier by Furth (51) that underfeeding led to a reduction of leukemia incidence in this strain, accompanied by involution of the thymus, and, therefore, the decrease in incidence might have been primarily due to this involution. The association of the thymus with neoplasia is an interesting development, and it may be noted in this connection that Sturm and Murphy observed that adrenalectomy in the rat leads to hypertrophy of the thymus together with an enhanced susceptibility to transplanted leukemia (52).

The relation of the secretion of the adrenal cortex to the development of malignant lymphatic disease has been one of the most interesting observations of the past decade. Earlier clinical studies had shown an atrophy or diminution of lymphoid tissue under conditions of stress (cf. 53) which now are known to be accompanied by high levels of circulating adrenocortical secretions. In 1943 Dougherty and White (54) reported that cortical secretions markedly inhibited the growth of the normal lymphocytes of experimental animals, followed the next year by the observations of Murphy and Sturm (55) and of Heilman and Kendall (56) on the inhibition of malignant lymphocytes by the same secretions. Further work on this problem was delayed until Kendall and his coworkers at the Mayo Clinic succeeded in isolating and separating several steroid components of the adrenal cortex, among which a compound designated E, later cortisone, was noted to be particularly inhibitory toward the growth of lymphoid tissue, whether normal or neoplastic (56). Among the crystalline adrenal cortex steroids are the following:

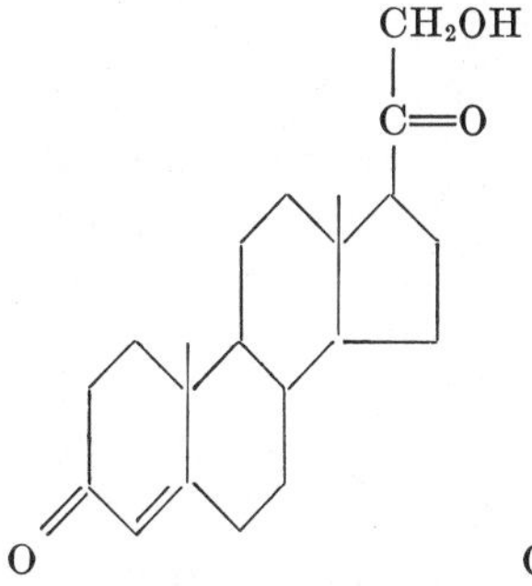

11-Deoxycorticosterone

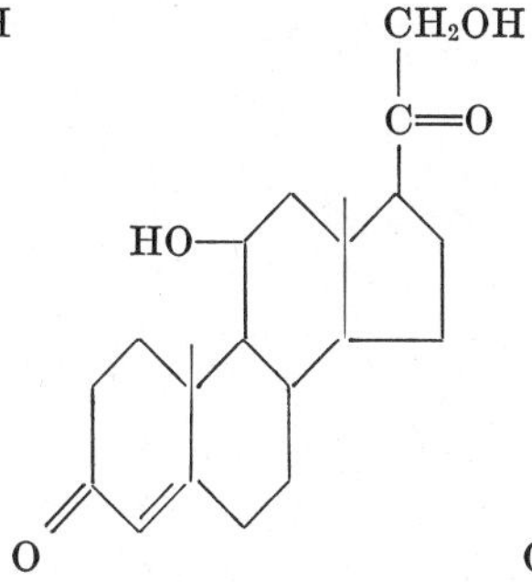

Corticosterone

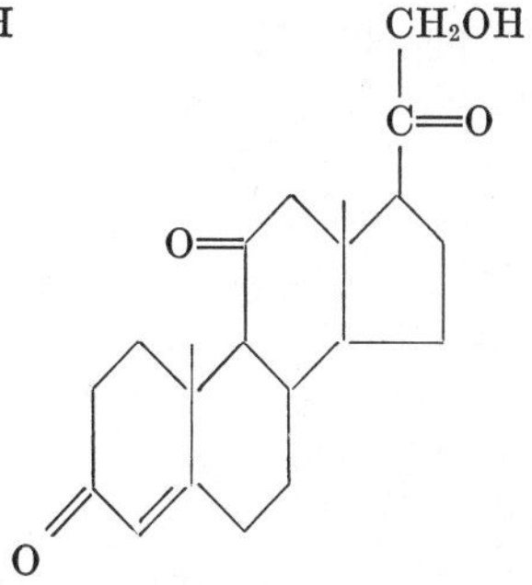

11-Dehydrocorticosterone (Compound A)

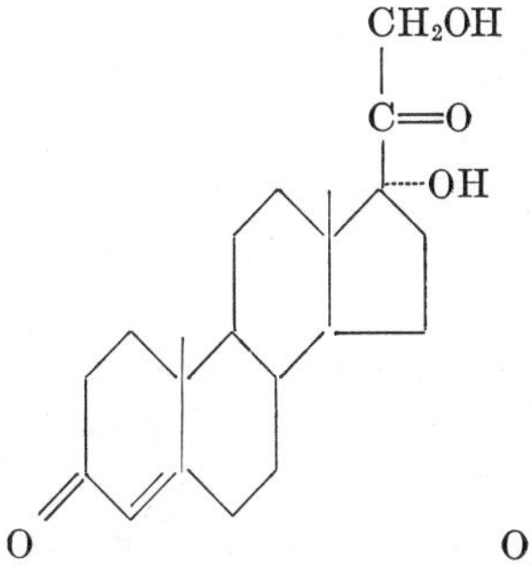

17-α-Hydroxydeoxycorticosterone (Compound S)

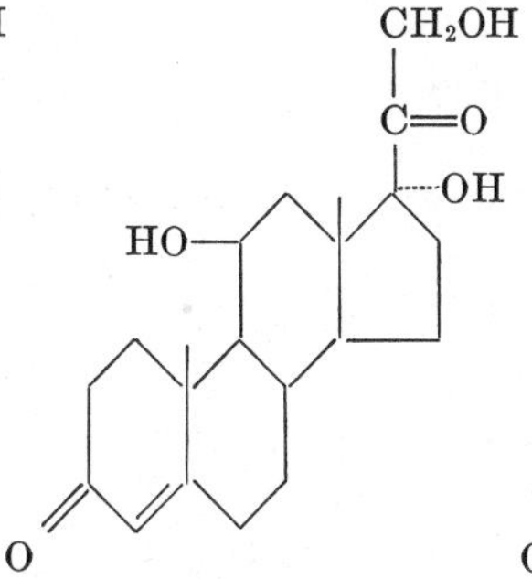

17-α-Hydroxycorticosterone (Compound F)

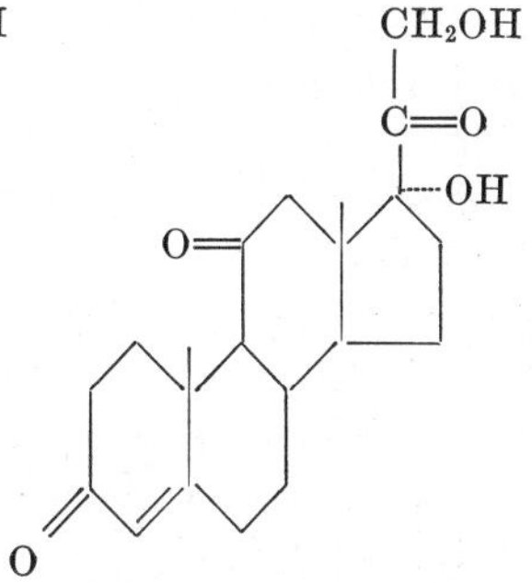

17-α-Hydroxy-11-dehydrocorticosterone (Compound E, "cortisone")

Parallel with the separation and identification of the adrenal cortex steroids went the purification of the polypeptide-like adrenocorticotrophic hormone of the anterior pituitary (ACTH), a task largely assumed by C. H. Li and his associates at Berkeley. The relatively small amounts of the materials available handicapped more extensive studies on their possible role in controlling malignant lymphatic disease, when in 1949 Hench, Kendall, and their associates at the Mayo Clinic made their first and dramatic announcement of the beneficial effects of cortisone (E) in the clinical treatment of rheumatoid arthritis (57). From that time forward, the accelerated development of organic chemical synthetic procedures, to some extent using plant sterols as intermediates, made the adrenal cortex steroids readily available for clinical and experimental studies. Indeed, the development of the use of the soya sterols and of the sapogenins has made possible the preparation of at least one of the steroids, namely, deoxycorticosterone, "in multiple kilos daily . . . a relatively simple task" (58). However, of the twenty-eight steroids which have been isolated from adrenal tissue (59), only cortisone has appeared so far to possess highly striking clinical features.

The biogenesis of the adrenal steroids has been studied in ingenious fashion by Pincus and his colleagues at Worcester, employing perfusion of the isolated adrenal (60). The perfusion medium was citrated homologous whole blood with and without added ACTH, the results showing that output of corticosteroids was greatly increased in the presence of the pituitary hormone, a finding attributed to synthesis, rather than release, of the extra steroids. An interesting observation in this connection was the need for the presence also of red cells to effect the ACTH stimulation of synthesis. The predominant steroid compounds so synthesized were 17-hydroxycorticosterone and corticosterone, with smaller amounts of cortisone, dehydrocorticosterone, and deoxycorticosterone. The former two compounds appear to be the end products of the adrenal corticosteroid synthetic systems, in which pregnenolone and progesterone are key intermediates, and from which cortisone and dehydrocorticosterone are secondary derivatives. Thus, by perfusion experiments it is fairly well established that cholesterol, acetate (61), or pregnenolone (from cholesterol?) is converted by the adrenal to progesterone, and thence by way of 17-hydroxyprogesterone to 17-hydroxycorticosterone (F). An oxidation at the 11-position would convert F to cortisone. The biosynthetic picture of the steroids is not entirely clear at the present time, nor is the exact position of ACTH in the numerous metabolic interconversions known. The entire subject is one of the most fascinating of our time, and it is curious and ironic that the alleviation of the distress of so many patients with lymphatic malignancy was delayed until it was found that arthritic patients were relieved by the same natural compounds.

The response of lymphoid tissue to ACTH is a general one in all species studied. Like the estrogenic hormones, this pituitary hormone produces a marked adrenal hypertrophy. In contrast, cortisone induces adrenal involution and, like testosterone, also thymic involution, while intense lymph node involution is accomplished by both ACTH and cortisone (cf. 62). The consequences of administration of the adrenal cortical steroids are widespread and involve many tissues of the body. Carbohydrate metabolism, protein metabolism, and salt balance are only some of the biological characteristics which are affected. As Ingle has well expressed it (63): "the consequences of cortical hormone action spread through the organism in a manner reminiscent of the waves caused by the impact of a stone in a pool of water, but the point of impact of the hormone remains unknown for the present."

The liver is a site of considerable steroid metabolism and is capable of transforming cortisone and related corticoids into a variety of metabolites in a basically similar pattern. The products are mainly compounds reduced in ring A, and it does not appear that 17-ketosteroids are major end products of hepatic metabolism (64). Perfusion studies involving cortisone in the rat liver led to the isolation from the perfusion fluid (citrated bovine blood) of allopregnan-3α,17α,21-triol-11,20-dione; allopregnan-3β,17α,21-triol-11,20-dione; allopregnan-3α,11β,17α,21-tetrol-20-one; allopregnan-3β,11β,17α,21-tetrol-20-one; Δ^4-pregnen-11β,17α,21-triol-3,20-dione; Δ^4-pregnen-17α,20β,21-triol-3,11-dione; and androsterone—thus five ketols, one glycol, and one 17-ketosteroid. In addition, paper chromatography of the perfusate revealed the presence of a considerably greater number of metabolic products than those actually isolated. The isolated ketol metabolites were all of the allo configuration and demonstrate the reductive nature of the reactions within the liver tissue, although the presence of androsterone shows the capacity of the liver to effect an oxidative reaction without the simultaneous reduction of ring A. Some of the reactions noted have been demonstrated after the incubation of cortisone and deoxycorticosterone with rat liver homogenates (65) and slices (66, 67).

The very considerable number of metabolic products of cortisone (and of other steroids) suggests that the study of the effect of the individual steroid hormones on isolated enzyme systems *in vitro* may have quite limited validity, a restricted usefulness comparable for the same reason to that of similar studies involving the carcinogenic agents. A considerable literature has accumulated on such investigations of hormones in isolated enzyme systems [cf. *Vitamins and Hormones* **10** (1952, and *Ann. N. Y. Acad. Sci.* **54** (1951) for reviews of this subject].

From 1949 on, the use of cortisone and ACTH in malignant diseases was intensively studied, principally at the Memorial Hospital in New York. A screening program was devised by Stock, Karnofsky, and Sugiura (68) in which the relative efficacy of the steroids was measured by the marked inhibition of the development of the chick embryo, and of the growth of lymphosarcoma in mice. The most active of the adrenal steroids in this respect were the 11-oxygenated compounds which includes cortisone. The clinical studies conducted by Pearson and Eliel (69) on patients with lymphoid tumors revealed marked temporary regression of the tumors, accompanied by a general wasting of protoplasm as shown by negative nitrogen, phosphorus, potassium, and calcium balances. The general features of Cushing's syndrome due to hypersecretion of the adrenal cortex had already become a familiar accompaniment of cortisone and ACTH therapy, and the generalized catabolic reactions induced by administration of the adrenal factors imposed a limitation on the extent of their use. Temporary remissions of acute leukemia, as in the case of mice (70, 71), are also accomplished by the use of the adrenal components. Whether the catabolic effect of cortisone can be clinically balanced by the anabolic effect of testosterone remains to be determined. Compound A is considerably weaker, and compound F slightly weaker, than cortisone in comparable dosages. The only conclusion possible at the present time is that administration of cortisone or ACTH either to patients or to experimental animals produces little effect on the growth of tumors other than those of lymphatic origin (72–74), and on these, the effect is definitely inhibitory if only temporary.

Carcinoma of the Prostate

The hormonal control of the development of many cases of prostatic carcinoma represents one of the achievements of scientific medicine. Combined with relatively specific biochemical techniques, the observation of the course of the disease and of its treatment may, in the majority of cases be accomplished in a uniquely exact manner. This work, with which the names of Huggins and Gutman are principally linked, has formed one of the most striking therapeutic researches of modern times, as well as one of the few clear-cut observations on the interrelationship between the endocrine system and clinical malignant disease.

Aged dogs frequently develop hyperplasia of the prostate similar to man. Huggins and his colleagues noted that administration of diethylstilbestrol reduced this hyperplasia and, moreover, that while testosterone stimulated, stilbestrol inhibited prostatic secretion (75). These findings suggested that, if normal adult prostatic epithelium could be made to atrophy by reducing the amount or neutralizing the effect of androgen, it should be possible to produce atrophy of malignant adult prostatic epithelium by castration or injection of estrogen (cf. 76). Estrogen administration in large amounts results in pituitary inhibition and testicular atrophy, and, thus, the use of this kind of hormone at sufficiently high levels is, in effect, a chemical castration. It will be noted that underlying the above assumption is the further assumption that the malignant prostate cells are not fully, if at all, autonomous; e.g., they are still controlled to some measure by the same body mechanisms which control the normal prostate cells.

The general validity of these deductions was demonstrated by Huggins and his colleagues in 1941 (77, 78) and independently by Herbst (79), who obtained, in the majority of cases of prostatic carcinoma tested, striking alleviation of clinical symptoms by means of surgical castration or injection of stilbestrol. Since these observations were published, the procedures have been widely employed and closely scrutinized. Sullivan, Gutman, and Gutman (80) described "results without precedent in the large experience of this Clinic (Squier)." In 1942, the *Journal of the American Medical Association* published a collection of papers by leading urologists, delivered as part of a symposium before the section on urology of the association

(81). In 1945 the proceedings of a similar and later symposium were published in the same journal (82) with amplification of, but no essential disagreement with, the observations and tentative conclusions expressed in the earlier symposium on the subject. The net impression gained from the contents of the papers in these symposia, and from the informal discussions which followed, is that either surgical castration or stilbestrol administration in daily doses of 1 to 2 mg., or some combination of both procedures, is frequently productive of a striking and rapid alleviation in the clinical symptoms of prostatic carcinoma. However, in view of the relatively short period of time during which the cases have been under observation, no claim for a permanent relief from the disease may be made at present. Opinion appears to be divided on the relative therapeutic efficacy of surgical *versus* chemical (estrogen administration) castration, but there seems to be no question that both procedures approximate the same clinical goal, although the choice of procedure may sometimes depend upon factors unrelated to the primary pathology, such as the psychic reaction of the patient to surgical castration. In cases of disseminated carcinoma, the skeletal metastases frequently regress and the primary tumor appears to subside, with accompanying relief from urinary distress.

Bilateral orchiectomy or estrogen administration affords some relief in cases of non-disseminated prostatic carcinoma, but it seemed to be the belief of some of the urologists reporting in the associations' 1945 symposium (Emmett and Greene, Bumpus *et al.*, 82) that these procedures are most efficacious when applied to advanced, metastasizing cases. Castration as a therapeutic or palliative measure for benign prostatic hypertrophy had been occasionally applied for the past half-century with lack of consistent success. Evidently, this procedure is most dramatic and effective when employed *in extremis*, e.g., in advanced metastasizing prostatic carcinoma, and thus forms, at the present time, the clinician's final weapon. The most recent report on the subject is that by Huggins (83).

After a period of favorable response to the procedures described above, many cases demonstrate a recurrence of the disease with fatal termination. This later recurrence may be due to the compensatory activity of accessory androgen centers in the body, as in the adrenal cortex. Raising of the level of estrogen dosage sometimes, but not always, controls such recurrences, but the discomfort attendant upon the increased feminizing use of estrogen, as exemplified in the "hot flashes" and in the painful swelling of the breasts which frequently ensue, renders this procedure dubious over any prolonged period of time. On the other hand, it is also possible that cases of the disease which recur after a period of favorable response, or which are refractory from the very start, may actually be in a largely autonomous state and independent of mechanisms of normal body control.

In cases of advanced cancer of the prostate which became reactivated after previous antiandrogen therapy, Huggins and Bergenstal (84) found that simultaneous bilateral adrenalectomy, with subsequent cortisone administration, resulted in several instances of marked clinical improvement. The same observation was made in several cases of advanced mammary cancer. In all these patients the gonads had been previously removed. The period of observation has been too short to evaluate the final outcome, but the technique provides another weapon in the maintenance of the cancer patient. In types of cancer other than prostatic or mammary, adrenalectomy provided no objective or subjective effects, which is in contrast with the regressive changes noted in several forms of tumors other than lymphatic in experimental animals after total adrenalectomy (85–87). Adrenalectomy as noted above appears to promote the incidence of lymphatic tumors (cf. 88).

Clinical judgment of the relative success or failure of the endocrine control of prostatic carcinoma possesses a unique and objective form of evidence in the level of phosphatase activity in the serum of patients with the disseminated form of the disease. A full description of this phenomenon is deferred to Chapter IX, at which place the present discussion is continued.

The mouse prostatic epithelium closely resembles that of the human (89), and Horning has been able to develop cancer in the mouse tissue by impregnating 20-methylcholanthrene in homologous, subcutaneous grafts. It appears that the actively secreting prostatic alveolus is not the focus of malignant change in this instance, but more probably the non-secreting, resting alveolar cells in the exhaustive phase of the secretory cycle. It will be recalled in this connection that Haddow had expressed the opinion that chemical carcinogens act more readily on tissues whose cellular activity had been depressed (90). In accord with these observations, Horning (91) noted that prostatic grafts in mice treated with stilbestrol plus methylcholanthrene yielded tumors more rapidly and in greater numbers than in similar grafts in which stilbestrol had been replaced by testosterone. It is thus probable that stilbestrol, by inhibiting the secretory phase of the prostatic epithelial cells, renders them more susceptible to the action of the carcinogen. The accord between theory on the one hand, and clinical observations on the other, is striking. Table 56 describes the findings.

TABLE 56

EFFECT OF HORMONES ON CARCINOGENESIS IN PROSTATIC GRAFTS (91)

Substances included in graft	Number of mice[1] with grafts	Number of mice which developed tumors
20-Methylcholanthrene alone	35	13
20-Methylcholanthrene + diethylstilbestrol	35	26
20-Methylcholanthrene + testosterone propionate	35	3

[1] Both *A* and *C3H* strains used.

References

(1) Lathrop, A. E. C., and Loeb, L., *J. Cancer Research* **1,** 1 (1916); Loeb, L., *J. Med. Research* **40,** 477 (1919).
(2) Cori, C. F., *J. Cancer Research* **10,** 265 (1926).
(3) Cori, C. F., *J. Exptl. Med.* **45,** 983 (1927).
(4) Murray, W. S., *J. Cancer Research* **12,** 18 (1928).
(5) Furth, J., and Butterworth, J. S., *Am. J. Cancer* **28,** 66 (1936).
(6) Murray, W. S., *Am. J. Cancer* **30,** 517 (1937).
(7) Wooley, G. W., *Proc. 7th Intern. Genetic. Congr. Edinburgh,* p. 318 (1939).
(8) Lacassagne, A., and Raynaud, A., *Compt. rend. soc. biol.* **131,** 586; **132,** 431 (1939).
(9) Lacassagne, A., *Am. J. Cancer* **37,** 414 (1939).
(10) Nathanson, I. T., and Andervont, H. B., *Proc. Soc. Exptl. Biol. Med.* **40,** 421 (1939).
(11) Jones, E. E., *Cancer Research* **1,** 787 (1941).
(12) Heiman, J., *Cancer Research* **4,** 31 (1944).
(13) Dobrovolskaia-Zavadskaia, N., and Zephioff, P., *Compt. rend.soc. biol.* **133,** 216; **134,** 79 (1940).
(14) Haagensen, C. D., Randall, H. T., and Auchincloss, R., *Proc. Soc. Exptl. Biol. Med.* **45,** 820 (1940).
(15) Bischoff, F., and Maxwell, L. C., *Am. J. Cancer* **27,** 87 (1936).
(16) Gardner, W. U., *Cancer Research* **2,** 476 (1942).
(17) Korteweg, R., and Thomas, F., *Am. J. Cancer* **37,** 36 (1939).
(18) Lipschutz, A., Bruzzone, S., and Fuenzalida, F., *Cancer Research* **4,** 179 (1944).
(19) Lipschutz, A., and Grisnall, J., *Cancer Research* **4,** 186 (1944).
(20) Heiman, J., *Cancer Research* **3,** 65 (1943).
(21) Hertz, R., Larsen, C. D., and Tullner, W. W., *J. Natl. Cancer Inst.* **8,** 123 (1947).
(22) Hertz, R., Cromer, J. K., Young, J. P., and Westfall, B. B., *Symposium on Steroids in Exptl. and Clin. Practice, Philadelphia,* p. 366 (1951).
(23) Zondek, B., *Lancet* **i,** 776 (1936).
(24) Smith, M. C., Slattery, P. A., Shimkin, M. B., Li, C. H., Lee, R., Clark, J. C., and Lyons, W. R., *Cancer Research* **12,** 59 (1952).
(25) Talalay, P., Takano, G. M. V., and Huggins, C., *Cancer Research* **12,** 838 (1952).
(26) Moon, H. D., Simpson, M. E., Li, C. H., and Evans, H. M., *Cancer Research* **10,** 297, 364, 549 (1950).
(27) Moon, H. D., Simpson, M. E., Li, C. H., and Evans, H. M., *Cancer Research* **11,** 535 (1951).
(28) Moon, H. D., Simpson, M. E., and Evans, H. M., *Science* **116,** 331 (1952).
(29) Griffin, A. C., Rinfret, A. P., and Corsigilia, V. F., *Cancer Research* **13,** 77 (1953).
(30) Escher, G. C., Heber, J. M., Woodard, H. Q., Farrow, J. H., and Adair, F. E., *Symposium on Steroids in Exptl. and Clin. Practice, Philadelphia,* p. 375 (1951).
(31) Nathanson, I. T., Engel, L. L., Kennedy, B. J., and Kelley, R. M., *Symposium on Steroids in Exptl. and Clin. Practice, Philadelphia,* p. 379 (1951).
(32) Douglas, M., *Brit. J. Cancer* **6,** 32 (1952).
(33) Albert, S., Heard, R. D. H., Leblond, C. P., and Saffron, J., *J. Biol. Chem.* **177,** 247 (1949).
(34) Lewison, E. F., Levi, J. E., Jones, G. S., Jones, H. W., Jr., and Silberstein, H. E.. *Cancer* **4,** 537 (1951).
(35) Daudel, P., Apelgot, S., Buu-Hoï, N. P., Costerousse, O., and Lacassagne, A., *Bull. soc. chim. biol.* **32,** 264 (1950).
(36) Patterson, E., Gilbert, C. W., and Gallagher, U. M., *Nature* **163,** 801 (1949).

(37) Twombly, G. H., McClintock, L., and Engelman, M., *Am. J. Obstet. Gynecol.* **56,** 260 (1948).
(38) Twombly, G. H., and Schoenewalt, E. F., *Cancer* **3,** 601 (1950); **4,** 296 (1951).
(39) Kennedy, B. J., Tibbetts, D. M., Nathanson, I. T., and Aub, J. C., *Cancer Research* **13,** 445 (1953).
(40) Segaloff, A., Gordon, D., Horwitt, B. N., Schlosser, J. V., and Murison, P. J. *Cancer* **4,** 319 (1951).
(41) Galton, D. A. G., *Brit. J. Cancer* **4,** 20 (1950).
(42) Homburger, F., Kasdon, S. C., and Fishman, W. H., *Proc. Soc. Exptl. Biol. Med.* **74,** 162 (1950).
(43) Homburger, F., Dart, R. M., Bonner, C. D., Brauche, G., Jr., Kasdon, S. C., and Fishman, W. H., *J. Clin. Endocrinol. and Metabolism.* **13,** 704 (1953).
(44) Foulds, L., *Brit. J. Cancer* **3,** 240 (1949).
(45) Andervont, H. B., *J. Natl. Cancer Inst.* **4,** 547 (1944).
(46) Dubnik, C. S., Morris, H. P., and Dalton, A. J., *J. Natl. Cancer Inst.* **10,** 815 (1950).
(47) Forkner, C. E., "*Leukemia and Allied Disorders.*" Macmillan Company, New York, 1938.
(48) Murphy, J. B., *Cancer Research* **4,** 622 (1944).
(49) Gardner, W. U., Dougherty, T. F., and Williams, W. L., *Cancer Research* **4,** 73 (1944).
(50) McEndy, D. P., Boon, M. C., and Furth, J., *Cancer Research* **4,** 377 (1944).
(51) Saxton, J. A., Boon, M. C., and Furth, J., *Cancer Research* **4,** 401 (1944).
(52) Sturm, E., and Murphy, J. B., *Cancer Research* **4,** 384 (1944).
(53) Bardeen, C. R., *J. Exptl. Med.* **2,** 501 (1897).
(54) Dougherty, T. F., and White, A., *Science* **98,** 367 (1943).
(55) Murphy, J. B., and Sturm, E., *Science* **99,** 303 (1944).
(56) Heilman, F. R., and Kendall, E. C., *Endocrinology* **34,** 416 (1944).
(57) Hench, P. S., Kendall, E. C., Slocumb, C. H., and Polley, H. F., *Proc. Staff Meetings, Mayo Clinic* **24,** 181 (1949).
(58) Julian, P. L., *Recent Progr. Hormone Research* **6,** 195 (1951).
(59) Reichstein, R., and Shoppee, C. W., *Vitamins and Hormones* **1,** 346 (1943).
(60) Hechter, O., Zaffaroni, A., Jacobsen, R. P., Levy, H., Jeanloz, R. W., Schenker, V., and Pincus, G., *Recent Progr. Hormone Research* **6,** 215 (1951).
(61) Hechter, O., Solomon, M. M., Zaffaroni, A., and Pincus, G., *Arch. Biochem. and Biophys.* **46,** 201 (1953).
(62) Money, W. L., Fager, J., and Rawson, R. W., *Cancer Research* **12,** 206 (1952).
(63) Ingle, D. J., *J. Clin. Endocrinol.* **10,** 312 (1950).
(64) Caspi, E. Y., Levy, H., and Hechter, O. M., *Arch. Biochem. and Biophys.* **45** 169 (1953).
(65) Fish, C. A., Hayano, M., and Pincus, G., *Arch. Biochem. and Biophys.* **42,** 448 (1953).
(66) Eisenstein, A. B., *Science* **116,** 520 (1952).
(67) Schneider, J. J., *J. Biol. Chem.* **199,** 235 (1952).
(68) Stock, C. C., Karnofsky, D. A., and Sugiura, K., *Symposium on Steroids in Exptl. and Clin. Practice, Philadelphia,* p. 50 (1951).
(69) Pearson, O. H., and Eliel, L. P., *Recent Progr. Hormone Research* **6,** 373 (1951).
(70) Law, L. W., and Spiers, R., *Proc. Soc. Exptl. Biol. Med.* **66,** 226 (1947).
(71) Burchenal, J. H., Stock, C. C., and Rhoads, C. P., *Cancer Research* **10,** 209 (1950).
(72) Donald, T. C., Jr., and Higgins, G. M., *Cancer Research* **11,** 937 (1951).
(73) Gottschalk, R. G., and Grollman, A., *Cancer Research* **12,** 651 (1952).

(74) Postlethwait, R. W., Moseley, V., McKee, K. T., Murdock, J. H., Jr., and McCord, W. M., *Cancer* **4,** 984 (1951).
(75) Huggins, C., and Clarke, P. J., *J. Exptl. Med.* **72,** 747 (1940).
(76) Mulligan, R. M., *Arch. Pathol.* **39,** 162 (1945).
(77) Huggins, C., Stevens, R. E., and Hodges, C. U., *Arch. Surg.* **43,** 209 (1941).
(78) Huggins, C., and Hodges, C. V., *Cancer Research* **1,** 293 (1941).
(79) Herbst, W. P., *J. Am. Med. Assoc.* **120,** 1116 (1942); *Trans. Am. Assoc. Genito-urinary Surg.* **34,** 195 (1941).
(80) Sullivan, T. J., Gutman, E. B., and Gutman, A. B., *J. Urol.* **48,** 426 (1942).
(81) *J. Am. Med. Assoc.* **120,** No. **4** (1942).
(82) *J. Am. Med. Assoc.* **127,** No. **2** (1945).
(83) Huggins, C., *J. Am. Med. Assoc.* **131,** 576 (1946).
(84) Huggins, C., and Bergenstal, D. M., *Cancer Research* **12,** 134 (1952).
(85) Ingle, D. J., and Baker, B. L., *Endocrinology* **48,** 313 (1951).
(86) Funk, C., Tomashefsky, P., Soukup, R., and Ehrlich, A., *Brit. J. Cancer* **5,** 280 (1951).
(87) Talalay, P., Takano, G. M. V., and Huggins, C., *Cancer Research* **12,** 838 (1952).
(88) Law, L. W., Bunker, L. E., Jr., and Norris, B. A., *J. Natl. Cancer Inst.* **8,** 157 (1947).
(89) Horning, E. S., *Brit. J. Cancer* **3,** 211 (1949).
(90) Haddow, A., *Brit. Med. Bull.* **4,** 417 (1947).
(91) Horning, E. S., *Brit. J. Cancer* **6,** 80 (1952).

Chapter VII

Chemotherapy

Introduction

This topic may be considered as involving the use of chemicals ordinarily foreign to the animal body, which, when administered to a tumor-bearing host at a site removed from the tumor, will adversely affect the latter without destroying the former. Excluded from consideration under this heading are synthetic drugs which are known to imitate the known functions of intrinsic, endogenous factors, such as the synthetic estrogens.

This is the area of last resort, when all other methods of therapy have failed, and yet potentially it is the only one capable of enduring merit. Despite the temporary successes of various forms of intrinsic therapy, attempts to use the resources of the body to combat that to which it has already yielded promise little permanent relief. The tumor is a new tissue with a metabolic pattern which, though peculiar to itself in an over-all sense, comprises enzymes which function qualitatively like similar enzymes in normal tissues. The metabolic functions of the tumor in many individual instances thus overlap those of normal tissues, and a chemical therapy which finds itself in this borderland has little hope of success. It is not the individual metabolic function or enzyme which is the target, but the metabolic pattern of the tumor, for the capacity of living systems to regenerate one of their crippled components is one of their characteristic features. The over-all metabolic pattern of the tumor is unlike that of any normal tissue, and perhaps only something foreign to the normal tissue will spare it but destroy the tumor.

Up to the time when the first edition of this monograph was published (1947), few compounds were known which appeared to possess a selective destructive action on tumors, and this chapter considered only such agents as the bacterial toxins, benzene and arsenite, colchicine, and the radioactive isotopes. Since that time, a remarkable acceleration of this area of cancer therapy has developed, with approaches which, though still largely empirical, have resulted in increasing the number of therapeutic weapons available for the treatment of cancer. Great screening programs, involving thousands of compounds prepared annually by industry, universities, and the research institutes, have been established at important centers of cancer research. Hundreds of these compounds have been found to be effective under the frequently arbitrary conditions imposed by the screening techniques. How many may be lost under such conditions may never be known. The debt which the establishment of these programs owes to the successful efforts of analogous screening programs in the field of antibiotics needs little elaboration, although it is amply clear that the problems faced by the former are not only far more difficult but not even biologically comparable with those of the latter, while the influence of the example of group effort backed by large financial resources, as illustrated by the development of the atomic bomb, must also have played its role in the public encouragement of the great chemotherapy programs. Behind all these reasons, of course, is the cancer patient, refractory to radiation and inaccessible to surgery, for whom something more must be done.

Many chemical agents have emerged from the screening programs, which, when administered to experimental animals bearing tumors, inhibit the further growth and sometimes produce the regression of these tumors simultaneously with strongly toxic effects, including severe weight loss, in the hosts. To some extent, these toxic effects may be due to resorption of tumor substance within the host, but all too frequently these agents produce similar pathologic manifestations in normal animals free of tumors. It is not improbable that, like the antibacterial drugs, the successful chemotherapeutic agents will be those most destructive to cells undergoing active metabolism and division. Cells in this category are to be found in non-neoplastic as well as in neoplastic tissues. Animals in toxemia have almost invariably a lowered food consumption, and a loss in tumor weight accompanied by a nearly proportionate loss in body weight is obviously not the solution to the problem. A second and equally important factor to consider in the evaluation of a chemotherapeutic agent is the fact that invariably a resistance develops to the continued administration of the agent. Indeed, in one known case, the host animal may even develop a dependence for the agent. The phenomena of drug resistance and dependence are among the most obscure in experimental therapeutics, and perhaps the most troublesome in actual practice. For these two reasons at least, namely, the toxicity of the drugs and the resistance developed to them, no agent has been found as yet to be completely effective in the treatment of cancer, whether in the mouse or in man. There are only agents which have more favorable ratios than others for the maximum tolerated dose to the minimum effective dose, and the use of different agents, either consecutively or in combination, appears to be the most frequently effective procedure.

The search for effective chemotherapeutic agents in cancer has been largely empirical, but of course analogous agents in malarial, cardiac, and infectious diseases were also once the happy results of accidental observation. The rationale generally appears to follow the discovery, not precede it, and sometimes no rationale can be found at all. The metabolism of tumors is not yet sufficiently known to allow prognostication as to the most rational and most favorable point of attack by chemicals of specific action, despite the many successes in other areas of the principle of antimetabolites. Until such knowledge is attained, it is only proper to encourage the exploration for any agent or group of agents which, when administered under satisfactory conditions, will adversely affect the tumor at doses well below the toxic level for the host. It might be supposed that the use of hormonal therapy would be based upon more rational principles, yet the curiously effective treatment of carcinoma of the male breast by castration plus estrogen administration must make the investigator prepared to accept many an apparent biological paradox. Among such paradoxes are Haddow's observation that chemicals which cause cancer may also cure it, and *vice versa*, an observation substantiated by the carcinogenic and carcinolytic properties of the nitrogen mustards, urethane, and stilbamidine, and Law's discovery that a transmissible leukemia in mice may pass from a susceptible to a dependent status in regard to amethopterin. The capacity for intellectual flexibility combined with scientific care is one of the demands in this field.

No attempt will be made in these pages to cover the burgeoning area of the chemotherapy of cancer. The most recent comprehensive review of the subject is by C. C. Stock (1). Karnofsky (2) and Gellhorn (3) have written surveys of the field of clinical cancer chemotherapy, and an able review by Skipper has recently appeared (3a). Dyer published in 1949 a list of the chemicals employed in therapeutic studies up to that date (4). A list of compounds which yielded negative results has been published by *Cancer Research* under the editorship of Stock (5), and the American Association for the Advancement of Science printed in 1947 a series of articles entitled *Approaches to Tumor Chemotherapy*. References to the use of radioactive isotopes in cancer therapy may be found in various reviews in the *Advances in Biological and Medical Physics* series, in the *Manual of Artificial Radioisotope Therapy* (New York), and in the monograph, *Isotopes in Biology and Medicine* (Madison). It is the purpose of this chapter to outline briefly the use of a few selected materials which have been found under limited conditions to affect unfavorably the growth of or cause damage to certain types of tumors. Although several examples will be described, it must be realized that thus far only a few, notably the nitrogen mustards and the antifolic acid agents, have had anything approaching extensive clinical trials, and these have been chiefly in the field of lymphatic diseases. Statistically these form a relatively small proportion of the total incidence of neoplastic diseases, but it has been one of the encouraging results of this program that some degree of comfort has been brought to even a few. The patience and persistence required in this field commands admiration, for if most men write their names on water, how true must this be of men who daily encounter failure and yet press on?

Screening Techniques

Since test procedures for potential chemotherapeutic agents involving human beings on a large clinical scale are out of the question, the screening of the thousands of available chemical compounds have had, perforce, to be accomplished with various experimental devices employing laboratory material. Like all scientific procedures, a compromise between the effective study of the chemical compounds and the resources, both in material and time available for experimentation, has inevitably led to the establishment of relatively arbitrary criteria in the evaluation of these compounds. The possible oversight of compounds ineffective in animals which might have been effective in man had they been tried may be matched by compounds active in animals and subsequently found inactive in man. These hazards are recognized by workers in this field (cf. Shear, 6), but there is no alternative. On the other hand, the number of compounds which have proved nearly equally effective in inhibiting the growth of neoplasms in both experimental animals and in man has encouraged and further established the usefulness of the laboratory screening programs.

To the uncertainties imposed by the choice of animal rather than human subjects are added those involved in the study of the inhibition of a limited number of experimental tumor types. At a single or over a narrow range of dosages of a given agent, one or more tumor types may prove to be susceptible and others may appear to be resistant. The question then arises whether the program should be diverted to the problem of the apparently resistant tumor types, which in some cases may turn out to be related to dosage or length of administration, or whether the demands of the program are met by the presence of susceptible tumor types alone. Many of the susceptible tumor types are of the transplanted variety, and the question also arises as to whether the inhibition is the resultant of a failure in successful grafting in the new host, a question which is only partially answered by varying the times of administration of the agent subsequent to the grafting. The successful growth of a transplanted tumor is markedly dependent on the dietary intake (7), and a toxic condition alone might produce an inhibition of tumor size (8). The progressive growth of a transplanted tumor is also dependent upon the genetic characteristics of the strain of animal in which it is implanted (cf. 9). Raising the protein level of the diet has sometimes diminished both the toxicity and the tumor-inhibitory capacity of more than one agent (10) (Table 57). On the other hand, many agents have been noted to induce a toxicity in tumor-bearing hosts without measurable effect on the tumors, but the designation of toxicity is not a precise term but the description of a generalized condition. Although an effective and an ineffective agent may each make the animal sick, their individual actions may be quite different. Few animal experimentalists, other than

TABLE 57

Comparison of Inhibiting Action of Various Agents on Growth of Walker Tumor in Rats Maintained on High (20%) and Low (5%) Protein Diets (10)

Therapeutic agent	Dose	Ratios of weight of tumor in untreated to treated animals on 20% protein diet	5% protein diet
X-Irradiation	100 r. per day—total, 800 r. whole body	2.9	5.7
Nitrogen mustard	2 × 10 mg. per kg. i.p.	2.1	9.0
2′-Chloro-4-dimethylaminostilbene	150 mg. per kg. i.p.	1.1	19.3
1,2,5,6-Dibenzanthracene	500 mg. per kg. i.p.	1.6	4.0

the careful nutritionists, take the trouble to measure each mouse's daily consumption of food or its daily weight status, and in many cases, when dealing simultaneously with thousands of animals, such efforts would be a physical impossibility.

The evaluation of the chemotherapeutic agents in the screening programs has been based on various criteria, among them failure of tumor implants to grow, inhibition of growth over a selected time period, increased rate of regression of tumors, increased survival periods of the host animals, and various cytological changes in the tumors. To these have been added determinations of the maximum tolerated doses and minimum effective doses of the active compounds, and interesting studies of their mechanism of action.

The cytologic screening procedure in Shear's laboratory has employed studies of a wide variety of compounds tested for their damage to sarcoma 37 in mice (11) which is observed both grossly and histologically. Among the effective compounds studied by this group have been the purified podophyllin derivatives (12, 13), a series of colchicine derivatives (14–16), and a number of plant preparations (17–19).

The use of transmissible leukemia in mice as a means of testing antileukemic agents such as benzene and arsenite was first developed in Furth's laboratory (20). This method has been adapted to the program of the Memorial Hospital group in New York (21) and others (22, 23), in which the survival times of the treated mice have been compared with those of untreated leukemic controls. Among the compounds found effective in these tests have been the nitrogen mustards and the folic acid analogues.

Haddow and his associates, in their studies on tumor inhibition by carcinogens (24), have dissected and weighed the implanted Walker 256 carcinoma in rats, as have Walpole and Hendry (25, 26) in their studies of the active epoxides and ethyleneimines. Tumor weights of treated mice have been determined in Kidder's laboratory (27) for the study of antipurine compounds. Measurement of tumor volumes in the living mice bearing sarcoma 180 has been employed by Stock and Rhoads (28) to study the effect of the folic acid analogues and nitrogen mustard, by Laszlo and Leuchtenberger (29), and by Schoenbach and his colleagues (30). The tumor-inhibitory capacity of various dyes has been studied in Margaret Lewis' laboratory by following the survival times of the treated tumor-bearing mice (31).

These have all been solid tumors. The use of the ascitic form of tumors has been recommended by Klein (32) and has been employed by Lettré (33) and by Sugiura and Stock (34). A partial screening of folic acid analogues using *Tetrahymena* has been reported by Kidder's group (35, 36). The use of tissue culture for screening purposes has been reported by Cornman (37), by Lettré (38), and by Biesele and his colleagues (39). The last-mentioned have employed a differential action on mouse sarcoma and embryonic mouse skin, both placed in glass tubes and treated with a variety of purines. Culture of tumors in eggs has been developed by Taylor *et al.* (40) to study the effect of folic acid antagonists, and by Karnofsky and his colleagues (41) to study the effect of nitrogen mustard-like compounds. The use of the regenerating liver in rats has recently been suggested (42).

The use of heterologous sites for growth of tumors, other than the developing chick embryo, has been described in an earlier chapter (II). Thus far the application of such procedures, as that of Greene involving transplantation to the anterior chamber of the eye, or that of Toolan involving the transplantation of human tumors to X-irradiated or cortisone-treated rats, to chemotherapy screening techniques has not been successfully developed. It is doubtful that human tumors growing under such circumstances would serve as a satisfactory filter for screening, for, although the tumor might remain human (and there may be doubt as to that), the host would still be an experimental animal. Moreover, the possible effect of the necessary cortisone or X-irradiation treatment of the rodent host raises an area of doubt in any chemotherapeutic trial, and, if the metabolism of the host is involved in the fate of the administered agent, there is no assurance that rodent and human mechanisms are sufficiently similar as to make a human tumor growing in a rat indistinguishable from the same tumor growing in a human being. All these objections might vanish if the curative agent ignored the host—and *vice versa*—and directly engaged the tumor in therapeutic struggle. However, no agent so far found to be at all palliative is without effect upon the host, and it seems probable that screening programs involving tumors separated from the natural host, whether in heterologous growths or in tissue culture, may possess some features of unreality. It is not impossible to conceive of a somewhat similar objection, although far less serious, in the use of transplanted tumors for screening, in place of spontaneous or primary induced tumors, but there must be some compromise with the practical demands inherent in programs involving the initial screening of hundreds or thousands of compounds. Finally, there is the philosophical and practical problem of whether any results in this area, obtained with laboratory animals, are applicable to human beings. As mentioned above, there is no alternative possible at present to the use of experimental animals, nor need this be a matter of great concern. There is a sufficiently strong body of evidence which indicates that cancer is cancer in any species, and failures in this field may perhaps be as readily ascribed to inadequate or faulty experimentation as to captious claims of insurmountable species differences.

Nitrogen Mustards and Related Compounds

Knowledge of the vesicants, inclusive of the so-called mustard gases, has been largely a by-product of activities connected with the last war. Mustard gas itself is di(2-chloroethyl)sulfide. Its properties are none too favorable for experimental studies, and attention shifted to its nitrogen analogues, such as methyl di(2-chloroethyl)amine or tri(2-chloroethyl)amine, which form hydrochlorides which are water-soluble and non-vesicant. The leucopenic and cytotoxic actions of these compounds were early recognized and led to various studies on the effect of these compounds in clinical lymphatic diseases. These clinical trials involved intravenous adminstration of the nitrogen mustard hydrochlorides in cases of Hodgkin's disease, lymphosarcoma, leukemia, and disorders of the hemopoietic system, with marked palliative effects and delay of the malignant processes in many of the cases studied. The early reports by clinical investigators in the United States (43–45) were confirmed in England (46, 47) and it seemed as though the use of these compounds might be an alternative to radiotherapy in the treatment of lymphatic diseases. The report by Rhoads (44) was cautious and pointed out the fact that, although the nitrogen mustards exert their most characteristic effects on rapidly-growing tissues, they do not distinguish between those normal or neoplastic, their predominant toxicologic effect is to damage the normal hemopoietic system which thereby sets a limit to their dosage, and the tumor regressions obtained are but temporary. Later considerations based on more clinical and experimental evidence have supported these initial views (48, 49). The most recent survey of this subject is by Klopp and Bateman (49a).

After the partial successes in the clinic, the study of these compounds was extended to laboratory animals with a wider variety of synthetic analogues. Lymphosarcoma and several forms of leukemia in mice were inhibited, whereas no change was noted with such tranplanted tumors as the mammary carcinoma or the melanoma (1, 50). Haddow *et al.* (51), working on the growth-inhibitory and carcinogenic effects of 4-aminostilbene, had noted the considerable (if transitory) degree of inhibition of the Walker 256 tumor in rats induced by administration of 4-N,N-di(2-chloroethyl)aminostilbene, and they subsequently prepared a wide series of haloalkylarylamines. The compounds were found to be much less toxic than the aliphatic representatives (51) and could be administered orally. In clinical trials of one of these, namely, β-naphthyl di(2-chloroethyl)amine (cf. 52), the compound was found to be effective in cases of Hodgkin's disease and of the chronic leukemias, but in lesser degree than the aliphatic methyl di(2-chloroethyl)amine hydrochloride administered by vein. The aliphatic nitrogen mustards on intravenous administration appear to have a palliative effect on bronchogenic carcinoma in man (53, 54), to an extent greater than that demonstrated for any tumors other than the lymphatic. This has been explained by the probably higher concentration of intravenously given drug which reaches the lungs, as compared with that which reaches tumors more distal (55). Of the many nitrogen mustards tested at the Memorial Hospital against sarcoma 180 and other tumors in mice, 3-di(2-chloroethyl)aminomethyl-4-methoxymethyl-5-hydroxy-6-methylpyridine dihydrochloride appeared to be highly effective (1).

Regional intra-arterial administration of methyl di(2-chloroethyl)amine hydrochloride together with aureomycin has been described by Klopp and his colleagues (55–57), a procedure in itself requiring a high degree of surgical skill, and which has produced therapeutic effects that could not have been achieved by intravenous administration. In essence the procedure results in the delivery of a large, concentrated dose of the drug to the tumor, thus obviating the diluting and detoxifying factors which reduce the dose delivered by vein. By these means, large doses of the agent were found to markedly affect carcinomas and sarcomas previously inoperable or inaccessible to radiation, and in some cases to subsequently make resection possible.

The nitrogen mustards cause chromosome damage with inhibition of mitosis and production of chromosome breaks similar to those produced by X-rays (58). The so-called radiomimetic effect of the nitrogen mustards has been emphasized by Boyland (59), and like X-rays these compounds are also carcinogenic. The fact that the nitrogen mustards will inhibit a large number of intracellular enzymes is not surprising in view of the highly reactive nature of this class of compounds in aqueous solution. The possible mechanisms involved in the inhibitory effect of X-irradiation on SH-enzymes have been partly attributed to the formation of peroxide-forming free radicals from water. That both the nitrogen mustards and X-rays produce marked and similar changes in the physical properties of such polymeric macromolecules as nucleic acid has been the subject of several investigations. Some of the mechanisms of action of these agents have been described in Chapter III on Carcinogenesis. The problem of whether both mustards and radiation function similarly in carcinogenesis or in therapy is only a special instance of the more general problem formulated in the Haddow paradox as to why the same agents may be both carcinogenic and therapeutic.

The sequence of events has been described in Chapter III whereby the suggestion of Goldacre, Loveless, and Ross (60) that the mustards acted by virtue of their ability to form links between chromosomes and thus inhibit mitosis led to the search among cross-linking agents in the textile industry for compounds with behavior biologically similar to that of the mustards. That the cross-linking hypothesis might not be correct was found only after this search did in fact reveal a number of most interesting compounds in the ethyleneimines, the epoxides, and the sulfonic acid esters. The carcinogenicity of these compounds has been alluded to (Chapter III), and their chemical reactivities have been described by Ross (61) and by Alexander (62).

The possible connection between the ethyleneimines and the nitrogen mustards stems from the possibility that the latter in aqueous solution cyclize as follows:

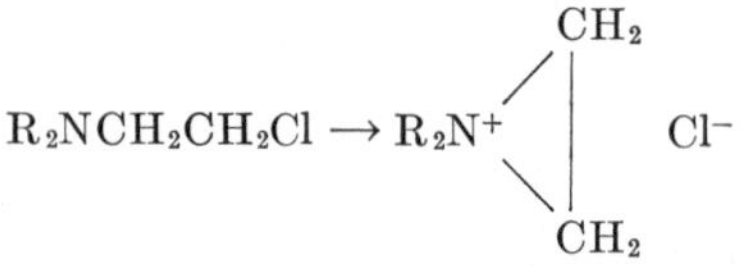

The most extensively studied of the ethyleneimines is the so-called triethylene melamine (TEM) otherwise 2,4,6-triethylene-imino-*s*-triazine, which was first employed for improving the finish of rayon fabrics. The compound can be given orally or intravenously (25, 26, 63, 64) and is effective against the same malignant tumors in man and in experimental animals which respond to the nitrogen mustards (65–67). Like the latter, it also depresses bone marrow function, and, beyond the favorable fact that together with the aromatic nitrogen mustards it can be given by mouth, it has no other apparent advantages over the intravenous administration of the aliphatic nitrogen mustards.

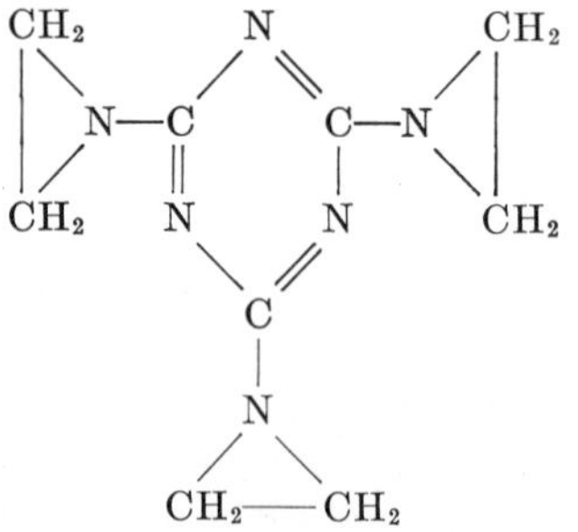

Triethylene melamine (TEM)

Extension of these studies to the ethylene phosphoramides has resulted in the preparation of compounds whose effect on lymphatic and other tumors in mice has been comparable with that of triethylene melamine (cf. 1).

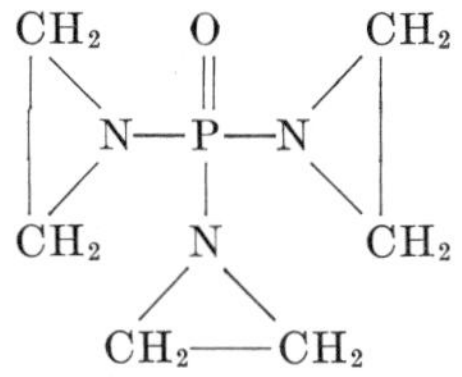

Triethylene phosphoramide

Phosphoramidase activity is present in plant and animal tissues, although the natural substrate is unknown. Using *p*-chloroanilinophosphoric acid, Gomori (67a) noted that this compound was more rapidly hydrolyzed at pH 5.4 to 5.8 in tumors than in adjacent normal tissues, although its high rate of spontaneous hydrolysis at this pH reduced the accuracy of the observations. Phosphorylated nitrogen mustards have been prepared in the expectation that on enzymatic hydrolysis they will liberate the mustard at neoplastic sites (67b).

The epoxides were found to be inhibitory to the Walker 256 tumor in rats at near-toxic levels (25, 26). The sulfonic acid esters have been noted to be inhibitory toward the Walker tumor (68), and one of them, namely, 1,4-dimethane sulfonoxy butane was found to be effective in producing clinical remissions in chronic myelogenous leukemia (52). It has been suggested that the sulfonic acid esters function by virtue of their reactivity with amino groups, a property which they must share with such agents as the nitrogen mustards (68).

$$H_3CO_2SO(CH_2)_4OSO_2CH_3$$

1,4-Dimethane sulfonoxy butane

Still another type of possible cross-linking as well as mercaptan-reactive agents are the quinones (69). 9,10-Phenanthraquinone, when incorporated in the food, has been found to inhibit the growth of a number of transplanted tumors in mice (70), although the actual amount of the compound reaching the tissues is unknown.

Rat liver choline oxidase is inhibited *in vitro* by methyl di(2-chloroethyl)-amine hydrochloride and by octyl-N,N^1-diethylenediamidophosphate (70a). It is apparently not affected by TEM, which suggests that for inhibition both an ethylenimine structure and a quaternary nitrogen are necessary.

Urethane

Phenylurethane was first noted by Lefèvre (71) to produce mitotic effects in plants resembling those described for colchicine. Subsequently Templeman and Sexton (72) studied the effects of several carbamates on the arrest of growth of cereals and other plants, and these effects suggested to Haddow the application of this class of compounds to the possible therapy of cancer (73). Haddow and Sexton observed that the administration of phenylurethane produced mitotic poisoning of the crypts of Lieberkühn in the mouse intestine and significant retardation of the growth of spontaneous mammary tumor in the mouse. Both urethane and phenylurethane markedly inhibited the growth of the Walker tumor in rats, and shortly thereafter these substances were used in clinical trials and found effective in the treatment of chronic myeloid leukemia (74).

The resemblance between the effects of X-irradiation and urethane therapy on the clinical and blood picture is readily apparent, and the synergistic action of both methods of treatment (75) as well as the antileukemic synergism between nitrogen mustard and urethane (76) have been reported. The use of urethane in other clinical conditions has been reviewed by Haddow (52). The compound is effective in the inhibition of mouse leukemia and other forms of experimental cancer (22, 77, 78) and has been shown by Skipper (79) to inhibit the incorporation of formate carbon into nucleic acid. The role of the antileukemic agents in purine and pyrimidine synthesis will be discussed further.

Urethane alone of all the carbamates is carcinogenic in mice and rats (pulmonary tumors) (see Chapter III) and as a therapeutic agent is relatively unique among this class of compounds (80). Like many narcotics, urethane has an inhibitory action on many types of enzymes, particularly the dehydrogenases, a property shared with compounds neither carcinogenic nor therapeutic. The mechanism of action of this curiously and doubtlessly deceptively simple compound remains obscure.

Antimetabolites

Studies of this category of compounds have included the following: folic acid antagonists, purine antagonists, vitamin antagonists, amino acid antagonists, and sugar antagonists.

Folic Acid Analogues. An antagonist to folic acid may be defined as a substance which possesses the property of inhibiting the growth of *Streptococcus faecalis R* or *Lactobacillus casei* in the presence of marginal levels of folic acid; reversal of inhibition occurs in the presence of added folic acid to the medium.

The studies by Lewisohn and his colleagues on the regressive effects of extracts of a number of natural materials on spontaneous mammary tumors in mice led to the report that folic acid was capable of causing complete regression of breast cancer in mice (81, 82). The same group subsequently showed that the active agent was the *L. casei* factor (83), identified as pteroyltriglutamic acid (84). Other investigators were unable to repeat

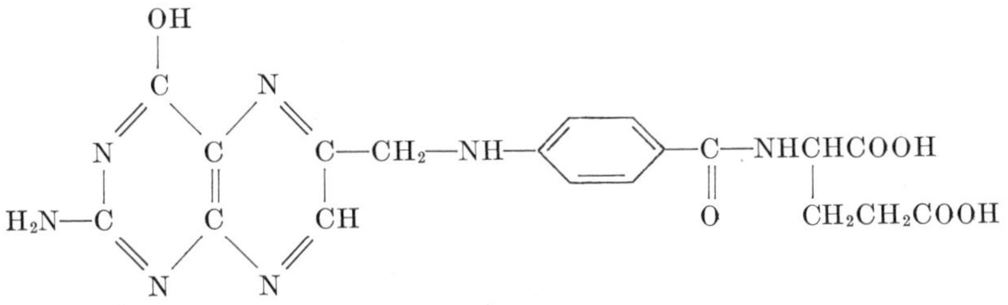

Pteridine p-Aminobenzoic acid Glutamic acid

Pteroylglutamic acid (Folic acid)

these observations (85, 86). Clinical study of pteroyldiglutamic and pteroyltriglutamic acids by Farber and his associates in Boston indicated that, although these compounds were non-toxic and little antineoplastic effects were observed, there were certain changes induced in the viscera and bone marrow of children with acute leukemia which suggested the possible value of further study with analogues of folic acid (87). The first compounds of this antifolic acid category studied, pteroylaspartic acid (An-Fol) and methylpteroic acid (Met-Fol), appeared to prolong the lives of a few children with acute leukemia, but it was not until the more powerful antifolic acid agent, 4-aminopteroylglutamic acid, known as aminopterin, was used that impressive remissions in the course of acute leukemia were observed (88). The accompanying toxicity of aminopterin emphasized the need for compounds in this cateogry which could be administered with less ensuing discomfort. This need was met by the preparation by chemists of the American Cyanamide Company (Lederle Laboratories Division under the late Y. SubbaRow) of 4-aminomethylpteroylglutamic acid, known as amethopterin, and 4-aminopteroylaspartic acid, referred to as amino-an-fol. The effective dose for remissions in children with acute leukemia lies between 3 and 5 mg. per day for amethopterin, and between 25 and 50 mg. per day for amino-an-fol, compared with the range of 0.5 to 1.0 mg. per day for aminopterin (89). The investigations on these compounds in childhood leukemia by Farber and his colleagues rank as one of the most careful and intensive in the history of clinical studies in cancer.

Experimentation on animals revealed that the 4-amino folic acid analogues were potent inhibitors of the development of leukemia in mice (90,91), although the antileukemic action of these compounds could be overcome not only by the administration of folic acid but still more actively by the folic acid metabolite known as the "citrovorum factor" (92; cf. 93–95). Other tumors in mice could also be retarded by the folic acid antagonists (96–99), the toxic manifestations including body weight loss, hypoplasia of the bone marrow, and intestinal lesions with diarrhea (100). The nearly equal susceptibility of normal bone marrow cells and of sarcoma 180 cells

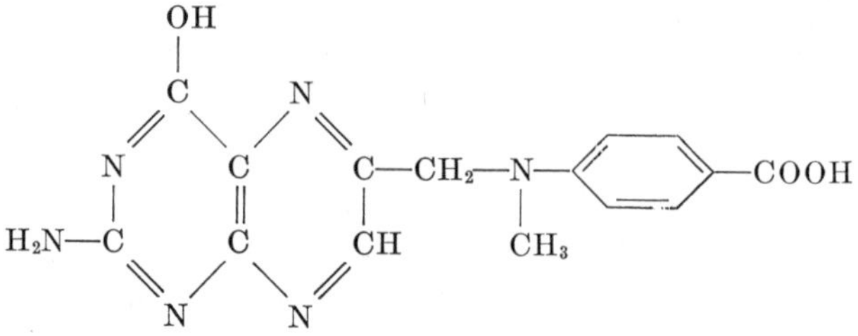

Methylpteroic acid (Met-Fol)

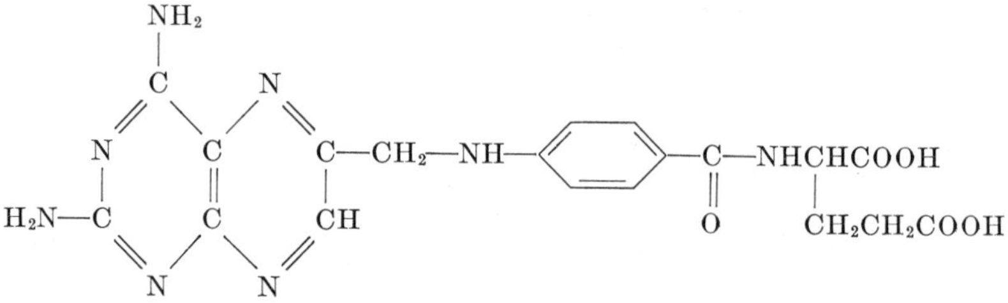

4-Aminopteroylglutamic acid (Aminopterin)

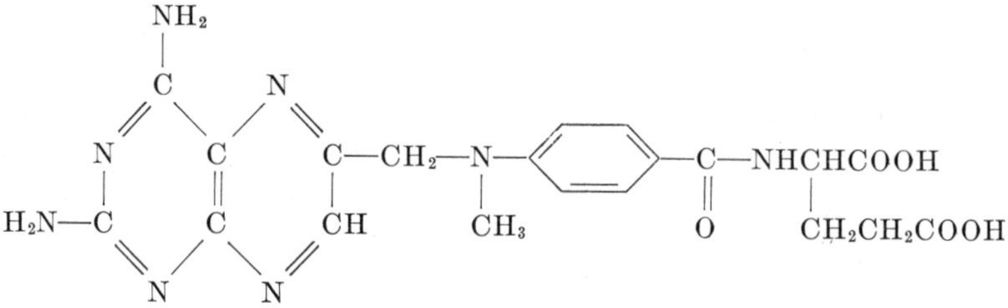

4-Aminomethylpteroylglutamic acid (Amethopterin)

to damage by amethopterin has been shown (101), thus indicating the limits to which the use of the antifolic acid drugs may be put.

Knowledge of the mechanisms of the action of the folic acid analogues in so far as they relate to the biosynthesis of the nucleic acids in leukemic mice is due to the brilliant investigations of Skipper and his colleagues. They have employed C^{14}-labeled formate as a precursor which, after injection, is incorporated into the 2- and 8-carbon atoms of the purine components of the nucleic acids, as well as into the carbon skeleton of the amino acids. Amethopterin inhibits nucleic acid synthesis as shown by the use of C^{14}-formate, and this inhibition can be partially reversed by administration of folic acid (102). That there is some measure of specificity in the action of the folic acid antagonists is shown by the fact that they do not inhibit incorporation of formate carbon into the tissues as a whole, but only (and that strongly) into the purine ring. It is possible that the inhibitory compounds function by preventing the conversion of folic acid to the citrovorum factor, a coenzyme or cofactor, essential to nucleic acid synthesis. The administration of the citrovorum factor thus eludes the otherwise inhibitory action of the folic acid analogues. An interesting observation in this connection is the prevention of the antileukemic action of amethopterin by administration of nucleic acid itself (103). Included in the inhibitory action of the antifolic drugs on purine synthesis would be, as expected, an inhibition of the adenine moiety of adenosine triphosphate (ATP) (104).

Studies of the mechanisms whereby leukemic cells become resistant to the folic acid antagonists have been pursued in many interesting experimental approaches. Following a general biological rule, leukemic cells in the mouse develop sooner or later a resistance against the inhibitory action of the various analogues of folic acid (105, 106), and in certain cases Law has observed that the variant cells may be dependent upon the 4-amino-substituted folic acid antagonists for optimal growth (107). In any event, the changes were noted to be stable, irreversible, and inheritable (108), and they appeared to arise through processes of mutation and selection (109). The use of such sublines of susceptible, resistant, and dependent leukemia in mice, combined with techniques of following the incorporation of C^{14}-formate, offered a most interesting opportunity for Skipper *et al.* (110) to approach the mechanism of action of the antifolic acid agents in such sublines. Their results, involving the effects of amethopterin on nucleic acid incorporation in the whole viscera, in leukemic cells susceptible to inhibition by this compound, and in leukemic cells from the same original strain which had become resistant to and then dependent on this compound for optimal growth, are given in Table 58.

Thus, amethopterin inhibits C^{14}-formate incorporation into the nucleic acid moieties of the leukemic cells and of the viscera in the susceptible subline. However, in the dependent subline, the drug causes an increase in incorporation of the label into the nucleic acids of the leukemia, and a decrease into the nucleic acids of the viscera of the same animals. There is evidently a different metabolic response of the susceptible and dependent leukemia sublines to the drug, whereas the nucleic acid metabolism in the viscera of the hosts of both sublines responds in the same way (by an inhibition) to the drug. Differences in the nucleic acid metabolism of the leukemic tissue are evidently not reflected in any observable differences, as far as the criteria employed are concerned, in the nucleic acid metabolism of the viscera of the hosts. Amethopterin has no effect on $P^{32}O_4$ incorporation into nucleotides (110a).

Only about 10 % of the formate carbon in the initial homogenates (Table 58) can be accounted for in terms of the nucleic acid bases (110). The difference is largely attributable to protein synthesis, and it is of interest that amethopterin produces relatively little change in incorporation of the label

TABLE 58

EFFECT OF AMETHOPTERIN ON C^{14}-FORMATE INCORPORATION INTO NUCLEIC ACIDS OF SUSCEPTIBLE (S) AND DEPENDENT (D) LEUKEMIA L1210 CELLS (110)

Tissue[1]	Treatment	Specific activities, μc./mole C					
		Initial homogenate	DNA[2]			RNA[3]	
			Guanine	Adenine	Thymine	Guanine	Adenine
Leukemia-S	None	4.2	206	227	100	309	308
Viscera-S	None	6.9	171	280		199	248
Leukemia-S	Amethopterin	1.8	34	39	10	54	112
Viscera-S	Amethopterin	5.6	26	16	4	70	90
Leukemia-D	None	1.8	55	51	24	85	86
Viscera-D	None	7.3	113	99		156	140
Leukemia-D	Amethopterin	4.8	127	115	51	162	156
Viscera-D	Amethopterin	4.9	15	10	3	37	35

[1] Viscera include livers, spleens, small intestines, kidneys, and testes.
[2] Deoxyribonucleic acid.
[3] Ribonucleic acid.

in the whole homogenates of the viscera, whether from susceptible or dependent leukemic sublines, although the incorporation into the nucleic acids of these viscera is markedly diminished. On the other hand, amethopterin produces a marked inhibition of incorporation into the whole homogenate of the susceptible leukemia cells, and a definite rise in incorporation into the whole homogenate of dependent leukemia cells. Superficially, it could be said that protein and nucleic acid metabolism appear to run parallal in the leukemic tissues, and independently in the visceral tissues, but this is clearly not the whole story. No matter what the explanations may be for the activating role of amethopterin on the dependent leukemia growth, it appears to act as folic acid would under similar circumstances, and the possibility might be considered that the cells of the variant subline have a complement of enzymes which would convert amethopterin to either folic acid or a folic acid-like compound capable of conversion to the citrovorum factor or to an effective derivative thereof. Thus, Kidder and his colleagues have found that *Tetrahymena* can use 4-aminopteroylglutamic acid (aminopterin) for growth in the absence of folic acid (35), presumably by virtue of the possession by this organism of an enzyme capable of converting the 4-amino group to a hydroxy group, and thereby the whole molecule to folic acid. The inhibition of the growth of this organism by amethopterin (36) is more difficult to explain on this basis, unless it is possible that the enzymatic deamination and demethylation of this compound occur too slowly to support normal, folic acid-requiring growth rates: the fact that amethopterin is capable of sparing suboptimal amounts of folic acid for the growth of *Tetrahymena* supports this possibility (36).

The formate incorporation technique has been employed to demonstrate interference with and inhibition of nucleic acid synthesis *in vivo* by 2,6-diaminopurine, 8-azaguanine, cortisone, arsenite, urethane, and nitrogen mustard (111), as well as by the folic acid analogues. However, the mechanism whereby this inhibition of nucleic acid synthesis is obtained may be different for the different antileukemic agents. Thus, when *E. coli* is grown in the presence of aminopterin and amethopterin, there is an accumulation of 4-amino-5-imidazolecarboxamide (112), one of the precursors, together with formate, of the purine skeleton. However, no such accumulation was noted in the presence of 2,6-diaminopurine, 8-azaguanine, urethane, or nitrogen mustard.

4-Amino-5-imidazolecarboxamide (112a) may be a purine precursor, converted to hypoxanthine by incorporation of an additional carbon atom, a step which is blocked by aminopterin (112b) as well as by sulfonamides. Rat liver is active in metabolizing the carboxamide, requiring the presence of DPN, ATP, Mg^{++}, some energy source such as ketoglutarate, succinate, fumarate, or malate, a methyl donor such as formate or methanol, and molecular oxygen (112c). It is probable that carboxamide ribosides and ribotides are formed prior to ring closure of the compound by formic acid (112d).

An important aspect of the use of these drugs, as with other therapeutic compounds, is the problem of their chemical purity. Thus, it has been noted that a sample of commercially available aminopterin contained over 20% pteroylglutamic acid (112e). Amethopterin has been found to contain appreciable quantities of 10-methylpteroylglutamic acid and smaller amounts of 4-amino-10-methylpteroic acid, aminopterin and pteroylglutamic acid (112f). The complications which the presence of these impurities introduce in the interpretation of experimental results need little emphasis. Where the antagonists appear to be utilized by resistant strains of *S. faecalis* and *Tetrahymena* and deamination and demethylation steps necessarily postulated, the question naturally arises whether the antagonists used possessed enough of the contaminants to account for the results obtained.

A schematic representation of the possible reactions involved is as follows,

Folic acid ——┼——→ Citrovorum factor (coenzyme of enzymes concerned with 1 carbon transfer, involving methionine, purine, serine, histidine, etc.)
↑
Aminopterin

——┼——→ Methionine
↑
Ethionine

whereby the use of two inhibitors may achieve a "sequential blocking" (Potter) or synergistic effect.

Purine Antagonists. Kidder and Dewey (113) in their nutritional studies on *Tetrahymena* noted that this organism requires guanine for growth and that 8-azaguanine would act as a potent antagonist in this system. In view of the evidence that dietary guanine was not incorporated as such into the nucleic acids of the rat, whereas adenine was so incorporated (114), Kidder and his associates felt that the 8-azaguanine might serve as an inhibitory agent in the conversion of adenine to guanine and thus block the growth of tissues dependent on rapid nucleic acid synthesis. When the compound was administered to mice bearing mammary and leukemic tumors, a remarkable inhibition in their growth was observed (115), which was subsequently confirmed by others (116–118). Toward several other types of tumors, such as the sarcomas and melanomas, 8-azaguanine proved to be ineffective (27, 116, 118, 119). At higher dosage levels, however, the growth of sarcoma 37 can be inhibited, together with observable damage to tumor and spleen (120).

Guanine could apparently reverse the inhibition of tumor growth produced by 8-azaguanine (27, 121), which is not quite consistent with the finding of Graff and his colleagues (122) that carcinostasis by 8-azaguanine does not involve synthesis of nucleic acid from guanine. It is possible that the action of 8-azaguanine may not be directly derived from its assumed influence in the nucleic acid metabolic systems but may function by diverting enzymes concerned with other systems (proteins?) from their normal path. 8-Aza-adenine is entirely ineffective toward tumors (27). 8-Azaguanine-C^{14} labeled in either C_2- or C_4-position and injected intraperitoneally into sarcoma 37-bearing mice has been found to be incorporated into the nucleic acid fraction of the tumor (122a). The relation of azaguanine to guanine has been again challenged in the finding that several nucleotides but not guanine are capable of reducing the carcinostatic effect of azaguanine (122b).

Gellhorn and his colleagues observed that tissues contained a deaminase which was capable of oxidizing 8-azaguanine to the non-carcinostatic 8-azaxanthine which is neither toxic nor curative (123). Differences in the activity of this enzyme among the mouse tumors, ranging from about 0.3 expressed as micrograms of NH_3-N evolved per 10^6 "cells" for the azaguanine-susceptible tumor 755, to about 3.0 on the same basis for tumor C-1498, which is azaguanine resistant, were observed. In view of the fact that the values for normal tissues in mice range from 0.56 for kidney, through 2.42 for liver and 4.18 for brain, to 16 for intestine, it would hardly seem probable that it might be the enzyme level in the tumor which would govern the level of effective dose of the active compound in the whole animal. The problem of why some tumors respond, and others do not, to the same agent is an extremely puzzling matter, requiring for at least a partial approach to the problem the investigation of a broad spectrum of metabolic activities.

The isolation of 8-azaguanylic acid from hydrolyzates of ribonucleic acids from various sources is further evidence of the ability of azaguanine to be incorporated into such materials (123a). Although it may be presumed that this may be one of the mechanisms whereby tumors are inhibited, it would be of interest to observe whether such incorporation occurred in the ribonucleic acid of tumors resistant to this agent.

Azaguanine, which, like other carcinostatic agents, is a mitotic poison (124), appears to function effectively in synergism with other agents. Thus, particularly good synergistic effects were noted with 8-azaguanine together with aminopterin in prolonging the survival of mice with leukemia to an extent greater than that with either agent alone (125, 126), or with 8-azaguanine and diethylstilbestrol in the carcinostatic effect on mammary tumors in *C57BL* mice (127). It will be recalled in this connection that Skipper (128, 129) had demonstrated an antileukemic synergism in mice between urethane and nitrogen mustard. The synergistic action in any case is difficult to interpret, but in practical therapy it offers the hope of alternative treatment with different agents. An example of this is afforded

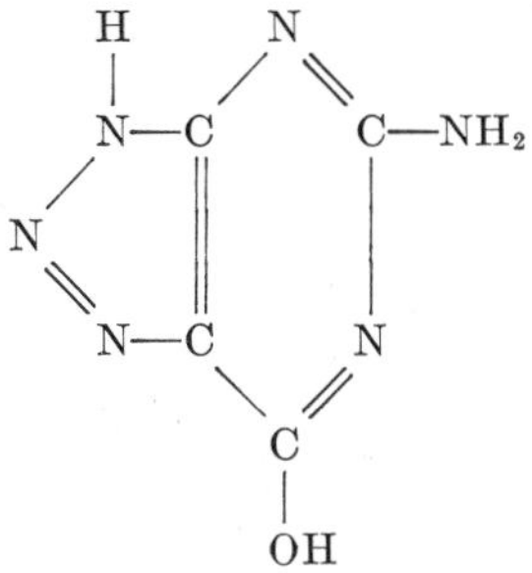

8-Azaguanine

by the enhanced carcinostatic action of 8-azaguanine on the 755 tumor in mice when the animals are pretreated with the non-carcinostatic riboflavin analogue, 6-chloro-9-(1′-D-sorbityl)-isoalloxazine (flavotin) (130). Since the action of flavotin could be reversed by riboflavin-5-phosphate (131), it would appear that such action might be concerned with an inhibition of some flavoprotein enzyme. There is considerably less xanthine oxidase in the tumor than in liver, and if the flavotin were uniformly distributed among the tissues it might be expected that the absolute inhibition of the enzyme in the tumor would be greater than in the liver. Such an observation has been reported (130) and, if confirmed, would suggest that the accumulation of xanthine through inhibition of its oxidase would lead to a further inhibition of guanase and hence permit a more prolonged action of azaguanine (130). An inhibition of guanase directly by 6-formylpteridine led to an augmentation of the carcinostatic action of azaguanine (132).

Other purine antagonists which have been suggested and tested on experimental cancers have been 2,6-diaminopurine (cf. 39), which is a precursor of nucleic acid guanine in the rat (133), and 6-mercaptopurine (134). Both

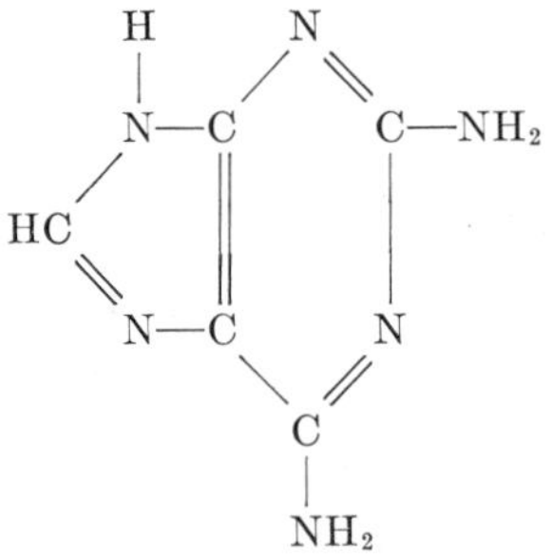

2,6-Diaminopurine

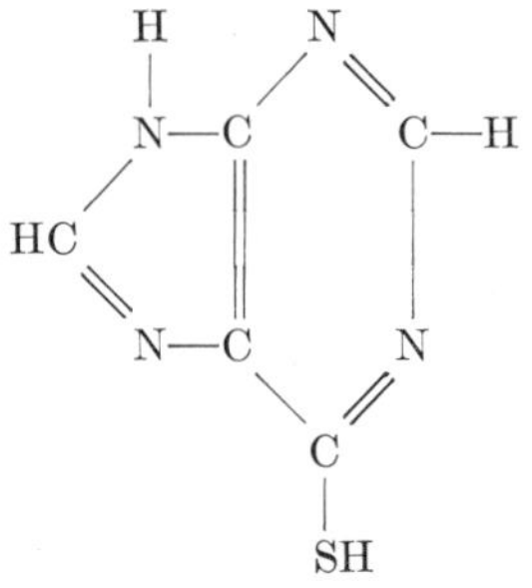

6-Mercaptopurine

2,6-diaminopurine and 6-mercaptopurine inhibit the growth of certain microorganisms, and this inhibition can be prevented specifically and perhaps competitively by adenine or guanine. The destructive action of 2,6-diaminopurine in mammalian bone marrow and intestinal epithelium may be due to interference with metabolic functions involving nucleic acid synthesis. Similarly, 6-mercaptopurine inhibits the growth of *Lactobacillus casei*, and this action is prevented by any of the four physiological purine bases (135); the drug appears to prevent utilization of hypoxanthine primarily, and of adenine secondarily, having little or no effect on the metabolism of guanine or xanthine. The compound inhibits xanthine oxidase and can be oxidized to bis-purinyl-disulfide which also has tumor-inhibitory capacities.

6-Mercaptopurine is very effective in destroying sarcoma 180 in mice (134), but, like the development of mercaptopurine-resistant strains of *L. casei*, resistant strains of sarcoma 180 can also be obtained after treatment of mice with the drug. The anticancer effect of the compound cannot, apparently, be reversed by treatment with any of the purines, a negative result which does not necessarily conflict with the hypothesis that the compound functions as a purine antagonist, since the specific purine metabolite which may be affected by it is not known. The toxic effects of the drug are similar to those induced by other inhibitors of tumors, such as the nitrogen mustards and antifolic acid agents, for they include progressive weight loss and damage to the intestinal epithelium and hematopoietic system.

When 2,6-diaminopurine is injected intraperitoneally into the mouse, a portion is converted to 2,6-diaminopurine riboside, and it is this compound which is incorporated into nucleotides (135a). The incorporation of 2,6-diaminopurine into the pentose nucleic acid guanine of the rat has been known for some time (135b). Certain 2,4-diaminopyrimidines possess antimalarial activity, and appear to act as antifolic agents. When given together with amethopterin, each at doses which were ineffective when singly administered, the effect was synergistic, and there was significant retardation in growth of leukemia in mice associated with an increase in survival time (135c).

General Considerations of Nucleic Acid Inhibitors. Much of the data on antipurine compounds has been derived from studies on microorganisms in which the inhibition of growth due to the addition of these compounds has been reversed by addition of certain purines. Thus, the growth inhibition due to the 4-aminopteroylglutamic acids for *S. faecalis* is reversed by addition of thymine plus purines, that of formamide and urethane for *E. coli* is reversed by 2,6-diaminopurine (3a), that of 2,6-diaminopurine for *L. casei* is reversed by adenine, guanine, and hypoxanthine, and that of 8-azaguanine for *T. gelii* is reversed by guanine. On the other hand, the only established case of prevention of the action of an antitumor agent is that of either folic acid, citrovorum factor, deoxyribonucleate, or vitamin B_{12} which can antagonize the effect of amethopterin on transplanted leukemia in mice (3a). To describe compounds as "purine antagonists" when one of the basic criteria of the use of such terminology is lacking, namely, the ability of purines to antagonize the antagonist, may be an illustration of a hypothesis stretched beyond its limits.

There are, however, two lines of evidence, both based on the use of tracer techniques, which relate several of the anticancer agents to nucleic acid metabolism. The first of these is based on the effect of these agents on the incorporation of known precursors such as formate into the purine skeleton, and the work of Skipper and his colleagues has shown the marked inhibition of such incorporation by the folic acid analogues, X-irradiation, etc. (cf. 3a). The second line of evidence is based upon the actual fixation of such agents as 8-azaguanine-2-C^{14} and 2,6-diaminopurine-2-C^{14} in small amounts in the nucleic acids isolated from mice previously treated with these compounds. The former type of evidence is more or less indirect, and the latter rather inconclusive, in relating the effect of the chemotherapeutic agents specifically to nucleic acid metabolism. Other tissue components are probably at least equally affected. However, there appears to be little question that purine synthesis is profoundly affected by a group of chemically quite unrelated therapeutic drugs, as well as by radiation of short wavelength. Cell physiology is only now emerging from two decades during which the secret of life, biosynthesis, and genetics were all uniquely bound to the structure of nucleic acids, to the stage where this class of compounds is only an equally important category with proteins, fats, and carbohydrates. The recent review by Skipper (3a) emphasizes the re-establishment of this equilibrium as far as the position of nucleic acids in the cancer problem is concerned. The antipurine effects noted may be considered at least one facet of the action of the effective drugs, without any implication in regard to uniqueness.

Vitamin Antagonists. Isoriboflavin added to a diet low in riboflavin has produced regression of transplanted lymphosarcomas in mice (136), the same effect being produced by diethylriboflavin in retarding the growth of rat tumors (137), as well as by administration of deoxypyridoxine coupled with a pyridoxine-deficient diet (138). These effects need further study. Avidin in the form of egg white has been fed to cancer patients with the hope of inducing a critical biotin deficiency sufficient to affect tumor growth (139), with negative results in both instances. From all available evidence (see Chapter V) it does not appear probable that any known vitamin deficiency would specifically affect tumor growth and spare normal body function.

Yet the fact that certain components, particularly the B vitamins, are usually low in cancer tissues has suggested that a uniform distribution of an inhibitor among the tissues of a tumor-bearing animal *in vivo* might produce a greater absolute effect on the tumor than on the normal tissues. Many of the B vitamins are prosthetic groups of specific enzyme systems, and an inhibition of the combination of prosthetic group with the protein component of the enzyme would be expected to lead to loss of the ability of the enzyme to function. The vitamin B_6 content, in micrograms per gram of wet weight, is for the tissues of male *C57BL* mice as follows (140): liver 5.28, kidney 4.16, heart 4.62, lungs 0.78, brain 2.84, testes 1.06, muscle 2.70, stomach 1.50, spleen 0.88, and the 755 transplanted tumor 0.69. In descending order of activity, the glutamic-aspartic transaminase system of which pyridoxal phosphate is an integral part is as follows: heart, liver, kidney, tumor, lung, and testis. Administration of deoxypyridoxine to the tumor-bearing mice results in an inhibition in the transaminase levels of these tissues to a degree roughly inversely as their activities. Using antimycin A as an inhibitor of the succinoxidase system, Reif and Potter (141) had previously shown that in general the degree of enzyme antagonism in a tissue was inversely proportional to the amount of enzyme in the tissue. It is therefore not surprising that administration of deoxypyridoxine to tumor-bearing animals produces an inhibition of tumor growth. Consistent with these findings is the observation that testosterone causes a decrease in the vitamin B_6 content of the 755 tumor in female *C57BL* mice without any effect on the growth of the tumor, but permitting thereby the use of carcinostatic doses of deoxypyridoxine otherwise too low to be effective when used alone for this purpose (140). However, if the diminished activity of transaminase is at least one of the key factors in the inhibition of the growth of the tumor, it is also clear that administration of deoxypyridoxine must also cause a marked impairment of transaminase in a number of presumably normal tissues in the tumor-bearing host (cf. 140), notably in the lungs and in the testes. The concept that it should be possible to completely inhibit an enzyme present in cancer tissue in small amounts while producing only minimal effects on the same enzyme present in other tissues in large amounts is ingenious and attractive (142, 143). However, it is based upon the frequently repeated and quite unwarranted generalization that enzyme levels are usually lower in tumors than in normal tissues. At the risk of anticipating data to be described in the following chapter, the results of studies of individual enzyme systems indicate that tumors occupy a median level among various tissues in respect to such systems; i.e., the activity of such systems in tumors may be lower than in those enzyme-rich normal tissues such as liver, but may be higher than in a great many other normal tissues. No single enzyme has yet been found whose activity in tumors is lower than that of the least active normal tissue, nor, for that matter, any enzyme in tumors more active than the most active normal tissue. As a working hypothesis, the use of multiple agents which might conceivably diminish specific components of tumors to levels far below those of any normal tissue, thus rendering them peculiarly vulnerable to the action of agents and dosage levels to which normal tissues would be relatively insensitive (cf. 140), has a great deal to recommend it; however, the cost to the host in terms of the inhibition in vital functions in non-neoplastic tissues must be carefully weighed.

Amino Acid Antagonists. The growth of a transplanted fibrosarcoma and of the Jensen sarcoma in rats has been reported to be inhibited by administration of DL-ethionine (144). The rationale for this experiment was based upon the relatively low methionine content of these tumors and the possibility that ethionine might serve as a competitive antagonist. It might have been of interest to see whether addition of methionine would have resulted in resumption of growth of the tumors, in view of the findings reported.

Glucose Antagonist. On the basis of the known competition of glucose, fructose, and glucosamine for the enzyme in brain tissue responsible for the phosphorylation of these sugars, Quastel and Cantero (145) studied the effect of D-glucosamine on the growth of sarcoma 37 in mice. Intraperitoneal injections of this compound even at high dosage levels produced no toxicity but did result in a considerable inhibition in the growth of the tumor accompanied by a prolongation in survival time of the treated tumor-bearing animals.

D-Glucoascorbic acid, a vitamin C antagonist (146), has no effect on the growth of transplanted tumors in either mice or guinea pigs, although it does reduce the ascorbic acid level in the animals (147).

Bacterial Metabolites

The clinical literature contains many scattered reports in which a favorable influence on the course of cancer was noted after a spontaneous attack of erysipelas, or other severe infection, or after the experimental infection of cancer patients with erysipelas (148–151). The earliest observation of this kind occurred in 1867 (148). Instead of using whole living bacteria, W. B. Coley prepared crude filtrates of various bacterial types which, for many years, he employed with cancer patients. The so-called Coley's toxins were employed by others with varying results, a favorable report being that of Lilienthal (152). To summarize briefly the general results obtained after bacterial infection or administration of bacterial products, it may be stated that, although reports of complete and permanent regression of human tumors are rare, a significant number of cases were reported to show partial and temporary regressions. The tumor in the course of successful treatment by the bacterial products demonstrates hemorrhage and necrosis. The subject was reviewed by Loeb in 1910 (153), by the Council on Pharmacy and Chemistry of the American Medical Association in 1934 (154) and, later, by Shear and Perrault (155). The history of Coley's efforts has been summarized by members of his family (156).

The clinical use of commercial preparations of the Coley toxins in cases of human cancer followed a rather heroic course, in that these preparations were rarely, if ever, standardized on the basis of their effect on animal tumors. Although granting the urgency for the use of these preparations, as well as the lack of suitable animal bioassays, the absence of standardization renders an evaluation of the findings rather difficult. Negative results might have been due to the use of non-potent preparations or of insufficient dosage of weak preparations, whereas positive results might have been due to the inclusion in such crude materials of adventitious impurities of non-bacterial origin from the media, etc. Furthermore, the use of crude toxins of unknown potency might well produce such side-reactions as to obscure or prevent the possible primary action on the tumor.

With the hope of averting the difficulties described above, Shear and his collaborators began a series of careful attempts (a) to isolate from bacterial cultures grown in known media and in pure form the material responsible for the effects of hemorrhage and necrosis in tumors, and (b) to devise a satisfactory method of bioassay to standardize the potency of such material (155, 157–159). These investigators succeeded in isolating from culture filtrates of *Bacillus prodigiosus* a highly active, hemorrhage-producing agent of high particle weight, which was almost completely polysaccharide in nature. Successive preparations were reproducible in activity within the limits of accuracy of the mode of assay, and about 0.1 γ of one of the more active preparations was found to be the minimum dose required to produce detectable hemorrhage in 50% of a group of mice bearing the transplanted sarcoma 37. The purified agent injected intraperitoneally into mice bearing either transplanted or primary induced sarcomas produced extensive hemorrhage and necrosis in the tumors. The over-all picture however, as Shear pointed out (155) in an admirably frank and lucid paper, was not quite satisfactory. Tumor-bearing mice were far more sensitive to the action of the polysaccharide at equal dosage than were normal mice, and doses tolerated by the latter were lethal to the former. Examination of the tumors after treatment with the agent revealed an inhomogeneous effect, in that only parts of the tumors had undergone hemorrhage, usually the central area, leaving the periphery undamaged and a source of continued growth. Doses of the agent sufficiently high to produce hemorrhage of the entire tumor were lethal to the animal; non-lethal doses resulted in affecting only part of the tumor. Finally, the primary injection of the polysaccharide apparently sets up an immunity in the tumor and in the animal to subsequent injections, so that the residual mass of the tumor remaining after the initial damage is unaffected by such subsequent injections. This is consistent with the finding that transplanted tumors accidentally contaminated with bacteria were much more resistant to the agent administered than were sterile tumors. The use of crude filtrates of organisms other than *Bacillus prodigiosus* subsequent to the use of the purified polysaccharide, in the hope, through varying bacterial material, of circumventing the immunity induced by the polysaccharide, resulted in severe and extensive fresh hemorrhage in the residual tumors, but the mortality was high.

Histologic sections of the tissues other than those of the tumors of treated mice revealed no great visible damage. Some nuclear degeneration occurs in normal dividing cells as in the intestinal epithelium. Observation of the tumors of treated mice by Algire has revealed that there is a severe and rapid drop in the total capillary volume which precedes the hemorrhage. The effect of the polysaccharide may thus be described by at least two consecutive stages, the first of which is an anoxia due to insufficient blood supply, leading to necrosis, and the second of which is incidental hemorrhage. A decrease in capillary volume may also occur in neighboring striated muscle.

Zahl *et al.* (160) employed active concentrates from two closely related and from one taxonomically remote bacterial species in similar immunizing experiments and reported that protection by immunization was found to be about as effective against the induction of tumor hemorrhage when the heterologous organisms were used as when the homologous were used. It is probable, however, that crude preparations of unrelated organisms may contain substances which are common as well as those which are different.

The mechanism for the primary effect of bacterial materials on certain types of tumors is still unknown. Although many species of bacteria are capable of elaborating substances potent in inducing hemorrhage in tumors, still others have given negative results. Zahl, Hutner and their collaborators (160, 161) have pointed out the general occurrence of tumor-hemorrhage potency in Gram-negative bacteria and its general absence in Gram-positive organisms. The relation of the tumor-hemorrhage phenomenon to anaphylaxis and immunity has been suspected. However, the bacterial polysaccharide produces hemorrhage in tumors without apparently requiring a sensitizing dose. Barrett (162) observed that hemorrhage could be induced in tumors of mice previously sensitized by horse serum after subsequent injection into such mice of a shocking dose of the serum, but the tumors of non-sensitized animals showed no hemorrhage on primary treatment with horse serum nor did they exhibit shock. It is probable that the mechanisms underlying the hemorrhage-producing results of the injection of bacterial product and of the injection of the shock-inducing horse serum are fundamentally different. Experimental animals as well as human cancer patients undergo some measure of shock after treatment with bacterial preparations or after induced bacterial infection, and Gardner *et al.* (163) suggested that the hemorrhagic phenomenon is a result of generalized vascular shock. It is possible that the newly formed capillaries of the growing tumor are more sensitive to the action of extrinsic agents than the blood vessels elsewhere in the host. The enhanced susceptibility to shock of the tumor-bearing as contrasted with the normal animal after treatment with the bacterial material suggests that it may be the decomposition products of destroyed tumor tissue which are responsible for the untoward symptoms and death of the former animal. In such an event shock would occur subsequent to the necrotizing effect of the agent on the tumor (cf. 164). Table 59, illustrative of data by Zahl, suggests that the presence within the body of a tumor is associated with an enhanced toxic effect of the antigenic polysaccharide (165). It was further noted by Zahl (165) that somatic antigens derived from three types of Gram-negative bacteria, although highly active *in vivo* in effecting tumor hemorrhage and necrosis in mice, possessed no effect on these tumors *in vitro*, thus emphasizing the probable systemic rather than direct mechanisms whereby these agents affect tumors.

The possible role of peripheral hypotension in the development of tumor ischemia as leading to tumor necrosis has been offered by Algire (166), whose admirable and ingenious experimental device of the transparent chamber has been described in Chapter II. There seems to be little doubt that the tumor blood supply is decreased by lowering the blood pressure

TABLE 59

EFFECT OF TUMOR EXTIRPATION ON THE SURVIVAL OF NORMAL AND OF SARCOMA 180-BEARING MICE RECEIVING THE SHEAR POLYSACCHARIDE (165)

Treatment	Per cent surviving after 48 hours
Normal mice receiving 0.3 LD_{50} of antigen	100
Sarcomatous mice receiving 0.3 LD_{50} of antigen	15
Sarcomatous mice receiving 0.3 LD_{50} of antigen, followed immediately by tumor excision	71
Sarcomatous mice receiving 0.3 LD_{50} of antigen, followed 2–3 hours later by tumor excision	80

in the arteries supplying the tumor, and that the reduction of tumor circulation is proportional to the duration and degree of the peripheral hypotension. Experimentally, the circulatory effects on the tumor followed by tumor damage appear to be the same after polysaccharide injection as those obtained through peripheral hypotension induced by histamine, namely, progressively increasing sluggish flow in arteries, accompanied by stasis of blood flow and occlusion of capillaries.

Chemical analysis of the tumor-necrotizing agent prepared by Shear revealed (167) that it is a phospholipid-polysaccharide peptide complex of which the carbohydrate represents about three-fourths of the total dry weight. The carbohydrate moiety consists of two parts, one a glucan which can be removed by the action of crude soybean β-amylase without loss of potency of the material, and the other a polysaccharide containing N-acetylglucosamine as a main constituent. The residual complex could not be further degraded without loss of potency.

The bacterial polysaccharides possess immunological, lethal, and tumor-necrotizing activities, and attempts by Creech and his associates to fractionate purified preparations of this class of compounds led to observations that indicated a ready separation of these activities (168). Thus, purified materials obtained from different bacterial strains showed considerable variation in all three activities, while isolation and fractionation techniques of a single material led to products of lower antigenicities and toxicities and higher tumor-necrotizing power. Simple storage of solutions for long periods of time appeared to decrease the tumor-necrotizing power, whereas freezing of such solutions appeared to enhance it, without in either case affecting antigenicity or toxicity. Passive immunization of tumor-bearing mice with rabbit antibody preparations toward the polysaccharide prior to injection of a large dose of the polysaccharide definitely decreased the lethality without affecting the tumor-necrotizing action (Table 60).

Another mouse tumor hemorrhagic agent from cultures of *E. coli* has been

TABLE 60

Passive Immunization against Lethal Action of a 50-γ Dose of Bacterial Polysaccharide in Sarcoma 37-Bearing Mice (168)

Group	Amount of γ-globulin, mg.	Per cent survivors after: 24 hours	4 days	10 days	21 days
Not immunized	0	43	43	42	27
Given normal globulin	1.5	73	47	47	33
Given immune globulin	1.5	87	83	80	66

prepared (169) which appears to be a complex polysaccharide containing polypeptide and phospholipid components. The peptide is apparently unessential for the antitumor effect, for it can be removed with trichloroacetic acid without loss of activity in the residual material. The high toxicity of the many bacterial polysaccharide preparations has acted as a deterrent to extensive clinical studies (cf. 170). However, their highly interesting theoretical possibilities suggest numerous experimental problems which can be developed by the use of laboratory animals. Thus, the administration of polysaccharide to mice produces a drop, but to man it produces a rise, in body temperature. Perhaps even a partial solution of these many problems may permit their reintroduction to clinical investigation.

Reports by Roskin and his associates on the therapeutic action of *Trypanosoma cruzi* and of an endotoxin prepared from it (cf. 171) have not been confirmed (172, 173). Studies on the action of antibiotics on tumors have been equivocal, and at the present time their effects on tumors are unclear (cf. 1). Administration of massive doses of terramycin and penicillin (174) and of aureomycin (175) to cancer patients led to rapidly progressive azotemia and effects compatible with intrahepatic obstructive jaundice. The screening of some thirty-three known antibiotics for their effect on sarcoma 180 in mice yielded negative results (176). Azaserine, a substituted L-serine, from a culture of a *Streptomyces*, $N_2CHC(=O)OCH_2CH(NH_2)COOH$, was found to have a marked inhibitory action against sarcoma 180 (176a).

An obvious difficulty in developing microbiological techniques and products for cancer therapy is the frequent metabolic lability of the cultures of microorganisms. The subject of the action of microorganisms and of their products in such therapeutic studies has been ably reviewed by Reilly (176b), and her feeling that screening tests for anticancer agents can be suitably tested only *in vivo* would meet with substantial agreement among most students in this field.

Benzene and Arsenic

The use of benzene and of potassium arsenite (in the form of Fowler's solution) has received attention in various clinical quarters as a chemotherapeutic treatment for human leukemia. The pertinent observations on these and related agents have been summarized by Forkner (177). Arsenite in particular was noted to exert favorable effects in cases of chronic myelogenous leukemia by frequently inducing a marked reduction in the leukocyte count and in the leukocytic infiltration of tissues and by improving the general clinical condition of the patients. Both benzene and arsenite (as well as X-radiation) have a depressant action on blood-forming tissues, and these agents have been most frequently employed in this form of neoplastic disease. More recently, injections of salts containing radioactive phosphorus have been employed in the treatment of various leukemias (see below).

Thorough studies of the effect of benzene and of arsenite on transmissible leukemia in several strains of mice have been reported by Flory *et al.* (178). The toxic level of dosage and the average weights of the experimental and control animals were noted throughout, and both myeloid and lymphoid types of leukemia were investigated. The results may be summarized as follows: Benzene and potassium arsenite retarded the development of one strain of myeloid leukemia and were ineffective against another strain. Only benzene was effective against a third strain with a myeloid chloroleukemia. Of the two chemicals, the best results were obtained with benzene, which occasionally doubled or tripled the period of survival of susceptible strains of mice. Of three lymphoid strains tested, none responded to arsenite and only one responded favorably to benzene. No organic arsenical or benzene derivative was as effective as potassium arsenite or benzene itself. The beneficial effect of the latter two chemicals was accomplished without causing loss of body weight. It is obvious that, in the experiments reported, the therapeutic effects were, on the whole, more striking with myeloid than with lymphoid strains, but it is equally clear that considerable variation in susceptibility toward the chemical agents may exist among several strains of the same type of leukemia. In no sense of the word is a cure of the disease effected in favorable cases but only a prolongation in survival.

Warren's studies of the effect of arsenite on the respiration and glycolysis of comparable normal and leukemic tissues revealed that the depressing effect on the respiration and the accelerating effect on aerobic acid production (Pasteur effect) brought about by this agent were of the same order of magnitude for both kinds of tissues (179). Although arsenite inhibits keto acid oxidation in kidney and liver, it fails to do so in bone marrow and in normal and leukemic leucocytes.

The use of the newer antileukemic agents has tended to relegate the arsenites to only occasional therapeutic studies. Tested on sarcoma 37 in mice, a large variety of aliphatic and aromatic derivatives of trivalent and pentavalent arsenic were found to be effective in damaging the tumor only when administered close to the maximum tolerated dose (180).

Plant Products—Colchicine and Podophyllin

A drug with an action partially resembling that of the bacterial polysaccharide is colchicine. This alkaloid, even at very low concentration, is capable of acting as a mitotic poison, arresting mitosis at the metaphase (181). Dividing cells, whether *in vitro*, as in tissue cultures of embryonic or tumor tissues (182), or *in vivo*, as in regenerating liver after partial hepatectomy (183), are highly sensitive to the drug. *In vitro* it is active at a dilution of 1 part in 100,000,000 (182). Colchicine is unique among the mitotic poisons in that it does not arrest the initial phase of cell division but, over a very wide range of concentrations, is capable of bringing such division to a standstill at metaphase. Ludford (181) ascribed the accumulation of arrested mitoses to failure of spindle formation. Chromosomes could apparently be formed and split for separation, but no spindle was observable (182). Those dividing cells which escape arrest of mitosis show various abnormalities (183), including increased chromosome numbers, *i.e.*, polyploidy (184, 185). The polyploidy is due to the repetition of an abortive dividing process whereby the absence of spindle formation leads to dividing chromosomes within a single nucleus.

The effect which colchicine exerts in arresting mitosis suggested that this alkaloid might be useful as a chemotherapeutic agent for cancer. However, when it is administered at dose levels just sufficient to arrest mitosis, little or no effect upon the growth of the tumor is discerned (181). Only when the drug is injected in very large doses, just below the minimum lethal dose and considerably in excess of that which arrests mitosis, is it possible to produce a partial and temporary regression of certain kinds of tumors (181, 186). However, at such high dose levels, hemorrhage is induced in susceptible tumors, and thus regression probably occurs not directly as a result of mitotic arrest but as a result of the destruction of the newly formed capillary endothelium in the tumors. In this respect at least, the action of the bacterial metabolites and of colchicine in producing regression of tumors is similar. Like the bacterial metabolites, colchicine is more toxic to tumor-bearing animals than to normal animals. Unless vascular damage is attained by high enough doses of colchicine, no inhibition of tumor growth occurs (187, 188). The tumors which respond most readily to treatment are the soft, highly cellular, rapidly growing types (181, 189). Very slow growing tumors are relatively resistant to the action of the drug. In this respect the action of colchicine resembles that of X-irradiation. After administration of colchicine there is a sharp drop in the ascorbic acid content of the tumor and in the respiration and glycolysis (187).

The disadvantages in the use of colchicine as a chemotherapeutic agent are due to (a) the lack of cytological specificity in its action (i.e., it is impossible to administer doses lethal to all the cells of a tumor without destroying essential dividing cells elsewhere in the body, such as in blood-forming tissues) and (b) the general toxicity, especially to the central nervous system.

The ratio for colchicine of MTD/MED is about 2, but for several derivatives prepared by Hartwell in Shear's laboratory this ratio is considerably higher (14). Thus, the ratio for colchiceinamide is about 20 (15), and for desmethylcolchicine it is about 8 (16). The expression given refers to the ratio of the maximum tolerated dose to minimum effective dose.

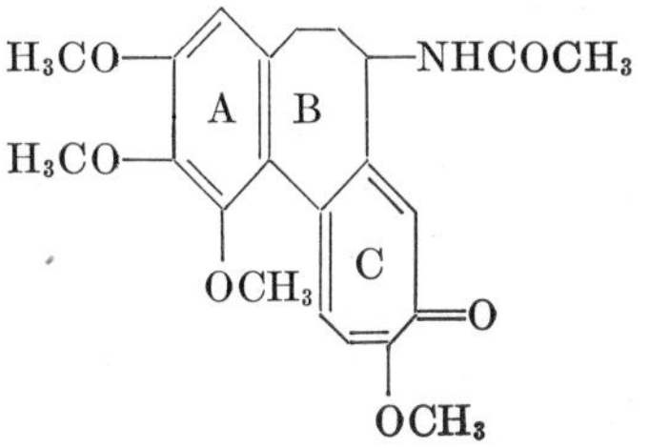

Dewar formula

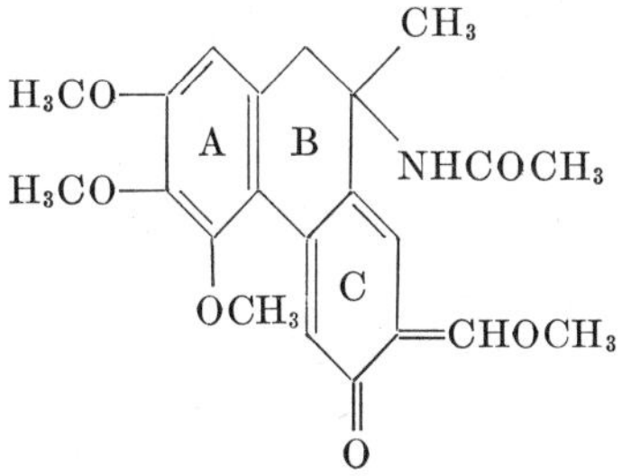

Windaus formula

Colchicine

Opening of the B ring of the Windaus structure would yield derivatives of diphenylethylamine, some of which have been found to be active in inhibiting tumor growth (190). Derivatives of diphenylpropylamine would be obtained by fission of the B ring of the Dewar structure, and many of these, too, are effective (14). Among the most active of the many colchicine derivatives studied in Shear's laboratory for their effect in inducing hemorrhage and necrosis after a single injection in mice carrying S-37 has been colchiceinamide in which an $—NH_2$ group has replaced the $—OCH_3$ group in the C ring of the Dewar structure (15). It is therefore possible to prepare derivatives of colchicine with the same tumor-damaging capacity as the parent compound but with less toxicity. How dependent the activity of these derivatives may be on structure is revealed by the complete ineffectiveness at lethal or near lethal doses of isocolchicine, in which the positions of the carbonyl and methoxy groups in the Dewar C ring of colchicine are exchanged (16). Simpler analogues of colchicine, representing degradations of its three-ring nucleus, such as biphenyl, fluorene, phenanthrene, and tropolone derivatives, are not particularly effective in damaging sarcoma 37 (191).

The distribution of colchicine is not quite the same when administered to normal mice and to mice bearing transplanted tumors. Thus, when radioactive colchicine (by biosynthesis) is injected into tumor-bearing mice, there is no uptake of this drug by the spleens of these animals, al-

TABLE 61

DISTRIBUTION OF RADIOACTIVE COLCHICINE IN ORGANS OF NORMAL AND TUMOR-BEARING MICE[1] (192)

Strain	Tumor	Intestine	Kidney	Liver	Spleen	Heart	Brain	Muscle	Tumor
C57BL	—	28.6	28.6	9.4	39.2	0	0	0	—
BAF-1	—	19.2	22.6	15.1	43.1	0	0	0	—
CF-1	—	18.3	26.2	7.4	47.1	0	0	0	—
C57BL	CR-180	46.2	28.5	17.6	0	—	—	—	5.7
BAF-1	Sarcoma	39.5	28.1	19.0	0	—	—	—	13.4
CF-1	Ascites	39.8	26.7	26.7	0	—	—	—	6.8
DBA × C3H	Mammary	38.2	30.7	18.5	0	—	—	—	12.3

[1] Counts expressed as per cent of total.

though their intestines take up more of the compound than do the intestines of normal animals (192) (Table 61). Uptake in this case refers to the whole molecule, as tested by ultraviolet absorption spectra and chromatography, and not just to the radioactivity alone.

It is well-known that tumor-bearing animals are more sensitive to colchicine than are normal animals. The injection of lyophilized tumor into normal mice together with radioactive colchicine gives substantially the same picture as that of a tumor *in situ*; i.e., there is an increase in intestinal and a decrease in spleen colchicine. This suggests that the tumor mass produces a substance which is humorally borne and which evokes an effect in distant tissues. Whether this material is the same which produces the marked lowering of the liver catalase level in tumor-bearing animals (see Chapter IX) remains for further investigation. Normal muscle homogenates injected into mice produce neither effect. It is interesting to note in this connection that there is an increased uptake of radioactive iodotyrosine in the intestines of tumor-bearing rats over that observed in normal animals (193). It would appear that not only the liver but also the intestinal epithelium is sensitive to the presence of a tumor in the host.

Podophyllin is a product from the mandrake or May apple root, which produces damage to tumors after a single subcutaneous injection (194). Four components of podophyllin with unequal effectiveness toward sarcoma 37 have been separated from crude podophyllin, namely, podophyllotoxin, quercetin, α-peltatin, and β-peltatin (12, 12a). The survival period of mice with leukemia has also been prolonged, and administration of the compounds caused weight loss only in tumor-bearing and not in normal animals (13). Generally, the maximum tolerated dose has been found to be well above the minimum effective dose, but the ratio apparently varies with the tumor type and host. The hypotensive effect of this class of drugs has been considered by Algire *et al.* (194a).

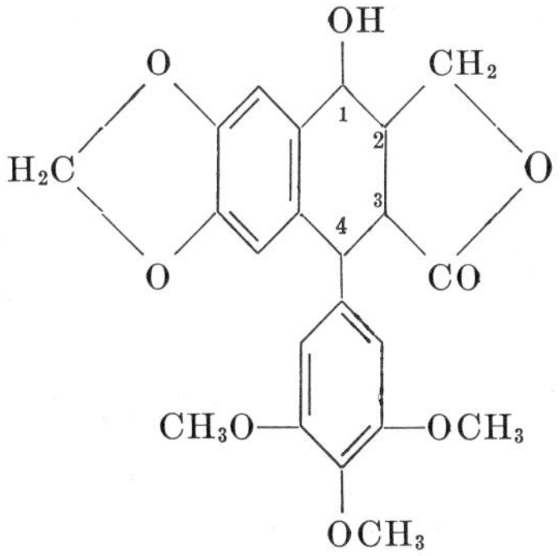

Podophyllotoxin

Quite significant studies of the effects of podophyllotoxin and related derivatives of podophyllin on the enzyme levels of the tumors of treated animals have been made by Leiter and his colleagues in Shear's laboratory (195). Subcutaneous injection of these compounds into mice bearing S-37 tumor results in a marked and rapid diminution of the cytochrome oxidase of the tumor during the first 8 hours after injection, the rate of which drop is proportional to the amount of drug administered, and which takes place well before any frank, histologic necrosis can be observed in the tumor. During this period no change from the normal level of cytochrome oxidase of the liver, kidneys, spleen, or testis of the treated animals could be noted, and indeed, even with supralethal doses of the active compounds, the diminution of the oxidase level of these tissues was relatively minor. Autolysis of the intact carcasses of tumor-bearing mice for periods up to 6 hours at 37° produced histological changes in the tumor similar to those observed after the same period following injection of podophyllotoxin, but no significant change in the cytochrome oxidase level was apparent. Not only cytochrome oxidase, but also cytochrome c, succinoxidase, and over-all respiration are reduced in the tumor after subcutaneous injection of acetylpodophyllotoxin (195a), although succinic dehydrogenase is not appreciably affected. The level of these systems in tissue other than tumor is nearly unaffected. It would appear that enzymatic changes can be detected in a tissue before histologic changes are evident (see changes in liver catalase activity in tumor-bearing animals, Chapter IX), and also that histologic changes need not necessarily imply general changes in enzymatic levels. Essentially similar observations have been made after administration to tumor-bearing mice of derivatives of colchicine, arsenic, antimony, and phenazine (196). The value of the program initiated by Leiter and his colleagues lies in introducing a possibly far more sensitive and specific criterion for screening antineoplastic drugs than that of histology, and in showing that a differential effect on the tumor and on the tissues of the host can be determined.

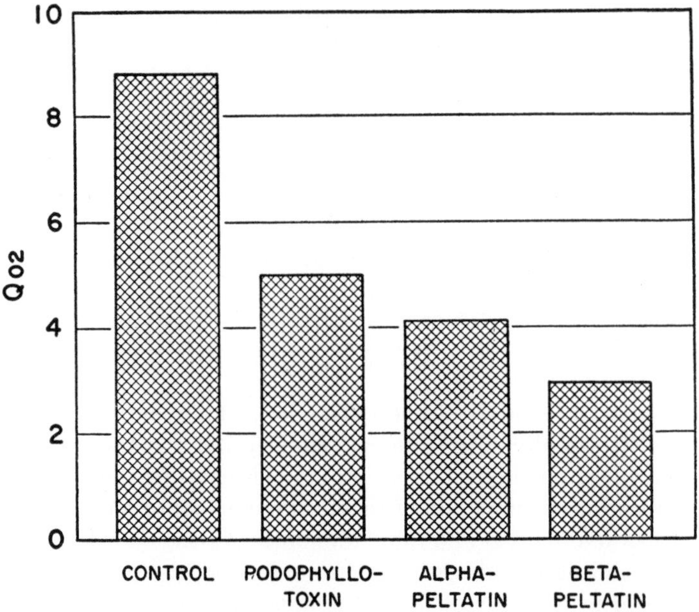

FIG. 25. Effect of podophyllin derivatives on cytochrome oxidase activity of sarcoma 37, 24 hours after a single subcutaneous injection. From Waravdekar, V. S., Domingue, A., and Leiter, J., *J. Natl. Cancer Inst.* **13,** 393 (1952).

An intensive program involving crude extracts of various plants, including those used as cathartics (17), diuretics (18), and pesticides (17), as well as several representatives of the conifers (19), has been developed by Belkin and his colleagues in Shear's laboratory. Most of these products produced toxicity in the mice studied, but a much smaller number were found to produce tumor damage (on S-37 and other tumors) at the same time. It may well be that not all forms of generalized toxicity lead also to tumor necrosis, but where tumor necrosis does occur there always appears to be some degree of toxicity in the host as well. The relatively large number of plants capable of inducing necrotic changes in the experimental tumors studied is rather surprising, and further studies in this area beyond the initial screening might prove of interest.

VIRUSES

The use of viruses as oncolytic agents is certainly one of the most curious developments in contemporary chemotherapeutic research, although since viruses are known to specifically destroy certain normal tissues there is no reason *a priori* why some should not have the specific property of destroying tumors. Many observers had found that viruses may infect the tumors of rodents (197, 198), and actually be carried in such tumors for so long a period of time as to suggest that malignant cells might not be able to develop an immunity to the virus. Under these conditions no effect on the growth of the tumor could be noted. In 1947, however, Turner and Mulliken (199) reported that a mouse-adapted strain of vaccinia could be directly introduced into sarcoma 180 in mice and attain high concentrations in the tumor without injury to the host. Upon transplantation, these virus-infected tumors grew more slowly and regressed more frequently than did uninfected controls. Recognizing that direct administration of an agent to the tumor is open to several objections, these authors employed intravenous administration with no effect on sarcoma 180, although the virus localized in the tumor in low titer (200).

On intraperitoneal injection of Russian encephalitis virus to mice bearing sarcoma 180, there is a rapid concentration of the virus in the tumor (201). The tumors grow for a short time, but, after 3 days, retransplantation of tumor pieces into virus immune animals shows only 50 % takes, and 6 days later all the transplanted tumors become necrotic. The use of virus-immune new hosts is essential, for the tumor pieces carry so much virus as to kill unimmunized hosts. The immune state of the animals itself has no effect on tumor growth. The original tumor-bearing animals, unimmunized, die with paralysis in 7 to 8 days. These animals must be originally unimmunized, for the adverse tumor effect does not initially occur in either actively or passively immunized mice. Although the virus appears in high titer in the tumor as much as one day after intraperitoneal inoculation, complete tumor destruction does not occur until about the sixth day, although this "latent" period can be reduced by giving larger doses of the virus (Fig. 26).

Moore (201) has studied the oncolytic action of a variety of viruses against several experimental tumors and noted that each virus appears to differ in its effect on different tumors (Table 62). The problem of tumor specificity is as cogent in the case of the viruses as it is with many other chemotherapeutic agents. A total of eleven viruses so far studied has been effective in inhibiting the growth of one or more experimental tumors, and the most active of these viruses have been neurotropic as well as tumor-tropic (cf. Fig. 26). It is possible to separate these properties, for by continuous passage through brain tissue the encephalitis virus loses its oncolytic properties, whereas after several passages through sarcoma 180 its relative oncolytic effectiveness increases (201). In either case its neurotropism does not significantly change. Virus strains can also be developed through several tissue passages which can destroy a tumor resistant to the original virus. The Bunyamwera virus has been noted to grow in and destroy the Ehrlich ascites tumor (202), and the Russian spring-summer encephalitis virus can apparently retard leukocytosis (without affecting survival) in mouse leukemia (203).

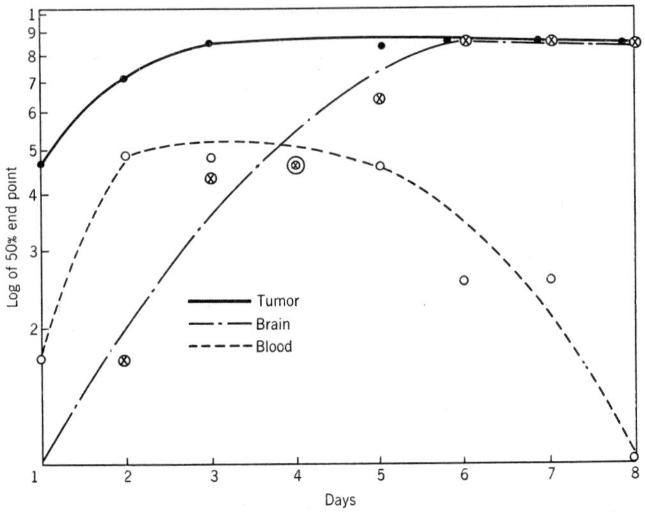

FIG. 26. Amount of virus in blood, brain, and tumor after intraperitoneal inoculation of Russian encephalitis virus into mice bearing sarcoma 180. From Moore, A. E., *Ann. N. Y. Acad. Sci.* **54,** 945 (1952).

TABLE 62

TUMOR DESTRUCTION BY VIRUSES (201)

	Tumor type					
Virus	Sarcoma S-180	Carcinoma E-0771	Osteo-sarcoma	Osteo-sarcoma	Sarcoma	Melanoma
Russian encephalitis	+	+	+	−	+	−
West Nile	+	±	+	+	+	−
Bunyamwera	−	±	+	+	−	−

The Mengo encephalitis virus multiplies at a faster rate in the Ehrlich ascites tumor of mice than it does in mouse brain (203a). Invasion of the tumor cells by the virus leads to destruction of the cells.

The Ehrlich ascites tumor has been employed in place of solid tumors as a test object for several viruses (204). This tumor was readily inhibited by the Bunyamwera and West Nile viruses, but not by several others, including the louping-ill virus which is so powerfully oncolytic against sarcoma 180 (205). Those viruses inactive against the ascites tumor may nevertheless multiply in the tumor cells but apparently do no damage.

Moore has classified the viruses in the following categories: (a) those which grow in a tumor and do not affect it, (b) those which grow in a tumor and destroy it, and (c) those which fail to grow in tumors (201). The virus of Russian encephalitis fails to grow in the melanoma, and the Eastern equine encephalitis virus fails to grow in sarcoma 180, although both these viruses grow in other tumors (206). The mechanism of action of the viruses is obscure. The fact that most if not all of the effective viruses are also neurotropic is suggestive in that tumor and brain must have some metabolic features in common. Like all attempts to interpret the many inconsistent observations in any area of cancer research, this too must await more fundamental information on virus-host relationships. But if interpretation can wait, therapy cannot, and several clinical trials have been made with certain of the viruses such as the West Nile and the Bunyamwera and Egypt 101 (207). Little if any effect on the growth of tumors in the patients tested was observed, although Pack (208) noted some improvement in a few cases of melanoma in patients treated with rabies virus. The practical difficulties in the way of a successful therapy using active viruses are obviously formidable, although the subject itself is fascinating from a theoretical standpoint. One of the most cogent of these difficulties is the finding of relatively obscure or foreign viruses, for the patient must not have previously been exposed and acquired an immunity to the virus applied therapeutically. In any event the patient becomes immune in a short time after receiving the virus, and the only way out of this difficulty is to develop variant strains or to use a wide spectrum of different viruses. The hazards in the use of these agents in peculiarly susceptible individuals are apparent, although sometimes the exchange of a hazard for a certainty is not a bad bargain.

Radioactive Isotopes

Treatment of neoplastic disease with radioactive chemicals is simply another form of radiation therapy, differing from X-ray or radium therapy in that the chemicals can be administered orally or parenterally and thus can be distributed throughout the body. If these radioactive chemicals are those which in the stable state participate in metabolic reactions, it would be expected that the radioactive forms would also be found in tissue metabolites under the same conditions. Treatment with such radioactive chemicals is, therefore, a kind of systemic therapy.

One of the most widely studied of the radioactive isotopes in neoplastic disease has been that of phosphorus (209–216). This isotope of phosphorus, P^{32}, has an unstable nucleus whose half-life is 14.3 days. It breaks down to yield sulfur and a β-particle. The β-particles produced have an average energy of 700 kv. and can penetrate several meters of air or about 2 to 4 mm. of tissue. Like its more familiar stable isotope it participates in many metabolic reactions, and, through its radiation properties, considerable information has been obtained as to its distribution throughout the body. Further discussion of the value of the use of radioactive isotopes is deferred to Chapter VIII, but it may be mentioned briefly here that it would be expected that, in regions of great metabolic activity and synthesis, materials normally serving as or in conjunction with metabolites would tend to accumulate in unusually large amount. If the normal isotope of phosphorus as phosphate accumulated or turned over rapidly metabolically in such regions, so too would the radioactive isotope of phosphorus. Thus, if neoplastic tissues take up more phosphorus, whether stable or radioactive, than do normal tissues, a possible mode of therapy based on administration of the unstable isotope can be devised. The studies of Marshak (217) did, indeed, show that tumors took up more radioactive phosphorus than did normal tissues. The subsequent investigations of Brues *et al.* (218) showed that a part of the radioactive isotope administered was synthesized into nucleic acid molecules. The retention of labeled phosphorus by lymphomatous tissue is much greater than by normal lymphatic tissue (219).

The only successful attempts at therapy by the use of P^{32} administered as sodium phosphate have been reported in cases of leukemia (209–216). Studies of the distribution of the isotope in patients with leukemia revealed that the deposition was greatest in those tissues which usually show the greatest infiltration of leukemic cells, namely, liver, spleen, kidney, and bone marrow (216). Thus, this localization, combined with the differential absorption by the rapidly growing leukemic cells (217), gives the radioactive isotope an opportunity favorable to the selective irradiation of leukemic cells. Another example of favorable localization is in the case of radioactive iodine (I^{131}, half-life 8 days) in tumors of the thyroid. With the hope that dyes might be selectively taken up and retained by tumors, radioactive elements such as Br^{82} (half-life 34 hours) have been incorporated in such substances (220). The results were not entirely favorable. The use of NaI^{131} to localize brain tumors after oral administration, or $Rb_2{}^{86}CO_3$ after intravenous administration (221, 222) has been a useful clinical tool. Radioactive colloidal metallic gold appears to have a limited benefit in mouse leukemia (223). Au^{198} is a β-emitter with a short half-life (224) and has been employed as a sol directly administered to the tumor mass (225) in which, under favorable circumstances, it remains. Negligible quantities are excreted, and the biologically effective half-life approximates the physical half-life (2.7 days). Some palliative effects in advanced cancer cases have been recorded by this treatment (224), which has an advantage in the employment of a single dose, and the disadvantage in the estimation of the dose levels since the amount of tissue involved is not readily measurable.

Other methods of administering β-emitters for localized irradiation have been the simultaneous injection of $Ag^{111}NO_3$ and KBr, or $AgNO_3$ and either KBr^{82} or KI^{131}, in order to effect precipitation in tumors *in situ* (224). $CrP^{32}O_4$ is also amenable to such a technique (226).

$La^{140}Cl_3$ is inhibitory to the growth of ascites tumors (227). Since stable $LaCl_3$ had no effect on the tumor cells, the toxicity must have been due to the radiation. Since the radioactive lanthanum salt was administered intraperitoneally, it came into relatively close contact with the tumor cells and appeared to be concentrated in the sediment of ascitic fluid containing the cells.

P^{32} therapy has been of value in the treatment of chronic leukemia, whether myeloid or lymphoid (228, 229). Good results have also been obtained in several cases of lymphosarcoma and of polycythemia (230–232). However, acute leukemic cases apparently were not benefited by the use of radioactive phosphorus. So far, the beneficial effects of external radiation procedures, such as X-radiation, run more or less parallel to those of P^{32} therapy, but the so-called radiation sickness is absent in the latter form of treatment. On the other hand, where massive radiation effects are desired, especially in localized areas, the radioactive chemicals cannot be administered except in doses damaging elsewhere.

In contrast with such elements as iodine which is largely localized in the thyroid gland, strontium in bone, and phosphorus in bone, bone marrow, leukemic tissue, and any rapidly growing tissue, sodium does not concentrate in any organ or group of organs but instead is, within a short time after its administration, distributed throughout the extracellular fluids of the body. Radioactive sodium, Na^{24}, emits penetrating β- and γ-rays and thus, by its wide distribution, can administer a rather uniform irradiation to the entire body. Its half-life period is 14.8 hours. Studies by Evans and Quimby (233) revealed that the subcutaneous administration of radioactive sodium (as the chloride) produced effects in mice essentially similar to those resulting from whole-body roentgen irradiation. The reduction in white and red blood counts and in the life-spans of the animals was similar for the two types of radiation. Ten microcuries of Na^{24} per gram of body weight injected subcutaneously in the normal mouse are equivalent in effect to 100 r. of heavily filtered 200-kv. roentgen rays. This ratio holds only for the mouse. In the human being the same number of microcuries would be equivalent to a considerably higher number of roentgens. This is partly due to the fact that the γ-rays are so penetrating that they escape from the small body of the mouse without giving up an appreciable portion of their energy, and to a lesser extent this is also true of the β-radiation, which is only about three-fourths effective. In man, practically all the β-rays and a considerable portion of the γ-rays are absorbed. Tests with Na^{24} on leukemic mice revealed that the leukemic cells are more sensitive to the radiation than are normal white cells, but the data are too recent to draw any conclusions as to the effectiveness of this form of therapy in mouse and still less in human leukemia.

The expected localization of I^{131} in the thyroid gland early suggested the use of this isotope for therapy of thyroid tumors (cf. 234). The results have not been generally satisfactory. One important reason for this may be seen in the studies of Morris and Wollman cited in Chapter IV, which showed that I^{131} uptake is least in the more malignant experimental thyroid tumors (235). The clinical application of this form of therapy has been ably reviewed by Rawson and Trunnell (236). A particularly careful study (237) in which I^{131} incorporation was followed by radioautographs revealed evidence of I^{131} concentration in only 46 cases of 100 of thyroid carcinoma in patients. Although I^{131} apparently selects normal thyroid follicles in preference to cancer tissue, the uneven, variable concentration of the isotope in both tissues is not only theoretically puzzling but exasperating in practice, for this inhomogeneous distribution emphasizes difficulties in calculating dosages on the assumption of a uniform distribution. Some thyroid follicles show no I^{131} activity, whereas neighboring follicles, morphologically indistinguishable, are heavily laden with the isotope (237).

Skipper and his colleagues have considered that, since C^{14} formate is taken up so much more rapidly by leukemic cells than by normal leukocytes, this material might serve as a therapeutic agent (238). They recognized, however, that the low energy of C^{14} disintegration (0.15 million electron volts) might militate against this idea and indeed found C^{14}-formate to be ineffective toward various mouse leukemias. Their suggestion that perhaps C^{11}-formate with its more energetic β-radiation and 20.5-minute half-life might be more effective is, as they admit, impracticable at this time.

It would appear that, with the exceptions noted, tumors as a rule do not selectively take up the radioactive isotopes but rather share in their distribution with other tissues. The unstable isotopes behave chemically like their stable forms. It is difficult to avoid the impression that, as a therapeutic agent for cancer, radiation of any kind is little more than a temporary and restricted stop gap.

The Problem of Resistance

The apparent resistance which a tumor develops to the administration of an agent is one of the key problems which efforts in the field of therapy have been compelled to consider. Closely allied to this problem are the interesting if vexatious differences in response which various tumors exhibit toward the same agent. These facts, together with numerous lines of evidence showing that the clinical course of cancer at different sites appears to have a quite different natural history in each case, have inclined many authorities to the belief that cancer is a spectrum of various neoplastic diseases.

Tumors are not biologically stationary, however, and as they grow may develop new characteristics. As will be shown in the following chapter, the metabolic pattern of a transplanted tumor has some characteristics different from those of the primary tumor from which it was derived, and on repeated transplantation may change still further. On the other hand, the metabolism of the primary tumor resembles in some characteristics that of the normal tissue of origin. But even in the primary tumor and subsequent transplants therefrom these characteristics may be present in unequal degree, as shown, for example, in the unequal iodine-concentrating capacities of the experimental thyroid tumors studied by Morris and Wollman. The significant biological studies of Foulds (239) on various tumors of the mouse have revealed what he refers to as "progressions" toward some final, malignant state. In the neoplastic alphabet, where A is a benign and Z the fully malignant state, a tumor may exist at any intermediate point, but it tends inexorably to develop toward Z. It may never reach Z, the ultimate stage, in the lifetime of the host, nor need it begin its career at A. Furthermore, it need not be, and probably never is, pure A, D, G, or X, but may be a mixture in different proportions. The administration of a therapeutic agent may affect cells in different stages of development to an unequal degree, leaving some actually unaffected. At the time of the later administration of the agent, not only are the resistant cells present, but they may have progressed to the next stage in the alphabet. Two different tumors may not exist in an identical biological alphabetical state, and the same agent effective on one combination may very well not be effective on another. The state of the resistant tumor is probably closer to Z. That the agent itself may accelerate this progression cannot be excluded from consideration (239), in view of the fact that most if not all of the effective therapeutic agents are also carcinogenic. Under such circumstances the end result would be an intractable and unresponsive malignancy hastened by the therapy itself. An alternative to so gloomy a prospect might be an effective therapy at each stage of the neoplastic progression. For so complicated a state of affairs to have any rational basis, the metabolic characteristics of each stage in the malignant progression must be apprehended. The differences from stage to stage are likely to be small and nearly imperceptible to ordinary methods of analysis. Even those differences noted above (cf. Chapter VIII) between the primary tumor and the first transplant generation are quantitatively relatively small, and no qualitative differences in regard to individual metabolic systems have ever been noted. The general metabolic patterns of all tumors at any stage resemble each other closely, and the detection of the probably few but crucial differences between stages will require the finest forms of microanalysis. When these differences are known, the varying degrees of responsiveness of different tumors to the same agent may no longer be so puzzling.

References

(1) Stock, C. C., *Advances in Cancer Research* **2**, 425 (1954).
(2) Karnofsky, D. A., *Ann. Rev. Med.* **3**, 283 (1952).

(3) Gellhorn, A., *Cancer Research* **13,** 205 (1953).
(3a) Skipper, H. E., *Cancer Research* **13,** 545 (1953).
(4) Dyer, H. M., "An Index of Tumor Chemotherapy," 1st ed. U. S. Government Printing Office, Washington, D. C., 1949.
(5) Negative Data from Experimental Cancer Chemotherapy Studies (C. C. Stock, ed.), *Cancer Research, Suppl.* No. **1** (1953).
(6) Shear, M. J., *in* "Clinical Problems in Cancer Research," p. 77. Sloan-Kettering Institute Seminar, 1948–1949.
(7) Tannenbaum, A., and Silverstone, H., *Advances in Cancer Research* **1,** 452 (1953).
(8) Lees, T. W., and Lees, J. C., *Cancer* **3,** 580 (1950).
(9) Leiter, J., and Kline, I., *J. Natl. Cancer Inst.* **14,** 449 (1953).
(10) Elson, L. A., *Acta Unio Intern. contra Cancrum* **7,** 600 (1951).
(11) Shear, M. J., and others *in* "Approaches to Tumor Chemotherapy," p. 236. American Association for the Advancement of Science, Washington, 1947.
(12) Leiter, J., Downing, V., Hartwell, J. L., and Shear, M. J., *J. Natl. Cancer Inst.* **10,** 1273 (1950).
(12a) Schrecker, A. W., and Hartwell, J. L., *J. Am. Chem. Soc.* **75,** 5916 (1953).
(13) Greenspan, E. M., Leiter, J., and Shear, M. J., *J. Natl. Cancer Inst.* **10,** 1295 (1950).
(14) Leiter, J., Downing, V., Hartwell, J. L., and Shear, M. J., *J. Natl. Cancer Inst.* **13,** 379 (1952).
(15) Leiter, J., Hartwell, J. L., Kline, I., Nadkarni, M. V., and Shear, M. J., *J. Natl. Cancer Inst.* **13,** 731 (1952).
(16) Leiter, J., Hartwell, J. L., Nllyot, G. E., and Shear, M. J., *J. Natl. Cancer Inst.* **13,** 1201 (1953).
(17) Belkin, M., and Fitzgerald, D. B., *J. Natl. Cancer Inst.* **13,** 139, 889 (1952–53).
(18) Belkin, M., Fitzgerald, D. B., and Felix, M. D., *J. Natl. Cancer Inst.* **13,** 741 (1952).
(19) Fitzgerald, D. B., Belkin, M., Felix, M. D., and Carroll, M. K., *J. Natl. Cancer Inst.* **13,** 895 (1953).
(20) Flory, C. M., Furth, J., Saxton, J. A., and Reiner, L., *Cancer Research* **3,** 729 (1943).
(21) Burchenal, J. H., *Cancer* **1,** 399 (1948).
(22) Law, L. W., *Proc. Soc. Exptl. Biol. Med.* **66,** 158 (1947).
(23) Kirschbaum, A., *Cancer Research* **11,** 741 (1951).
(24) Haddow, A., Harris, R. J. C., Kon, G. A. R., and Roe, E. M. F., *Trans. Roy. Soc. (London)* **A 241,** 147 (1948).
(25) Hendry, J. A., Rose, F. L., and Walpole, A. L., *Brit. J. Pharmacol.* **6,** 201 (1951).
(26) Hendry, J. A., Homer, R. F., Rose, F. L., and Walpole, A. L., *Brit. J. Pharmacol.* **6,** 235, 357 (1951).
(27) Kidder, G. W., Dewey, V. C., Parks, R. E., Jr., and Woodside, G. L., *Cancer Research* **11,** 204 (1951).
(28) Stock, C. C., and Rhoads, C. P., *in* "Evaluation of Chemotherapeutic Agents," p. 181. Columbia University Press, New York, 1949.
(29) Laszlo, D., and Leuchtenberger, C., *Science* **97,** 515 (1943).
(30) Goldin, A., Greenspan, E. M., and Schoenbach, E. B., *Cancer* **5,** 153 (1952).
(31) Lewis, M. R., and Goland, P. P., *Cancer Research* **13,** 130 (1953).
(32) Klein, G., Klein, E., and Klein, E., *Cancer Research* **12,** 484 (1952).
(33) Lettré, H., *Z. physiol. Chem.* **268,** 59 (1941).
(34) Sugiura, K., and Stock, C. C., *Cancer Research* **11,** 284 (1951).

(35) Kidder, G. W., Dewey, V. C., and Parks, R. E., Jr., *Proc. Soc. Exptl. Biol. Med.* **78,** 88 (1951).
(36) Dewey, V. C., Kidder, G. W., and Parks, R. E., Jr., *Proc. Soc. Exptl. Biol. Med.* **78,** 91 (1951).
(37) Cornman, I., *Science* **99,** 247 (1944).
(38) Lettré, H., *Angew. Chem.* **63,** 421 (1951).
(39) Biesele, J. J., Berger, R. E., and Clarke, M., *Cancer Research* **12,** 399 (1952).
(40) Taylor, A., *Texas Repts. Biol. and Med.* **8,** 227 (1950).
(41) Ridgway, L. P., and Karnofsky, D. A., *Ann. N. Y. Acad. Sci.* **55,** 203 (1952).
(42) Ultmann, J. E., Hirschberg, E., and Gellhorn, A., *Cancer Research* **13,** 14 (1953).
(43) Goodman, L. S., Wintrobe, M. M., Dameshek, W., Goodman, M. J., Gilman, A., and McClennan, M. I., *J. Am. Med. Assoc.* **132,** 126 (1946).
(44) Rhoads, C. P., *J. Am. Med. Assoc.* **131,** 656 (1946).
(45) Jacobson, L. O., Spurr, C. L., Barron, E. S. G., Smith, T. R., Lushbaugh, C., and Dick, G. F., *J. Am. Med. Assoc.* **132,** 263 (1946).
(46) ApThomas, M. I. R., and Cullumbine, H., *Lancet* **i,** 899 (1947).
(47) Wilkinson, J. F., and Fletcher, F., *Lancet* **ii,** 540 (1947).
(48) Gellhorn, A., and Jones, L. O., *Am. J. Med.* **6,** 188 (1949).
(49) Karnofsky, D. A., and Burchenal, J. H., *Am. J. Med.* **8,** 767 (1950).
(49a) Klopp, C., and Bateman, J. C., *Advances in Cancer Research* **2,** 255 (1954).
(50) Bass, A. D., and Freeman, M. L. H., *J. Natl. Cancer Inst.* **7,** 171 (1946).
(51) Haddow, A., Kon, G. A. R., and Ross, W. C. J., *Nature* **162,** 824 (1948).
(52) Haddow, A., *Practitioner* **167,** 36 (1951).
(53) Lynch, J. P., Ware, P. F., and Gaensler, E. A., *Surgery* **27,** 368 (1950).
(54) Boyland, E., Clegg, J. W., Koller, P. C., Rhoden, E., and Warwick, O. H., *Brit. J. Cancer* **2,** 17 (1948).
(55) Klopp, C. T., Alford, T. C., Bateman, J., Berry, G. N., and Winship, T., *Ann. Surg.* **132,** 811 (1950).
(56) Bateman, J. C., Cornman, I., Grice, P. M., Kennelley, J., and Klopp, C. T., *Cancer* **6,** 275 (1953).
(57) Barberio, J. R., Berry, G. N., Bateman, J., Cromer, J. K., and Klopp, C. T., *Cancer* **6,** 280 (1953).
(58) Darlington, C. D., and Koller, P. C., *Heredity* **1,** 187 (1947).
(59) Boyland, E., and Horning, E., *Brit. J. Cancer* **3,** 118 (1949).
(60) Goldacre, R. J., Loveless, A., and Ross, W. C. J., *Nature* **163,** 667 (1949).
(61) Ross, W. C. J., *Advances in Cancer Research* **1,** 397 (1953).
(62) Alexander, P., *Advances in Cancer Research* **2,** 1 (1953).
(63) Lewis, M. A., and Crossley, M. L., *Arch. Biochem.* **26,** 319 (1950).
(64) Burchenal, J. H., Johnston, S. F., Cremer, M. A., Webber, L. F., and Stock, C. C., *Proc. Soc. Exptl. Biol. Med.* **74,** 708 (1950).
(65) Karnofsky, D. A., Burchenal, J. H., Armistead, G. C., Jr., Southam, C. M., Bernstein, J. L., Craver, L. F., and Rhoads, C. P., *Arch. Internal. Med.* **87,** 477 (1951).
(66) Crossley, M. L., Allison, J. B., Wainio, W. W., and Muenzen, J. B., *J. Natl. Cancer Inst.* **12,** 305 (1951).
(67) Buckley, S. M., Stock, C. C., Crossley, M. L., and Rhoads, C. P., *Cancer* **5,** 144 (1952).
(67a) Gomori, G., *Proc. Soc. Exptl. Biol. Med.* **69,** 407 (1948).
(67b) Friedman, O. M., and Seligman, A. M., *J. Am. Chem. Soc.* **76,** 655, 658 (1954).
(68) Haddow, A., and Timmis, G. M., *Abstr. 5th Intern. Cancer Congr. Paris* (1950).

(69) Sexton, W. A., "Chemical Constitution and Biological Activity."E. & F. N. Spon, London, 1949.
(70) Powell, A. K., *Brit. J. Cancer* **5,** 264 (1951).
(70a) Miller, Z., *Arch. Biochem. and Biophys.* **47,** 137 (1953).
(71) Lefèvre, J., *Compt. rend.* **208,** 301 (1939).
(72) Templeman, W. G., and Sexton, W. A., *Nature* **156,** 630 (1945).
(73) Haddow, A., and Sexton, W. A., *Nature* **157,** 500 (1946).
(74) Patterson, E., ApThomas, I., Haddow, A., and Watkinson, J. M., *Lancet* **i,** 677 (1946).
(75) Dustin, P., *Rev. belge pathol. et méd. exptl.* **19,** 115 (1949).
(76) Skipper, H. E., *Cancer* **2,** 475 (1949).
(77) Murphy, J. B., and Sturm, E., *Cancer Research* **7,** 417 (1947).
(78) Weir, D. R., and Heinle, R. W., *Proc. Soc. Exptl. Biol. Med.* **66,** 268 (1947).
(79) Skipper, H. E., *Texas Repts. Biol. and Med.* **4,** 543 (1950).
(80) Skipper, H. E., and Bryan, C. E., *J. Natl. Cancer Inst.* **9,** 391 (1949).
(81) Leuchtenberger, C., Lewisohn, K., Laszlo, D., and Leuchtenberger, R., *Proc. Soc. Exptl. Biol. Med.* **55,** 204 (1944).
(82) Leuchtenberger, C., Leuchtenberger, C., Laszlo, D., and Lewisohn, R., *Science* **101,** 46 (1945).
(83) Lewisohn, R., Leuchtenberger, C., Leuchtenberger, R., and Keresztesy, J., *Science* **104,** 436 (1946).
(84) Hutchings, B. L., Stokstad, E. L. R., Rohonos, N., and Sloan, N. H., *Science* **99,** 371 (1944).
(85) Sugiura, K., *in* "Approaches to Tumor Chemotherapy," p. 208. American Association for the Advancement of Science, Washington, D. C., 1947.
(86) Morris, H. P., *in* "Approaches to Tumor Chemotherapy," p. 195. American Association for the Advancement of Science, Washington, D. C., 1947.
(87) Farber, S., Diamond, L. K., Mercer, R. D., Sylvester, R. F., and Wolff, J. A., *New Engl. J. Med.* **238,** 787 (1948).
(88) Farber, S., 10th Edwin R. Kretschmer Memorial Lecture, *Proc. Inst. Med. Chicago* **18** (14), (1951).
(89) Farber, S., *Blood* **4,** 160 (1949).
(90) Burchenal, J. H., Kushida, M. N., Johnston, S. F., and Cremer, M. A., *Proc. Soc. Exptl. Biol. Med.* **71,** 559 (1949).
(91) Burchenal, J. H., Johnston, S. F., Kushida, M. N., Robinson, E., and Stock, C. C., *Proc. Soc. Exptl. Biol. Med.* **71,** 381 (1949).
(92) Burchenal, J. H., Babcock, G. M., Broquist, H. P., and Jukes, T. H., *Proc. Soc. Exptl. Biol. Med.* **74,** 735 (1950).
(93) Sauberlich, H. E., and Baumann, C. A., *J. Biol. Chem.*, **176,** 165 (1948).
(94) Broquist, H. P., Stokstad, E. L. R., and Jukes, T. H., *J. Biol. Chem.* **185,** 399 (1950).
(95) Bond, T. J., Bardos, T. J., Sibley, M., and Shive, W., *J. Am. Chem. Soc.* **71,** 3852 (1949).
(96) Goldin, A., Mantel, N., Venditti, J. M., and Greenhouse, S. W., *J. Natl. Cancer Inst.* **13,** 1463 (1953).
(97) Bennette, J. G., *Brit. J. Cancer* **6,** 377 (1952).
(98) Schoenbach, E. B., Goldin, A., Goldberg, B., and Ortega, L. G., *Cancer* **2,** 57 (1949).
(99) Stock, C. C., Biesele, J. J., Burchenal, J. H., Karnofsky, D. A., Moore, A. E., and Sugiura, K., *Ann. N. Y. Acad. Sci.* **52,** 1360 (1950).
(100) Philips, F. S., and Thiersch, J. B., *J. Pharmacol. Exptl. Therap.* **95,** 303 (1949).

(101) Thiersch, J. B., and Stock, C. C., *Cancer* **2,** 863 (1949).
(102) Skipper, H. E., Nolan, C., Newton, M. A., and Simpson, L., *Cancer Research* **12,** 369 (1952).
(103) Skipper, H. E., Bell, M., and Chapman, J., *Cancer* **4,** 357 (1951).
(104) Skipper, H. E., Morgan, C., and Bennett, L. L., Jr., *Cancer Research* **12,** 413 (1952).
(105) Burchenal, J. H., Robinson, E., Johnston, S. F., and Kushida, M. N., *Science* **111,** 116 (1950).
(106) Law, L. W., and Boyle, P. J., *Proc. Soc. Exptl. Biol. Med.* **74,** 599 (1950).
(107) Law, L. W., *Proc. Soc. Exptl. Biol. Med.* **77,** 340 (1951).
(108) Law, L. W., *J. Natl. Cancer Inst.* **11,** 849 (1950).
(109) Law, L. W., *Nature* **169,** 628 (1952).
(110) Skipper, H. E., Bennett, L. L., Jr., and Law, L. W., *Cancer Research* **12,** 677 (1952).
(110a) Williams, A. D., Winzler, R. J., and Law, L. W., *Cancer Research* **14,** 135 (1954).
(111) Skipper, H. E., Mitchell, J. H., Jr., Bennett, L. L., Jr., Newton, M. A., Simpson, L., and Eidson, M., *Cancer Research* **11,** 145 (1951).
(112) Edwards, P. C., Skipper, H. E., and Johnson, R. P., *Cancer* **4,** 398 (1951).
(112a) Shive, W., Ackermann, W. W., Gordon, M., Getzendauer, M. E., and Eakin, R. E., *J. Am. Chem. Soc.* **69,** 725 (1947).
(112b) Woolley, D. W., and Pringle, R. B., *J. Am. Chem. Soc.* **72,** 634 (1950).
(112c) Miller, Z. and Warren, L., *J. Biol. Chem.* **205,** 331 (1953).
(112d) Greenberg, G. R., *J. Am. Chem. Soc.* **74,** 6307 (1952).
(112e) Zakrzewski, S. F., and Nichol, C. A., *J. Biol. Chem.* **205,** 361 (1953).
(112f) Nichol, C. A., Zakrzewski, S. F., and Welch, A. D., *Proc. Soc. Exptl. Biol. Med.* **83,** 272 (1953).
(113) Kidder, G. W., and Dewey, V. C., *J. Biol. Chem.* **179,** 181 (1949).
(114) Brown, G. B., Roll, P. M., Plentl, A. A., and Cavalieri, L. F., *J. Biol. Chem.* **172,** 469 (1948).
(115) Kidder, G. W., Dewey, V. C., Parks, R. E., Jr., and Woodside, G. L., *Science* **109,** 511 (1949).
(116) Gellhorn, A., Engelman, M., Shapiro, D., Graff, S., and Gillespie, H., *Cancer Research* **10,** 170 (1950).
(117) Law, L. W., *Cancer Research* **10,** 186 (1950).
(118) Sugiura, K., Hitchings, G. H., Cavalieri, L. F., and Stock, C. C., *Cancer Research* **10,** 178 (1950).
(119) Stock, C. C., Cavalieri, L. F., Hitchings, G. H., and Buckley, S. M., *Proc. Soc. Exptl. Biol. Med.* **72,** 565 (1949).
(120) Finkelstein, M., and Thomas, P. A., *Cancer Research* **11,** 801 (1951).
(121) Goldin, A., Greenspan, E. M., and Schoenbach, E. B., *J. Natl. Cancer Inst.* **11,** 319 (1950).
(122) Graff, S., Engelman, M., Gillespie, H. B., and Graff, A. M., *Cancer Research* **11,** 388 (1951).
(122a) Mandel, H. G., Carló, P.-E., and Smith, P. K., *J. Biol. Chem.* **206,** 181 (1954).
(122b) Gellhorn, A., Hirshberg, E., and Kells, A., *J. Natl. Cancer Inst.* **14,** 935 (1954).
(123) Hirschberg, E., Kream, J., and Gellhorn, A., *Cancer Research* **12,** 524 (1952).
(123a) Lasnitzki, I., Mathews, R. E. F., and Smith, J. D., *Nature* **173,** 346 (1954).
(124) Woodside, G. L., Kidder, G. W., Dewey, V. C., and Parks, R. E., Jr., *Cancer Research* **13,** 289 (1953).
(125) Goldin, A., Greenspan, E. M., and Schoenbach, E. B., *Cancer* **5,** 153 (1952).

(126) Law, L. W., *Cancer Research* **12,** 871 (1952).
(127) Shapiro, D. M., *Cancer Research* **12,** 713 (1952).
(128) Skipper, H. E., *Cancer* **2,** 475 (1949).
(129) Skipper, H. E., Chapman, J. B., and Bell, M., *Cancer Research* **11,** 109 (1951).
(130) Dietrich, L. S., and Shapiro, D. M., *Cancer Research* **13,** 699 (1953).
(131) Shapiro, D. M., and Fugmann, R. A., *Proc. Soc. Exptl. Biol. Med.* **81,** 239 (1952).
(132) Shapiro, D. M., Kream, J., and Dietrich, L. S., *Proc. Soc. Exptl. Biol. Med.* **81,** 616 (1952).
(133) Bendich, A., Furst, S. S., and Brown, G. B., *J. Biol. Chem.* **185,** 423 (1950).
(134) Clarke, D. A., Philips, F. S., Sternberg, S. S., Stock, C. C., Elion, G. B., and Hitchings, G. H., *Cancer Research* **13,** 593 (1953).
(135) Elion, G. B., Hitchings, G. H., and VanderWerff, H., *J. Biol. Chem.* **192,** 505 (1951).
(135a) Wheeler, G. P., and Skipper, H. E., *J. Biol. Chem.* **205,** 749 (1953).
(135b) Bendich, A., and Brown, G. B., *J. Biol. Chem.* **176,** 1471 (1948).
(135c) Nadel, E. M., and Greenberg, J., *Cancer Research* **13,** 865 (1953).
(136) Stoerck, H. C., and Emerson, G. A., *Proc. Soc. Exptl. Biol. Med.* **70,** 703 (1949).
(137) Aposhian, H. V., and Lambooy, J. P., *Proc. Soc. Exptl. Biol. Med.* **78,** 197 (1951).
(138) Stoerck, H. C., *J. Biol. Chem.* **171,** 437 (1947).
(139) Rhoads, C. P., and Abels, J. C., *J. Am. Med. Assoc.* **121,** 1261 (1943).
(140) Shapiro, D. M., Shils, M. E., and Dietrich, L. S., *Cancer Research* **13,** 703 (1953).
(141) Reif, A. E., and Potter, V. R., *Cancer Research* **13,** 49 (1953).
(142) Boyland, E., *Yale J. Biol. and Med.* **20,** 321 (1948).
(143) Ackermann, W. W., and Potter, V. R., *Proc. Soc. Exptl. Biol. Med.* **72,** 1 (1949).
(144) Levy, H. M., Montañez, G., Murphy, E. A., and Dunn, M. S., *Cancer Research* **13,** 507 (1953).
(145) Quastel, J. H., and Cantero, A., *Nature* **171,** 252 (1953).
(146) Woolley, D. W., "A Study of Antimetabolites." John Wiley and Sons, New York, 1952.
(147) Sokoloff, B., Eddy, W. H., Powella, R., Beaumont, J., and Relos, H., *Cancer Research* **13,** 639 (1953).
(148) Busch, E., *Berlin. klin. Wochschr.* **3,** 245 (1866); **5,** 137 (1868).
(149) Bruns, P., *Bruns' Beitr. klin. Chir.* **3,** 443 (1888).
(150) Rosenrauch, C., *Clinique* **28,** 324 (1933).
(151) Sakhov, G., and Rosiisky, D., *Acta Med. U.R.S.S.* **2,** 145 (1939).
(152) Lilienthal, H., *J. Mt. Sinai Hosp., N. Y.* **10,** 623 (1944).
(153) Loeb, L., *J. Am. Med. Assoc.* **54,** 262 (910).
(154) Council on Pharmacy and Chemistry, *J. Am. Med. Assoc.* **103,** 1067 (1934).
(155) Shear, M. J., and Perrault, A., *J. Natl. Cancer Inst.* **4,** 461 (1944).
(156) Nauts, H. C., Swift, W. E., and Coley, B. L., *Cancer Research* **6,** 205 (1946).
(157) Shear, M. J., and Turner, F. C., *J. Natl. Cancer Inst.* **4,** 81 (1943).
(158) Hartwell, J. L., Shear, M. J., and Adams, J. R., Jr., *J. Natl. Cancer Inst.* **4,** 107 (1943).
(159) Shear, M. J., Perrault, A., and Adams, J. R., Jr., *J. Natl. Cancer Inst.* **4,** 99 (1943).
(160) Zahl, P. A., Hutner, S. H., and Cooper, F. S., *Proc. Exptl. Biol. Med.* **54,** 48, 187 (1943).
(161) Zahl, P. A., Hutner, S. H., Spitz, S., Sugiura, K., and Cooper, F. S., *Am. J. Hyg.* **36,** 224 (1942).

(162) Barrett, M. K., *J. Natl. Cancer Inst.* **2,** 625 (1942).
(163) Gardner, R. E., Bailey, G. H., and Hyde, R. R., *Am. J. Hyg.* **29,** 1 (1939).
(164) Brues, A. M., and Shear, M. J., *J. Natl. Cancer Inst.* **5,** 195 (1944).
(165) Zahl, P. A., *J. Natl. Cancer Inst.* **11,** 279 (1950).
(166) Algire, G. H., and Legallais, F. Y., *J. Natl. Cancer Inst.* **12,** 399 (1951).
(167) Rathgeb, P., and Sylvén, B., *J. Natl. Cancer Inst.* **14,** 1109 (1954).
(168) Creech, H. J., Hamilton, M. A., Nishimura, E. T., and Hankwitz, R. F., *Cancer Research* **8,** 330 (1948).
(169) Ikawa, M., Koepfli, J. B., Mudd, S. G., and Niemann, C., *J. Natl. Cancer Inst.* **13,** 157 (1952).
(170) Reimann, S. P., and Nishimura, E. T., *J. Mich. State Med. Soc.* **48,** 453 (1949).
(171) Roskin, G., *Cancer Research* **6,** 363 (1946).
(172) Hauschka, T. S., Saxe, L. H., Jr., and Blair, M., *J. Natl. Cancer Inst.* **7,** 189 (1947).
(173) Hauschka, T. S., and Goodwin, M. B., *Science* **107,** 600 (1948).
(174) Bateman, J. C., Barberio, J. R., Grice, P. M., Klopp, C. T., and Pierpont, H., *Arch. Internal Med.* **90,** 763 (1952).
(175)Bateman, J. C., Barberio, J. R., Cramer, J. K., and Klopp, C. T., *Antibiotics & Chemotherapy* **3,** 1 (1953).
(176) Reilly, H. C., Stock, C. C., Buckley, S. M., and Clark, D. A., *Cancer Research* **13,** 684 (1953).
(176a) Stock, C. C., Reilly, H. C., Buckley, S. M., Clarke, D. A., and Rhoads, C. P., *Nature* **173,** 71 (1954).
(176b) Reilly, H. C., *Cancer Research* **13,** 821 (1953).
(177) Forkner, C. E., "Leukemia and Allied Disorders." Macmillan Co., New York, 1938.
(178) Flory, C. M., Furth, J., Saxton, J. A., and Reiner, L., *Cancer Research* **3,** 729 (1943).
(179) Warren, C. O., *Am. J. Physiol.* **139,** 719 (1943).
(180) Leiter, J., Downing, V., Hartwell, J. L., and Shear, M. J., *J. Natl. Cancer Inst.* **13,** 365 (1952).
(181) Ludford, R. J., *J. Natl. Cancer Inst.* **6,** 89 (1945).
(182) Ludford, R. J., *Arch. exptl. Zellforsch Gewebezücht.* **18,** 411 (1936).
(183) Brues, A. M., Marble, B. B., and Jackson, E. B., *Am. J. Cancer* **38,** 159 (1940).
(184) Blakeslee, A. F., *J. Genet.* **65,** 72 (1941).
(185) Tennent, R., and Liebow, A. A., *Yale J. Biol. and Med.* **13,** 39 (1940).
(186) Lits, F. J., Kirschbaum, A., and Strong, L. C., *Am. J. Cancer* **34,** 196 (1938).
(187) Boyland, E., and Boyland, M. E., *Biochem. J.* **31,** 454 (1937).
(188) Andervont, H. B., *J. Natl. Cancer Inst.* **1,** 361 (1940).
(189) Boyland, E., and Boyland, M. E., *Biochem. J.* **34,** 280 (1940).
(190) Lettré, H., and Fernholz, H., *Z. physiol. Chem.* **278,** 175 (1943).
(191) Leiter, J., Hartwell, J. L., Kahler, J. S., Kline, I., and Shear, M. J., *J. Natl. Cancer Inst.* **14,** 365 (1953).
(192) Back, A., and Walaszek, E. J., *Cancer Research* **13,** 552 (1953).
(193) Scott, K. G., and Stone, R. S., *Cancer* **3,** 722 (1950).
(194) Belkin, M., *J. Pharmacol. Exptl. Therap.* **93,** 18 (1948).
(194a) Algire, G. H., Legallais, F. Y., and Anderson, B. F., *J. Natl. Cancer Inst.* **14,** 879 (1954).
(195) Waravdekar, V. S., Domingue, A., and Leiter, J., *J. Natl. Cancer Inst.* **13,** 393 (1952).

(195a) Waravdekar, V. S., Paradis, A. D., and Leiter, J., *J. Natl. Cancer Inst.* **14,** 585 (1953).
(196) Leiter, J., Paradis, A. D., and Waravdekar, V. S., *J. Natl. Cancer Inst.* **14,** 177 (1953).
(197) Rivers, T. M., and Pearce, L., *J. Exptl. Med.* **42,** 523 (1925).
(198) Levaditi, C., and Haber, P., *Rev. immunol.* **3,** 5 (1937).
(199) Turner, J. C., and Mulliken, B., *Cancer Research* **7,** 774 (1947).
(200) Turner, J. C., and Mulliken, B., *Cancer* **3,** 354 (1950).
(201) Moore, A. E., *Ann. N. Y. Acad. Sci.* **54,** 945 (1952).
(202) Love, R., Koprowski, H., and Cox, H. R., *Cancer Research* **13,** 350 (1953).
(203) Southam, C. M., and Epstein, J. D., *Cancer Research* **13,** 581 (1953).
(203a) Koprowska, I., and Koprowski, H., *J. Natl. Cancer Inst.* **14,** 627 (1953).
(204) Koprowska, I., and Koprowski, H., *Cancer Research* **13,** 651 (1953).
(205) Moore, A. E., *Cancer* **2,** 525 (1949).
(206) Koprowski, H., and Norton, T. W., *Cancer* **3,** 874 (1950).
(207) Southam, C. M., and Moore, A. E., *Cancer* **5,** 1025 (1952).
(208) Pack, G. T., *Arch. Dermatol. and Syphilol.* **62,** 694 (1950).
(209) Erf, L. A., Tuttle, L. W., and Lawrence, J. H., *Ann. Internal Med.* **15,** 497 (1941).
(210) Kenney, J. M., *Cancer Research* **2,** 130 (1942).
(211) Lawrence, J. H., *Radiology* **35,** 51 (1940).
(212) Lawrence, J. H., Scott, K. G., and Tuttle, L. W., *New Intern. Clinics* (2) **3,** 33 (1939).
(213) Warren, S., *New Engl. J. Med.* **223,** 751 (1940).
(214) Jones, H. B., Chaikoff, I. L., and Lawrence, J. H., *Am. J. Cancer* **40,** 243 (1940).
(215) Lawrence, J. H., and Scott, K. G., *Proc. Soc. Exptl. Biol. Med.* **40,** 694 (1939).
(216) Warren, S., *Cancer Research* **3,** 334 (1943).
(217) Marshak, A., *Science* **92,** 460 (1940).
(218) Brues, A. M., Tracy, M. M., and Cohn, W. E., *J. Biol. Chem.* **155,** 619 (1944).
(219) Scott, K. G., *Cancer Research* **5,** 365 (1945).
(220) Moore, F. D., Tobin, L. H., and Aub, J. C., *J. Clin. Invest.* **22,** 161 (1943).
(221) Chou, S. N., Moore, G. E., and Marvin, J. F., *Science* **115,** 119 (1952).
(222) Zipser, A., and Freedberg, A. S., *Cancer Research* **12,** 867 (1952).
(223) Hahn, P. F., Skipper, H. E., Carothers, E. L., and Bernard, L. J., *Cancer* **4,** 634 (1951).
(224) Hahn, P. F., *in* "A Manual of Artificial Radioisotope Therapy," p. 186. Academic Press, New York, 1951.
(225) Hahn, P. F., Goodell, J. P. B., Sheppard, C. W., Cannon, R. O., and Francis, H. C., *J. Lab. Clin. Med.* **32,** 1442 (1947).
(226) Jones, H. B., Wrobel, C. J., and Lyons, W. R., *J. Clin. Invest.* **28,** 783 (1944).
(227) Lewin, R., Stern, K. G., Ekstein, D. M., Woidowsky, L., and Laszlo, D., *J. Natl. Cancer Inst.* **14,** 45 (1953).
(228) Kenney, J. M., *Cancer Research* **2,** 130 (1942).
(229) Diamond, H. D., and Craver, L. F., *Cancer* **4,** 999 (1951).
(230) Hall, B. E., Watkins, C. H., Hargraves, M. M., and Giffen, H. Z., *Am. J. Med. Sci.* **209,** 712 (1945).
(231) Warren, S., *Am. J. Med. Sci.* **209,** 701 (1945).
(232) Stroebel, C. F., and Hall, B. E., *in* "A Manual of Artificial Radioisotope Therapy," p. 53. Academic Press, New York, 1951.
(233) Evans, T. C., and Quimby, E. H., *Am. J. Roentgenol.* **55,** 55 (1946).
(234) Wollman, S. H., *J. Natl. Cancer Inst.* **13,** 815 (1953).

(235) Wollman, S. H., Scow, R. O., Wagner, B., and Morris, H. P., *J. Natl. Cancer Inst.* **13,** 785 (1953).

(236) Rawson, R. W., and Trunnell, J. B., *in* "A Manual of Artificial Radioisotope Therapy," p. 103. Academic Press, New York, 1951.

(237) Fitzgerald, P. J., Foote, F. W., Jr., and Hill, R. F., *Cancer* **3,** 86 (1950).

(238) Skipper, H. E., Bell, M., and Chapman, J. B., *Cancer Research* **12,** 371 (1952).

(239) Foulds, L., *Ann. Roy. Coll. Surgeons Engl.* **9,** 93 (1951).

THE PROPERTIES OF TUMORS

Chapter VIII

Chemistry of Tumors

Introduction

Every normal tissue, except possibly some rudimentary relics, carries on a specific and unique function. To effect this function, the particular tissue is metabolically (as well as morphologically) differentiated and possesses a chemical structure and pattern of enzymatic catalysis peculiar to itself. The life of the animal or plant thus represents the harmonious integration of a number of individual metabolic mosaics.

The metabolic pattern is as distinguishing a feature of each tissue as is the gross or microscopic morphology and constitutes a functional characterization of the tissue. Each of the enzymes behaves qualitatively in much the same way in all tissues. Quantitatively, however, the distribution of the enzymes varies in each of the tissues, and it is this quantitative distribution which constitutes the individual mosaic of each tissue. Although the pattern itself is based on a quantitative distribution of each of the enzymes, the net biological result of the various catalytic systems in each intact tissue is actually a qualitative one, for these systems are not independent but interrelated, and the particular direction which the individual metabolism of each tissue will take may be dependent upon, among other factors, the relative proportion of rate-determining systems.

In extracts or suspensions of the tissues, in which the possible influence of the gross cellular structure is removed, the activity of each enzyme may be quantitatively determined by employing the appropriate substrate in such concentration as to make the enzyme the limiting rate factor. When many representative systems in each tissue have thus been studied, the tissue may be said to be enzymatically characterized.

Thus, given a suspension or extract of a tissue unknown to the analyst, identification of the tissue can be made on this basis by employing standardized techniques. A tissue extract high in cystine desulfurase activity may have been derived from liver, from kidney, or from pancreas. If, in addition, it has a high arginase and catalase activity, the choice is narrowed to that of either liver or kidney. Finally, if the extract or suspension has a quite high alkaline phosphatase activity, it could only have come from the kidney. Bone tissue and the intestinal mucosa both have a very high activity of alkaline phosphatase, but neither has much catalase or arginase activity. These two tissues may, however, be distinguished, among other methods, by the very high activity of esterase in the intestinal mucosa as contrasted with that of bone. It is possible to distinguish between cardiac and skeletal muscle on the basis of the very high cytochrome oxidase activity in the former tissue. This kind of systematic analysis may be extended to any number of catalytic systems among a wide variety of normal tissues and suggests a method based upon function to supplement the purely morphological characterization.

Tumors, like the normal tissues from which they arise, possess chemical substances, enzymes, etc., and their existence, too, must be at least partially explicable in terms of a chemical and metabolic pattern. A comparison of the pattern of a tumor with that of the normal tissue from which it arose may be expected to reveal the metabolic and chemical changes which are the consequence of neoplasia. Such a comparison has its limitations, for, among other things, the normal tissue under scrutiny is, unlike the tumor, a resting non-growing tissue. To make the comparison more valid, a normal, growing tissue, such as fetal or regenerating tissue, must be included. Such a study has been accomplished by several investigators, employing the following four homologous hepatic tissues: normal, resting liver, hepatoma, fetal liver, and regenerating liver after partial hepatectomy. It is impossible to assume, *a priori*, that the neoplastic transformation of one type of tissue is the same for every other type of tissue, and, therefore, such comparative studies should include all available sets of homologous tissues in as many species as are available, viz., liver and hepatoma, muscle and rhabdomyosarcoma, skin and epidermal carcinoma, prostate and prostatic carcinoma, lymph nodes, and lymphoma, etc. Furthermore, it is equally unwise to assume that each enzyme or chemical component alters during the neoplastic transformation in exactly the same way, and, therefore, as many such systems must be investigated as is possible. Far too many generalizations on tumor metabolism have been expressed in the past on the basis of studies of a single enzyme in a pair of quite unrelated tissues within a single species of animal.

Studies such as those described in the preceding paragraph may be expected to yield (a) an over-all comparison of normal tissues as a class and of cancerous tissues as a class, as well as (b) specific comparisons of individual tissues as each undergoes a neoplastic transformation. Such studies imply and demand a wide scope of operation, necessitating the ready availability of large numbers of diverse types of neoplastic tissues obtained in fresh and unaltered condition and controlled by independent morphologic examination. Cancer is a pathologic manifestation or series of manifestations, the taxonomy of which is within the province of the morphologist and upon which many other pathologic manifestations impinge. The chemical description of a tumor has little meaning unless it is read against the background of pathology and is rigidly controlled by microscopic criteria. There is only one kind of normal tissue, but there may be a number of different neoplasms which arise from this normal tissue. Thus, on a chemical basis, the liver in one mouse is practically identical with the liver in every other mouse (save for possible minor differences among inbred mice strains). But the tumors which arise from the liver may be cholangiomas (arising from the bile ducts), hepatomas (arising from the liver cells), or sarcomas (arising from the connective tissue). Furthermore, the hepatomas may vary considerably in the degree to which they resemble or depart from the characteristics of the normal liver. Similar phenomena occur in nearly all cases of the transformation of normal tissues into tumors and, in the particular case of human tumors, have given rise to elaborate systems of gradation of tumor malignancy.

Tumors may, therefore, differ not only qualitatively within the same type but, in respect to the proportion of tumorous cells, also quantitatively. Thus two tumors of similar type may have in one case 10 % of epithelial cells and in the other case 90 % of epithelial cells. Unless an adequate base line is introduced, comparisons of such tissues are not feasible. Such wide variations generally occur in primary tumors which arise directly from the normal tissue of origin. In experimental cancer research, this difficulty is largely obviated by employing tumors the cellular elements of which have been largely concentrated by many generation transplants. In the case of human tumors, metastases could serve in this connection. However, the limitation in the study of late generation transplants of tumors is sufficiently obvious, because the very concentration of particular cells, by repeated selection or by other means, yields a somewhat artificial picture. It should be remembered that, if tumors are frequently inhomogeneous as to cell type, so too are many normal tissues, for muscle, kidney, etc., are far from being homogeneous in this regard. Indeed, certain transplanted tumors may have a higher proportion of one cell type than many normal tissues.

The lack of cellular homogeneity, whether in normal or in tumor tissues, is hardly a deterrent to investigation, but its recognition is necessary. Such inhomogeneity is uniform among normal tissues of the same kind and almost invariably uniform among tumors in late generation transplants. The chemical study of such tissues presents few difficulties from this angle. On the other hand, the tumor arising directly from the normal tissue, or in relatively early generation transplants when alterations may sometimes occur, requires microscopic criteria as controls for both a qualitative decription of the tumor itself and for a basis of knowledge of the principal contributing factors (proportion of active cells) to the chemical properties of of the tissue.

The historical development of chemical approaches to the characterization of cancerous tissues falls roughly into three parts. The first of these relates to the scattered investigations of pioneer, chiefly clinical, workers, who investigated from time to time a few chemical components in whatever tissues were at hand. Much of this work may be summarized by saying that most tumors appear to have qualitatively the same kind of enzymes and other components as normal tissues. These observations probably led to the misconception frequently repeated in medical texts and in the writings of non-chemical oncologists of the present day, namely, that the chemical properties of tumors are practically indistinguishable from those of normal tissues. Another error arising from this early lack of systematic investigation, and also perpetuated, has been due to generalizations that tumors are higher in certain components and lower in other components on the basis of comparison of such unrelated tissues as liver and sarcomas, or muscle and epitheliomas.

The second phase of chemical studies on tumors may be said to be that of Warburg. It is instructive to assess the approach of Warburg to this area, for it embraced the first scientific attitude toward the handling of the problem. Warburg first developed the most appropriate experimental methods for his studies, then systematically utilized a variety of tissues, reported data on many samples of each tissue under different experimental conditions, and, most important of all, centered his attention on the problem of cancer. These were self-evident approaches and methods, but they were lacking in most of the work in this field. Many of Warburg's interpretations and conclusions have subsequently been modified by later workers but his approach to the subject may serve as a model.

The third, or contemporary, phase may be considered as differing fundamentally from the first two in laying emphasis on the comparative studies of tumors of known histogenesis and of the normal tissues of origin of these tumors. The development of this third phase had to wait for the preparation of suitable carcinogenic agents and for the development of inbred strains of experimental animals. It is an illustration of the increasingly greater interdependence of various workers in the field of cancer research.

The first experimental studies along these lines were conducted by various Japanese workers who had succeeded in inducing hepatomas in experimental animals through the feeding of azo dyes. These studies were further widened and intensified in various laboratories in the United States.

Cancer is a problem of abnormal growth, and it might be expected that study of the energetics of the catalytic systems concerned with intracellular synthetic reactions would be highly revealing. That is, however, a problem for the future. Research on the phenomena of the cancer cell can progress little faster than comparable research on normal cell mechanisms. Thus far, the analytical chemist has only the task of uninspired digging within the cancer cell, of mapping the chemical spectrum of the cancer cell, and, to further mix the metaphor, of running, among other things, the enzyme gamut from A for aconitase to Z for zymase. Up to now no evidence for a "cancer enzyme" has emerged. However, there may be a "cancer pattern" of several enzymes within cancerous tissues. Little by little the outline of the pattern has slowly come into view, and the interesting regularity and uniformity of this pattern has perhaps been even more than might have been expected.

So far as is known, cancer tissues do not differ from normal tissues in the kind of enzymes or other components but rather in their relative amount or activity. It is not known whether the changes in the enzyme pattern of a tumor as compared with the pattern of the tissue of origin precede, follow, or accompany the neoplastic transformation. Enzymes can be studied in tissue extracts, in tissue homogenates, and in surviving tissue slices. More recently, the study of the intracellular particulates obtained by methods of differential centrifugation of the homogenate has been added as a combined morphological and biochemical approach to the characterization of tissues. Each approach has its advantages and disadvantages. The use of extracts or homogenates discloses the potentialities of the tissues under a given set of conditions but is not in itself evidence for the customary activity of the integrated cell. The use of tissue slices permits of more physiological experimental conditions, but the activity as measured depends greatly on the conditions chosen and on the rates of diffusion and permeability of the substrates. Complete freedom from possible aggregation effects and experimental artifacts cannot yet be excluded from the study of differentially centrifuged intracellular particulates. No approach is flawless, but each can be rendered useful for the particular purpose in mind, provided that its limitations are understood. The present purpose is chiefly a comparison of normal and neoplastic tissues, and for the most part those studies have been described wherein such a comparison has been made under identical experimental conditions.

Chemical Concentration or Activity and the Proportion of Active Epithelial Cells in Tumors

Tumors, and particularly primary tumors, are likely to be heterogeneous, being composed of mixtures in various proportions of cellular and noncellular elements, viz., cancer cells, connective tissue cells, fibers, etc. Attempts have been made in various ways to correlate the chemical properties of tumors with the cellularity. These have been chiefly concerned with (a) the visual estimation under the microscope of the number of active cancer cells within a particular area, or (b) the estimation of so-called nucleoprotein phosphorus.

The determination of nucleoprotein phosphorus dates back to Kossel's studies at the end of the last century. Kossel washed ground animal tissues with dilute acid, followed by alcohol and ether (1). The residue was represented as nucleoprotein, and the distribution of the residual phosphorus among various tissues closely followed the order of nucleus-cytoplasmic ratios of the intact tissues. This procedure, with some modifications, has at times been followed up to the present (2-5). It is obviously crude, but it does permit of a rough comparison between the nucleic acid phosphorus of widely varying tissues and provides an approximate index of cellularity in tissues with many non-cellular elements.

There are two objections to the use of the so-called nucleoprotein phosphorus, namely (a) the possibility that non-lipid phosphorus may not be entirely nucleoprotein phosphorus, and (b) the possibility that not all cells within a tumor have the same proportion of nucleic acid. Thus, a tumor composed of a few cells of high nucleic acid content would give the same phosphorus value as a tumor composed of many cells of low nucleic acid content. There is at present no evidence that all cancer cells have the same proportion of nucleic acid, or even that any one kind of cancer cell has the same proportion of this acid at all stages. Indeed, as Caspersson and Santesson have shown by ultraviolet absorption studies, many epithelial tumors have varying proportions of two main kinds of cells, one kind at or near the periphery of the tumor and containing much nucleic acid, and another kind nearer the center of the tumor and relatively poorer in nucleic acid (6).

The visual estimation of tissue entities under the microscope is the most direct and still the most unequivocal method of determining the cellularity of a given tissue. What promises to be a most useful and accurate procedure of determining the relative proportion of the various components present in a sample of tissue is that of Chalkley (7). This method depends upon the repeated estimation, at various settings of the microscope, of the proportion of the various tissue components. The technique is free from subjective error and, with a sufficient number of readings, is capable of attaining a high degree of accuracy in the most heterogeneous types of tissue (Fig. 27).

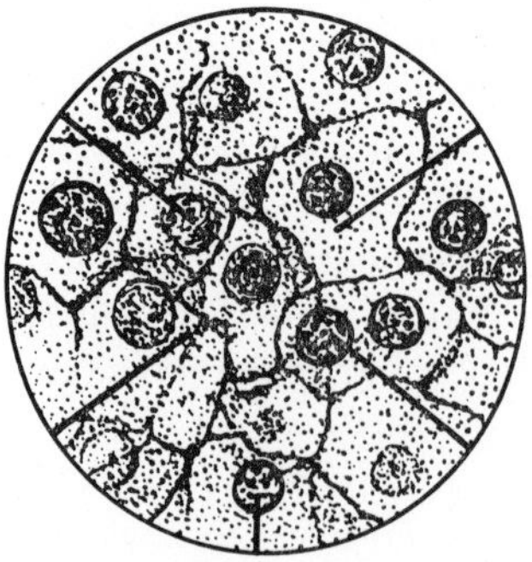

FIG. 27. Point pattern as seen in making measurements. The upper point is focused on a nucleus to serve as reference. The reading is one hit on nucleus, three on cytoplasm (lower right point is over a nucleus, but latter is not in focus). From Chalkley, H. W., *J. Natl. Cancer Inst.* **4**, 47 (1943).

The methods described are rather time-consuming and, to some degree, elaborate. For many purposes it is not necessary to employ them. Thus in working with transplanted tumors in experimental animals, such tissues already contain a very high proportion of cellular elements, and the enzymatic activity may be approximately related to the total weight of the tissue taken. Extracts of tissues may be presumed to have leached out the cellular elements, the fibrous connective tissue remaining undissolved, and, hence, comparisons between tissues may be placed on the basis of total nitrogen or other components per unit aliquot of such extracts. On the other hand, when working with primary tumors, it is sometimes the case that the enzymatic data may vary considerably from one specimen of the same kind of tumor to the other, and only quite careful comparisons, based on fairly exact calculation of the proportion of cellular components, will bring such disparate data into line. Thus, Greenstein *et al.* (8) noted that several specimens of human thyroid adenomas yielded cytochrome oxidase values varying from 0.38 to 1.42. When such data were placed on a basis relative to the proportion of epithelial cells present, a consistent result could be obtained (cf. Fig. 28). Similar findings have been noted by Rosenthal and Drabkin (9) and others.

In addition to the cellular and fibrous elements, tumors have varying areas of central necrosis. These ill-defined areas represent pools of cell-disintegration products, etc., and customarily are larger, the faster the growth rate of the tumor. For enzymatic studies on tumors, the necrotic areas are usually carefully removed and discarded, and the data given in terms of non-necrotic tumor material. In fact, all the data presented in this monograph are on this basis. On the other hand, it may be of interest to know the enzymatic activity per unit of entire tumor mass and not

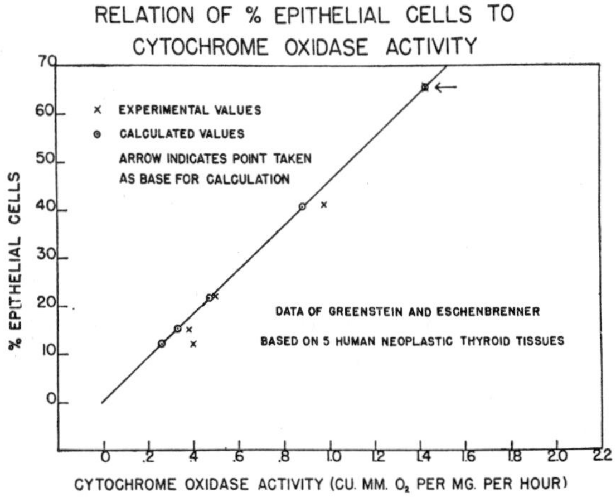

FIG. 28. Enzymatic activity and the proportion of epithelial cells. Courtesy of Dr. H. W. Chalkey.

necessarily of the growing, non-necrotic portion. In this connection, the work of Waldschmidt-Leitz and McDonald demonstrated that with increasing necrosis of transplanted rat tumors the activity per unit weight of total tumor mass of cathepsin, phosphatase, and purine deaminases decreased, that of arginase increased, thereby suggesting that the former three enzymes existed for the most part in the cellular elements of the tumors, whereas arginase tended to accumulate in the necrotic areas (10). The distribution of hexone bases, of purines, and of monoamino acids is nearly identical in the growing and in the necrotic areas of the Jensen rat sarcoma (11), whereas the content of citric acid in milligrams per 100 g. wet weight is nearly ten times as great in the necrotic as in the viable portion of the Walker 256 tumor (12).

All methods of computing a base line for the comparison of the chemical properties of different sorts of tissues have some disadvantages, whether from the standpoint of essential accuracy or of the time consumed in their operation. The choice which the investigator makes is a matter of personal discretion. As no method is completely perfect, it may be assumed that claims of differences in chemical properties between different tissues will carry more conviction, the greater such differences appear to be. Precisely because most base lines of comparison are weak, no claim of "greater than" or "less than" should be made unless the evidence in its favor is overwhelming. That abhorrent phrase, "a statistically significant difference," may have validity when computing the behavior of a very large population but has little meaning when comparing the relative activity or concentration of a chemical hidden together with scores of others within some half-dozen samples of tissues. It is possible that very small differences between tissues may indeed be crucial, but their detection is a matter of refinement in experimental technique rather than of calculations based upon probability. The quantitative chemical analysis of catalytic and other systems within raw tissues is an admittedly hazardous undertaking, and the results therefrom can only be conservatively described.

The Metabolism of Normal Tissues, of Primary Tumors, and of Transplanted Tumors

In the comparison of the properties of tissues in normal and neoplastic states it is possible to recognize, roughly, several stages. First, there is the normal tissue of origin of the tumor. Second, there is the precancerous stage of this normal tissue, viz., a possible stage, or stages, of transition between the normal and the primary neoplastic states. Third, there is the primary neoplasm, which may be benign or malignant in nature. If benign, there is the possibility of stage four, namely, the malignant tumor which arises from the preceding primary benign tumor. Five, there is the metastasis of the tumor within the same host, or the transplant of the tumor to new hosts. Furthermore, there may be substages in the last-mentioned category whereby the transplanted tumor may alter from one type into another through successive generation transplants.

1. *The Normal Tissue.* The properties of the normal tissue of origin of the tumor form the base line of comparison with the altered states characteristic of the tumor. These properties are generally invariable over the greater part of the life span of the host.

2. *The Normal Tissue during the Preneoplastic State.* One of the important questions occurring in the problem of carcinogenesis is whether the neoplastic state arises suddenly and abruptly or whether there is a preceding period of gradual transition of the normal tissue to this state. To answer this question even partially, a knowledge of the properties of the normal tissue and of the primary neoplasm is essential. If such properties vary widely between the two states, a study of the normal tissue during the period when a carcinogenic agent is applied may be expected to reveal possible stages of transition. Such precancerous tissues may be obtained either by biopsy or by the sacrifice of a few animals from time to time among a large number under treatment by the carcinogenic agent. The results obtained in this sort of study have been somewhat conflicting. A partial listing follows.

Ascorbic Acid Levels. The administration of 1,2,5,6-dibenzanthracene (13), and of 4-dimethylaminoazobenzene, 2-acetaminofluorene, 7-hydroxy-2-acetaminofluorene, and azobenzene (14) results in a rise in hepatic ascorbic acid in rats and in mice. The phenomenon may be considered to be associated in part with an increased metabolic activity of the liver incident to detoxication processes.

Hepatomas in Rats. Normal liver has a low rate, hepatoma a high rate, of anaerobic glycolysis. Nakatani *et al.* (15) observed that the livers of rats fed 4-dimethylaminoazobenzene showed a gradual increase in anaerobic glycolysis during the period of feeding. Orr and Stickland could not confirm this observation (16). Normal rat liver has a relatively low, rat hepatoma an extremely high, alkaline phosphatase activity. Woodard (17) noted that the average alkaline phosphatase activity of the former tissue was 0.16 unit, that of the latter was 1.6 units, whereas the activity of the precancerous liver during the period of feeding of the azo dye was 0.4 unit. That this increase in alkaline phosphatase activity during azo dye feeding may be localized in areas of rapidly proliferating biliary epithelium and infiltrating leukocytes, and not in the hepatoma cells themselves, forms a concept advanced by Pearson, Novikoff, and Morrione (18) on the basis of their histochemical studies on the livers of rats. Even on the assumption that the histochemical phosphatase test can be employed to distinguish morphological structures, it is difficult to accept this concept, since the transplanted hepatomas of the rat, carried through many generation transplants, retain their high and constant alkaline phosphatase activity from one generation to the next. It would be hard to assume the same amount of proliferating biliary epithelium and infiltrating leukocytes in each transplant. Furthermore, Mulay and Firminger (19) noted a slightly higher alkaline phosphatase value for hepatomas than for cholangioma tissue. As in the experiments of Woodard mentioned above, these authors noted an increase in the alkaline phosphatase of the livers of rats fed azo dyes prior to the appearance of tumors. Unlike the development of the rat hepatoma, in the development of the Lucké frog renal carcinoma, acid phosphatase considerably increases in activity, whereas alkaline phosphatase markedly diminishes (20).

The esterase activity of rat liver appears to remain at the normal level throughout the period of feeding by the host of 4-dimethylaminoazobenzene, dropping in value only when the tumor makes its appearance (21). On the other hand, the levels of uricase (22) and of cathepsin (casein at pH 5) (21) appeared to rise during the period of dye feeding and dropped to values lower than the normal only when the tumor appeared. A still-different picture emerged when the level of asparaginase activity was followed, for, with feeding of the dye, the activity of this enzyme in the liver steadily diminished to that low level characteristic of the tumor (23). The diminution of these enzymes in the liver during feeding of the dye could be prevented by inclusion in the diet of liver powder, a reflection no doubt of the protective action of the riboflavin present in this material.

The proportion of arginine, as followed by the extent of the Sakaguchi reaction on the whole livers, appears to rise progressively during the period of feeding of the dye, from an average value of 414 mg. at the beginning to 530 mg. at the end of 100 days; the value for the tumor is 555 mg. (24). During this period of time the specific gravity of the liver progressively diminishes (25) from 1.088 to 1.067, the value of 1.060 being characteristic of the tumor. Since both the water and lipoid contents of the liver rise in the preneoplastic phase, this change in the specific gravity of the liver is readily interpretable.

The incorporation of P^{32} can be roughly correlated with the degree of mitotic activity of the liver, as shown in Fig. 29, which represents data on the livers of normal rats, of rats fed 3′-methyl-4-dimethylaminoazobenzene, and on the hepatomas which ultimately develop (26).

Hepatic xanthine oxidase, which is a flavoprotein enzyme, diminishes in level during the feeding of 4-dimethylaminoazobenzene, but a similar decrease can also be observed by placing the rats on a purified 21% casein diet. However, a difference between the effects of the two agencies may be noted in the corresponding levels of blood xanthine oxidase, which also drops during depletion of the liver enzyme by feeding the azo dye, but which rises during feeding of the pure protein (27). Choline oxidase (28) of the

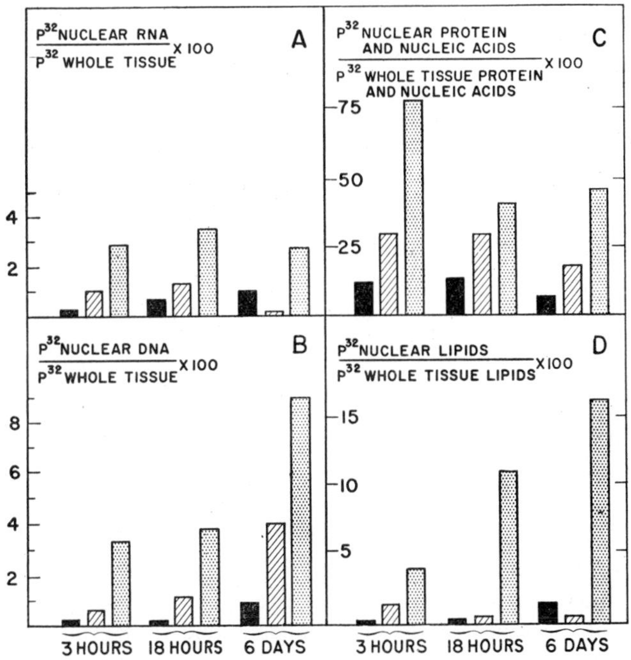

FIG. 29. Per cent uptake of P^{32} in nuclear fractions with respect to whole-tissue homogenate or fractions. Solid, shaded, and unshaded areas represent normal, precancerous, and tumor liver tissue in rats fed 3′-methyl-4-dimethylaminoazobenzene. From Griffin, A. C., Cunningham, L., Brandt, E. L., and Kupke, D. W., *Cancer* **4**, 410 (1950).

rat liver also diminishes during the feeding of 3′-methyl-4-dimethylaminoazobenzene, being quite rapid from the very beginning of the feeding period (25 % of normal after only 14 days), and finally dropping to less than 5 % of that of the normal liver. At pH 7.2 or 7.8, normal livers oxidize choline only to betaine, whereas the preneoplastic liver produces more betaine aldehyde; at pH 6.7, the former produces both betaine and its aldehyde, whereas the latter oxidizes choline little if at all.

Cantero and his colleagues (29) have noted that the hepatic depolymerases for both ribonucleic and deoxyribonucleic acids rise to a maximum value somewhere at the half-way mark during the course of feeding 4-dimethylaminoazobenzene to rats and decrease thereafter to the normal value at the hepatoma stage. This maximum period apparently corresponds with the development of a cirrhotic stage of the liver.

One of the most interesting developments in this area of cancer research has been the determination of the enzymes associated with each of the particulate components in tissue homogenates (cf. 30). Thus the whole-tissue homogenate has been fractionated by differential centrifugation into nuclei (about 500 × g), large granules or mitochondria (about 3000 × g), and small granules or microsomes (about 20,000 × g), leaving in the final supernatant solution proteins too small to be sedimented at these speeds. The application of these techniques to the tissues of animals undergoing carcinogenesis has been an active area of investigation. Because of the considerable amount of work involved, the greater part of these studies has been conducted on rat livers at a single period after feeding the azo dyes, generally 4 to 6 weeks. In many cases dyes of different potency were employed, and in all cases the average composition of the liver fractions after exposure to the dye for about 4 weeks approached that of the corresponding tumor fractions which arose at a later date. One of the most important general observations made from these studies was that cell divisions can occur in which the rate of accumulation of one cell constituent does not keep pace with the rate of cell division; this conclusion, however, holds not only during carcinogenesis but also during normal regenerative processes (31).

Figures 30 to 33 are representative of data on the effect of feeding azo dyes of varying potency on certain intracellular liver fractions of the rat (32). These dyes were fed for a period of 4 weeks, and the effects induced were roughly proportional to the potency of the dyes, as expected. There was an increase in protein and deoxyribonucleic acid in the nuclear fraction, decreases in the protein, riboflavin (except when the 2-methyl derivative of the azo dye was used) and ribonucleic acid in the large granule fraction, and increases in ribonucleic acid in the supernatant, soluble fraction. Protein-bound azo dye was present in each of the fractions, being greatest in the supernatant fluid. Several of these findings have also been noted

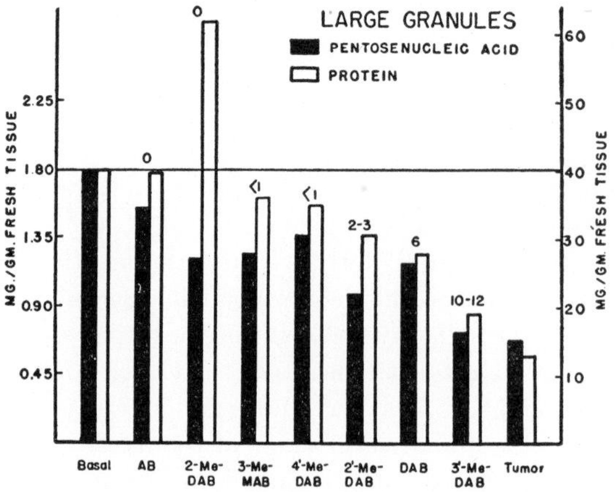

FIG. 30. Levels of ribonucleic acid and protein in the large-granule fraction from livers of rats fed various aminoazo dyes, and from liver tumors induced by 4-dimethylaminoazobenzene. From Price, J. M., Miller, E. C., Miller, J. A., and Weber, G. M., *Cancer Research* **10**, 18 (1950).

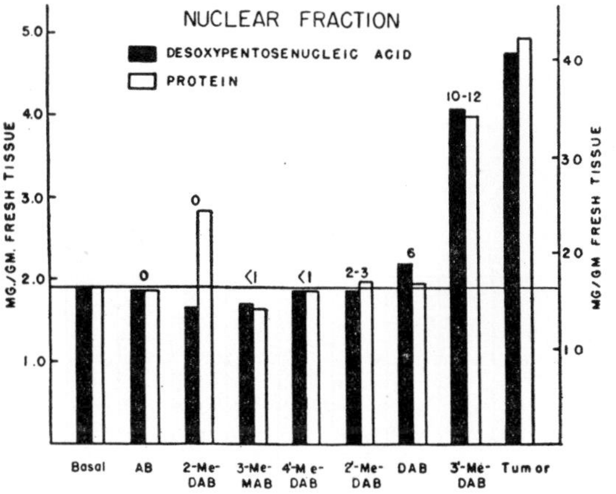

FIG. 31. Levels of deoxyribonucleic acid and protein in the nuclear fraction from livers of rats fed various aminoazo dyes, and from liver tumors induced by 4-dimethylaminoazobenzene. From Price, J. M., Miller, E. C., Miller, J. A., and Weber, G. M., *Cancer Research* **10,** 18 (1950).

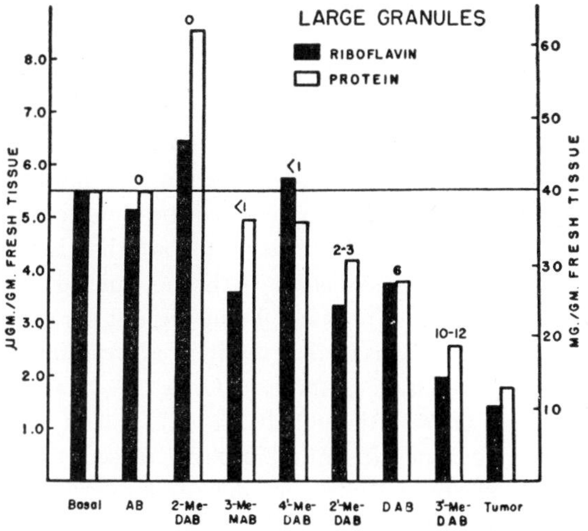

FIG. 32. Levels of riboflavin and protein in the large-granule fraction from livers of rats fed various aminoazo dyes, and from liver tumors induced by 4-dimethylaminoazobenzene. From Price, J. M., Miller, E. C., Miller, J. A., and Weber, G. M., *Cancer Research* **10,** 18 (1950).

by others (33). Assays for succinoxidase and oxalacetate oxidase systems (34) showed that the former correlated well with the values for mitochondrial or large-granule protein, in accordance with the fact that the enzyme is located on this fraction. Thus the succinoxidase activity decreased with increasing carcinogenicity within the C-methyl series of azo dye deriva-

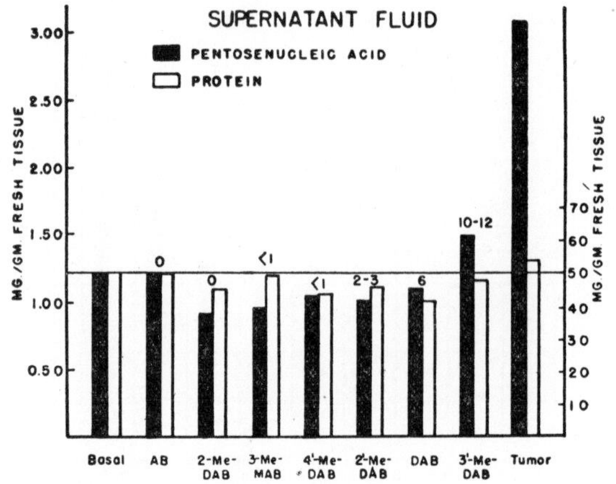

FIG. 33. Levels of ribonucleic acid and protein in the supernatant fluid fraction from livers of rats fed various aminoazo dyes, and from liver tumors induced by 4-dimethylaminoazobenzene. From Price, J. M., Miller, E. C., Miller, J. A., and Weber, G. M., *Cancer Research* **10,** 18 (1950).

tives but increased in the peculiar case of the 2-methyl derivative which produces an increase in mitochondrial protein. No change in the level of the oxalacetate oxidase system was noted in the same samples. The increase in mitochondria in the case of the non-carcinogenic 2-methyl-4-dimethylaminoazobenzene suggests that the number of these forms may be the resultant of independent cell and mitochondrial multiplication. The various dyes apparently influence these separate factors in different ways.

In this connection it is of interest to point out that in liver practically all the deoxyribonucleate is associated with the nuclear fraction, ribonucleic acid is present in all the fractions, being highest per gram of protein in the small granules, and riboflavin is present in all fractions, being highest per gram of protein in the large granules. On a 12% casein diet, the number of nuclei per gram of fresh tissue $\times 10^{-6}$ is 137, and on feeding 3'-methyl-4-dimethylaminoazobenzene this number is increased to 336; the calculated amount of deoxyribonucleate per nucleus in micrograms $\times 10^{6}$ in the former case is 14.0, and in the latter 11.4 (32). Thus, it is the number of nuclei rather than their deoxyribonucleate content which is altered by ingestion by the animal of the carcinogen. Like riboflavin, vitamin B_6 is highest in the large-granule fraction, decreases during the ingestion by the rat of 4-dimethylaminoazobenzene, and is reduced to about one-fifth the normal value in the large granules of the liver tumor (in terms of weight of fresh tissue) (35), a reflection of the reduction in the amount of this fraction in the tumor; on the basis of unit weight of protein in this fraction, there is little change. Feeding the dye also results in an increase of glutamic acid in the nuclear proteins, of arginine in the large-granule proteins, and of cystine and tryptophan in the supernatant fluid proteins, while the proteins in each fraction of the liver tumor contain less methionine and more cystine than the proteins in the corresponding fractions of normal liver (36). It cannot be said, however, that these changes in amino acid levels are of any considerable order of magnitude.

The difference in the effect of the 2-methyl (non-carcinogenic) and the 3′-methyl (highly carcinogenic) derivatives of 4-dimethylaminoazobenzene is of considerable significance. Striebich, Shelton, and Schneider (37) demonstrated by direct counting procedures a large increase in the number of mitochondria induced by the former dye, and a marked decrease induced by the latter dye. The increase of mitochondria in the former case occurred without any increase in cellularity of the liver. It was noted by Potter and his colleagues (34) that, although succinoxidase increased proportionately to the increase in mitochondria, oxalacetate oxidase did not. Similarly, Schneider *et al.* (38) noted that, although total nitrogen content and cytochrome c reductase actively increased in the livers of animals fed the 2-methyl derivative, the increase was in no way as great as the increase in mitochondrial numbers, and the uricase, octanoxidase, and nuclease activities of these livers did not increase at all. The increase in numbers of mitochondria under these conditions apparently did not result in an increase in "normal" mitochondria. On the other hand, the decrease in mitochondria as a result of feeding the 3′-methyl derivative gave fewer but still "normal" mitochondria. The viewpoint of these authors (38) is that the preneoplastic liver cell contains fewer mitochondria of approximately normal biochemical composition, whereas the liver tumor cell contains the same number of mitochondria of greatly altered biochemical properties.

In order to see whether the changes in the morphological fractions of the liver could be correlated with the carcinogenic action of the dye, Price *et al.* (39) studied the effect of 4-dimethylaminoazobenzene on two species which are resistant to the dye, namely, mice, in which liver tumors develop only very slowly, and hamsters, in which liver tumors never develop. They were fed the dye for 4 months, in contrast with analogous studies on rats fed for only 4 weeks. As almost expected, the composition of the liver fractions of the hamster was unaltered from the normal. On the other hand, the dye produced changes in the relative composition of the mouse liver similar to those in the liver of the rat. Thus, the increase in the protein content of the nuclear fraction and the decrease in the protein content of the mitochondria were almost of the same magnitude as found in the rat. In both species there was a decrease in the ribonucleic acid of large and small granules, and a decrease in riboflavin and vitamin B_6 in the large granules. However, an increase in protein and decrease in ribonucleate in the supernatant fluid were not found in the livers of rats fed the dye.

Another type of control study has involved the use of regenerating rat liver after partial hepatectomy, a tissue of fast but controlled growth rate. Novikoff and Potter (40), as well as Stowell (41), found a considerable increase in ribonucleic acid in whole regenerating liver, with a maximum at 2 to 3 days after the operation. Brues, Drury, and Brues (42) demonstrated that there is no significant increase in the number of hepatic cells during the first day of regeneration, although the liver increases in weight by 50 to 60 %, and Bucher, Scott, and Aub (43) obtained evidence for a humoral mechanism for control of liver cell mitoses when they found an increased rate of mitosis in the non-operated parabiotic partner of a partially hepatectomized rat. During the first 24 hours of regeneration, the average liver cell showed an increase of 83 % in deoxyribonucleate, an increase of 62 % in ribonucleate, and an increase of 17 % in protein N (44). Thereafter, the deoxyribonucleate and ribonucleate returned to normal, and the protein content decreased. The initial increases in ribonucleate occurred in the supernatant and small-granule fraction, and those of the protein in the nuclear and small-granule fractions. Thus, during the first few days of rapid growth, the ratio of ribonucleate to protein increased in all fractions. The relative amounts of protein and ribonucleate in the various fractions of the liver tumor cells are quite different from either normal or regenerating liver, for in these cells the ratios of these constituents is normal in the nuclear and small-granule fractions, and abnormal in the large-granule and supernatant fluid fractions. Normal, regenerating, and neoplastic liver all

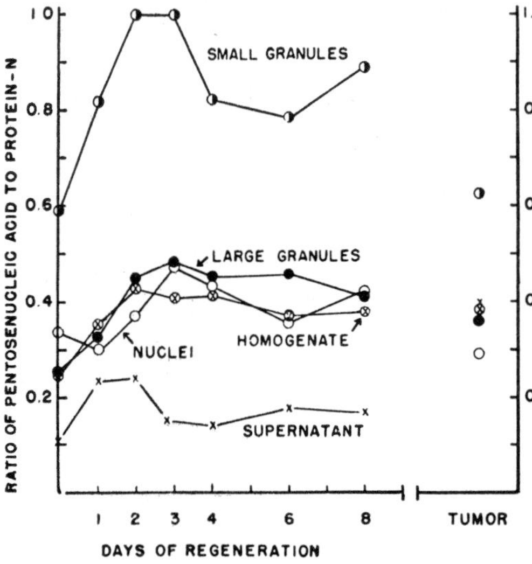

FIG. 34. Ratio of ribonucleic acid to protein nitrogen in normal and regenerating liver and in liver tumors. From Price, J. M., and Laird, A. K., *Cancer Research* **10**, 650 (1950).

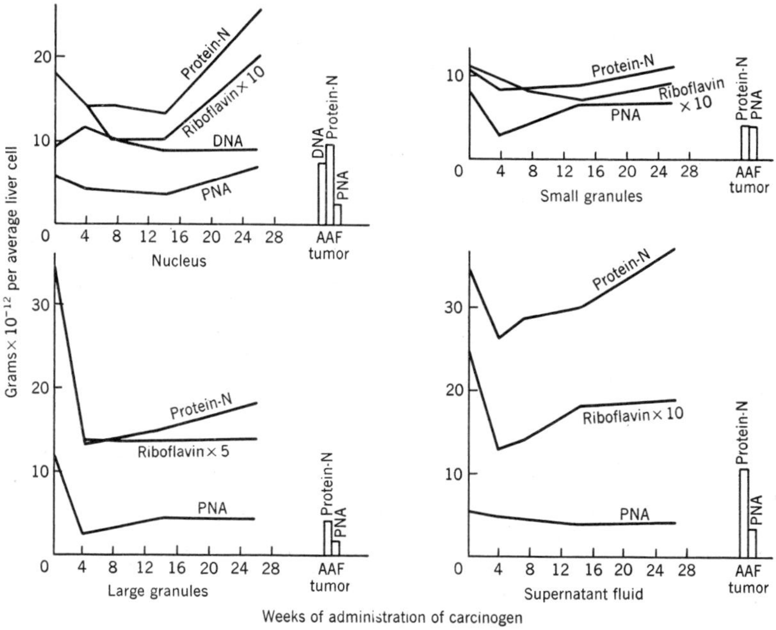

FIG. 35. Changes in cell constituents of the livers of rats fed 2-acetylaminofluorene. From Laird, A. K., and Miller, E. C., *Cancer Research* **13**, 464 (1953).

have points of resemblance and of difference, and the tumor is not simply a tissue with a rapid growth rate (cf. Fig. 34).

Not only the azo dyes but also 2-acetylaminofluorene produces marked biochemical effects in the liver of the host animal. Thus Griffin *et al.* (45) found that the concentrations of total nitrogen, riboflavin, and ribonucleic acid decreased on feeding this compound to levels of the final tumor, whereas the deoxyribonucleate remained nearly normal. Similar decreases were reported by others (46). As shown in Fig. 35, there is considerable depletion in all of the intracellular fractions at about 4 weeks. These minimum values were either maintained or slowly rose toward the normal. As a rule, the tumor cells contained about half as much of each constituent as was found in the liver cells after 4 weeks of treatment. The damaged cells, the tumor cells, and the normal cells contained about the same amount of deoxyribonucleic acid; however, there was in contrast with all other constituents a rise in its value at 4 weeks. In general the picture of acetaminofluorene carcinogenesis is similar to that shown by the active azo dyes (31).

Another liver carcinogen is carbon tetrachloride, and the chemical changes in mouse liver produced by this compound have been found by Stowell and his associates (47–49) to include a marked decrease, after a single feeding, of succinoxidase, cytochrome oxidase, esterase, and acid and alkaline phosphatase. Resynthesis of new enzyme occurred during the regenerative phase, all enzymes studied with exception of cytochrome oxidase being restored rapidly. Considerable overlapping between the initial necrosis and subsequent regeneration is evident under these conditions, and the enzyme levels are consequently difficult to apprehend unless histological criteria are employed.

Studies of the electrochemical properties of the soluble proteins of the livers of rats fed the azo dyes have shown that the electrophoretic patterns of the preneoplastic and normal liver proteins are nearly indistinguishable (50, 51). The authors cited have demonstrated that the electrophoretic pattern of the eventual liver tumor is quite different, an increase in proportion of faster-moving components taking place apparently at the expense of the slower-migrating components of the normal (or preneoplastic) liver. With different experimental conditions than those used above, e.g., the use of the whole homogenate from frozen livers of female rats instead of only the soluble fraction from fresh liver homogenates of male rats, and with buffers of different composition and pH, another group of investigators reported that the electrophoretic pattern of the preneoplastic liver bore a closer resemblance to that of the tumor (increase in faster and decrease in slower components) than to that of normal liver (52). The claim was also made that the liver homogenates of young, rapidly growing rats also showed this "tumor pattern," although Sorof, Claus, and Cohen (53) showed that the soluble fraction from rapidly growing regenerating liver gave an electrophoretic pattern indistinguishable from the normal. Like all conflicting results which depend basically on differences in experimental techniques and conditions, any attempt to reconcile them would be futile. The important point of agreement, apparently, is that of the remarkably uniform electrophoretic pattern which is exhibited by the soluble proteins of a large variety of tumors.

The major portion of the soluble protein-bound azo dyes is associated with proteins representing about one-half of the supernatant proteins, or about one-fourth of the proteins of rat liver (53), and which sediment as a symmetrical single component with 3.6 S. Electrophoretic analysis at pH 8.6 indicated the presence of two components, one of them previously referred to as "h," representing about one-fourth of the total.

Electrophoretic analyses of the soluble proteins of the rat liver during regeneration and after a 9-day fast indicate the absence of a specific or preferential reserve protein pool, for the pattern does not change. No one of the nine electrophoretic components of the liver is metabolically more labile than the others, a finding in agreement with that of Luck (54), who observed that the proteins of various liver fractions were diminished relatively proportionately during inanition.

During administration of 4-dimethylaminoazobenzene to rats, the albumin of the blood plasma markedly diminishes and the γ-globulin equally markedly increases (55, 56). Similar variations in albumin and γ-globulin concentrations are observed after partial hepatectomy (56, 57) but in this case the α- and β-globulins also appear to increase in concentration (56).

During the feeding of the rat with 4-dimethylaminoazobenzene, there is a progressive diminution in the catalase activity of the liver (58, 59), which may be related to the formation of protein-bound dye. It is for this reason that a control study of the liver catalase level of the rabbit or guinea pig fed the dye would have been of interest, since the kidney catalase of the dye-fed rat did not change in its activity (58).

Pulmonary Tumors in Mice. The alkaline phosphatase activity of the normal lung tissue of *A* strain mice is roughly four times that of the pulmonary tumors which develop from this tissue. Greenstein and Shimkin (cf. 60) studied the lungs of mice which had been injected intravenously with methylcholanthrene from the time of injection until the time when nodules just appeared 6 weeks later. The alkaline phosphatase activity of the lungs of such treated mice was consistently that characteristic of normal lung tissue.

Epidermal Carcinoma in Mice. Carruthers and Suntzeff (61) noted that, after an application of a solution of methylcholanthrene to the skin of mice, there was a progressive fall in the content of certain mineral constituents (calcium, iron, etc.) until constant low values were reached characteristic of the skin cancer. These are diffusible constituents, and their alteration may possibly be accomplished by toxic agents unrelated to carcinogenic capacity. Nevertheless, the results are striking, and, in general, the changes in the early (precancerous) stages are in a direction taken by the ultimate tumor (i.e. low Ca, Fe, etc.) (Fig. 36). In the carcinomas so produced, alkaline phosphatase activity was high both in the stroma and in epidermal cells adjacent to the stroma but was almost absent from cells far removed (62). Only biotin of the B vitamins studied decreased in the skin as a result of methylcholanthrene treatment (63).

Indeed, these studies in Cowdry's laboratory (cf. 64) of progressive changes in the epidermis during methylcholanthrene carcinogenesis form one of the most highly organized series of investigations in cancer research. Figure 37, from data of Carruthers (65), illustrates further the fate of several enzyme systems during the course of epidermal carcinogenesis. Only cytochrome oxidase rises significantly prior to cancer formation. Studies of the amino acid composition of the dried epidermal tissues by Roberts and his associates are described in Table 63 (66). It cannot be said that any striking changes in the proportion of the amino acids occur during the neoplastic change of the tissue, or in the cancer itself compared with the normal tissue of origin. In this respect, the findings are consistent with those of others who have noted the rather similar amino acid

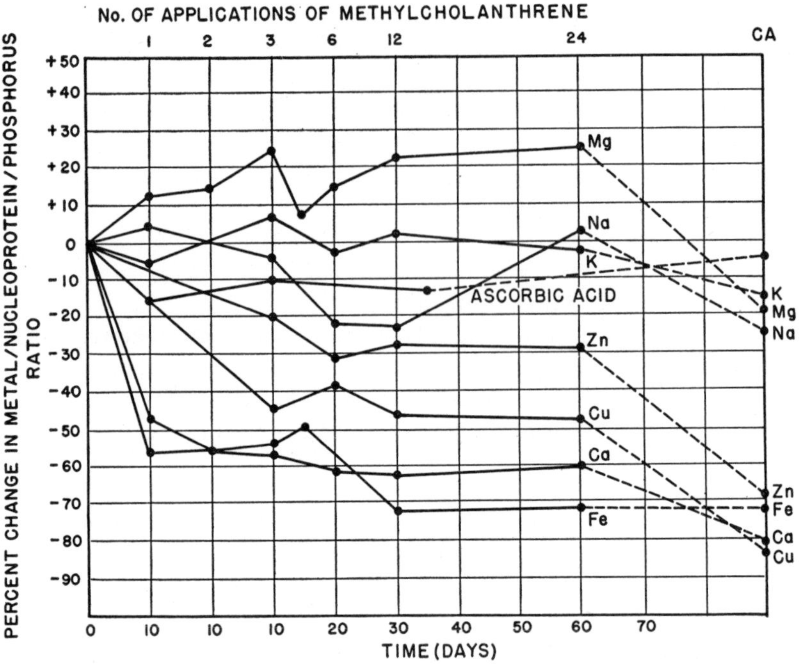

FIG. 36. Changes in the concentration of various components of the mouse skin in epidermal carcinogenesis induced by methylcholanthrene. CA represents carcinoma. The dotted lines designate the change from late hyperplastic epidermis to carcinoma. From Carruthers, C., and Suntzeff, V., *J. Biol. Chem.* **159**, 647 (1945). Similar to these findings was the marked and rapid reduction in epidermal lipid after even a single application of methylcholanthrene to the skin (68).

patterns for most animal proteins, whether normal or neoplastic (cf. 67 and below).

On the whole, the study of normal tissues during precancerous periods is not very decisive. If all the cells of a given tissue developed so that the entire tissue turned into a tumor, there might be a more logical basis for such study. However, the primary tumor rarely involves the entire normal organ and usually appears singly or in nodules in various areas. It would appear as if only a relatively few cells of the normal tissue had undergone a neoplastic transformation. The analyst cannot predetermine which cells of a given tissue will undergo this transformation, and, hence, he is compelled to study the entire tissue. Thus, if the few cells which form the tumor later actually alter before the tumor appears, the recognition of their presence through the determination of the properties of the entire tissue mass may well be obscured by the resulting dilution. That only a few cells in a normal tissue undergo alteration is indicated by the fact that the tissue adjacent to the tumor is, with few exceptions, almost

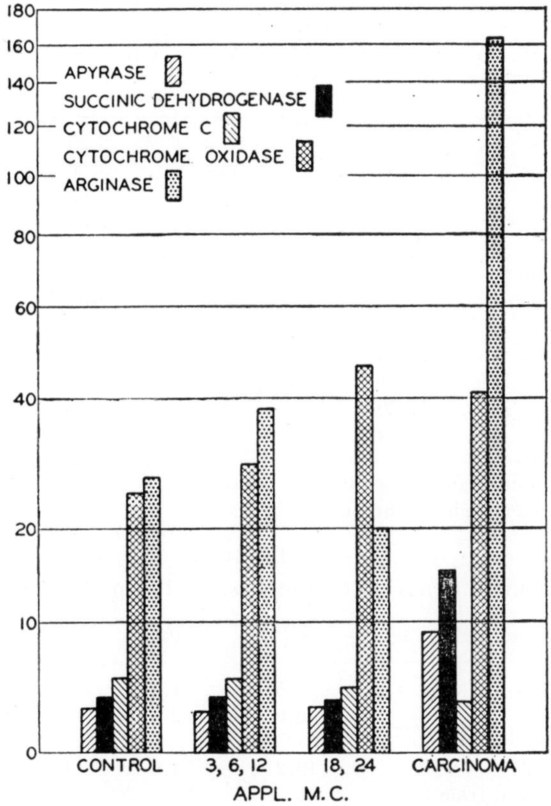

FIG. 37. Levels of enzyme activity after 3, 6, and 12 weeks, after 18 to 24 weeks and after the epidermis has become cancerous as a result of methylcholanthrene application. From Carruthers, C., *Cancer Research* **10**, 255 (1950).

invariably indistinguishable in chemical properties from that of normal tissue. It is also possible that precancerous events occur uniformly throughout all the cells of the tissue for which either contemporary methods of chemical analysis are as yet too crude to recognize, or else such events actually occur without significant changes in the chemical properties of individual enzyme systems within these cells. Where the chemical properties of the cancer differ considerably from those of the normal cells, the presence of a few cancer cells may escape histologic detection and yet be chemically revealed in the analysis of the whole tissue. The only useful approach by which this whole problem can ultimately be solved is through the use of histochemical methods of analysis of tissues undergoing carcinogenesis. At the present time, it is difficult to avoid the tentative impression that the neoplastic transformation is relatively abrupt and sudden.

3–4. *The Primary Tumor.* The chemical properties of a tumor differ in

TABLE 63

CONTENT OF INDIVIDUAL AMINO ACIDS[1] (66)

Amino acid	Normal skin	Benzene alone	Benzene + MCA[2]	Skin carcinoma
Lysine	5.15	5.08	6.29	8.18
Isoleucine	2.65	2.58	3.26	3.83
Leucine	4.17	4.19	4.69	5.28
Methionine	0.91	0.74	1.09	1.20
Valine	2.84	3.05	3.23	3.86
Phenylalanine	1.46	1.39	1.95	1.89
Threonine	2.43	2.26	2.62	3.17
Histidine	3.33	3.24	3.57	3.40
Glutamic acid	7.90	7.86	8.65	7.72
Cystine	1.51	2.38	2.06	1.42
Arginine	11.50	13.79	13.53	11.34
Tryptophan	0.98	1.71	1.10	1.60

[1] In terms of milligrams N per 100 mg. total N.

[2] MCA = 20-methylcholanthrene.

TABLE 64

GLYCOLYTIC BEHAVIOR OF HOMOLOGOUS RABBIT TISSUE (69)

Tissue	$Q_A^{N_2}$[1]	$Q_A^{O_2}$[2]	*R.Q.*	Q_{O_2}
Normal skin	1.5[3]	1.4	0.89	1.0
Benign Shope virus papilloma	6.9	2.8	0.84	3.0
Transplanted V-2 carcinoma derived from papilloma	10.2	4.6	0.67	3.2
Transplanted Brown-Pearce carcinoma	11.8	—	—	—

[1] Anaerobic glycolysis.

[2] Aerobic glycolysis.

[3] On the basis of epidermal cells this value would approach that of the papilloma

TABLE 65

METABOLISM OF HUMAN ENDOMETRIUM (70)

State of tissue	Q_{O_2}	$Q_A^{O_2}$	$Q_A^{N_2}$
Proliferative phase	16.9	1.4	9.7
Secretory phase	16.3	1.0	8.5
Decidua	16.4	0.8	14.2
Hyperplasia	16.5	1.1	11.2
Adenomyosis[1]	16.5	1.2	10.6
Carcinoma	13.3	10.0	14.2

[1] Benign lesion, between normal and malignant growth states.

varying degree among themselves from those of the normal tissue of origin. Some functions are increased when a normal tissue becomes neoplastic, others decrease, and still others are unaltered. The evidence for these differences forms the bulk of the present chapter and is described below.

The primary neoplasm may be benign in nature, in which case it differs relatively little from the normal tissue of origin. Thus, Berenblum *et al.* (5) observed that there was little difference in the glycolyzing capacity of normal rabbit skin and of benign skin papillomas induced with the Shope virus. The benign tumor can, however, undergo a malignant transformation and the properties of the malignant tumor, compared with the benign tumor, differ more on the whole than do the properties of the benign tumor and the normal tissue of origin. This is illustrated in Tables 64 and 65.

The comparison of a transplanted malignant tumor in the rabbit with a primary papilloma, even though the former was originally derived from the latter, may not be entirely proper. As shown below, there may be differences alone between a primary and a transplanted tumor of the same kind. Nevertheless, the differences observed between the rabbit skin, papilloma, and transplanted V2 carcinoma depicted in Table 64 are more or less consistent with differences noted between primary benign and malignant lesions (*vide ultra*). Greenstein *et al.* noted that the oxidative capacity of a human rectal adenoma differed markedly from that of rectal adenocarcinoma, values for the former tissue falling within the range of normal tissues, values for the latter tissue falling within the range characteristic of malignant lesions (8). It is, nevertheless, interesting to note from Table 64 that there are distinguishable differences in certain cases between the virus-induced papilloma and the carcinoma, and in these differences the benign papilloma appears to stand somewhere between the normal tissue on one hand and the the malignant carcinoma on the other.

5. *The Transplanted Tumor.* The tumor which arises primarily at a certain focus within a normal tissue will possess certain chemical properties which may be either similar to or quite different from those of the tissue of origin. When the tumor is transplanted into a new host animal, generally in a new and different site within the animal, it might be expected that, in certain respects, the transplanted tumor will have properties different from both those of the primary tumor and of the normal tissue of origin. The transplanted tumor, if it is to grow, must make an adjustment to a new and essentially foreign environment, and, thus, a hepatoma residing previously within a liver and nourished by the portal circulation may have to become adjusted to living and growing under the skin with an arterial circulation. In the course of this accommodation, a certain selection of cellular elements with high survival value may ensue, and hence it is prob-

TABLE 66

ENZYMATIC ACTIVITY IN NORMAL RAT LIVER AND IN PRIMARY AND TRANSPLANTED RAT HEPATOMAS (71, 72)

Tissue	Arginase[1]	Catalase[2]	Acid phosphatase[3,4]	Alkaline phosphatase[3,4]	Urea synthesis[5]	Ribonucleodeaminase[6]	Deoxyribonucleodeaminase[6]	Cystine desulfurase[7]	Dehydropeptidase I[8]	Dehydropeptidase II[8]	Succinic oxidase[9]	Cytochrome oxidase[10]	Cytochrome c[11]	Riboflavin[12]	BAA amidase[13]	Esterase[14]
Normal Liver	213	2.0	25	4	0.12	20	4	45	80	80	88	392	90	29	32	312
Primary hepatomas[15]	40	0.1	28	270	0.01	22	5	0	80	40	26	134	20	4	36	120
Transplanted hepatoma 31[16]	21	0.0	52	542	0.00	58	38	0	80	5	22	124	30	5	56	104
Transplanted Jensen sarcoma	46	0.0	22	44	—	52	0	0	78	0	18	129	12	4	43	83
Transplanted epithelioma	48	0.0	32	18	—	50	5	0	80	0	—	—	—	—	40	72
Liver of tumor-bearing rat[17]	120	0.2	25	4	—	—	—	45	—	—	—	—	—	17	—	100

[1] In terms of ratio of per cent arginine hydrolyzed in 2 hours to the cube root of the total N per milliliter in the tissue extract.

[2] In terms of the rate of oxygen evolution at 25° from a mixture of 5 ml. phosphate buffer, 1 ml. hydrogen peroxide at 29%, and 1 ml. tissue extract containing 0.6 mg. total N.

[3] In terms of the ratio of per cent phenylphosphate hydrolyzed to the total N in 1 ml. of tissue extract, at either pH 4.6 or 9.5.

[4] Woodard (17) noted a nearly 50% rise in the acid phosphatase activity of the primary rat hepatoma. This investigator also independently noted the very considerable rise in the alkaline phosphatase value, employing β-glycerophosphate as substrate. Recently, phenolphthalein esters of phosphoric acid have been introduced as substrates for the phosphatases (78, 79).

[5] In terms of urea formed after 2 hours incubation of tissue slices with citrulline and ammonia. Data on the primary hepatoma recalculated from those of Dickens and Weil-Malherbe (77).

[6] In terms of ammonia N in milligrams $\times 10^3$ evolved in digests of 1 ml. tissue extract (equivalent to 160 mg. tissue) plus 1 ml. 0.5% sodium nucleate after 5 hours incubation.

[7] In terms of per cent ammonia N evolved from digests of cystine or cystine peptides with tissue extracts.

[8] In terms of per cent hydrolysis of glycyldehydroalanine or chloracetyldehydroalanine.

[9, 10] Values of succinic oxidase and cytochrome oxidase from Schneider and Potter (73); units in terms of cubic millimeters oxygen consumed per milligram dry weight per hour with succinate and ascorbate respectively and in presence of excess cytochrome c.

[11] Values of cytochrome c in primary hepatoma from Du Bois and Potter (75); cytochrome c in transplanted hepatoma from Shack (76). Cytochrome c expressed as micrograms per gram wet weight of tissue.

[12] Values from Robertson and Kahler (74) in terms of micrograms per gram wet weight of tissue.

[13] In terms of per cent hydrolysis after 2 hours of incubation of benzoylarginineamide with tissue extracts. These data were obtained at pH 7. At pH 5 (153) or pH 6 (152), the activity of the primary hepatoma toward BAA is very much greater than that of liver.

[14] In terms of average ratio of increase in titer of 0.1 *N* alcoholic KOH to the milligram wet weight of tissue used after 2 hours of incubation of methylbutyrate.

[15] Induced by ingestion of 4-dimethylaminoazobenzene.

[16] Originally induced by ingestion of 4-dimethylaminoazobenzene; late generation transplants.

[17] Rats bearing either transplanted hepatoma 31 or transplanted Jensen sarcoma.

TABLE 67

THE RATE OF METHYLENE BLUE DECOLORIZATION IN EXTRACTS OF NORMAL RAT LIVER AND OF PRIMARY AND TRANSPLANTED RAT HEPATOMAS (72)[1]

Mixture	Decolorization rate (minutes^{-1} × 10^4) in:		
	Normal liver	Primary hepatoma	Transplanted hepatoma
1 ml. Extract + 1 ml. H_2O + 1 ml. dye	640	640	5
1 ml. Extract + 1 ml. ribonucleate + 1 ml. dye	600	550	370
1 ml. Extract + 1 ml. deoxyribonucleate + 1 ml. dye	190	184	23

[1] Aqueous extract of tissues equivalent to 166 mg./ml. Dye concentration 0.62 mM. Nucleates at 2.5 mg./ml.

able that a concentration of cells possessing a high order of autonomy is achieved by the tumor transplant.

A comparison of rat hepatic tissues is presented in Tables 66 and 67 (cf. 71, 72) and includes data on the Jensen transplanted rat sarcoma and on a transplanted rat epithelioma.

There are evidently several categories of components of the normal rat rat liver which differ in the changes of concentration or activity when the liver becomes neoplastic. Certain catalytic functions of the liver alter in the primary neoplastic transformation; others apparently do not alter at all. Of the components which are at the same level in the primary hepatoma, some may alter on transplantation, others may not alter at all on transplantation.

It is evident that, in the case of this particular tumor (i.e., the rat hepatoma), certain enzyme systems are more sensitive to the primary neoplastic transformation than are others. It may thus be necessary in certain cases, when making comparisons between tissues, to distinguish between primary and transplanted tumors. In any event, the values of the various components in the primary tumor do not appear to be discontinuous between the normal tissue and the transplant, but approach those of either one or the other.

The primary hepatoma stands functionally somewhere between the normal liver and the transplanted hepatoma (Table 68). In the components in category I it stands nearer the transplanted tumor; in the components in category II, it is nearly identical with normal liver. The components in category IV are those which have altered to such an extent in the primary neoplastic transformation that subsequent transplantation produces no further change, whereas the components in category III, although undergoing a change in level as a result of the primary neoplastic transformation, can still alter further when the tumor is transplanted. Cate-

TABLE 68

CATEGORIES OF RAT LIVER COMPONENTS BASED UPON ALTERATIONS IN CONCENTRATION OR ACTIVITY IN PRIMARY HEPATOMAS AND IN HEPATOMA TRANSPLANTS (71)

Category I[1]	Category II[2]	Category III[3]	Category IV[4]	Category V[5]	Category VI[6]
Arginase[7]	Acid phosphatase[8]	Arginase[7]	(exo)Cystine desulfurase[8]	Acid phosphatase[8]	Ribonucleodepolymerase[8]
Catalase[7]	Ribonucleodeaminase	Catalase[7]	Succinic oxidase	Ribonucleodeaminase	Deoxyribonucelodepolymerase
Diphosphopyridinenucleotide	Deoxyribonucleodeaminase	Alkaline phosphatase[8]	Cytochrome	Deoxyribonucleodeaminase	Amylase[8]
Alkaline phosphatase[8]					Creatine
Urea synthesis	Dehydropeptidase I	Urea synthesis	Cytochrome c		Creatinine
(Exo) Cystine desulfurase[8]	Dehydrogenase systems responsible for methylene blue decolorition	Dehydropeptidase II	Riboflavin[7]	Dehydrogenase systems responsible for methylene blue decolorization	
Dehydropeptidase II		BAA amidase	Esterase[7]		
Succinic oxidase					
Cytochrome oxidase	Adenosine[9] triphosphatase				
Cytochrome c					
Riboflavin[7]					
Esterase[7]					
Transaminase[9]					
Glyoxylase[9]					
Histidase[9]					
BAA amidase					

[1] Components which differ in primary hepatoma from normal liver. To this category would also be added the glycolytic capacity.

[2] Components which do not differ in primary hepatoma from normal liver.

[3] Components which differ in primary hepatoma from normal liver and which change further on transplantation.

[4] Components which differ in primary hepatoma from normal liver and which do not change further on transplantation.

[5] Components which do not differ in primary hepatoma from normal liver but do change on transplantation.

[6] Components which probably do not differ in primary hepatoma from normal liver, e.g., components which are at same level in transplanted hepatomas as in normal liver.

[7] Definitely lowered in livers of tumor-bearing rats.

[8] Not altered from normal in livers of tumor-bearing rats.

[9] No data available on transplanted hepatomas.

gory V is an interesting one, for this includes components which are apparently resistant to the primary neoplastic transformation but markedly alter as a result of transplantation. The components in category VI evidently survive in level, not only the primary neoplastic transformation of the liver, but the subsequent transplantation as well.

Beyond the fact that the enzyme systems involving oxygen (cytochrome oxidase, etc.) do not alter further than the primary hepatoma, i.e., do not change on transplantation, and that the deaminases and dehydrogenases for the nucleic acids behave in parallel fashion, little or no generalizations as to types of components can be drawn from the categories in Table 68 at the present time. It would be difficult to believe that these separate categories of components occur capriciously. There must be some underlying reasons why certain chemical components survive or are affected by the neoplastic transformation and the subsequent transplantation, but it must be frankly confessed that these reasons are not clear at the moment.

One suggestive factor arises from these observations which, although it anticipates discussion in Chapter IX, may nevertheless be mentioned here. The livers of tumor-bearing rats and mice reflect, in the level of certain components, the presence of a tumor in a distant site. Thus, in animals carrying a wide variety of subcutaneously implanted tumors, the level of activity of hepatic catalase, arginase, riboflavin, etc., may be considerably lowered below the normal value. This phenomenon is a part of the general systemic effect elicited by tumors. From the data given in Table 66, it would hardly be expected that the components in category II would be those affected by a tumor in a distant site, and, indeed, this is the case. Only category I would be expected to include components which might be affected by such a condition, and, as noted above, this actually occurs in the case of catalase, etc. It must, however, also be noted that not all the components in category I are systemically affected by the presence of a distant tumor—only a few are so markedly affected. The striking feature of this alteration in level of the few hepatic components affected is that the change is in the direction which the tumor takes, and, since this is, in the case of these components, in a downward direction, so too is the direction in the level of the hepatic components. The liver of the cancerous animal is, therefore, also "cancerous."

It is possible, therefore, to conceive of several categories of hepatic tissues varying in increasing divergence from the properties of normal liver and thus in the direction of increasing malignancy, namely (a) the normal liver, (b) the liver of a tumor-bearing animal in which a few components in category I are already changing in the direction of a hepatoma (whether the distant tumor is a transplanted hepatoma or not), (c) the preneoplastic liver, (d) the primary hepatoma with some properties of normal liver and some properties of (e) the transplanted hepatoma, with a very few properties of the normal liver, but with many more quite different from those of the normal liver.

The observations described hold, of course, only for the tissues studied. It may be that, in the case of other kinds of tumors, few if any differences will be noted between primary and transplanted tumors and, if so, perhaps not necessarily involving the same components as in the case of rat hepatic tissues. The primary hepatoma, whether in mice or in rats, evidently possesses some characteristics of benign lesions (near identity in certain functions with liver) and of malignant lesions (divergence in certain functions from liver) and, hence, may be a poor test case in this instance. Nevertheless, certain of the changes in properties which the primary tumor reveals as compared with the normal liver, on the one hand, and with the transplant of the tumor, on the other, are quite striking and suggestive. Tumors arising from highly functional normal tissues other than liver sometimes carry over from these tissues one or more functions which are the imprint (or legacy) of the tissue of origin. Thus, the osteogenic sarcoma frequently has a high alkaline phosphatase characteristic of bone, adrenal carcinomas may have fatty layers similar to those of the adrenal gland, and the prostatic carcinoma very frequently has the high acid phosphatase of the normal prostatic epithelium. The behavior of the last mentioned tumor in man is not known, but the first two tumors in experimental animals quite frequently lose trace of these specialized functions through transplantation.

It is necessary to point out that there is an element of uncertainty in the conclusions drawn from the data in Tables 66 and 67, due to the fact that no data are available on the primary tumor which on transplantation formed the readily transplantable tumor now known as hepatoma 31. The data given are those obtained on hundreds of samples of hepatoma 31 and on an equal number of samples of primary hepatomas induced in the same way as the original primary tumor which gave rise to hepatoma 31 (namely, by ingestion of 4-dimethylaminoazobenzene). The data on all the samples of hepatoma 31 were consistent within a few per cent and so, too, were the data on all the samples of the primary tumor studied. This consistency is worthy of emphasis in view of the findings on the mouse hepatomas described below. Nevertheless, the possibility must be envisaged that the primary tumor which gave rise to the rat hepatoma 31 was an exception among primary hepatomas otherwise uniform and that it had properties more nearly like those of the transplant which originated from it than like those of the usual primary hepatomas. According to this possibility, the chemical properties of hepatoma 31 are those not only of a transplanted but of a transplantable tumor. The primary rat hepatoma is rarely successfully transplanted even into animals of the same stock, but whether this is due (a) to the too close similarity of the tumor to normal liver as revealed by the data in Tables 66 and 67 and, hence, to an essential benignancy in character of the former, or (b) to a lack of genetic homogeneity in the animal stocks used cannot be answered at the present time. The possibility raised above, namely, that the parent primary tumor of hepatoma 31 may have been exceptional, is probably far-fetched but, in the absence of evidence to the contrary, cannot be dismissed. The proper conduct of studies of this kind would obviously involve successive investigations of primary tumors and of successfully transplanted tumors to which they give rise.

Nearly all transplanted tumors possess many functional properties at close to the same quantitative level, and, although this phenomenon is described in more detail below as it applies to mouse tissues, it may be observed to some extent in the data on the transplanted hepatoma 31 and on the transplanted epithelioma and Jensen rat sarcoma in Table 66. With few exceptions, the properties of the hepatoma resemble more nearly those of the epithelioma and sarcoma than they do those of normal liver.

The primary mouse hepatoma, in certain instances, shows characteristics generally ascribed to benign tumors. Dickens and Weil-Malherbe (77) found that the spontaneous hepatoma which arises in mice of the *CBA* strain possesses many functions similar to, and at as high a degree as, normal mouse liver.

Studies on primary hepatomas induced in *A* strain mice by carbon tetrachloride administration revealed a considerable lack of uniformity in the enzymatic pattern (80). Among a dozen or more samples of this tumor, the cystine desulfurase activity varied from sample to sample, with values ranging from that high level characteristic of normal liver to that of zero characteristic of all tumors. In hepatomas induced in this strain of mice by chloroform administration, the cystine desulfurase activity, although lower than that of normal liver, was always present; the alkaline phosphatase activity, on the other hand, was always considerably higher than that of normal liver. In respect to the level of the latter enzyme, the mouse hepatoma resembles the rat hepatoma, the neoplastic transformation of the liver involving, in these cases, a considerable rise in the alkaline phosphatase activity. In respect to the former enzyme (cystine desulfurase), the mouse hepatoma preserves some function of the normal mouse liver. On transplantation of the mouse hepatoma induced by the above-mentioned agents, the level of cystine desulfurase in the early generation transplants is not greatly changed from that of the primary tumor, whereas that of alkaline phosphatase rises well above that of the primary tumor (Table 69). The variability among the transplants in each transplant generation was difficult to determine because so very few tumors "took" in each generation. The impression gained, however, was that

TABLE 69

ENZYMATIC ACTIVITY IN MOUSE HEPATIC TISSUES[1] (80)

Tissue	Cystine desulfurase	Alkaline phosphatase
Normal liver	9 ± 0.5	4 ± 0.2
Transplanted hepatoma 587[2]	0 ± 0.1	5 ± 0.2
Transplanted hepatoma 98/15[3]	0 ± 0.1	1 ± 0.1
Transplanted hepatoma 7A/77[4]	0 ± 0.1	4 ± 0.1
Transplanted hepatoma A[5]	0 ± 0.1	0
Livers of mice bearing transplanted hepatomas 587 and 7A/77	9 ± 0.5	4 ± 0.2
Liver plus primary hepatoma induced by CCl_4[6]	7	—
Liver plus primary hepatoma induced by CCl_4[7]	9	—
Liver plus primary hepatoma induced by CCl_4[8]	7	—
Liver excised from primary hepatomas induced by CCl_4	9 ± 0.5	—
Primary hepatomas induced by CCl_4 excised from liver[9]	4 ± 4.0	—
Primary hepatomas induced by $CHCl_3$ excised from liver	4 ± 2.0	20 ± 4
First-generation transplant of hepatoma induced by $CHCl_3$	3	—
Second-generation transplant of hepatoma induced by $CHCl_3$	3	90
Third-generation transplant of hepatoma induced by $CHCl_3$	4	—
Fourth-generation transplant of hepatoma induced by $CHCl_3$	4	120
Fifth-generation transplant of hepatoma induced by $CHCl_3$	3	150
Sixth-generation transplant of hepatoma induced by $CHCl_3$	2	204

[1] For activity units cf. Table 66. All animals of *A* strain except where noted.

[2] Originally spontaneous in *A* strain mouse; beyond twelfth-generation transplant.

[3] Originally spontaneous in *C3H* strain mouse; beyond twelfth-generation transplant.

[4] Originally induced by CCl_4 in *A* strain mouse; beyond twelfth-generation transplant.

[5] Originally induced by aminoazotoluene in *C3H* strain mouse; beyond twelfth-generation transplant.

[6] Total weight of liver plus tumor = 7.8 g.

Total weight of liver plus tumor = 5.2 g.

[8] Total weight of liver plus tumor = 6.0 g.

[9] Fourteen separate samples used; several samples were pooled from different animals, other samples were each obtained from a single animal. Values of cystine desulfurase activity for the latter group of samples were 0, 2, 3, 6, and 8; values for the former samples were 1, 4, 4, 6, 6, 7, 7, and 8.

smaller differences in enzymatic activity existed between the few transplants in each transplant generation than occurred among the primary hepatomas in the parent mice. In view of the uniformity among the primary and transplanted rat hepatomas, the relative variability among the primary and early transplanted mouse hepatomas furnishes an interesting contrast.

The phosphatase determinations reported in Table 69 were performed according to the usual macrochemical techniques. Analogous techniques on a histochemical scale revealed essentially similar findings (Eschenbrenner). These most useful histochemical methods, developed principally by Gomori (81), and applied to sectioned tissues on microscope slides, although only semiquantitative in scope, are important in revealing sites of phosphatase (or other enzyme) activity within the cell—a form of enzyme topography. The possibility of artifacts arising by the use of this technique, owing to unselected and adventitious areas of precipitation, cannot however, be overlooked.

Through the use of histochemical staining, Wachstein (82) noted a considerable decrease in the alkaline phosphatase activity in the livers of stock albino mice injected intraperitoneally with a mixture of chloroform and liquid petrolatum. The difference between these results and those of Eschenbrenner, who noted a rise in the activity of this enzyme in the livers of *A* strain mice fed the chemical (cf. also Table 69), may be due as much to the dosage and method of dosage as to differences in the genetic constitution of the animals employed.

The primary tumors induced by chloroform administration were transplanted with difficulty even in animals of the same inbred strain, a very low percentage of "takes" being noted. The retention of cystine desulfurase in the primary tumor and of its successive early transplant generations suggests that these tumors still carry sufficient vestiges of the normal tissue of origin, namely liver, to reduce the possibility of generally successful and ready transplantation.

In contrast with these data are the results on the hepatomas in late-generation transplants given in the upper part of Table 69. The results on several samples of each of these tumors are invariably uniform from one sample to another, and the enzymatic data on these tissues are largely indistinguishable from those obtained on other transplanted tumors of quite different etiology and histogenesis (*vide ultra*). Whether the characteristics of the transplanted chloroform-induced hepatoma will, in later generation transplants, come to resemble those of the other hepatomas described in Table 69 is a matter for the future. No data are available on the primary tumors or the early generation transplants thereof which produced the established hepatomas given by number in the table. These latter tumors, it should be pointed out, are readily transplantable. It may be wondered whether they arose from primary tumors with zero cystine desulfurase activity. Further studies on primary hepatomas in the mouse, either of spontaneous origin or induced by other agents, such as aminoazotoluene, would go far in clarifying many of the issues raised by the above findings. It may be that the response of the liver of *A* strain mice to oral administration of the halogenated aliphatic hydrocarbons forms a special case in the general field of carcinogenesis. The variability in such response may be a reflection of delicate adjustments made by the liver cells to the numerous factors, such as dosage and intervals between dosages, which are concerned in the neoplastic transformation of this tissue, adjustments obviously made unequally even in mice of an inbred strain. These findings are exceptional among the rather consistent enzymatic levels observed hitherto among hepatomas in rats and in tumors induced in other sites in rats and mice through other agents and, hence, are especially interesting on this account.

There is other evidence pointing to the possibility that tumors in late generation transplants may alter radically from the characteristics of early generation transplants. This is well illustrated by the case of an osteogenic sarcoma which arose spontaneously in a *C3H* mouse and which was carried consecutively through many transplant generations. Up to the sixth-generation transplant, the tumor formed bone, was encapsulated, and metastasized regularly and consistently to the lungs. Beyond the sixth-generation transplant, the tumor lost the capacity to produce bone, became highly anaplastic in appearance with many mitotic figures, and very invasive and rapidly growing in character. The phosphatase activity also changed markedly in this transition, as noted in Table 70 (83).

There is apparently a general tendency for tumor cells which possess a special function to lose this after a number of transplantations, especially if, during that time, there is an increase in growth rate. In addition to the case of the osteogenic sarcoma described above, an example of a transplantable mouse adrenal cortical tumor (84) supplies confirmatory evidence. In the early generation transplants of this adrenal tumor, cells containing lipid droplets and resembling the cells of the *zona fasciculata* of the normal adrenal gland were numerous. In later generation transplants in which the growth rate had greatly increased, such cells were no longer in evidence. Apparently, the expression of specialized functions is not to be generally expected in cells which have achieved a rapid growth rate. Which is

TABLE 70

ACID AND ALKALINE PHOSPHATASE ACTIVITY IN EARLY AND LATE GENERATION TRANSPLANTS OF A MOUSE OSTEOGENIC SARCOMA[1] (83)

Tissue	Acid phosphatase	Alkaline phosphatase
Adult normal bone in mice	50	420
Osteogenic sarcoma in mice, third-generation transplant	135	1100
Osteogenic sarcoma in mice, seventeenth-generation transplant	21	1

[1] For units of activity, cf. Table 66.

prior, the loss of function or the increase in growth rate, or whether both effects occur simultaneously, is not known at the present time.

One of the most important problems in cancer research is concerned with the question of why primary tumors metastasize. This problem is particularly acute in the case of man, for the social environment generally preserves the tumor-bearing host of this species until the metastasizing lesions are fatal. It might be expected that, in general, autologous transplantation within the same animal would be more readily achieved than heterologous transplantation from one animal to another. The criteria for the latter would be correspondingly more severe than for the former. It has been noted that, for a tumor to be readily transplantable, a considerable divergence in its chemical properties from those of the tissue of origin is to be expected. This divergence in properties is essentially a reflection of the degree of autonomy of the tumor. The transplant may be considered to be representative of the primary tumor in an equally or a greater autonomous form. It seems probable that, for metastasis, a lower degree of autonomy, or a correspondingly smaller divergence from normal of the chemical properties of the primary tumor compared with that necessary for heterologous transplantation, would be required. It is possible that the level of an enzyme such as cystine desulfurase, determined in a primary tumor through biopsy where possible, could serve as a prognosis of subsequent metastasis and as collateral evidence with histologic criteria of the degree of malignancy of the tumor. Indeed, the chemical criterion may be even more decisive than that of the microscopic, for, as noted above, experimentally induced tumors which are histologically indistinguishable (hepatomas induced in mice by halogenated aliphatic hydrocarbons) may be readily distinguished by enzymatic methods. Since certain tumors change their characteristics in later generation transplants, it is possible that, although the first metastasis of a tumor may be relatively benign and slow-growing, later and successive metastases from this first metastasis may demonstrate striking changes with increasing divergence in chemical properties from the original primary tumor accompanied by increased growth rate.

The late-generation transplant in an experimental animal represents a quite late stage in the development of a tumor. In effect, it is Z in the neoplastic alphabet to the normal tissue's A. Studies of the intermediate stages have barely been touched upon. These intermediate stages occur in profusion in the clinic, and for further progress in this field a more substantial cooperation between laboratory and clinic must be achieved than has, regrettably, been the case up to now. But before these intermediate stages can be adequately recognized, it is necessary to establish the chemical phenomena revealed by the extremes of the scale, namely, the fully normal and the frankly malignant.

The Chemical Pattern of Normal and of Neoplastic Tissues

The activity of a number of individual enzyme systems and the concentration of several components, each studied under comparable conditions in a wide variety of normal and neoplastic tissues in several species and strains of animals, is described below. The data in these tables and in the pertinent literature are first discussed generally, in the form of a group of tentative conslusions, and then specifically, as they relate to individual systems in homologous tissues. *Unless otherwise noted, these conclusions relate specifically to established transplanted tumors.*

General Conclusions

(*a*) Each normal tissue is characterized by the possession of an individual pattern of enzymatic activity which may serve to distinguish it from all other tissues.

(*b*) Tumors have qualitatively the same enzymes as normal tissues. There is always the possibility that future research may reveal the presence of an enzyme or enzymes in neoplasms unique to these tissues and absent in all normal tissues. On the other hand, it is also possible that neoplasms might be characterized by the lack of one or more enzymes known to occur in normal tissues. The tumors studied are all lacking in cystine desulfurase and dehydropeptidase II. Inasmuch as normal tissues, with the exception of liver, kidney, and pancreas, are also lacking in cystine desulfurase and in dehydropeptidase II, it would not be entirely correct to say that tumors are characterized by the absence of these enzymes. The same line of reasoning would also apply to the limited case of pepsin and rennin, for these enzymes, although absent in the gastric adenocarcinoma and presumably all other other tumors, are also absent in all normal tissues except one, the gastric mucosa.

(*c*) The enzymatic pattern of a tumor is largely independent of its age, of its growth rate, and of the strain of animal in which it is grown. This conclusion is partially supported by reports in the literature (85, 86) and on unpublished work by the writer. The enzymatic activity of transplanted, primary induced, and spontaneous tumors is the same for each tumor type when it makes its appearance as in later stages of growth of the tumor. A particular tumor growing in a group of even closely related animals may grow at a different rate in each animal; nevertheless, the enzymatic pattern of the tumor is the same, regardless of the growth rate. A tumor which originated in a particular strain can, under certain circumstances, be transplanted and successfully grown in another strain; for example, sarcoma 37 can be transplanted to and grown in, mice of strains *DBA*, *C*, *C57 Black*, *I*, *and Y*, and the melanotic melanoma S-91 which originated in a pigmented *JAX-DBA* strain mouse has been successfully transplanted to, and grown in, albino mice of the *C* strain (87). The enzymatic activity of sarcoma 37 and of melanoma S-91, respectively, is, however, the same, regardless of the strain of mouse in which these tumors are grown (87). These observations strongly suggest that the tumor is, enzymatically at least, an autonomous, independent entity which preserves to a considerable extent its individuality, regardless of the nature or condition of the host.

(*d*) The range of activity of each enzyme and of concentration of such components as the vitamins is much narrower among tumors than among normal tissues; i.e., tumors possess a more uniform and less diverse chemical pattern than normal tissues. Neoplasms may arise in animals either spontaneously or by induction through a wide variety of unrelated known extrinsic agents. Whatever the cause or origin of the tumor may be, the tumor ends by possessing a chemical pattern very largely the same as that of other tumors of quite different etiology or histogenesis. One of the earliest observations of this nature was made by the Coris in 1925, who noted that the lactic acid and sugar contents of a sarcoma were very nearly the same as those of a carcinoma (88). In the case of the mouse hepatomas, where relatively slight differences may appear in the activity of certain enzymes (catalase, xanthine dehydrogenase, deoxyribonucleodepolymerase) these differences appear to be related to the strains of mice in which the tumors are grown and are independent of the etiology of the tumors. The level of alkaline phosphatase in the hepatomas, which in certain instances may be abnormally high, may perhaps be a reflection of initial liver damage and obstruction by the carcinogen and quite unrelated to the neoplastic transformation. On the other hand, the patterns of the lymphoma in three different strains of mice are nearly identical. Judging by the data, it would be difficult, indeed, to distinguish on a chemical basis among sarcomas, carcinomas, lymphomas, and adenocarcinomas. To take a strikingly extreme case, the enzymatic patterns of the normal gastric mucosa and of the normal liver are qualitatively and quantitatively vastly different, but those of the gastric adenocarcinoma (induced by methylcholanthrene) and of the hepatoma (spontaneous or induced by aminoazotoluene or carbon tetrachloride) are very nearly the same. The degree of similarity in enzymatic pattern among the tumors is usually highest, the further away the tumors stand from their normal tissues of origin, i.e., the number of transplant generations. In many respects, in primary tumors especially and sometimes in early generation transplants, some resemblance to the functions of the normal tissue of origin is retained, such as dehydropeptidase and adenosine triphosphatase in the hepatoma, and prostatic acid phosphatase in the prostatic adenocarcinoma. It should be emphasized, however, that, no matter what differences may be observed among the tumors, these differences are generally smaller than those found among different kinds of normal tissues.

A possible exception to the generalization expressed above may be the case of the osteogenic sarcoma. In this tumor, the phosphatase values are, as might be expected, phenomenally high, far exceeding those of all the other tumors studied. A high alkaline phosphatase activity is associated with osteoblastic activity. Since this activity represents a specialized structural function, the osteogenic sarcoma, like the prostatic carcinoma, may be placed in a separate category. At the present time, the relation of the phosphatase activity of the osteogenic sarcoma to that of the normal osteoblastic cells is not known. To clarify this point, the activity of the epiphysis of normal growing bone should be employed for comparison; in the case of mice this determination would be rather difficult.

Tumors thus tend chemically to resemble each other more than they do normal tissues or than normal tissues resemble each other.

(*e*) When a normal tissue becomes neoplastic, many of the specific functional activities markedly decrease or are lost altogether. This conclusion is largely derived from a comparison of the enzymatic activities and component concentrations of the following pairs of homologous tissues: liver and hepatoma, lymph nodes and lymphoma, intestinal mucosa and intestinal adenocarcinoma, and gastric mucosa and gastric adenocarcinoma. Many enzymes of high activity in the normal tissues are markedly reduced in the neoplasms derived from them. The liver is characterized by a high activity of arginase, catalase, and cystine desulfurase, as well as by a high concentration of flavin; lymph nodes contain an active deoxyribonucleodepolymerase; intestinal mucosa is high in alkaline phosphatase and esterase; and the gastric mucosa is the site of peptic activity. In the neoplasms originating from these tissues the enzymes noted are either reduced in activity or else have virtually disappeared. This general reduction in activity goes far in explaining why tumors have a narrower range of enzymatic activity than have normal tissues. To a large extent the diversity of the chemical pattern in normal tissues is due to the presence of certain systems in very high, as well as very low, degree.

(*f*) The range of values for tumors is usually between the extremes of the corresponding values for normal tissues. Thus, the metabolic activity of tumors is not lower than *all* normal tissues; it is only lower than the *highest* values characteristic of certain normal tissues, but it is frequently higher than those very *low* values in certain other normal tissues. Arginase is high in normal liver and low in brain (246 and 3, respectively); the average tumor value is between these extremes (roughly 40). Similar results hold for the several metabolic systems which act on the nucleic acids, etc., for tumors stand somewhere in between the respective extremes of the normal tissues. It might even appear that, when a normal tissue was low in some catalytic function, the latter would rise in value when the tissue became neoplastic in order to reach the median value. Perhaps this is the reason why the deaminases for the nucleates, which are relatively low in liver, rise in activity value when this tissue becomes neoplastic, reflecting in this way increased nuclear (mitotic) activity.

It cannot be said, therefore, that 'tumors are lower (or higher) in activity than normal tissues," but only that their activity is lower (or higher) in respect to certain specified normal tissues. Tumors do not stand outside the metabolic range of normal tissues. What appears to be true, however, is that the activity of each catalytic system in tumors rarely stands at the top of the metabolic range but is nearly always either somewhere in between or at or near the lower extreme of the range for normal tissues. When an enzyme in a normal tissue rises in activity when the tissue becomes neoplastic it does not exceed the value for the most active normal tissue; i.e., hepatoma cathepsin does not exceed spleen cathepsin (89), nor does rat hepatoma phosphatase exceed kidney or intestinal mucosa phosphatase (90). Conversely, when an enzyme in a normal tissue falls in activity when the tissue becomes neoplastic, it does not drop in activity below the value for the least active normal tissue. Most striking of the systems which in tumors stand at the lowest range of the normal tissues, are the oxidases.

However, although the normal tissue may be most active in a particular enzyme, information is often lacking on the tumor derived from this normal tissue. Thus, although hepatoma cathepsin may be higher in activity than liver cathepsin but lower than spleen cathepsin, the question may be raised as to what is the level of spleen tumor cathepsin. In this case, it might be expected that the activity of the last-mentioned would be lower than that of the normal spleen, but no data are available. In cases where liver is the most active tissue, the hepatoma is always less active.

It is possible that the maximum activity of the enzymes elicited in extracts or suspensions of the normal tissues is never fully utilized in the intact tissues. A certain proportion of the concentration of these enzymes may be employed as a reserve, the extent of this reserve depending, in part, upon the availability of specific substrates. The difference between the total and reserve activity would thus be the activity utilized for maintenance of the tissue. When the normal tissue becomes neoplastic, the possible reserve activity presumably disappears. Apparently tumors possess little if any enzymatic reserve of certain systems.

(*g*) Tumors tend to converge, enzymatically, to a common type of tissue. The nearly identical pattern of tumors suggests that they approach a chemically similar type of tissue. However, a tumor may not lose all vestiges of the tissue of its origin and indeed may, in the primary stage, retain several of the functions of the latter tissue. The mouse hepatomas may have more benign than malignant characteristics, and it possible that the more a neoplasm approaches the malignant state (through successive transplantations?), the fewer vestiges of the normal tissue of its origin are preserved and the more it approaches a type of dedifferentiated tissue presumably common to all neoplasms.

A final piece of evidence in favor of a fundamentally similar metabolism for all tumors (at least in mice and rats) is the fact that they produce identical systemic effects in the hosts which bear them. Thus, the liver catalase activity is very considerably reduced in rats and in mice bearing all kinds of tumors except very slow-growing ones, but not in such animals bearing a rapidly growing embryonal tissue implant. This topic is considered in the following chapter (IX), but it may be cited here as a basis for the concept that all tumors, irrespective of their origin or etiology, possess metabolic and chemical properties not only in common but of nearly the same order of magnitude.

Conclusions Relating to Special Systems

Enzymes of Oxidation-Reduction. One of the most striking features of the metabolism of tumors is their relatively low content of aerobic catalytic systems, i.e., cytochrome, succinic, and D-amino acid oxidases, cytochrome c, catalase, and flavin (4, 8, 73–76, 85, 91). The rate of anaerobic reduction of methylene blue (92) is apparently different for liver and for transplanted hepatoma in the fresh extracts of these tissues but is of nearly the same order of magnitude in the dialyzed extracts. It may be that, to a considerable extent, the difference between the normal and the neoplastic tissues in this case is due to the relative amount of dialyzable and oxidizable substrates in the two kinds of tissue.

From the calculations of Shack (76), it cannot be said that tumors are necessarily deficient in the cytochrome system, but only that such tissues have just enough to take care of their respiration. Normal tissues, or at least certain normal tissues, appear to have more of a reserve of this system. The oxidative response of tissues is considered below.

From the severe decrease in the cytochrome system and in catalase when normal liver becomes neoplastic, as well as in the marked effect of a distant tumor in lowering the liver catalase and blood hemoglobin of the host, it would appear that there is some factor, either operative during the neoplastic transformation or else within the neoplasm itself, which is antagonistic to the synthesis of iron porphyrins, the prosthetic groups of these biologically active proteins.

The iron-containing components of normal liver, catalase, cytochrome oxidase, and cytochrome c are considerably reduced when the liver becomes neoplastic. The exact physiologic function of catalase is not known. It is identified by its high rate of splitting of hydrogen peroxide. The peroxide is normally produced by the action of such oxidases as employ molecular oxygen in the oxidation of substrates (xanthine, D-amino acids, etc.).

Catalase destroys the peroxide so formed. In the presence of alcohols, the peroxide plus catalase yields the corresponding aldehydes, and thus the enzyme may participate in coupled oxidations (93). The level of this enzyme is strongly lowered not only in neoplasms but also in the tissues of tumor-bearing animals. Cytochrome oxidase is a participant in the respiration cycle in all tissues, and its substrate is the readily identifiable tissue component, cytochrome c. Of the various cytochromes in tissues, only cytochrome c and cytochrome oxidase have been isolated. For the synthesis of catalase and of cytochrome oxidase by the tissues, a definite level of copper in the diet of the host animal has been found necessary (94). In this connection it is interesting to note that the copper content of hepatomas is lower than that of normal liver.

Catalase activity in the rat hepatoma is reduced to an almost negligible amount as compared with that of normal liver. The reduction is not so marked in mouse as in rat hepatomas, but here, too, the activity is much less than normal and appears to be slightly related to the strain of mouse in which the hepatoma appears. The activity of catalase in induced and spontaneous hepatoma in *C3H* mice is very nearly the same, but the activity of the induced and spontaneous hepatomas in *A* mice is quite different in the two types of tumor and different also from that in the *C3H* mice. The cytochrome oxidase activity is very nearly the same for hepatomas in all the mice strains.

The catalase (and arginase) activity of the induced tumor in *I* mice is the same as that found in the same tumor transplanted to F_1 hybrids of this strain with *C3H* and with dilute brown mice (86). Hybridization, at least for the first generation, does not affect the enzymatic properties of the tumor. Furthermore, in any one hepatoma in a given mouse strain the enzymatic activity is invariably independent of the age or the growth rate of the tumor.

Both cytochrome oxidase and cytochrome c are reduced to nearly the same extent in the rat hepatoma. This reduction is of some interest when it is considered that the respiration (in which these components participate) is practically the same in the hepatoma and in normal and regenerating liver. Shack (76) has pointed out that the liver, whether resting or regenerating, has, in contrast with the hepatoma, a considerable reserve of the oxidase–cytochrome system. When *p*-phenylenediamine in addition to glucose was added to liver and to hepatoma, the former tissue responded by a greater oxygen consumption than did the latter. Since the hepatomas do not possess an oxidative reserve, they can respond to demands for more energy by the supply of substrates only by an increase in glycolysis, whereas normal and regenerating liver (the latter, like the hepatoma, is also rapidly growing) may respond by increased oxidation. The oxygen consumption of the hepatoma is thus limited by the cytochrome system. This concept assists in the general interpretation of the high glycolysis of most tumors whose cytochrome oxidase values fall within the range of the hepatomas.

Xanthine dehydrogenase, D-amino acid oxidase, and succinic oxidase either have in common a known riboflavin structure or require riboflavin in the diet for their proper level of function (95, 96). With one exception, xanthine dehydrogenase is present in greatly diminished activity in the hepatomas as compared with normal liver. The value for the hepatoma in the *I* strain is the same as that of normal liver. The drop in the two hepatomas of the *C3H* strain is very nearly the same and the drop in the two hepatomas in the *A* strain is very nearly the same but different from that in the *C3H* strain. The riboflavin content of all the mouse hepatomas, however, is very nearly the same and is considerably lower than the value for normal liver. Since xanthine dehydrogenase, D-amino acid oxidase, and succinic oxidase are apparently associated with flavin, it is not surprising to find their activity reduced in the riboflavin-low hepatomas, but it is equally clear that there is no exact correlation between the drop in riboflavin content in the tumor and the drop in either amino acid oxidase or xanthine dehydrogenase activity. Shack (76) suggested that the lowering of the D-amino acid oxidase activity may be owing to a deficiency in the protein component as well as in the flavin prosthetic group (cf. 91). The lack of determinable D-amino acid oxidase activity in normal mouse liver is noteworthy since it is so high in rat liver, and both tissues are almost equally high in flavin.

The oxidation chain in tissues is presumed to involve the action of molecular oxygen on cytochrome oxidase previously reduced by the reduced form of cytochrome c. The latter in turn is reduced by the flavoprotein enzymes. The iron and flavin systems are thus closely linked in the respiration cycle of animal tissues. However, although both cytochrome oxidase and D-amino acid oxidase are reduced in activity when the liver becomes neoplastic, the latter is reduced to a much greater extent. The fall in activity of the amino acid oxidase is also much greater than that of xanthine dehydrogenase. Since the last two enzymes are flavoproteins and there appears to be more than enough flavin in the tumor to account for their combined activity, the unequal fall in their activity would lend weight to the suggestion that the fall is caused by changes in the protein moiety of these enzymes. In any event, the change of liver cells from normal to neoplastic is accompanied by an unequal change in these as in many other enzyme systems.

No data have yet been obtained on L-amino acid oxidase in tumors. This enzyme in liver and kidney contains riboflavin phosphate as prosthetic group (97).

Coenzyme I, which participates in the oxidation mechanism, contains

TABLE 71

COENZYME I OXIDASE AND ITS COMPONENTS (99)

Tissue	Coenzyme I oxidase	Diaphorase	Cytochrome c reductase	Cytochrome c	Cytochrome oxidase
Liver	+++	++++	+++++	++	+++
Kidney	++++	++++	++++	+++	++++
Heart	+++++	++++	++++	++++	++++
Brain	++	++	+++	++	+++
Muscle	+	+	+	++	+++
Sarcoma 37	+	+	++	+	+
Adenocarcinoma	+	+	++	+	+
Hepatoma 98/15	+	+++	+++++	+	++

nicotinic acid amide as a component and, hence, is related to the B vitamins. The content of coenzyme I is considerably lower in the rat hepatoma as compared with normal rat liver (98). The series of respiratory enzymes which constitute the system which oxidizes reduced diphosphopyridine nucleotide (coenzyme I or DPN) includes the flavoprotein diaphorase which directly oxidizes $DPNH_2$, cytochrome c reductase which mediates the oxidation reaction between $DPNH_2$ and cytochrome c, and cytochrome oxidase. The relative levels of these systems is described in Table 71 (99). The low oxidase values of the tumors are attributable to the low and limiting cytochrome levels, despite, in the case of hepatoma 98/15, a normal level of cytochrome c reductase.

Energy-yielding reactions within the cell involve the oxidation of carbohydrates and fats, and these reactions may be aerobic and anaerobic. Closely associated with many of these reactions are mechanisms of phosphate transfer. The intermediary metabolism of carbohydrates has generally been described under two headings, namely, glycolysis, which consists in the fission of the carbohydrate molecule by a series of fermentative reactions to yield lactic acid (in animal tissues), and respiration, which involves a number of oxidative decarboxylations. The subject of glycolysis is reserved to a later section. The mechanisms of respiration whereby carbohydrates and fats are oxidized by molecular oxygen to carbon dioxide and water must include reactions other than decarboxylation alone to account for the complete oxidation of these substances. The water formed as an end product probably arises through the action of dehydrogenase systems. The oxygen is activated by a series of electron transport systems such as the cytochromes and flavoproteins thus: The source of much of

$$\text{Food-stuff} \xrightarrow{2H} \text{Pyridine nucleotides} \xrightarrow{2e\,+\,1H^+} \text{Flavoprotein} \xrightarrow{2e\,+\,2H^+}$$

$$\text{Cytochrome b} \xrightarrow{1e} \text{Cytochrome c} \xrightarrow{1e} \text{Cytochrome a} \xrightarrow{1e}$$

$$\text{Cytochrome oxidase} \xrightarrow{1e} 1/2\ O_2 + 2H^+ + 2e \rightarrow H_2O$$

the carbon dioxide in tissue respiration appears to be pyruvic acid, and a series of reactions whereby this decarboxylation may occur in animal

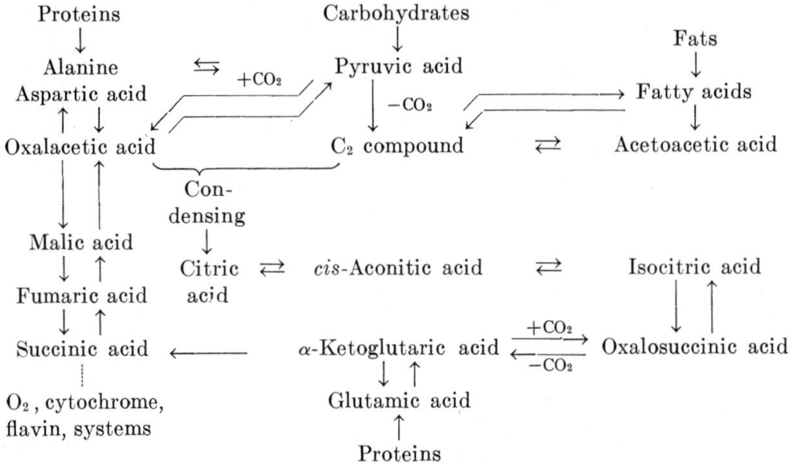

THE KREBS CYCLE

tissues has been developed by Krebs (cf. 100), and named by others the Krebs or tricarboxylic acid cycle. The basis of the theory upon which this series of reactions rests is the observation by Knoop and Martius of the chemical oxidation by hydrogen peroxide of an alkaline mixture of oxalacetic acid and pyruvic acid to yield citric acid (101). The enzymatic synthesis of citric acid has been accomplished by Stern and Ochoa by means of a liver system and adenosine triphosphate with oxalacetic acid, acetate, and coenzyme A (102). A complete exposition of this important if unsettled field is beyond the scope of this monograph, and the excellent summations by Dickens (103) and by Krebs (100) may serve in this connection.

The generally low level of the cytochrome components in tumors has been mentioned above. However, it was evident before these findings were made that Warburg's observations on the nearly equal oxygen consumption by normal and malignant tissue slices (104) posed a problem for which the relative glycolytic activities of these two types of tissues offered no solution. Since the concepts involved in the Krebs cycle offered some hope of resolving this evident discrepancy, Weinhouse and his collaborators entered into a study of the individual reactions of this cycle in normal and in tumor tissues (105-109). The anaerobic breakdown of glucose in normal and in cancer cells involves the formation of 3-carbon acids (110, 111), and the oxidative phase in which pyruvic acid is completely oxidized through the Krebs cycle also appears to be identical both qualitatively and quantitatively in normal tissues and in tumors (105). Palmitic acid also appears to be oxidized completely by normal and by malignant tissues via

TABLE 72

RADIOACTIVE CITRATE FROM OXIDATION OF RADIOACTIVE PRECURSORS (105)

Mouse tissue	Substrate	Quinidine citrate, counts/min.
Heart	Glucose	150
Liver	Glucose	126
Kidney	Glucose	2480
Hepatoma	Glucose	1225
Mammary tumor	Glucose	1750
Rhabdomyosarcoma	Glucose	1000
Ehrlich ascites tumor	Glucose	910
Mammary tumor	Acetate	293
Mammary tumor	Palmitate	74
Hepatoma	Palmitate	138
Rhabdomyosarcoma	Palmitate	83

TABLE 73

OXIDATION OF LABELED GLUCOSE, PALMITIC ACID, AND LACTIC ACID (105)

Tissue	Rate of conversion to carbon dioxide for:[1]		
	Glucose	Palmitic acid	Lactic acid
Rat kidney	111	40	152
Rat brain	93		112
Rat heart	87		148
Rat liver	23	10	44
Rat muscle	7		3
Rat hepatoma	44	14	61
Mouse hepatoma	38	20	87
Mouse rhabdomyosarcoma	35	17	72
Mouse mammary tumor	26	11	65

[1] As microatoms of substrate carbon oxidized to CO_2 per gram dry tissue per hour.

the citric acid cycle (Tables 72-74). The individual enzymes of the Krebs cycle showed, as might be expected, activities in normal and tumor tissues of comparable rates (106) (Tables 72-74). The presence of the "condensing enzyme" in tumors definitely establishes the capacity of neoplastic tissues to synthesize citric acid. Administration of fluoroacetate to tumor-bearing rats leads to no evidence of an accumulation of citric acid in the tumors (112) (Table 75), such as occurs in all normal tissues except liver. It seems probable that in nearly all normal tissues the oxidation of citric acid is blocked by fluoroacetate, at some point or points not clearly known at present. In tumors, as in normal liver, fluoroacetate does not cause citrate to accumulate, but the reasons may not be the same for both types of tissues. The presence of an alternative pathway to acetoacetate may be the explanation in liver, and the absence of a fluoroacetate-susceptible system may be the explanation in the case of tumors. Thus, *in vitro*

TABLE 74

ENZYMES OF THE KREBS CITRIC ACID CYCLE (106)

Tissue	Assay for:[1]							
	Condensing enzyme	Aconitase	Fumarase	Lactic dehydrogenase	Malic dehydrogenase	Isocitric dehydrogenase	Oxalacetic decarboxylase	Ketoglutarate oxidase
Mouse muscle				520	330	16		
Rat liver		25	66					7.7
Mouse liver	1.5	33	132	200	256	11	3.2	
Rat heart		72	96	320	383	56		
Rat kidney		50	62	104	173	66		11.3
Mouse kidney								4.0
Rat muscle		12						
Rat hepatoma			133	238	540	13	2.5	2.4
Mouse hepatoma	2.9	8	62	108	288	15	0.8	2.1
Mouse rhabdomyosarcoma	1.5	4	50	190	180	7	2.2	3.3
Mouse mammary tumor	3.3	4	50	168	380	16	1.2	3.2
Mouse ascites				165	200	5	3.5	

[1] Units in original paper (106).

TABLE 75

EFFECT OF FLUOROACETATE ON CITRATE CONTENT OF NORMAL AND TUMOR TISSUES[1] (12)

Rat tissues	Before injection	One hour after injection
Brain	57	212
Heart	49	632
Lung	75	285
Thymus	55	525
Liver	47	50
Kidney	56	1029
Spleen	59	652
Testis	73	114
Blood	54	74
Muscle	31	54
Pancreas	53	276
Walker 256 tumor	49	42
Flexner-Jobling tumor	121	90
Jensen tumor	85	66
Primary hepatoma	85	60

[1] As micrograms per gram wet weight of tissue.

studies have shown that, when spleen cells are incubated with oxalacetic and acetic acids, no citrate accumulates unless fluoroacetate is added, and it is possible that citric acid in this tissue is metabolized as fast as it is formed; on the other hand, when tumor cells are incubated with oxalacetate and acetate, citrate accumulates in the absence of fluoroacetate, and the addition of fluoroacetate produces only a very small increase in this component (113). It is, therefore, possible that the tumor accumulates this metabolite faster than it can break it down. The rate-limiting factor or factors in normal and malignant tissues are not known at present. No matter what the level of efficiency of the process may be, it is clear that the Krebs cycle is wholly operative in both kinds of tissues.

The accumulation of lactic acid in tumors is a familiar phenomenon. Both this substance and its precursor, pyruvic acid, are metabolized by way of the Krebs cycle, and the specific enzyme entity which catalyzes the equilibrium between these two components is lactic dehydrogenase. The coenzyme for this factor is diphosphopyridine nucleotide (DPN). Extensive studies by Meister on a variety of tumors have shown that the mean apodehydrogenase level (in the presence of excess DPN) is nearly the same for normal as for cancerous tissues (114) (Table 76). The accumulation of lactic acid in tumors is not likely due to a decrease in the level of the apodehydrogenase in these tissues. A deficient oxidation of lactate to pyruvate in tumors could conceivably arise from a low concentration of the coenzyme, or from an excess of the reduced form of the coenzyme (cf. 115). Actually, the oxidized form predominates in both normal and tumor tissues (116) (117). Recent analyses (117) reveal that liver contains 268–446 γ of DPN per gram of fresh tissue, hepatoma contains about 85 γ,

TABLE 76

Lactic Dehydrogenase Activity of Normal and Neoplastic Mouse Tissues[1] (114)

Normal tissues	Activity	Neoplastic tissues	Activity
Liver	428	Hepatoma 112B	669
Kidney	369	Hepatoma 13/8	381
Spleen	144	Primary lung tumor	466
Pancreas	155	Lymphoma 1	292
Brain	228	Thymoma	316
Cardiac muscle	292	Sarcoma 37	428
Skeletal muscle	972	Gastric adenocarcinoma	332
Lung	83	Harding-Passey melanoma	162
Intestinal mucosa	732	Melanoma S-91	367
Gastric mucosa	201	Primary, mammary tumor	299
Submaxillary gland	137	Transplanted mammary tumor	389
Thymus	188	Granulosa cell tumor	257
Lymph nodes	209	Myoepithelioma	492
Ovary	116	Lymphoma 2	335
Testis	203	Rhabdomyosarcoma	250
Lactating breast	373		
Uterus	140		

[1] Mean values as moles $\times 10^{-8}$ pyruvate reduced per milligram total homogenate N per minute.

muscle contains 268–451 γ, and rhabdomyosarcoma contains about 95 γ. The corresponding values of $DPNH_2$ on the same basis are 114–200, about 26, 9–19, and about 32 γ. That tumors may have a relatively low content of factors concerned with electron transport is suggested by their low B-vitamin levels as compared with normal tissues (see below).

The earlier studies on the formation of lactic acid from glucose (glycolysis) were performed with tissue slices, and the failure to observe this reaction in homogenates was attributed to the need for the mechanisms inherent in the intact cell. The important experiments of LePage (118, 119) established the ability of whole-tissue homogenates, whether normal or neoplastic in origin, to carry out glycolysis of hexosediphosphate at nearly equal levels when such homogenates are fortified with added DPN. Weinhouse subsequently found that pyruvate, oxalacetate, and a number of other components of the citric acid cycle could be oxidized by homogenates strongly fortified with DPN (120). There is an active DPN-ase in tumors (121) which can be inhibited by nicotinamide (cf. 118, 119). There seems to be no change, however, in the level of this enzyme in liver when the latter becomes cancerous (121). Another approach to maintaining the metabolic integrity of the tissue homogenate has been to conserve high-energy phosphate. Thus, the apparent deficiency of certain oxidative activities in tumor homogenates has been related to the excessive breakdown of adenosine triphosphate (ATP) (122), so that when phosphate breakdown was suppressed by addition of fluoride, oxalacetate and pyruvate could be readily oxidized by homogenates of the Flexner-Jobling carcinoma (123) in the presence of added ATP. The synthesis of high-energy phosphate bonds during glycolysis and during certain types of aerobic oxidations probably provides much of the energy required for cell maintenance and growth. It is not likely that this requirement will be identical for all tissues, and, thus, the addition of fluoride to a number of different tumor homogenates provides a different degree of oxidative response for each tumor (124). In such tumor homogenates under conditions of anaerobic glycolysis, considerable pyruvic acid disappears, to an extent which cannot be accounted for in terms of lactic acid formation; one of the apparently major conversion products of pyruvate is propanediol phosphate ($CH_3CHOHCH_2OPO_3H_2$) (125). A logical intermediate in this reductive reaction would be acetol phosphate (126).

The oxidation of pyruvate, citrate, α-ketoglutarate, succinate, fumarate, and malate can be accomplished by tumor homogenates in the presence of added DPN, and, under these conditions, the level of oxidation in the tumor mitochondria on a per milligram of nitrogen basis is of the same order of magnitude as that of the mitochondria of normal tissues (107). With exception of succinate, there is a considerable rise in the level of oxidation

TABLE 77

EFFECT OF DPN ADDITION TO TISSUE MITOCHONDRIA (107)

Substrate	Oxygen consumed per milligram mitochondrial N in: Normal mouse liver, No added DPN	Normal mouse liver, Added DPN	Hepatoma 7A77, No added DPN	Hepatoma 7A77, Added DPN
None	37	49	15	44
Pyruvate	150	145	30	250
Citrate	176	215	14	153
α-Ketoglutarate	142	180	100	214
Succinate	145	165	125	116
Fumarate	130	156	15	143
Malate	160[1]	164[1]	33	176

[1] Rat liver.

of the Krebs cycle components in tumors (Table 77) when DPN is added, indicating that the potential glycolytic capacities of the two kinds of tissues are similar. When the mitochondrial particles are isolated with great care from isotonic sucrose homogenates in such a way as to exclude ATP-ase activity, net phosphate uptake can be measured in absence of added fluoride (126), and under such conditions it has been possible to demonstrate high net rates of ATP synthesis by tumor mitochondria during the oxidation of α-ketoglutarate and succinate (127), and in the presence of added DPN. In this case also, the requirement of hepatoma for DPN is greater than that of liver, but when this cofactor is added, the phosphorylation and oxidation reactions of normal and of tumor mitochondria approach the same order of magnitude. The requirement of tumor mitochondria for DPN may be linked to an intense DPN-ase activity of the cytoplasmic particles (128). Under conditions conducive to oxidative phosphorylation reactions related to succinate, the uptake of P^{32} into phospholipid and nucleic acid fractions of the mitochondrial particles of the tumor cell can be demonstrated (129). Coupled phosphate esterification and Krebs cycle intermediates oxidation are full properties of tumors, and the available evidence indicates that, under optimal conditions, both normal and cancer tissues can carry out these functions at nearly equal levels. The explanation for that tumor cul-de-sac, lactic acid, is still elusive.

The level of pyruvic acid in normal tissues is very low, as is that of α-ketoglutaric acid, except in brain and kidney (129); both α- keto acids are relatively high in concentration in neoplastic tissues (Table 78).

The synthesis of the fatty acid carbon chain in tumors has received relatively little attention, compared with that of proteins and nucleic acids. It would appear that the primary rat hepatoma possesses the ability to incorporate carbon of radioactive acetate and glucose into fatty acids *in*

TABLE 78

α-KETO ACIDS IN NORMAL AND TUMOR TISSUES OF FED RATS[1] (129)

Tissue	Pyruvic acid	α-Ketoglutaric acid	Oxalacetic acid
Brain	0.77	1.25	< 0.02
Heart	0.29	0.21	0.10
Kidney	0.29	2.35	0.08
Liver	0.14	0.26	0.11
Muscle	0.71	0.28	0.09
Flexner-Jobling tumor	1.50	1.75	0.09
Jensen sarcoma	1.55	0.78	0.04
Walker 256 tumor	1.95	1.15	0.03
Arterial blood	1.19	0.50	< 0.02
Venous blood	3.20	0.49	< 0.02

[1] Milligrams per cent.

TABLE 79

INCORPORATION OF CARBON FROM UNIFORMLY LABELED GLUCOSE INTO NON-PHOSPHOLIPID FATTY ACID OF LIVER AND HEPATOMA SLICES (107)

Tissue	Conversion capacity[1]	
	Fatty acids	Respiratory carbon dioxide
Liver	0.01	6
Hepatoma	0.5	40
Sarcoma	0.3	40

[1] Microatoms of substrate carbon incorporated into the product per gram of dry weight of tissue per hour.

vitro (107, 130, 131). The rates of lipogenesis in the tumors is generally considerably less than that of normal tissues, as measured by incorporation of acetate into lipids. However, when glucose is used as the carbon source, slices of hepatoma incorporate this carbon far more rapidly into the fatty acids than do slices of liver (107), a difference due to the relative ability of these tissues to utilize glucose as shown by the very low rate of glucose oxidation by liver, e.g., the low rate of incorporation of the glucose carbon in the respiratory carbon dioxide (Table 79). The special capacity of the neoplastic cell for autonomous protein synthesis may not be reflected in the synthesis of fats, for calculation of the rates of lipid synthesis from *in vitro* studies on tumors yields values much too low to account for the actual amount of fat present (107). It is therefore probable that tumor growth may constitute a drain upon the lipid resources of the host. The capacity of tumors to oxidize fatty acids is considerably less than of liver (109, 132, 133) (Table 80). The hepatoma loses the capacity to produce acetoacetate from fatty acids, characteristic of the normal liver (109), but curiously

TABLE 80

FATTY ACID OXIDATION (107, 132)

Tissue	Oxidation or conversion of:					
	Acetate	Butyrate	Hexanoate	Octanoate	Octanoate	Palmitate
Mouse liver	49.0	82.5	85.1	85.7	104	17.2
Hepatoma 112B			12.4	6.7		
Hepatoma 98/15	18.9	51.3	5.0	−2.1	45	11.4
Mammary tumor	5.9	12.0			0.6	5.4
Sarcoma 37	5.6	9.8			0.2	8.7
Rhabdomyosarcoma	7.2	15.8			0.6	10.7

TABLE 81

CONVERSION OF BUTYRATE TO ACETOACETATE AND OXIDATION OF LATTER (107)

Tissue	Conversion of butyrate	Oxidation of acetoacetate
Mouse liver	88	26.8
Hepatoma	4	55.1
Mammary tumor	3	20.2
Sarcoma 37	1	32.8
Rhabdomyosarcoma	6	20.4

enough the capacity to oxidize acetoacetate is not only retained in the hepatoma but actually raised in level above that of the liver (Table 81). Hepatoma homogenates oxidize choline at a rate less than 5% that of normal liver (28). The major portion of the total capacity of liver to oxidize octanoate is present in the mitochondrial fraction (cf. 134, 135), as is also the capacity to oxidize oxalacetic acid (136) and succinic acid (137). Cytochrome c is also found mainly in association with mitochondria (137). However, many of the glycolytic functions (138), as well as isocitric dehydrogenase (139), are principally found in the soluble fraction of normal tissues and of tumors, and it would appear that the Krebs cycle reactions are not exclusive properties of the mitochondria. Actually, when so many interrelated enzymatic reactions are considered, their distribution among the subcellular fractions is somewhat difficult to interpret, for the level of activity of any one of the enzymes in one fraction may be markedly affected by cofactors present in other fractions (cf. 139) and by reactions necessarily coupled with each other in different fractions. This mutual effect may of course be either additive or subtractive, and the peculiar phenomena displayed when one or more combinations of subcellular fractions are studied are well illustrated by the observations of Potter *et al.* (140).

The interpretation of the results of blocking the reactions of the Krebs cycle by addition of fluoroacetate suffers from the fact that the tissues must first convert this substance to a toxic fluorotricarboxylic acid (141). The use of malonate as an inhibitor does not possess this disadvantage, and by means of this reagent applied *in vivo* it was found that succinate accumulates in tumors to an extent comparable to that of other tissues, i.e., 3 to 5 μM per gram of wet weight in 2 hours (142). The radioactivity of injected acetate-1-C^{14} is rapidly incorporated into this succinate in normal tissues, and hardly at all in tumors (142a). It is of interest that, as succinate accumulates in the tumor of malonate-treated rats, the content of free glutamate and aspartate correspondingly decreases, suggesting the origin of one from the other. Another kind of *in vivo* enzyme inhibitor which has been employed is antimycin A, which characteristically and reversibly inhibits the succinoxidase of various tissues when administered to rats (143). This approach represents one of the few rational attempts at a chemotherapy and is based upon the possibility of totally inhibiting enzymes present in tumors at lower levels than in normal tissues, thereby destroying the former without permanent damage to the latter. The apparently rapid reactivation of the inhibited enzyme may impose a barrier to the application of this ingenious approach.

The direct oxidation of hexose monophosphate can be accomplished by TPN-linked dehydrogenases without passing through the hexosediphosphate stage. The first product of this oxidation is the lactone of 6-phosphogluconic acid, which, by further oxidative decarboxylation yields ribose-5-phosphate (143a). Since one of the main functions of the direct oxidative pathway may be to supply ribose-5-phosphate for incorporation into ribonucleic acid and coenzymes, it would be expected to play an important part in the metabolism of tumors. It is therefore of interest to note that the levels of glucose-6-phosphate dehydrogenase and of 6-phosphogluconate dehydrogenase in various rat and mouse transplanted tumors are not particularly elevated but tend to fall within the range of normal tissues (143b).

Enzymes of Protein Metabolism. The proteins are molecules of high molecular weight which, when hydrolyzed by acids, alkalies, or proteolytic enzymes, yield a variety of α-amino acids. The course of protein metabolism is, briefly, as follows. Ingested protein is hydrolyzed at various internal peptide bonds by gastric pepsin at an acid pH, yielding primarily a mixture of relatively low molecular weight polypeptides. This mixture, plus any undigested protein, passes into the intestinal tract, where pancreatic secretion produces the hydrolysis of the residual protein and the polypeptide mixture to smaller peptides and free amino acids. The smaller peptides are finally hydrolyzed by intestinal mucosal secretion to the free amino acids, so that the final digestion product of the ingested protein is the mixture of α-amino acids of which it was originally composed. The amino acids are absorbed from the gut into the blood stream in which they pass to the liver and begin their course of intracellular metabolism. The subsequent passage of the amino acids is not well known. They are undoubtedly transported humorally to other tissues, and in each tissue they are reconstituted into proteins characteristic of that tissue or of its secretions by a variety of intracellular proteolytic enzymes generally grouped under the designation of cathepsins. These intracellular cathepsins act optimally in the hydrolysis of proteins at a pH of 3.5 to 5.0. On smaller amino acid combinations such as the di- or tripeptides, they act optimally at higher pH values, e.g., 7 to 9. The equilibrium mixtures invariably lie far to the side of hydrolysis, and the conditions for biosynthesis of the proteins are as yet not understood, except for the obvious fact that some external source of energy is necessary to couple with the reaction in order to drive it toward synthesis. The problem of accounting for the fate of the individual amino acids is further complicated by the fact that they do not merely rest patiently in the cell waiting their turn to be synthesized to proteins but undergo a variety of enzymatic reactions whereby they are converted to compounds related to the sugars and to the fats, as well as to other kinds of α-amino acids. It is impossible to cover adequately the entire subject of protein metabolism in this brief section, and attention will be paid only to those several reactions studied in connection with cancer. It is not improbable that the topic of protein metabolism and the biosynthesis of proteins may be the core of the cancer problem. A simple allusion to one of the most common phenomena of cancer should suffice to substantiate this, namely, the fact that protein is laid down in the growing tumor at the expense of the body protein of the host. Anabolism in the tumor, catabolism in the host—the answer to this paradoxical situation might illuminate entirely the perplexities offered by the problem of cancer. In the few phenomena described below, and elsewhere in this monograph, little light has been shed on this fundamental question.

Pepsin and rennin, which are specialized functions of the gastric mucosa, disappear when this mucosa becomes neoplastic (144). No data are available on the proteolytic systems of neoplastic pancreas or intestinal mucosa.

A number of proteolytic systems have been studied in liver, and in the hepatoma which arises from it. As a rule, those enzymes which hydrolyze peptide bonds are generally higher in activity in the hepatoma than in normal liver. This includes preeminently cathepsin, aminopeptidases, and aminodehydropeptidases. The activity of these enzymes is measured in terms of their hydrolytic rates and bears no relation to the problem of synthesis in the hepatoma unless it is assumed that synthesis is simply a reversal of hydrolysis.

Taking first the specific hepatic systems: histidase activity (145), and the urea-synthesizing mechanisms, whether the citrulline or ornithine plus ammonia system (146), or the ornithine-glutamic acid system (147; cf. 148), as well as the glutamine or asparagine transaminase-deamidase system (149; cf. 150), are all considerably lower in the hepatoma than in normal liver, or else absent altogether. Arginase, another component of the urea cycle, is also markedly reduced in the tumor (151) (Table 66). Another hepatic system considerably reduced in the hepatoma is that responsible for the synthesis of *p*-aminohippuric acid (147). This enzyme system is associated with the mitochondrial fraction of liver (148), and, although the mitochondria concentration is less in hepatoma than in liver, this decrease does not explain the virtually complete disappearance of the enzyme in the tumor. When ammonia is added to slices of liver or of hepatoma suspended in a glucose-containing medium, the rate of disappearance of the ammonia is distinctly greater in the former than in the latter tissue (146; cf. 77). The ammonia consumed is presumed to enter into a synthetic reaction with glucose or its conversion products. In view of the rapid growth characteristics of the hepatoma, it is somewhat surprising to find that the ammonia consumption is less than in normal liver, but it is possible that the synthetic processes of the tumor require other factors and perhaps other conditions than those experimentally employed.

Systems in liver shared to greater or less degree with other normal tissues show different responses to the neoplastic transformation. The higher level of cathepsin in hepatoma, using proteins as substrates, has been mentioned (89). When α-benzoyl-arginineamide is used as substrate, the hepatoma is again more active than is normal liver (152, 153). Catheptic enzymes are known to be activated in their hydrolytic reactions by various agents such as sulfhydryl groups. The ultrafiltrates of hepatomas contain less catheptic activators than do comparable ultrafiltrates of normal liver (154). Glutathione appears to be a major cathepsin activator in normal liver and in hepatoma and is considerably reduced in amount in the latter tissue. However, fetal livers have a low glutathione concentration, but their ultrafiltrates possess very high catheptic-activating capacity, and it would appear that some other tissue component than glutathione must function in this situation. The observations mentioned above of the higher catheptic activity of hepatoma were noted in systems to which an optimal amount of activator had been added, and the results indicated the higher concentration of catheptic protein in the tumor. It is curious that this higher concentration of enzyme protein should be accompanied by a diminution in the amount of its activator. This is, however, not an isolated instance, for in the case of such conjugated proteins as the riboflavin- and pyridoxal-enzyme proteins, the neoplastic transformation is accompanied by a disparate change in the relative amounts of both apoenzyme and prosthetic group.

The glutamic acid-pyruvic acid transaminase system is lower in hepatoma

TABLE 82

Protein Metabolic Systems in Normal Liver and Hepatoma[1] (149, 155a, 161)

Substrate	System	Activity in		
		Liver	Hepatoma	Fetal liver
Glutamine	Glutaminase I[2]	166	1000	1300
Glutamine	Transaminase-deamidase[2]	48	28	32
Asparagine	Transaminase-deamidase[2]	50	18	22
Glycylalanine	Aminopeptidase[3]	920	4520	—
Alanylglycine	Aminopeptidase[3]	1340	6060	—
Glycylleucine	Aminopeptidase[3]	4230	7240	—
Leucylglycine	Aminopeptidase[3]	580	2580	—
Glycylphenylalanine	Aminopeptidase[3]	2360	6970	—
Phenylalanylglycine	Aminopeptidase[3]	300	900	—
Glycyldehydroalanine	Dehydropeptidase I[2]	60	384	—
Glycyldehydrophenylalanine	Dehydropeptidase I[2]	12	0	—
Glycyldehydroalanine	Dehydropeptidase I[3]	96	280	—
Glycyldehydronorleucine	Dehydropeptidase I[3]	16	9	—
Acetylalanine	Acylase[2]	30	23	—
Acetylleucine	Acylase[2]	35	33	—
Acetylmethionine	Acylase[2]	70	67	—
Acetylglutamic acid	Acylase[2]	41	42	—
Acetyldehydroalanine	Dehydropeptidase II[2]	3	0	—
Acetyldehydroleucine	—	0	0	—
Cystine	Cystine desulfurase[2]	2	0	—

[1] Cf. references for experimental details.
[2] Rat tissues.
[3] Mouse tissues.

than in normal liver (155), and the phosphate-activated glutaminase system is increased in the tumor (Table 82) (155a).

Transaminase systems in mouse lymphomas, involving alanine-α-ketoglutarate, aspartic-α-ketoglutarate, alanine-oxalacetate, and glutamic-oxalacetate, are at about the same order of magnitude of activity as in various normal lymphatic tissues, such as thymus and spleen (156).

The peptidase systems of tissues form a complex of a number of enzymes, and attention will be focused chiefly on those which do or do not require a free α-amino group on the acyl residue of the peptide chain. The latter may be considered to be intracellular carboxypeptidases or acylases; the former may be designated as aminopeptidases. Aminopeptidases acting on natural, L-amino acid-containing peptides are found in the soluble fraction of all tissues at a relatively high activity. When liver is converted to a hepatoma, this activity rises very considerably (89, 149) regardless of the nature of the amino acids in the peptide (Table 82). Aminodehydropeptidases (dehydropeptidases I), which act upon peptides in which the terminal residue has an α,β-unsaturated bond, are also found in high activity in normal tissues, chiefly in the kidney in which it is associated with the particulate fraction, in contrast with other tissues in which it is soluble (147). This enzyme is multiple in nature (158). Thus, kidney particulates readily hydrolyze all known glycyldehydroamino acids, but there is a soluble fraction which hydrolyzes only glycyldehydroalanine (159, 160) In view of this multiple nature, it is not surprising that in hepatoma only the activity toward glycyldehydroalanine is increased, whereas that toward other glycyldehydroamino acids is diminished (149, 161) (Table 100). There may therefore occur in the neoplastic transformation of liver not only the known reduction in the number of particulates but also an increase in certain soluble enzyme systems.

The intracellular acylases are soluble systems, and those which act upon such substrates as acetyl-L-amino acids are found in all tissues. The neoplastic transformation of liver is accompanied by no change in the level of this enzyme, using a variety of acylated L-amino acids (149) (Table 82). The intracellular acylase (dehydropeptidase II) is effective only toward acetyldehydroalanine (149) and is found only in liver, kidney, and pancreas (162); the neoplastic transformation of liver results in a nearly complete disappearance of this enzyme. The quite different distribution of the aminopeptidase and aminodehydropeptidase on the one hand, and that of the acylase and dehydroamino acid acylase on the other, is presumptive evidence that the enzymes acting upon the saturated and unsaturated peptides are separate systems. This is emphasized by the following observations (163). When the soluble fraction of rat liver homogenates is heated at 60° and pH 6.2, a large part of the total activity of this fraction toward chloroacetyl-L-alanine is destroyed, whereas little if any of the activity toward chloroacetyldehydroalanine is affected. The residual activity after the heat treatment is nearly equal for the two substrates, and further attempts to separate this activity in respect to the two substrates was unsuccessful. It would appear that there may be two soluble acylases in liver, namely an acylase for N-acyl-L-amino acids which is relatively heat-labile, and an acylase which does not distinguish between N-acyl-L-amino acids and N-acyldehydroalanine and which is relatively heat-stable. The latter enzyme bears some resemblance to renal acylase I (160, 164) and is probably the one designated earlier as dehydropeptidase II. The neoplastic transformation of the liver is apparently accompanied by a loss of the latter of these systems and a retention in nearly unaltered amount of the former. The fraction of the total activity toward chloroacetyl-L-amino acids which is present in the lost dehydropeptidase II is relatively small, and hence the activity remaining in the hepatoma is nearly the same as in the liver. The third soluble hepatic system, namely that toward glycyldehydroalanine, is inactivated at 48°. It is therefore possible to demonstrate the presence of each of the three hepatic systems separately. This separate identity is consistent with the observation that one system rises (glycyldehydroalanine), one system disappears (chloroacetyldehydroalanine), and one system does not change (chloroacetyl-L-alanine) when the liver becomes a hepatoma (163).

Cystine desulfurase, like dehydropeptidase II, is found only in liver, kidney, and pancreas, and like this enzyme is virtually absent in the hepatoma. The hydrolytic rates of amino acid amides are generally lower in hepatoma than in normal liver. Further characterization of the individual systems in tumors is desirable, if only to obtain some concept of the fine structure of the metabolic pattern in these tissues. The loss of dehydropeptidase II and of cystine desulfurase in tumors simply emphasizes the specific function which these enzymes must exert in certain normal tissues; they evidently play no role in basic metabolic reactions concerned with malignant tissues. The high value in all tumors for the activity of the enzyme acting on glycyldehydroalanine alone of all the dehydropeptides studied may of course be due to association with some other soluble system more crucial to tumor metabolism, or it may reflect some basic metabolic need in these malignant tissues not shared by peptides involving other dehydroamino acids. Again, it should be emphasized that these are all lytic reactions, and their connection with the synthetic reactions characteristic of malignant tissue is quite obscure at the present time. Indeed, in the case of the dehydropeptides a class of substances of no known biological origin has been considered, although the process of α,β-unsaturation, as Knoop first pointed out in the case of amino acid oxidation, may well be a biological mechanism. It is of interest in this connection to emphasize the fact that such difficulties in transposition of interpretations of peptidase distribution from one tissue to the other occur only when dehydropeptide substrates are considered. Thus, with a large variety of chloroacetyl- and glycyl-L-amino acids studied under identical conditions with homogenates of kidney and liver, the ratio of hydrolytic rates for each substrate by the two tissues were in every instance close to 3. With a similar group of glycyldehydroamino acids, the corresponding ratios varied from 32 for glycyldehydroalanine to 155 for glycyldehydronorvaline, and to 650 for glycyldehydrophenylalanine; the ratio for chloroacetyldehydroalanine was 7 (160). There appears to be something exceptional in the behavior and distribution of the dehydropeptidases, and the curious position of this class of enzymes is rather challenging.

Under normal conditions in normal tissues it can be expected that the template by which proteins are synthesized is ordinarily nearly flawless, and that each side chain fits into its proper niche along the polypeptide chain. It is possible to conceive, however, that if this template (specific genic nucleic acid?) alters or is altered even slightly, one or more side chains may not fall into their proper and usual position in the polypeptide chain—that is to say, proper and usual for the normal proteins of the cell—and a new and foreign protein is thus synthesized on the polypeptide chain skeleton of the old. Such a protein will no longer be amenable or respond to those normal systems of control which preserve the equilibrium of the cell and, hence, will keep on multiplying indefinitely. The altered template thus functions like the sorcerer's apprentice in calling into being unwanted products in excess. The possibility is not excluded that the picture drawn may be pertinent to the problem of the origin and continued growth of the cancer cell. To throw light on this possibility experimentally, it is necessary to show that the proteins, or at least a significant fraction of the proteins, of a tumor are different from the proteins of the normal tissue of origin. Up to the present time this problem has received relatively little chemical attention. The distribution of sulfur among normal tissues and tumors of any one species appears to be similar. Immunologic studies have not been entirely conclusive.

The report by Kögl and Erxleben in 1939 concerning the presence of D-amino acids in tumor proteins has failed of confirmation in numerous quarters. The report, however, stimulated work on the investigation of the enzymatic hydrolysis of peptides containing D-amino acids participating in the peptide bond. D-Peptidase activity was noted in most animal tissues, both normal and neoplastic, and the following conclusions were drawn (164a): (a) the activity is not greatly different in normal tissues and in tumors; (b) there is no distinction between the ratio of the activities on L- and D-peptides of extracts from normal and from cancerous tissues; and (c) the activation (by manganese and cysteine) and the inhibition behavior of the D-peptidases of normal and cancerous tissue is very nearly the same.

Enzymes of Nucleic Acid Metabolism. The nucleic acids consist for the most part of polymerized tetranucleotides of high molecular weight with specific physical properties. Two major types of nucleic acid exist, one containing deoxyribose as the sugar component and found exclusively in the nuclei of cells as part of the chromatin, the other containing ribose as the sugar component and found in both nucleus (generally associated with the nucleolus) and cytoplasm. Thymus nucleic acid and yeast nucleic acid have customarily been employed as models, respectively, of deoxyribonucleic acid and of ribonucleic acid. The metabolism of the two types of nucleic acid, although following essentially similar lines, apparently requires different enzymatic systems, at least in the earlier stages, when the large molecules are attacked.

Aqueous solutions of thymus nucleate are highly viscous and show intense streaming birefringence. Yeast nucleate is almost completely insoluble in acid solutions. When these two types of nucleic acid are incubated with tissue extracts at neutral pH, a progressive diminution in these properties occurs. The enzymes responsible have been designated deoxyribonucleodepolymerase and ribonucleodepolymerase (164b, 164c). Simultaneously, ammonia and phosphate derived from the nucleates appears in the mixtures. The deamination proceeds with the hydrolysis of two of the three available amino groups in each type of nucleate, the susceptible groups being derived from the adenine and guanine moieties. The depolymerase, dephosphorylase, and deaminase for ribonucleate can be distinguished from those for the deoxyribonucleate by employing dialyzed instead of fresh tissue extracts. The enzymes for the former substrate are unaffected, whereas the enzymes for the latter substrate vanish in activity. The enzymatic action on deoxyribonucleate can, however, be restored in the dialyzed extract by the addition of any one of a wide variety of salts of alkali and alkaline earth metals as well as of certain organic bases. This restoration in activity does not occur when the anion of an otherwise effective cation is fluoride, bicarbonate, or phosphate. Indeed, these anions when added to fresh tissue extracts considerably inhibit the deamination and dephosphorylation of deoxyribonucleate, and to a lesser extent that of ribonucleate. In any event, the metabolism of the deoxyribonucleic acid requires the presence of salt, whereas the metabolism of the ribonucleic acid to all appearances does not require the presence of salt. The normally active ion for the metabolism of the former nucleate is probably magnesium, although a wide variety of divalent cations, acting at optimal concentrations which may vary for each cation, can also serve in this connection *in vitro* (164d). The depolymerase for deoxyribonucleic acid appears to be associated chiefly with the mitochondria of the cytoplasm (164e, 164f), a curious fact in view of the complete limitation of the substrate for this enzyme to the nucleus. The latter entity is practically completely devoid of the enzyme.

The deamination and dephosphorylation capacities for nucleotides and nucleates vary from tissue to tissue. The hepatoma is considerably more active than normal liver. The inorganic phosphate which appears in digests of the nucleates with dialyzed normal tissues (plus added salt in the case of deoxyribonucleate) is almost invariably greater than in fresh extracts of these tissues. This might be interpreted as being due to either (a) the presence of an inhibitor, or (b) the presence of phosphate acceptors in the fresh extract. No other phosphate ester studied, including the nucleotides, glycerophosphate, etc., yields more phosphate in dialyzed than in fresh tissue extracts, and it would appear as if this were a unique property of the nucleic acids (e.g., as phosphate donors). The phosphate split from the nucleates in dialyzed hepatoma extracts is no greater than in fresh extracts, a striking contrast with liver, which suggests that the hepatoma is lacking in either inhibitor or acceptors of phosphate from nucleates. In many respects, the extracts of tumors are comparatively "empty" of dialyzable components. Tumors have little luxury margin.

When the nucleates are incubated with fresh tissue extracts in cellophane bags, the outer fluid being in considerable excess and containing Mg^{++} and Na^{+} chlorides in at least 0.005 *M* concentration, it is noted that these substrates are invariably split into particles capable of passing through the cellophane membrane (<12,000 to 18,000 in molecular weight). With all tissues except pancreas, ammonia also appears in the dialyzate, and the rate of deamination very closely parallels that of splitting. Addition of fluoride, phosphate, and bicarbonate inhibits almost completely the splitting and deamination of deoxyribonucleate and inhibits only relatively slightly those of ribonucleate. In the absence of any added salt, the splitting and deamination of ribonucleate is little affected, but those of deoxyribonucleate are completely inhibited. The deamination of guanine and of the ribonucleotides is not especially sensitive to the presence or absence of salts, although fluoride inhibits to some extent the deamination of the nucleotides. It is not yet clear whether, under these conditions, deamination precedes splitting or *vice versa*. Since the rates of splitting and of deamination are so very nearly the same, it is possible that one of these two reactions may be either spontaneous (non-enzymatic) or also extremely rapidly enzymatic. A third possibility might be based upon the presence in tissues of two enzymes with nearly identical rates for the splitting and deamination of nucleic acids. The case of the pancreas is instructive in this respect. Extracts of this tissue rapidly split the nucleates but do not deaminate them, in spite of the fact that there are present in such extracts active deaminases for the purine nucleotides and free guanine. At the present time it would appear that the capacities of tissues to split and to deaminate and dephosphorylate the nucleates are due to separate phenomena. In all cases studied, the rates of deamination, of dephosphorylation, and of splitting of ribonucleate in fresh tissue digests exceeded those of deoxyribonucleate. This may have been due to the fact that the preparations of the latter were invariably more highly polymerized than were those of the former, and the depolymerization of the deoxyribonucleate imposed a lag over the entire series of reactions.

When the nucleates are incubated in test tubes with fresh extracts of liver or of *transplanted* hepatomas (of the rat or mouse), the deamination and dephosphorylation by the tumors far exceeds that by the normal homologous tissue. This is brought out particularly well by successive dilution experiments. On the other hand, the deamination rate by other tumors either equals or falls considerably behind that of their respective normal tissues of origin (especially in the case of deoxyribonucleate), and in this respect the hepatomas may be considered to be exceptional. Under dialytic conditions of incubation as described in the preceding paragraph, the rates of splitting (and of deamination) of the nucleates by liver and hepatoma, thymus and thymoma, etc., are all very nearly of the same order of magnitude. The deamination of the nucleates within the test tube by the primary rat hepatoma is equal to that of normal liver. Both tissues are considerably less active than the transplanted hepatoma. The splitting (and deamination) of the nucleates by extracts of each of these three tissues under dialytic conditions is, however, of the same order.

It is obviously not proper to draw conclusions on the basis of comparison of two such different procedures as incubation in closed tubes on the one hand, and in dialysis sacks on the other, for the experimental conditions are not the same. Nevertheless, the near uniformity among normal and neoplastic tissues observed by the dialytic procedure as contrasted with the results in non-dialyzed digests prompts inquiry as to the possible reasons therefor. The data on the depolymerases for the two kinds of nucleic acid reveal that the activities of these enzymes are the same in normal liver and in the hepatoma, whether mouse or rat, and indeed they are of nearly the same order of magnitude for all tissues, whether normal or neoplastic, within each species. The splitting phenomenon of the nucleates under dialytic conditions may thus be a reflection of depolymerase activity, whereas the deamination of the nucleates within closed systems (test tube) may be to a considerable extent independent of depolymerase activity. Until this problem is finally elucidated, the deamination of the nucleates will be referred respectively to ribonucleodeaminase and to deoxyribonucleodeaminase without commitment as to the molecular size of the substrate.

It is of interest to note a certain parallelism in characteristics between the amidase for benzoylarginineamide and the deaminases for the nucleic acids. Both types of enzymes are present in normal liver and in the primary rat hepatoma, both enzymes increase in activity in the transplanted rat hepatoma, and among normal tissues these enzymes are most active in spleen, least active in muscle, and intermediate in activity in liver, kidney, and brain. Both benzoylarginineamidase and deoxyribonucleodeaminase are strongly inhibited by phosphate. The parallelism among various tissues of the amidase and catheptic proteinase, on the one hand, and of the nucleodeaminase on the other, lends some weight to the viewpoint that protein metabolism and nucleic acid metabolism are interrelated. Intracellular nucleases have been found to be closely associated with cathepsins, and indeed, from the criteria that both activities are dependent upon free —SH groups and both function optimally at an acid pH, they appear at the present time to be due to the same protein complex (164g). Newer chromatographic techniques, however, have succeeded in partially separating these activities.

Extended studies on the rate of decolorization of methylene blue in extracts of liver and of hepatoma in the presence of the nucleates revealed the pronounced retarding effect of the nucleates on the decolorization rate in liver extracts and the pronounced accelerating rate in extracts of the transplanted hepatoma (165). At every dye concentration employed in hepatoma extracts, ribonucleate accelerated the decolorization rate of the dye more than did the deoxyribonucleate. The difference in effect of the two nucleates in liver extracts on the one hand and in hepatoma extracts on the other reveals a striking qualitative difference in the properties of the two kinds of homologous tissues. (As shown above in Tables 66 and 67, the properties in these respects of the primary hepatoma and of the liver are identical; these properties markedly alter only in the transplant.) This difference is further revealed in that, under all conditions employed and with increasing amounts of dye present, the relative decolorization rate in liver extracts rises, that in hepatoma extracts falls. The same phenomena hold in the case of mouse as in the case of rat hepatic tissues. The capacity of the tumor extracts to utilize the presence of ribonucleate even far more than that of deoxyribonucleate in the oxidation of substrates through methylene blue is noteworthy. Whether the added nucleates in the hepatoma extracts function catalytically (i.e. as hydrogen transporters), or are simply used as substrates, cannot be answered at the present time. The rapid turnover of the nucleates in hepatoma tissue, ribonucleate more than deoxyribonucleate, as compared with liver, has been reported by Brues *et al.* (166). Furthermore, the higher rate of deamination of the nucleates in the tumor may be related to the acceleration of dye decolorization rate, i.e., furnishing of oxidizable groups.

The dialysis studies reveal that the decolorization rates of dialyzed liver and hepatoma extracts are of the same order; the difference between fresh extracts of these tissues must probably lie in the relative amounts of dialyzable substrates. This is, however, not the entire story, for the decolorization rate can be restored in large measure to the dialyzed extract by adding coenzyme I (diphosphopyridine nucleotide) and bicarbonate (166), the response still being greater in the case of the liver than of the hepatoma. The results with dialyzed tissues also suggest that molecules of high molecular weight may participate in metabolic (oxidative) reactions. The much lower decolorization rate of methylene blue in fresh extracts of tumors as compared with that in fresh extracts of certain normal tissues has also been observed by Heinlein (167).

The total content of ribonucleic acid and of deoxyribonucleic acid in hepatomas appears to be somewhat higher than that of normal or regenerating liver (168–171). Both hepatoma and fetal liver have a higher proportion of deoxyribonucleic acid and a lower proportion of ribonucleic acid than the comparable adult tissue (172, 173). These findings are in agreement with those of Stowell (174), who noted by photometric procedures a

TABLE 83

NUCLEIC ACID CONSTITUENTS OF VARIOUS ORIGINS (176–180)

Nucleic acid and origin	Molar proportions of constituents				
	Adenine	Guanine	Cytosine	Uracil	Thymine
Yeast ribonucleic acid	3.2	3.1	3.0	1.0	
Pancreas ribonucleic acid	3.6	8.8	4.5	1.0	
Fowl sarcoma ribonucleic acid	1.1	3.7	2.2	1.0	
Yeast deoxyribonucleic acid	1.8	1.0	1.0		1.9
Thymus deoxyribonucleic acid	1.6	1.2	1.0		1.5
Mouse sarcoma deoxyribonucleic acid		1.1			1.0
Rat sarcoma deoxyribonucleic acid		1.2			1.0

slightly higher content per unit volume and per cell of deoxyribonucleic acid in epidermoid carcinomas than in normal human epidermis. However, there is apparently less deoxyribonucleate in a transplanted squamous cell mouse carcinoma than in normal mouse skin (169). Stowell analyzed sections photometrically of twenty various types of human tumors and noted that the deoxyribonucleic acid content per unit volume of 18 was definitely higher than in adjacent normal tissue (174). Qualitatively, the nucleic acids isolated from tumors appear to be the same as those isolated from normal tissues (175). Quantitatively, however, the newer methods of chromatographic separations and analysis have revealed distinct differences among the constituents of nucleic acids, depending upon their origin (Table 83) (176–180). Physicochemically, tumor deoxyribonucleic acid closely resembles in its properties of ionization, light absorption, and viscosity the nucleic acid of the thymus (181). The gross macromolecular structure of the nucleic acid with its hydrogen-bonding may not be greatly different among the various nucleic acids, but the evidence which has emerged during the past few years on the heterogeneity of this class of substances, based in part on analytical data, has required interpretation in terms of intimate structure as well as composition. This problem has been ingeniously considered by Stern, who has suggested possible modes of variation based on the sequence or spatial orientation of the component nucleotides in reference to the backbone of the polynucleotide chain, as well as on variations in chain length or degrees of polymerization (182, 183). Further evidence on the internal variations possible in the molecular structure of nucleic acid arose from the observations that each of the nucleotides produced by hydrolysis of ribonucleic acid exists in two isomeric forms (cf. 184 and 185), and that phosphate esterification at the 5′-position is equally as significant as at the 2′ and 3′-positions (185). The 5′-phosphate is the major bond in ribonucleic acid, with other links of phosphate at either the 2′- or 3′-position or both (185a). Ribonuclease is most probably a phosphodiesterase which is specific for the non-3′-phosphate bonds of the pyrimidine nucleoside phosphate esters. Schmidt, Cubiles, and Thannhauser had earlier shown that this enzyme hydrolyzes the linkages involving pyrimidine nucleotides but not those involving purine nucleotides (185b).

Potter (185c) has considered the ribose and deoxyribose moieties of nucleic acids as essential metabolites, which are formed from glucose metabolites by the action of enzymes which must compete with other enzymes whose function is to convert the same metabolites to pyruvic acid, lactic acid, and finally CO_2. When glucose-1-C^{14} was given to rats with tumor, the ribose in the nucleic acid of the tumor had 2,000 c.p.m. per gram of tissue at 1 hour and 4,380 c.p.m. at 5 hours, whereas the liver component had 0 and 534 c.p.m. respectively; the deoxyribose of the tumor had 650 and 2,260 c.p.m. at these time intervals, whereas the corresponding deoxyribose in the liver had 0 and 0 c.p.m. at these times. These observations are remindful of the administration of glycine-C^{14} to similar rats whereby the tumor steadily gained radioactivity on the whole tissue basis, whereas normal tissues lost radioactivity.

Although, as described below, there appears to be a relative constancy in the amount of deoxyribonucleic acid per nucleus in mammalian cells, excluding polyploidy, it is probable that this nuclear component is composed of at least two fractions which can be distinguished by their differing solubilities in saline (186). Moreover, these two fractions are metabolically dissimilar, for with the aid of C^{14}-formate it was observed that the isotope was incorporated and retained to an unequal extent in the purine and pyrimidine bases of the two fractions. Each tissue apparently possesses a different pattern of biosynthesis of the two deoxyribonucleic fractions, suggesting a metabolic heterogeneity in each tissue. A heterogeneous distribution of P^{32} in the mononucleotides of rat and mouse liver deoxyribonucleic acid has also been noted (187), and it is probable that the biosynthesis of the nucleic acid bases results largely from exchange type of reactions, rather than from a simultaneous assembling of all the components on a template. However, if there are a large number of nucleic acids of different base composition, the bases might be renewed at the same rates, but the mixtures of such heterogeneous nucleic acids would behave as if there were an unequal renewal (186). Aside from the fact that ribonucleic acid is distributed among the nucleus and various cytoplasmic fractions, the heterogeneity of this cell component in terms of composition (Table 83) and of metabolic behavior is now well known (188, 189). Thus, the nuclear ribonucleic acid is synthesized at a rate considerably greater than that of the cytoplasm fractions (190-193). Evidence from the natural occurrence of 4-amino-5-imidazolecarboxamide as a nucleoside or nucleotide (194, 195) suggests that under some conditions ribose addition may occur prior to ring closure of the purine base. Little is known of the extent of the distribution of different fractions of each of the nucleic acid types in neoplastic tissue, or of their metabolic origin and fate. Since each tissue possesses its own pattern of nucleic acid biosynthesis, it would be expected that malignant tissue, even though its total content might not be greatly different from that of normal tissues, must possess a distribution of the nucleic acids and a metabolic pattern peculiar to itself.

The ratio of cytoplasmic to nuclear volume is 5.85 for rat liver and 3.04 for the primary rat hepatoma (173). Since both normal liver and hepatoma have the same size distribution of nuclear volumes (196), it follows that the cytoplasmic volume in the hepatoma is about one-half as great as that in the liver cell, and that, roughly, there are about twice as many cells per unit volume in hepatoma as in liver. Consequently, on the basis of the data (173), the deoxyribonucleic acid content in the nucleus is about the same for hepatoma as for liver, but the content of ribonucleic acid is greater in the cytoplasm of the hepatoma than of the liver (cf. 197). In leukemic spleens of mice, there is no change in the content of deoxyribonucleic acid from normal, although there is a considerable increase in the content of total ribonucleic acid (198), the greater part of this increase occurring in the nuclear fraction and the small, submicroscopic granules. The increase in deoxyribonucleic acid in tumors may be due more to an increase in the number of nuclei than to an increase in amount of this component per nucleus. Ribonucleic acid is found in both nucleus and cytoplasm, and it is difficult to interpret its changes during neoplasia except by following its amount in each of the subcellular fractions (cf. 199). Both normal mouse spleen and leukemic mouse spleen contain close to 0.5 mg. deoxyribonucleic acid per milligram of nitrogen, or about 15 mg. per gram of spleen (198), but the ribonucleic acid to nitrogen ratios in the nuclear and small-granule fractions of the former rise from 0.07 and 0.3, respectively, to 0.3 and 0.5. Somewhat lower figures have been reported for the deoxyribonucleic acid phosphorus in normal mouse splenic lymphocytes, the average value being 0.49×10^{-9} mg. per lymphocyte (200); per lymphocyte in leukemic mice the values ranged from 0.66 to 0.72×10^{-9} mg. Similar figures for samples of bone marrow aspirated from patients with lymphocytic leukemia were 0.68×10^{-9} mg., and from patients with granulocytic leukemia, 0.82×10^{-9} mg., per cell (201). These values were considerably decreased after therapeutic X-irradiation. X-irradiation itself reduces the incorporation of P^{32} into the nucleic acids of tumors (201a). Analysis of highly polymerized deoxyribonucleic acids from leukemic, diseased but not leukemic, and normal human spleens for molar amounts of the bases revealed in all cases a nearly similar preponderance of adenine and thymine over guanine and cytosine, the total amount of purines versus pyrimidines being nearly equimolar (201b).

The apparent constancy of the deoxyribonucleic acid of the rat liver nucleus during carcinogenesis (32, 197, 202) permits calculation of the cell

TABLE 84

DEOXYRIBONUCLEIC ACID CONTENT OF INDIVIDUAL NUCLEI OF ANIMAL CELLS

Source	Micrograms × 10^6
Liver of man, cattle, hog, dog, rabbit, rat, mouse, horse, and sheep	5.0–14.0
Kidney of man, cattle, hog, dog, rabbit, rat, and mouse	5.0– 9.0
Thymus of cattle	6.4– 7.2
Pancreas of cattle	6.9
Tumors of fowl, rat liver, and mouse ascites cells	5.1–14.0
Mouse spleen	6.6
Leukemic mouse spleen	7.4

composition using this component as a standard of reference (203) and further permits a calculation of the number of cells and thereby a measure of growth. Data in Table 84 are based upon the results of Griffin *et al.* (204, 205), as calculated by Davidson and Leslie (203). The diminution in protein content of the liver during carcinogenesis affects mainly the mitochondria, although the small granules are also involved (32). In the rat liver, carcinogenesis affects the cytoplasm more than the nucleus, at least in terms of the considerable drop in protein. No matter whether the liver tumor is induced by an azo dye or by aminofluorene, it ends up by being lower in protein, ribonucleic acid, and riboflavin *per cell* than is the normal liver. Davidson and Leslie (206) have suggested that normal embryonic growth and differentiation are accompanied by an increasing protein content of the dividing cells; if the decreased protein content of malignant cells is equally universal, it would provide an interesting contrast.

The amount of deoxyribonucleic acid in the nuclei of tumors has been estimated as about 6×10^{-6} γ per nucleus for liver tumors (197), 10 to 14×10^{-6} γ (32) and 14×10^{-6} γ per nucleus for mouse ascites tumor cells (207). For a fowl tumor, a value of 5.1×10^{-6} γ per nucleus has been estimated (203) (Table 85). The ascites tumor cells contain about twice as much of this compound as do normal somatic mouse cells, and so, too, do the fowl tumor cells in relation to normal fowl somatic cells. However, many types of ascites tumors appear to differ considerably in their deoxyribonucleic content, much larger values being found with sarcomas and carcinomas, and relatively low or average values being noted with lymphomas (208). It does not seem likely that these differences can be correlated with different growth rates, for there is no apparent relation of nucleic acid content to the mitotic index or survival time (208). These differences in content may simply be an expression of polyploidy and not necessarily related to neoplasia. On the other hand, some of the variations in values may be ascribed to the experimental procedures employed (cf. 209). When polyploidy is taken into consideration, the average deoxyribonucleic acid content

TABLE 85

CHEMICAL COMPOSITION OF LIVER AND LIVER TUMORS REFERRED TO CONTENT OF DEOXYRIBONUCLEIC ACID (203–205)

Component	Milligrams of component per milligram of deoxyribonucleic acid in: Liver	Liver tumor
Nitrogen	9.5	2.7[1]
Phosphorus	1.1	0.4[1]
Ribonucleic acid as ribose	0.6	0.2[1]
Nitrogen	9.3	6.2[2]
Phosphorus	1.1	0.7[2]
Ribonucleic acid as ribose	0.5	0.4[2]

[1] Induced by 3′-methyl-4-dimethylaminoazobenzene.
[2] Induced by 2-acetylaminofluorene.

of individual nuclei of the liver, thymus, spleen, and liver tumor of the rat is nearly constant, at about $6 \times 10^{-6}\ \gamma$ per nucleus (210). The deoxyribonucleic acid content may indeed be a reflection of the number of its diploid cell units. Colchicine treatment of mice with the Ehrlich ascites tumor markedly prolongs the survival of the hosts, but the content of deoxyribonucleic acid per cell of exposed and control ascites tumor cells remains the same (211), namely about $14 \times 10^{-6}\ \gamma$ per cell (212). The content per cell of the Ehrlich tumor is approximately twice that found in normal diploid nuclei, thus corresponding to tetraploid nuclei, whereas the lymphoma nuclei, containing $6.8 \times 10^{-6}\ \gamma$ of deoxyribonucleic acid (212), show their diploid character (cf. 213). There is an appreciable quantity of ribonucleic acid in the nuclei of the ascites tumors, of the order of $4 \times 10^{-6}\ \gamma$ in the Ehrlich, and $2 \times 10^{-6}\ \gamma$ in the lymphoma (212), but comparisons with corresponding normal, homologous cells are lacking. The deoxyribonucleic acid content of the Ehrlich ascites cells is about twice, that of the ribonucleic acid about fivefold, the corresponding values for non-tumorous exudate cells (214). Where more exact comparisons have been made in the case of normal mouse spleen and the spleens of mice with leukemia (215), it is found that the deoxyribonucleic acid per nucleus is $6.6 \times 10^{-6}\ \gamma$ for the former, and $7.4 \times 10^{-6}\ \gamma$ for the latter, whether slow or fast growing; on the other hand, the ribonucleic acid of the nuclei of the slowly developing leukemic spleen increases 1.6 times the normal amount, but to 4.2 times the normal in the case of the rapidly developing transplanted leukemia. It is unlikely that the increase in ribonucleic acid is anything other than a reflection of the characteristics of normal, rapid growth and is not based necessarily on neoplastic growth (215, 216).

An interesting analysis of the total nucleic acid content of the nuclei of the normal and malignant cells of the uterine cervix of women has shown normal values of 9.3 and $6.2 \times 10^{-6}\ \gamma$, depending on whether the nuclear volumes are computed, respectively, as an elliptical cylinder or an ellipsoid, whereas for the malignant cells comparable values are 35×10^{-6} and $23 \times 10^{-6}\ \gamma$ (217). However, there appears to be a trimodal distribution of values in the category of abnormal and cancer cells, as shown in Fig. 38, with averages for the subgroups of 17, 38, and $67 \times 10^{-6}\ \gamma$ respectively. The curves in Fig. 38 are theoretical, with maxima at 9×10^{-6} for the normal, and at 18, 36, and $72 \times 10^{-6}\ \gamma$ for the subgroups of the cancer categories. When calculated on the basis of an ellipsoidal model for the nucleus, the total nucleic acid contents of the three subgroups of cancer cells are 11, 25, and $45 \times 10^{-6}\ \gamma$, and the frequency-distribution curves can be

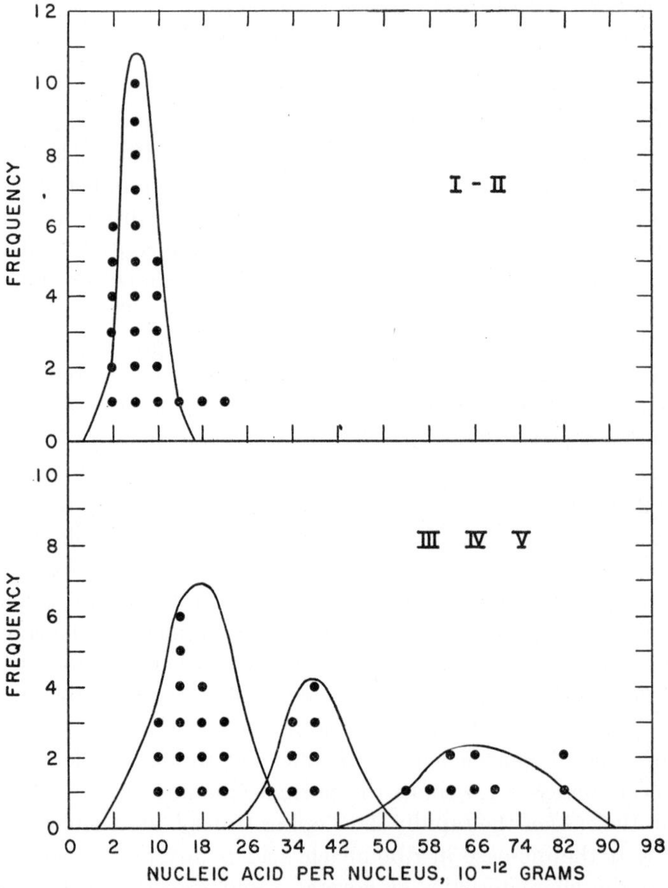

FIG. 38. Frequency of occurrence (ordinate) of nucleic acid per nucleus (abscissa) for cells of classes I and II combined (epithelial cells with no atypical features) and for cells of classes III, IV, and V combined (abnormal cells and those fairly and definitely conclusive for cancer) of the human uterine cervix. From Mellors, R. C., Keane, J. F., Jr., and Papanicolaou, G. N., *Science* **116,** 265 (1952).

drawn with maxima at 6 (for the normal), and at 12, 24, and 48 γ (for the cancerous). There appears to be a distinct geometrical progression in the total nucleic acid of the interphase nucleus of the squamous cancer cell which may be related to the following mechanisms of growth: (a) the acquisition of an even integral multiple of the fundamental number of chromosomes, or polyploidy, (b) a reduplication of the mass of individual chromosomes without division, and (c) a geometrical increment in the heterochromatin or nucleolar (ribonucleic acid) apparatus (217).

A great many of the estimations of total nucleic acids in tissues have relied upon ultraviolet spectrophotometry and the characteristic absorption maximum for these compounds at 2600 Å. With the availability of infrared spectrophotometers, attempts have been made to estimate the level of these components in tissue preparations at 8.1, 9.3, and 10.3 μ (218, 219), and some degree of correlation of the absorption intensities at these wavelengths with nucleic acid-rich cells has been noted. The technical difficulties due to interference by other cellular components in the region of 8 to 11 μ remain formidable.

Examination of the data reveals few differences between tissues of any considerable order of magnitude. However, this may be an instance where relatively small differences in the chromosomal component (deoxyribonucleate) would lead to enormous differences in the functional elements synthesized at this locus. On the other hand, the quantitative differences in nucleic acid content may be relatively unimportant in comparison with possible qualitative differences between the nucleic acids of normal and of tumor tissues. It is quite possible that nucleic acids from different sources may possess individual specificities, but only physical isolation of these materials and subsequent analysis plus biological testing (on tissue culture?) could decide this point. The interesting specificity demonstrated by the deoxyribonucleic acid of a certain type of *pneumococcus* in transforming other types is suggestive of the possible role of this material under certain circumstances in functioning as a transmissible mutating agent, (cf. 220).

Carcinogenic agents may apparently be divided into two categories (220a), namely those (methylcholanthrene, urethane, azo dyes) which have no effect on deoxyribonucleic acid with transforming activity, and those (nitrogen mustards) which completely inactivate it even at very low levels.

The results obtained so far appear to support the concept of Vendrely and and Vendrely (221) of an almost identical content of deoxyribonucleic acid in the somatic cells of all mammals, the value of this content being half for haploid cells. It would be expected that this generalization would hold for malignant as well as for normal cells, and indeed it seems that the measurement simply of content will supply no explanation of the neoplastic process. In view of the heterogeneous character of the nucleic acids even in the same cell, it is necessary to consider the distribution of the various nucleic acid types, for it is not likely that this distribution can remain identical in different tissues.

Mutations induced in microorganisms by ultraviolet radiation occur optimally at wavelengths which are those characteristic of the maximum absorption of nucleic acid, namely, at about 2600Å.; at such wavelengths profound alterations occur in the molecular properties of deoxyribonucleic acid. The mutant strains of microorganisms developed by irradiation procedures are frequently characterized by the loss of one or more enzyme systems, a result which is analogous to that of the neoplastic transformation of a normal animal tissue induced by any one of a number of carcinogenic agents, including ultraviolet radiation. It is no doubt quite far-fetched to draw an analogy between an animal tumor and a microorganismal mutant, but it is possible that the mechanisms involved in the alterations leading to both, and the adaptations and adjustments required in both, may not be entirely dissimilar. Considerable information exists suggestive of a linking of nucleic acids with gene mechanisms, but in the absence of evidence for the isolated gene any attempt to identify the latter as a nucleoprotein must be treated with some reserve. Nevertheless, there is evidence that growth and reduplication are associated with the presence of nucleic acid, and the relation of the latter type of substance with the gene may thus be strongly inferred. Since the genic material exerts a controlling influence over the multitudinous functional processes of the cell, it may be assumed that it accomplishes this not by a remote and olympian form of control but by specific kinds of chemical interaction with the cellular components involved in individual reactions, i.e., enzymes.

Esterases and Phosphatases. Esterase (butyrate) activity is high in normal intestinal mucosa and liver and drops when these tissues become neoplastic (222). Total lipids tend to decrease in tumors. Histochemical methods of demonstrating esterase by the use of β-naphthyl acetate have been developed by Seligman (223). The β-naphthol released by enzymatic action is combined with diazotized naphthylamine as the stabilized salt with naphthalene-1,5-disulfonic acid to yield an insoluble purple-red pigment. By the use of this method, the generally low non-specific esterase activity of a series of human tumors could be demonstrated (224). Phosphatomonoesterase (acid and alkaline phosphatase) shows interesting differences. The values for acid phosphatase in the normal mouse tissues are fairly constant, and so too are the values of this enzyme in all the mouse tumors studied, only, in the latter case, of a slightly lower order of magnitude (60, 90). Alkaline phosphatase values for normal mouse tissues show greater variation from tissue to tissue; in tumors the range narrows, except for the osteogenic sarcoma (60, 90). In the cases of the rat hepatoma induced by ingestion of 4-dimethylaminoazobenzene and the mouse hepatoma induced by ingestion of chloroform, there is an exceptionally high alkaline phosphatase value (17, 60, 90). The reason for this unusual finding is obscure, but it may be concerned with bile duct elements, either within the tumor or associated with the neoplastic transformation.

The splitting of the phosphate esters by liver and by hepatoma varies somewhat according to the nature of the substrate. With the exception of the nucleates, the other phosphate esters are less susceptible to extracts of mouse hepatoma than to mouse liver. Magnesium is a frequent activator and in the case of pyrophosphatase is indispensable. The relative dephosphorylation behavior in fresh and in dialyzed extracts has been alluded to above.

Acid phosphatase is present in the cytoplasm of liver cells in much larger amount than alkaline phosphatase. Both enzymes (in liver cells) are also present in high activity in the chromosomes of dividing nuclei (82). Adenosine triphosphatase of liver does not apparently alter in the hepatoma (225).

The greatest activity of alkaline phosphatase for all body tissues is found in the small intestine, and this enzyme also apparently nearly disappears in the intestinal adenocarcinoma. The gastric adenocarcinoma contains little or no alkaline phosphatase, and, in both types of adenocarcinoma, the acid phosphatase is reduced to about half the activity of the normal mucosa.

Kutscher and Wolbergs (226) first demonstrated the presence of a highly active acid phosphatase (optimum pH 5.0) in normal prostate tissue, but the only comparison of this enzyme performed under the same conditions with carcinomatous prostate tissue is in the report by Gutman and Gutman (227). The relative activity of acid phosphatase at pH 5.06 of the tumor was 156 (normal prostate = 100).

The acid phosphatase in the carcinomatous prostate is definitely but not greatly increased over that of the normal tissue. No data appear to exist in relation to the alkaline phosphatase activity of the tumor, but Gutman, et al. (228) and Woodard (229) have reported that the normal prostate contains very little of this enzyme. Of considerable clinical importance has been the discovery that the serum of patients with disseminated carcinoma of the prostate contains large amounts of the acid phosphatase (227).

Additional information concerning the phosphatase activity of prostatic carcinoma has been derived from extensive studies on the sites of osteoplastic bone metastases secondary to carcinoma of the prostate gland (228). Studies of the lumbar vertebrae and ribs of a patient with disseminated prostatic cancer revealed high acid phosphatase values and suggested that metastatic tumor cells arising from the tumor retain the high acid phosphatase activity of the primary cancer. It is necessary, however, to attempt to differentiate the activity of the phosphatase in the metastasis from that of the proliferating bone. Increased alkaline phosphatase activity is char-

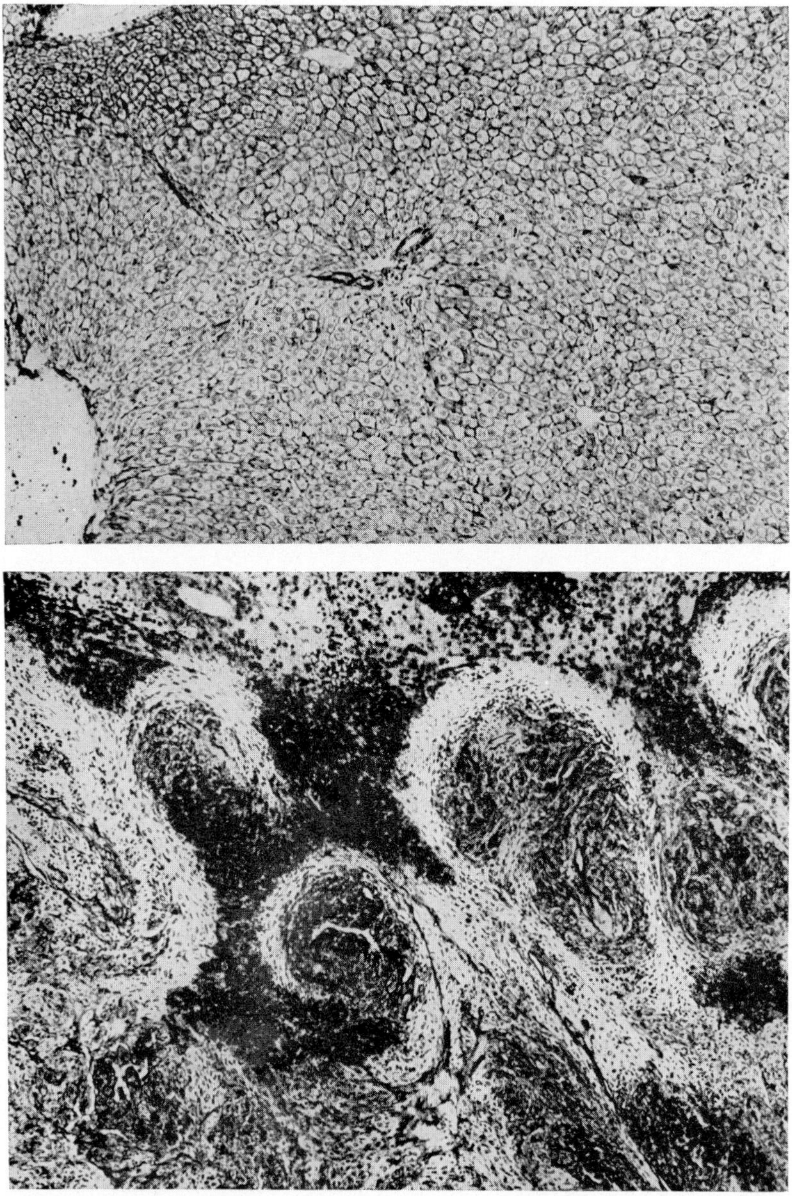

FIG. 39. Photomicrographs (×90) (top) of normal liver of rat and (bottom) of fifteenth generation transplant of a rat hepatoma induced with 4-dimethylaminoazobenzene, both stained for alkaline phosphatase activity under the same conditions. Black areas and lines indicate site of enzyme activity. Note cellular detail in normal liver. In the hepatoma cellular detail is obscured by intense deposition of silver salts as a result of high phosphatase activity. From White, J., Dalton, A. J., and Edwards, J. E., *J. Natl. Cancer Inst.* **2,** 539 (1942).

acteristic of growing bone in children, of hyperplastic bone (229), and of the osteoblastic type of osteogenic sarcoma (230). The bones studied in the case of disseminated prostatic carcinoma had not only a high acid, but also a high alkaline, phosphatase activity. Since the acid phosphatase activity of bones is very low, the presence of this enzyme at the site of the metastasis betrays the presence of prostatic tissue, but the high alkaline phosphatase activity at this site must in turn be related in some fashion to the osteoplastic character of the prostatic metastasis. Determinations of the phosphatase activity at pH 9 of the primary carcinoma of the prostate would be of value in ascertaining the contribution of the skeletal metastasis to the total activity at the site of the metastasis, including that of proliferating bone.

It is interesting to consider in this connection the alkaline phosphatase values for the hepatomas in rats induced with 4-dimethylaminoazobenzene. The normal liver has a very low alkaline phosphatase activity, but the hepatoma is extremely active in this enzyme. White and Edwards (231),

TABLE 86

COMPOSITION OF LIPIDS OF MAMMARY TISSUES OF MICE (254)

Lipid	Milligrams per milligram of protein N in:		
	Normal resting	Pregnancy-stimulated	Carcinoma
Total fat	67.2	43.0	1.03
I_2 number	71.9	72.9	101.0
Neutral fat	66.5	42.4	0.35
Cholesterol, total	0.16	0.065	0.13
Free	0.14	0.057	0.11
Esterified	0.02	0.008	0.02
Phospholipid, total	0.52	0.53	0.55
Sphingomyelin	0.10	0.10	0.12
Lecithin	0.17	0.26	0.08
Cephalin	0.25	0.17	0.35

TABLE 87

LIPID COMPOSITION OF WALKER 256 TUMOR AT STAGES IN ITS GROWTH (255)

Lipid	Weeks of tumor growth			
	1	2	3	4
Total lipid	28.06	14.83	13.93	14.22
Neutral fat	18.95	5.36	3.58	2.78
Total fatty acids	22.74	10.47	8.79	8.77
Total cholesterol	2.25	2.00	2.68	2.26
Cholesterol esters	1.03	0.81	1.21	0.92
Free cholesterol	1.22	1.19	1.47	1.34
Phospholipid	6.18	6.93	6.85	8.57

TABLE 88

ENZYMATIC ACTIVITY IN THE NORMAL TISSUES OF MICE[1-3] (60, 71, 72, 86, 90, 144, 146, 151, 259, 270–273)

Tissue	Arginase[4]	Catalase[5]	Xanthine dehydrogenase[6]	Acid phosphatase[7]	Alkaline phosphatase[8]	Deoxyribonucleodepolymerase[9]	Ribonucleodepolymerase[10]	Esterase[11]	Cytochrome oxidase[12]	Cystine desulfurase[13]	Deoxyribonucleodeaminase[14]	Ribonucleodeaminase[14]	Amidase for BAA[15]	Dehydropeptidase II[16]	Dehydropeptidase I[17]
Liver	246	8.00	10	12	4	14	0.12	411	8	6	7	16	34	15	20
Hyperplastic breast[18]	67	0.02	45	18	9	8	0.04	—	—	—	—	—	—	—	—
Lymph nodes	20	0.02	240	49	8	25[19]	0.46	25	3	0	25	60	—	0	—
Bone marrow	4	0.01	45	22	23	7	0.60	—	—	—	—	—	—	—	—
Spleen	6	0.12	30	73	17	16	0.28	106	2	—	88	96	35	—	21
Kidney	42	3.20	15	15	1072	10	0.08	108	11	3	64	82	7	23	22
Skeletal muscle	4	0.01	92	19	2	12	0.07	13	6	0	0	0	3	0	18
Cardiac muscle	7	0.01	50	18	12	9	0.04	13	19	0	—	—	—	0	—
Skin	27	0.01	45	30	5	10	0.17	3	—	0	—	—	—	0	—
Lung	50	0.22	>300	33	36	8	0.06	68	4	0	0	34	—	0	—
Intestinal mucosa	80	0	6	34	2789	15	0.68	973	1	0	5	10	—	0	20
Gastric mucosa	4	0	>300	27	17	6	0.27	48	1	0	—	—	—	0	—
Thymus[20]	2	0	>300	5	3	3	0.12	3	—	0	—	—	—	0	—
Pancreas	8	0.01	30	10	1	5	0.78	1820	2	2	—	—	7	4	19
Brain	3	0	15	15	12	4	0.18	7	10	0	0	30	11	0	20
Adult bone	—	—	—	50	420	—	—	1	—	0	—	—	—	—	—

[1] No normal tissue other than gastric mucosa possesses peptic activity.

[2] Each tissue was investigated in the following strains: *C*, *C3H*, *A*, and *DBA*. No significant strain differences or sex differences with the same strain were observed. These strains were selected for study because nearly all the mouse tumors studied appear in them. All data are averaged from the tissues of several animals.

[3] Each enzyme was investigated under identical conditions in all the tissues studied. All data are presented to show the extremes of activities, and are not always given in kinetic terms. The data on the heart and brain, with the exception of those pertaining to esterase, cytochrome oxidase, and cystine desulfurase, are hitherto unpublished. Also hitherto unpublished are the data for bone esterase and skin, nodes, gastric and intestinal mucosa, cytochrome oxidase. The contribution of residual blood to the enzymatic activity of the extracts was negligible; cf. for liver catalase. Residual blood in the lung may account for 3% of the total alkaline phosphatase determined on extracts of this tissue.

[4] In terms of the average ratio of the per cent hydrolysis of arginine after 2 hours incubation at 38° to the cube root of the total N per milliliter of tissue extract.

[5] In terms of the rate of oxygen evolution in milliliters per second at 25° of a mixture of 1 ml. of 29% hydrogen peroxide, 5 ml. phosphate buffer at pH 6.9, and 1 ml. of tissue extract containing 2.4 mg. total N.

[6] In terms of the time in minutes required to decolorize at 25° under anaerobic conditions a mixture of 1 ml. tissue extract containing 2.6 mg. total N, 1 ml. phosphate buffer at pH 6.9, 1 ml. xanthine solution (0.023%), and 1 ml. methylene blue solution (0.04%). The lower values in the table refer, of course, to the more active tissues.

[7] In terms of the average ratio of the per cent hydrolysis of phenyl phosphate after 1 hour incubation at 38° to the total N per milliliter of tissue extract; pH at 4.6.

[8] Same as 7, except that pH was 9.5.

[9] In terms of the decrease in viscosity after ½ hour incubation at 30° of a mixture containing 3 ml. of 1% sodium thymonucleate and 3 ml. of a tissue extract (1.23 mg. N per milliliter).

[10] In terms of the increase in milligrams of acid-soluble phosphorus after 2 hours incubation at 38° of a mixture of 1 ml. of 3% sodium yeast nucleate, 1 ml. of tissue extract containing 0.4 mg. N, and 1 ml. veronal buffer at pH 7.0.

[11] In terms of the average ratio $\times 10^4$ of the increase in the titer of 0.1 *N* alcoholic KOH to the milligrams of wet tissue used per milliliter of extract after 2 hours incubation at 37°. Methyl-*n*-butyrate was used as the substrate.

[12] In terms of the cubic millimeters of oxygen absorbed per milligrams wet weight of tissue suspension per hour (at 38°). Cytochrome c present in excess (1×10^{-4} *M*) in the presence of *p*-phenylenediamine.

[13] In terms of the increase in moles $\times 10^6$ of ammonia N after 4 hours incubation at 37° of a mixture of 1 ml. tissue extract (equivalent to 300 mg. wet tissue), 1 ml. phosphate buffer at pH 7.2, and 1 ml. L-cystine solution (0.025 *M* in 0.1 *N* NaCl).

[14] In terms of ammonia nitrogen in milligrams $\times 10^3$ evolved in digests of 1 ml. tissue extract (equivalent to 160 mg. tissue) plus 1 ml. 0.5% sodium nucleate after 5 hours incubation at 37°.

[15] In terms of per cent splitting of 6.2 mg. benzoylarginineanide incubated with extract of tissue equivalent to 333 mg. tissue after 2 hours incubation at 37°. See footnote 13 in Table 66.

[16] In terms of increase in moles $\times 10^6$ ammonia N after 2 hours incubation of 1 ml. tissue extract (equivalent to 300 mg. tissue) plus 1 ml. of 25×10^{-6} *M* solution of chloracetyldehydroalanine. Incubation period chosen arbitrarily, and values are not linear.

[17] Same as footnote 16, only using glycyldehydroalanine.

[18] Induced by subcutaneous implantation of stilbestrol pellets.

[19] Probably somewhat higher than the value given.

[20] Animals 2 months of age.

TABLE 89

ENZYMATIC ACTIVITY IN THE NEOPLASTIC TISSUES OF MICE[1-3] (cf. TABLE 88)

Tumor	Strain	Arginase	Catalase	Xanthine dehydrogenase	Acid phosphatase	Alkaline phosphatase	Deoxyribonucleodepolymerase	Ribonucleodepolymerase	Esterase	Cytochrome oxidase	Deoxyribonucleodeaminase	Ribonucleodeaminase	Amidase for BAA	Dehydropeptidase I
Hepatoma 1[4]	*I × DBA*	40	0.60	10	10	1	11	—	—	—	—	—	—	—
Hepatoma A[4]	*C3H*	34	0.05	38	21	0	21	0.26	172	3	40	42	—	—
Hepatoma 98/15[5]	*C3H*	30	0.08	35	22	1	21	0.30	—	3	44	50	34	20
Hepatoma 7A/77[6]	*A*	37	0.80	18	22	4	15	0.29	207	4	—	—	—	—
Hepatoma 587[5]	*A*	33	0.24	20	21	5	15	0.27	103	4	42	50	32	20
Mammary carcinoma	*C3H*	114	0.01	30	21	22	20	0.27	26	6	—	—	—	20
Lymphoma 72942[5]	*A*	26	0.01	25	10	10	4	0.17	—	—	—	—	—	—
Lymphoma Y-103[5]	*DBA*	31	0.01	40	12	4	4	0.11	—	—	25	60	—	—
Lymphoma 163[5]	*C3H*	28	0	22	12	6	4	0.12	8	1	—	—	—	—
Pigmented melanoma[7]	*DBA*, *C*	49	0.01	—	19	1	3	0.09	27	2	—	—	28	20
Sarcoma 37	*DBA*, C, Y	49	0	15	23	2	3	0.16	6	2	—	—	25	20
CR-180	*DBA*	49	0	15	21	2	3	0.15	6	2	0	43	—	18
Intestinal adenocarcinoma	*A*	26	0	30	19	3	14	0.20	11	3	2	10	—	22
Gastric adenocarcinoma	*C3H*	—	—	—	16	0	6	—	—	—	—	—	—	—
Squamous cell carcinoma of stomach	*A*	52	0	17	6	3	3	0.16	19	3	—	—	32	21
Lung tumor F	*A*	29	0	25	11	1	3	0.11	6	2	0	34	30	19
Sarcoma[8]	*C3H*	25	0	22	19	2	4	0.12	6	2	—	—	—	—
Spindle-cell sarcoma	*C3H*	28	0	40	12	1	4	0.10	6	2	—	—	—	—
Rhabdomyosarcoma	*C*	28	0	42	8	24	15	0.18	—	—	—	—	—	—
Osteogenic sarcoma[9]	*C3H*	27	0	35	135	1100	3	0.10	—	—	—	—	—	—

[1] All tumors, including the gastric adenocarcinoma, are lacking in peptic activity as well as in cystine desulfurase and dehydropeptidase II.

[2] Enzymatic activity determined exactly as for the normal tissues described in Table 88. See this table for references and terms of activity. With the exception of esterase and of cystine desulfurase, data on the spindle-cell sarcoma, lymphoma 163, and lung tumor F are hitherto unpublished. Data are averaged in each case from a study of several specimens. All necrotic areas were removed from the tumors before study of the latter.

[3] With exception of the spontaneous mammary carcinoma and the primary sarcoma induced by methylcholanthrene, all the tumors studied were transplants in late generation.

[4] Originally induced by injection of 2-amino-5-azotoluene.

[5] Originally spontaneous.

[6] Originally induced by injection of carbon tetrachloride.

[7] The cytochrome oxidase activity of the melanotic and amelanotic melanomas are nearly identical. The melanotic tumor contains an active tyrosinase and dopa oxidase, together with a cyanide-insensitive system or systems which oxidize *p*-phenylenediamine; the amelanotic melanoma is completely lacking in all these enzymes.

[8] Primary tumor induced by administration of methylcholanthrene.

[9] Representing an early (third) transplant of this tumor; the later (seventeenth, etc.) transplants lost the osseous elements together with the phosphatase activity.

TABLE 90

ENZYMATIC ACTIVITY IN NORMAL AND NEOPLASTIC TISSUES OF THE RAT[1] (72)

Tissues	Arginase	Catalase	Acid phosphatase	Alkaline phosphatase	Ribonucleodeaminase	Deoxyribonucleodeaminase	Dehydropeptidase I	Dehydropeptidase II	Exocystine desulfurase	BAA amidase (benzoyl-arginineamidase)	Cytochrome oxidase	Esterase
Normal:												
Liver	213	2.0	25	4	20	4	20	20	45	32	11.8	312
Kidney	60	1.0	95	1500	80	60	22	20	16	12	14.0	70
Pancreas	4	0.1	18	3	10	0	17	10	8	8	—	1600
Spleen	10	0.4	42	21	96	84	20	0	0	50	4.3	82
Brain	3	0	16	14	32	0	18	0	0	0	13.0	4
Muscle	8	0.1	16	2	0	0	18	0	0	0	6.3	4
Neoplastic:												
Transplanted hepatoma 31	21	0	52	542	50	36	20	1	0	56	3.1[2]	104
Transplanted Jensen sarcoma	46	0	22	44	52	0	19	0	0	43	1.6[2]	83
Transplanted tumor 2226[3]	48	0	32	18	50	5	20	0	0	40	2.0	72

[1] Enzymatic activity in terms given in Table 88.

[2] According to Schneider and Potter (73) the cytochrome oxidase activity of hepatoma 31 and the Jensen sarcoma is very nearly the same.

[3] Very anaplastic epithelial type of tumor.

in a description of the pathology of this tumor, point out that the presence of this enzyme in considerable amount may be associated with the capacity for bone formation and in one of the transplants of this tumor membranous bone formation was observed. Although the studies on the skeletal metastases of prostatic carcinoma have been highly interesting and suggestive, it is unfortunate that only skeletal metastases have been investigated. The bone itself, and particularly growing bone, is rich in alkaline phosphatase, and for this reason the results on this enzyme at sites of osteoplastic metastases may be confusing. Further studies on the primary carcinoma or on metastases to non-osseus tissues low in alkaline phosphatase would go far toward clearing up the problem.

Figure 39 shows the Gomori histochemical stains for alkaline phosphatase activity in liver and in hepatoma. Seligman has introduced a new histochemical procedure for the phosphatases, which depends upon the use of α-naphthylphosphate (232). The α-naphthol is coupled with diazotized aminoanthroquinone to yield an insoluble brown-red pigment. In this method employing the insoluble azo technique, alkaline and acid phosphatase may be portrayed on the same slide by different colored pigments.

The chemical composition of bone has made extensive studies of the phosphatase mechanism in this tissue desirable. The role of this enzyme in bone formation has been reviewed (233, 234), and studies of the phosphatase activity in normal and neoplastic bone have been reported by several investigators (229-231).

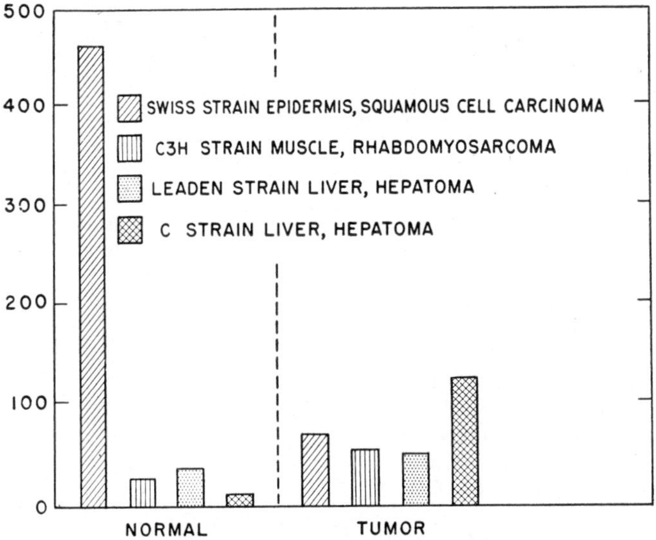

FIG. 40. Citric acid content of various tumors and their normal homologues in micrograms per gram. From Miller, H., and Carruthers, C., *Cancer Research* **10,** 636 (1950).

Alkaline phosphatase has long been known to occur in high activity at sites of ossification in embryos and in children (230, 234). It has been suggested that this enzyme hydrolyzes the phosphoric esters in the blood to bring about a local increase in the concentration of the phosphate ions,

TABLE 91

CYTOCHROME OXIDASE, CYTOCHROME C AND SUCCINIC OXIDASE IN NORMAL AND NEOPLASTIC RAT TISSUES

Tissue	Cytochrome oxidase				Cytochrome c					Succinic oxidase
Reference	(73)[1]	(276)[2]	(76)[3]	(8)[3]	(75)[4]	(276)[5]	(76)[4]	(8)[6]	(4)[7]	(73)[1]
Normal:										
Heart	974	9.7	69	40.2	371	2.34	—	—	—	219
Kidney	549	4.7	—	14.0	247	1.36	—	—	1430[8]	195
Skeletal muscle	180	2.3	8	6.3	97	0.68	—	—	—	36
Brain	420	3.5	—	13.0	50	0.35	—	—	375[8]	49
Liver	392	1.7	31	11.8	90	0.24	80	8.6	607	88
Spleen	195	1.6	10	4.3	43	0.21	—	—	—	23
Lung	92	1.3	—	—	21	0.14	—	—	24	18
Neoplastic:										
Primary hepatoma[9]	134	—	—	—	20	—	—	—	—	26
Transplanted hepatoma[10]	124	—	7	3.1	—	—	30	—	—	22
Flexner-Jobling tumor[11]	91	—	—	—	12	—	—	—	—	16
Walker 256 tumor[11]	62	—	—	—	9	—	—	—	71	9
Jensen sarcoma[11]	129	—	3	1.6	12	—	—	1.2	—	18
Tumor R-256	—	2.9	—	—	—	0.02	—	—	—	—
Spontaneous tumor	—	2.4	—	—	—	0.01	—	—	51	—

[1] In terms of cubic millimeters oxygen consumed per milligram dry weight per hour with ascorbate or succinate as respective substrates and in presence of excess cytochrome c.

[2] Activity units per milligram dry weight. One unit causes increase in oxygen consumption of 10 cu. mm. per hour.

[3] In terms of cubic millimeters oxygen consumed per milligram fresh weight in presence of *p*-phenylenediamine.

[4] Micrograms per gram wet weight.

[5] Milligrams per gram dry weight.

[6] Milligrams per 100 g. wet weight.

[7] Micrograms per gram dry weight.

[8] Cortex only.

[9] Induced by ingestion of 4-dimethylaminoazobenzene.

[10] Originally induced by ingestion of 4-dimethylaminoazobenzene.

[11] Originally spontaneous.

thereby leading to excess of the solubility product of the calcium phosphophates which enter into the structure of bone (235). If phosphatase activity runs parallel to osteogenesis it would be expected that the osteogenic tumors would be high in this enzyme, and the data reveal that this is indeed the case. It seems probable that phosphatase is synthesized by the osteoblasts.

The control tissues for the tumors mentioned were the long bones of adult mice and of human beings. If the growing bones of young mice or children had been selected for the control tissues, the ratio of tumor to control phosphatase would certainly be smaller. Nevertheless, the data reveal a marked increase in the bone phosphatase of the tumors, particularly of the osteoblastic type. The plasma phosphatase in patients with bone tumors also tends to increase markedly. This will be discussed elsewhere.

It is of interest to consider the marked similarity in the great increase of phosphatase activity in osteogenic sarcoma and in the bones at the sites of osteoplastic metastases from primary carcinoma of the prostate. It has been suggested that certain metastases stimulate the production of alkaline phosphatase by osteogenic cells at the site of the metastasis (228). Whether the initiation of osteogenesis is a function of the metastatic tumor cell or whether the latter carries with it all the materials ready-made for osteogenesis, including a large amount of alkaline phosphatase, can perhaps be better answered by study of the primary prostatic carcinoma or perhaps of metastases to non-osseous tissues naturally low in alkaline phosphatase.

Vitamins. The range of concentration of the B vitamins and of ascorbic acid is lower and considerably narrower in tumors than in normal tissues (see Fig. 41) (236, 237). As certain of the B vitamins serve metabolically in part as prosthetic groups of some of the enzymes, it would be expected

TABLE 92

COMPARATIVE CYTOCHROME OXIDASE ACTIVITY OF THE NORMAL TISSUES OF VARIOUS SPECIES[1] (8)

Tissue	Cytochrome oxidase activity of:				
	Man	Mouse[2]	Rat[3]	Guinea pig	Rabbit
Liver	2.8	8.0	11.8	4.2	2.9
Spleen	0.4	2.0	4.3	0.9	0.8
Kidney	3.6	11.0	14.0	5.4	4.7
Heart	8.2	18.6	40.2	9.6	9.5
Brain	3.9	9.6	13.0	6.0	4.9
Skeletal muscle	2.4	2.8	6.3	1.6	2.0

[1] In terms of cubic millimeters oxygen consumed per milligram wet weight per hour.

[2] Strains *A* and *C3H* mice. No strain differences observed.

[3] Buffalo rats.

that the general phenomena exhibited by the latter in neoplastic tissues would be followed more or less by the former (*vide infra*). Thus, riboflavin phosphate appears to be associated with xanthine dehydrogenase and with amino acid oxidase, and pyridoxyl phosphate is associated with transaminase. These enzymes are decreased in hepatomas as compared with normal liver; the decrease in the tumor may, however, be due as much to decrease of or alteration in the protein moiety as to decrease in the prosthetic group.

TABLE 93

CYTOCHROME OXIDASE, CYTOCHROME c AND SUCCINIC OXIDASE IN MISCELLANEOUS TISSUES OF VARIOUS ANIMAL SPECIES

Species and tissue	Cytochrome oxidase			Cytochrome c		Succinic oxidase
Reference	(276)[1]	(73)[2]	(76)[3]	(276)[4]	(75)[5]	(73)[2]
Rat:						
Early whole embryo	1.1	—	—	0.03	—	—
Late whole embryo	1.1	—	—	0.18	—	—
Skeletal muscle	2.3	—	—	—	—	—
Diaphragm muscle	0.72	—	—	—	—	—
Large intestine	0.36	—	—	—	—	—
Mouse:						
Yale tumor I[6]	—	88	—	—	16	19
Ear tumor[7]	—	64	—	—	11	19
Mammary tumor[8]	—	88	6.1	—	14	28
Hepatoma E[9]	—	—	6.2	—	—	—
Hepatoma 98/15	—	—	4.8	—	—	—
Gastric adenocarcinoma	—	—	3.0	—	—	—
Intestinal adenocarcinoma	—	—	4.4	—	—	—
Hepatoma 587	—	—	5.1	—	—	—
Hepatoma 7A/77	—	—	6.2	—	—	—
Leukosis 72942	—	—	6.1	—	—	—
Leukosis Y-103	—	—	7.4	—	—	—
Melanoma	—	—	3.6	—	—	—
Sarcoma 37	—	—	6.3	—	—	—
Sarcoma CR-180	—	—	5.5	—	—	—
Hepatoma 1	—	—	6.3	—	—	—
Chicken:						
Rous sarcoma[10]	—	44	—	—	12	11

[1] Cf. footnote 2, Table 91.
[2] Cf. footnote 1, Table 91.
[3] Cf. footnote 3, Table 91.
[4] Cf. footnote 5, Table 91.
[5] Cf. footnote 4, Table 91.
[6] Induced by estrin administration.
[7] Induced by ultraviolet irradiation.
[8] Spontaneous.
[9] This and later mouse tumors were all late generation transplants. For origin of the hepatomas compare Table 89.
[10] Induced by virus.

TABLE 94

CYTOCHROME C CONTENT OF EPITHELIAL TISSUES OF VARIOUS SPECIES (4)

Tissue	Species	Cytochrome c content, γ/g. dry weight
Kidney cortex	Mouse	1105
	Rabbit	354
	Dog	302
	Pig	271
	Man	45
	Horse	137
Liver	Mouse	525
	Rabbit	125
	Horse	24
Brain cortex	Mouse	479
	Rabbit	252
Lung	Rabbit	45
	Man	9
Colon mucosa	Rabbit	97
	Man	39
Gastrointestinal[1] adenocarcinomas	Man	30

[1] Includes two gastric and four rectal tumors.

TABLE 95

D-AMINO ACID OXIDASE AND URICASE IN RAT TISSUES

Tissue	D-Amino acid oxidase (76)			Uricase (91)
	Cu. mm. O_2/mg. wet weight/hr.	Cu. mm. NH_3/ mg. wet weight/hr.	Flavin adenine dinucleotide, γ/g.	Cu. mm. O_2/mg. dry weight/hr.
Osborne-Mendel rats:				
Normal liver	0.24[1]	0.354	61	2.8
Regenerating liver	0.19	—	52	—
Fetal liver	0.035	—	11.5	—
Transplanted hepatoma 31	0.022[1]	0.032	10.2	0.2
Normal kidney	1.61	—	60	—
Buffalo rats:				
Normal liver	0.102	—	60	—
Jensen sarcoma	0	—	7.5	—
Strain *A* mice:				
Normal liver	0	0	78	—
Hepatoma 587	0	—	32	—
Hepatoma 7A/77	0	—	32	—
Strain *C3H* mice:				
Normal liver	0	0	81	—
Hepatoma 98/15	0	—	32	—
Normal kidney	0.54	—	—	—

[1] Lan (91) observed similarly that the activity of D-amino acid oxidase in normal rat liver was roughly ten times as great as in the transplanted hepatoma. It appeared as if a part of the deficiency in the tumor was due to reduced amount of coenzyme.

In human tumors, regardless of origin, the vitamin B_6 content falls within the relatively narrow range of 0.33 to 1.35 γ per gram of tissue, which is of an order of magnitude characteristic of the values for those normal tissues low in vitamin B_6 content; the normal human tissues range from 0.26 to 8.9 γ per gram, the highest value referring to liver (238). The biotin content of these tumors range from 0.02 to 0.16, whereas the normal tissues range from 0.03 to 0.66 γ per gram. The ascorbic acid content of human tissues is considerably less than that of the corresponding tissues of several animal species, and, in general, the content of ascorbic acid is somewhat higher in human tumors than in the adjacent, non-neoplastic tissue (239). The differences are, however, not striking. Dehydroascorbic and diketogulonic acids are practically absent (240). The systematic studies on the B-vitamins by R. J. Williams and his associates (277–280) are collected in Table 96.

Rat hepatomas induced by 3′-methyl-4-dimethylaminoazobenzene, as well as other kinds of tumors, accumulate dietary α-tocopherol more rapidly than does liver tissue, and in vitamin E depletion the tumors also yield up their stores more slowly (241). The concentration of α-tocopherol in liver is 37.7 γ per gram, and in the hepatoma it is 4.9; the corresponding

TABLE 96

B VITAMIN CONTENT OF NORMAL AND NEOPLASTIC TISSUES (277–280)

Riboflavin[1]		Nicotinic acid[1]		Biotin[2]		Pantothenic acid[1]	
Normal[3]	Neoplastic[4]	Normal[3]	Neoplastic[4]	Normal[3]	Neoplastic[4]	Normal[3]	Neoplastic[4]
Liver 13–41	Human 1-6	Liver 54–174	Human 11–30	Liver 620–1160	Human 5–97	Liver 31–112	Human 3–11
Heart 12–36	Mouse 2–6	Heart 120	Mouse 20–29	Heart 160–390	Mouse 70–166	Heart 16–50	Mouse 23–39
Brain 2–4	Rat 3	Brain 60	Rat 19	Brain 76–100	Rat 30	Brain 13–28	Rat 5
Lung 2–4		Lung 18–51		Lung 19–78		Lung 5–9	
Spleen 3		Spleen 50		Spleen 40–73		Spleen 5–9	
Kidney 27		Kidney 30–117		Kidney 580–790		Kidney 16–34	
Muscle 2		Muscle 50–81		Muscle 21–52		Muscle 5–10	

[1] In terms of micrograms per gram wet weight of tissue.

[2] In terms of micromicrograms per gram wet weight of tissue.

[3] Includes mouse, rat, and human tissues.

[4] Includes about twenty human tumors, three mouse tumors, and two rat tumors. The content of vitamins in rats receiving a purina diet is considerably higher than in those on a rice-carrots diet.

values for vitamin A are, respectively, 52.0 and 9.1. The rapid accumulation of vitamin E by tumors is unlike that of vitamins A or D, and in its slow loss from tumors it is unlike riboflavin. Vitamin E storage in tumors appears to be unlike that of all other vitamins.

Folic acid is essential for leukocyte maturation (242). Analysis of normal and leukemic human leukocytes for this compound (inclusive of folinic acid) revealed a much higher content in the latter than in the former cells (243). The folic acid conjugase is present in equal activity levels in both types of cells, and there is nearly the same proportion of free folic acid in each. In terms of millimicrograms per cubic centimeter of packed leukocytes, the mean folic acid values (total) for normal persons is 80, for patients with chronic lymphocytic leukemia it is 120, with lymphosarcoma it is 250,

TABLE 97

Content of Ascorbic Acid in Normal and Neoplastic Tissues[1] (237)

Tissue	Ascorbic acid
Normal:	
Rat liver	21
Regenerating rat liver	18
Fetal rat liver	20
Mouse liver	32
Rat lymph nodes	48
Mouse lymph nodes	46
Mouse pyloric stomach	22
Mouse small intestine	55
Mouse hyperplastic mammary tissue	9
Mouse lung	24
Mouse muscle	4
Mouse forestomach	38
Neoplastic:	
Transplanted rat hepatoma 31	32
Transplanted mouse hepatoma 587	30
Transplanted mouse hepatoma 98/15	22
Rat lymphosarcoma	29
Mouse leukosis 72942	38
Mouse leukosis Y-103	70
Mouse gastric adenocarcinoma	21
Mouse intestinal adenocarcinoma	43
Mouse spontaneous mammary tumor	34
Mouse lung tumor	33
Mouse rhabdomyosarcoma	26
Mouse squamous cell carcinoma	19
Mouse sarcoma CR-180	19
Mouse sarcoma S-37	20
Rat Jensen sarcoma	39

[1] In terms of milligrams per 100 g. wet weight of tissue.

with chronic granulocytic leukemia 155, and with acute granulocytic leukemia it is 455. Thus, the more rapidly proliferating cells contain more folic acid, a characteristic established for a wide variety of tumors (244). The greater part of the total folic acid content of leukocytes occurs as folinic acid.

Hyalouronidase. One of the characteristics of tumor growth is that of invasiveness, i.e., the capacity to invade and break down adjacent normal tissue. The thought has frequently been entertained that this capacity may be due to the presence of factors at the periphery of the tumors which degrade the supporting connective tissue structure of neighboring normal tissues. To some extent, this concept arises by analogy to the known properties of several bacterial species which possess the property of invasiveness. The responsible bacterial agent has been noted to facilitate the spreading of various materials in the skin when simultaneously administered; it has also been noted to depolymerize and degrade complex mucopolysaccharides. The spreading factor and the enzyme complex responsible for the degradation of the mucins are thus frequently considered to be identical, and the designation of the complex has been that of hyalouronidase (245, 246). Of all animal tissues, testis contains the most active enzyme (247, 248). Extracts of tumors generally possess a very weak hyalouronidase (249-252). Extracts of the Rous sarcoma contain a highly viscous mucin with little or no evidence of a mucinase (251). The low level of

TABLE 98

ADENOSINE TRIPHOSPHATASE IN NORMAL AND NEOPLASTIC RAT TISSUES (225)

Tissues	Activity[1]	
	Without calcium	With calcium
Normal:		
Heart	—	27.3
Skeletal muscle	—	23.3
Lung	—	21.8
Kidney	—	20.3
Submaxillary gland	—	16.4
Spleen	—	13.0
Liver	—	12.9
Pancreas	—	11.5
Smooth muscle	—	8.2
Brain	—	7.0
Neoplastic:		
Jensen sarcoma	2.0	20.2
Primary hepatoma	1.9	11.8
Walker tumor	1.6	11.5
Flexner-Jobling tumor	1.3	8.0

[1] In terms of micrograms inorganic phosphorus split off substrate per milligrams fresh tissue in 15 minutes.

mucinase activity in tumors does not encourage the belief that this enzyme complex plays any unusual role in the invasiveness of these growths. Indeed, it might appear that reports of the presence of this enzyme in tumors might have been based on measurements of contaminating bacterial rather than tumor mucinases (253). It is worthy of note, however, that a hyalouronidase inhibitor exists in blood serum which is distinctly elevated in cases of metastasized malignant tumors (253).

Non-Catalytic Components. Analyses of these materials with few exceptions do not reveal differences between comparable normal and neoplastic tissues of the same striking order of magnitude as do the catalytic systems in these tissues. Nevertheless, these data are interesting and important, and it is quite possible that relatively small differences in such ostensibly inert components as salts may, in specific cases, lead to relatively large differences in catalytic properties. As matters stand, however, the overall similarity in analysis of such components as proteins, carbohydrates, salts, etc., between comparable tissues of the same species suggests that the proportion of materials which enter into the architecture of homologous tissues within the same species is likely to be similar throughout and implies a similar framework. The content of phosphatides and of fatty acids in the rat hepatomas is lower than in normal liver, but that of both free and esterified cholesterol is much greater.

That there may be a lipid pattern associated with varying states of physiological activity among homologous tissues is suggested by data on resting and pregnancy-stimulated mammary glands and mammary gland carcinomas of mice (254) (Table 86). Both composition and relative amounts of lipid differ considerably in these three comparable tissues, the differences being extremely marked in the total fat content, whereas all three tissues contain approximately the same amount of total phospholipid. The composition of the phospholipid fraction differs among the tissues, for the stimulated mammary glands possess nearly twice as much lecithin as the resting glands, and four times as much as the tumors; they also contain considerably more cephalin than the resting glands, and only about half as much as the tumors. All three tissues have approximately equal amounts of sphingomyelin. It would appear that, although similar amounts of total essential lipid may be present in homologous tissues, the character of this fraction may differ considerably, depending upon the physiological state of the tissues. The enormous drop in total and neutral fat when a normal tissue becomes malignant is not an unusual phenomenon.

In many tumors, phospholipid appears to account for about half the total lipids, but this calculation may depend upon the age of the tumor. Thus, Boyd and McEwen (255) (Table 87) observed during the growth of the Walker 256 tumor in rats that although total lipid, neutral fat, and fatty acids declined during the early stages of growth, the proportion of phospho-

TABLE 99

ACTIVITY OF PROTEINASE, PEPTIDASE, AND DESULFURASE IN NORMAL AND NEOPLASTIC TISSUES

Tissue	Proteinase[1] (282)	Peptidase[2] (281)	BAA amidase (71)		Exocystine desulfurase[4] (99)				Dehydropeptidase II[5] (71)				Dehydropeptidase I[6] (71)			
	Rat	Rat	Rat	Mouse	Rat	Mouse	Rabbit	Guinea pig	Rat	Mouse	Rabbit	Guinea pig	Rat	Mouse	Rabbit	Guinea pig
Liver	0.038	0.18	32	34	11	8	4	3	20	15	12	12	20	18	13	15
Regenerating liver	0.030	—	32	—	11	—	—	—	20	—	—	—	20	—	—	—
Transplanted hepatoma	0.085	0.40	56	33	0	0	—	—	1	0	—	—	20	18	—	—
Fetal liver	—	—	18	—	5	—	1	—	5	—	3	—	20	—	12	—
Primary hepatoma	—	—	36	—	0	—	—	—	10	—	—	—	20	—	—	—
Spleen	—	—	50	35	0	0	0	0	0	0	0	0	19	17	12	16
Kidney	—	—	12	7	4	3	3	2	20	23	14	16	22	21	14	19
Brain	—	—	0	11	0	0	0	0	0	0	0	0	18	17	15	20
Muscle	—	—	0	3	0	0	0	0	0	0	0	0	18	16	12	14
Pancreas	—	—	8	7	2	1	1	2	10	4	3	10	17	20	15	15
Intestinal mucosa	—	—	—	—	—	—	—	—	—	2	—	—	—	20	—	—
Intestinal adenocarcinoma	—	—	—	—	—	0	—	—	—	0	—	—	—	19	—	—
Melanoma	—	—	—	—	—	0	—	—	—	0	—	—	—	23	—	—
S-37	—	—	—	—	—	0	—	—	—	0	—	—	—	21	—	—
CR-180	—	—	—	—	—	0	—	—	—	0	—	—	—	20	—	—
Brown-Pearce tumor	—	—	—	—	—	—	0	—	—	—	0	—	—	—	16	—
Squamous cell tumor	—	—	—	—	—	0	—	—	—	0	—	—	—	17	—	—
Fibrosarcoma	—	—	—	—	—	—	—	0	—	—	—	0	—	—	—	18
Jensen sarcoma	—	—	43	—	0	—	—	—	0	—	—	—	19	—	—	—
Lung tumor F	—	—	—	—	—	0	—	—	—	0	—	—	—	16	—	—
Serum[7]	—	—	—	—	0	—	0	0	0	—	0	0	4	—	7	7

[1] Hemoglobin as substrate at pH 7.0; data refer to tyrosine chromogen released after 10 minutes per milligram N in extract.

[2] Data in terms of milliliter 0.1 *N* NaOH required in formol titration with 0.05 *N* DL-leucylglycine as substrate.

[3] Data refer to per cent hydrolysis of benzoylarginineamide in 2 hours incubation in tissue extracts equivalent to 333 mg. tissue per milliliter. These data were obtained at pH 7. See footnote 13 in Table 66.

[4] Data refer to ammonia N in moles 10^6 split from either diglycylcystine or dichloracetylcystine (each yielding identical results) as substrate in 25×10^{-6} moles concentration. Incubation period 2 hours with 1 ml. extract equivalent to 166 mg. tissue. Cystine used alone gives identical results as peptides.

[5] Same as footnote 4 only chloracetyldehydroalanine used as substrate.

[6] Same as footnote 4 only glycyldehydroalanine used as substrate.

[7] Human serum does not split cystine peptides or chloracetyldehydroalanine but actively splits glycyldehydroalanine, the activity in terms corresponding with other data in Table 99 being 4–6. Recent work by Meister and Greenstein has shown that dehydropeptidase I activity may be considerably elevated in the serum of patients with liver damage, e.g., tuberculosis, neoplastic involvement, etc.

lipid and of cholesterol, the so-called "essential lipid," remained fairly constant throughout the growth of the tumor. Throughout its life history, the only marked change in lipid concentration of the tumor is the early decline in neutral or storage fat values.

The content of non-protein nitrogen, of amino nitrogen, and of creatine and creatinine is practically the same in hepatomas as in normal liver. Creatine is formed by the interaction of choline, methionine, glycine, and

TABLE 100

Susceptibility of Glycyldehydroamino Acids to Liver and Hepatoma Fractions (163) (cf. 283)

Tissue	Fraction	Substrates					
		Glyclydehydro-alanine		Glycyldehydro-norvaline		Glycyldehydro-phenylalanine	
		Rate[1]	% Total	Rate[1]	% Total	Rate[1]	% Total
Mouse liver	Homogenate	13.5	—	2.5	—	0.5	—
	Supernatant	35.4	90	3.8	68	0.0	0
	Sediment	2.5	10	1.0	32	0.5	100
Mouse hepatoma	Homogenate	20.0	—	2.3	—	0.0	—
	Supernatant	56.0	96	6.2	95	0.0	—
	Sediment	1.5	4	0.2	5	0.0	—

[1] In terms of micromoles hydrolyzed per hour per milligram N.

TABLE 101

β-Glucuronidase Activity in Human Neoplastic and Adjacent Uninvolved Tissues (288)

Tissue	Range of β-glucuronidase units[1] in: Pathological lesions	Adjacent tissue
Breast cancer	900–3650	62–168
Benign fibroadenoma	393	325
Mastitis	1810–16,100	770–1042
Gastric cancer	817–3180	191–1270
Colon cancer	827–5250	449–2490
Pancreas cancer	172–463	326
Uterine cancer	884	199
Benign leiomyoma	165–425	173–1370
Ovarian cancer	1410–2740	295–605
Chondrosarcoma	572	242
Penile cancer	1855	325
Lung sarcoma	940	483

[1] Defined as 1 γ of phenolphthalein liberated from phenolphthalein mono-β-glucuronide per hour per gram of wet tissue at 38°.

arginine (256, 257). The amidination of glycine may occur in the kidney, but the methylation of guanidoacetic acid occurs in the liver (258). The capacity to produce creatine (and creatinine), which represents a phase of amino acid metabolism, is yet another system that is apparently completely retained when the liver becomes neoplastic (259).

The proportion of water in the hepatomas, irrespective of origin, strain, or species of animal, appears to be distinctly higher than in normal liver. If this water is mainly extracellular, it might be expected that the sodium- and chloride-ion concentrations would also be higher in the tumors. This is indeed the case. The proportion of potassium in the tumor is apparently very high. Iron is lower in the tumor than in normal liver and this is in keeping with the finding of decreased iron-containing enzyme systems in the hepatomas as well as in other tumors. A possible exception to the generalization that tumors have a higher water content than do normal tissues may be the case of interstitial tumors of the dog testis (260).

The higher potassium and lower calcium content of tumors as compared

TABLE 102

GLUCURONIDASE AND ESTERASE ACTIVITY LEVELS IN MOUSE MAMMARY TISSUES (294)

Strain	Glucuronidase levels in:		Esterase levels in:	
	Normal mammary	Mammary tumor	Normal mammary	Mammary tumor
C3H	4	51	11,500	4600
Z	25	70	16,100	4400
ZD8F$_1$	82	170	21,000	1800
D8	92	174	15,000	1700
A	89	156	13,000	5000
AJKF$_1$	112	191	10,500	1170
C	119	194	8,850	1150

TABLE 103

HYDROLYTIC RATES OF 2,4- AND 3,5-DIKETO ACIDS BY LIVER AND HEPATOMA (299, 300)

Tissue	Activity toward:	
	2,4-Diketovaleric acid[1]	3,5-Diketohexanoic acid[1]
Normal rat liver	5.70	2.64
Primary rat hepatoma	0.33	0.97
Normal mouse liver	8.78	2.79
Hepatoma 112B	2.60	0.91
Hepatoma 98/15	—	0.89
Azotoluene-induced hepatoma	3.04	1.11

[1] Expressed as micromoles substrate hydrolyzed per hour per milligram N.

with their normal tissues of origin appears to be a nearly universal phenomenon (261-263). Potassium appears to play an indispensable and unique role in tissue protein synthesis (264), although the mechanism of its utilization is at present unknown. Potassium ions are indispensable in certain enzymatic reactions, and this may be the reason for its need (cf. 265).

An interesting, but at present obscure, observation is that of the uniformly higher isotopic potassium ratio (K^{39}: K^{41}) as compared with mineral potassium in all tumors studied, both in man and in animals, as compared with normal tissues (266). It would appear that the heavy isotope K^{41} was definitely lower in tumors as well as in the tissues of tumor-bearing animals. The uniformity in all tumors studied is consistent with other observations on catalytic and non-catalytic components of such tissues (*vide infra*), as, for example, citric acid (267). This uniformity of citric acid among tumors is also revealed in Fig. 40, based on data by Miller and Carruthers (268). The figure particularly shows the median level of this component in tumors,

TABLE 104

CATHEPSINS IN NORMAL AND NEOPLASTIC MOUSE TISSUES (89)

Tissue	Activity[1]
Normal: [2]	
Spleen	0.22
Liver	0.07
Kidney	0.08
Lung	0.09
Muscle	0.05
Intestine	0.04
Lymph node	0.20
Bone marrow	0.13
Embryo liver	0.14
Neoplastic:	
Spontaneous mammary tumor[2]	0.15
Hepatoma E[2]	0.10
Spindle cell sarcoma[2]	0.10
Hepatoma 587[3]	0.14
Intestinal adenocarcinoma[3]	0.11
Squamous cell carcinoma[3]	0.07
Melanoma[4]	0.16
Adrenal cortical carcinoma[5]	0.10
Sarcoma CR-180[5]	0.07

[1] In terms of milligrams tyrosine after 10 minutes; all tumors were transplants except spontaneous mammary tumor; pH 4.6.

[2] *C3H* strain.

[3] *A* strain.

[4] *DBA* strain.

[5] *C* strain.

which is somewhere between the very high value in normal skin and the very low value in normal liver. Thus, when skin becomes neoplastic the citrate content decreases, and when liver becomes neoplastic the citrate content rises. The role of the last-mentioned is of importance, and its relatively high concentration in bone and in the young embryo is of interest. The citric acid content in terms of milligrams per 100 g. fresh tissue for hu-

TABLE 105

AMMONIA N AND INORGANIC PHOSPHATE P EVOLVED IN DIGESTS OF SINGLE NUCLEOTIDES OF EQUIMOLECULAR MIXTURES OF FOUR DIFFERENT NUCLEOTIDES AND OF RIBONUCLEATE AND DEOXYRIBONUCLEATE IN FRESH AND IN DIALYZED TISSUE EXTRACTS[1] (301)

Tissue	Ammonia N and phosphate P evolved from:													
	Sum of four[2] nucleotides in fresh or dialyzed extracts		Mixture of four[3] nucleotides in fresh or dialyzed extracts		YNA in[4] fresh extracts		YNA in[4] dialyzed extracts		TNA in[4] fresh extracts		TNA in[4] dialyzed extracts		TNA[4] in dialyzed extracts + salts	
	N	P	N	P	N	P	N	P	N	P	N	P	N	P
Rat:														
Liver	90	269	44	106	20	55	56	124	5	40	0	0	20	130
Kidney	96	340	94	300	80	225	92	228	58	180	0	0	102	220
Spleen	98	250	90	52	96	25	96	65	80	6	0	0	90	180
Brain	50	160	50	60	32	10	42	70	0	0	0	0	0	25
Pancreas	30	118	30	60	0	0	0	78	0	0	0	0	0	32
Muscle	40	86	8	40	0	0	0	11	0	0	0	0	0	0
Mouse:														
Liver	94	268	62	140	16	25	46	110	6	28	0	0	20	120
Hepatoma 587	96	240	60	120	50	60	—	40	50	66	—	0	—	60
Hepatoma 98/15	—	—	—	—	70	60	—	—	54	60	—	—	—	—

[1] Incubation period 5 hours at 37°. Data in terms of micrograms ammonia N or inorganic phosphate P over those in controls; digests consisted of 1 ml. tissue extract (equivalent to 166 mg. tissue) plus 1 ml. substrate solution.

[2] Sum of N or P evolved from individual digests of adenylic, guanylic, cytidylic, and uridylic acids, at respective concentrations per milliliter of 1.24 mg., 1.28 mg., 1.20 mg., and 1.20 mg. If all nucleotides were in 1 ml. solution, their sum would be equivalent to 5 mg. ribonucleate.

[3] Represents N or P evolved from mixtures of nucleotides described in footnote 2, all in 1 ml. solution. Equivalent to 5 mg. ribonucleate.

[4] Concentration of nucleates 5 mg. per milliliter water solution. YNA denotes ribonucleate, TNA denotes deoxyribonucleate. Salts added to dialyzed extracts with YNA yield no more N and P than fresh extracts. Salts added to dialyzed extracts plus TNA at 0.01 M may be halides (except fluoride) of alkali or alkaline earth metals (except beryllium), and of organic bases.

TABLE 106

DEAMINASES FOR RIBONUCLEIC ACID, DEOXYRIBONUCLEIC ACID, AND PURINES IN NORMAL AND NEOPLASTIC ANIMAL TISSUES (301–303)

Tissue	Ammonia nitrogen in digests of:[1]								
	Yeast nucleate	Thymus nucleate	Adenylic acid	Adenine	Guanylic acid	Guanine	Guanosine	Cytidylic acid	Cytosine
Normal:									
Rat spleen	96	84	50	0	47	48	50	0	0
Rat kidney	80	60	48	0	50	40	44	0	0
Rat brain	32	0	0	0	52	52	50	0	0
Rat liver	20	4	40	0	48	42	55	0	0
Rat fetal liver	32	8	50	0	48	0	30	0	0
Rat muscle	0	0	0	0	30	0	42	0	0
Rat pancreas	10	0	36	0	25	30	30	0	0
Mouse spleen	96	88	50	0	50	50	42	0	0
Mouse kidney	82	64	42	—	40	45	48	40	0
Mouse lymph nodes	60	25	52	0	—	54	48	0	0
Mouse brain	30	0	35	—	47	40	42	0	0
Mouse liver	16	7	40	0	50	43	50	0	0
Mouse lung	34	0	—	—	—	—	—	—	—
Mouse intestine	10	5	50	0	42	48	42	0	0
Mouse thymus	55	14	40	0	43	50	50	0	0
Mouse muscle	0	0	—	—	—	—	—	0	0
Neoplastic:									
Rat Jensen sarcoma	52	0	—	—	—	—	—	—	—
Primary rat hepatoma	22	5	—	—	—	—	—	0	0
Rat hepatoma 31	58	38	42	0	50	50	50	0	0
Mouse hepatoma 587	50	42	48	0	48	45	48	0	0
Mouse hepatoma 98/15	50	44	45	0	45	50	50	0	0
Mouse hepatoma E	42	40	—	—	—	—	—	—	—
Mouse lymphoma 1885	60	25	50	0	—	55	48	—	—
Mouse sarcoma 180	43	0	—	—	—	—	—	—	—
Mouse lung tumor F	34	0	—	—	—	—	—	—	—
Mouse intestinal adenocarcinoma	10	2	50	0	52	48	48	0	0
Mouse thymoma	41	1	50	0	50	43	48	0	0

[1] In terms of milligrams N $\times 10^3$ from 5 mg. nucleate or equivalent purine in aqueous extract of tissue equivalent to 160 mg. 150 $\times 10^{-3}$ mg. N corresponds to deamination of 3 atoms of amino nitrogen in nucleate, 50 $\times 10^{-3}$ mg. N to complete deamination of purines. Incubation period 5 hours at 37°

TABLE 107

DECOLORIZATION VELOCITY OF METHYLENE BLUE IN AQUEOUS EXTRACTS OF NORMAL LIVER AND OF TRANSPLANTED HEPATOMA 31 IN MALE OSBORNE-MENDEL RATS[1] (92)

Methylene blue, mM.	Xanthine, mM.	YNA, mg.	TNA, mg.	Decolorization rate, min.$^{-1}$ × 10^4 Liver	Hepatoma
0.016	0	0	0	—	450
	0	2.5	0	—	10,000
	0	0	2.5	—	400
0.031	0	0	0	—	178
	0	2.5	0	—	5,000
	0	0	2.5	—	222
	1.6	0	0	—	230
	1.6	2.5	0	—	5,000
	1.6	0	2.5	—	2,500
0.062	0	0	0	—	56
	0	2.5	0	—	3,333
	0	0	2.5	—	164
	1.6	0	0	—	56
	1.6	2.5	0	—	3,333
	1.6	0	2.5	—	1,428
0.155	0	0	0	5,000	24
	0	2.5	0	2,500	1,666
	0	0	2.5	556	62
	1.6	0	0	3,333	33
	1.6	2.5	0	2,500	2,000
	1.6	0	2.5	1,250	909
0.31	0	0	0	2,000	10
	0	2.5	0	1,429	833
	0	0	2.5	333	36
	1.6	0	0	1,667	20
	1.6	2.5	0	1,429	769
	1.6	0	2.5	667	58
0.62	0	0	0	714	5
	0	2.5	0	667	370
	0	0	2.5	294	23
	1.6	0	0	769	11
	1.6	2.5	0	667	222
	1.6	0	2.5	476	24
1.24	0	0	0	218	—
	0	2.5	0	218	—
	0	0	2.5	111	—
	1.6	0	0	250	—
	1.6	2.5	0	227	—
	1.6	0	2.5	178	—

TABLE 107—(*Continued*)

Methylene blue, mM.	Xanthine mM.	YNA,[2] mg.	TNA, mg.	Decolorization rate, min.$^{-1}$ × 10^4	
				Liver	Hepatoma
2.48	0	0	0	39	—
	0	2.5	0	91	—
	0	0	2.5	48	—
	1.6	0	0	121	—
	1.6	2.5	0	111	—
	1.6	0	2.5	105	—
4.96	0	0	0	4	—
	0	2.5	0	66	—
	0	0	2.5	18	—
	1.6	0	0	14	—
	1.6	2.5	0	18	—
	1.6	0	2.5	10	—

[1] Aqueous extract of tissues equivalent to 166 mg./ml. Mixtures consisted of 1 ml. extract, 1 ml. dye, 1 ml. water or substrates so that total volume was 3 ml. Temperature, 25°. Anaerobic conditions maintained throughout by employment of tubes evacuated and sealed at 18 mm. mercury. End point at 98% decolorization; pH 7.1. Concentrations given are of stock solutions. YNA refers to sodium yeast nucleate, TNA to thymus nucleate, the ribose and deoxyribose forms, respectively. At low dye concentrations in liver extracts the rates were too fast to measure; at high dye concentrations in hepatoma extracts the rates were so low as to render measurement impracticable.

man benign prostatic hypertrophy is about 645, and for the cancer, about 74 (269).

Rondoni and Cudkowicz (268a) have analyzed liver, kidney, and tumors for their content of hydrogen peroxide by titration of the KCN-treated tissues with titanium salts. There appears to be about 3 to 4 γ of H_2O_2 per milligram dry weight of kidney, about 1 γ on the same basis in the Walker rat tumor, and about 0.2 γ on the same basis in rat liver. The relatively high level of peroxide in tumors may be due in part to their low level or absence of catalase.

Carbohydrate Metabolic Systems. Amylase, which is probably composed of at least two separate enzymes, including phosphorylase (274), acts upon glycogen with the liberation of reducing groups. The activity of this enzyme system in the hepatomas differs little from that in normal liver (85). This is interesting in view of the fact that the rat hepatoma is nearly devoid of glycogen. The mouse hepatomas, on the other hand, all contain glycogen in quantities which at present are not known (275). The amylase system is retained in the hepatoma independently of the capacity of the latter to store glycogen. Orr and Stickland (16) have pointed out that the substrate for glycolysis in the liver is glycogen, in the rat hepatoma it is glucose. Glycogen may be unnecessary in the hepatoma, but if so the reason

TABLE 108

(Calculated data from Table 107)

EFFECT OF YNA AND TNA ON DECOLORIZATION VELOCITY IN AQUEOUS EXTRACTS OF NORMAL LIVER AND OF TRANSPLANTED HEPATOMA 31 IN MALE OSBORNE-MENDEL RATS (92)

Methylene blue, mM.	Change in decolorization velocity, min.$^{-1}$ × 10^4, in.							
	YNA (yeast nucleate)				TNA (thymus nucleate)			
	No xanthine[1]		Xanthine[2]		No xanthine[3]		Xanthine[4]	
	Liver	Hepatoma	Liver	Hepatoma	Liver	Hepa-toma	Liver	Hepatoma
0.016	—	+9550	—	—	—	− 50	—	—
0.031	—	+4822	—	+4770	—	+ 44	—	+2270
0.062	—	+3277	—	+3277	—	+108	—	+1372
0.155	−2500	+1642	−833	+1967	−4444	+ 38	−2083	+ 876
0.31	− 577	+ 823	−238	+ 749	−1667	+ 26	−1000	+ 38
0.62	− 47	+ 365	−102	+ 211	− 420	+ 18	− 293	+ 13
1.24	0	—	− 23	—	− 107	—	− 72	—
2.48	+ 52	—	− 10	—	+ 9	—	− 16	—
4.96	+ 62	—	+ 4	—	+ 13	—	− 4	—

[1] Values = Velocity in presence of YNA − Velocity in water alone.
[2] Values = Velocity in presence of xathine + YNA − Velocity in xanthine alone.
[3] Values = Velocity in presence of TNA − Velocity in water alone.
[4] Values = Velocity in presence of xanthine + TNA − Velocity in xanthine alone.

TABLE 109

DECOLORIZATION VELOCITY OF METHYLENE BLUE IN AQUEOUS EXTRACTS OF NORMAL LIVER AND OF TRANSPLANTED HEPATOMA 587 IN STRAIN *A* MALE MICE[1] (92)

Methylene blue, mM.	Xanthine, mM.	YNA[2], mg.	TNA,[2] mg.	Decolorization rate, min.$^{-1}$ × 10	
				Liver	Hepatoma
0.62	0	0	0	6666	909
	0	5 —	0	2500	500
	0	0	5	500	72
	1.6	0	0	4000	666
	1.6	5	0	1818	303
	1.6	0	5	1333	152
1.24	0	0	0	135	7
	0	5	0	125	35
	0	0	5	49	14
	1.6	0	0	185	69
	1.6	5	0	145	58
	1.6	0	5	101	40

[1] Aqueous extract of tissues equivalent to 166 mg./ml. Mixtures consisted of 2 ml. extract, 1 ml. dye, and water or solutions of substrates to bring total volume to 5 ml.; temperature, 23°. Anaerobic conditions maintained throughout by employment of tubes evacuated and sealed at 18 mm. mercury. End point at 98% decolorization; pH, 7.1. Concentrations given are of stock solutions.

[2] YNA refers to yeast nucleate; TNA to thymus nucleate.

for the presence of the amylase system becomes obscure. The relative proportion of glucose in the rat hepatoma is low, that of lactic acid is high, as compared with that of the normal liver, and this, in view of the greater glycolysis in the former tissue, is not surprising (*vide ultra*). The Jensen sarcoma is yet another tumor which contains little or no glycogen but does contain a very active amylase (11). Phosphorylase, as measured by inorganic phosphate liberation from glucose-1-phosphate in presence of cysteine and adenylic acid, is at the same level in liver and in hepatoma, despite the greatly decreased glycogen content of the latter (284). In the absence of added adenylic acid, the liver activity decreases by half, but the tumor phosphorylase nearly disappears.

Sulfuric acid esters of sugars of high molecular weight are observed in rapidly growing mesenchymal tumors (285), and the suggestion has been made that these compounds are derived from the granules of the mast cells.

TABLE 110

DIALYSIS STUDIES, EFFECT OF VARIOUS SUBSTANCES ON THE DECOLORIZATION RATE OF METHYLENE BLUE IN DIALYZED AQUEOUS TISSUE EXTRACTS OF NORMAL LIVERS AND OF TRANSPLANTED HEPATOMA 587 IN STRAIN *A* MALE MICE[1] (92)

Solutions added to extracts and methylene blue[2] ml.						Decolorization rate, $min.^{-1} \times 10^4$	
Distilled water	Saline[3]	Coenzyme (DPN)[4]	Coenzyme-saline[5]	YNA[6]	TNA[6]	Liver	Hepatoma
2	—	—	—	—	—	36	24
1	1	—	—	—	—	105	121
1	—	—	—	1	—	105	80
—	1	—	—	1	—	143	205
1	—	—	—	—	1	51	33
—	1	—	—	—	1	83	100
1	—	1	—	—	—	36	23
—	1	1	—	—	—	2000	833
—	—	1	—	1	—	47	23
—	—	1	—	—	1	43	26
—	—	—	1	1	—	1111	833
—	—	—	1	—	1	1000	714

[1] The aqueous tissue extracts, equivalent to 333 mg./ml., were dialyzed 24 hours against distilled water.

[2] Mixtures consisted of 1 ml. dialyzed extract, 1 ml. methylene blue at 0.62×10^{-3} *M* concentration, and 2 ml. added solutions.

[3] Composition in grams per liter: sodium chloride, 6.8; potassium chloride, 0.4; calcium chloride, 0.2; magnesium sulfate, 0.1; sodium dihydrogen phosphate, 0.125; and sodium bicarbonate 2.2. The saline is the same as that used by Dr. W. R. Earle for tissue-culture studies.

[4] The diphosphopyridine nucleotide (DPN) was made up at 1.6×10^{-3} *M* concentration in distilled water.

[5] 1.6×10^{-3} *M* concentration in saline solution.

[6] 1 mg./ml. distilled water; YNA = yeast nucleate, TNA = thymus nucleate.

TABLE 111

NUCLEIC ACIDS IN NORMAL AND NEOPLASTIC TISSUES

Tissue	Nucleo-protein phosphorus[1]	Nucleotide N[2]	Nucleoside N + free purine N[2]	Total acid-soluble purine N[2]	RNA	DNA	Ratio RNA/DNA	References
Normal rat liver	449	30.6	9.7	40.3	75.3[3]	17.6[3]	4.3	(170)
Regenerating rat liver	512	36.1	10.9	47.0	72[3]	18[3]	4.0	(170)
Fetal rat liver	908	17.1	7.3	24.4	49.5[3]	33.7[3]	1.5	(170)
Primary rat hepatoma	535	17.3	9.9	27.3	71[3]	19.5[3]	3.6	(170)
Nuclei of rat liver	—	—	—	—	—	38.3[4]	—	(168)
Nuclei of transplanted rat hepatoma	—	—	—	—	—	21.8[4]	—	(168)
Adult sheep liver	231	—	—	—	65[3]	19[3]	3.5	(172)
Fetal sheep liver	592	—	—	—	61[3]	24[3]	2.6	(172)
Normal rat liver	350	—	—	—	754[5]	236[6]	3.2	(173)
Primary rat hepatoma	555	—	—	—	715[5]	513[6]	1.4	(173)
Normal mouse lung	—	—	—	—	238[5]	586[6]	0.4	(173)
Transplanted lung tumor	—	—	—	—	800[5]	950[6]	0.8	(173)

[1] In terms of milligrams per 100 g. dry weight of tissue.

[2] In terms of milligrams per 100 g. tissue.

[3] As per cent total P in extracted tissue powder; RNA = ribonucleic acid, DNA deoxyribonucleic acid P.

[4] As deoxyribonucleic acid in terms of per cent dry weight of isolated nuclei (lipid present).

[5] In terms of milligrams ribonucleic acid per 100 g. wet weight of tissue.

[6] In terms of milligrams deoxyribonucleic acid per 100 g. wet weight of tissue.

TABLE 112

RIBONUCLEINASE ACTIVITY OF RAT TISSUES AND VARIOUS TUMORS (304)

Tissue	Activity[1]
Pancreas	16.7
Spleen	2.1
Kidney	1.6
Submaxillary	1.0
Lung	1.0
Liver	0.4
Cardiac muscle	0.4
Skeletal muscle	0.3
Walker tumor 256[2]	1.1
Flexner-Jobling carcinoma[2]	0.6
Yale No. I adenocarcinoma[3]	0.8
Fibrosarcoma[3]	0.5

[1] In terms of cubic millimeters carbon dioxide liberated from bicarbonate per milligram wet weight of tissue per hour in the presence of yeast nucleate. This enzyme is probably identical with those referred to as ribonucleodepolymerase and polynucleotidase.

[2] Rat tumor.

[3] Mouse tumor.

TABLE 113

ACID AND ALKALINE PHOSPHATASE ACTIVITY IN NORMAL AND NEOPLASTIC ANIMAL TISSUE[1] (60, 90)

$Q_{acid} > Q_{alk.}$			$Q_{acid} = Q_{alk.}$			$Q_{acid} < Q_{alk.}$		
	Q_{acid}	$Q_{alk.}$		Q_{acid}	$Q_{alk.}$		Q_{acid}	$Q_{alk.}$
Lymph nodes (mouse)	49	8	Bone marrow (mouse)	22	23	Intestinal mucosa (mouse)	34	2789
Pancreas (mouse)	10	1	Brain (mouse)	15	12			
Pancreas (rat)	18	3	Brain (rat)	16	14			
Liver (rat)	25	4	Lung (mouse)	33	36	Kidney (mouse)	15	1072
Liver (mouse)	12	4	Mammary tumor (mouse)	21	22	Kidney (rat)	95	1500
Liver (rabbit)	14	3	Lymphoma (mouse)	10	10	Blood serum (rat)	0.4	9
Fetal liver (rabbit)	22	0				Jensen sarcoma (rat)	22	44
Fetal liver (rat)	48	27				Liver tumor (rat)	52	542
Regenerating liver (rat)	29	3				Liver tumor (mouse)	20	120
Muscle (mouse)	19	2						
Muscle (rat)	16	2						
Spleen (mouse)	73	17						
Spleen (rat)	42	21						
Skin (mouse)	30	5						
Skin (rat)	8	5						
Gastric mucosa (mouse)	27	17						
Hyperplastic breast (mouse)	18	9						
Intestinal tumor (mouse)	19	3						
Gastric tumor (mouse)	16	0						
Lung tumor (mouse)	16	1						
Liver tumor (mouse)	10	1						
Endothelioma (mouse)	12	4						
Melanoma (mouse)	19	1						
Sarcoma 37 (mouse)	23	2						
CR-180 (mouse)	21	2						
Sarcoma (mouse)	19	2						

[1] In terms of Q, the ratio at either pH 4.6 or pH 9.5 of the per cent hydrolysis of $M/200$ phenylphosphate after 1 hour incubation to milligrams total N in extract of tissue.

TABLE 114

PHOSPHATASES IN FRESH AND IN DIALYZED EXTRACTS OF NORMAL MOUSE LIVER AND OF TRANSPLANTED MOUSE HEPATOMA 587 (305)

Substrate	pH	Mg. tissue per ml.	Incubation time, hr.	Salt	Activity of appropriate phosphatase[1]			
					Liver		Hepatoma	
					Fresh	Dialyzed	Fresh	Dialyzed
Phenylphosphate	4.6	83	2	—	77	68	58	57
Phenylphosphate	4.6	83	2	Mg	77	70	58	62
Phenylphosphate	4.6	83	2	Ca	77	69	58	57
Phenylphosphate	9.6	83	2	—	60	66	18	20
Phenylphosphate	9.6	83	2	Mg	86	90	18	25
Phenylphosphate	9.6	83	2	Ca	64	70	17	20
β-Glycerophosphate	4.6	83	2	—	30	35	19	20
β-Glycerophosphate	4.6	83	2	Mg	30	35	16	20
β-Glycerophosphate	4.6	83	2	Ca	30	35	18	20
β-Glycerophosphate	9.6	83	2	—	56	60	14	20
β-Glycerophosphate	9.6	83	2	Mg	56	70	20	30
β-Glycerophosphate	9.6	83	2	Ca	56	66	12	20
β-Glycerophosphate	6.8	83	2	—	18	20	10	14
β-Glycerophosphate	6.8	83	2	Mg	30	40	14	19
β-Glycerophosphate	6.8	83	2	Ca	19	23	10	15
Adenylic acid	6.8	42	1	—	50	52	40	42
Adenylic acid	6.8	42	1	Mg	60	64	60	60
Adenylic acid	6.8	42	1	Ca	55	60	60	52
Guanylic acid	6.8	42	1	—	60	64	40	42
Guanylic acid	6.8	42	1	Mg	64	68	68	70
Guanylic acid	6.8	42	1	Ca	60	62	55	60
Cytidylic acid	6.8	42	1	—	60	64	42	46
Cytidylic acid	6.8	42	1	Mg	64	68	50	54
Cytidylic acid	6.8	42	1	Ca	60	62	48	50
Uridylic acid	6.8	42	1	—	90	94	90	94
Uridylic acid	6.8	42	1	Mg	98	100	94	94
Uridylic acid	6.8	42	1	Ca	90	92	88	92
Ribonucleate	6.8	166	5	—	25	110	60	50
Ribonucleate	6.8	166	5	Mg	40	130	94	100
Ribonucleate	6.8	166	5	Ca	25	120	64	58
Deoxyribonucleate	6.8	166	5	—	28	0	66	0
Deoxyribonucleate	6.8	166	5	Mg	40	140	84	65
Deoxyribonucleate	6.8	166	5	Ca	40	132	78	65
Pyrophosphate	6.8	10	0.5	—	0	0	0	0
Pyrophosphate	6.8	10	0.5	Mg	160	248	106	80
Pyrophosphate	6.8	10	0.5	Ca	0	0	0	0

[1] In terms of micrograms inorganic phosphate P above controls. Digests consisted of 1 ml. extract of tissue at concentrations designated plus 1 ml. substrate solution. Extract concentration chosen in range where splitting of substrate is proportional to dilution of extract. Substrates in milligrams per milliliter as follows: disodium phenylphosphate 1.09 (complete splitting = 155 γ P), sodium β-glycerophosphate 0.97 (complete splitting = 160 γ P), sodium pyrophosphate 2.2 (complete splitting = 320 γ), all ribonucleotides at 3.5×10^{-3} M (complete splitting = 109 γ P), both nucleates 5 (complete splitting = 440 γ P). Concentrations of MgCl and $CaCl_2$ 0.01 M in digests. Nucleotides first neutralized with NaOH before digesting. Nucleates used as sodium salts.

TABLE 115

CHEMICAL ANALYSIS OF NORMAL RAT LIVER AND OF TRANSPLANTED RAT HEPATOMA (281)

Component	Normal liver		Hepatoma	
	Fresh weight, %	Dry weight, %	Fresh weight, %	Dry weight, %
Water	71.38	0	81.93	0
Ash	1.634	5.17	1.391	7.70
N	3.200	11.18	2.315	12.81
P	0.321	1.12	0.253	1.40
S	0.264	0.921	0.207	1.148
Na	0.305	1.064	0.314	1.737
K	0.029	0.101	0.089	0.492
Ca	0.009	0.031	0.0034	0.019
Mg	0.019	0.066	0.023	0.126
Fe	0.0035	0.0121	0.0014	0.008
I	0.0025	0.009	0.0018	0.0098
Cl	0.161	0.564	0.180	0.998
Phosphatide	2.60	9.06	1.48	8.17
Free cholesterol	0.184	0.643	0.233	1.289
Total cholesterol	0.268	0.936	0.357	1.976
Fatty acids	3.09	10.81	1.09	6.00
Total P (d)	0.321	1.120	0.253	1.400
Inorganic P (a)	0.063	0.221	0.064	0.354
Acid-soluble P (b)	0.094	0.326	0.104	0.576
Lipoid P (c)	0.103	0.360	0.059	0.327
Protein P (d − b + c)	0.124	0.434	0.090	0.498
Organic P (d − a)	0.258	0.899	0.189	1.046
Nonprotein N	0.172	0.601	0.227	1.256
Amino N	0.107	0.374	0.138	0.764
Creatinine	0.005	0.017	0.003	0.017
Creatine	0.005	0.017	0.005	0.028
Urea	0.030	0.105	0.041	0.227
Uric acid	0.014	0.049	0.020	0.111

TABLE 116

ACID AND ALKALINE PHOSPHATASE ACTIVITY IN NORMAL ADULT HUMAN TISSUES[1] (306)

Tissues	Acid phosphatase	Alkaline phosphatase
Prostate	522	1.3
Prostate	792	0.8
Prostate	2284	0.9
Kidney	4.6	2.9
Kidney	2.4	6.7
Kidney	3.1	2.3
Liver	1.6	1.2
Liver	2.4	2.1
Liver	2.6	10.6
Duodenum	3.1	11.3
Duodenum	0.9	5.9
Duodenum	0.8	4.0
Vertebra	2.5	8.8
Vertebra	1.9	3.0

[1] In terms of units per gram fresh tissue. One unit equivalent to release of 1 mg./hr. of phenol from phenylphosphate at 37°.

Little study has been made of the enzymes, e.g., mucinases, which act upon these substrates in tumors.

β-Glucuronidase is an enzyme which Fishman and his associates have found to be present in high concentration in tissues exposed to estrogen stimulation and which, in such malignant neoplasms and their effusion fluids as those of the breast, ovary, stomach, colon, uterus, penis, and lung, exists at a generally higher level of activity than that of the adjacent uninvolved tissues (Table 101) (286-290). β-Glucuronidase may be involved in metabolic conjugation processes with glucuronic acid as the conjugating substance. Thus, glucuronidogenic substances such as menthol, when fed to animals, induce an increase in the β-glucuronidase activity of various

TABLE 117

CHEMICAL ANALYSIS OF NORMAL AND CARCINOMATOUS HUMAN LUNG (307)

Component		Normal lung	Lung carcinoma	lung sarcoma
Dry material		21.9%	18.4%	15.8%
Composition, per cent dry material				
Nitrogen		10.9	10.79	10.07
Phosphorus		0.43	0.51	0.39
Lipoid		11.26	8.89	7.25
Cholesterol		2.24	2.2	1.35
Carbohydrate		1.79	2.76	2.28
Protein-N		9.75	9.75	8.86
Residual-N		1.20	1.38	1.2
Nitrogen Distribution				
Protein-N	Per cent total N	89.2	86.9	88.0
Residual-N	Per cent total N	10.8	13.1	12.0
Proteose	Per cent residual N	14.7	23.7	78.2
Diamino acids	Per cent residual N	2.3	6.8	4.6
Monoamino acids	Per cent residual N	83.9	72.8	17.2
Carbohydrate Distribution, mg.% dry material				
Free sugar		108.0	0	32.9
Bound but not to protein		358.5	1348.0	316.4
Protein-bound sugar		1323.0	1502.0	173.1
Phosphorus Distribution, mg.% dry material				
Inorganic P		105.3	114.6	127.8
Lipoid P		126.6	74.1	42.9
Protein P		162.9	263.1	196.3

tissues (286). However, the tissue function responds specifically to hormonal stimulation, for stilbestrol stimulates liver but not kidney β-glucuronidase, whereas testosterone and methylandrostenediol produce a striking increase of this enzyme in kidney but not in liver (287). Cyclic changes in the activity of the enzyme occur in normal human endometrium, closely paralleling titers of blood and urinary estrogens during the menstrual cycle (291). It might appear from the viewpoint of several investigators (286-293) that β-glucuronidase levels can serve as a partial index of cellular growth, and perhaps that the metabolic conjugation products involved might be needed by the growing cells (cf. 287). The high level of the enzyme in tumors might be due to a response to some stimulating agent which may be an estrogen or adventitiously related to it. β-Glucuronidase is also higher in mouse mammary tumors than in the normal tissues of mice (293, 294), and among the various mouse strains considerable differences both in β-glucuronidase and in esterase have been noted (Table 102). The relative levels of β-glucuronidase in normal liver and mammary gland are more or less the same, and the relative levels in the mammary tumors reflect the characteristics of the tissues of origin.

Glycogen appears to be another intracellular constituent which varies considerably throughout the menstrual cycle, reaching high values in the endometrium during the secretory phases and dropping to low values in the proliferative phases. In fundal adenocarcinoma of the endometrium, there seems to be no clear-cut response of glycogen, for of a large series studied, both differentiated and undifferentiated, some tumors had a high, and some a low, content of glycogen (295).

The hydrolytic action of tissue preparations on diketo acids was first observed by Meister and Greenstein (296). Whether the tissue catalyst

TABLE 118

WATER AND ELECTROLYTE CONTENT OF TESTICULAR TUMORS OF THE DOG AND OF NORMAL, CRYPTORCHID AND ESTROGENIZED TESTIS[1] (260)

Tissue	Water	Fat	Cl	Na	K	Ca	Mg	N
Normal testis	873.0	20.3	60.3	45.6	90.9	0.86	5.0	16.6
Testis from which tumors were removed	868.8	19.0	67.2	57.4	85.2	—	—	—
Interstitial cell tumors	846.0	87.1	66.8	58.1	72.2	—	—	—
Lobulated tumors I (low fat)	838.9	5.2	53.0	36.9	104.6	—	—	22.0
Lobulated tumors II (high fat)	829.9	56.8	58.2	50.8	86.8	—	—	21.3
Cryptorchid	852.9	16.2	62.8	60.1	76.1	—	—	—
Estrogen	842.2	21.6	67.8	60.7	83.2	—	—	—

[1] In terms of mean values per kilogram fat-free tissue.

which hydrolyzes 2,4-diketo acids to pyruvic acid and the corresponding fatty acid (296) is the same which hydrolyzes the 3,5-diketo acids to acetic and acetoacetic acids (297, 298) remains a moot point. Both actions result in a hydrolysis of a C-acyl group, and both types of substrate are hydrolyzed considerably slower by hepatomas than by normal liver (299, 300)

TABLE 119

CITRIC ACID CONTENT OF NORMAL AND NEOPLASTIC TISSUES[1] (308)

Normal		Neoplastic	
Rabbit:			
Liver	2.8	Brown-Pearce carcinoma	13.6
Skeletal muscle	2.5	—	—
Kidney	6.0	—	—
Brain	4.6	—	—
Mouse:			
Skin	12.2	Crocker sarcoma	14.2
Fur	133.0	Crocker sarcoma	14.3
Seminal vesicles	128.0	Crocker sarcoma (little necrosis)	12.3
Muscle	2.8	Crocker sarcoma (largely necrotic)	7.7
Viscera and brain	4.6	—	—
Rat:			
—	—	Walker 256 tumor	16.6
—	—	Walker 256 tumor	18.4
—	—	Guerin tumor	16.8
Man:			
Gastric mucosa	2.0	Seminoma of testis	9.9
Skin	5.3	Uterine fibroadenoma	5.0
—	—	Gastric carcinoma	2.7
—	—	Carcinoma of vulva	8.8
—	—	Carcinoma of vulva	7.0

[1] In terms of milligrams per 100 g. wet weight of tissue.

TABLE 120

CONTENT OF CREATINE AND CREATININE IN NORMAL AND NEOPLASTIC HEPATIC TISSUES[1] (259)

Tissue	Total creatine chromogen	True creatine	Total creatinine chromogen	True creatinine
Normal rat liver	33	11	1.4	1.4
Transplanted rat hepatoma 31	32	10	1.5	1.5
Normal mouse liver	34	6	1.2	1.1
Transplanted mouse hepatoma 587	33	5	1.2	1.2

[1] Values given in terms of milligrams per 100 g. wet tissue. True creatine and creatinine values are obtained by measuring the decrease in chromogen (alkaline picrate) after digestion with specific bacterial enzyme for creatinine.

(Table 103). The δ-lactone of 3,5-diketohexanoic acid is also metabolized by liver with the preliminary opening of the lactone ring (297), and the system responsible is also measurably reduced when rat liver becomes neoplastic (300); however, mouse hepatomas in contrast possess nearly normal levels of this system. It is not improbable that these C-acylase systems are related to the metabolic systems involved in the oxidation of the fatty acids. These take a precipitate drop in the course of the neoplastic transformation of normal tissues.

The Over-All Enzyme Pattern

Among the general conclusions mentioned above, it was stated that the range of activity of various enzymes and other components in tumors is narrower than that of the same enzymes, etc., in normal tissues, and that the range for a particular component in tumors might occur near the upper part of the range of the same component in normal tissues, near the lower part of the range for another component, and somewhere in the middle part of the normal range for still a third component. Extensive data on normal and neoplastic tissues of mice and rats have been reported in Tables 63 to 120, and, on the basis of these data, the enzymes studied may be apportioned among the above three categories. In no sense is such a comparison exact, for it burdens the data with assumptions as to relative weight and uniformity which are not warranted. Moreover, such a comparison does not reveal how individual enzyme systems alter in the event of the neoplastic transformation of each individual normal tissue. (A more exact comparison of this kind is given in the case of hepatic tissues in the following section.) All that can be claimed for the present comparison is that it suggests, on the basis of the data so far available, which enzymes, respectively, are as active in tumors as in the most active normal tissues, which are as little active as the least active normal tissues, and which fall somewhere between the extremes of the normal range.

Among the most active enzymes in tumors are those concerned with protein metabolism, e.g., benzoylarginineamidase (BAA amidase), and dehydropeptidase I. The inclusion of xanthine dehydrogenase in this category may be due to the role of this enzyme in the active nucleic acid metabolism in tumors. Among the least active enzymes in tumors are the iron-containing catalysts (catalase and cytochrome oxidase), the phosphoric acid and fatty acid esterases, and the systems concerned with the metabolism of cystine. The systems described in the second column of Table 121 are better evaluated when compared among pairs of homologous normal and neoplastic tissues.

The Properties of Homologous Hepatic Tissues

The hepatic tissues lend themselves particularly well to comparisons of the metabolism of tissues which are resting and of those undergoing con-

TABLE 121

RANGE IN ENZYMATIC ACTIVITY IN MOUSE AND RAT TUMORS AS COMPARED WITH THE RANGE AMONG NORMAL TISSUES[1]

Enzymes in tumors which stand in the upper normal range of activity	Enzymes in tumors which stand in the middle of the normal range of activity	Enzymes in tumors which stand in the lower normal range of activity
Dehydropeptidase I[2]	Arginase[3]	Catalase[4]
Benzoylarginineamidase[5] (BAA amidase)	Acid phosphatase[6]	Cytochrome oxidase[7]
Xanthine dehydrogenase[8]	Ribonucleodepolymerase[9]	Alkaline phosphatase[10]
	Deoxyribonucleodepolymerase[11]	Esterase[12]
	Ribonucleodeaminase[13]	Cystine desulfurase[14]
	Desoxyribonucleodeaminase[15]	Dehydropeptidase II[16]

[1] Based on data in Tables 63–120. Osteogenic sarcoma in mice and the hepatoma in rats excluded from consideration of phosphatase levels.

[2] Most active normal tissue, kidney; least active normal tissue, skeletal muscle.

[3] Most active normal tissue, liver; least active normal tissue, thymus.

[4] Most active normal tissue, liver; least active normal tissue, thymus.

[5] Most active normal tissue, spleen; least active normal tissue, skeletal muscle.

[6] Most active normal tissue, spleen; least active normal tissue, thymus.

[7] Most active normal tissue, cardiac muscle; least active normal tissue, intestinal mucosa.

[8] Most active normal tissue, intestinal mucosa; least active normal tissue, lung.

[9] Most active normal tissue, pancreas; least active normal tissue, skeletal muscle.

[10] Most active normal tissue, intestinal mucosa; least active normal tissue, pancreas.

[11] Most active normal tissue, lymph nodes; least active normal tissue, thymus.

[12] Most active normal tissue, pancreas; least active normal tissue, thymus.

[13] Most active normal tissue, spleen; least active normal tissue, skeletal muscle.

[14] Most active normal tissue, liver; least active normal tissue, brain.

[15] Most active normal tissue, spleen; least active normal tissue, skeletal muscle.

[16] Most active normal tissue, kidney; least active normal tissue, brain.

trolled or uncontrolled growth. Thus there is (a) the normal adult resting liver, (b) regenerating liver after partial hepatectomy, (c) fetal liver and (d) the hepatoma. The last three mentioned are growing tissues, but (b) and (c), in contrast with (d), involve controlled growth. At certain periods of growth of the regenerating liver, particularly in the earlier stages, the rate exceeds that of the hepatoma (309).

The first to investigate these tissues was Burk (310) (Table 122), who noted their glycolytic and respiratory properties. As a whole, the metabolic behavior of the hepatoma and of fetal liver is nearly similar and quite different from that of the nearly similar metabolic properties of resting adult liver and regenerating liver after partial hepatectomy. The high anaerobic glycolysis of fetal liver may likely be due to the erythropoietic elements and not to the true liver cells, but, in any event, it is

TABLE 122

Comparison of the Metabolism of Homologous Rat Hepatic Tissues[1] (310)

Tissue	$Q_A^{O_2}$	Q_{O_2}	*RQ*	$Q_A^{N_2}$	*MOQ*	*U*
Normal liver	1.5	6.0	0.70	1.0	−0.3	−11.0
Regenerating liver	1.5	6.4	0.64	1.8	0.1	−11.0
Fetal liver	0.6	6.0	1.00	8.0	1.2	−5.2
Hepatoma (primary)[2]	6.0	6.4	0.87	12.1	2.9	−0.7

[1] *Q* values based on initial dry weights. Q_{O_2}, $Q_A^{N_2}$, and $Q_A^{O_2}$ = cubic millimeters oxygen consumption, anaerobic, and aerobic acid production per milligram per hour. *RQ* = repiratory quotient = $\frac{Q_{CO_2}}{Q_{O_2}}$. *MOQ* = Meyerhof oxidation quotient = $3\left(\frac{Q_A^{N_2} - Q^{O_2}}{Q_{O_2}}\right)$. *U* = fermentation excess = $Q_A^{N_2} - 2\,Q_{O_2}$.

[2] Induced by feeding 4-dimethylaminoazobenzene.

difficult to distinguish between them. It is true, however, that nucleated erythroid cells, such as chick bone marrow erythroblasts (produced by acetylphenylhydrazine injection) and the normal rabbit bone marrow erythroid cells, have a high anaerobic glycolysis, comparable to that of embryonic livers (310, 311). What is indeed striking is the similar metabolic behavior of resting and regenerating liver and the dissimilar metabolic behavior of the hepatoma. It is evident that, in the case of regenerating liver, it is possible to have rapid growth in the absence of appreciable glycolysis. This is, however, controlled growth. In the case of the hepatoma, there is presented an ostensibly uncontrolled growth accompanied by extensive glycolysis. The four homologous rat hepatic tissues thus fall, metabolically, into two main categories, resting and regenerating liver on the one side and hepatoma and fetal liver on the other.

The investigation of a number of individual enzymes in these tissues was subsequently undertaken by others (Tables 123 and 124).

With the exception of xanthine dehydrogenase, the activity of all enzymes studied is nearly the same in normal adult and in regenerating liver. It may be that the altered xanthine dehydrogenase activity in the latter tissue is related to the increased rate of nucleic acid turnover (*vide ultra*, (166)). On the whole, and from the standpoint of the enzymes studied, normal adult and regenerating liver are nearly identical. In the case of regenerating mouse liver, although there is a rapid restoration of the normal level of enzymes and other chemical components, there is a persistent incomplete restoration of cell numbers, resulting in the presence of a smaller number of cells containing correspondingly greater amounts of chemical constituents (311a).

The enzymatic activity of fetal liver and of the transplanted hepatoma appear to run parallel when compared with the activity of normal and

TABLE 123

ACTIVITY OF ENZYMES IN HOMOLOGOUS RAT HEPATIC TISSUES[1,2]

Tissue	Arginase	Catalase	Xanthine dehydrogenase	Acid phosphatase	Alkaline phosphatase	Deoxyribonucleodepolymerase	Ribonucleodepolymerase	Amylase[3]	Urea synthesis[4]	Esterase	(Exo) cystine desulfurase	Cytochrome oxidase[5]	D-Amino acid oxidase[5]	Deoxyribonucleodeaminase	Ribonucleodeaminase	Amidase for BAA[6]	Riboflavin[7]	Dehydropeptidase II	Dehydropeptidase I
Normal liver	213	6.8	14	25	4	7	0.09	1.5	0.14	312	9	31	0.24	4	20	32	29	20	20
Regenerating liver	250	6.8	27	29	3	6	0.08	1.6	0.12	303	9	30	0.20	4	20	32	25	20	20
Fetal liver	60	0.4	>300	48	27	6	0.08	1.5	0	152	5	12	0.04	8	32	18	6	5	20
Transplanted hepatoma 31	21	0	28	52	542	5	0.07	1.5	0	104	0	7	0.02	38	58	56	5	1	20

[1] Each enzyme studied under identical conditions in all four tissues. Activity terms of enzymes, except where noted, same as in Table 66. Necrotic areas removed from tumors. Activity of cytochrome oxidase was studied in suspensions of the tissues; urea synthesis was observed with tissue slices; all other enzymes investigated in extracts. All tissues were obtained from Osborne-Mendel rats. The regenerating liver was taken from animals 48 hours after 60–70% of the liver was excised. Fetal liver was taken at about 2 weeks of pregnancy. Hepatoma 31 was in late generation transplants.

All data, with the exception of cytochrome oxidase and D-amino acid oxidase (Shack, (76)) and riboflavin (Robertson and Kahler, (74)), were from Greenstein *et al.*, (60, 71, 92, 146, 270–273).

[2] Cohen *et al.* (316) noted that the transaminase and glyoxalase activity of normal adult and regenerating rat liver was very nearly the same, whereas the activity of these enzymes was much lowered in the livers of rats fed 4-dimethylaminoazobenzene. Potter (225) observed that the adenosine triphosphatase activity of the primary hepatoma in rats was nearly the same as that of normal liver, whereas that of the fetal liver of this species was much lower in activity.

[3] This is probably a mixture of at least 2 enzymes. The activity is given in terms of the increase in titer of 0.02 *N* thiosulfate after iodine treatment of a mixture incubated 2 hours at 39° of 2 ml. 1% glycogen solution in 1% sodium chloride, 1 ml. phosphate buffer at pH 6.9, and 1 ml. extract containing 2.6 mg. total N.

[4] Activity in terms of the milligrams per milliliters of urea nitrogen synthesized after 2 hours' incubation of a mixture of 2 ml. rat serum, 0.25 ml. ammonium chloride solution, 0.25 ml. of citrulline solution and 40–50 mg. (dry weight) of tissue slices.

[5] Data given in terms of cubic millimeters oxygen absorbed per milligram wet weight of tissue per hour at 38°.

[6] Value for primary hepatoma was 36. The amidase activity was estimated by the percentage hydrolysis of benzoylarginineamide hydrochloride in a mixture of 1 ml. substrate (6.2 mg.) plus 1 ml. tissue extract (equivalent to 333 mg. tissue) incubated for 2 hours at 38°. This amidase, according to Bergmann, may actually be a tissue protease. See footnote 13 of Table 66.

[7] In terms of micrograms per gram wet weight of tissue.

TABLE 124

EFFECT OF NUCLEATES ON THE RATE OF METHYLENE BLUE DECOLORIZATION IN AQUEOUS EXTRACTS OF HOMOLOGOUS RAT HEPATIC TISSUES[1] (92)

Methylene blue, mM.	Yeast nucleate, mg.	Thymus nucleate, mg.	Decolorization rate, min.$^{-1}$ × 10^4, in.			
			Adult liver	Regenerating liver[2]	Fetal liver[3]	Transplanted hepatoma[4]
0.155	0	0	5000	—	83	24
0.155	2.5	0	2500	—	53	1666
0.155	0	2.5	556	—	25	62
0.620	0	0	714	333	33	5
0.620	2.5	0	667	245	27	370
0.620	0	2.5	294	159	17	23

[1] Mixtures composed of 1 ml. fresh aqueous extract (equivalent to 166 mg. tissue), 1 ml. sodium nucleate solution and 1 ml. methylene blue solution. Temperature 28°.

[2] 48 hours after operation.

[3] From rats approximately 2 weeks pregnant.

[4] Corresponding values for the primary hepatoma are nearly identical with those for normal liver (71).

regenerating liver. When the activity of any one enzyme in the hepatoma is less than, greater than, or equal to the activity of the same enzyme in normal adult or regenerating liver, so too is the activity of that enzyme, respectively, in the fetal liver. Arginase, catalase, xanthine dehydrogenase, esterase, the urea-synthesizing systems, cystine desulfurase, and cytochrome and D-amino acid oxidases are all lower in activity in both fetal liver and the hepatoma than in normal or regenerating liver. Acid and alkaline phosphatase and the deaminases for ribonucleic and deoxyribonucleic acids are all higher in activity in fetal liver and the hepatoma than in normal or regenerating liver. Amylase and the two nucleic acid depolymerases are nearly identical in activity in all four tissues. Other workers have noted an increase in hepatic alkaline phosphatase levels during regeneration (312–314). On the basis of histochemical studies on punch biopsies of human liver, there appears to be little if any correlation between the level of this enzyme and the diagnosis of hepatoma in man (315). Alkaline phosphatase is an enzyme highly responsive to a number of pathologic stimuli *in vivo*, and to various metal and organic cofactors as well as substrate types *in vitro*, and any combination of these serves to explain the many discrepancies in the literature concerned with this enzyme.

The relative enzymatic activity of fetal and adult liver is the same in the rabbit (85) and in the cat (317) as in the rat (Table 123). West and Woglom (318) observed that the biotin content of both tumor and embryo tissues deviated in the same direction from the corresponding normal adult levels (Fig. 41). In view of the presence of hematopoietic elements in fetal liver, the analogy of this tissue to the hepatoma should not, per-

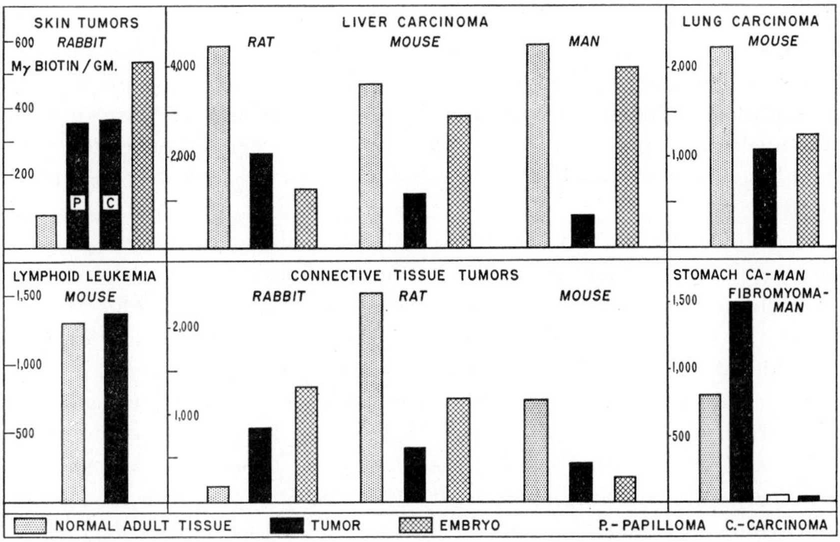

FIG. 41. Comparison of the biotin contents of certain tumors with analogous normal adult and embryo tissues. From West, P. M., and Woglom, W. H., *Cancer Research* **2,** 324 (1942).

haps, be carried too far. Nevertheless, the evidence of a nearly similar pattern of fetal and neoplastic hepatic tissue suggests that neoplasms may revert to a more primitive and less-differentiated metabolism.

Studies of the decolorization rate of methylene blue in extracts of the four homologous rat hepatic tissues are described in Table 124 (92). The data may be appraised in two separate ways. First, by reading the table vertically, a comparison of the effect of addition of yeast nucleate (YNA) and of thymus nucleate (TNA) reveals that, in extracts of adult liver, regenerating liver, and fetal liver, the decolorization rate of the dye is decreased, the decrease being greater in the case of addition of thymus than of yeast nucleate. On the other hand, in the presence of the nucleates, the decolorization rate of the dye is increased in the hepatoma, the increase being greater in the case of the yeast than of the thymus nucleate. This (vertical) comparison demonstrates a qualitative difference between the normal tissues, i.e., adult, regenerating, and fetal liver on the one hand, and the neoplastic hepatic tissue on the other. It would appear that, at the same level of methylene blue used and under the same experimental conditions, the neoplasm can utilize the nucleic acids at a rate considerably greater than that of the three normal tissues. It may be wondered (*vide ultra*) whether under these conditions the hepatoma does not actively metabolize the nucleic acids, the yeast (ribonucleic) nucleic acid at a faster rate than the thymus (deoxyribonucleic) nucleic acid, and both at a rate considerably in excess of that by the normal tissue homologues. No matter what the interpretation may be, it is clear that, at the concentrations of dye used, in hepatoma extracts the nucleates accelerate the rate of methylene blue decolorization whereas in normal hepatic tissue extracts the nucleates depress this rate. The low decolorization rates in fetal liver and hepatoma extracts are most probably due to the lack of available substrates.

Second, when the data in Table 124 are read horizontally, it is noted (a) that the order of magnitude of the decolorization rate is nearly the same for adult and regenerating liver in the presence or absence of added nucleoates; (b) with one significant exception, the order of magnitude of the decolorization rate of fetal liver and of the hepatoma is very nearly the same—the exception occurring in the presence of yeast nucleate—and this order of magnitude is very much less than that characteristic of the adult and regenerating livers. The capacity of hepatoma extracts to decolorize methylene blue in the absence of added nucleates or in the presence of thymus nucleate is very much like that of fetal liver, but, in the presence of yeast nucleate, this capacity of the hepatoma is more like that of adult or regenerating liver.

Thus, on the basis of the horizontal scanning of the data in Table 124 the hepatoma resembles fetal liver in certain respects and adult liver in other respects, whereas on the basis of the vertical scanning of the data it resembles none of the normal hepatic tissues. The effect of yeast nucleate in extracts of the hepatoma is noteworthy. If the rate of hydrogen transport in the presence of the nucleates is dependent upon a prior deamination of the nucleates, it will be noted from Table 105 that the rate of enzymatic deamination is greater in hepatoma than in liver extracts, greater in the case of yeast than of thymus nucleate and, thus, consistent with the data in the last column of Table 124.

That the hepatoma can utilize yeast and thymus nucleates in metabolic processes at a rate higher than in normal liver is revealed by the experiments of Brues *et al.* (166) (Table 125). The rate of turnover of the nucleic acid phosphorus, as measured by P^{32}, is higher in the hepatoma than in normal liver, and, of this nucleic acid phosphorus, the turnover is higher in the case of ribonucleic than of deoxyribonucleic acid. Higher than in either hepatoma or normal liver is the rate of turnover of nucleic acid phosphorus in regenerating liver. The rate of growth of the regenerating liver is also higher than that of the hepatoma, and, apparently, the metabolic turnover of nucleic acid keeps pace with this rate. The rate of metabolic turnover of the phospholipids exceeds that of the nucleic acids (166).

There is an enormous increase in activity of many enzymes in the course of development of late embryonic rat tissues to early postnatal life, the

TABLE 125

SPECIFIC ACTIVITIES OF NUCLEIC ACID PHOSPHORUS EXPRESSED AS PER CENT OF INORGANIC PHOSPHATE SPECIFIC ACTIVITIES USING P^{32} AS INDICATOR (166)

Tissue	Days after injection of P^{32}	Nucleic acid phosphorus in tissues: Ribonucleic acid	Nucleic acid phosphorus in tissues: Deoxyribonucleic acid
Normal adult rat liver	3	54.9	10.6
Normal adult rat liver	8	123	20.8
Regenerating rat liver	3	230	180
Regenerating rat liver	13	314	576
Transplanted rat hepatoma	3	171	64.0

adult level being reached in 10 to 15 days after birth for cytochrome oxidase, succinic dehydrogenase, and adenosine triphosphatase (319).

The sulfur distribution in the four homologous rat hepatic tissues is consistent with the metabolism and enzyme studies (320).

At this time it is impossible to remain unimpressed by the general, if not complete, similarity in the biochemical aspects studied of fetal liver and the hepatoma. Fetal liver possesses a certain enzyme pattern and protein sulfur distribution, both of which alter to a quite different pattern and distribution in the adult liver. When, however, the adult liver becomes neoplastic, the adult pattern and distribution alters again (reverts?) to an enzyme pattern and a protein sulfur distribution largely characteristic of those of fetal liver. The morphologic resemblance of tumors and fetal tissues, which goes far back to the earliest days of microscopic studies on cancer, are thus reflected in modern chemical investigations on these tissues.

TABLE 126

SULFUR DISTRIBUTION IN NORMAL AND NEOPLASTIC RAT HEPATIC TISSUES[1] (320)

Tissues	Total sulfur[2]	Cystine[3]-cysteine sulfur	Methionine sulfur[4]	Cysteine sulfur[3]	Cystine sulfur[5]	Cystine-cysteine sulfur + methionine sulfur
Adult liver	0.136	0.109	0.022	0.026	0.083	0.131
Regenerating liver	0.134	0.106	0.028	0.026	0.080	0.134
Fetal liver	0.130	0.069	0.055	0.016	0.053	0.124
Transplanted hepatoma 31	0.131	0.064	0.068	0.016	0.048	0.132

[1] All data given in terms of milligrams per milligram total N in the tissue extracts.
[2] By alkaline peroxide fusion.
[3] From Table 135 below.
[4] By method of McCarthy and Sullivan.
[5] Calculated by difference.

The assumption has been made that the normal, adult tissue alters or reverts to a primitive, fetal metabolic pattern when it becomes neoplastic. The possibility must also be envisaged that the tumor may arise from embryonal residues within the normal, adult tissue.

It must be recalled (*vide infra*) that the comparisons drawn among the homologous hepatic tissues include only those on the transplanted rat hepatoma. The primary hepatoma resembles in many respects the tissue of its origin (Tables 66–68), and, hence, for present purposes, the maximum-altered tissue, namely, the transplanted tumor, was employed. The complete list of homologous hepatic tissues may, therefore, be given in the order of increasing divergence from the normal adult: (a) normal resting or regenerating liver, (b) the liver of the tumor-bearing animal, (c) the primary hepatoma, and (d) the transplanted hepatoma and fetal liver. It is of interest in this connection that the level of catalytic components in the fetal liver is more nearly equivalent to that of the transplanted rather than the primary hepatoma (due to the resemblance in many respects of the latter to normal liver). If the transplanted tumor represents a frankly malignant state, it is significant to note that the only normal comparable tissue which at all resembles this state is the fetal tissue. Generalizations on tumors can only be made, where such generalizations can be made at all, on transplanted tumors, for these tissues, regardless of etiology or histogenesis, tend toward a common type.

The Oxidative Response of Normal and Neoplastic Tissues

Of the various chemical approaches to the study of malignancy in tissues, the solution of the problems concerned with metabolism and respiration ranks among the most important. The complex and interrelated functions by which living tissues are maintained require the ready availability of sources of energy. To some extent, these sources of energy are supplied by the oxidation of substances of relatively low molecular weight, amino acids, sugars, and fatty acids. In primitive forms of life, the energy derived from the oxidation of these metabolites may be obtained entirely under anaerobic conditions (fermentation). In the higher animals there are present, in addition to anaerobic systems, oxidation mechanisms whereby molecular oxygen is utilized (respiration). Most of the tumors which have been studied appear to obtain a considerable part of their energy from fermentation processes (321, 322), although they exhibit considerable respiration. The study of this anomalous phenomenon requires a knowledge of the individual tissue systems concerned with both anaerobic and aerobic types of metabolism.

The activation of molecular oxygen for the purposes of intracellular oxidation is performed in part by iron-containing, cyanide-sensitive, cata-

TABLE 127

OXYGEN CONSUMPTION OF MALIGNANT, BENIGN, AND NORMAL RABBIT TISSUES TO *p*-PHENYLENEDIAMINE AND SUCCINATE IN GLUCOSE-PHOSPHATE MEDIUM (69)

Tissue	Percentile increase in Q_{O_2} with *p*-phenylenediamine	Percentile increase in Q_{O_2} with succinate
Normal:		
Spleen	122	94
Lung	195	67
Skin	198	136
Embryonic liver	248	100
Pancreas	265	—
Kidney cortex	300	287
Kidney medulla	305	348
Brain	330	390
Retina	345	59
Ovary	345	390
Liver	430	900
Leg muscle	845	2100
Adrenal gland	835	730
Heart muscle	1510	210
Diaphragm fascia	1720	2340
Diaphragm muscle	7360	8900
Neoplastic:		
V-2 carcinoma	69	36
Brown-Pearce tumor	85	34
Sarcoma RSI	119	28
Virus papilloma	63	22
Virus fibroma	64	29

lytic systems which are capable of existing reversibly in reduced (ferrous) and oxidized (ferric) states. Knowledge of these systems is by no means complete, but the best available data indicate that they are composed of several components, each of which is a conjugated protein containing a hemin nucleus as the prosthetic group. Each of the components, when in the reduced condition, gives sharply defined absorption bands in the visible region of the spectrum and by this means has been separately identified (323, 324). The generic term for these components is "cytochrome," and the various components have been given the designations cytochrome oxidase, cytochrome a, cytochrome b, cytochrome c, etc. Only two of these components have so far been isolated in relatively pure form, cytochrome oxidase (325, 326) and cytochrome c (327), and the mode of action of only these substances of all the cytochromes is understood at least partially. The main cyclic pathway by which these components utilize molecular oxygen in the oxidation of a given metabolite is as follows:

$$\text{Molecular } O_2 + \text{reduced cytochrome c} \xrightarrow{\text{Cytochrome oxidase}} \text{Oxidized cytochrome c} \tag{1}$$

$$\text{Oxidized cytochrome c} + \text{metabolite} \rightarrow \text{Oxidized metabolite} + \text{reduced cytochrome c} \tag{2}$$

Thus, molecular oxygen does not act directly upon the metabolite but only indirectly through the mediation of the cytochrome oxidase-cytochrome c system. Neither cytochrome c nor cytochrome oxidase is autoxidizable. Taken together, the two components will cause an uptake of oxygen if cytochrome c is in the reduced state. For oxidation by cytochrome c, the metabolite may need to be prepared through reduction by a suitable dehydrogenase and, thus, in certain cases, as in the oxidation of succinic acid, dehydrogenase systems involving flavin nucleotides and phosphopyridine nucleotides must be added to the above scheme.

The normal tissues of animals contain the cytochrome oxidase-cytochrome c system to greater or less degree, heart muscle being by far the most active, liver and kidney intermediate, and spleen and lung among the least active. In all the normal tissues studied, the activity of cytochrome oxidase and the concentration of cytochrome c run roughly parallel. In comparison with such highly active tissues as heart and kidney, the activity of tumors is low; on the other hand, the activity of the tumors is of the same order of magnitude as that of such tissues as spleen and lung.

Salter and his colleagues developed a novel and interesting method for estimating the relative cytochrome system level in normal and neoplastic tissues (328–330). They determined (A) the oxygen consumption of tissue slices or suspensions alone, and (B) the oxygen consumption of the same samples of tissues after the addition of excess metabolite (succinate or *p*-phenylenediamine), and observed that the percentile increase in oxidation of (B) over (A) was invariably smaller in the case of neoplastic than normal tissues. According to these authors, practically all normal tissues fell into one class with a high percentile increase in oxidation on addition of substrate, whereas practically all neoplastic tissues fell into another class with a correspondingly low percentile increase in oxidation on addition of substrate, the former of magnitude over 100%, the latter of magnitude varying from −30 to +30 (Figs. 42–44).

Similar studies were conducted subsequently by Kidd, Burk, *et al.* (69) and by Rosenthal and Drabkin (9). The former investigators, like Salter *et al.*, employed glucose in their medium; the latter investigators omitted this material from their studies. Kidd, Winzler, and Burk studied the normal and neoplastic tissues of the rabbit and noted that, whereas the latter tissues yielded average Q_{O_2} values in the presence of glucose that

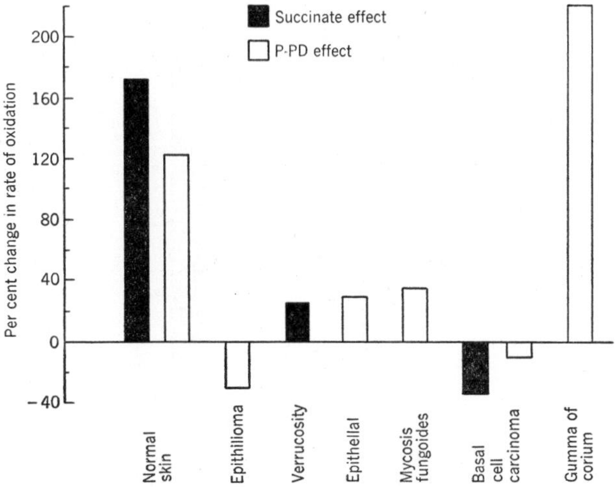

FIG. 42. Comparison of oxidative behavior of normal human skin and cutaneous lesions. From Roskelley, R. C., Mayer, N., Horwitt, B. N., and Salter, W. T., *J. Clin. Investigation* **22,** 743 (1943).

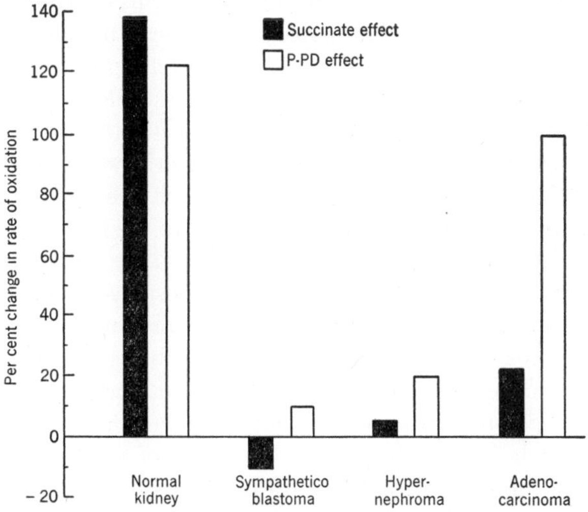

FIG. 43. Comparison of normal human kidney with human renal neoplasms. From Roskelley, R. C., Mayer, N., Horwitt, B. N., and Salter, W. T., *J. Clin. Investigation* **22,** 743 (1943).

were increased 120% at the most upon the addition of *p*-phenylenediamine and less than 40% by succinate, the increase in the Q_{O_2} of the former tissues was 120 to 7400% on addition of *p*-phenylenediamine and 59 to 9000% on addition of succinate.

In glycolytic properties, the benign rabbit papilloma resembles the

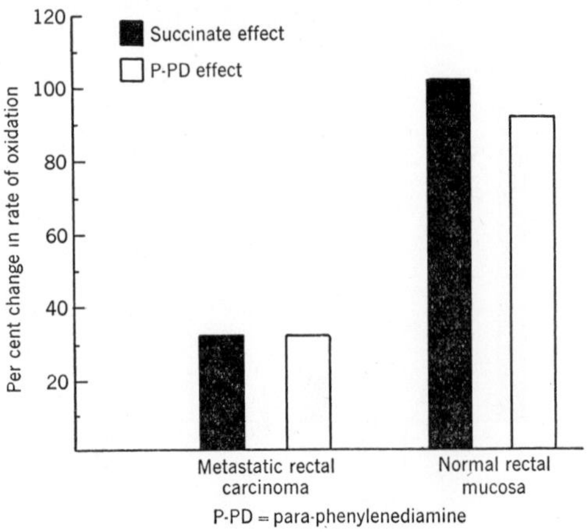

FIG. 44. Comparison of normal rectal mucosa and carcinoma of rectum. From Roskelley, R. C., Mayer, N., Horwitt, B. N., and Salter, W. T., *J. Clin. Investigation* **22,** 743 (1943).

normal skin more than it does the malignant carcinoma which develops from this benign lesion. On the other hand, in terms of oxidative response to added substrate, the benign tumor resembles the malignant tumor much more than it does normal skin. It is, therefore, possible to separate the characteristics of the benign tumor by these criteria, a possibility which further emphasizes the fact that, in some respects, the benign tumor resembles the normal tissue of origin, whereas in others it already possesses some functions of the malignant tumor into which it evolves or develops.

Rosenthal and Drabkin noted that, in respect to the increase in oxidation after addition of substrate, normal epithelial tissues fall into two main groups, namely (a) tissues with high oxidative responses toward *p*-phenylenediamine or succinate (liver, kidney cortex, brain, and muscle), and (b) tissues with low responses toward the two test substrates (gastrointestinal mucosa, lung, and possibly, skin, mammary gland, and lymphatic tissues). Benign and malignant rat tumors, as well as human cancers, show remarkably uniform oxidative responses of a low order of magnitude, similar to that range found in normal tissue group b. Thus, the percentile increases were 3000 to 6000 for liver, 450 to 550 for kidney, 250 to 350 for brain and for the submaxillary gland, 50 to 150 for mucosa and lung, and 120 to 300 for neoplasms. It would appear, therefore, from the work of these authors that the percentile increase of tumors fell within the range characteristic of those normal tissues with the lowest values of percentile increase, and thus there is a certain overlapping of the values of tumors and of certain normal tissues. That a certain amount of overlapping in the pertinent values for normal tissues and tumors might occur was also pointed out by Warren (331), who showed that the percentile increase in Q_{O_2} of normal rabbit marrow on addition of *p*-phenylenediamine or of succinate was quite low and of the order of magnitude characteristic of those of tumors.

The investigations described may be considered as involving a comparison of state A (the resting oxidation in the tissue) and state B (the oxidation by the tissue in the presence of added substrate). Response (A–B) appears to be high in the case of such normal tissues as liver, kidney, brain, and muscle, whereas it is low in the case of such normal tissues as lung and spleen and of tumors. Greenstein *et al.* carried the analysis of normal and neoplastic tissues one step further by comparing state B above with what may be called state C (i.e., the oxidation by the tissue in the presence of added substrate and added cytochrome c) (8). It is possible, therefore, to make comparisons of a tissue from state A to state C inclusive, using tissue suspensions throughout. Comparisons of response (B–C) among normal and neoplastic tissues reveal values smallest for normal tissues and largest for frankly malignant tissues (Table 128).

The values of $v_{\text{obs.}}$ in Table 128, referring to the rate of oxygen consumption by the tissue suspensions in the presence of *p*-phenylenediamine but in the absence of *added* cytochrome c, reveal the over-all activity of the cytochrome oxidase-cytochrome c systems inherent in these suspensions. That cytochrome c is never present in excess in any of the tissues studied is shown by the fact that, when an excess is added, the oxygen consumption is increased. In the presence of *p*-phenylenediamine, the addition of increasing amounts of cytochrome c to a fixed amount of cytochrome oxidase produces an increasing velocity of oxygen consumption up to a point beyond which further additions are without effect. The maximum velocity ($V_{\text{max.}}$) reached is directly proportional to the activity of different preparations of cytochrome oxidase or the actual amount used of the same preparation of oxidase. The enzyme substrate relations under these conditions can be represented by the Michaelis-Menton equation

$$v = \frac{V_{\text{max.}} \times S}{K_{\text{M}} + S}$$

where $V_{\text{max.}}$ is the maximum velocity elicited by the oxidase preparation in the presence of excess cytochrome c, v is the velocity of oxygen uptake in the presence of cytochrome *c* of concentration S, and K_{M} is the dissociation constant of the oxidase-cytochrome complex. The values of $v_{\text{calc.}}$ obtained by this equation are very nearly the same as the values of $v_{\text{obs.}}$ determined experimentally (Table 128). Data on rat tissues examined in this way reveal similar findings. In those cases where $v_{\text{obs.}}$ is appreciable enough to be determined with some accuracy, it is possible, therefore, to calculate the respiration of the suspensions when the concentration of

TABLE 128

CYTOCHROME OXIDASE, CYTOCHROME C AND COPPER IN NORMAL AND NEOPLASTIC HUMAN TISSUES[1, 2] (8)

Tissue	Number of tissues studied[3]	Cytochrome oxidase, $V_{max.}$[4]	Cytochrome c[5]	Copper[5]	$v_{obs.}$[6]	$v_{calc.}$[7]	Response (calc.)[8]
Normal:							
Heart muscle	5	8.2	10.2	0.3	4.0	4.0	100
Skeletal muscle	5	2.4	2.4	0.2	0.7	0.5	375
Diaphragm muscle	3	2.9	2.8	—	0.9	0.7	333
Liver	5	2.8	2.3	0.8	0.8	0.6	400
Kidney	5	3.6	2.4	0.5	1.0	0.8	375
Brain	5	3.9	2.3	0.3	0.9	0.8	400
Thyroid	5	0.6	1.0	0.2	0.1	0.08	750
Spleen	5	0.4	0.8	0.2	(>0)	0.03	1000
Pancreas	5	0.5	0.8	0.2	0.1	0.05	1000
Adrenal	4	0.7	0.8	0.3	—	0.06	1000
Intestine	4	0.5	0.9	0.2	0.1	0.06	857
Stomach	4	0.5	0.9	0.2	0.1	0.06	857
Uterus	1	0.4	0.7	0.1	(>0)	0.03	1200
Bladder	5	0.4	0.7	0.04	(>0)	0.03	1200
Prostate	4	0.2	0.8	0.2	(>0)	0.02	1000
Lung	5	0.4	0.7	0.2	(>0)	0.03	1200
Neoplastic:							
Thyroid adenoma	5	0.38–1.42	0.9–1.6	0.2–0.4	(>0)–0.22	0.04–0.20	600–1000
Dermatofibrosarcoma protuberans	1	0.68	0.6	0.4	(>0)	0.04	1500
Hypertrophied prostate	4	0.40–0.42	0.9–1.4	0.4	(>0)	0.03–0.05	644–1000
Early prostatic adenocarcinoma	1	0.32	0.8	0.2	(>0)	0.03	1200
Granulosa cell ovarian tumor	1	0.90	1.3	0.2	0.12	0.11	750
Uterine fibromyoma	2	0.34–0.48	0.7–0.8	0.2	(>0)	0.02	1200–1500
Giant cell tumor	2	0.54–0.68	1.3–1.6	0.3	0.12	0.07–0.10	600–750
Chondrosarcoma	1	0.68	1.0	0.2	0.12	0.07	1000
Mixed parotid tumor	1	0.70	1.4	0.3	0.12	0.08	750
Synovioma	1	0.54	0.8	0.3	(>0)	0.04	1200
Spindle-cell sarcoma	1	0.48	0.7	—	(>0)	0.02	1500
Connective tissue tumor	1	0.42	0.6	—	(>0)	0.02	1500
Melanoma[9]	3	0.30–0.35	0.7–0.8	0.4–0.5	[11]	0.02	1200–1500
Desmoid tumor	1	0.56	0.9	0.2	(>0)	0.04	1000
Epidermoid carcinoma	3	0.34–0.44	0.3–0.4	—	(>0)	0.01–0.02	2000–3000
Meningioma	2	0.32–0.34	0.3–0.4	0.1	(>0)	0.01	2000–3000
Bronchogenic carcinoma[10]	1	0.42	0.3	0.2	(>0)	0.01	3000
Lymphosarcoma[10]	1	0.22	0.3	0.2	(>0)	0.01	3000

TABLE 128—(*Continued*)

Tissue	Number of tissues studied[3]	Cytochrome oxidase, $V_{max.}$[4]	Cytochrome c[5]	Copper[5]	$v_{obs.}$[6]	$v_{calc.}$[7]	Response (calc.)[8]
Early gastric adenocarcinoma	1	0.22	0.9	0.2	(>0)	0.01	1200
Gastric adenocarcinoma	4	0.28–0.38	0.4–0.6	0.3–0.4	(>0)	0.01	2000–3000
Colonic adenocarcinoma	6	0.38–0.50	0.4–0.5	0.2–0.3	(>0)	0.01–0.02	2000–3000
Large rectal adenoma	1	0.82	0.9	0.5	0.12	0.08	1000
Rectal adenocarcinoma	5	0.36–0.50	0.4–0.7	0.2–0.3	(>0)	0.01–0.03	1500–3000
Mammary carcinoma	7	0.24–0.48	0.2–0.4	0.2	(>0)	0.00 0.02	3000–6000

[1] Neoplastic tissues obtained within 2 hours after operation from the Memorial and New York Hospitals. Normal tissues obtained 1–4 hours after accidental death through the medical examiner's office of Queen's County, N. Y. Tissues from five normal subjects were studied. Neoplastic tissues obtained at autopsy are so noted. Necrotic areas removed from the tumors.

[2] Control studies on rat tissues performed under the same conditions as were the human tissues revealed that the time interval of standing of the tissues and the mode of death of the normal subjects had no apparent influence on the findings. Variations in normal tissues given in original report (8).

[3] Normal tissues were obtained from four males and one female. Descriptions of the neoplasms are given in the original report.

[4] Activity given in terms of cubic millimeter oxygen taken up per hour per milligram wet weight of tissue. Cytochrome c added in excess (1×10^{-4} M) plus *p*-phenylenediamine. Activity designated as $V_{max.}$.

[5] Concentration given in terms of milligrams per 100 g wet tissue.

[6] $v_{obs.}$ refers to cubic millimeter oxygen taken up per hour per milligram wet weight of tissue in presence of *p*-phenylenediamine but no added cytochrome c. Where this quantity was too small to measure accurately the designation (>0) has been used.

[7] $v_{calc.}$ refers to cubic millimeter oxygen per milligram wet weight of tissue calculated from the experimental quantities of cytochrome oxidase ($V_{max.}$), and cytochrome c, and the Michaelis-Menten equation (Lineweaver and Burk, (332); Stotz, Altschul, and Hogness, (333). Concentrations of cytochrome c for this purpose are calculated in terms of moles per liter (mol. wt. 16,000); the Michaelis-Menten constant, K_M , is 6.0×10^{-6}.

[8] The response (calc.] is given as % by the expression:

$$\frac{V_{max.} - v_{(calc.)}}{v_{(calc.)}} \times 100 = \frac{K_M}{\text{Cytochrome c}} \times 100$$

[9] Two melanotic and one amelanotic.

[10] Autopsy specimens.

[11] One of the specimens of melanotic melanoma gave an oxygen uptake in the presence of excess cytochrome c of 0.72 cu.mm./hr./mg.; with buffer instead of cytochrome c, the uptake was 0.48, and with 0.01 *M* KCN instead of either buffer or cytochrome c it was 0.40. The other specimen of melanotic melanoma gave an oxygen uptake in the presence of excess cytochrome c of 1.50 cu.mm./hr./mg.; with water or 0.01 *M* KCN in place of the cytochrome c it was 1.20.

cytochrome c in the tissue is known. Conversely, from the values of the cytochrome oxidase ($V_{max.}$), the respiration of the suspension ($v_{obs.}$), and K_M, it is possible to calculate the concentration of cytochrome c.

By the "response" of the tissue suspension is meant the proportionate increase in the oxygen consumption of the suspension (in the presence of *p*-phenylenediamine) when an excess of cytochrome c is added. The response, in per cent, may be calculated from the following expression:

$$\text{Per cent response} = \frac{V_{max.} - v_{(calc.)}}{v_{(calc.)}} \times 100$$

or

$$\frac{K_M}{S} \times 100$$

The response is, therefore, inversely proportional to the cytochrome c content and is independent, because of its excess, of the cytochrome oxidase. Under these conditions the limiting factor in the respiration of the tissue suspensions is the concentration of cytochrome c.

The tissues described in Table 128 may be divided into the following categories:

Category a. Calculated per cent response range, 100 to 400. Only normal tissues, namely, heart, skeletal and diaphragm muscle, liver, kidney, and brain. The incidence of neoplasia among these tissues is relatively uncommon.

Categories b and b′. Calculated per cent response range, 600 to 1200. The former category (*b*) is composed of the normal tissues of thyroid, spleen, pancreas, adrenal, intestine, stomach, uterus, bladder, prostate, and lung. The incidence of neoplasia among these tissues is relatively high. The latter category (*b′*) is composed of the neoplastic tissues, thyroid adenomas, hypertrophied prostates, early prostatic adenocarcinoma, granulosa cell tumor of the ovary, uterine fibromyomas, giant cell tumors, chondrosarcoma, mixed parotid tumor, synovioma, desmoid tumor, early gastric adenocarcinoma, and large rectal adenoma. These neoplasms are either benign in nature or else represent an early manifestation of malignancy.

Category c. Calculated response range, 1500 to 6000. Only neoplastic tissues, including spindle-cell sarcoma, malignant melanomas, epidermoid, mammary and bronchogenic carcinomas, malignant meningiomas, lymphosarcoma, and gastric, colonic, and rectal adenocarcinomas. These neoplasms are all frankly malignant.

Data taken from the literature (Schneider and Potter, 73, 334; Shack, 76; Stotz, 323), reveal that, in analogy with and similar to the case of the human tissues, the rat tissues may be divided into a *category a* with lowest calculated response and including only normal tissues, heart and skeletal muscle, liver, kidney, and brain; *categories b and b′* with intermediate response values and including, respectively, the normal tissues spleen and lung, and the neoplasm hepatoma; and, finally, a *category c* with highest response values, and including the neoplasms tumor 256, the Flexner-Jobling and the Walker carcinomas, and the Jensen sarcoma (Greenstein *et al.*, 8). There is little doubt about the tumors in category *c* being malignant, but whether the hepatoma is truly malignant is debatable.

In all tissues of any category, in relation to the content of cytochrome c, cytochrome oxidase is present in excess (cf. 334, 335). This excess is relatively small for the tissues of category *a*, relatively large for the tissues of category *c*, and intermediate in value for the tissues of categories *b* and *b′*. The various categories are thus based fundamentally upon the relation of cytochrome c to cytochrome oxidase. It is evident that malignancy is characterized by the widest disparity between the components of the cytochrome oxidase-cytochrome c system. In relation to the activity of cytochrome oxidase, malignant tissues have the lowest proportion of cytochrome c. It is for this reason that, when to such tissue suspensions an excess of cytochrome c is added, the response in the form of proportionate increase in oxygen consumption is the greatest. From these findings the following generalization may be drawn: *Malignant tissues, in comparison with normal tissues and benign tumors, are characterized not only by possessing the lowest concentrations of cytochrome c but also by possessing the greatest disparity between the components of the cytochrome oxidase-cytochrome c system.*

Finally, it may be pointed out that the range of activity of cytochrome oxidase and of the concentration of cytochrome c and copper among all the neoplasms is much narrower than that of the same components, respectively, among all the normal tissues (Table 128). This is in accord with the observations on the animal tissues (Tables 66, 88 and 89). The copper content of the tissues studied bears little or no relation to the activity of the cytochrome system.

Studies on free cancer cells, as in the Ehrlich, Krebs 2, and *DBA* thymoma ascites tumors, by direct spectroscopic means have revealed fairly high values of cytochrome c in relation to cytochrome oxidase (336), values which indeed appear to exceed that of the cytochrome c content of the rapidly respiring yeast cell. Whether these observations reflect actual differences between free-living cells and solid tumors or differences in the experimental techniques of spectroscopy and manometry is not clear at the present time.

Glycolytic Reactions in Normal and Neoplastic Tissues

The observation that the chemical reactions in working muscle involved the breakdown of carbohydrate and the appearance of lactic acid is quite old and has formed the basis of one of the major lines of work in the fields of biochemistry and physiology. It has been stated in the beginning of this chapter that each tissue can be described in terms of a characteristic enzymatic or metabolic pattern. Thus, presented with a particular substrate, each tissue will metabolize this substrate through a series of reactions to a final product or products which may be (a) the same for each tissue but formed at different rates, or (b) different for each tissue, both results being due to the nature of the metabolic pattern of the tissue. Every tissue yields lactic acid when glucose is metabolized, more being formed under anaerobic than under aerobic conditions. It is seemingly characteristic of tumor tissues that they possess a relatively higher rate of lactic acid production under both anaerobic and aerobic conditions, than do many normal tissues. This implies an accumulation of lactic acid in tumors, because (a) the particular system or systems concerned with its further degradation is lacking, (b) because tumors possess one or more highly active systems which rapidly degrade glucose to this product, or (c) because of some unusual feature in the metabolic pattern of tumors, the degradation of glucose is at some stage diverted to the formation of this product. The choice of any explanation becomes still more difficult when it is considered that the high glycolysis of tumors occurs in the presence of a normal level of respiration. There is little knowledge as to what constitutes an optimal content of enzymes in the cell, or which of the many integrated and alternative metabolic pathways is the preferable.

The metabolism of carbohydrate in outline form, whether in animals or in plants, is given on the following page.

Pyruvate holds a central position in carbohydrate metabolism. As noted from the sequence of events from glycogen (or glucose) to pyruvic acid, these steps involve, for the main part, phosphorylations, hydrolyses, splitting of the central C-C bond in the hexose, and molecular rearrangements. Other systems may also be involved. Thus, the phosphorylation of glucose by adenosine triphosphate involves (a) reduced pyridine nucleotide and (b) inorganic phosphate which may be linked with nuclease activity in the production of (c) free guanine. Moreover, this phosphorylation can be inhibited by anterior pituitary extract (and adrenal cortex extract), and the inhibition can be counteracted by insulin (337). But from pyruvate on, the pathways of metabolism diverge in many different directions. In yeast, for example, pyruvate is decarboxylated in the presence of diphosphothiamine to yield eventually ethyl alcohol and carbon dioxide; this is the fermentative phase of carbohydrate metabolism in plants. In animals, the utilization of pyruvic acid is more complicated, and is outlined simply on page 449.

These are only a few of the reactions in which pyruvate participates in

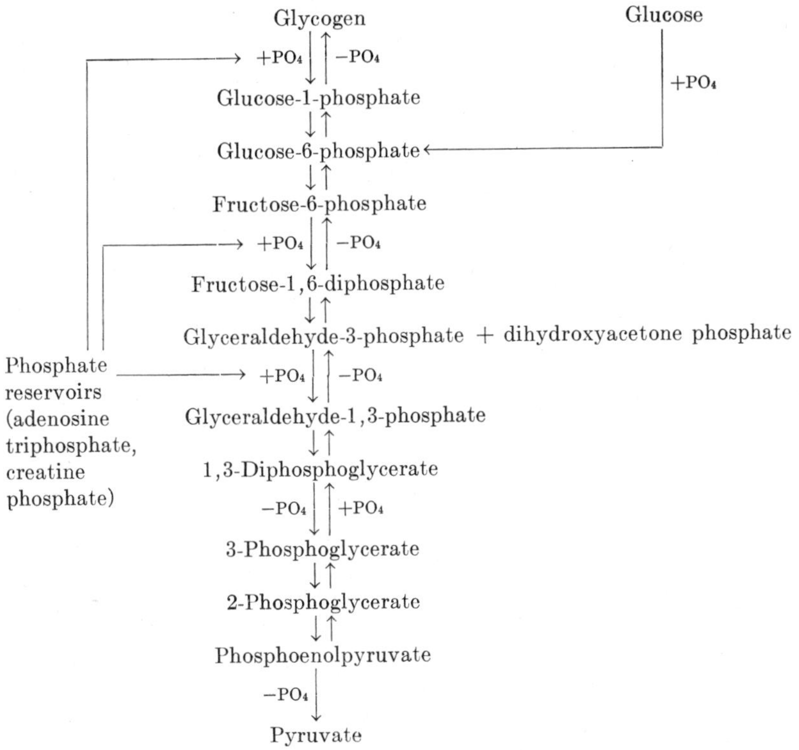

cellular metabolism. A more complete description of the fate of pyruvate via the Krebs citric acid cycle has been given earlier in this chapter. It should be mentioned that this substance is derivable not only from split

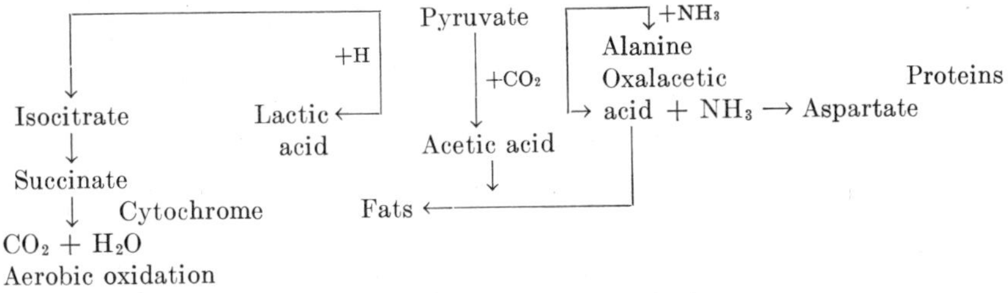

products of the sugars but also of proteins (alanine, cystine, serine, etc.) and of fats. The above scheme, however, sketchy as it may be, reveals that lactic acid is only one of the many products derivable from pyruvate in animal tissues. Under aerobic conditions, it may be a relatively minor product; under anaerobic conditions, however, it is a major product of the metabolism of carbohydrate.

For the conversion of pyruvate to lactate in appreciable amounts, anaerobic conditions are usually necessary and the presence of diphosphopyridine nucleotide (DPN) (coenzyme I) is essential (338). This statement holds principally for normal animal tissues, and thus lactic acid may be considered the chief end product of fermentation (anaerobic metabolism) in such tissues. In the presence of oxygen, the formation or accumulation of lactate may be partially or wholly suppressed (Pasteur effect), and pyruvate may be utilized through a number of multiple pathways yielding products ultimately oxidized via the cytochrome system and molecular oxygen.

$$\text{Pyruvate} + \text{DPN}\cdot 2\text{H} \rightleftarrows \text{Lactate} + \text{DPN}$$

In Warburg's classic studies on tumors (321), the observation was made that, whereas slices of a number of normal tissues and tumors produced lactic acid from glucose or glycogen rapidly in the absence of oxygen, practically only cancer tissues slices showed an unusual ability to produce lactic acid from glucose in the presence of oxygen. The relative Pasteur effect was apparently deficient to a greater or less degree in most tumors (cf. Table 129).

The respiration rates of cancer and of normal tissues appeared to be, by and large, very nearly of the same order of magnitude, and to account for the high aerobic glycolysis in tumors Warburg postulated that the respiratory mechanism in such tissues was damaged as a result of the neoplastic transformation. High anaerobic glycolysis appeared to be a general property of growing or multiplying tissues, since it was found in embryo tissue and testis, but in these normal tisues glycolysis was largely abolished by the presence of oxygen. In most tumors, the high anaerobic glycolysis was relatively little reduced when oxygen was admitted to the system; the same, however, could be said of placenta (Table 129).

That lactic acid actually is produced from the tumor within the living animal was shown by several investigators (339, 340), who observed that the venous blood leaving a tumor contained less glucose and more lactate than did venous blood in a comparable tumor-free site in the same animal.

Since lactic acid, because of the presence of the polar hydroxyl group adjacent to the carboxyl, may be considered a relatively strong organic acid, its accumulation within the tumor should produce a lowering of the pH, provided that the rate of glycolysis exceeds both the diffusion of the acid products from the malignant cells and the diffusion of buffers from the arterial circulation into the cells and provided that the rate of supply of the glucose to the cells is sufficiently high.

By means of an ingenious experimental device involving the insertion

TABLE 129
GLYCOLYTIC METABOLISM OF TISSUES

Tissue	Ref.	Q_{O_2}[1]	$Q_A^{O_2}$[2]	$Q_A^{N_2}$[3]	MOQ[4]	U[5]
Normal:						
Muscle fascia (rat)	(321)	tr.	tr.	tr.	—	—
Kidney (rat)	(321)	21	0	3	0.4	−39
Thyroid (rat)	(321)	13	0	2	0.4	−24
Liver (rat)	(321)	12	0.6	3	0.6	−21
Intestinal mucosa (rat)	(321)	12	1.6	4	1.0	−20
Spleen (rat)	(346)	12	2	8	1.5	−16
Testis (rat)	(321)	12	0	8	2.0	−16
Thymus (rat)	(321)	6	0.6	8	3.6	− 4
Brain cortex (rat)	(321)	11	2.5	19	4.5	− 3
Pancreas (rabbit)	(321)	5	0	3	2.0	− 7
Submaxillary (rabbit)	(321)	4	0	3	2.2	− 5
Pancreas (dog)	(321)	3	0	4	4.0	− 2
Lymph node (man)	(321)	4	2	5	2.2	− 3
Embryo (rat)	(321)	13	6	23	3.9	− 3
Retina (rat)	(321)	31	45	88	4.2	+26
Placenta (rat)	(346)	7	10	14	1.7	0
Neoplastic:						
Jensen sarcoma (rat)	(321)	9	17	34	5.6	+16
Jensen sarcoma (rat)	(344)	9	18	32	4.7	+14
Flexner-Jobling carcinoma (rat)	(321)	7	25	31	2.6	+17
Flexner-Jobling carcinoma (rat)	(346)	8	20	29	4.3	+13
Spontaneous tumors (mouse)	(346)	14	8	25	3.6	− 3
Tar carcinoma (mouse)	(344)	20	15	25	1.5	−15
Sarcoma 37 (mouse)	(344)	15	12	28	3.2	− 2
Melanoma (mouse)	(344)	9	6	16	3.3	− 2
Yale tumor I (mouse)	(347)	7	7	16	4.0	+ 2
Spontaneous tumors (mouse)	(345)	11	9	16	2.0	− 6
Rous sarcoma (chicken)	(321)	5	20	30	6.0	+20
Bladder carcinoma (man)	(321)	10	24	36	3.6	+16
Sarcoma (man)	(321)	5	16	28	7.2	+18
Carcinoma of larynx (man)	(321)	8	15	19	1.5	+ 3

[1] Respiration in terms of cubic millimeters oxygen per milligram dry tissue per hour.

[2] Aerobic glycolysis in terms of cubic millimeters lactic acid equivalent per milligram dry tissue per hour.

[3] Anaerobic glycolysis in terms similar to those of footnote 2.

[4] Meyerhof oxidation quotient in terms of $3\left(\frac{Q_A^{N_2} - Q_A^{O_2}}{Q_{O_2}}\right)$, which is a measure of the Pasteur effect in relation to respiration.

[5] Fermentation excess in terms of $Q_A^{N_2} - 2Q_{O_2}$

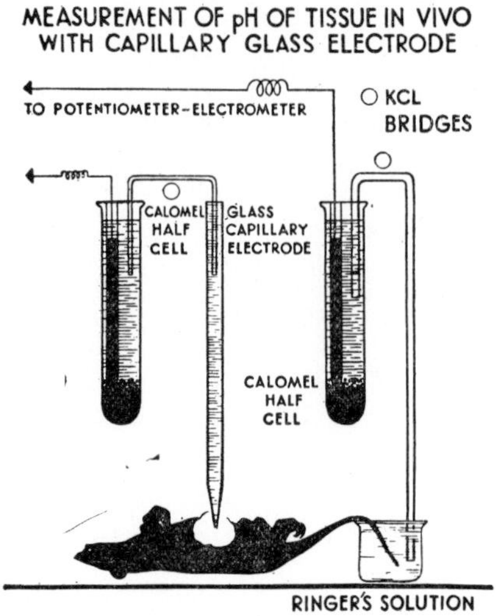

FIG. 45. Device for measuring pH *in vivo*. From Kahler, H., and Robertson, W. v. B., *J. Natl. Cancer Inst.* **3,** 495 (1943).

of fragile electodes of very small diameter directly into the tumor mass of the living animal, Voegtlin *et al.* (341) demonstrated that the administration of glucose, whether subcutaneous or intraperitoneal, was followed very quickly by a drop in pH of 0.4 to 0.6 unit. The pH of the tumor may drop from 6.9 to 6.3 without the occurrence of any pulmonary respiratory symptoms indicative of a systemic acidosis, thus indicating that the increased acid production is largely confined to the tumor and that the excess lactate carried off in the venous circulation is quickly metabolized by the normal tissues. Kahler and Robertson (342) compared the hydrogen ion concentration of the liver and of a transplanted hepatoma in fasted rats (Figs. 45 and 46). The pH of the former tisssue was 7.4, that of the latter was 7.0, thus considerably more acid. When the rats were supplied with excess glucose, the pH of the liver tissue remained unaltered whereas that of the hepatoma dropped to 6.4. It should be pointed out that the decrease in pH shown by tumors in glucose-treated animals may be due not only to lactic acid formed but to other acids as well, e.g., phosphoric. However, the greater proportion of the acids is unquestionably lactic acid. The Coris (88) found that the lactic acid content of the mouse mammary carcinoma was 0.034 %; after glucose administration the content of this acid rose to 0.137 %.

A flood of reports followed the pioneer observations of Warburg, and the data of a number of investigators, among them Dickens (cf. 77), Elliott (343), and Crabtree (344), rather conclusively showed that tumors, as a class of tissues, were distinguished by a high anaerobic glycolysis. Dickens and Simer (345) went further and ascribed a low respiratory quotient

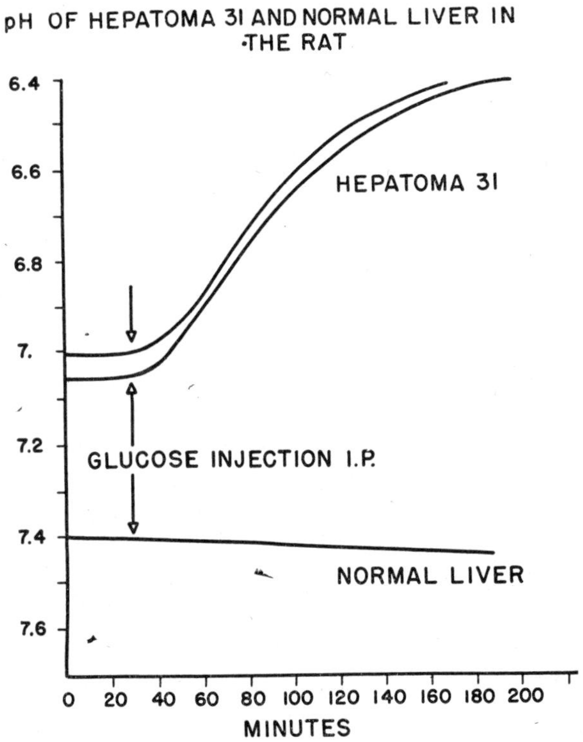

FIG. 46. Effect of glucose administration on pH of liver and of hepatoma. Courtesy of Dr. H. Kahler.

(Q_{CO_2}/Q_{O_2}) to tumors in general. In addition, and with few exceptions (344, 346), the aerobic level of glycolysis in tumors appeared also to be high but in no respect as high as the anerobic glycolytic level.

The fact that this high rate of glycolysis is accompanied by a normal level of respiration is perhaps incongruous. However, the respiratory level in normal tissues may only be a fraction of that available, whereas in tumors it is already at its optimum (see p. 481). The former tissues respond to addition of substrate by increase in oxidation, the latter by glycolysis.

The general uniformity in behavior of cancerous tissues as a class (cf. 347) led Burk to suggest the following criteria of malignancy (322):

Q_{O_2}	$Q_A^{O_2}$	$Q_A^{N_2}$	Meyerhof oxidation quotient	Absolute Pasteur effect	Fermentation excess, (U)	Respiratory quotient
2–10	0–15	8–20	3–6	8–15	−5 to +25	0.75–0.9

where Q_{O_2}, $Q_A^{O_2}$, and $Q_A^{N_2}$ are experimentally determined quantities, relating respectively to the respiration (oxygen consumption in cubic millimeters per milligram initial dry tissue per hour), aerobic glycolysis and anaerobic glycolysis (lactic acid production in equivalent of carbon dioxide per milligram dry tissue per hour); the Meyerhof oxidation quotient is described as $3(Q_A^{N_2} - Q_A^{O_2})/Q_{O_2}$, thus a measure of the Pasteur effect where the coefficient refers to the fact that three molecules of lactic acid are equivalent to one molecule oxygen by virtue of measuring the inhibition of lactic acid formation in relation to oxygen consumption; the absolute Pasteur effect $= Q_A^{N_2} - Q_A^{O_2}$; the fermentation excess U is described as $Q_A^{N_2} - 2Q_{O_2}$, which quantity is $Q_A^{O_2}$ when the Meyerhof oxidation quotient is set arbitrarily as 6; and the respiratory quotient is described as Q_{CO_2}/Q_{O_2}, which is unity when carbohydrate is burned. Thus, nearly all cancer tissues show a moderately high respiration rate, a moderately low respiratory quotient, and a definitely high sustained aerobic and anaerobic glycolysis. It should be noted that, according to the above criteria, the absolute Pasteur effect may be appreciable, although the "per cent Pasteur effect", i.e., the per cent inhibition of glycolysis by oxygen, may be relatively small. That is to say, although in most normal tissues the per cent Pasteur effect may be between 60 and 100, and in tumors between 20 and 40, the absolute amount may be considerably greater in the latter tissues than in the former (cf. 348, 349).

Burk's criteria of malignancy are sufficiently inclusive for the glycolytic and respiratory phenomena under consideration and appear to cover the pertinent facts as they are related to tumors. These criteria are only the latest of many attempts by various investigators, first and foremost among them Warburg and Dickens, to describe tumor phenomena on a uniform basis. Many of these blanket definitions had a good deal of truth in them. Yet it is curious to note how quickly such proposed criteria were repudiated, sometimes by their original proponents, not because new data on tumors were inconsistent with such criteria but actually because a few normal tissues met them. Warburg himself had reported that mammalian retina possessed a high aerobic as well as anaerobic glycolysis, although he considered that some sort of damage had occurred in the preparation of this fragile tissue (321). As evidence accumulated that certain normal tissues possessed some characteristics ascribed to tumors, i.e., high aerobic glycolysis in the kidney medulla (350) and jejunal mucosa (no Pasteur effect) (351), high aerobic glycolysis and low respiratory quotient in synovial membrane (352), and high aerobic glycolysis, etc., in myeloid cells of the rabbit bone marrow (331), it was felt in many quarters that no such thing as a specific tumor metabolism existed.

To make matters still more complex, Warburg had calculated from the somewhat arbitrary expression of U, the fermentation excess, that the values of this quantity were negative for nearly all normal tissues except for retina (which shows unusually high respiration and glycolysis and, hence, may be exceptional) and positive for nearly all malignant tumors of the rat and of the human. However, the subsequent data of Murphy and Hawkins and of Crabtree indicated that certain mouse tumors had negative U values (due largely to the high respiration of these tissues). It soon became clear that, as far as glycolytic metabolism was concerned, there was some degree of overlapping in properties of certain normal tissues and certain tumors, and it appeared that no clear-cut distinction could be made between these two classes of tissues on the basis of these metabolic criteria.

It is, perhaps, easy to see in so overly pessimistic a conclusion the swing of the pendulum from an over-optimism. The early experiments of Warburg had given the general impression that in the respiratory and glycolytic phenomena the basis of the neoplastic character was revealed. If this were so, then no completely normal tissue could share in these phenomena and no tumor could resemble normal tissues in any respect. Like so many similar examples in the field of cancer research, too much was claimed and too much was hoped for in the beginning. Yet, if there is no evidence at present of a *specific* tumor metabolism, there is evidence of a *uniform* tumor metabolism. This theme has been well stated by Dickens (345). The fact that certain normal tissues possess properties which in particular instances overlap those of tumors does not invalidate this conclusion.

It is not always advisable to lump all normal tissues in one category and all tumors into another category, because tumors arise, in the first place, from normal tissues and apparently never lose all traces of their origin. The negative U values of the mouse tumors may be simply an indication of another set of properties of the normal tissues preserved when such tissues become neoplastic, a phenomenon not at all unusual in the mouse. It must be reiterated that tumors are not an identical tissue type but represent a convergence toward such an identical tissue type and that some tumors (which may be classed as malignant) possess properties differing more from normal tissues than do other tumors (which may be classed as benign) and which resemble more the tissue of origin. The only generalization in this connection which appears to be nearly universally applicable is that, whenever a normal tissue becomes neoplastic, those properties which change are always accomplished in the same direction as are encountered in other kinds of tumors, and thus tumors may be said to converge toward a uniform type of tissue.

As may be seen from the abbreviated sketch of carbohydrate metabolism depicted above, the phenomenon of glycolysis is not simply glucose $\rightarrow$ lactic acid but rather a very complicated sequence of consecutive and concurrent reactions involving phosphorylation, oxidation-reduction, molecular rearrangements, and hydrolyses. It might be quite too much to expect that the metabolic pattern involving scores of individual reactions was such in every normal tissue that at no one point would it resemble in certain respects the metabolic pattern of a tumor. Indeed, as Tables 71–120 on individual enzymes in normal and neoplastic tissues indicate, the activity of each enzyme in tumors falls somewhere within the range of that enzyme in normal tissues, sometimes near the upper end of the range, more often near the lower end of the range, but never outside the normal range. It is little wonder, therefore, that in measuring some over-all phenomenon involving a great many individual systems some degree of overlapping of properties between normal tissues and tumors occurs. As the tables cited further reveal, however, the range of activity of each of the enzymes is narrower among tumors than among normal tissues; the picture of a uniform respiratory and glycolytic pattern in tumors by Burk (*vide infra*) is thus consistent with this phenomenon and, indeed, since it is based on an enzymatic pattern, could hardly be otherwise.

The glycolytic phenomenon as the experimenter measures it in the manometer, e.g., by adding glucose to the tissue slice suspended in bicarbonate and measuring the carbon dioxide evolved by the acid formed, is an over-all reaction and is composed of so many individual reactions as to be yet too complicated for ready interpretation. The need for knowing the nature of the individual steps intermediate between glucose and lactic acid, before glycolysis can be understood, has long been appreciated. Warburg's early prophecy of a deficient respiratory mechanism in tumors has been sustained by the observation of very low levels of oxidases in these tissues. Yet, these limited systems, unlike those in normal tissues, may function at their optimal capacities.

The resemblance in many respects of plant and animal tumors has been noted. The metabolism of carbohydrate in animal tissues which leads under anaerobic conditions to the accumulation of lactic acid leads in plant tissues to the accumulation of alcohol. Studies on the respiratory behavior of green plant tissues are complicated by the accompanying process of photosynthesis, and the vessels in which such behavior is investigated must be shielded from sources of light. The results of respiration studies in the presence and absence of oxygen on bacteria-free crown-gall tumors and on healthy plant tissues revealed little differences in order of magnitude between normal and pathologic tissues (353).

One of the puzzling features of glycolysis in tumors has been the accumulation of lactic acid in these tissues. Perhaps this accumulation may not be very important. It is by now sufficiently clear that tumors contain all the enzymes associated with glycolysis and with the Krebs cycle, and homogenates of normal tissues when sufficiently fortified can glycolyze at greater rates than those of tumors (119). The low rates of glycolysis frequently observed for normal tissue slices may have been due to the inability of these tissues *in vitro* to accomplish the initial phosphorylation step in the formation of hexosediphosphate. The hexokinase reaction *in vivo* is probably under hormonal control. It may be tentatively formulated as follows:

$$\text{Adenosine triphosphate} + \text{glucose} \rightarrow \text{Adenosine diphosphate} + \text{Glucose-6-phosphate}$$

The possibility of the existence of a non-phosphorylating glycolysis in tissues was advanced some time ago (354) because of the relatively slow action of normal and tumor tissue slices on hexosediphosphate (355). Although this possibility cannot be completely excluded, non-phosphorylating glycolysis must represent only a very small proportion of the total glycolysis of tumors. Thus, the glycolysis of glucose, fructose, and hexosediphosphate by fortified tumor extracts proceeds at close to the same rate as in tumor slices (356). It is probable that glycolysis in the homogenates is dependent in part on the ratio of phosphorylating and dephosphorylating enzymes present. Although tumor homogenates contain large amounts of ATP-ase activity relative to the hexokinase content (357), it has been shown that the latter is sufficiently great in tumors to allow all the glucose used in anaerobic glycolysis of the tumor slices to pass through the stage of the hexokinase reaction (358). The tumor enzyme readily phosphorylates glucose (and mannose). In view of the large amount of ATP-ase in tumor homogenates compared with hexokinase, either exogenous hexokinase must be added or the ATP-ase inhibited in order to obtain a steady rate of glycolysis. Octyl alcohol has been used for such inhibition, as has fluoride. LePage has analyzed a number of transplanted and primary tumors for various intermediates of the Embden-Meyerhof glycolytic scheme (359) (Table 130). Much the same pattern of intermediates is present in tumors as in normal tissues, although the former have a considerably higher content of lactic acid and a lower glycogen level. Essentially similar observations have been made by others (360), and in this case some evidence pointing to a somewhat higher level of esterified phosphate in more rapidly growing tumors has been adduced. It is also possible to isolate some of these intermediates (ATP, ADP, glucose-6-phosphate, etc.) from tumors in yields approximating those from muscle (361). There is again little doubt but that the Embden-Meyerhof scheme of phosphorylative glycolysis is operative in tumors and that there is no evidence that glycolysis follows a different pathway in tumors. Despite the apparent quantitative differences between glycolysis in tumors and normal tissues, several of the enzyme systems involved appear to function at nearly similar levels in the two types of tissues. Thus, ATP-ase (225) and lactic dehydrogenase (114) of various normal and neoplastic rat tissues are about the same order of magnitude. That the ATP content of hepatomas is higher than that of normal liver has further been shown (361a).

TABLE 130

EMBDEN-MEYERHOF GLYCOLYSIS INTERMEDIATES[1] (359)

Component	Brain	Muscle	Liver	Kidney	Heart	Primary liver tumor	Flexner-Jobling tumor	Walker 256 tumor	Jensen sarcoma	Mouse ear carcinoma
Lactic acid	141	188	230	155	578	582	862	824	637	704
Glycogen[2]	531	3480	28,450	81	2460	462	67	65	43	56
Acid-soluble P	2390	5070	3040	2530	3200	2720	2650	2430	2130	2950
Inorganic P	495	748	417	497	730	795	1035	622	580	726
Organic P	1895	4322	2623	2033	2470	1925	1615	1808	1550	2224
Phosphocreatine	311	1630	274	116	219	0	92	116	78	94
Adenylic acid	151	150	144	213	329	255	131	171	183	251
Adenosine diphosphate	27	59	330	48	65	129	49	25	46	135
Adenosine triphosphate	179	542	8	138	105	58	106	152	142	161
Glucose-1-phosphate	61	80	42	42	175	106	104	130	106	156
Glucose-6-phosphate	185	250	423	264	249	542	278	454	393	500
Fructose-6-phosphate	30	33	24	17	53	28	7	14	17	37
Hexosediphosphate	6	7	17	4	7	19	5	6	5	11
Phosphoglyceric acid	98	140	183	102	209	122	119	148	98	165
"Coenzymes"	17	17	35	16	25	—	—	—	—	—
Free pentose P	42	22	48	72	50	—	—	—	—	—
Per cent of organic P accounted for	80	81	70	68	65	79	72	86	91	89

[1] As micromoles per 100 g.
[2] As hexose.

Averages are reported of 72 for the former and 50 for the latter (γ of 7 minutes hydrolyzable P per 100 mg. dry weight). At the same time, as Potter and Lieb had found, there is no difference in ATP-ase activity between the two tissues. The values for aldolase in sarcoma 39 and the Walker 256 tumor are lower than those for muscle, about the same as those for liver, brain, and heart, and higher than those for kidney, spleen, and testis (362) (Table 131).

Glycolytic studies have been made in the whole animal, in tissue slices, in tissue homogenates, and in subcellular fractions of the homogenate. It is also possible to carry out such studies on free cells, as in leukocytes (363) and in ascites cells (364–366). Both normal and leukemic myeloid cells possess an active aerobic glycolysis, whereas lymphatic leukemic lymphocytes and blast forms have low aerobic glycolytic rates. With glucose

TABLE 131

ALDOLASE ACTIVITY IN NORMAL AND TUMOR TISSUES[1] (362)

Tissue	Activity	Tissue	Activity
Muscle	74,000	Spleen	4,800
Brain	15,800	Testis	2,900
Heart	15,600	Sarcoma 39	14,000
Liver	12,100	Walker 256 tumor	15,600
Kidney	7,800		

[1] As microliters of hexosediphosphate split per hour per gram of fresh tissue.

TABLE 132

METABOLISM OF NORMAL AND LEUKEMIC LEUKOCYTE HOMOGENATES[1] (363)

Tissue	Oxygen consumption	Glucose utilization	Lactic acid
Normal	0.40	1.40	3.01
Chronic myelocytic leukemia	0.12	0.52	1.27
Chronic lymphocytic leukemia	0.11	0.31	0.48

[1] In terms of millimoles per 10^{10} cells per hour.

and hexosediphosphate as substrates, the oxygen consumption, glucose utilization, and lactic acid production are significantly higher in normal than in leukemic cell *homogenates* (Table 132). Human lymphatic tissue, whether thymus, lymph nodes, or spleen, from normal or from cancerous patients, has an extremely low oxidase activity, and little correlation can be made with various pathologic variables (367).

Washed ascites tumor cells possess high rates of anaerobic and aerobic glycolysis in the presence of glucose or fructose (364) and in general behave as do other tissues in respect to their component enzymes, i.e., loss of inorganic phosphate simultaneously with oxidation of succinate, and phosphorylation of glucose by extracts at about the same rate as the anaerobic glycolysis by the whole tumor cell (hexokinase reaction). The oxidative metabolism of these cells is inhibited by large quantities of glucose (366). The ascitic plasma contains an active acid phosphatase, an almost negligible alkaline phosphatase, β-glucuronidase, "pseudo"-cholinesterase, and several glycolytic enzymes, but does not possess the ability to glycolyze hexosediphosphate to lactate (364). The plasma is virtually free of triosephosphate dehydrogenase, but has a high aldolase activity. The presence of aldolase in ascites fluid has been shown by Warburg and Hiepler (365), who have also shown the presence of little sugar and much lactate in this fluid. The calculations of Warburg and Hiepler for the *in vivo* metabolism of the ascites cell are of considerable interest. Thus, if 1 ml. of ascites fluid contains 250 cu. mm. of cells, and if a mouse has 5 ml. of ascites fluid, there will be $5 \times 250 \times 0.175 = 220$ mg. dry weight of cells which form 220

$\times$ 50 = 11,000 cu. mm. of lactic acid per hour, equivalent to 44 mg. of glucose. The total blood sugar of the mouse is of the order of 4 mg. The potential metabolism of the ascites cells is obviously not realized *in vivo*, and the ascites fluid must contain, as observed, very little fermentable sugar. The tumor cell evidently lives on the relatively small amounts of sugar and oxygen which diffuse into it through the surrounding fluid.

The ascites tumor cells apparently contain active dehydrogenases for glucose-6-phosphate, 6-phosphogluconate, isocitric acid, and lactic acid (368). The former two enzymes also occur in the plasma. The direct oxidation of glucose-6-phosphate by the tumor cell extracts suggests that this system may contribute by way of triphosphopyridinenucleotide to the over-all respiration of the cell (368). Glucose dehydrogenase is probably not present, since glucose is unable to reduce pyridine nucleotides under conditions whereby triphosphopyridinenucleotide is readily reduced by glucose-6-phosphate. The Ehrlich ascites tumor cells contain an active glutathione reductase. The lactic acid formed is of the L(+) configuration (369).

There is generally an apparently higher consumption of oxygen by tumor tissues in the absence of glucose than in its presence (cf. 370). Warburg *et al.* (371) had shown that the metabolism of tumors in animals kept in insulin convulsions was little affected, while tumor slices studied in the sera of normal animals and in the sera of animals in insulin shock demonstrated a higher Q_{O_2} in the latter than in the former medium (372). Addition of glucose to the hypoglycemic serum reduces its excess oxygen consumption in the presence of the tumor slices (372).

These experiments illustrate the dilemma which constantly confronts the investigator who employs manometric methods, namely, the problem of adequate and meaningful controls. Thus, a biological system may possess a particular respiration when treated with a known substrate, but is the control to this experiment the value for the respiration of the system alone and in the absence of the substrate? A tissue system carries on a specific endogenous metabolism, and the addition of a compound which may be metabolized by this system may nevertheless itself affect the endogenous reactions of the tissue. Under such conditions, the use of the tissue system alone as a control is illusory. Manometric measurements with tissue controls have been frequently employed to calculate the ratio of aerobic glycolysis to equivalent respiration or that of lactic acid production to glucose consumption in the presence of oxygen, whereby values of 5.1 to 17.7 have been noted for malignant tumors (373). When lactic acid production and glucose consumption of Brown-Pearce tumor slices respiring in normal rabbit serum were chemically assayed (372), a ratio of 0.63 was observed, or, for every 100 mg. of glucose metabolized, 63 mg. was glycolyzed and 37 mg. was oxidized or otherwise altered; on the assumption that all the glucose not glycolyzed was completely burnt, the glycolysis to respiration ratio becomes 63/37 = 1.7. When this ratio was determined under identical conditions by the usual manometric procedures, the equivalent value was found to be 6.2 (372). The discrepancy does not invalidate the accepted concept that tumors convert a large share of administered glucose to lactic acid under aerobic conditions, but it is of sufficient magnitude to emphasize the Liebigian dictum that all physiological investigation must rest upon chemical analysis.

Advantages of the use of homogenates for studying the complete dissimilation of glucose are: (a) they contain all metabolic factors, (b) there are no cell membrane barriers, and (c) they contain all structural components of the cell. A serious disadvantage is their high endogenous metabolism, which makes direct manometric estimations of oxidation of added substrate almost impossible. Weinhouse and his collaborators have used C^{14}-labeled glucose and measured the incorporation of radioactivity with respiratory CO_2 as a measure of the oxidation of glucose in slices of normal and neoplastic tissues (105).

When whole-tissue homogenates were suitably fortified, they oxidized glucose rapidly (373a). The requirements for glucose oxidation in homogenates of *C3H* mouse hepatoma 98/15 are the same as in normal tissues; i.e., there is the same dependence on DPN and Mg^{++}, and in the complete system (inclusive of ATP and fumarate), oxygen consumption and glucose oxidation are similar in magnitude to that of liver. "No qualitative differences are apparent in the requirements and the pattern of glucose oxidation between the liver and its neoplastic counterpart. Obviously more data are necessary to establish quantitative differences, if any" (373a).

The observations that tissue slices, including those of tumors, show little or no response in oxygen uptake to addition of glucose (except for brain) are probably due to the substitution by glucose for endogenous metabolites (373a). A requirement for active homogenates is apparently the presence of intact subcellular structures.

Proteins in Normal and Neoplastic Tissues

The distinguishing biochemical characteristics of a species lie fundamentally in the nature of its proteins (374). There are hints in recent work (375, 376) that the nucleic acids may share in this specificity, but to date only the proteins are definitely known to possess a striking uniqueness. This differentiation in the proteins of various species has been almost entirely accomplished by sensitive immunologic methods. That there may be minor protein differences among individuals even within the same species is now familiar from studies of so-called blood groupings. It would further appear that, although the possession of a uniquely constructed protein architecture is the distinguishing chemical feature of each species, there may be a certain degree of similarity in such architecture in the proteins of closely related species.

Attempts to distinguish the proteins of homologous tissues in different species by means of chemical analysis have so far revealed that, on the whole, the amino acid composition of these proteins is rather similar. Thus, Bailey (377) found that the values for nitrogen, sulfur, amide nitrogen, cystine-cysteine, methionine, tyrosine, and tryptophan in each of the preparations of myosin of the rabbit, dog, ox, chicken, fish, and lobster were practically identical from one species to another. Similar results were obtained by a study of the whole muscle proteins (378). Block (379) found that the nitrogen, histidine, lysine, arginine, cystine-cysteine, tyrosine, and tryptophan values for the brain proteins of the human, monkey, cow, sheep, rat and guinea pig were very nearly the same from one species to another. It might thus appear on the surface that, although the architecture of the proteins in several species might vary widely, the proportion of the building blocks in the proteins of homologous tissues among these species is very nearly the same. However, closer investigation of such proteins has revealed striking differences in the sulfur distribution in the comparable tissues of different species (320, 380–382).

In the analysis of proteins for cystine and cysteine, both amino acids are estimated together by means which make no distinction between them. From the data given above, it would appear that their sum was very nearly the same in homologous proteins of different species. Recently developed experimental techniques, however, designed to estimate cystine and cysteine separately, have yielded results which show that, although the sum of these two amino acids may be the same in homologous proteins of different species, their relative ratio differs markedly for each species. Within the proteins of each species this ratio is very nearly a constant quantity. The first indication of this phenomenon came about through a study of the purified nucleoprotein fraction of the liver in various animal species (380, 381) (Tables 133 and 134).

From the results in Table 133, it is noted that (a) similar to the observations of others on homologous tissue proteins the proportion of most of the amino acid constituents of the homologous nucleoproteins of the liver of different species is very nearly the same from one species to the other; (b) however, this protein fraction does differ in each species in the relative proportion of cystine to cysteine whereby the cystine-cysteine in the rabbit protein is nearly entirely cysteine, whereas in the rat the greater part of the cystine-cysteine moiety is composed of cystine; and (c) the mercaptan groups of the cysteine moieties of the proteins are exposed within the native protein inasmuch as no further groups are released by denaturation procedures.

Further investigations of the sulfur distribution in the whole organs of

TABLE 133

ANALYTICAL VALUES FOR FAT-FREE LIVER NUCLEOPROTEIN PREPARATIONS (380, 381)

Source	N, %	Amide N, %	P, %	Total S, %	Free SH in native protein as cysteine, %	Free SH[1] in denatured protein as cysteine, %	Cystine-cysteine, %	Methionine, %	Tyrosine, %	Tryptophan, %
Rabbit	15.6	1.0	0.8	1.0	1.3	1.3	1.3	3.0	3.8	1.3
Rabbit	15.6	1.0	0.8	1.2	1.4	1.4	1.3	3.1	3.9	1.3
Rabbit	15.6	0.9	0.8	1.2	1.4	1.4	1.4	2.9	4.0	1.5
Rabbit	15.7	1.0	0.8	1.1	1.2	1.2	1.5	3.1	4.0	1.5
Calf	15.6	1.0	0.8	1.1	0.7	0.7	1.4	3.2	3.9	1.4
Calf	15.7	1.0	0.8	1.1	0.7	0.7	1.4	3.1	3.9	1.5
Cow	15.8	1.0	0.9	1.2	0.6	0.6	1.5	3.1	3.7	1.7
Rat	15.6	0.9	0.9	1.2	0.2	0.2	1.3	3.0	3.8	1.5
Rat	15.7	1.0	0.8	1.2	0.2	0.2	1.4	3.1	3.8	1.5
Transplanted rat hepatoma	15.8	0.9	0.7	1.1	0.2	0.2	1.4	2.9	3.6	1.5

[1] Denatured in 8 *M* guanidine HCl.

TABLE 134

PROPORTION OF FAT IN LIVER NUCLEOPROTEIN PREPARATIONS[1] (380, 381)

Source	Cold ether extract, %	Hot alcohol-acetone-ether extract, %	Fat from hot alcohol-acetone-ether extract, %	
			N	P
Rabbit	4.4	10.1	0.7	1.6
Rabbit	4.5	12.5	0.6	1.6
Rabbit	4.0	9.6	0.7	1.9
Rabbit	3.9	12.5	0.7	2.2
Calf	5.1	13.1	0.7	1.9
Calf	16.3	21.5	0.6	1.5
Cow	5.8	15.3	0.8	2.2
Rat	5.5	14.7	0.8	2.1
Rat	5.3	15.0	0.8	2.2
Transplanted rat hepatoma	—	15.0	0.8	2.0

[1] The liver nucleoprotein fraction consists of a lipid-nucleic acid-protein complex.

different species revealed data in conformity with the above findings (320) (Table 135).

The problem of sulfur distribution in various tissues, as it applies to the state of oxidation of the tissue protein sulfur groups, involves the level of glutathione in these tissues. The sulfur group of the tripeptide is in equilibrium with corresponding groups on the surface of protein molecules in the tissue. Values of glutathione in normal rat liver range in terms of milli-

TABLE 135

CYSTINE AND CYSTEINE IN THE EXTRACTABLE PROTEINS OF NORMAL AND NEOPLASTIC TISSUES[1] (320)

Tissues	Cystine-cysteine[2] Rat	Cystine-cysteine[2] Rabbit	Cysteine[3] Rat	Cysteine[3] Rabbit	Cystine[4] Rat	Cystine[4] Rabbit	Cystine:cysteine Rat	Cystine:cysteine Rabbit
Normal:								
Adult liver	0.41	0.43	0.10	0.25	0.31	0.18	3.1	0.7
Regenerating liver[5]	0.40	—	0.10	—	0.30	—	3.0	—
Fetal liver[6]	0.26	0.11	0.06	0.05	0.20	0.06	3.3	1.2
Kidney	0.40	0.44	0.10	0.24	0.30	0.20	3.2	0.8
Spleen	0.38	0.28	0.09	0.16	0.29	0.12	3.2	0.8
Brain	0.36	0.36	0.11	0.24	0.25	0.12	2.3	0.5
Heart	0.38	0.40	0.11	0.20	0.27	0.20	2.4	1.0
Skeletal muscle	0.28	0.26	0.08	0.18	0.20	0.08	2.5	0.5
Lung	0.20	0.20	0.04	0.11	0.16	0.09	4.0	0.8
Pancreas	0.26	0.24	0.05	0.16	0.21	0.08	4.2	0.5
Average	—	—	—	—	—	—	3.1	0.7
Neoplastic:[7]								
Hepatoma 31	0.24	—	0.06	—	0.18	—	3.0	—
Jensen sarcoma	0.23	—	0.05	—	0.18	—	3.6	—
Walker 256 carcinoma	0.26	—	0.06	—	0.20	—	3.3	—
Flexner-Jobling carcinoma	0.28	—	0.07	—	0.21	—	3.0	—
Brown-Pearce tumor	—	0.31	—	0.18	—	0.13	—	0.7
Average	—	—	—	—	—	—	3.2	—

[1] All data given in terms of milligram per milligram of total nitrogen in the tissue extracts.

[2] By the Folin-Marenzi method on hydrochloric acid + formic acid hydrolyzates.

[3] By porphyrindin titration of the proteins denatured in guanidine hydrochloride.

[4] Calculated by difference, i.e., by subtraction of cysteine from cystine-cysteine.

[5] 2 days after partial hepatectomy.

[6] From rats 2 weeks, and from rabbits 20 days pregnant.

[7] All tumors were transplants.

grams per 100 g. wet weight from 204 (383) to 270 (384). The glutathione content of the primary rat hepatoma is about 11% lower (384), that of the transplanted rat hepatoma about 24% lower (385), than that of normal rat liver. Glutathione contributes very little (less than 5%) to the values of "cysteine" in Table 135, but the relative values for this component in the tissue proteins is in accord with the relative glutathione content of the two tissues. Rabbit liver contains 316 mg. of glutathione per 100 g. of tissue (386), and the higher glutathione content in this tissue over that in the corresponding tissue of the rat is reflected in the higher cysteine values for the proteins of the rabbit as contrasted with those for the rat (Tables 133 and 135).

It would appear that the cystine-cysteine ratio may be a value characteristic for each species and that, although there exist appreciable similarities in the protein composition of homologous tissues of different species, there also exist profound differences.

Neoplasms arise from normal tissues and possess metabolic characteristics at once similar to and different from those of the latter tissues. The question that is raised in the present connection is concerned with whether the proteins of the neoplasm differ from or are similar to those of the normal tissue of its origin. The enzymes are protein in nature, and it might be asked, when the enzymatic activity of a neoplasm differs from its normal tissue of origin, whether one tissue has more of the same enzyme protein than the other, or whether such a difference is qualitative in nature and based upon different enzyme proteins in each tissue.

From the data in Table 133, it is noted that the purified nucleoprotein fraction of the transplanted rat hepatoma is nearly indistinguishable in amino acid composition from that of the normal rat liver. It is nevertheless possible that the proteins of these two tissues may differ in the content of components other than those studied and perhaps also in terms of molecular configuration. The cytoplasmic ribonucleoprotein components of normal and cancer tissues appear to possess similar ultracentrifugal ($S = 28, 40, 50$, and 70) and electrophoretic behavior, although their relative amounts may vary among themselves (386a).

The distribution of sulfur in the total extractable proteins of four diverse but transplanted rat tumors (Table 135) is very nearly identical. The sulfur distribution of the hepatoma proteins is much more like that of the other rat tumors than it is like that of the proteins of the normal adult liver. This implies a close degree of correlation among tumors within the same species and is consistent with the enzymatic findings described above, which reveal a generally consistent metabolic pattern among tumors as compared with normal tissues. However, the cystine:cysteine ratio for the rat tissues is 3.1 for all the normal tissues and 3.2 for all the tumors; thus, in this respect it may be concluded that rat tumors are composed of rat protein. Similarly, the cystine:cysteine ratio for the normal rabbit tissues is 0.7 and that of the transplanted Brown-Pearce tumor is also 0.7. Thus, it would appear that this tumor is composed of rabbit protein. These conclusions might well be termed self-evident, but these are the first analytical data which reveal them.

It should be pointed out that the above figures hold for rat and rabbit tumors growing respectively in rats and in rabbits, so that parenchyma and stroma proteins are derived from the same species. It would be of interest to examine the proteins of a tumor growing in an alien species, as in the guinea pig eye, where the parenchyma may be mouse or human, etc., and the stroma is guinea pig.

The total sulfur of acetone powders of normal rat liver has been reported as 1.32 %, and that of the primary rat hepatoma as 1.34 % (387). Alkaline treatment of the acetone powders of a variety of human and rat tumors yielded elemental sulfur in much greater quantities than from similar preparations of normal adult tissues so treated. Each of the subcellular morphologic entities of normal liver yielded much less elemental sulfur than did the corresponding fractions of tumor. These interesting observations suggest different modes of combination of cystine or cysteine in the proteins of normal and malignant tissues (387).

The evidence that tumors resemble each other more than they do normal tissues, or more than normal tissues resemble each other, is further supported by immunologic observations (388). Studies on a protein fraction with catheptic properties from various rat tissues revealed that the particular fraction from the transplanted hepatoma resembled that of the transplanted Jensen sarcoma more than it did the comparable fraction of the normal liver of the same species (Table 136). The consistency in the implications of the data in Tables 133–136 is noteworthy.

Kubowitz and Ott (389) isolated an enzyme in crystalline form from the Jensen rat sarcoma which is concerned with the following reaction:

$$\text{Pyruvic acid} + \text{dihydropyridine nucleotide} \leftrightarrows \text{Lactic acid} + \text{pyridine nucleotide}$$

This enzyme was identical in all respects studied, catalytic as well as immunologic, with an enzyme of similar specificity isolated from rat muscle. Although this is but a single example, it would not seem likely that the enzymes in normal and neoplastic tissues of the same species would differ very greatly qualitatively. In view of the evidence portrayed by the similar cystine-cysteine ratios of the proteins, whether normal or neoplastic, within each species (Tables 133 and 135), it may be assumed that the proteins of such tissues are at least closely similar, and, hence, the enzymatic differences between such tissues may, with some confidence, be ascribed to quantitative rather than to qualitative variations.

More recent data by Sauberlich and Baumann emphasize in striking fashion the resemblance of the amino acid composition of many animal tissues, regardless of species, or whether normal or neoplastic (67) (Table (137). It must be pointed out, however, that not all animal tissues possess the same amino acid composition, and the resemblance referred to is not unlimited. Thus, collagen is characterized by exceptionally high values of glycine and proline, and the globins are rich in the hexone bases. Many other exceptions can be cited. In the case of a mammary fibrosarcoma, somewhat high values for glycine and for proline were observed (67), and it is probable that this tumor is composed of a large proportion of connective tissue.

TABLE 136

Precipitin Tests with Antiserums to Cathepsins Using Different Concentrations of Cathepsins as Antigens and Serums Diluted 1:2 (388)

Source of antigens	Antiserum to hepatoma 31 cathepsin					Antiserum to normal rat liver cathepsin				
	Dilutions of antigen					Dilutions of antigen				
	1:1,000[1]	1:10,000	1:100,000	1:1,000,000	1:10,000,000	1:1,000[1]	1:10,000	1:100,000	1:1,000,000	1:10,000,000
Hepatoma 31:										
Preparation 1	+++++	+++	+	+	+	++	+	0	0	0
Preparation 2	+++++	++	+	+	+	+++	+	+	0	0
Preparation 3	++++	++	+	+	+	+++	++	0	0	0
Jensen sarcoma:										
Preparation 37	++	+	+	+	0	+++	+	0	0	0
Preparation 38	++	+	+	+	0	+++	+	0	0	0
Preparation 40	++	+	+	+	0	++	+	0	0	0
Normal rat liver:										
Osborne-Mendel	(+++)					(++++)	++	+	+	+
strain	(+++)	+	0	0	0	(+++)	++	+	+	+
N.C.I. stock	+++	+	0	0	0	++++	++	+	+	+
Normal rat kidney	+	+	0	0	0	+	+	0	0	0
Normal rat spleen	+	0	0	0	0	+	+	0	0	0
Spleens of rats bearing Jensen sarcoma	+	+?	0	0	0	+	+	0	0	0
Beef spleen	0	0	0	0	0	0	0	0	0	0
Rat muscle albumin	0	0	0	0	0	0	0	0	0	0
Hepatoma 31 albumin	0	0	0	0	0	0	0	0	0	0
Rat liver albumin	0	0	0	0	0	0	0	0	0	0

[1] 1:1,000 is equivalent to 1 mg. dry weight of antigen per milliliter.

Tissues, like serum, possess amino acids not only bound in protein linkage but also in the free state (cf. 391). In relatively high concentration in serum and in tissues are glutamic acid, aspartic acid, glycine, alanine, glutamine, and serine. The relative amounts of these substances vary somewhat in different tissues and in serum, but their absolute amounts are higher in tissues. Simple, free diffusion does not seem a likely factor in any possible equilibrium between the tissue and serum. Some normal tissues have long been known to possess extractives peculiar to themselves, e.g., carnosine in muscle, and, more recently, γ-aminobutyric acid in brain. Comparisons of the free amino acid patterns by two-dimensional chromatography in homologous normal and cancer tissues of the mouse (muscle

TABLE 137

Amino Acids in Various Animal Tissues[1] (67)

Amino acids	Four rat tumors[2]	Fibrosarcoma[3]	Normal rat tissues[4]	Beef[5]	Pork[5]	Mammary fibrosarcoma	Collagen[5]
Arginine	5.4–6.2	5.9	5.0–6.0	6.2	6.2	6.8	7.3–9.0
Glutamic acid	11.7–13.3	12.0	10.4–15.0	15.2	—	10.2	11.4
Glycine	5.1–6.3	4.5	4.9–6.1	5.0	—	17.1	24–30
Histidine	1.9–2.7	2.5	2.0–2.4	3.5	3.2	1.2	0.7–0.9
Isoleucine	4.3–5.6	4.5	4.8–5.2	5.3	4.8	2.5	1.3–1.8
Leucine	7.2–8.9	7.5	7.3–9.1	7.8	7.8	4.7	3.1–3.3
Lysine	6.5–8.3	7.5	6.5–8.3	8.0	8.1	5.2	3.2–3.7
Methionine	1.9–2.0	1.8	2.2–2.5	2.7	2.5	1.2	0.8–0.9
Phenylalanine	3.7–4.4	3.8	3.4–4.5	3.9	4.0	3.5	2.0–2.4
Threonine	3.1–5.1	3.8	3.5–4.1	4.5	4.6	2.4	1.7–2.4
Tryptophan	0.9–1.0	—	1.2–1.4	1.1	1.1	0.26	—
Valine	4.4–5.3	5.2	4.3–6.1	5.2	5.2	3.2	2.4–2.8

[1] In terms of per cent amino acids in fat-free, dry tissues, corrected to 16% N.

[2] Tumors include Flexner-Jobling, a subcutaneous sarcoma, and two hepatomas.

[3] Data of Dunn *et al.* (390).

[4] Includes muscle and liver.

[5] Compiled from the data of other investigators by Sauberlich and Baumann (67).

and rhabdomyosarcoma, liver and hepatoma, epidermis and squamous cell carcinoma, and lymph nodes and lymphosarcoma) revealed that each normal tissue has a distribution of amino acids characteristic for that tissue, whereas all the tumors, regardless of derivation or source, showed very similar patterns (392). It is of interest to emphasize in these observations that the neoplastic tissues yielded the same pattern of free amino acids whether they originated from a normal tissue with a high content of free amino acids, such as epidermis, or a tissue relatively low in these constituents, such as muscle. Epidermis has a very high content of free amino acids (392), as well as of urea and non-protein nitrogen (393), and the decrease in non-protein nitrogen in the skin tumor has been observed. Glutamine is also present in lower amounts in the tumors than in liver or normal skin. Free alanine and glycine as well as proline appear in a considerably elevated concentration in lymphomas of mice as compared with normal lymphatic tissues (156). Taurine is apparently present in most of the tissues of the mouse, both normal and neoplastic. A curious observation, at present inexplicable, is the observation of the relatively high content of histamine in sarcomas (394).

One of the most unusual scientific controversies in modern times originated 15 years ago when Kögl and Erxleben published the first of a long series of papers which have dealt with the presence of D-glutamic acid in tumor proteins (395). The controversy is unusual, not because of the claim that a D-amino acid may exist in a protein, for the presence of D-amino acids in a variety of natural polypeptides is well-established, but because in all these 15 years no one has yet confirmed the original observation. During this period, the proponents have stubbornly adhered to their claims. The topic has been recently reviewed by Miller (396) and by Wiltshire (397). The crux of the problem lies in the ready racemization which both combined and free L-glutamic acids undergo in the boiling strong HCl necessary to hydrolyze the proteins. The most recent papers by Kögl and his collaborators (398–400) deal with the injection of isotope-labeled L- or D-glutamic acid in large amounts under the skin of rats with benzpyrene-induced tumors. Hydrolysis by acid of the dried tumor led to the isolation of the glutamic acid fraction from which L-glutamic acid could be crystallized. From the mother liquor of the latter crystallization DL-glutamic acid could be isolated. When labeled L-glutamic acid was administered, neither the L- nor the DL-glutamic acid preparations from the tumor hydrolyzates contained appreciable isotope. When labeled D-glutamic acid was administered, however, the isolated L-glutamic acid from the tumor hydrolyzates was again isotope-free, but the DL-glutamic acid fraction contained much of the label. The assumption that the L-component of the latter racemate was isotope-free led to the calculation of a considerable concentration of the isotope in the D-glutamic acid moiety. On the basis of these apparently clear-cut results, Kögl and his collaborators drew the conclusion that D-glutamic acid is incorporated as such into the tumor protein, whereas the L-glutamic acid is diluted in the body as a consequence of the many metabolic conversions involving this compound. If these observations are correct, they would tend to negate the criticism based upon the racemization of protein-bound glutamic acid during acid hydrolysis, for it would be expected that under such conditions the isotope concentration would be the same in the L- and D-moieties of the racemate. It would have been of interest in this connection to have subjected the DL-glutamic acid fraction to the action of glutamic acid decarboxylase, not only to establish the purity of this fraction, but to have definitely established that all the label was present in the D-enantiomorph, since the latter can readily be separated from γ-aminobutyric acid.

A possible explanation for these observations lies in the well-known fact that free amino acids are frequently found associated even with highly purified proteins. This is a phenomenon familiar to investigators concerned with end-group analysis of proteins, and its existence has been a stumbling-block to the acceptance of much of the incorporation studies of amino acids into tissue preparations *in vitro*. Kögl's source materials have been the crude, insoluble mass of proteins of tissues which were extracted first with saline and then with water. If free amino acids are removed with difficulty from proteins even after several crystallizations and dialyses, it would not be expected that simple washing of a crude protein mass could accomplish this purpose. As noted above in the findings of Astrup, Roberts, and others, glutamic acid in the free state is one of the more common components of many tissues. Kögl and his collaborators have not excluded the possibility that the tumor may take up administered D-glutamic acid without necessarily incorporating it into its proteins. The studies of Christensen and his colleagues have shown that cancer cells have a greater ability to accumulate free amino acids than have normal cells (401). There is no proof that such accumulated amino acids enter into synthetic reactions to form proteins, although in the case of the natural L-amino acids the inference is strong. It may well be that sites of unusual synthetic activity would tend to accumulate natural as well as unnatural amino acids, and the fact that the latter may be found in hydrolyzates of crude proteins from these sites does not mean that they were *a priori* constituents of such proteins. On the other hand, this attempt to explain Kögl's findings must be reconciled with the numerous observations from many laboratories which show that the D-glutamic acid content of normal tissues is fully as high as that of cancer tissues (cf. 396 and 397). At the present time these differences are irreconciliable, and, attractive though the Kögl hypothesis may be, it must, for the present at least, be subject to the Scotch verdict—not proved.

It therefore appears that amino acid analyses *per se* may not be of too great value in distinguishing tumor from normal proteins, but there still remains the possibility that the arrangement and sequence of the amino acid residues in the respective proteins might result in physical and biological properties sufficiently different as to be distinguishable by experiment. The evidence cited by Kubowitz and Ott (389) on the practical identity of lactic dehydrogenase from muscle and from tumor might tend to extinguish the hope of realizing this possibility. Nevertheless, this enzyme is only a single entity in a much larger protein mass and need not be representative of the tissues as a whole. Rodewald and Klein (402) fed cancer tissue to mice and noted marked and persistent liver damage, a phenomenon completely absent when normal tissues were so fed. The action of pepsin on proteins of homologous blood plasma leads to the formation of low molecular weight polypeptides which, in contrast with the low molecular weight polypeptides obtained similarly from heterologous blood plasma, possess a pronounced and immediate growth-promoting effect on fibroblasts *in vitro* (403). The peptic digests of avian tumors and of normal avian tissues after neutralization present an analogous picture in their respective effects on the growth of pure chick myoblasts in dialyzed cultures *in vitro* (404). In all cases, where the effect of the digested tumor tissue supplemented or not with glutamine, cystine, or glutathione was compared with that of similarly digested normal tissues, the latter invariably induced a much higher growth rate of the culture. These interesting experiments might suggest a difference in the structure or amino acid sequence in the proteins of the normal and malignant tissues studied—in so far as these proteins are susceptible to the action of pepsin. They remain somewhat ambiguous, however, in part because homologous pairs of well-defined individual proteins from analogous normal and tumor tissues were not studied, and in part because the presence of growth accelerators in the normal tissues were by no means excluded. Nevertheless, since pepsin is known to be a highly selective endopeptidase, parallel experiments on pure protein from well-characterized and comparable biological sources should prove of great value.

Instead of studying the massed proteins of the tissue as a whole, it is sometimes convenient to investigate the properties of one of the limited, subcellular fractions. Thus, Hogeboom and Schneider (405) isolated mitochondria from normal *C3H* mouse liver and from transplanted hepatoma 98/15 grown in the same strain and subjected the proteins of the disintegrated particles to ultracentrifugal analysis (Table 138). The ultracentrifugal pattern of regenerating mouse liver was the same as that of normal liver, and, whereas there are four distinguishable sedimenting peaks when the mitochondria are disintegrated by pressure, there are only three when sonic vibration is used as a disintegrating agent. With either procedure, the hepatoma mitochondrial proteins demonstrate the presence of only three peaks. There seems, therefore, to be a qualitatively different protein picture in the mitochondria of normal and regenerating mouse liver on the one hand, and of the hepatoma on the other. The apparent absence of component 2 from the hepatoma mitochondria might represent the loss of some specialized hepatic function.

Among the more sensitive physicochemical methods of characterizing proteins is that of electrophoresis, which depends upon the net charge on the protein surface at any given pH. Some of the results of measuring the mobilities of the soluble proteins of liver and hepatoma during azo dye carcinogenesis have been described earlier in this volume. These may be summarized as demonstrating that the major portion of the protein-bound dye

TABLE 138

SEDIMENTATION CONSTANTS OF MITOCHONDRIAL PROTEINS (405)

Preparation	Disintegration	Sedimentation constant, Svedbergs: Component 1	Component 2	Component 3	Component 4	Range of total protein concentration, %
Normal liver mitochondria	Pressure	3.8	5.1	7.5	About 10–11	1.4–2.3
	Sonic	3.7	6.3	Absent	About 11–13	1.7–2.2
Hepatoma mitochondria	Pressure	3.7	Absent	7.6	About 12–15	0.6–2.6
	Sonic	3.8	Absent	8.0	About 12–13	0.5–1.6

migrated with the slowly migrating *h* components (406), which, in the tumors themselves, are present in greatly reduced quantity (50, 51); electrophoretic analyses of the soluble proteins of the rat liver after partial hepatectomy, or after inanition, showed no essential difference from those of normal rat liver (53). Comparison of the protein spectrum of liver and hepatoma is complicated by the fact that much less protein is extractable from the tumor. Thus, at pH 5 (in order to exclude nucleoproteins), protein nitrogen in extracts of the hepatoma is only about 8 % of the total nitrogen (51). The tumor is relatively rich in nuclear material, and the decreased amount of extractable proteins might reflect the diminished amount of cytoplasm available. Although the soluble proteins of the hepatoma give an electrophoretic diagram quite different from that of liver, the diagram of the hepatoma resembles very closely those of extracts of all other types of tumors studied (51, 406–409), thus providing another piece of evidence in favor of the essentially similar chemical composition of all tumors. Electrophoretic measurements on extracts of mouse muscle and rhabdomyosarcoma revealed three major components in the former, and seven in the latter (407). None of the components of the tumor appeared to be comparable with those of normal muscle, and, although the myosin fraction which was extracted in smaller amount from the tumor had the same solubilities as normal myosin, its mobility was quite different, and its viscosity much less in magnitude.

To some extent the electrophoretic diagrams of soluble tumor proteins resemble in mobility those of the comparable components of blood serum, although the relative amounts of the components are considerably different (51, 409). Thus, in hepatoma extracts there is less of a component with the mobility of serum albumin, and more of one with the mobility of serum α_2-globulin (51). The cryoglobulin (precipitable from serum at 4°) (cf. 410) present in the serum of patients with lymphosarcoma and other pathologic conditions possesses a mobility equaled by a protein in large amount in extracts of the lymphosarcoma (411).

All the investigators in this area agree on the difficulty in resolving the various electrophoretic components and emphasize the possibility that, owing to protein-protein interaction, several individual components may be associated with each peak. The results appear to be invariably reproducible, and therefore such association is not adventitious. Much interesting information has been obtained by the electrophoretic technique, and more will be anticipated as this approach is extended to include a wider variety of normal and malignant tissues. Perhaps in conjunction with methods of chromatography and specific adsorption on gels and on ion-exchange resins the proteins of normal tissues and of tumors may be further compared and, by means of these techniques, separated and identified.

Incorporation or Uptake Studies

The availability of C^{14} or N^{15} has permitted the synthesis of labeled amino acids and thereby has provided a tool for following the course of events when such amino acids are placed in juxtaposition with tissues whether *in vivo* or *in vitro*. It has generally been assumed that, if a labeled amino acid is brought into such juxtaposition and if, after a suitable period of time, analysis of tissues or of tissue components reveals the presence of the label, the amino acid has been incorporated into the proteins or other components of such tissues. Since only the fate of the label has generally been followed, rather than that of the labeled molecule administered—which would require multiple labeling and subsequent isolation—the presence of the label in the tissues is a reflection of several metabolic factors. These include the rates of metabolic interconversions of the administered amino acids, the rates of synthesis of the metabolic products into the amino acids actually incorporated into the tissue proteins, and the rates of diffusion from the sites of metabolic activity to the tissues in which incorporation is studied, as well as the rates of diffusion away from these tissues of their catabolic products. Since the classic experiments of Schoenheimer (412), the incorporation of isotopically labeled amino acids into body proteins has been used as an indicator of the biosynthesis of proteins (cf. 413). A great deal of information derived by experiment has accrued over the past years, but the results have been most difficult of interpretation (cf. 414). In part, this situation is due to a lack of adequate and clear-cut concepts as to what constitutes either protein structure or protein synthesis. Under such circumstances, the term incorporation is vague and meaningless, for it is not known whether the labeled amino acid is progressively synthesized together with other amino acids into longer and longer peptide chains until the latter reach protein status, or whether the peptide chain of preformed proteins can open at two adjacent peptide bonds and permit the exchange of amino acids with no net change in protein mass. The conditions necessary for the synthesis of only a single peptide bond is not known at the present time, except for the fact that in many instances some external source of energy is essential, and numerous transfer and exchange reactions such as transpeptidation, transamidation, and similar reaction sequences illustrate what may only be a few examples of the wealth of biological alternatives which pass under the designation of protein synthesis. Since it is not the amino acid administered which is necessarily incorporated but the isotopic label, it seems often excessive to go to the trouble of synthesizing labeled amino acids, when, for example, $C^{14}O_2$ in juxtaposition to tissues leads to an incorporation of C^{14} into the amino acids of the protein (415). Since protein synthesis in tissues requires a very balanced diet among the amino acids offered (416) and can be inhibited by an excess of any one of them (417), it is not likely that a single administered amino acid offered to a tissue would be incorporated as such. Thus, after N^{15}-labeled glycine was given to rats, the label was found not only in tissue glycine but in many other amino acids as well (418). When the possibilities of protein-amino acid interaction without chemical exchange are taken into consideration, with concomitant non-specific adsorption (cf. 419–422), together with the fact that few studies of incorporation have been made on highly purified proteins, it is no wonder that many workers in this field of research have tended to substitute the less committing and compromising designation of uptake for that of incorporation.

Of critical importance is the use of labelled compounds to determine the rates of reaction in tissues, and the expression "turnover" refers to the process whereby compounds may remain at constant levels and yet be involved in continual metabolic activity. The limitations and qualifications of the method have been critically considered by Reiner, who has pointed out that a knowledge of the mechanisms involved in reactions in which the administered labelled compound participates is necessary for proper interpretation (422a). Thus, a pathological condition which blocks a pathway whereby a labelled precursor is diluted would be expected to raise the slope of the specific activity curve of the final product without necessarily having any direct effect on the rate of actual synthesis of that final product.

It would be expected that tumor tissue, perhaps more than any other type of growing tissue, would most dramatically illustrate the associated phenomena of protein synthesis, for the tumor possesses the uniquely parasitic property of growing, if need be, at the expense of the host. Among the earliest studies of this problem were those of Shemin and Rittenberg (423), who fed glycine-N^{15} to rats bearing sarcoma R-39. The essential findings were that the label was taken up by tumor and by liver at nearly equal rates but was excreted from the former tissue far less rapidly than from the latter; the half-time of the tumor as so measured was nearly twice as much (12 days) as that of the liver (7 days). However, in muscle or skin, the half-life was even greater than for the tumor. Perhaps these early experiments might have been taken as warnings of the difficulties in interpretation to come. Rats bearing a transplanted lymphosarcoma and injected with C^{14}-labeled tyrosine possessed a higher label concentration after 6 hours and after 3 days in intestinal mucosa and in kidney than in the tumor (424). Similar results were obtained on administering methionine labeled with S^{35} to rats with tumors (425). After feeding C^{14}-labeled glycine by stomach tube to rats with primary azo dye-induced hepatomas, it was found that the non-cancerous portion of the livers took up the label much more rapidly than did the cancerous portion, but also lost it faster (426). In the experiments with labeled tyrosine, the tumor took up the label more rapidly than did the liver (425), and these opposing findings illustrate the limitations imposed on the use of single amino acids in such studies. Thus, when labeled glycine with C^{14} in either methylene or carboxyl is given to rats, much of the label in the liver tissue is found in serine (427). The metabolism of glycine and of tyrosine is certainly not the same in all particulars, and no generalizations in regard to the uptake by tissues of amino acids are applicable on the basis of the behavior of any one of them (cf. 428). With rats bearing the Flexner-Jobling carcinoma, the label from glycine-2-C^{14} reaches an optimum in liver, tumor, and kidney at about 12 hours (429); liver has a much higher uptake than tumor. Histidine-2-C^{14} provides a formate precursor supplying carbon to positions 2 and 8 of uric acid, and when administered to hepatoma-bearing rats the label is incorporated into the purines and choline methyl groups of the tumor as it is in normal liver (430). The hepatoma choline, however, contains the isotope only in the methyl groups and, unlike liver choline, not in the ethanolamine moiety; this suggests that the tumor may lack the capacity the carry out the necessary sequence in this instance of condensing formate with glycine and decarboxylating serine.

In vitro studies using tissue slices or homogenates incubated with labeled amino acids have also been employed (Table 139). The rate of uptake of labeled glycine or alanine by slices of hepatoma was found to be considerably greater than by slices of normal liver (431), a finding in disagreement with the results of *in vivo* studies involving these tissues and labeled glycine (426), as well as with other *in vivo* studies (429). It may be that the discrepancy is due to contact of the slices with a higher, localized concentration of amino acid (414, 426). The uptake *in vitro* by the lymphosarcoma cell occurs at about the same rate for labeled glycine as it does for the normal spleen cell (113), but there is a greater stimulation of the uptake by the tumor after addition of glucose which may be a reflection of the lower level of energy-yielding metabolites ordinarily present in the

TABLE 139

UPTAKE OF ISOTOPE OF LABELED AMINO ACIDS *in Vitro*

Tissue	Labeled compound	Incubation time, hr.	Micromoles per gram of protein per hour	Reference
Rat liver slices	Alanine	3.5	0.6	(431)
Rat hepatoma slices	Alanine	3.5	5.1	(431)
Rat fetal liver slices	Alanine	3.5	3.6	(431)
Mouse liver homogenate	Alanine	4	0.06	(421)
Mouse tumor homogenate	Alanine	4	0.3	(421)
Rat liver slices	Glycine	3.5	3.0	(431)
Rat hepatoma slices	Glycine	3.5	8.9	(431)
Mouse liver homogenate	Glycine	4	0.1	(421)
Mouse tumor homogenate	Glycine	4	0.1	(421)

tumor (113). It is nevertheless of interest that the amounts of uptake of glycine-2-C^{14} by the Ehrlich ascites tumor were equally rapid under both aerobic or anaerobic conditions (432). With homogenates, the uptake of labeled compounds can be noted, but the extent of uptake is much smaller than with whole cells or with slices. All the subcellular fractions take up amino acids, the nuclei being particularly active in this respect (428, 433, 434); the label from glycine-2-C^{14} is found in the nucleic acids, proteins, and fats (434).

The uptake by ascites cells suspensions of radioactive phenylalanine can be inhibited by the presence of *o*-fluorophenylalanine or β-2-thienylalanine (434a). These antagonists also inhibited uptake of valine, leucine, and lysine, although phenylalanine itself could inhibit the uptake of these amino acids. The general effect of phenylalanine and of its analogs upon the other amino acids may thus be ascribed to an imbalance phenomenon.

In vitro studies involving non-labeled amino acids and ascites tumors tend to support the findings with labeled amino acids. Thus, when mice bearing the Ehrlich ascites tumor were fed glycine or L-alanine, the tumor cells accumulated the free amino acid more rapidly than did the cells of the liver (401). Peptides are also accumulated by the ascites cells (435). In fact, the tumor cells tend to concentrate all α-amino acids, whether of the L- or D-configuration (436), but there must be some sort of selective use of these amino acids for actual synthesis of protein. Thus, the available evidence indicates that D-lysine is not incorporated into the protein molecule (437). There is no apparent exchange in the *in vitro* concentration of taurine, β-alanine, and triiodothyronine in the ascites tumor cells (437a).

Tissues therefore tend to concentrate, accumulate, take up, or incorporate amino acids for the undoubted purpose of protein synthesis, but it may be wondered whether the quantitative data so far obtained with labeled compounds present an adequate picture of such synthesis, if by synthesis a net increase in amount of protein is meant. The liver is a protein-synthesizing tissue and a site of intense metabolic activity, and its relatively rapid uptake of labeled metabolites is to be expected. This more rapid uptake than by muscle, for instance, does not reflect a more rapid growth. The more rapid uptake by liver than by hepatoma *in vivo* can be ascribed to the superior circulation of the former; the converse which occurs *in vitro* has been ascribed to the experimental conditions. The comparison of *in vitro* and *in vivo* findings rarely leads to a happy solution, and it may be doubted whether a protein-synthesizing tissue which does not grow can be adequately compared with a protein-synthesizing tissue which grows—at least when protein synthesis is the sole issue.

Studies on the biosynthesis of the nucleic acid components have tended to be more exact, for in many cases the purines and pyrimidines have been isolated after administration of the labeled materials. The first evidence that the purines of nucleic acid could be synthesized from small molecules was the observation by Barnes and Schoenheimer that isotopic ammonia was incorporated into the purines in the rat, and into uric acid in the pigeon (438). The incorporation into the carbon atoms of the purine ring of carbon from glycine, formate, and CO_2 was determined much later (439, 440).

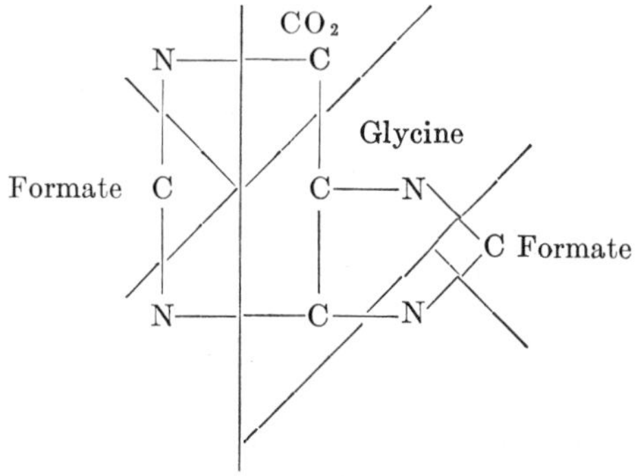

The label of isotopic glycine (glycine-2-C^{14}) is rapidly incorporated into the purines of both deoxyribonucleate and ribonucleate (429, 441). When administered to rats bearing the Flexner-Jobling carcinoma, it appears that, unlike the case of protein uptake, the isotope is incorporated more rapidly and reaches a higher peak in purines of both types of nucleic acids of the tumor than in the corresponding components of the liver (441). Ribonucleic acid exists in both nucleus and cytoplasm, and the rate of incorporation of P^{32} into each fraction differs considerably (442). The label from both glycine and phosphate, as well as from adenine-8-C^{14} (443) is incorporated at a much higher specific activity into the nuclear ribonucleate than into the cytoplasmic variety (441). At the same time, a reverse situation holds for the proteins, since the highest uptake of glycine label is found in the microsomal fraction (cf. 428). There appears on the whole to be no clear-cut correlation between protein and nucleic acid synthesis, and the nucleic acid metabolism of tumors appears to be qualitatively similar to but quantitatively more rapid than that of liver.

Orotic acid is known to be a precursor of nucleic acid pyrimidines (444), and the incorporation of radioactive orotic acid into the uridylic acid of tumors is about seven to ten times as great as that into the cytidylic acid, whereas in normal tissues and regenerating liver, the ratio is about 2:1 to 4:1 (445). Adenine-8-C^{14} is incorporated at a more rapid rate into the deoxyribonucleate of hepatoma than of liver (443), and both adenine and orotic acid (189) are rapidly incorporated into the nuclear ribonucleate fraction. Of particular interest are experiments in which both P^{32} and C^{14}-glycine were simultaneously administered to tumor-bearing rats, for, although there appears to be a much lower phosphorus incorporation into deoxyribonucleate than into ribonucleate (cf. 166, 442, 446–448), the incorporation of C^{14} into the purine bases is approximately equal for the two kinds of nucleic acid (441); the tumor components behave qualitatively similar. On the other hand, orotic acid appears to be a poor precursor for deoxyribonucleate purines, and, although N^{15}-orotic acid and P^{32}-phosphate reach higher values in nuclear ribonucleate than in cytoplasmic ribonucleate and both have a higher rate of turnover than deoxyribonucleate, the ratio of ribonucleate turnover to that of deoxyribonucleate is considerably different for the two tracers (449). All the nucleic acid fractions turn over more rapidly during regeneration, the increase in phosphorus being greater than for nitrogen; however during hepatic regeneration the increase in turnover is greatest for the cytoplasmic ribonucleate. In the Flexner-Jobling tumor, the nuclear ribonucleic acid is more active (441), but a comparison of regenerating liver and a tumor which does not arise from the hepatic cell may have doubtful validity.

The phosphorus uptake of mouse tumors is rapid, and the malignant tissues tend to retain phosphate for a long time in contrast with normal tissues (450), but the specific activity of P^{32}-treated squamous cell carcinoma is similar to that of epidermis (451).

It has generally been assumed that higher organisms cannot use exogenous pyrimidines for nucleic acid synthesis, yet observations seem to indicate that uracil can be incorporated as such into the nucleic acids of the hepatoma (452) (Table 140). It is possible that uracil may serve as a nutritional factor for tumor tissues, and this possibility is not inconsistent with the observation of the relatively rapid turnover of cytidylic acid in a number of tumors (445). Uracil is apparently an effective precursor of uridylic acid, but not of purine nucleotides nor of deoxypentose pyrimidine nucleotides (452).

A final comment may be made concerning the possibility of so-called isotope effects which emerge in tracer studies of biological systems when labeled and unlabeled molecules differ in their chemical and physical properties (cf. 453). These effects have some importance in evaluating kinetic tracer data in biological reactions, but for many of the reactions described above they play a relatively minor role.

TABLE 140

Distribution of Uracil-2-C^{14} Radioactivity (452)

Fraction	Normal liver	Hepatoma[1]
Acid-soluble (c.p.m.)	3,200	75,000
Total nucleic acid (c.p.m./mg.)	5	40
Protein (c.p.m./mg.)	2	3

[1] Induced by acetylaminofluorene in Wistar rats.

Intracellular Distribution of Chemical Components

In an earlier section (p. 338) the distribution of a number of chemical components among the intracellular morphologic entities of liver undergoing carcinogenesis was described. After 4 weeks of feeding of the azo dyes, this distribution in the liver approached that of the tumors which arose at a later date. Representative data on a variety of chemical components are described in Table 141. Briefly summarized, the essential observations are as follows. Homogenate: higher in hepatoma—cathepsin, protein, deoxyribonucleic acid, ribonucleic acid, DPN-cytochrome reductase; lower in hepatoma—riboflavin, vitamin B_6, Co-A, pantothenic acid, succinoxidase, cytochrome oxidase, and ATP-ase. Nuclei: higher in hepatoma—cathepsin with hemoglobin as substrate but not leucine amide as substrate, protein, deoxyribonucleic acid, ribonucleic acid, and cytochrome reductase; lower in hepatoma—cathepsin with leucine amide as substrate, vitamin B_6, Co-A, pantothenic acid, succinoxidase, cytochrome oxidase, and ATP-ase—there is little if any change in riboflavin. Large granules (mitochondria): higher in hepatoma—cathepsin with hemoglobin as substrate, deoxyribonucleic acid in rat but not in mouse tissues, and cytochrome reductase; lower in hepatoma—cathepsin with leucine amide as substrate, protein, ribonucleic acid, riboflavin, vitamin B_6, Co-A, pantothenic acid, succinoxidase, cytochrome oxidase, and ATP-ase. Small granules: higher in hepatoma—cathepsin with hemoglobin as substrate, and ATP-ase; lower in hepatoma—cathepsin with leucine amide as substrate, Co-A, and pantothenic acid. Supernatant: higher in hepatoma—cathepsin with hemoglobin as substrate, protein, ribonucleic acid, ATP-ase, and cytochrome reductase; lower in hepatoma—cathepsin (leucine amide), vitamin B_6, Co-A, pantothenic acid, and succinoxidase.

The greater proportion of cathepsin is found in the mitochondria, deoxyribonucleic acid in the nucleus (almost wholly), ribonucleic acid in the small granules, riboflavin in mitochondria and supernatant, vitamin B_6 in mitochondria and supernatant, Co-A and pantothenic acid in nuclei, large granules, and supernatant, succinoxidase and cytochrome oxidase in the large granules (mitochondria), ATP-ase in nuclei and large and small granules, and cytochrome reductase chiefly in the small granules. This distribution holds generally for both liver and hepatoma. The cathepsin data are curious not only in that the relative activities in liver and hepatoma fractions are different, depending on whether hemoglobin or leucine amide is used as substrate but also because the higher activity of the tumor homogenate toward leucine amide is not reflected in any of its subcellular fractions. The former may be due to the fact that cathepsin (like dehydropeptidase I mentioned above) is a complex of several proteolytic enzymes, and thus at least two enzymes are studied with the two substrates; the latter may be due to the presence of catheptic (leucine amide) inhibitors

TABLE 141

INTRACELLULAR DISTRIBUTION OF CHEMICAL COMPONENTS IN LIVER AND HEPATOMA

Component	Ref.[1]	Homogenate		Nuclei		Large granules		Small granules		Supernatant	
		Liver	Hepatoma	Liver	Hepatoma	Liver	Hepatoma	Liver	Hepatoma	Liver	Hepatoma
Cathepsin (hemoglobin)[2]	(454)	0.033	0.120	0.052	0.120	0.087	0.237	0.038	0.069	0.009	0.113
Cathepsin (leucine amide)[3]	(454)	81.4	101.4	53.8	22.9	152.8	65.7	93.3	38.6	662.8	148.5
Protein[4]	(455)	123	129	23	42	36	14	14	14	49	60
Deoxyribonucleic acid[4]	(455)	2.37	5.72	2.20	4.73	0.14	0.33	0.00	0.09	0.00	0.19
Deoxyribonucleic acid[5]	(456)	27.9	31.6	22.4	25.3	1.55	1.09	3.96	4.65	—	—
Ribonucleic acid[4]	(454)	5.27	6.88	0.87	1.57	1.47	0.71	1.08	1.32	1.56	3.25
Ribonucleic acid[5]	(456)	92.9	97.5	10.2	16.0	15.6	10.3	48.7	38.8	15.3	25.7
Riboflavin[6]	(454)	5.7	3.9	0.8	0.8	2.6	1.4	0.9	0.6	1.7	1.5
Vitamin B_6[6]	(35)	6.0	1.8	0.5	0.2	2.0	0.5	0.3	0.2	3.0	1.2
Coenzyme A[7]	(457)	174	30	39	3	95	9	4	0	33	8
Pantothenic acid[6]	(457)	126	17	33	3	63	3	5	0.4	30	6
Succinoxidase[8]	(458)	383	86.7	25.4	10.0	289	48.5	—	—	—	—
Succinoxidase[8]	(459)	4,250	755	842	128	2,400	455	—	—	184	58
Cytochrome oxidase[8]	(458)	1,012	322	54.6	29.4	748	203	—	—	—	—
Cytochrome oxidase[8]	(459)	6,860	1,520	1,360	195	5,390	964	292	247	0	0
ATP-ase[9]	(458)	865	802	231	100	416	98	—	—	—	—
ATP-ase[9]	(456)	1,580	907	495	342	790	117	240	318	80	125
DPN-cytochrome reductase[10]	(460)	6.95	8.80	0.63	1.30	1.97	2.40	4.12	4.56	0.24	0.69

[1] References 35, 454, 455, 457, and 458 are to primary hepatoma in rats; references 456, 459, and 460 involve transplanted hepatoma 98/15 in *C3H* strain mice.

[2] As mg. milligrams tyrosine liberated per milligram N.

[3] As micromoles substrate hydrolyzed per milligram N.

[4] As milligrams per gram fresh tissue.

[5] As micrograms per 100 milligrams fresh tissue.

[6] As micrograms per gram fresh tissue.

[7] As Lipmann units per gram fresh tissue.

[8] As cubic millimeters O_2 per 100 milligrams fresh tissue.

[9] As micrograms phosphorus liberated per 100 milligrams fresh tissue.

[10] As micromoles cytochrome c reduced by 100 milligrams fresh tissue.

present in the crude liver homogenate. The cathepsins of the nuclei possess a further distinction, for, whereas hemoglobin is hydrolyzed by crude homogenates of liver to yield an increase both in tyrosine color with the Folin reagent and in soluble nitrogen, the nuclei act upon this substrate to yield only an increase in soluble nitrogen, with no increase in tyrosine color (461). Studies on the amino acid concentration of the various intracellular fractions of liver and of hepatoma revealed no striking differences for any of the amino acids (462).

A new mitochondrial component of tissues recently described (463) is of smaller dimensions than that hitherto designated under this name and has therefore been called "small mitochondria." Like "large mitochondria" they possess a high succinoxidase activity, but in contrast thereto they have a very low ribonucleic acid to protein ratio. It is likely that this new subcellular component will have to be taken into consideration in future studies.

The studies described have largely dealt with comparisons on a subcellular level of liver and hepatoma. Similar studies of the distribution of succinoxidase in the particulate fractions of lactating mouse breast and of mammary tumors showed no difference in the distribution of this enzyme in the fractions of the normal and malignant tissues. The levels of activity in corresponding fractions were practically the same, and it made no difference whether the tissues were derived from mice of high or low cancer incidence strains (464).

Liver and kidney possess a high mitochondrial content in terms of protein nitrogen, whereas pancreas and submaxillary gland have a very high proportion of microsomal material with a very low proportion of mitochondria (464a). Thymus, adrenal, and tumors in general are characterized by relatively low proportions of the cytoplasmic particulate fractions. Among various types of tumors, the amounts of protein and ribonucleic acid in corresponding cell fractions are very nearly the same.

Correlation of Metabolism of Normal and Tumor Tissues with Concentration of Crucial Components

Respiration and the Cytochrome System. The aerobic respiration of tissues is dependent upon the cytochrome system. It will be noted from the foregoing tables that the content of cytochrome c and the activity of cytochrome oxidase are lower in the hepatoma than in the liver. Nevertheless, the respiration of both kinds of tissue is very nearly the same. Thus, the Q_{O_2} value for normal liver and for hepatoma slices is about 6 (310), the cytochrome c content is, respectively, 80 γ and 30 γ per gram dry weight (75), and the cytochrome oxidase activity is, respectively, 103 and 38 cu. mm. per milligram dry weight per hour (76).

Shack has calculated from these data that the oxygen consumption of tumor tissue slices is limited by the cytochrome system whereas liver (and various other normal tissues) possess a considerable reserve (76). If it is assumed that the cytochrome oxidase and cytochrome c interact as if in solution, i.e., neglecting the role of cellular structure, it is possible to calculate the maximum oxygen uptake via cytochrome oxidase-cytochrome c by employing the Michaelis-Menten constant for the reaction given by Stotz (323):

$$v = \frac{V_{\text{max.}} \times S}{Km + S}$$

where S is the cytochrome c concentration in moles per liter, v is the velocity of oxidation at submaximal concentrations of cytochrome c, $V_{\text{max.}}$ is the maximum velocity of oxidation in the presence of excess cytochrome c (cytochrome oxidase activity), and K_M is the equilibrium constant of the reaction. Stotz *et al.* (333) found the value of K_M in reaction mixtures of purified beef heart oxidase and cytochrome c to be 5.8×10^{-6} moles per liter; Greenstein *et al.* (8) found this value to be 6.0×10^{-6} moles per liter. If the molecular weight of cytochrome c be taken as 16,000, the equation yields for liver

$$V = \frac{103 \times 4 \times 10^{-6}}{6 \times 10^{-6} + 4 \times 10^{-6}} = 42 \text{ cu.mm. } O_2\text{/mg./hr.}$$

and for hepatoma

$$V = \frac{38 \times 1.2 \times 10^{-6}}{6 \times 10^{-6} + 1.2 \times 10^{-6}} = 6 \text{ cu. mm. } O_2\text{/mg./hr.}$$

Thus the respiration of the hepatoma tissue slice may be accounted for nearly entirely by the content of cytochrome c, whereas the respiratory activity of the normal liver tissue slice may be accounted for by only a fraction of all the cytochrome c presumably available. It would appear that the normal tissue possesses a considerable cytochrome reserve and, hence, can satisfy any additional energy requirements by an increased oxidation. Since the tumor does not possess this oxidative reserve, demands for more energy must be satisfied by other mechanisms, perhaps by increased glycolysis.

Glycolysis and Aldolase. An interesting similar type of calculation with the above was made by Warburg and Christian in the case of aldolase (465). This enzyme, which splits hexose into two trioses, is part of the glycolytic chain of reactions.

The glycolytic rate of red blood cells is 105 cu. mm. lactic acid per hour, and the aldolase activity in the same quantity of cells (1 ml.) is 1900 cu. mm. triosephosphate per hour. Thus, in the red blood cells there is roughly 18 times as much aldolase as is necessary to account for their glycolysis.

On the other hand, the glycolytic rate of the Jensen sarcoma is roughly

40, and the aldolase activity in the same amount of tissue expressed in the same manometric units is also 40 (465). Red cells and sarcoma are hardly comparable tissues, but it is significant, however, to note that just as the cytochrome c is the limiting factor in the respiration of the hepatoma, so also is aldolase the probable limiting factor in the glycolysis in sarcoma tissue. Like the liver, which possesses a considerable oxidative reserve, the normal red cells possess a considerable glycolytic reserve.

So far as has been calculated from the available data, it would appear that tumors function to the limit of their available catalytic systems whereas normal tissues have the advantage of a considerable reserve of such systems. The neoplastic transformation is evidently accompanied by a loss of this reserve. Like embryonic tissues, the tumor appears to possess a primitive economy. The luxury of reserve which the normal tissue enjoys must be the result of eons of evolutionary development.

Melanotic and Amelanotic Melanomas

It has long been known that melanomas may or may not contain the melanin pigment. The presence of the pigment in the melanotic tumor is due to the possession by this tumor of oxidases which catalyze the oxidation of tyrosine and dihydroxyphenylalanine (dopa) to melanin. In studies of suspensions of the Harding-Passey melanotic tumor in mice, Hogeboom and Adams found that tyrosine and dihydroxyphenylalanine were converted into melanin through the catalytic uptake of five and of four atoms of oxygen, respectively (466). The course of events may very probably be represented as follows (467):

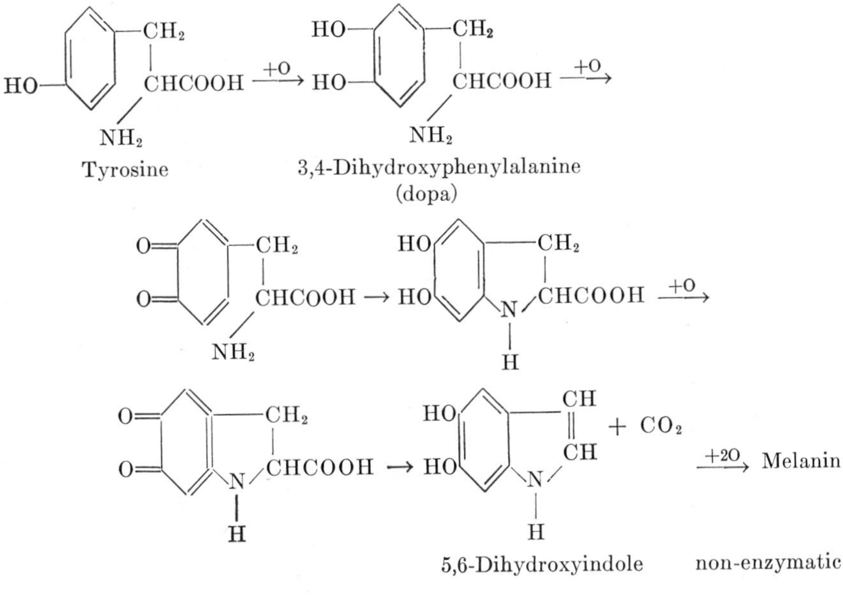

The discovery of the presence of phenolic oxidases in an animal tissue, hitherto believed to be a nearly exclusive property of plant tissues, is a matter of interest, and the transplanted melanoma, which can be grown in quantity, presents an unrivaled source for the preparation of such oxidases. Protein fractions with tyrosinase and dopa oxidase activity can be separated in aqueous extracts of the melanoma by appropriate salting-out techniques at definite pH ranges (466). The tyrosinase and dopa oxidase reactions can be completely abolished in the presence of cyanide. In the course of an investigation of the cytochrome oxidase activity of a large number of human tumors, Greenstein *et al.* (8) employed the more or less customary control determination of the oxygen uptake of the tissue homogenate in the presence of cyanide (autoxidizable components). *p*-Phenylenediamine was employed routinely as the oxidizable substrate throughout. In all types of tumors but one, the oxygen consumption in the presence of cyanide was negligible. The striking exception consisted in the pigmented (but not the non-pigmented) melanoma.

This observation led to studies which revealed the presence in melanotic melanomas, whether in spontaneous tumors in man (8) or in transplanted tumors in the mouse (87), of a powerful, largely cyanide-insensitive enzyme system which oxidizes *p*-phenylenediamine. The nature of this system is unknown; spectroscopic examination of suspensions of the tumors reveals no bands characteristic of cytochrome b.

In contrast with the pigmented melanoma, the amelanotic melanoma possesses no enzymes capable of oxidizing tyrosine, dihydroxyphenylalanine or *p*-phenylenediamine in the presence of cyanide (87). For this comparison, an excellently controlled material was available through the work of Algire (468), who developed amelanotic portions of the melanotic mouse tumor (S-91) separately from the pigmented portions. Thereby, the comparisons of pigmented and non-pigmented tumors could be made on materials arising from a single source (Figs. 47 and 48).

Thus, the melanotic melanomas, in contrast to the amelanotic melanomas, are characterized by the possession of (1) cyanide-sensitive tyrosinase, (2) cyanide-sensitive dopa oxidase, and (3) an enzymatic system, or systems, which oxidizes *p*-phenylenediamine and which is largely cyanide-insensitive. These three enzyme systems appear to be present in amounts which are directly related to the darkness of color of the melanoma (8). It has been claimed that dopa oxidase exists in the normal melanoblast (469, 470), but the evidence, as in comparable efforts to observe a skin tyrosinase, has been inconclusive; the dilution of the enzymes, if they were present, precluded, in any event, a definite estimation.

Many normal tissues such as heart, kidney, liver, and brain, as well as many animal tumors, when in suspension, absorb oxygen in the presence of *p*-phenylenediamine, the normal group absorbing more per milligram than

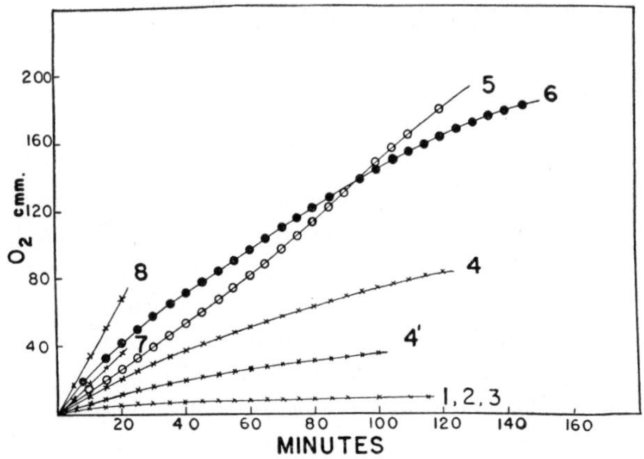

FIG. 47. Oxygen consumption of suspension of melanotic and amelanotic mouse melanomas. Curves 1, 2, 3 represent data on the amelanotic melanoma S-91 (transplanted mouse tumor) suspensions treated respectively with tyrosine (pH 6.5), dihydroxyphenylalanine (pH 6.5), and *p*-phenylenediamine (pH 7.2); curve 4, data on the melanotic melanoma suspensions (S-91 or Harding-Passey) in buffer and treated with *p*-phenylenediamine (pH 7.2); curve 4′ same as curve 4, except that 1 ml. of 0.01 *M* KCN was added in place of 1 ml. buffer; curves 5, 6, and 8, data on the melanotic melanoma suspensions (S-91 or Harding-Passey) in buffer treated respectively with tyrosine (pH 6.5), dihydroxyphenylalanine (pH 6.5), and *p*-phenylenediamine plus excess cytochrome c (pH 7.2); curve 7, data on the amelanotic melanoma suspensions S-91 treated with *p*-phenylenediamine and excess cytochrome c (pH 7.2). From Greenstein, J. P., and Algire, G. H., *J. Natl. Cancer Inst.* **5,** 35 (1944).

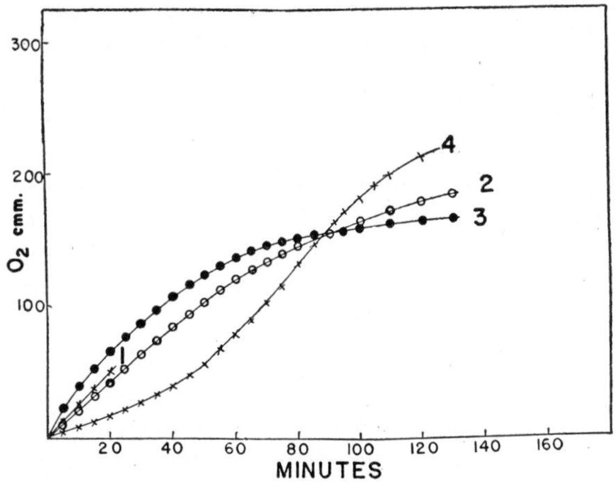

FIG. 48. Oxygen consumption of suspensions of a human melanotic melanoma. Curve 1 represents data in the presence of *p*-phenylenediamine and excess cytochrome c (pH 7.2); curve 2, data on suspensions in the presence of *p*-phenylenediamine plus either phosphate buffer or 0.01 *M* cyanide; curves 3 and 4, data obtained on suspensions treated respectively with dihydroxyphenylalanine (pH 6.5) and tyrosine (pH 6.5). From Greenstein, J. P., Werne, J., Eschenbrenner, A. B., and Leuthardt, F. M., *J. Natl. Cancer Inst.* **5,** 55 (1944).

the tumor group. In either case the oxygen uptake is almost completely abolished by addition of cyanide. The uptake of oxygen by these tissues is due to the cytochrome oxidase-cytochrome c system. The distinguishing characteristic of the melanotic melanomas lies, therefore, not so much in the presence of a highly active oxidizing system for *p*-phenylenediamine, which all normal and tumor tissues possess in varying degree, but in the fact that a considerable proportion of this system is insensitive to cyanide. The cytochrome oxidase activity (cyanide-sensitive) is, however, nearly equal in melanotic and amelanotic melanomas (87).

The transplantable mouse melanoma S-91 after homogenization is almost entirely soluble in water and consists in large measure (over 90%) of a pseudoglobulin to which all the melanin pigment is attached (471). Analysis of the conjugated protein yielded the following values in per cent of dry weight: nitrogen, 15.8; phosphorus, 0; amide nitrogen, 1.0; sulfur, 1.6; sulfate-sulfur, 0; cystine-cysteine, 2.5; methionine, 2.0; tyrosine, 2.7; and tryptophan, 1.0. The pseudoglobulin forms a gray-black powder. When digested with pancreatin for thirty days, the melanin can be isolated in the form of a jet black material like coal dust. Analyzed in the same fashion as the protein from which it was derived, the melanin yields the following values in per cent: nitrogen, 11.0; sulfur, 2.5; cystine-cysteine, 1.4; methionine, 8.9; tyrosine, 1.9; and tryptophan, 1.3. Thus, a residue of protein still remained attached to the melanin after enzymatic digestion of the conjugated protein. From these data it would appear that, at the point or points of attachment of the pigment to the protein, there is a relatively high proportion of the sulfur-containing amino acids, particularly that of methionine. Arginine is also present in the protein residue attached to the melanin. When this melanin preparation was treated with concentrated HCl at a high temperature for several hours, a black powder of nearly pure melanin was recovered in 35% yield (471). This recovered material gave a nitrogen value of 8.8% and contained no sulfur; the nitrogen value is characteristic of that found in the melanin pigment formed enzymatically from tyrosine (467).

Subsequent studies by Burk and his associates (472) on slices of melanotic and amelanotic mouse melanomas showed that the metabolic quotients of these tissues were comparable with those of other mouse tumors (Table 142). In contrast with this similarity among the various tumors, was the observation that addition of *p*-phenylenediamine caused a considerably greater stimulation of oxygen consumption in the case of the three melanomas than of the other tumors listed, a somewhat lesser effect being noted on addition of succinate. These observations suggest that in the melanomas the ratio of oxidized to reduced cytochrome c may be higher than in other tumors, nearly approaching that of normal tissues. That this stimulation of oxygen consumption by *p*-phenylenediamine is blocked by cyanide

TABLE 142

METABOLISM OF TISSUE SLICES OF MOUSE MELANOMAS (472)

Tumor	$Q_A^{N_2}$	$Q_A^{O_2}$	Q_{O_2}	Q_{CO_2}
Harding-Passey melanoma	11.0	2.1	4.6	4.1
Cloudman melanoma	11.8	3.0	5.0	3.8
Algire amelanotic melanoma	14.8	5.2	7.2	6.0
Earle sarcoma	12.0	5.6	7.7	6.4
Barrett adenocarcinoma	17.6	10.4	9.4	8.6
Malignant tumors in general	8–25	2–15	3–10	2–9

is consistent with the view that the cytochrome system is involved. However, the cytochrome oxidase level of the melanoma (in homogenates) is no greater than that of other tumors, and the fact that the stimulation of oxygen consumption is of the same order, whether the melanomas are melanotic or amelanotic, appears to remove this effect from considerations of melanin synthetic mechanisms. In homogenates, the oxidation of *p*-phenylenediamine occurs only with melanotic tumors, and in this instance the effect is relatively insensitive to cyanide (87), an illustration of the difficulty in drawing comparisons of results based upon work with tissue slices on the one hand and with homogenates on the other.

The Cloudman melanoma possesses two types of cytoplasmic granules, one capable of pronounced melanization, the other incapable of or at least limited in its melanization (473). The derived amelanotic melanoma of Algire possesses the latter type of granules. On the other hand, all the cytoplasmic granules of the Harding-Passey melanoma possess the strongly melanized type of granules. After being isolated by centrifugation, all three types contain cytochrome oxidase and cytochrome c, the Harding-Passey granules also possessing tyrosinase and dopa oxidase activities, the amelanotic melanoma granules possessing neither, and the Cloudman melanoma granules possessing only dopa oxidase and not tyrosinase activity (473). A careful study of the factors involved in studying the respiration of melanoma tissues has been made by Riley *et al.* (474), and methods have been described for the chromatography of the melanoma particulates on diatomaceous earth (475). There is a possibility that the metabolism of melanocytes may be influenced by a pituitary factor to which the designation of melanocyte-stimulating hormone (MSH) (475a, 475b) has been applied.

For the past few years, the New York Academy of Sciences has conducted several conferences on the biology and chemistry of melanin (cf. 476 and 477). A review of the subject by Lerner and Fitzpatrick (478) is also available.

The chemistry of the melanin pigment is of considerable biological interest, and its study can be facilitated by the availability of melanotic melanomas in quantity. However, in view of the fact that amelanotic melanomas may be equally as malignant as the pigmented variety, it is difficult not to believe that the mechanisms for melanin production are quite separate from, and independent of, the cancerous capacities of the melanoma and may be, in the case of the pigmented tumor, only an adventitious retention of a property of the normal cell of origin.

Strain Differences in Mice

It might be expected that the continued inbreeding of mice strains would tend to segregate not only biological but also chemical characteristics (which amount to the same thing). Thus the liver xanthine dehydrogenase of the *C3H* strain is less active than that of the *JK* strain (479), the liver catalase of the *C57 Black* strain is less active than that of the *DBA*, *C*, *Y*, *I*, and *C3H* strains (270), and the serum esterase levels are different in the *C57 Black*, *C3H*, and *I* strains of mice (480, 481). Attempts have been made to correlate these enzyme findings, together with similar observations on hemoglobin (482), porphyrins (483), and ascorbic acid (484) with the relative incidence of mammary tumors in the various strains. The reports of individual investigators, when concerned with only one chemical factor in each of two strains, often show differences correlated with tumor incidence. When all the data are collected from all the investigators, however, no consistent correlation of this nature can be demonstrated (485) (Table 143).

Recently, Chitre *et al.* (486) examined the livers of mice of the *A*, *C3H*, and *C57 Black* strains for their content of nicotinic acid, riboflavin, ascorbic acid and glutathione and noted (a) that the former two components were at nearly the same concentration in all three strains, (b) that ascorbic acid was highest in the A strain, and (c) that glutathione was highest in the *A* strain. From their data, the authors drew the conclusion that no definite relationship was evident between the susceptibility of the various strains to spontaneous mammary tumors and the content of liver components studied.

So far, it is apparent that biochemical differences between strains and relative mammary tumor incidence in strains cannot yet be equated. Many factors enter into the genesis of mammary tumors (Chapter IV). To avoid the complications inherent in the consideration of each of these factors among a number of different strains of mice, the proper approach is to employ a single strain of mice of ascertained tumor incidence and to significantly alter this tumor incidence by appropriate foster-nursing or other means. In this way, all factors but one are kept ostensibly constant, and any subsequent biochemical differences between the treated and untreated mice may, with some confidence, be related to the tumor incidence.

This was the technique employed by Khanolkar and Chitre (480) and subsequently by Shimkin, Greenstein, and Andervont (481). The former investigators reported that the serum esterase of *C3H* and of *C57 Black* mice could be altered by reciprocal foster-nursing in such way that the level of this enzyme resembled that of the foster-mother strain. The latter investigators failed to observe analogous changes in *C* strain mice foster-nursed on *C3H* females (Table 143). Regardless of the merits of these respective findings, the method itself has a sound basis and is capable of opening up many interesting problems. That serum esterase itself is unrelated to the incidence of mammary cancer in inbred strains of mice has been shown by Tuba (489). There certainly is little or no theoretical basis for the particular study of this enzyme in connection with the origin of murine breast tumors.

Other studies on serum factors in mice of inbred strains have revealed high antiproteolytic reactions in mice of the *JK* and *BC* strains, low reactions in the *F* strain, and intermediate values in mice of the *A*, *C3H*, and *C57* strains (490), whereas mice of the *C57BL* strain possess a far higher frequency of natural antisheep agglutinins at much higher titers and a much more vigorous response to injections of sheep and human red cells, than do mice of the *C3H*, *DBA*, *MALB*, *BALB*, and *AKm* strains (491).

Among the most dramatic differences in enzyme level in mice, not only of different strains but of different sublines of the same strain, are those shown for liver glucuronidase activity (Table 144) (492). It may be pertinent to question whether the two *CBA* sublines, or two of the *C3H* sublines, are sublines only by genetic convention and do not rather represent new strains entirely. The differences in liver glucuronidase level in the inbred strains are also reflected in the corresponding levels of spleen and of kidney in these strains: thus, the activity in liver, spleen, and kidney of the *A* (Heston) strain is, respectively, 3.5, 3.6, and 1.7; for the *C3H* (Andervont) strain it is 0.36, 1.6, and 0.24; and for the *CBA* (Andervont) strain it is 0.30, 1.3, and 0.27. It is probable that the marked strain differences in tissue β-glucuronidase activity are due to actual differences in the amount of enzyme protein (493). The kidney enzyme, which increases in activity after testosterone administration, is increased by amounts which depend upon the animal strain, and the fundamental problem is raised as to whether or not sex hormone effects in general might not be considerably influenced by hereditary constitution (494). The high glucuronidase activity of the liver of several of the mice strains is dependent upon the presence of a single dominant gene; strain *C3H* would thus carry the recessive alleles (495). Observed segregation ratios obtained in various crosses between strains agree with those expected of a trait determined by a single dominant gene.

TABLE 143

CHEMICAL DIFFERENCES IN STRAINS OF MICE[1, 2] (485)

Strain	Sex	Mammary tumor incidence	Liver xanthine dehydrogenase[3]		Liver catalase[4]	Liver ascorbic acid[5]	Hemoglobin[6]		Serum esterase[7]		Harderian glands[8]	Kidney nonhemin iron[9]
C3H	M	Low	0.81	10	2.0	387	—	—	7.9	6.6	Low Fl	52
C3H	F	High	0.81	10	2.0	322	—	—	11.4	7.2	High Fl	50
A	M	Low	—	10	2.0	—	—	—	—	7.2	—	—
A	F	High	—	10	2.0	—	—	11.9	—	7.2	—	—
DBA	M	Low	—	10	2.0	344	—	—	—	—	—	—
DBA	F	High	—	10	2.0	467	—	—	—	—	—	—
RIII	M	Low	—	—	—	349	13.4	—	—	—	—	59
RIII	F	High	—	—	—	360	14.7	—	—	—	—	74
CBA	M	Low	—	—	—	349	14.8	—	—	—	—	59
CBA	F	Low	—	—	—	306	16.0	14.2	—	—	—	97
JK	M	Low	1.64	—	—	—	—	—	—	—	Low Fl	—
JK	F	Low	1.64	—	—	—	—	—	—	—	Low Fl	—
C57	M	Low	—	—	1.0	216	—	—	6.9	3.7	—	—
C57	F	Low	—	—	1.0	175	—	—	6.7	3.2	—	—
C	M	Low	—	10	2.0	—	—	—	10.9	—	—	—
C	F	Low	—	10	2.0	—	—	—	10.2	—	—	—
I	M	Low	—	—	2.0	—	—	—	15.0	—	—	—
I	F	Low	—	—	2.0	—	—	—	14.4	—	—	—
Cf[10]	M	Medium	—	—	—	—	—	—	10.5	—	—	—
Cf	F	High	—	—	—	—	—	—	10.2	—	—	—
C3Hf[11]	M	Low	—	—	—	—	—	—	—	4.7	—	—
C3Hf	F	Low	—	—	—	—	—	—	—	4.9	—	—
C57f[10]	M	High	—	—	—	—	—	—	—	6.0	—	—
C57f	F	High	—	—	—	—	—	—	—	5.3	—	—

[1] Animals show no visible presence of tumors.

[2] Riboflavin content of livers of *A*, *C3H*, and *C57* mice is uniformly close to 35 γ/g. wet weight, nicotinic acid content close to 115 γ on same basis (486). Ascorbic acid in milligrams per cent is for males of the following strains: *A*, 36; *C3H*, 26; *C57*, 25; for females, 30, 25, and 19. Glutathione in milligrams per cent is for males of the following strains: *A*, 308; *C3H*, 284; *C57*, 233; for females, 293, 214, and 221.

[3] Activity units in first column refer to ratio: 5/decolorization time for 200 mg. liver and 1 ml. 0.001 *N* methylene blue. Activity units of data in second column refer to decolorization time in minutes of mixture of 1 ml. tissue extract (2.6 mg. *N*), 1 ml. phosphate buffer at pH 7.2, and 1 ml. methylene blue (0.04%).

[4] Activity refers to rate of evolution of oxygen at 25° in milliliters per second from mixture of 1 ml. tissue extract (0.6 mg. *N*), 1 ml. hydrogen peroxide (29%), and 5 ml. phosphate buffer at pH 7.2.

[5] Micrograms per gram liver.

[6] Grams per cent. Reference first column (487).

[7] Data in both columns refer to increase in phenolphthalein titer of milliliters 0.01 *N* NaOH in mixture of 5 ml. phosphate buffer at pH 8.8, butyrate ester, and 0.1 ml. fresh serum. First column represents data with 0.22 ml. methyl butyrate. Second column represents data obtained with unknown amount of ethyl butyrate.

[8] Degree of red fluorescence under ultraviolet light illumination.

[9] All mice 300–400 days old. Results in terms of micrograms per gram (488).

[10] Strains foster-nursed with *C3H* females.

[11] Strains foster-nursed with *C57* females.

TABLE 144

LIVER GLUCURONIDASE ACTIVITY IN INBRED MICE (492)

Strain	Mean activity, γ phenolphthalein/mg. wet weight/hr. at pH 4.5
C3H (Heston)	0.44
C3H (Bittner)	0.19
C3H (Andervont)	0.33
A (Heston)	3.5
A (Bittner)	4.3
CBA (Andervont)	0.28
CBA (Strong)	3.9
BALB (Heston)	4.0
DBA (Heston)	4.0
RIII (Andervont)	4.2
I (Andervont)	4.4
C57BL (Heston)	4.2

TABLE 145

SERUM ESTERASE AND β-GLUCURONIDASE IN MICE (496)

Strain	Esterase units	β-Glucuronidase units
Z	26,700	363
C3H	32,100	718
C57	25,600	1120
A	37,700	1950
C	55,200	—

There is apparently no association with the gene for β-glucuronidase and those for the three-coat color genes, brown, Agouti, or albinisim. Both β-glucuronidase and esterase in serum reflect genetic background (496) (Table 145).

The red blood cells of the *C3H* mice strain and of the *C57 Black* react at different rates with antitumor rabbit sera (prepared against the mammary tumor in *C3H* mice) (497). A hemolytic factor is present in the red blood cells of the *C3H* mouse which is not present in those of the *C57BL* mouse (498); when the *C57* mice acquire the milk agent through nursing *C3H* mothers, however, their erythrocytes exhibit hemolysis. On the other hand, erythrocytes from *C3H* × *C57BL* hybrids who were nursed by *C57BL* mothers showed much less hemolysis than those from pure strain *C3H* mice. It is possible that these phenomena may be ascribed to the presence or absence of the milk agent in these strains, since it is known that red cells in the *C3H* strain carry the agent (499). The hemolysins in the tumors themselves do not differ qualitatively from those present in normal tissues (500).

References

(1) Kossel, A., *Z. physiol. Chem.* **7,** 7 (1882).
(2) Javallier, M., *Bull. soc. chim. biol.* **11,** 644 (1929).
(3) Carruthers, C., and Suntzeff, V., *J. Natl. Cancer Inst.* **3,** 217 (1942).
(4) Rosenthal, O., and Drabkin, D. L., *J. Biol. Chem.* **150,** 131 (1943).
(5) Berenblum, I., Chain, E., and Heatley, N. G., *Biochem. J.* **33,** 68 (1938).
(6) Caspersson, T., and Santesson, L., "Studies on Protein Metabolism in the Cells of Epithelial Tumors." Norstedt, Stockholm, 1942.
(7) Chalkley, H. W., *J. Natl. Cancer Inst.* **4,** 47 (1943).
(8) Greenstein, J. P., Werne, J., Eschenbrenner, A. B., and Leuthardt, F. M., *J. Natl. Cancer Inst.* **5,** 55 (1944).
(9) Rosenthal, O., and Drabkin, D. L., *Cancer Research* **4,** 487 (1944).
(10) Waldschmidt-Leitz, E., and McDonald, E., *Z. physiol. Chem.* **219,** 9 (1933).
(11) Edlbacher, S., and Baumann, W., *Z. Krebsforsch.* **47,** 191 (1937); **44,** 441 (1936).
(12) Haven, F. L., Randall, C., and Bloor, W. R., *Cancer Research* **9,** 90 (1949).
(13) Daff, M., Hoch-Ligeti, C., Kennaway, E. L., and Tipler, M. M., *Cancer Research* **8,** 376 (1948).
(14) Elson, L. A., Kennaway, E. L., and Tipler, M. M., *Brit. J. Cancer* **3,** 148 (1949).
(15) Nakatani, M., Nakano, K., and Okara, Y., *Gann* **32,** 240 (1938).
(16) Orr, J. W., and Stickland, L. H., *Biochem. J.* **35,** 479 (1941).
(17) Woodard, H. Q., *Cancer Research* **3,** 159 (1943).
(18) Pearson, B., Novikoff, A. B., and Morrione, T. G., *Cancer Research* **10,** 557 (1950).
(19) Mulay, A. S., and Firminger, H. I., *J. Natl. Cancer Inst.* **12,** 917 (1952).
(20) Lucké, B., and Schlumberger, H., *Physiol. Revs.* **29,** 91 (1949).
(21) Kishi, S., and Haruno, K., *Gann* **42,** 69 (1951).
(22) Mori, K., and Shimojo, K., *Science* **117,** 683 (1953).
(23) Kishi, S., and Haruno, K., *Ber.* **85,** 836 (1952).
(24) Mori, K., and Ito, H., *Gann* **42,** 41 (1951).
(25) Mori, K., and Momoki, S., *Gann* **42,** 33 (1951).
(26) Griffin, A. C., Cunningham, L., Brandt, E. L., and Kupke, D. W., *Cancer* **4,** 410 (1951).
(27) Westerfeld, W. W., Richert, D. A., and Hilfinger, M. F., *Cancer Research* **10,** 486 (1950).
(28) Woodward, G. E., *Cancer Research* **11,** 918 (1951).
(29) Cantero, A., Dacust, R., and de Lamirande, G., *Science* **112,** 221 (1950).
(30) Schneider, W. C., and Hogeboom, G. H., *Cancer Research* **11,** 1 (1951).
(31) Laird, A. K., and Miller, E. C., *Cancer Research* **13,** 464 (1953).
(32) Price, J. M., Miller, E. C., Miller, J. A., and Weber, G. M., *Cancer Research* **10,** 18 (1950).
(33) Cunningham, L., Griffin, A. C., and Luck, J. M., *Cancer Research* **10,** 194 (1950).
(34) Potter, V. R., Price, J. M., Miller, E. C., and Miller, J. A., *Cancer Research* **10,** 28 (1950).
(35) Price, J. M., Miller, E. C., and Miller, J. A., *Proc. Soc. Exptl. Biol. Med.* **71,** 575 (1949).
(36) Schweigert, B. S., Guthneck, B. T., Price, J. M., Miller, J. A., and Miller, E. C., *Proc. Soc. Exptl. Biol. Med.* **72,** 495 (1949).
(37) Striebich, M. J., Shelton, E., and Schneider, W. C., *Cancer Research* **13,** 279 (1953).
(38) Schneider, W. C., Hogeboom, G. H., Shelton, E., and Striebich, M. J., *Cancer Research* **13,** 285 (1953).

(39) Price, J. M., Miller, J. A., and Miller, E. C., *Cancer Research* **11,** 523 (1951).
(40) Novikoff, A. B., and Potter, V. R., *J. Biol. Chem.* **173,** 223 (1948).
(41) Stowell, R. E., *Arch. Pathol.* **46,** 164 (1948).
(42) Brues, A. M., Drury, D. R., and Brues, M. C., *Arch. Pathol.* **22,** 658 (1936).
(43) Buchner, N. L. R., Scott, J. F., and Aub, J. C., *Cancer Research* **10,** 207 (1950).
(44) Price, J. M., and Laird, A. K., *Cancer Research* **10,** 650 (1950).
(45) Griffin, A. C., Cook, H., and Cunningham, L., *Arch. Biochem.* **24,** 190 (1949).
(46) Rutman, R. J., Cantarow, A., and Paschkis, K. E., *Cancer Research* **12,** 293 (1952). See reference 452.
(47) Tsuboi, K. K., Stowell, R. E., and Lee, C. S., *Cancer Research* **11,** 87 (1951).
(48) Tsuboi, K. K., and Stowell, R. E., *Cancer Research* **11,** 221 (1951).
(49) Stowell, R. E., Lee, C. S., Tsuboi, K. K., and Villasana, A., *Cancer Research* **11,** 345 (1951).
(50) Sorof, S., Cohen, P. P., Miller, E. C., and Miller, J. A., *Cancer Research* **11,** 383 (1951).
(51) Eldredge, N. T., and Luck, J. M., *Cancer Research* **12,** 801 (1952).
(52) Hoffman, H. E., and Schechtman, A. M., *Cancer Research* **12,** 129 (1952).
(53) Sorof, S., Claus, B., and Cohen, P. P., *Cancer Research* **11,** 873 (1951); cf. Sorof, S., Golder, R. H., and Ott, M. G., *Cancer Research* **14,** 190 (1954).
(54) Luck, J. M., *J. Biol. Chem.* **115,** 491 (1936).
(55) Cook, H. A., Griffin, A. C., and Luck, J. M., *J. Biol. Chem.* **177,** 373 (1949).
(56) de Lamirande, G., and Cantero, A., *Cancer Research* **12,** 330 (1952).
(57) Roberts, S., and White, A., *J. Biol. Chem.* **180,** 505 (1949).
(58) Mori, K., and Manoki, S., *Gann* **43,** 431 (1952).
(59) Euler, H., von, Hasselquist, H., and Eriksson, E., *Arkiv. Kemi* **4,** 487 (1952).
(60) Greenstein, J. P., *in* "Research Conference on Cancer." American Association for the Advancement of Science, Washington, D. C., 1945; *cf.* also *Ann. Rev. Biochem.* **14,** 643 (1945).
(61) Carruthers, C., and Suntzeff, V., *J. Biol. Chem.* **159,** 647 (1945); *cf.* also, *Cancer Research* **6,** 296 (1946).
(62) Biesele, J. J., and Biesele, M. M., *Cancer Research* **4,** 751 (1944).
(63) Tatum, E. L., Ritchey, M. G., Cowdry, E. V., and Wicks, L. F., *J. Biol. Chem.* **163,** 675 (1946).
(64) Cowdry, E. V., *Advances in Cancer Research* **1,** 57 (1953).
(65) Carruthers, C., *Cancer* **10,** 255 (1950).
(66) Roberts, E., Caldwell, A. L., Clowes, G. H. A., Suntzeff, V., Carruthers, C., and Cowdry, E. V., *Cancer Research* **9,** 350 (1949).
(67) Sauberlich, H. E., and Baumann, C. A., *Cancer Research* **11,** 67 (1951).
(68) Wicks, L. F., and Suntzeff, V., *J. Natl. Cancer Inst.* **3,** 221 (1942).
(69) Kidd, J. G., Winzler, R. J., and Burk, D., *Cancer Research* **4,** 547 (1944).
(70) Dreyfuss, M. L., *Am. J. Cancer* **38,** 551 (1940).
(71) Greenstein, J. P., and Leuthardt, F. M., *J. Natl. Cancer Inst.* **6,** 197, 203, 211 (1946); also Greenstein, J. P., and Chalkley, H. W., *J. Natl. Cancer Inst.* **6,** 207 (1946).
(72) Greenstein, J. P., and Leuthardt, F. M., *J. Natl. Cancer Inst.* **6,** 317 (1946).
(73) Schneider, W. C., and Potter, V. R., *Cancer Research* **3,** 353 (1943).
(74) Robertson, W. von B., and Kahler, H., *J. Natl. Cancer Inst.* **2,** 595 (1942).
(75) Du Bois, K. P., and Potter, V. R., *Cancer Research* **2,** 290 (1942).
(76) Shack, J., *J. Natl. Cancer Inst.* **3,** 389 (1943).
(77) Dickens, F., and Weil-Malherbe, H., *Cancer Research* **3,** 73 (1943).
(78) Bray, T., and King, E. J., *J. Pathol. Bacteriol.* **55,** 315 (1943).

(79) Huggins, C., and Talalay, P., *J. Biol. Chem.* **159,** 399 (1945).
(80) Greenstein, J. P., and Eschenbrenner, A. B., unpublished data.
(81) Gomori, G., *Proc. Soc. Exptl. Biol. Med.* **42,** 23 (1939); *Arch. Pathol.* **40,** 121 (1946).
(82) Wachstein, M., *Arch. Pathol.* **46,** 57 (1945).
(83) Barrett, M. K., Dalton, A. J., Edwards, J. E., and Greenstein, J. P., *J. Natl. Cancer Inst.* **4,** 389 (1944).
(84) Dalton, A. J., Edwards, J. E., and Andervont, H. B., *J. Natl. Cancer Inst.* **4,** 329 (1943).
(85) Greenstein, J. P., Edwards, J. E., Andervont, H. B., and White, J., *J. Natl. Cancer Inst.* **3,** 7 (1942).
(86) Greenstein, J. P., Jenrette, W. V., Mider, G. B., and Andervont, H. B., *J. Natl. Cancer Inst.* **2,** 293 (1941).
(87) Greenstein, J. P., and Algire, G. H., *J. Natl. Cancer Inst.* **5,** 35 (1944).
(88) Cori, C. F., and Cori, G. T., *J. Biol. Chem.* **64,** 11 (1925).
(89) Maver, M. E., and Dunn, T. B., *J. Natl. Cancer Inst.* **6,** 49 (1945).
(90) Greenstein, J. P., *J. Natl. Cancer Inst.* **2,** 511 (1942).
(91) Lan, T. H., *Cancer Research* **4,** 37 (1944).
(92) Chalkley, H. W., and Greenstein, J. P., *J. Natl. Cancer Inst.* **6,** 119 (1945).
(93) Keilin, D., and Hartree, E. F., *Biochem. J.* **39,** 293 (1945).
(94) Schultze, M. O., and Kuiken, K. A., *J. Biol. Chem.* **137,** 727 (1941).
(95) Axelrod, A. E., and Elvehjem, C. A., *J. Biol. Chem.* **140,** 725 (1941).
(96) Axelrod, A. E., Potter, V. R., and Elvehjem, C. A., *J. Biol. Chem.* **142,** 85, (1942).
(97) Blanchard, M., Green, D. E., Nocito, V., and Ratner, S., *J. Biol. Chem.* **161,** 583 (1945).
(98) Kensler, C. J., Sugiura, K., and Rhoads, C. P., *Science* **91,** 623 (1940).
(99) Lenta, M. P., and Riehl, M. A., *Cancer Research* **12,** 498 (1952).
(100) Krebs, H. A., *Advances in Enzymol.* **3,** 191 (1943).
(101) Knoop, F., and Martius, C., *Z. physiol. Chem.* **242,** 1 (1936); Martius, C., **279,** 96 (1943).
(102) Stern, J. R., and Ochoa, S., *J. Biol. Chem.* **179,** 491 (1949).
(103) Dickens, F., *in* "The Enzymes," Vol. 2, Part 1, p. 624. Academic Press, New York, 1951.
(104) Warburg, O., *Abhandl. deut. Akad. Wiss. Berlin* No. **3,** (1947).
(105) Weinhouse, S., Millington, R. H., and Wenner, C. E., *Cancer Research* **11,** 845 (1951).
(106) Wenner, C. E., Spirtes, M. A., and Weinhouse, S., *Cancer Research* **12,** 44 (1952).
(107) Wenner, C. E., and Weinhouse, S., *Cancer Research* **13,** 21 (1953).
(108) Medes, G., Thomas, A., and Weinhouse, S., *Cancer Research* **13,** 27 (1953).
(109) Weinhouse, S., Allen, A., and Millington, R. H., *Cancer Research* **13,** 367 (1953).
(110) Meyerhof, O., and Wilson, J. R., *Arch. Biochem.* **21,** 1 (1949).
(111) Novikoff, A. B., Potter, V. R., and LePage, G. A., *Cancer Research* **8,** 203 (1948).
(112) Potter, V. R., and Busch, H., *Cancer Research* **10,** 353 (1950).
(113) Kit, S., and Greenberg, D. M., *Cancer Research* **11,** 495, 500 (1951).
(114) Meister, A., *J. Natl. Cancer Inst.* **10,** 1263 (1950).
(115) Euler, H. von, Malmberg, M., and Gunther, G., *Z. Krebsforsch.* **45,** 425 (1937).
(116) Fisher, A., and Schlenk, F., *Texas Repts. Biol. and Med.* **6,** 346 (1948).
(117) Jedeikin, L., and Weinhouse, S., Unpublished data, courtesy of Dr. Weinhouse.
(118) LePage, G. A., *J. Biol. Chem.* **176,** 1009 (1948).
(119) LePage, G. A., *Cancer Research* **10,** 77 (1950).

(120) Weinhouse, S., *Cancer Research* **11,** 585 (1951).
(121) Quastel, J. H., and Zatman, L. J., *Biochim. et Biophys. Acta* **10,** 256 (1953).
(122) Potter, V. R., *Cancer Research* **11,** 565 (1951).
(123) Potter, V. R., and Lyle, G. G., *Cancer Research* **11,** 355 (1951).
(124) Siekevitz, P., and Potter, V. R., *Cancer Research* **13,** 513 (1953).
(125) Groth, D. P., LePage, G. A., Heidelberger, C., and Stoesz, P. A., *Cancer Research* **12,** 529 (1952).
(126) Kielley, W. W., and Kielley, R. K., *J. Biol. Chem.* **191,** 485 (1951).
(127) Kielley, R. K., *Cancer Research* **12,** 124 (1952).
(128) Williams-Ashman, H. G., and Kennedy, E. P., *Cancer Research* **12,** 415 (1952).
(129) LePage, G. A., *Cancer Research* **10,** 393 (1950).
(130) Olson, R. E., *Cancer Research* **11,** 571 (1951).
(131) Zamecnik, P. C., Loftfield, R. B., Stephenson, M. L., and Steele, J. M., *Cancer Research* **11,** 592 (1951).
(132) Baker, C. G., and Meister, A., *J. Natl. Cancer Inst.* **10,** 1191 (1950).
(133) Vestling, C. S., Williams, J. N., Jr., Kaufman, S., Maxwell, R. E., and Quastler, H., *Cancer Research* **9,** 639 (1949).
(134) Schneider, W. C., *J. Biol. Chem.* **176,** 259 (1948).
(135) Kennedy, E. P., and Lehninger, A. L., *J. Biol. Chem.* **172,** 847 (1948).
(136) Schneider, W. C., and Potter, V. R., *J. Biol. Chem.* **177,** 893 (1949).
(137) Schneider, W. C., and Hogeboom, G. H., *J. Biol. Chem.* **183,** 123 (1950).
(138) LePage, G. A., and Schneider, W. C., *J. Biol. Chem.* **176,** 1021 (1948).
(139) Hogeboom, G. H., and Schneider, W. C., *J. Biol. Chem.* **186,** 417 (1950).
(140) Potter, V. R., Lyle, G. G., and Schneider, W. C., *J. Biol. Chem.* **190,** 293 (1951).
(141) Buffa, P., Peters, R. A., and Wakelin, R. W., *Biochem. J.* **48,** 467 (1951).
(142) Busch, H., and Potter, V. R., *Cancer Research* **12,** 660 (1952).
(142a) Busch, H., *Cancer Research* **13,** 789 (1953).
(143) Reif, A. E., and Potter, V. R., *Cancer Research* **13,** 49 (1953).
(143a) Dickens, F., *Biochem. J.*, **32,** 1626 (1938).
(143b) Glock, G. E., and McLean, P., *Biochem. J.* **56,** 171 (1954).
(144) Greenstein, J. P., and Stewart, H. L., *J. Natl. Cancer Inst.* **2,** 631 (1942).
(145) Masayama, T., Iki, H., Yokoyama, T., and Hasimoto, M., *Gann* **32,** 303 (1938).
(146) Greenstein, J. P., *J. Natl. Cancer Inst.* **3,** 293 (1942).
(147) Tung, T. C., and Cohen, P. P., *Cancer Research* **10,** 793 (1950).
(148) Kielley, R. K., and Schneider, W. C., *J. Biol. Chem.* **185,** 869 (1950).
(149) Greenstein, J. P., Fodor, P. J., and Leuthardt, F. M., *J. Natl. Cancer Inst.* **10,** 271 (1949).
(150) Meister, A., Sober, H. A., Tice, S. V., and Fraser, P. E., *J. Biol. Chem.* **197,** 319 (1952).
(151) Greenstein, J. P., Jenrette, W. V., Mider, G. B., and White, J., *J. Natl. Cancer Inst.* **1,** 687 (1941).
(152) Greenstein, J. P., and Leuthardt, F. M., *J. Natl. Cancer Inst.* **8,** 77 (1947).
(153) Zamecnik, P. C., and Stephenson, M. L., *Cancer Research* **7,** 326 (1947).
(154) Zamecnik, P. C., and Stephenson, M. L., *Cancer Research* **9,** 3 (1949).
(155) Cohen, P. P., Hekhuis, G. L., and Sober, E. K., *Cancer Research* **2,** 405 (1942); cf. Cohen, P. P., *Cancer Research* **5,** 626 (1945).
(155a) Errera, M., and Greenstein, J. P., *J. Natl. Cancer Inst.* **7,** 285 (1947).
(156) Kit, S., and Awapara, J., *Cancer Research* **13,** 694 (1953).
(157) Price, V. E., Meister, A., Gilbert, J. B., and Greenstein, J. P., *J. Biol. Chem.* **181,** 535 (1949).
(158) Greenstein, J. P., Price, V. E., and Leuthardt, F. M., *J. Biol. Chem.* **175,** 953 (1948).

(159) Robinson, D. S., Birnbaum, S. M., and Greenstein, J. P., *J. Biol. Chem.* **202,** 1 (1953).
(160) Rao, K. R., Birnbaum, S. M., and Greenstein, J. P., *J. Biol. Chem.* **203,** 1 (1953).
(161) Levintow, L., Fu, S-C. J., Price, V. E., and Greenstein, J. P., *J. Biol. Chem.* **184,** 633 (1950).
(162) Greenstein, J. P., *Advances in Enzymol.* **8,** 117 (1948).
(163) Birnbaum, S. M., and Greenstein, J. P., *Bull. Res. Council of Israel* (in press).
(164) Shack, J., *J. Biol. Chem.* **180,** 411 (1949).
(164a) Maschmann, E., *Biochem. Z.* **313,** 129, 151, 156 (1942).
(164b) Greenstein, J. P., and Jenrette, W. V., *Cold Spring Harbor Symposia Quant. Biol.* **9,** 236 (1941).
(164c) Greenstein, J. P., *Advances in Protein Chem.* **1,** 210 (1944).
(164d) Miyaji, T., and Greenstein, J. P., *Arch. Biochem. and Biophys.* **32,** 414 (1951).
(164e) Schneider, W. C., and Hogeboom, G. H., *J. Biol. Chem.* **198,** 155 (1952).
(164f) Webb, M., *Exptl. Cell Research* **5,** 16, 27 (1953).
(164g) Maver, M. E., and Greco, A. E., *J. Biol. Chem.* **181,** 861 (1949).
(165) Greenstein, J. P., and Chalkley, H. W., *J. Natl. Cancer Inst.* **6,** 143 (1945).
(166) Brues, A. M., Tracy, M. M., and Cohn, W. E., *J. Biol. Chem.* **155,** 619 (1944).
(167) Heinlein, H., *Z. Krebsforsch.* **30,** 506 (1930).
(168) Dounce, A. L., *J. Biol. Chem.* **151,** 235 (1943).
(169) Carruthers, C., and Suntzeff, V., *Cancer Research* **6,** 8 (1946).
(170) Davidson, J. N., and Waymouth, C., *Biochem. J.* **38,** 375, 379 (1944).
(171) Davidson, J. N., and Waymouth, C., *Brit. J. Exptl. Pathol.* **25,** 164 (1944).
(172) Davidson, J. N., and Waymouth, C., *Biochem. J.* **38,** 39 (1944).
(173) Schneider, W. C., *Cancer Research* **5,** 717 (1945).
(174) Stowell, R. E., *Cancer Research* **5,** 283, 295 (1945); **6,** 426 (1946).
(175) Klein, G., and Beck, J., *Z. Krebsforsch.* **42,** 163 (1935).
(176) Vischer, E., and Chargaff, E., *J. Biol. Chem.* **176,** 715 (1948).
(177) Chargaff, E., Vischer, E., Doniger, R., Green, C., and Misani, F., *J. Biol. Chem.* **177,** 405 (1949).
(178) Vischer, E., Zamenhof, S., and Chargaff, E., *J. Biol. Chem.* **177,** 425 (1949).
(179) Woodhouse, D. L., *Brit. J. Cancer* **3,** 510 (1949).
(180) Beale, R. N., Harris, R. J. C., and Roe, E. M. F., *J. Chem. Soc.* **1950,** 1397.
(181) Shack, J., Jenkins, R. J., and Thompsett, J. M., *J. Natl. Cancer Inst.* **13,** 1435 (1953).
(182) Stern, K. G., *Yale J. Biol. and Med.* **19,** 937 (1947).
(183) Stern, K. G., *in* "The Chemistry and Physiology of the Nucleus," p. 1. Academic Press, New York, 1952.
(184) Loring, H. S., and Luthy, N. G., *J. Am. Chem. Soc.* **73,** 4215 (1951).
(185) Cohn, W. E., and Volkin, E., *J. Biol. Chem.* **203,** 319 (1953).
(185a) Volkin, E., and Cohn, W. E., *J. Biol. Chem.* **205,** 767 (1953).
(185b) Schmidt, G., Cubiles, R., and Thannhauser, S. J., *J. Cellular Comp. Physiol.* **38,** 61 (1951).
(185c) Schmitz, H., Potter, V. R., and Hurlburt, R. B., *Cancer Research,* **14,** 58 (1954).
(186) Bendich, A., Russell, P. J., Jr., and Brown, G. B., *J. Biol. Chem.* **203,** 305 (1953).
(187) Volkin, E., and Carter, C. E., *J. Am. Chem. Soc.* **73,** 1519 (1951).
(188) Marshak, A., and Calvet, F., *J. Cellular Comp. Physiol.* **34,** 451 (1949).
(189) Hurlbert, R. B., and Potter, V. R., *J. Biol. Chem.* **195,** 257 (1952).
(190) Jeener, R., and Szafarz, D., *Arch. Biochem.* **26,** 54 (1950).
(191) Barnum, C. P., and Huseby, R. A., *Arch. Biochem.* **29,** 7 (1950).
(192) Bennett, E. L., *Biochim. et Biophys. Acta* **11,** 487 (1953).

(193) Smellie, R. M. S., McIndoe, W. M., and Davidson, J. N., *Biochim. et Biophys. Acta* **11,** 559 (1953).
(194) Greenberg, G. R., *J. Am. Chem. Soc.* **74,** 6307 (1952).
(195) Gots, J. S., *Nature* **172,** 256 (1953).
(196) Biesele, J. J., *Cancer Research* **4,** 540 (1944).
(197) Mark, D. D., and Ris, H., *Proc. Soc. Exptl. Biol. Med.* **71,** 727 (1949).
(198) Petermann, M. L., Alfin-Slater, R. B., and Larack, A. M., *Cancer* **2,** 510 (1949).
(199) Price, J. M., Miller, E. C., and Miller, J. A., *J. Biol. Chem.* **173,** 345 (1948).
(200) Menten, M. L., Willms, M., and Wright, W. D., *Cancer Research* **13,** 729 (1953).
(201) Menten, M. L., and Willms, M., *Cancer Research* **13,** 733 (1953).
(201a) Sherman, F. G., and Forssberg, A., *Arch. Biochem. and Biophys.* **48,** 293 (1954).
(201b) Uzman, L. I., and Desoer, C., *Arch. Biochem. and Biophys.* **48,** 63 (1954).
(202) Cunningham, L., Griffin, A. C., and Luck, J. M., *Cancer Research* **10,** 211 (1950).
(203) Davidson, J. N., and Leslie, I., *Cancer Research* **10,** 587 (1950).
(204) Griffin, A. C., Nye, W. N., Noda, L., and Luck, J. M., *J. Biol. Chem.* **176,** 1225 (1948).
(205) Griffin, A. C., Cook, H., and Cunningham, L., *Arch. Biochem.* **24,** 190 (1949).
(206) Davidson, J. N., and Leslie, I., *Nature* **165,** 49 (1950).
(207) Klein, E., Kurnick, N. B., and Klein, G., *Exptl. Cell. Research* **1,** 127 (1950).
(208) Klein, G., *Exptl. Cell Research* **2,** 518 (1951).
(209) Albert, S., Johnson, R. M., and Wagshal, R. R., *Science* **117,** 551 (1953).
(210) Cunningham, L., Griffin, A. C., and Luck, J. M., *J. Gen. Physiol.* **34,** 59 (1950).
(211) Klein, G., Klein, E., and Klein, E., *Cancer Research* **12,** 484 (1952).
(212) Leuchtenberger, C., Klein, G., and Klein, E., *Cancer Research* **12,** 480 (1952).
(213) Hauschka, T. S., and Levan, A., *Anat. Record* **111,** 467 (1951).
(214) Goldberg, L., Klein, E., and Klein, G., *Exptl. Cell Research* **1,** 543 (1950).
(215) Petermann, M. L., and Schneider, R. M., *Cancer Research* **11,** 485 (1951).
(216) Mizen, N. A., and Petermann, M. L., *Cancer Research* **12,** 727 (1952).
(217) Mellors, R. C., Keane, J. F., Jr., and Papanicolaou, G. N., *Science* **116,** 265 (1952).
(218) Blout, E. R., and Mellors, R. C., *Science* **110,** 137 (1949).
(219) Woernley, D. L., *Cancer Research* **12,** 516 (1952).
(220) Avery, O. T., MacLeod, C. M., and McCarty, M., *J. Exptl. Med.* **79,** 137 (1944).
(220a) Zamenhof, S., Leidy, G., and Reiner, B., *Proc. Am. Assn. for Cancer Res.* (1954).
(221) Vendrely, R., and Vendrely, C., *Experientia* **5,** 327 (1949).
(222) Greenstein, J. P., *J. Natl. Cancer Inst.* **5,** 31 (1944).
(223) Nachlas, M. M., and Seligman, A. M., *J. Natl. Cancer Inst.* **9,** 415 (1949).
(224) Cohen, R. B., Nachlas, M. M., and Seligman, A. M., *Cancer Research* **11,** 709 (1951).
(225) Potter, V. R., and Liebl, G. J., *Cancer Research* **5,** 18 (1945).
(226) Kutscher, W., and Wolbergs, H., *Z. physiol. Chem.* **236,** 237 (1935).
(227) Gutman, A. B., and Gutman, E. B., *J. Clin. Invest.* **17,** 473 (1938).
(228) Gutman, A. B., Sproul, E. E., and Gutman, A. B., *Am. J. Cancer* **28,** 485 (1936).
(229) Woodard, H. Q., *Cancer Research* **2,** 497 (1942).
(230) Franseen, C. C., and McLean, R., *Am. J. Cancer* **24,** 299 (1935).
(231) White, J., and Edwards, J. E., *J. Natl. Cancer Inst.* **2,** 535 (1942).
(232) Seligman, A. M., *J. Natl. Cancer Inst.* **9,** 427 (1949).
(233) Kay, H. D., *Physiol. Revs.* **12,** 384 (1932).
(234) Folley, S. J., and Kay, H. D., *Ergeb. Enzymforsch.* **5,** 159 (1936).
(235) Robison, R., *Biochem. J.* **17,** 286 (1923).

(236) Taylor, A., Pollack, M. S., and Williams, R. J., *Science* **96,** 322 (1942).
(237) Robertson, W. van B., *J. Natl. Cancer Inst.* **4,** 321 (1943).
(238) Ballantyne, R. M., and McHenry, E. W., *Cancer Research* **9,** 689 (1949).
(239) Goth, A., and Littmann, I., *Cancer Research* **8,** 349 (1948).
(240) Dyer, H. M., and Ross, H. E., *J. Natl. Cancer Inst.* **11,** 313 (1950).
(241) Swick, R. W., and Baumann, C. A., *Cancer Research* **11,** 948 (1951).
(242) Daft, F. S., and Sebrell, W. H., *Public Health Repts.* (*U.S.*) **58,** 1542 (1943).
(243) Swendseid, M. E., Bethell, F. H., and Bird, O. D., *Cancer Research* **11,** 864 (1951).
(244) Pollack, M. A., Taylor, A., and Williams, R. J., *Univ. Texas Publ.*, No. **4237,** 56 (1942).
(245) Chain, E., and Duthie, A., *Brit. J. Exptl. Pathol.* **21,** 324 (1940).
(246) Meyer, K., Chaffee, E., Hobby, G. L., and Dawson, M. H., *J. Exptl. Med.* **73,** 309 (1941).
(247) Madinaveitia, J., and Quibell, T. H. H., *Biochem. J.* **34,** 625 (1940).
(248) McClean, D., and Hale, C. W., *Biochem. J.* **35,** 159 (1941).
(249) Duran-Reynals, F., and Stewart, F. W., *Am. J. Cancer* **15,** 2790 (1931).
(250) Boyland, E., and McClean, D., *J. Pathol. Bacteriol.* **41,** 560 (1935).
(251) Pirie, A., *Brit. J. Exptl. Pathol.* **23,** 277 (1942).
(252) Balazs, E. A., and Euler, J. von, *Cancer Research* **12,** 326 (1952).
(253) Kiriluk, L. B., Kremen, A. J., and Glick, D., *J. Natl. Cancer Inst.* **10,** 993 (1950).
(254) Johnson, R. M., and Dutch, P. H., *Arch. Biochem. and Biophys.* **40,** 239 (1952).
(255) Boyd, E. M., and McEwen, H. D., *Can. J. Med. Sci.* **30,** 163 (1952).
(256) Schoenheimer, R., "The Dynamic State of Body Constituents." Harvard University Press, Cambridge, 1942.
(257) du Vigneaud, V., Cohn, M., Chandler, J. P., Schenck, J. P., and Simmonds, S., *J. Biol. Chem.* **140,** 625 (1941).
(258) Borsook, H., and Dubnoff, J. W., *J. Biol. Chem.* **160,** 635 (1945).
(259) Greenstein, J. P., *J. Natl. Cancer Inst.* **3,** 287 (1942).
(260) Huggins, C., and Eichelberger, L., *Cancer Research* **4,** 447 (1944).
(261) Brunschwig, A., Dunham, L., and Nichols, S., *Cancer Research* **6,** 230 (1946).
(262) Dunham, L., Nichols, S., and Brunschwig, A., *Cancer Research* **6,** 233 (1946).
(263) Epstein, A., *Z. Krebsforsch.* **38,** 63 (1932).
(264) Cannon, P. R., Frazier, L. E., and Hughes, R. H., *Metabolism* **1,** 49 (1952).
(265) Boyer, P. D., Lardy, H. A., and Phillips, P. H., *J. Biol. Chem.* **149,** 529 (1943).
(266) Lasnitzki, A., and Brewer, S. K., *Cancer Research* **2,** 494 (1942).
(267) Dickens, F., *Biochem. J.* **35,** 1011 (1941).
(268) Miller, H., and Carruthers, C., *Cancer Research* **10,** 636 (1950).
(268a) Rondoni, P., and Cudkowicz, A., *Experientia* **9,** 348 (1953).
(269) Barron, E. S. G., and Huggins, C., Proc. Soc. Exptl. Biol. Med. **62,** 195 (1496).
(270) Greenstein, J. P., and Andervont, H. B., *J. Natl. Cancer Inst.* **2,** 345 (1942); **4,** 283 (1943).
(271) Greenstein, J. P., and Thompson, J. W., *J. Natl. Cancer Inst.* **4,** 63, 271, 275 (1943).
(272) Greenstein, J. P., *J. Natl. Cancer Inst.* **3,** 491 (1943).
(273) Greenstein, J. P., and Leuthardt, F. M., *J. Natl. Cancer Inst.* **5,** 39 (1944).
(274) Cori, G. T., and Cori, C. F., *Proc. Soc. Exptl. Biol. Med.* **39,** 337 (1938).
(275) Strong, L. C., and Smith, G. M., *Bull. assoc. franç. étude cancer* **26,** 694 (1937).
(276) Stotz, E., *J. Biol. Chem.* **131,** 555 (1939).

(277) Pollack, M. S., Taylor, A., Taylor, J., and Williams, R. J., *Cancer Research* **2,** 739 (1942).
(278) Taylor, A., Pollack, M. S., Hofer, M. J., and Williams, R. J., *Cancer Research* **2,** 744 (1942).
(279) Pollack, M. S., Taylor, A., Woods, A., Thompson, R. C., and Williams, R. J., *Cancer Research* **2,** 748 (1942).
(280) Taylor, A., Pollack, M. S., Hofer, M. J., and Williams, R. J., *Cancer Research* **2,** 752 (1942).
(281) Kishi, S., Fujiwara, T., and Nakahara, W., *Gann* **31,** 1, 51, 355, 556 (1937); **32,** 469 (1938).
(282) Maver, M. E., Mider, G. B., Johnson, J. M., and Thompson, J. W., *J. Natl. Cancer Inst.* **2,** 277 (1941).
(283) Carter, C. E., and Greenstein, J. P., *J. Natl. Cancer Inst.* **7,** 51 (1946).
(284) Goranson, E. S., McBride, J., and Weber, G., *Cancer Research* **14,** 227 (1954).
(285) Sylvén, B., "Ester Sulfuric Acids of High Molecular Weight and Mast Cells in Mesenchymal Tumors." Norstedt, Stockholm, 1945.
(286) Fishman, W. H., *J. Biol. Chem.* **136,** 229 (1940); **169,** 7 (1947).
(287) Fishman, W. H., *Ann. N. Y. Acad. Sci.* **54,** 548 (1951); cf. Riotton, G., and Fishman, W. H., *Endocrinology* **52,** 692 (1953).
(288) Fishman, W. H., and Anlyan, A. J., *Cancer Research* **7,** 808 (1947).
(289) Fishman, W. H., and Bigelow, R., *J. Natl. Cancer Inst.* **10,** 1115 (1950).
(290) Fishman, W. H., Markus, R. L., Page, O. C., Pfeiffer, P. H., and Homburger, F., *Am. J. Med. Sci.* **220,** 55 (1950).
(291) Odell, L. D., and Burt, J. C., *Cancer Research* **9,** 362 (1949).
(292) Anlyan, A. J., Gamble, J., and Hoster, H. A., *Cancer* **3,** 116 (1950).
(293) Kerr, L. M. H., Campbell, J. G., and Levvy, G. A., *Biochem. J.* **44,** 487 (1949); **46,** 278 (1950).
(294) Cohen, S. L., and Bittner, J. J., *Cancer Research* **11,** 723 (1951).
(295) Atkinson, W. B., Gall, E. A., and Gusberg, S. B., *Cancer* **5,** 138 (1952).
(296) Meister, A., and Greenstein, J. P., *J. Biol. Chem.* **175,** 573 (1948).
(297) Meister, A., *J. Biol. Chem.* **178,** 577 (1949).
(298) Witter, R. F., and Stotz, E., *J. Biol. Chem.* **176,** 501 (1948).
(299) Meister, A., *J. Natl. Cancer Inst.* **9,** 125 (1948).
(300) Meister, A., *J. Natl. Cancer Inst.* **10,** 75 (1949).
(301) Greenstein, J. P., Carter, C. E., Chalkley, H. W., and Leuthardt, F. M., *J. Natl. Cancer Inst.* **7,** 9 (1946).
(302) Greenstein, J. P., and Chalkley, H. W., *J. Natl. Cancer Inst.* **6,** 61 (1945).
(303) Carter, C. E., and Greenstein, J. P., *J. Natl. Cancer Inst.* **7,** 29 (1946).
(304) Bain, J. A., and Rusch, H. P., *J. Biol. Chem.* **153,** 659 (1944).
(305) Greenstein, J. P., Carter, C. E., and Leuthardt, F. M., *J. Natl. Cancer Inst.* **7,** 47 (1946).
(306) Gutman, A. B., and Gutman, E. B., *Proc. Soc. Exptl. Biol. Med.* **39,** 529 (1938).
(307) Lustig, B., *Biochem. Z.* **284,** 367 (1936).
(308) Dickens, F., *Biochem. J.* **35,** 1011 (1941).
(309) Brues, A. M., Drury, D. R., and Brues, M. C., *Arch. Pathol.* **22,** 658 (1936).
(310) Burk, D., *in* "Symposium on Respiratory Enzymes." Madison, University of Wisconsin Press, 1942.
(311) Tamiya, C., *Biochem. Z.* **189,** 175 (1927).
(311a) Tsuboi, K. K., Yokoyama, H. O., Stowell, R. E., and Wilson, M. E., *Archiv. Biochem. and Biophys.* **48,** 275 (1954).
(312) Norberg, B. O., *Acta Physiol. Scand.* **19,** 246 (1949).

(313) Oppenheimer, M. J., and Flock, E. V., *Am. J. Physiol.* **149,** 418 (1947).
(314) Sulkin, N. M., and Gardner, J. H., *Anat. Record* **100,** 143 (1948).
(315) Cleveland, F. P., Richfield, D. F., Gall, E. A., and Schiff, L., *Arch. Pathol.* **49,** 333 (1950).
(316) Cohen, P. P., Hekhuis, G. L., and Sober, E. K., *Cancer Research* **2,** 405 (1942); *cf.* Cohen, P. P., *Cancer Research* **5,** 626 (1945).
(317) Cohen, P. P., and Hekhuis, G. L., *Cancer Research* **1,** 620 (1941).
(318) West, P. M., and Woglom, W. H., *Cancer Research* **2,** 324 (1942).
(319) Potter, V. R., Schneider, W. C., and Liebl, G. J., *Cancer Research* **5,** 21 (1945).
(320) Greenstein, J. P., and Leuthardt, F. M., *J. Natl. Cancer Inst.* **5,** 111 (1945).
(321) Warburg, O., "The Metabolism of Tumors." Constable and Co., London, 1930.
(322) Burk, D., *Cold Spring Harbor Symposia Quant. Biol.* **7,** 420 (1939).
(323) Stotz, E., *in* "Symposium on Respiratory Enzymes." University of Wisconsin Press, Madison, 1942.
(324) Keilin, D., and Hartree, E. F., *Proc. Roy. Soc.* (*London*) **B 127,** 167 (1939).
(325) Keilin, D., and Hartree, E. F., *Proc. Roy. Soc.* (*London*) **B 125,** 171 (1938).
(326) Haas, E., *J. Biol. Chem.* **148,** 481 (1943).
(327) Keilin, D., and Hartree, E. F., *Proc. Roy. Soc.* (*London*) **B 122,** 298 (1937).
(328) Craig, F. N., Bassett, A. M., and Salter, W. T., *Cancer Research* **1,** 869 (1941).
(329) Roskelley, R. C., Mayer, N., Horwitt, B. N., and Salter, W. T., *J. Clin. Invest.* **22,** 743 (1943).
(330) Mayer, N., *Cancer Research* **4,** 345 (1944).
(331) Warren, C. O., *Cancer Research* **3,** 621 (1943).
(332) Lineweaver, H., and Burk, D., *J. Am. Chem. Soc.* **56,** 658 (1934).
(333) Stotz, E., Altschul, A. M., and Hogness, T. R., *J. Biol. Chem.* **124,** 745 (1938).
(334) Schneider, W. C., and Potter, V. R., *J. Biol. Chem.* **149,** 217 (1943).
(335) von Euler, H., and Skarzynski, B., "Biochemie der Tumoren." Ferdinand Enkel, Stuttgart, 1942.
(336) Chance, B., and Castor, L. N., *Science* **116,** 200 (1952).
(337) Colowick, S. P., and Price, W. H., *J. Biol. Chem.* **159,** 563 (1945); Price, W. H., Cori, C. F., and Colowick, S. P., *J. Biol. Chem.* **160,** 633 (1945); Price, W. H., Slein, M. W., Colowick, S. R., and Cori, G. T., *Federation Proc.* **5,** 150 (1946).
(338) Warburg, O., and Christian, W., *Biochem. Z.* **286,** 81 (1936).
(339) Cori, C. F., and Cori, G. T., *J. Biol. Chem.* **65,** 397 (1925).
(340) Bierich, R., and Rosenbohm, A., *Z. physiol. Chem.* **214,** 271 (1933).
(341) Voegtlin, C., Fitch, R. H., Kahler, H., Johnson, J. M., and Thompson, J. W., *U. S. Public Health Service, Public Health Bull.* No. **164,** 15 (1935).
(342) Kahler, H., and Robertson, W. van B., *J. Natl. Cancer Inst.* **3,** 495 (1943).
(343) Elliott, K. A. C., *in* "Symposium on Respiratory Enzymes." Madison (1942); *cf.* also, Elliott, K. A. C., and Greig, M. E., *Biochem. J.*, **31,** 1021 (1937).
(344) Crabtree, H. G., *Biochem. J.* **23,** 536 (1929).
(345) Dickens, F., and Simer, F., *Biochem. J.* **24,** 1301 (1930); **25,** 985 (1931).
(346) Murphy, J. B., and Hawkins, J. S., *J. Gen. Physiol.* **8,** 115 (1925).
(347) Belkin, M., and Stern, K. G., *Cancer Research* **3,** 164 (1943).
(348) Burk, D., Sprince, H., Spangler, J. M., Boon, M. C., and Furth, J., *J. Natl. Cancer Inst.* **3,** 249 (1942).
(349) Hall, V. E., *Cancer Research* **4,** 785 (1944).
(350) Dickens, F., and Weil-Malherbe, H., *Biochem.* J. **30,** 659 (1936).
(351) Dickens, F., and Weil-Malherbe, H., *Biochem. J.* **35,** 7 (1941); *cf.* Dickens, F., *Nature* **145,** 512 (1940).

(352) Bywaters, E. G. L., *J. Pathol. Bacteriol.* **44**, 247 (1937).
(353) White, P. R., *Cancer Research* **5**, 302 (1945).
(354) Needham, J., and Lehmann, H., *Biochem. J.* **31**, 1210 (1937).
(355) Boyland, E., and Boyland, M. E., *Biochem. J.* **32**, 321 (1938).
(356) Boyland, E., Boyland, M. E., and Greville, G. D., *Biochem. J.* **31**, 461 (1937).
(357) Meyerhof, O., and Wilson, J., *Arch. Biochem.* **21**, 22 (1949).
(358) Boyland, E., Goss, G. C. L., and Williams-Ashman, H. G., *Biochem. J.* **49**, 321 (1951).
(359) LePage, G. A., *Cancer Research* **8**, 193 (1948).
(360) Goldfeder, A., and Albaum, H. G., *Cancer Research* **11**, 118 (1951).
(361) LePage, G. A., *Cancer Research* **8**, 197 (1948).
(361a) Fujii, T., and Ohnishi, J., *Gann* **44**, 67 (1953).
(362) Sibley, J. A., and Lehninger, A. L., *J. Natl. Cancer Inst.* **9**, 303 (1949).
(363) Beck, W. S., and Valentine, W. N., *Cancer Research* **13**, 309 (1953).
(364) Kun, E., Talalay, P.. and Williams-Ashman, H. G., *Cancer Research* **11**, 855 (1951).
(365) Warburg, O., and Hiepler, E., *Z. Naturforsch.* **7b**, 193 (1952).
(366) McKee, R. W., Lonberg-Holm, K., and Jehl, J. A., *Cancer Research* **13**, 537 (1953).
(367) Steinberg, M. A., Stern, K. G., and Rottino, A., *J. Natl. Cancer Inst.* **12**, 971 (1952).
(368) Williams-Ashman, H. G., *Cancer Research* **13**, 721 (1953).
(369) Brin, M., *Cancer Research* **13**, 748 (1953).
(370) Burk, D., Sprince, H., Spangler, J. M., Kabat, E. A., Furth, J., and Claude, A., *J. Natl. Cancer Inst.* **2**, 201 (1941).
(371) Warburg, O., Wind, F., and Negelein, E., *Klin. Wochschr.* **5**, 829 (1926).
(372) Steckel, R. H., and Murlin, J. R., *Cancer Research* **11**, 330 (1951).
(373) Burk, D., *in* "Some Fundamental Aspects of the Cancer Problem." Science Press, New York, 1937.
(373a) Wenner, C. E., Dunn, D. F., and Weinhouse, *J. Biol. Chem.* **205**, 409 (1953).
(374) Toennies, G., *Cancer Research* **7**, 193 (1947).
(375) Chargaff, E., Crampton, C. F., and Lipschitz, R., *Nature* **172**, 289 (1953).
(376) Brown, G. L., and Watson, M., *Nature* **172**, 339 (1953).
(377) Bailey, K., *Biochem. J.* **31**, 1406 (1937).
(378) Beach, E. F., Munks, B., and Robinson, A., *J. Biol. Chem.* **148**, 431 (1943).
(379) Block, R. J., *J. Biol. Chem.* **119**, 765; **120**, 467 (1937).
(380) Greenstein, J. P., and Jenrette, W. V., *J. Natl. Cancer Inst.* **1**, 91 (1940).
(381) Greenstein, J. P., Jenrette, W. V., and White, J., *J. Natl. Cancer Inst.* **2**, 305 (1941).
(382) Greenstein, J. P., *J. Natl. Cancer Inst.* **3**, 61 (1942); *cf.* Neurath, H., Greenstein, J. P., Putnam, F. W., and Erickson, J. O., *Chem. Rev.* **34**, 157 (1944).
(383) Thompson, J. W., and Voegtlin, C., *J. Biol. Chem.* **70**, 793 (1926).
(384) Kinosita, R., *J. Japan. Gastroenterol. Assoc.* **37**, 513 (1938).
(385) Greenstein, J. P., *J. Natl. Cancer Inst.* **3**, 61 (1942).
(386) Yamamoto, K., *Mitt. med. Akad. Kioto* **29**, 817 (1940).
(386a) Petermann, M. L., Mizen, N. A., and Hamilton, M. G., *Cancer Research*, **13**, 372 (1953); *Proc. Am. Assn. for Cancer Research* (1954).
(387) Ghosh, D., and Lardy, H. A., *Cancer Research* **12**, 232 (1952).
(388) Maver, M. E., and Barrett, M. K., *J. Natl. Cancer Inst.* **4**, 65 (1943).
(389) Kubowitz, F., and Ott, P., *Biochem. Z.* **314**, 94 (1943).
(390) Dunn, M. S., Feaver, E. R., and Murphy, E. A., *Cancer Research* **9**, 306 (1949).

(391) Astrup, T., Carlström, G., and Stage, A., *Acta Physiol. Scand.* **24,** 202 (1951).
(392) Roberts, E., and Frankel, S., *Cancer Research* **9,** 645 (1949).
(393) Roberts, E., and Frankel, S., *Cancer Research* **9,** 231 (1949).
(394) Rosenthal, S. M., *J. Natl. Cancer Inst.* **10,** 89 (1949).
(395) Kögl, F., and Erxleben, H., *Z. physiol. Chem.* **258,** 57 (1939).
(396) Miller, J. A., *Cancer Research* **10,** 65 (1950).
(397) Wiltshire, G. H., *Brit. J. Cancer* **7,** 137 (1953); *Biochem. J.* **55,** 46 (1953).
(398) Kögl, F., *Experientia* **5,** 173 (1949).
(399) Kögl, F., Klein, A. J., Erxleben, H., and van Veersen, G. J., *Rec. trav. chim.* **69,** 822 (1950).
(400) Kögl, F., Erxleben, H., Klein, A. J., and van Veersen, G. J., *Rec. trav. chim.* **69,** 834, 841 (1950).
(401) Christensen, H. N., and Henderson, M. E., *Cancer Research* **12,** 229 (1952).
(402) Rodewald, W., and Klein, H., *Naturwissenschaften* **31,** 277 (1943).
(403) Fischer, A., *Acta Physiol. Scand.* **4,** 207 (1942).
(404) Fischer, A., *Enzymologia* **14,** 15 (1950).
(405) Hogeboom, G. H., and Schneider, W. C., *Science* **113,** 355 (1951).
(406) Sorof, S., and Cohen, P. P., *Cancer Research* **11,** 376 (1951).
(407) Miller, G. L., Green, E. U., Miller, E. E., and Kolb, J. J., *Cancer Research* **10,** 148 (1950).
(408) Roberts, S., and White, A., *J. Biol. Chem.* **178,** 151 (1949).
(409) Barry, G. T., *Cancer Research* **10,** 694 (1950).
(410) Lerner, A. B., and Watson, C. J., *Am. J. Med. Sci.* **214,** 410, 416 (1947).
(411) Abrams, A., Cohen, P. P., and Meyer, O. O., *J. Biol. Chem.* **181,** 237 (1949).
(412) Schoenheimer, R., and Rittenberg, D., *Physiol. Revs.* **20,** 218 (1940).
(413) Borsook, H., *Physiol. Revs.* **30,** 206 (1950).
(414) Zamecnik, P. C., *Cancer Research* **10,** 659 (1950).
(415) Peters, T., and Anfinsen, C. B., *J. Biol. Chem.* **182,** 171 (1950).
(416) Cannon, P. R., "Some Pathologic Consequences of Protein and Amino Acid Deficiencies." Charles C Thomas, Springfield, 1948.
(417) Van Pilsum, J. F., and Berg, C. P., *J. Biol. Chem.* **183,** 279 (1950).
(418) Ratner, S., Rittenberg, D., Keston, A. S., and Schoenheimer, R., *J. Biol. Chem.* **134,** 665 (1940).
(419) Melchior, J. B., and Tarver, H., *Arch. Biochem.* **12,** 301 (1947).
(420) Levine, M., and Tarver, H., *J. Biol. Chem.* **192,** 835 (1951).
(421) Winnick, T., Peterson, E. A., and Greenberg, D. M., *Arch. Biochem.* **21,** 235 (1949).
(422) Winnick, T., *Arch. Biochem.* **27,** 65 (1950).
(422a) Reiner, J. M., *Arch. Biochem. and Biophys.* **46,** 53, 80 (1953).
(423) Shemin, D., and Rittenberg, D., *J. Biol. Chem.* **153,** 401 (1944).
(424) Winnick, T., Friedberg, F., and Greenberg, D. M., *J. Biol. Chem.* **173,** 189 (1948).
(425) Kremen, A. J., Hunter, S. W., Moore, G. E., and Hitchcock, C. R., *Cancer Research* **9,** 174 (1949).
(426) Griffin, A. C., Bloom, S., Cunningham, L., Teresi, J. D., and Luck, J. M., *Cancer* **3,** 316 (1950).
(427) Goldsworthy, P. D., Winnick, T., and Greenberg, D. M., *J. Biol. Chem.* **180,** 341 (1949).
(428) Borsook, H., Deasy, C. L., Haagen-Smit, A. J., Keighly, G., and Lowy, P. H., *J. Biol. Chem.* **187,** 839 (1950).

(429) Tyner, E. P., Heidelberger, C., and LePage, G. A., *Cancer Research* **12,** 158 (1952).
(430) Reid, J. C., Landefeld, M. O., and Simpson, J. L., *J. Natl. Cancer Inst.* **12,** 929 (1952).
(431) Zamecnik, P. C., Frantz, I. D., Jr., Loftfield, R. B., and Stephenson, M. L., *J. Biol. Chem.* **175,** 299 (1948).
(432) LePage, G. A., *Cancer Research* **13,** 178 (1953).
(433) Siekevitz, P., *J. Biol. Chem.* **195,** 549 (1952).
(434) Lang, K., Lang, H., Siebert, G., and Lucius, S., *Biochem. Z.* **324,** 217 (1953)
(434a) Rabinovitz, M., Olson, M. E., and Greenberg, D. M., *Proc. Am. Assn. for Cancer Research* (1954).
(435) Christenson, H., and Rafu, M. L., *Cancer Research* **12,** 495 (1952).
(436) Christenson, H., and Riggs, T. R., *J. Biol. Chem.* **194,** 63 (1952).
(437) Miller, L. L., Bly, C. G., Watson, M. L., and Bale, W. F., *J. Exptl. Med.* **94,** 431 (1951).
(437a) Christensen, H. N., Hess, B., and Riggs, T. R., *Cancer Research* **14,** 124 (1954).
(438) Barnes, F. W., Jr., and Schoenheimer, R., *J. Biol. Chem.* **151,** 123 (1943).
(439) Sonne, J. C., Buchanan, J. M., and Delluva, A. M., *J. Biol. Chem.* **166,** 395 (1946); **173,** 69, 81 (1948).
(440) Heinrich, M. R., and Wilson, D. W., *J. Biol. Chem.* **186,** 447 (1950).
(441) Tyner, E. P., Heidelberger, C., and LePage, G. A., *Cancer Research* **13,** 186 (1953).
(442) Barnum, C. P., and Huseby, R. A., *Arch. Biochem.* **29,** 7 (1950).
(443) Griffin, A. C., Davis, W. E., Jr., and Tifft, M. O., *Cancer Research* **12,** 707 (1952).
(444) Arvidson, H., Eliasson, N. A., Hammarsten, E., Reichard, P., von Ubisch, H., and Bergstrom, S., *J. Biol. Chem.* **179,** 169 (1949).
(445) Weed, L. L., *Cancer Research* **11,** 470 (1951).
(446) Eliasson, N. A., Hammarsten, E., Reichard, P., Åqvist, S., Thorell, B., and Ehrensvärd, G., *Acta Chem. Scand.* **5,** 431 (1951).
(447) Hammarsten, E., and Hevesy, G. von, *Acta Physiol. Scand.* **11,** 335 (1946).
(448) Davidson, J. N., and McIndoe, W. M., *Biochem. J.* **45,** xvi (1949).
(449) Anderson, E. P., and Åqvist, S., *J. Biol. Chem.* **202,** 513 (1953).
(450) Jones, H. B., Chaikoff, I. L., and Lawrence, J. H., *Am. J. Cancer* **40,** 243 (1940).
(451) Costello, C. J., Carruthers, C., Kamen, M. D., and Simoes, R. L., *Cancer Research* **7,** 642 (1947).
(452) Rutman, R. J., Cantarow, A., Paschkis, K. E., and Allanoff, B., *Science* **117,** 282 (1953); *cf.* Rutman, R. J., Cantarow, A., and Paschkis, K. E., *Cancer Research,* **14,** 111, 115, 119 (1954).
(453) Buchanan, D. L., Nakao, A., and Edwards, G., *Science* **117,** 541 (1953).
(454) Maver, M. E., and Greco, A. E., *J. Natl. Cancer Inst.* **12,** 37 (1951).
(455) Price, J. M., Miller, J. A., Miller, E. C., and Weber, G. M., *Cancer Research* **9,** 96 (1949).
(456) Schneider, W. C., Hogeboom, G. H., and Ross, H. E., *J. Natl. Cancer Inst.* **10,** 977 (1950).
(457) Higgins, H., Miller, J. A., Price, J. M., and Strong, F. M., *Proc. Soc. Exptl. Biol. Med.* **75,** 462 (1950).
(458) Schneider, W. C., *Cancer Research* **6,** 685 (1946).
(459) Schneider, W. C., and Hogeboom, G. H., *J. Natl. Cancer Inst.* **10,** 969 (1950).
(460) Hogeboom, G. H., and Schneider, W. C., *J. Natl. Cancer Inst.* **10,** 983 (1950).

(461) Maver, M. E., Greco, A. E., Lovtrup, E., and Dalton, A. J., *J. Natl. Cancer Inst.* **13,** 687 (1952).
(462) Schweigert, B. S., Guthneck, B. T., Price, J. M., Miller, J. A., and Miller, E. C., *Proc. Soc. Exptl. Biol. Med.* **72,** 495 (1949).
(463) Laird, A. K., Nygaard, O., Ris, H., and Barton, A. D., *Exptl. Cell Research* **5,** 147 (1953).
(464) Dmochowski, L., and Stickland, L. H., *Brit. J. Cancer* **7,** 250 (1953).
(464a) Laird, A. K., Exptl. Cell Research **6,** 30 (1954).
(465) Warburg, O., and Christian, W., *Biochem. Z.* **314,** 399 (1943).
(466) Hogeboom, G. H., and Adams, M. H., *J. Biol. Chem.* **145,** 273 (1942).
(467) Evans, W. C., and Raper, H. S., *Biochem. J.* **31,** 2162 (1937).
(468) Algire, G. H., *J. Natl. Cancer Inst.* **5,** 151 (1944).
(469) Bloch, B., *Am. J. Med. Sci.* **177,** 609 (1929).
(470) Laidlaw, G. F., *Am. J. Pathol.* **8,** 477 (1932).
(471) Greenstein, J. P., Turner, F. C., and Jenrette, W. V., *J. Natl. Cancer Inst.* **1,** 377 (1940).
(472) Burk, D., Algire, G. H., Hesselbach, M. L., Fischer, C. E., and Legallis, F. Y., *in* "The Biology of Melanomas," p. 437. New York Academy of Sciences, New York, 1948.
(473) duBuy, H. G., Woods, M. W., Burk, D., and Lackey, M. D., *J. Natl. Cancer Inst.* **9,** 325 (1949).
(474) Riley, V., Hobby, G. L., and Burk, D., *in* "Pigment Cell Growth," p. 231. Academic Press, New York, 1953.
(475) Riley, V., Hesselbach, M. L., Fiala, S., Woods, M. W., and Burk, D., *Science* **109,** 361 (1949).
(475a) Zondek, B., and Krohn, J., *J. klin. Wochschr.* **11,** 405 (1932).
(475b) Frieden, E. H., and Bozer, J. M., *Proc. Soc. Exptl. Biol. Med.* **77,** 35 (1951).
(476) "The Biology of Melanomas." New York, 1948.
(477) "Pigment Cell Growth." Academic Press, New York, 1953.
(478) Lerner, A. B., and Fitzpatrick, T. B., *Physiol. Revs.* **30,** 91 (1950).
(479) Figge, F. H. J., and Strong, L. C., *Cancer Research* **1,** 779 (1941).
(480) Khanolkar, V. R., and Chitre, R. G., *Cancer Research* **4,** 128 (1944).
(481) Shimkin, M. B., Greenstein, J. P., and Andervont, H. B., *J. Natl. Cancer Inst.* **5,** 29 (1944).
(482) Strong, L. C., and Francis, L. D., *Arch. Pathol.* **23,** 202 (1937).
(483) Figge, F. H. J., Strong, L. C., Strong, L. C., Jr., and Shambron, S., *Cancer Research* **2,** 335 (1942).
(484) Kennaway, E. L., Kennaway, N. M., and Warren, F. L., *Cancer Research* **4,** 245 (1944).
(485) Greenstein, J. P., *in* "Mammary Tumors in Mice." American Association for the Advancement of Science, Washington, D. C., 1945.
(486) Chitre, R. G., Ambegaokar, S. D., and Joshi, N. G., *Ann. Biochem. and Exptl. Med. (India)* **4,** 87 (1944).
(487) Goulden, F., and Warren, F. L., *Cancer Research* **4,** 421 (1944).
(488) Warren, F. L., and Goulden, F., *Cancer Research* **4,** 417 (1944).
(489) Tuba, J., *Cancer Research* **12,** 113 (1952).
(490) Cliffton, E. E., Elliott, D. W., and Nero, W. J., *Cancer Research* **9,** 422 (1949).
(491) Davidsohn, I., and Stern, K., *Cancer Research* **9,** 426 (1949).
(492) Morrow, A. G., Greenspan, E. M., and Carroll, D. M., *J. Natl. Cancer Inst.* **10,** 1199 (1950).
(493) Sie, H-G., and Fishman, W. H., *Cancer Research* **13,** 590 (1953).

(494) Fishman, W. H., and Farmelant, M. H., *Endocrinol.* **52,** 536 (1953).
(495) Law, L. W., Morrow, A. G., and Greenspan, E. M., *J. Natl. Cancer Inst.* **12,** 909 (1952).
(496) Cohen, S. L., and Bittner, J. J., *Cancer Research* **11,** 723 (1951).
(497) Adelsberger, L., *Cancer Research* **11,** 653 (1951).
(498) Adelsberger, L., *Cancer Research* **11,** 658 (1951).
(499) Bittner, J. J., *Ann. N. Y. Acad. Sci.* **49,** 69 (1947).
(500) Ponder, E., and Nesmith, J., *Cancer Research* **12,** 104 (1952).

Chapter IX

Chemistry of the Tumor-Bearing Host

Introduction

The effects described in this chapter are those elicited in the animal as a consequence of the presence of a tumor. Many striking and clear-cut phenomena have been noted as a result of the study of such effects. The unhappily familiar cachexia of patients with advanced neoplastic disease is a clinical symptom of these effects, sometimes considerably exaggerated, sometimes masked as a result of secondary causes such as bacterial infection, generalized toxemia, malnutrition, and psychic depression, but nevertheless fundamentally due to systemic alterations produced by the tumor on the host. These effects have been studied in a number of empirical ways, including (a) changes in the enzyme pattern or in the concentration of components of the blood, (b) changes in the enzyme pattern or in the concentration of chemical components of tissues at a site removed from that of the tumor and (c) quantitative changes in the components or qualitative alterations due to the appearance of new components in the urine. Excluding consideration of changes of non-neoplastic origin, the effects elicited by the tumor may be produced either by a liberation into the blood stream of material elaborated by the tumor or by an abstraction by the tumor of some component or components in the blood stream essential for the maintenance and proper function of the distant tissue. In only a few instances is it possible to decide between these alternatives.

Inasmuch as the effects in the tumor-bearing animal are noted on the basis of quantitative changes, a framework of reference for the normal animal is naturally implied. A knowledge of the biochemistry and physiology of normal tissue function is prerequisite to an understanding of the effects induced by neoplastic disease. In genetically heterozygous populations, as in human beings, individual biochemical variation, apart from relatively slight effects due to age or sex, is likely to be small. In homozygous populations, as in inbred strains of mice, a certain segregation of biochemical characteristics in each strain may be expected, and, hence, a separate framework of reference for each strain must be constructed. In short, the comparison of biochemical characteristics in normal and in tumor-bearing animals must be adequately controlled if it is to be significant.

However, when the secondary effects alluded to above (cachexia, etc.) intervene in the course of neoplastic disease, a new framework of reference must be considered in order to isolate properly the specific effects induced by neoplasia alone. This would necessitate the investigation of the systemic effects induced in the host by all kinds of pathological states, a task admittedly enormous, but one worth the effort not only to the study of cancer but of other disease states as well. Up to the present, such new biochemical frameworks of reference against various pathologic states have been little investigated. The normal state, together with the few facts available on changes from the normal induced by other diseases, must serve as the only available basis of comparison with the data derived from the tumor-bearing host.

In order to narrow any systemic effect observed to the influence of the tumor itself, it is necessary to correlate such effect with the growth of the tumor. Where experimental animals are employed, the tumors should be free from ulceration and infection, and the systemic effect should be observed at intervals during the growth of the tumor within the period when the animals appear to be healthy and vigorous. Study of the fate of the systemic effect when the tumor is removed is a further means of correlating cause and effect, for, if the reaction is reversed subsequent to the loss of the tumor, this reaction, in the absence of extraneous factors, must have been originally evoked by the tumor. Finally, it is advisable to study several components in the various tissues of the tumor-bearing host. Whereas a general toxic condition might affect all or most of the components of a tissue, a specific effect elicited by the tumor might be directed only toward certain components.

A vast literature has evolved from studies on the tumor-bearing host. It is evident that the establishment of one or more specific systemic effects would have important theoretical bearings in cancer research and that, if such effects were observable in readily accessible sites, they would be of great value in the diagnosis and prognosis of neoplastic disease in man. The greater part of these studies has been conducted on blood and urine, which, in the case at least of human beings, have been the most available materials. The techniques of serum investigations have included those of immunology. For the most part, the results of the immunological studies have been controversial and inconclusive. With no intent to dismiss these studies summarily, the fact that they are not sufficiently established at the present time renders their treatment here inadvisable. There is little or no valid evidence that the serum of the cancerous host contains antibodies for cancer cells or their components, in the way that the serum contains antibodies for bacteria. Similarly, several of the widely discussed serochemical studies based upon cytolytic and proteolytic reactions (Abderhalden, Freund-Kaminer, Fuchs, v. Christiani, Waldschmidt-Leitz, etc.) will not be discussed here. It is possible that the concepts upon which these reactions are based may be well-founded and capable of experimental proof. Until such time, however, when these tests are performed according to practices which appeal to the experienced biochemist any final assessment of their value must be postponed.

To the reader who has studied the vast literature of cancer sero- and urinary chemistry, the subject appears to be as much a sequence of psychological as chemical phenomena. The urgency of the immediate task may perhaps have been the most frequent offender. Perhaps the advisable approach would be not to insist at the very start that a rigorous, practical and specific test for neoplastic disease be established, but that the readily observed changes in the tissues or excreta of tumor-bearing hosts be more closely examined, even if such changes appear to occur in conditions other than cancer. On further, closer scrutiny, such changes in the cancerous individual might eventually be distinguished from those in the non-cancerous individual. Even in those cases in which this may be unsuccessful, such information has an independent interest of its own.

That evidence has been selected and described in the present chapter which illustrates marked systemic effects elicited in the tumor-bearing host, namely (a) changes in the enzymatic pattern and components of liver, kidney, adrenal, etc., (b) changes in the enzymatic pattern and the components of the blood, and (c) changes in the steroid pattern of the urine.

Specific Systems in Tissues

Hepatic Dysfunction in Man. In a striking study on eight hepatic functions, Abels, Rekers, Binkley, Pack, and Rhoads (1) demonstrated that patients with gastrointestinal cancer revealed a high incidence of failure to maintain these functions. These functions were tested for on the following: plasma prothrombin, serum bilirubin, serum proteins, vitamin A, urinary excretion of glucuronates, mean corpuscular volume of erythrocytes, urinary and fecal excretion of urobilinogen, and serum cholesterol and cholesterol esters. Five groups of individuals were studied: (a) normal patients, (b) patients with various forms of gastrointestinal cancer, (c) patients whose gastrointestinal cancer had been removed, (d) patients with atrophic gastritis, and (e) patients with oral leukoplakia. In all cases the nutritional status was noted. Of these groups, only (b) showed marked hepatic dysfunction. The fact that the patients in group (c), i.e., those whose tumors were removed at operation, showed a low incidence of such dysfunction strongly suggests that the changes noted in the patients in group (b) are reversible. There seems to be little doubt that hepatic insufficiency is a concomitant phenomenon with cancer and, as the authors emphasize, such damaged livers impose an additional hazard to those normally accompanying operative procedures.

The hypoproteinemia in the patients with neoplastic disease is largely attributable to decrease in serum albumin. The decrease in this component

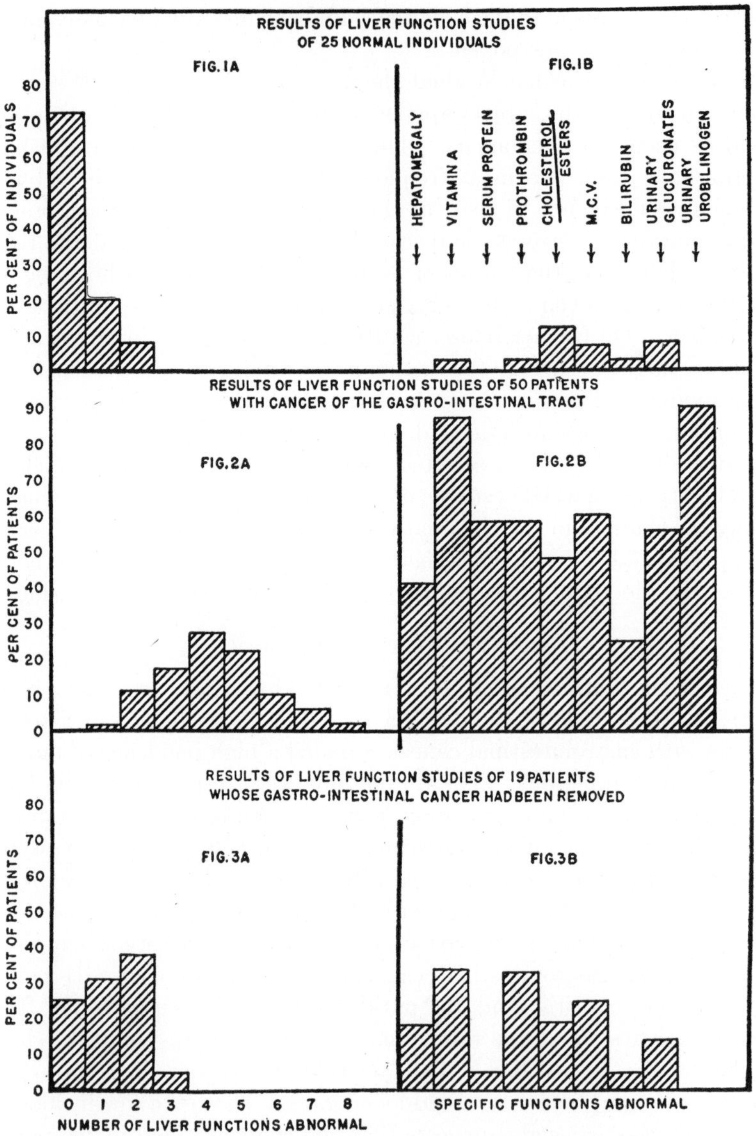

FIG. 49. Liver function studies in man. From Abels, J. C., Rekers, P.E., Binkley, G. F., Pack, G. T., and Rhoads, C. P., *Ann. Internal Med.* **16**, 221 (1942).

was observed to be due to impaired fabrication by the liver and not to a decreased dietary intake of protein. Table 146 illustrates these findings.

The osmotic pressure of serum is due chiefly to the albumin component, and results in accord with those of Abels *et al.* have been observed in rats

TABLE 146

THE CONCENTRATIONS OF TOTAL PROTEIN, ALBUMIN, AND GLOBULIN IN THE SERUM OF PATIENTS WITH CANCER OF THE GASTROINTESTINAL TRACT (IN G./100 ML.) (1)

Patient	Diet	Total serum protein[1]	Serum albumin[2]	Serum globulin
F. B.	Adequate	6.6	4.2	2.3
D. S.	Adequate	6.2	3.4	2.8
A. N.	Adequate	6.1	3.7	2.4
S. G.	Adequate	5.9	2.8	3.1
F. K.	Adequate	5.9	3.3	2.5
J. M.	Adequate	6.4	3.9	2.5
F. R.	Adequate	5.3	3.2	2.1
H. G.	Adequate	5.9	3.9	2.0
D. M.	Adequate	5.4	3.0	2.4
J. R.	Inadequate	4.8	3.3	1.4
E. W.	Inadequate	5.7	4.2	1.3
K. P.	Inadequate	4.6	2.9	1.7

[1] Assumed abnormal when less than 6.6.
[2] Assumed abnormal when less than 4.0 associated with globulin of more than 2.0.

bearing the transplanted Jensen sarcoma during successive stages of growth of the tumor (2) (Table 147).

Problems of Nitrogen and Lipid Metabolism. Among the seemingly unique properties of the growing tumor is its capacity to grow at the expense of the host, i.e., to build up protein in a host in negative nitrogen balance (cf. Chapter V). The transfer of nitrogen from the body tissues to the tu-

TABLE 147

COLLOID OSMOTIC PRESSURE OF SERA OF RATS BEARING THE TRANSPLANTED JENSEN SARCOMA (2)

Days following inoculation	Osmotic pressure at 23°, mm. H_2O		
0 (control)[1]	310	347	320
2	290	321	309
5	284	289	285
7	261	254	278
8	265	254	270
10	256	262	280
12	240	230	252
14	217	218	242
17	222	200	205
19	205	200	199
21[2, 3]	200	208	207

[1] Averaged 8.6 g. per cent total serum protein.
[2] Averaged 6.8 g. per cent total serum protein.
[3] Animals died shortly thereafter.

mor is accompanied by a progressive loss of total body lipid as well. The evidence of a one-way passage of protein or its precursors from the metabolic pool to the growing tumor has led to the concept by Mider (3) (5) of the tumor as a "nitrogen trap." Whether a reversal of this process might occur in the case of the regressing tumor remains to be seen (cf. 4).

Studies by Mider and his colleagues (5) on the Walker 256 tumor in rats clearly illustrate the basic problems concerned with the translocation of nitrogen to neoplasm. Using pair-fed animals, it is possible to show three distinct phases of growth of the tumor. During the first stage up to about 10 days after visible growth, the tumor grows slowly but progressively, and the body gains weight at the same time. The second stage is characterized by a more rapid growth of the tumor, the animals become anoretic, and the host tissues begin to lose weight. During both stages, both pair-fed tumorous and control rats excrete almost identical amounts of nitrogen. Rats which survive this second stage pass into a relatively brief third stage during which the tumor grows slowly, the host's tissues lose nitrogen at a rapid rate, and the tumorous rats excrete excessive amounts of ammonia and urea in their urine (Fig. 50). During the second stage of tumor growth a considerable hyperlipemia develops, which disappears subsequently as the store of body lipids is depleted (6) (20). It would appear that in the

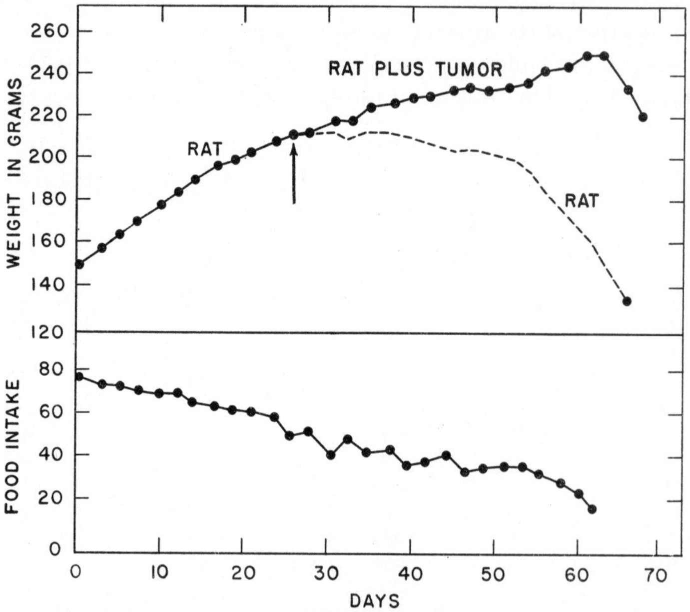

FIG. 50. Weight changes in male rat bearing Walker carcinoma. The rat carcass loses weight progressively soon after growth of tumor is noted (arrow). From Mider, G. B , Tesluk, H., and Morton, J. J., *Acta Unio Intern. Contre Cancrum* **6,** 409 (1948).

first stage the major source for the tumor protein is the diet, whereas in the second stage the dietary intake is not sufficient to supply the needs of the growing tumor, and the resources of the host are drawn upon. During this second stage, the liver of the cancerous host appears to hypertrophy (7, 8), and the liver enlarges in proportion to the total weight of the animal (i.e., carcass plus tumor) (8, 9). However, in the ante-mortem stage of growth of the tumor, there is a precipitate drop in the weight of the liver, as if in the final phase of the life of the cancerous host even the liver surrenders both its functions and its substance to the needs of the tumor (7). The potential sources of tumor nitrogen other than the diet arise from the musculature, but it is of interest that nitrogen must also be diverted, if only temporarily, to the needs of a hyperplastic liver and spleen in the cancerous host (7). The liver response may be homeostatic in origin, as such anabolic reactions may also occur in pregnancy (10). The decrease in size of the liver late in tumor development (11) reflects the general disintegration of the body economy. Although it is known that part of the weight increase of the livers of tumor-bearing animals is due to an increase in water content (12), the hyperplasia is correlated with increase in total nitrogen.

When rats bearing the Walker 256 tumor are deliberately placed on a low protein diet to the extent that the animals are in negative nitrogen balance, the tumors will grow, as in the case of the mice studied by F. R. White (13), but the tumors are smaller, and there is a less profound systemic effect induced in the host (14). Thus, in the protein-depleted, tumorous animals there is no change in the weight of the liver, nor any evidence of hypervolemia; there is, however, an increase in the water content of the liver, and the concentration of liver protein in both depleted and non-depleted tumorous animals is diminished. In the case of sarcoma R-1 in rats, the water content of the tumor increases and the protein content diminishes, as the level of dietary protein decreases (14a).

The question may logically be raised concerning the mechanism of the diversion of nutriments and body proteins to tumor proteins. One answer may be that the demands of the tumor effect an imbalance of the normal steady state, and thus homeostatic mechanisms attempt to restore some sort of equilibrium. Associated with this phenomenon may be the production by the tumor of a circulating toxin which accelerates the catabolism of the body tissues. The respective normal and cancerous patterns may be represented as follows:

$$\text{Normal: Amino acids} \rightarrow \text{Liver} \rightleftarrows \text{Plasma} \rightleftarrows \text{Tissues}$$

$$\text{Cancerous: Amino acids} \rightarrow \text{Liver} \rightleftarrows \underset{\substack{\downarrow \\ \text{Tumor}}}{\text{Plasma}} \rightleftarrows \text{Tissues}$$

There appears to be an increased turnover of protein, as measured by

TABLE 148

Body and Tissue Weights of Fed and Fasted Rats[1] (16)

Tissue	Initial	Protein %	Fed 5 days	Protein %	Fasted 5 days	Protein %
Body	— 174		173 182		172 118	
Tumor	4.14	12.1	12.97	17.2	7.52	17.3
Brain	1.62		1.67		1.66	
Liver	7.00	21.2	9.17	21.9	3.51	25.8
Kidneys	1.28		1.29		1.00	
Thymus	0.39		0.35		0.06	
Spleen	0.92		2.58		0.59	
Heart	0.57		0.56		0.39	

[1] Flexner-Jobling tumors implanted 10 days, one group sacrificed, one group fed normally 5 more days, and one group fasted during same 5 days. Weight on basis of fresh tissue.

C^{14}-labeled glycine, in the liver and plasma proteins of tumor-bearing animals (15). A careful study of the growth of the Flexner-Jobling tumor in rats fed and fasted for 5 days revealed that the proteins of this tumor are not available to the host during starvation and that the tumor serves essentially as a one-way, nitrogen trap (16). In these experiments, within 5 days, the weight of tumor protein increased 345 % in the fed rats and 160 % in the fasted rats; the latter lost 31 % of their body weight and 39 % of their liver weight during the same period (Table 148). Injection of glycine-2-C^{14} showed that in both fasted and fed groups the total radioactivity of the liver and kidney proteins diminishes, whereas the total radioactivity of the tumor increases. The nucleic acid apparently changes in parallel fashion. Since the tumors are necrotic, it would appear that the radioactivity, if released by autolysis, must be efficiently reincorporated into the growing portions to demonstrate the rapid net increase in radioactivity. There is an increased specific and total radioactivity of the deoxyribonucleotides in the livers of tumor-bearing animals as measured both by P^{32} and glycine-2-C^{14} incorporation (17, 18). This latter effect may only be a reflection of rapidly growing tissue elsewhere in the host, for it also occurs in pregnancy.

An indication of possible autolytic phenomena in the livers of animals with tumors elsewhere is provided by data from Dunn's laboratory on some of the free amino acids present in the hepatic tissues (19) (Table 149). There is an elevation in the free amino acids which is greater the larger the size of the tumor.

The total weight loss from non-neoplastic organs and tissues of cancerous subjects exceeds that lost by the normal partner of the pair-fed experiment (5). The carcass (rat minus tumor) of the cancerous host contains less

TABLE 149

FREE AMINO ACIDS IN LIVERS OF NORMAL AND CANCEROUS RATS[1] (19)

State of animals	Amino acids, γ/g. protein			
	Glycine	Methionine	Serine	Threonine
Normal	45.6	5.24	55.9	16.5
Cancerous (small tumor)	53.5	4.78	56.9	18.4
Cancer (large tumor)	62.3	8.30	83.0	33.2

[1] UCLA fibrosarcoma.

nitrogen than do the bodies of the pair-fed controls, but the sum of the tumor and carcass nitrogen yields a nitrogen value not greatly different from that of the normal animal. Nitrogen balance studies in tumor-bearing rats have shown that the tumors contain more nitrogen than is stored by their hosts during the period of tumor growth (5) (Fig. 51). There is little question but that, left to its own devices, the cancerous rat, plagued by anorexia, does not ingest enough nitrogen to take care of the continued demands of both neoplastic and non-neoplastic tissue and answers the problem by breaking down the latter tissue to supply the former.

When the rat is not left to its own devices but is forcibly fed during the period of tumor growth, the tumorous rats do not lose as much carcass weight, as do animals on an *ad libitum* regimen, but they do reveal the typical systemic effects due to the presence of a cancer, namely, anemia, enlarged adrenals, decrease in liver catalase, and increase in liver nitrogen (20, 21). Both nitrogen and sodium chloride are apparently retained in the tumor-bearing animals under these conditions to a greater extent than

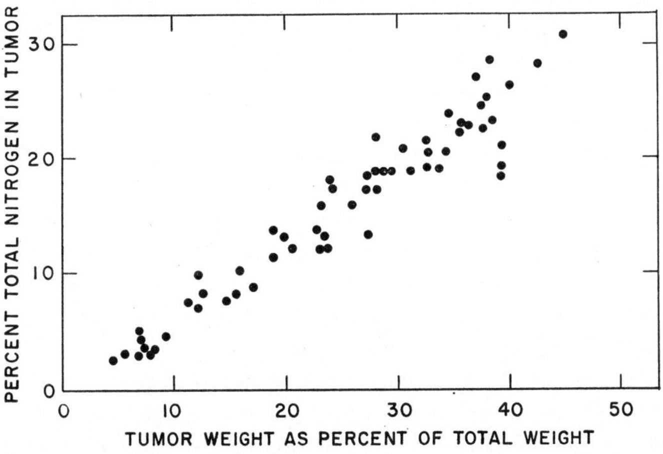

FIG. 51. Walker carcinoma of rat contains a larger proportion of total body nitrogen as growth progresses. From Mider, G. B., Tesluk, H., and Morton, J. J., *Acta Unio Intern. contre Cancrum* **6,** 409 (1948).

TABLE 150

Systemic Effects in Force-Fed Walker 256 Rats (20)

Effect on Ingle high fat diet	Normal	Cancerous
Adrenal weight, mg.	37.9–42.8	80.4–98.5
Liver catalase, $K \times 10^4$	3900–4300	2060–3900
Water in liver, %	68.0	73.0
Lipid, %	17.3	37.3
Nitrogen, mg./g. dry weight	87.0	92.5
Nitrogen, mg./g. fat-free dry weight	120.0	161.5

in normal animals, the former being due to increase in amount of protein being synthesized, the latter to increase in water content of the liver, tumor, and perhaps other tissues (20). The force-fed diet, containing a high fat content, induces in the tumorous rats a considerable lipemia not present in the normal rats receiving the same diet. In conjunction with this lipemia in the tumorous rat is an increase in its liver lipid content (Table 150). The fatty livers noted on the Ingle high fat diet may be due to a dietary choline deficiency, for this condition does not occur with diets (force-fed) containing a high fat content plus water-soluble vitamin mixtures (21). It is of interest that the hypertrophy of the adrenals in the tumorous rat can be reduced by administration of testosterone without any apparent effect on the growth of the tumor (22). Systemic effects on the tumorous host may thus occur in the absence of loss of carcass weight, but it must be pointed out that the proportionate size of the tumor in relation to total body weight may be considerably greater in rats left to feed *ad libitum*, and under such circumstances the degree of systemic effect may be greater. However, it is only by the forced feeding of a high fat diet that the striking inability of the cancerous rat to deal metabolically with fat can be expected to be revealed (21). Whether the forced diet is high in fats, carbohydrates, or protein, there invariably occurs the characteristic increase in weight of the adrenals, spleen, liver, and thymus in the tumorous hosts (21).

The enlarged adrenal in the tumorous host is low in ascorbic acid and in cholesterol (23, 24), and Begg has suggested (25) that these findings would be compatible with an exhaustive hypofunction of the adrenal cortex, particularly emphasized in the lessened liver glycogen (26) and lymph node hypertrophy (27) observed in tumor-bearing mice. These phenomena merit further study.

The principal effect of forced feeding is to reduce the degree of protein depletion of the carcass, but not to prevent such depletion, in rats bearing the Walker 256 tumor, and thereby it further confirms the concept of the tumor as a nitrogen trap. When the tumor weight begins to approach 30 % of the total weight of the rat, even forced feeding does not prevent a marked loss of carcass protein (28). Forced feeding of an adequate diet simply permits the cancerous host to grow a larger tumor in absolute terms without as much carcass weight loss as does free or paired feeding and perhaps seemingly prolongs the first phase of tumor growth described above (29). At the same time, such tube-feeding experiments, especially with extremely high fat diets, illustrate the possibly different requirements of the normal and of the cancerous rat for choline (21). It may be that the extreme hyperlipemia in the cancerous rat under these conditions is due to a response to the demands of the tumor for unsaturated fatty acids needed for the formation of phospholipids, etc. (30). This, however, can only be a partial explanation.

The growth of tumors in rats under paired-feeding conditions is accompanied by a loss of total lipid from the host, and it would appear that this may be due to the increased caloric requirements of the host (6). That there actually is a caloric deficit acquired during the growth of the Walker tumor in rats, a deficit equal to the caloric value of the lipid lost by the cancerous animal, has been shown by bomb calorimetry (31). The lipids lost from the body during tumor growth are apparently completely burnt, since there is no evidence of ketosis. The caloric value of rat lipid extracted from different carcasses possesses a mean value of 9.11 $\pm$ 0.03 calories (31). By dividing the caloric loss from the carcass minus the caloric value of the tumor by 9.11, a figure is obtained for each tumorous rat representative of the calculated lipid loss. This figure agrees very well with the observed lipid loss obtained by subtracting the total lipid in the host's carcass from the lipid in the pair-fed control sacrificed on the day that the first palpable tumor is noted. Thus, for the series of animals studied by Mider and his colleagues, the lipid lost in cancerous and normal rats calculated from caloric data is about -13.40 to -27.4 g. and about -0.4 to -6.7 g., respectively; the observed values are -8.1 to -27.9 g. and -1.5 to -11.3 g. respectively (31). The expenditure by the host of energy derived from fat and carbohydrate during the period of tumor growth is proportional to the size of the tumor.

The increased energy requirement associated with growth of a tumor, largely met by the combustion of lipid, should result in an increased metabolic rate. Basal metabolic studies on individual experimental animals with tumors pose many difficult technical problems. Studies on cancer patients have revealed caloric deficits and increasing energy expenditure in the presence of rapidly growing tumors (32), but many other observations have suggested bizarre metabolic patterns in cancer patients which are inexplicable in terms of known metabolic reactions (29). Some patients store nitrogen despite a calculated caloric deficit (32), and there seems to be no consistent ratio between the amount of nitrogen stored by a cancerous patient and the amount of weight gained (32, 33), whereas some individuals store nitrogen while losing weight. Frequently an increase in body weight simply means an increase in retention of electrolyte and water. Each one of these phenomena is encountered in experiments on laboratory animals, but rarely, apparently, does the human being provide in his behavior an exact copy of all that found in the laboratory rat. As Mider has pointed out (29), the conclusions drawn from the behavior of the tumorous rat apply to only about 80% of the subjects studied, and the other 20% represent widely variable responses. It is small wonder that in a more heterogeneous and far less well-controlled group of human patients the proportion of individuals with variable responses is certainly greater than the 20% found in rats. Nevertheless, the basic principles derived from the study of the majority of a group of laboratory animals may, when skilfully applied, illuminate the course of neoplastic disease in individual cases of human beings.

Hepatic, Renal, and Erythrocyte Catalase Activity. One of the earliest reports on the systemic effect of tumors was made by Brahn (34), who observed very low liver catalase values in human beings who had died as a result of various forms of cancer. Later work showed that, of all the individual enzyme systems studied in the livers of mice and rats bearing a wide variety of tumors, the activity of catalase was by far the most affected. This peroxide-splitting enzyme is apparently very considerably reduced only in the livers and to only a small extent in the kidneys (35–41). The decrease in the liver catalase is progressive with the growth of the tumor. Moreover, the effect of the tumor upon the activity of this liver enzyme was found to be reversible, for the complete removal of the tumor, whether by surgical excision or by spontaneous regression in certain strains, resulted in a restoration of the liver catalase activity to the normal level. Further evidence that the effect produced on the liver catalase is due to the tumor and not to any growing tissues present in the animal has been adduced from the failure of growing, subcutaneously implanted whole embryo tissue mashes to affect in any way the liver catalase activity of the animal (41); the liver catalase activity of pregnant animals is also normal throughout gestation.

The effect elicited by subcutaneous transplanted tumors in rats is illustrated in Table 151. The number of Osborne-Mendel rats employed in the studies described in Table 151 and in subsequent similar investigations totaled well over 100. When the hepatoma weighed 10 g. or more, i.e., at least 5% of the total body weight of the animal, no exception was ever found in the observations of a lowered liver catalase in the tumor-bearing animals of both sexes. The livers of about 200 Buffalo rats of both sexes bearing the transplanted Jensen sarcoma were also examined for catalase activity, and here, too, when the tumor weight was 5% or more of the total body weight of the animal, the liver catalase activity was

TABLE 151

EFFECT OF THE PRESENCE OF TUMORS ON THE LIVER AND KIDNEY CATALASE ACTIVITY OF RATS[1] (36, 39)

Tissue	Remarks[2]	Catalase activity[3]
1. Normal rat liver[4]	Animals 5 wk. to 1 yr. old	1.7
2. Regenerating liver in normal rats[5]	Animals 5 wk. to 1 yr. old	1.6
3. Livers of rats carrying transplanted hepatoma 31[6]	Tumors 4 wk. old; host rats 9–10 wk. old	0.1
4. Livers of rats from which transplanted hepatomas were excised[6]	24 hr. after operation	1.0
	48 hr. after operation	1.8
	72 hr. after operation	1.8
	96 hr. after operation	1.3
	168 hr. after operation	1.6
5. Livers of rats described under (4) reinoculated with fresh hepatoma[6]	Second tumors 4 wk. old; host rats about 14 wk. old	0.1
6. Livers of rats described under (5) from which second hepatoma was excised[6]	24 hr. after operation	0.9
	48 hr. after operation	1.8
	72 hr. after operation	1.8
7. Regenerating liver in rats carrying transplanted hepatoma 4 wk. old[6]	24 hr. after removal of lobes	0.3
	48 hr. after removal of lobes	0.3
	72 hr. after removal of lobes	0.1
	120 hr. after removal of lobes	0.1
8. Livers of rats described under (7) from which hepatoma was excised[6]	24 hr. after removal of tumor 6 days after removal of lobes	1.0
	48 hr. after removal of tumor 7 days after removal of lobes	1.6
	72 hr. after removal of tumor 8 days after removal of lobes	1.8
9. Livers of rats carrying transplanted Jensen sarcoma[7]	Tumors 4 wk. old; host rats 12–14 wk. old	0.1
10. Kidneys of normal Osborne-Mendel rats	Animals 5 wk. to 1 yr. old	1.0
11. Kidneys of rats bearing transplanted hepatoma 31	Animals 4 wk. old; host rats 9–10 wk. old	0.8
12. Kidneys of normal Buffalo rats	Animals 12–14 wk. old	1.3
13. Kidneys of rats bearing transplanted Jensen sarcoma[7]	Tumors 4 wk. old; host rats 12–14 wk. old	1.1
14. Blood of normal rats[8]	Animals 12–14 wk. old	1.4
15. Blood of rats carrying transplanted Jensen sarcoma[8]	Tumor 4 wk. old; host rats 12–14 wk. old	1.4

[1] Animals killed by decapitation. See (37) for discussion of influence of residual blood in the liver on determination of catalase activity.

[2] Age of tumor refers to time elapsed since implantation.

[3] In terms of milliliters oxygen evolved per second at 25° of a mixture containing 1 ml. tissue extract (0.6 mg. total N), 1 ml. 29% hydrogen peroxide, and 5 ml. phosphate buffer at pH 6.9. Blood catalase activity determined on mixture of 0.05 ml. blood hemolyzed in 5 ml. distilled water, plus 1 ml. 29% hydrogen peroxide.

[4] Osborne-Mendel and Buffalo rats (male or female).

[5] Same as footnote 4. Lobes removed 24–96 hr. before.

[6] Osborne-Mendel rats (male or female).

[7] Buffalo rats (male or female).

[8] Blood collected fresh through decapitation.

invariably lower than normal. The lowest values were found in animals with the largest tumors. The catalase activity of the liver, which was the same in the normal rats of both strains, decreased proportionately with the growth of the hepatoma or sarcoma, never leveling off at any time that the tumor was growing, and reaching its lowest level with the death of the animal. On the basis of the experimental technique employed, the lowest level of liver catalase activity reached was about one-twentieth that of normal. At the time that this work was done, hepatoma 31 grew in Osborne-Mendel rats at about the same rate as the Jensen sarcoma grew in Buffalo rats, and the rate of decrease in the liver catalase activity with growth of the tumor in both kinds of rats was practically the same. Regenerating liver in animals with tumors behaved like non-regenerating (normal adult) liver under the same circumstances (Table 151). Quite frequently, the hepatic catalase in rats in whom the subcutaneous or intramuscular tumor had just been freshly implanted, e.g., 1 or 2 days before, showed a distinct rise in level of activity (36). Thereafter, there was a steady diminution in this level. It may be that the initial rise in the hepatic catalase level is a reflection of the adjustment of the host to the establishment of a foreign tissue and has nothing to do with the latter as a tumor *per se*.

Hepatoma 31 was an encapsulated tumor and grew under the skin of the inoculated animal. The complete surgical excision of this tumor was readily accomplished, and the restoration of the liver catalase activity to to the normal value followed within a day or two after the operation. A second inoculation of the tumor into the animal from which the first had been excised again resulted in a decrease in the liver catalase; excision of the second tumor again resulted in a restoration of the enzyme activity to the normal level (Table 151). The Jensen sarcoma was implanted intramuscularly and subsequently invaded the surrounding tissue; complete excision of this tumor was difficult if not impossible. Attempts to remove most of the sarcoma led to a partial and only temporary restoration of the liver catalase activity of the operated animals for, with subsequent growth of the remaining tumor tissue, the liver catalase activity dropped again.

Tumors of all kinds which grow at a rapid rate in various strains of mice of both sexes also produce a marked lowering of the liver catalase activity. The fastest growing tumors produce the greatest drop in the liver catalase activity in mice. As in the case of rats, the effect on the liver enzyme runs parallel with the growth of the tumor, reaching the lowest level at the death of the animal. Again, as in the case of rats, the optimum effect observed is of the very first order, for the activity may drop to less than one-twentieth of the normal liver catalase value. Up to the present time, several hundred mice of various strains, bearing many kinds of tumors, whether transplanted, induced, or spontaneous, have been studied. The only exceptions to the otherwise invariable observation of a lowered liver catalase in these animals were two. These were (a) mice bearing extremely slow-growing tumors, such as the transplanted intestinal adenocarcinoma in *A* mice, and the transplanted hepatoma A in *C3H* mice, and (b) *C57 Black* mice bearing the rapidly growing transplanted sarcoma 37. Exception (a) may be explained on the following basis: There is probably a competition between the rate by which the tumor in some way causes a lowering of the liver catalase activity and the rate by which the animal's body attempts to repair this deficiency. In the case of slow-growing tumors the latter effect in all probability predominates. Exception (b) may have its origin in the fact that the liver catalase activity of normal strain *C57 Black* mice is very much lower than that of all the other strains studied (five in number) (Table 152). It may be possible, therefore, that, in the livers of this strain of mice, with an abnormally low catalase activity to begin with, the otherwise universal effect of a fast-growing tumor may be either imperceptibly small or non-existent (37).

The problem of removing tumors from mice to see whether the tumor effect on the liver catalase is reversible is similar to that of the Jensen sarcoma in rats; i.e., it is difficult under ordinary circumstances to remove the subcutaneous tumor completely without removing, fatally, a large part of the animal at the same time. The question of reversibility has, however, been answered by investigating the liver catalase activity (a) of *I* strain mice in which the intracutaneous (abdominal) implantation of sarcoma 37 is followed by the progressive growth of the tumor for about 3 weeks, at the end of which time the tumor begins to regress visibly and steadily until by the end of another 3 weeks or so the tumor disappears, and (b) of *DBA*, *Y*, and *C* strain mice in the tails of which sarcoma 37 is intracutaneously implanted. The tumor grows steadily in this site, and, after a certain lapse of time, the tails are amputated. In either case, (a) or (b), the animal loses the tumor, and in both cases the liver catalase activity is restored to the normal level within a few days (37) (Figs. 52 and 53).

The effect which the growth rate of a tumor exerts upon the depression of the liver catalase activity is particularly well illustrated by the relative rate of growth of sarcoma 37 in the abdomen or in the tail, and in the corresponding level of liver catalase activity of the respective animals. There is available here the controlled circumstance of one and the same tumor growing in two different sites in different animals of the same strain. The caudal implants of sarcoma 37 grow at nearly the same rate in *DBA*, *C*, and *Y* strains. The abdominal implants of this tumor grow at nearly the same rate in these strains. But the rate of growth of the caudal implants is only about half that of the abdominal implants. Correspondingly, the rate of decrease in the liver catalase activity of the mice of all strains with

TABLE 152

THE EFFECT OF THE PRESENCE OF TUMORS ON THE LIVER AND KIDNEY CATALASE ACTIVITY OF MICE[1] (37, 39, 41)

Strain	Tumor[2]	Age of tumor[3]	Activity of liver[4]	Activity of kidney[4]
C3H		—	2.0	1.0
C3H	Transplanted hepatic A	270	1.9	0.9
C3H	Spontaneous mammary	18	1.9	—
C3H	Spontaneous mammary	35	1.6	—
C3H	Spontaneous mammary	60	0.7	0.2
C3H	Transplanted gastric adenocarcinoma	21	0.3	0.6
C3H	Transplanted cerebral	90	0.3	—
C3H	Primary sarcoma[5]	14	0.5	0.5
C3H	Transplanted endothelioma	30	0.1	—
A		-	2.0	—
A	Transplanted intestinal	90	1.9	—
A	Spontaneous mammary	35	1.0	—
A	Transplanted pulmonary	42	0.3	—
A	Transplanted lymphoma	9	1.4	—
A	Transplanted lymphoma	20	0.6	—
A	Transplanted lung tumor F	30	0.5	—
C		—	2.0	—
C	Transplanted hemangioma	60	0.7	—
C	Transplanted sarcoma 37	24	0.1	—
DBA		—	2.0	0.8
DBA	Transplanted hepatic	20	0.3	0.7
DBA	Transplanted melanoma	40	1.2	0.8
DBA	Transplanted sarcoma 37	18	0.1	0.4
DBA	Transplanted CR-180	18	0.1	0.6
Y		—	2.0	—
Y	Transplanted sarcoma 37	18	0.1	—
I		—	2.0	—
I	Transplanted sarcoma 37	12	0.4	—
I	Transplanted sarcoma 37	35[6]	1.9	—
C57 Black		—	1.0	—
C57 Black	Transplanted sarcoma 37	10	0.9	—
C3H	Embryo mash	60	2.0	—
DBA	Embryo mash	60	2.0	—

[1] Animals killed by decapitation. See (37) for discussion of influence of residual blood in catalase determinations.

[2] Transplanted tumors grown subcutaneously or intracutaneously.

[3] Age of transplanted tumor refers to days elapsed since implantation. Age of spontaneous and induced tumors is only approximate and refers to time elapsed since tumors were palpable.

[4] In terms of milliliters of oxygen evolved per second at 25°, of mixture of 1 ml. tissue extract (0.6 mg. total N), 1 ml. 29% hydrogen peroxide, and 5 ml. phosphate buffer at pH 6.9.

[5] Induced by injection of methylcholanthrene.

[6] At this "time" the tumor had completely regressed.

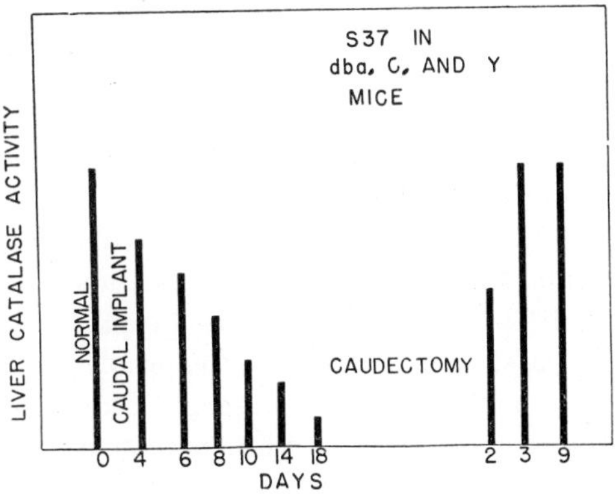

FIG. 52. The effect of intracutaneous implantation in the tail and of removal of sarcoma 37 by caudectomy on the liver catalase activity of various strains of mice. The ordinate represents the rate of O_2 evolution in milliliters per second at 25° of a mixture of 1.0 ml. liver extract containing 0.6 mg. total N, 5.0 ml. phosphate buffer at pH 6.9, and 1.0 ml. 29% hydrogen peroxide. Normal liver activity is 2.0 ml./sec. in all strains. From Greenstein, J. P., and Andervont, H. B., *J. Natl. Cancer Inst.* **2,** 345 (1942).

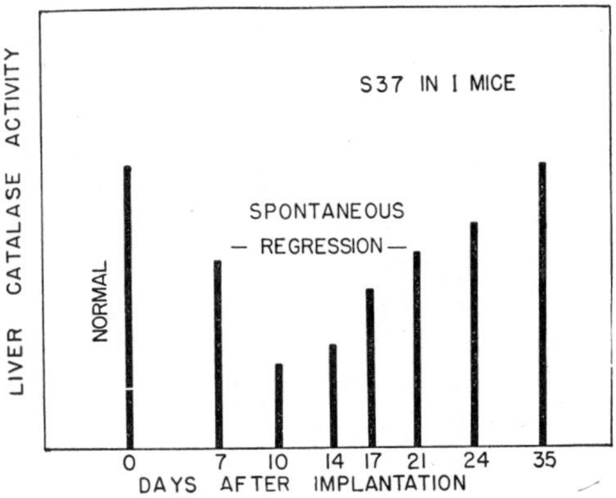

FIG. 53. The effect of intracutaneous implantation in the abdomen and of subsequent regression of sarcoma 37 on the liver catalase activity in *I* strain mice. The ordinate represents the rate of O_2 evolution in milliliters per second at 25° of a mixture of 1.0 ml. liver extract containing 0.6 mg. total N, 5.0 ml. phosphate buffer at pH 6.9, and 1.0 ml. 29% hydrogen peroxide. Normal liver activity is 2.0 ml./sec. From Greenstein, J. P., and Andervont, H. B., *J. Natl. Cancer Inst.* **2,** 345 (1942).

caudal implants of the tumor is about half that of mice with abdominal implants (37).

The liver catalase activity of the kidney in tumor-bearing rats and mice is also depressed below the normal value, but the proportionate drop from the normal is not as great in the kidney as in the liver (39). The liver catalase may drop to one-twentieth the normal activity, the kidney catalase to one-half. In some cases this disparity in the depression of activity in the two tissues leads to the curious finding that, per gram of tissue, the kidney in tumor-bearing animals has an equal or higher catalase activity than the liver. The possibility that the effect produced on the kidney may be reversible has not been investigated.

In tumor-bearing animals with greatly lowered liver catalase activity and less lowered kidney catalase activity, the catalase activity of the red blood cells is normal (39). Liver, kidney, and erythrocytes are the principal tissues in which catalase is found. To the problem of how the liver and the kidney catalase is affected by the presence of a tumor in a distant site is added the further complication of why the catalase in each of the two tissues should be affected in different degrees while the erythrocyte catalase is completely unaffected. Further study along fundamental lines in normal as well as in cancerous animals, e.g., the sites at which enzymes are synthesized, is clearly desirable.

Although the mechanism of the reduction in the liver catalase activity of tumor-bearing animals is not at present understood, one significant fact emerges from the study of this phenomenon, viz., that practically all tumors, regardless of their classification, if they grow fast enough, will produce this phenomenon in practically all species and strains of animals studied. Hepatomas, lymphomas, sarcomas, carcinomas, etc., all exert a systemic effect as revealed by the depression of the liver catalase activity. It has been demonstrated in the previous chapter that nearly all transplanted tumors possess so uniform an enzymatic pattern as to render them nearly indistinguishable from each other. As a further corollary it was stated that, enzymatically, tumors tended to converge toward a common type of tissue. It will be readily appreciated that the similar effect upon the liver catalase activity produced by a wide variety of tumors is in harmony with these concepts. Tumors, in a general sense, apparently present in themselves not only a rather uniform set of chemical components but also produce a more or less uniform effect on the hosts which contain them. This effect is not produced simply because the tumor is a growing tissue, for embryonic tissue, growing at the same rate as many tumors, does not elicit the effect (41). This effect is something which nearly all tumors, as tumors, possess in common.

In the first edition of this monograph, the writer, summing up the observations accumulated in his laboratory, stated that the tumor may produce the effects noted either by giving off some toxic product to the circulation or else by abstracting from the circulation some material essential to the normal maintenance of the liver catalase. On the basis of observations showing that the catalase activity of mixtures of homogenates of normal liver and of tumor were additive (38), it was concluded that the liver of the cancerous animal does not contain the normal amount of catalase plus an inhibitor, but that it simply contains less catalase; i.e., the synthesis of the enzyme in the liver is interfered with in some manner.

Since 1947, when those lines were written, much valuable information on this problem has accrued from various laboratories, and it may be concluded that the effect of a tumor in decreasing markedly the level of liver catalase of the host is by now a well-established phenomenon (cf. 42). However, the essential answers to many of the questions raised by this problem have not as yet been answered. Perhaps the most basic of these questions is why only hepatic catalase is so markedly lowered in the cancerous animal, whereas many other hepatic enzymes are apparently unaffected (see below). Studies with radioactive iron (43) have served to illuminate one paradoxical situation, namely that of the normal level of erythrocyte catalase in the presence of greatly reduced hepatic catalase in the tumor-bearing animal, for these studies have revealed the independent course of the biosynthesis of the catalase in the two sites. The subjection of animals to various dietary and hormonal stresses, whereby not only catalase but many other enzymes are simultaneously affected, offers little help to a general solution of the problem. A prolonged period of starvation in which the decrease in the level of hepatic enzymes more or less parallels the decrease in hepatic protein yields results which are no more than to be expected (44). The observations that mice irradiated with X-rays (45) and that rats with advanced murine leprosy possess a lowered hepatic catalase level is of interest, but they would be significant to the problem if the level of other hepatic enzymes in such animals had been shown to be unaffected (46). The effect of the tumor is apparently selective among the hepatic systems, and any interpretation of the mechanism of the hepatic catalase decrease in tumor-bearing animals must take this factor of selectivity into consideration.

Before reviewing the more recent work in this area of research, it should be pointed out that catalase is an enzyme whose activity is measured with considerable experimental difficulty and uncertainty. The reaction between catalase and hydrogen peroxide to yield water and oxygen is simple enough, but the explosive nature of the reaction, and the need to work in a two-phase system involving an emerging gas, imposes difficulties not ordinarily encountered in simpler, homogeneous systems. A critical consideration of the kinetics of the catalase-peroxide system has been published (47). The very precise, rapid methods developed by Chance (48) are admirable, but they depend upon the use of physical equipment and highly purified enzyme preparations not generally available. It is unnecessary to belabor a point quite familiar to workers concerned with this system, but it should be pointed out that comparisons of crude tissue preparations with different catalase contents may well yield differences in activity which will vary depending upon the conditions chosen. Thus, in the writer's experience, incubation of homogenates of the livers of normal and of tumorous animals will show very great differences in activity at high peroxide substrate concentrations, and lesser differences as the peroxide concentration is lowered. The toxic effect of peroxide itself on catalase is well known, but is the apparently greater damaging effect of hydrogen peroxide on the hepatic catalase of the tumorous rat due to the possibility that there is less actual catalase protein in the liver of this animal and hence a greater ratio of substrate to enzyme than normal, or are the proteins in such a liver rearranged in such a way as to afford less protection against the action of the substrate on an otherwise normal catalase-protein complex in that liver? When carefully performed in a single laboratory, manometric and titrimetric methods of catalase assay are in agreement (46), and, although practically all the evidence from the newer work is in accord that hepatic catalase is markedly reduced in activity in the tumorous host, the magnitude of the levels determined generally varies from one laboratory to the other. In the face of so marked a phenomenon, these quantitative differences are not serious, since they are all in the same direction, but they should perhaps be borne in mind.

Among the more promising of the newer assay methods for catalase, and one readily applicable to the study of homogenates, is that of Greenfield and Price (cf. 68). This procedure employs a pressure traducer and a continuous recorder system to record the pressure change of the oxygen evolved from the hydrogen peroxide during the initial period of the reaction. The data are expressed in terms of first order reaction kinetics, and the method has been used to follow the fractionation of the livers of normal and of tumor-bearing animals (see below).

A lowering of hepatic catalase level in rats carrying the Jensen sarcoma without appreciable change in the levels of kidney and erythrocyte catalase has been noted by Appelman *et al.* (49), which is in accord with earlier reports (39). It is further stated (49) that the decrease in liver catalase is accompanied by enlargement of liver and spleen. The enlargement of these organs unquestionably accompanies the later phases of tumor growth, but the hepatic catalase effect may be observed before this enlargement begins. Studies of the effect of animal tumors growing in egg culture on the liver catalase levels of the embryo chick have revealed a decreased enzymatic activity on a unit nitrogen basis (50, 51). In view of the enlarged liver in such cases, calculations of liver catalase activity on a whole-liver basis reveal an unchanged or slightly higher activity than normal (50, 51). Such calculations are arithmetical expressions of temporary and unrelated biological phenomena. In the three phases of tumor growth described by Mider, the liver of the host first remains at its normal size, then it enlarges, and finally it either reverts to its normal size or decreases below normal size. During all these three phases, after a brief, initial rise, the liver catalase steadily diminishes until it reaches a constant, minimum level. At no time is there an apparent relation between catalase level and liver size. As stated above, catalase activity levels are frequently a function of experimental technique, but many recent results suggest that the liver catalase level of tumor-bearing animals falls to at least 50% of the normal. At the same time, no data on enlarged livers in tumorous animals have ever shown an increase in weight double that of normal, and the relatively small increases in liver weight, more frequent in female than in male tumor-bearing rats (49, 52), show the presence of a superimposed hormonal effect. Furthermore, the increase in liver weight is frequently a function of age of the tumorous host, the older animal having the greater tendency to such an increase (52). The younger animal, as Yeakel suggests, already has a liver enlarged to the physiological maximum, and the additional stress imposed by the presence of a tumor in the host does not produce a demonstrable effect upon the liver weight. The data in Table 151 concerned rats 9 to 10 weeks old and bearing tumors. Finally, it should be pointed out that pregnancy causes enlargement of the liver (10) without a change in liver catalase (41).

Studies by Weil-Malherbe and Schade (53) on the effect of the Jensen sarcoma on hepatic catalase levels have shown that in extreme cases the drop in such level may reach 5% of the normal. The presence of a high or low protein diet (8 and 45% casein, respectively) has no appreciable effect in either case on the mean level of catalase activity in the livers of the tumorous hosts, which was about 25% of normal. These findings might suggest either that nutritional factors were non-operative or that the effects of the tumor on the liver catalase level were large in proportion to the possible nutritional effects. In protein-depleted rats bearing the Jensen sarcoma, the lowering of the liver catalase activity is not as severe as in normally fed rats bearing the same tumor, but this may be related to the smaller size of the tumor in the starved animals (54). It will be recalled that the presence of the tumor tends to compel the liver at some stage to incorporate nitrogen, and that this increased level of hepatic nitrogen should be accompanied by a diminution in one of the liver components is essentially a paradoxical circumstance. When animals are forced-fed, as in the experiments of Begg and Dickinson (20), the tumor-bearing rats lose little if any carcass weight but develop the typical systemic effects such as loss of liver catalase activity to about half that of normal, anemia, adrenal hypertrophy, and loss of adrenal sudanophilia. Thus, with high or low protein diets, with protein depletion, or with forced feeding, the tumor-bearing animal's lowered hepatic catalase is relatively little altered, and it is difficult to avoid the impression that this enzymatic effect is relatively independent of the nutritional status of the host (Tables 153 and

TABLE 153

EFFECT OF DIET ON LIVER CATALASE LEVELS IN JENSEN SARCOMA RATS (53)

Diet	Body weight/ tumor weight	Days after transplantation	Catalase, % of normal
Cube diet	4.20	22.1	14
High protein	6.53	19.1	29
Low protein	5.61	18.1	28

TABLE 154

EFFECT OF DIETARY PROTEIN ON LIVER CATALASE LEVELS IN RATS BEARING WALKER 256 TUMOR (55)

Diet	Initial body weight, g.	Time, days	Changes in carcass weight, g.	Liver, g./100 g.	Hemoglobin, g./100 ml.	Catalase, $K \times 10^4$
25% protein, normal	114	14	+59	5.8	13.3	2522
25% protein, tumor	113	14	+ 8	9.2	7.8	1342
6% protein, normal	115	14	−12	5.0	15.1	2487
6% protein, tumor	111	14	−24	6.6	8.7	1170

TABLE 155

EFFECT OF TUMOR ALTERATION ON LIVER CATALASE IN FEMALE RATS[1] (56)

Group	Tumor, % of body weight	Mean liver weight		Hemoglobin, g./100 ml.	Catalase, $K \times 10^4$
		Per 100 g. body weight	Per 100 g. carcass weight		
Control	—	3.6	3.6	14.7	2842
Benign tumor	51	3.1	6.3	11.4	2609
Benign-malignant tumor	49	3.1	6.2	8.9	1600
Malignant tumor	30	3.7	5.4	9.1	1353

[1] Benign tumor in female Sprague-Dawley rats, which undergoes malignant transformation whereby it becomes transplantable.

154) (53, 55), of the body weight of the host, or of the liver size (cf. 56) (Table 155).

Some of the concomitant systemic effects on the tumor-bearing host are described in Table 156 (25). It is interesting to note a brief rise in hemoglobin and in liver catalase in the early stage of growth of the tumor (cf. 36), followed by the progressive diminution in these constituents as the tumor grows. As suggested above, the initial rise in these levels may not be specific for a tumor *per se* but simply representative of the adjustment of the host to the establishment of a foreign tissue.

Concomitant with the depression of the liver catalase of the tumor-bearing animal is a decrease in hemoglobin. It is possible by frequent bleedings to induce a drop in the hemoglobin level of the normal animal to about 50% of the usual level, but there is a relatively very small decrease in the liver catalase of such an animal (55). The presence of a growing, malignant tumor, on the other hand, can induce a 50% drop in blood hemoglobin together with a 50% drop, or more, in the liver catalase level. This is further evidence that the heme proteins of the erythrocyte and of the liver have different histories, and that a tumor induces effects over and beyond those due to "ordinary" disturbances of body growth (cf. 55).

It may well be that the hepatic catalase depression in tumorous animals is a specific illustration of the effect of a cancer toxin. The revival of this old concept, hitherto somewhat nebulous, has been facilitated since it can be tested on a reasonably well-defined chemical system derived from a particular organ within the host. The development of this problem has resulted in recent years in a series of penetrating studies from several laboratories. Adams injected mice subcutaneously with homogenized S-37, S-2146, and CR-180 tissue and observed a marked diminution in the hepatic catalase of such animals at 24 and 48 hours after injection, a rise to normal by the fourth day, and thereafter a progressive decrease to a value considerably less than that of the normal level of this enzyme by the tenth day (57, 58) (Fig. 54). The purpose of homogenization was apparently to delay the effects of tumor growth, for, when larger pieces of tumor

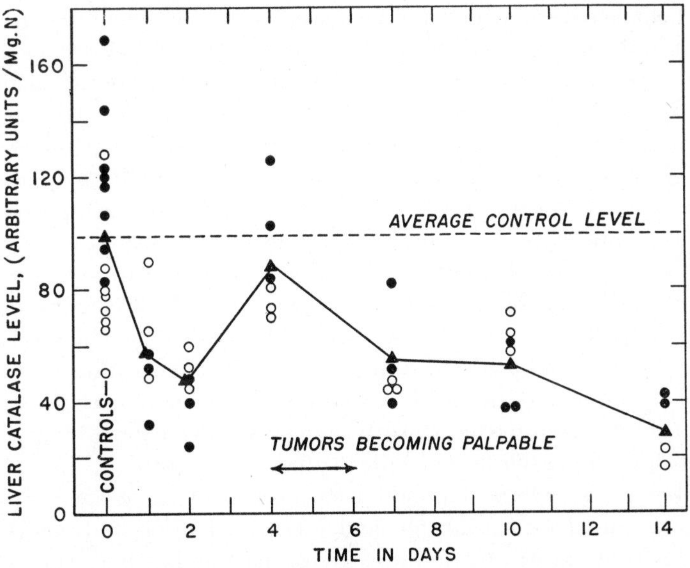

FIG. 54. Liver catalase of mice after injection of sarcoma 37 homogenate. Open circles, -females; black circles,—males; triangles represent arithmetic mean values. From Adams, D. H., *Brit. J. Cancer* **4,** 183 (1950).

TABLE 156

Associated Systemic Effects in Rats Bearing Walker 256 Tumors[1] (25)

Tumor size	Body weight	Adrenal weight	Thymus weight	Hemoglobin	Liver catalase	Adrenal cholesterol	Adrenal ascorbic acid
Control	170	15.4	387	15.4	1570	4.68	0.413
10 mm.	160	17.5	420	16.2	2079	4.16	0.372
20 mm.	161	18.8	324	11.8	1596	3.79	0.324
30 mm.	173	21.3	288	10.7	1332	3.25	0.314
40 mm.	182	30.2	156	8.6	753	2.97	0.238

[1] Body weight in grams; adrenal and thymus weight in milligrams; hemoglobin in grams per 100 ml.; liver catalase as $K \times 10^4$ at 0.1 mg. N per milliliter; and adrenal components in milligrams per 100 mg. Animals fed *ad libitum.*

were inoculated and an earlier and more rapid evidence of tumor growth occurred, the rise of the liver catalase at the fourth day was obscured or obliterated (57), and the progressive decrease in liver catalase from the time of inoculation observed by others in the case of mice (37, 41) was observed. No significant effect on the liver catalase level was noted by Adams with homogenates of normal tissues, including embryos (57; cf. 41). It appeared probable, therefore, that the homogenization of the tumors prior to inoculation and the course of the liver catalase levels subsequent to inoculation revealed the following consecutive phenomena: (a) the initial drop in the hepatic catalase shortly after inoculation of the tumor homogenate and due to the release of a toxic material from the tumor into the host; (b) the restoration to the normal level of liver catalase at the fourth day due to exhaustion of the supply of toxin with concomitant restorative powers of the host; and (c) beyond the fourth day, when the tumor began to be actually palpable, and thereafter during the course of its progressive growth, the familiar progressive diminution in the liver catalase level of its host (Fig. 54). With still finer homogenization of the tumor, the initial drop in catalase activity reached its lowest level at 1 day after inoculation, the normal restoration was advanced to 7 days, and the delay in tumor growth caused the lowering of the liver catalase levels to proceed only after the tenth day (57). The dependence of the catalase level on tumor weight is shown in Fig. 55 (57). When the tumor tissue was homogenized in citric acid, subcutaneous inoculation of the homogenates into mice resulted in a nearly immediate decrease in liver catalase without any observable tumor growth (58).

The possibility of the humoral transmission of some agent from the tumor was raised by Lucké (59) and was tested by a study of the liver catalase activity in parabiotic rats with one partner bearing a tumor. The collected data are given in Table 157, whereby it is noted that (a) parabiosis *per se* has no effect on the enzyme level in the liver, (b) although in

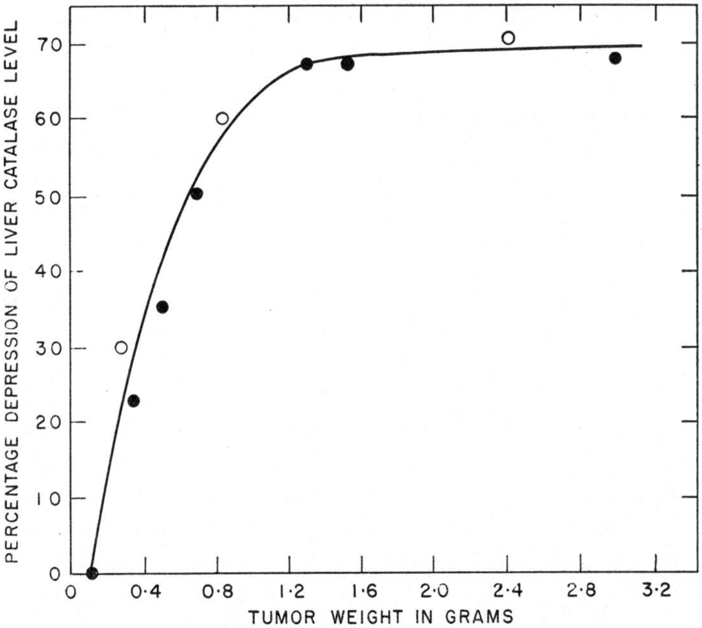

FIG. 55. Progressive diminution in liver catalase level to constant and minimal value with increasing weight of sarcoma 37 in mice. Open circles, -females; black circles, -males. From Adams, D. H., *Brit. J. Cancer* **4,** 183 (1950).

TABLE 157

LIVER CATALASE ACTIVITY IN SINGLE AND PARABIOTIC RATS (59)

Status of rats	Liver catalase activity, mean per 0.03 mg. N
Single rats, normal	0.814
Parabiotic rats:	
Partner A, normal	0.826
Partner B, normal	0.817
Single rats, with tumor	0.608
Parabiotic rats:	
Partner A, with tumor	0.535
Partner B, without tumor	0.660

single rats with tumors (Walker 256) the liver catalase activity is reduced, an apparently greater depression occurs in tumor-bearing parabionts, and (c) the liver catalase activity in the non-tumor-bearing partner in the parabiotic union is reduced to the level of single rats bearing the tumor. In view of these findings and the fact that the blood flow through the anastomoses is small in comparison to the total blood volume of each of the partners, it is possible that the toxic agent either is elaborated in relatively large amounts by the tumor or disappears relatively slowly from the blood stream (59).

At the same time, Nakahara attempted to arrive at the chemical basis of the problem, namely, to isolate from tumor tissues the agent which might be responsible for the effect on the liver catalase of the host. Using relatively crude fractionation techniques, Nakahara and his coworkers (60–62) succeeded in isolating a fraction, apparently protein-like and heat-stable in nature, from a number of human tumors which, when injected into normal mice, produced a marked diminution in their level of hepatic catalase. This observation was important, not so much because a chemical component of a tumor could produce an effect *in vivo* on a specific liver enzyme, but because the component derived from one species was effective on the hepatic function of another species. Perhaps this is not too exceptional when the therapeutic action of beef insulin in cases of human diabetes is recalled, but it does mark one of the few observations which suggest that the metabolism of the cancer cell and the systemic effects derivable from it may be similar in different species. The agent responsible for the effect noted was designated by Nakahara as "toxohormone" (61). Fractionation in a similar manner of the normal tissues adjacent to the tumors studied led to the isolation of materials which, at the same dosage levels, had no effect on the liver catalase of mice injected with such materials. The active tumor agent produced in normal mice the characteristic thymic involution of tumor-bearing mice, but not the equally characteristic increase in adrenal weight (62). The suggestion was made by Nakahara that the tumor agent may function generally by affecting protein metabolism, and specifically by interfering with the metabolism of iron and thereby the synthesis of iron-containing enzyme proteins (62).

Using implants of rat and human homogenates in mice, Adams noted no change in the liver catalase activity of the host animals (58), a phenomenon at first sight explicable on grounds of species differences but probably due to the small proportion of agent present in the amount of homogenate employed for the injection. The agent represents apparently only a relatively minute fraction of the total homogenate, and in Nakahara's early experiments the human materials injected per mouse represented several grams of wet weight of the original human tissues from which the material had been isolated. Nevertheless, with the same amount of mouse homogenate injected into mice, Adams had noted profound effects upon their liver catalase, and the possibility therefore remains either that mouse tumors per unit weight contain more of the toxic agent than do the tumors of other species (cf. 62), or that the mouse liver catalase is more sensitive to, and receptive of, the effect of the agent from mouse tumors.

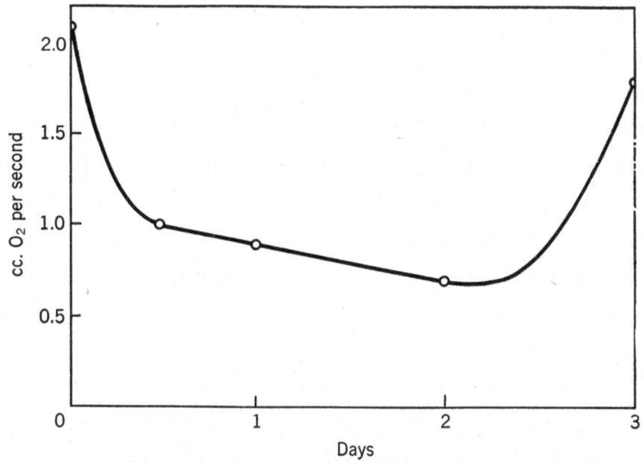

FIG. 56. Liver catalase activity of mice at various intervals after a single intraperitoneal injection of active tumor fraction. From Greenfield, R. E., and Meister, A., *J. Natl. Cancer Inst.* **11,** 997 (1951).

In any event, the question is academic, since the appearance of purified fractions from tumors has made the use of tumor homogenates unnecessary.

The fractionation of mouse mammary tumor tissue was conducted on a relatively large scale in the writer's laboratory by Greenfield and Meister (63), and several fractions were obtained which when injected intraperitoneally into normal mice produced a marked and reversible decrease in their liver catalase activity (Fig. 56). Similar fractions obtained from normal tissues possessed at the same dosage levels little if any effect on the liver catalase activity of the host. Equally as important as these was the observation that injection of an amount of the tumor factor which in the normal mouse resulted in a marked decrease of liver catalase produced no significant change in the levels of the following enzymes in the same liver: lactic dehydrogenase, dehydropeptidase I, and glutamic-alanine transaminase. The active tumor fractions were found to be very stable to heat, as noted by Nakahara, and in addition they were very stable to boiling 6 *N* HCl (63). Similar fractions from the viable and the necrotic areas of the same tumor possessed identical anticatalase activities, so that it may be assumed that the necrotic area of a tumor is not the site of origin of these fractions. Of possibly related interest in this connection is the observation of a unique antigen in a transplanted lymphosarcoma in rats, which is absent from all normal tissues studied (63a).

When fractions from normal tissues are injected at levels very much higher than those derived from tumors, there frequently appears in normal mice a distinct lowering of their liver catalase activity (63). With due allowance in the interpretation of an effect after the administration of a large amount of ill-defined material, it is not impossible to consider the factor which produces a decrease in liver catalase as being more or less widely distributed among normal tissues, but present in tumors in abnormally large amounts. This possibility is further emphasized by the *in vitro* studies of Hargreaves and Deutsch (64) Starting with the observation that there exists within sea urchin eggs a heat-stable catalase inhibitor which can be demonstrated in lysates of these organisms (65), it was found that boiled extracts of tumors, and, to a much lesser extent, boiled extracts of certain normal tissues such as liver and spleen, could inhibit *in vitro* the activity of crystalline catalase and of other iron porphyrin enzymes (64). The active component of the extract can be obtained from both rat and human tumors and apparently functions through a reversible combination with the enzyme at the iron porphyrin group, since mixtures of catalase and inhibitor absorb much less at 405 mμ than does the catalase alone (Fig. 57). Control experiments in which the extract containing active inhibitor is replaced by muscle extract which contains little or no catalase inhibitor show no change in the absorption spectrum of catalase in the region of the Soret band. Enzymes lacking the iron porphyrin group are not affected by extracts of the tumor. These are lactic dehydrogenase, succinic dehydrogenase, ascorbic acid oxidase, cholinesterase, and arginase (64). Greenfield and Meister (63) had noted that lactic dehydrogenase as well as dehydropeptidase I and glutamic-alanine transaminase in the livers of normal animals were not affected *in vivo* by ad-

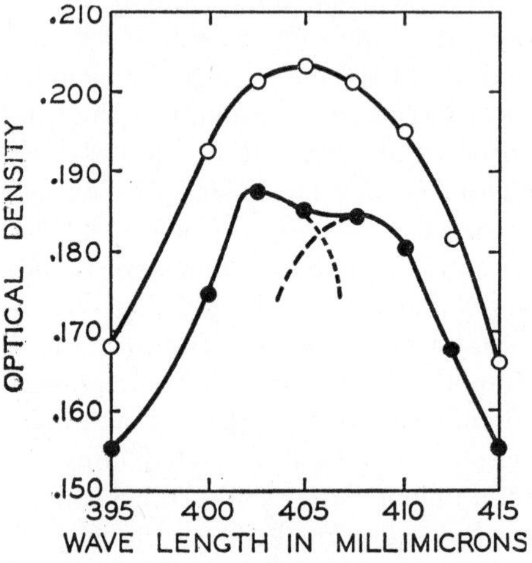

FIG. 57. Effect of tumor *kochsaft* preparation on absorption spectrum of crystalline catalase. Upper curve, 10 units of catalase. Lower curve, 10 units of catalase plus 1 unit of inhibitor. Unit of inhibitor refers to amount which, after incubation at 0° to 2° with catalase, inactivates 1 unit of the enzyme. Control experiments with muscle *kochsaft* and catalase show no change in absorption at 405 mμ. From Hargreaves, A. B., and Deutsch, H. F., *Cancer Research* **12,** 720 (1952).

ministration of a tumor fraction to the intact animals. Hargreaves and Deutsch observed only a partial inhibition *in vitro* of cytochrome oxidase by tumor extract. In the livers of tumor-bearing animals, the level of this enzyme is not changed from the normal (66, 67).

Earlier experiments by the writer (38) and by Nakahara and Fukuoka (61) had shown that *in vitro* mixtures of liver and tumor homogenates, or liver homogenates plus the toxohormone, yielded catalase activity levels characteristic of the liver homogenate alone; i.e., there appeared to be no effect *in vitro* of the inhibitor on the catalase component of the liver homogenate. These findings have been interpreted by Hargreaves and Deutsch as being due to the presence of an enzyme or some factor in the liver homogenate which inactivates the inhibitor, and they demonstrated the capacity of tumor extracts to inhibit the catalase activity of liver homogenates when both together were incubated at 0° prior to assay. The ready dissociability of the inhibitory agent from the catalase molecule assists in the understanding of the rapid restoration of liver catalase in animals from whom the tumor was extirpated, and of the failure to observe lowered liver catalase in animals with very slowly growing tumors. On the basis of these observations Hargreaves and Deutsch suggest that the *in vivo* catalase inhibition phenomenon is very likely due to a suppression of the normal enzyme level and not to an actual lowering of the concentration of the catalase (64). The end result is, of course, the same, but experiments on actual physical isolation of the liver catalase from tumor bearing rats carried out by Greenfield and Price (68) in the writer's laboratory show that there is actually less catalase than normal in such livers.

When extracts of liver are stirred with a calcium phosphate gel, nearly all the catalase present in the extracts is adsorbed on the gel. Since catalase exists in liver tissue in a complex with other proteins (69) it is probable that these accompanying proteins are also adsorbed. Elution of the protein mixture from the gel, and transfer of the solution brought to pH 5.7 (close to the isoelectric point of catalase) to a column of calcium phosphate gel prepared in the presence of cellulose powder (68), leads to adsorption on the column. Four successive elutions with phosphate buffer under different conditions, as shown in Fig. 58, lead to complete removal of the protein from the column. In this figure, normal rat livers and the livers of tumor-bearing animals were treated in identical fashion, and the very considerable differences in the relative amounts of protein in the four bands relating to the normal liver and to the liver of the tumor-bearing animal are clearly apparent. These two kinds of livers came from animals of the same sex, and originally from the same litter, and histologic examination of the livers revealed no observable difference between them. The livers weighed the same, and their homogenates prepared under identical circumstances had the same amounts of total nitrogen and iron (68). The

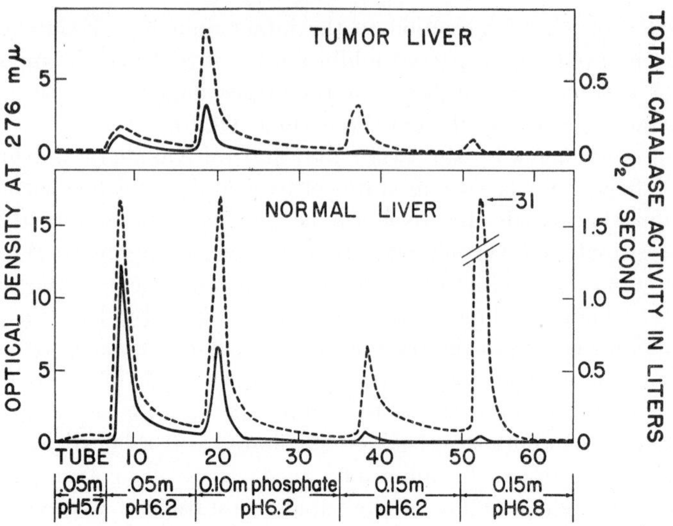

FIG. 58. Chromatograms of the catalase-protein complex isolated from the livers of normal and of tumor-bearing rats under identical conditions and adsorbed on calcium phosphate-cellulose powder columns. Dotted lines refer to protein (left ordinate); continuous line to catalase activity (right ordinate). From Greenfield, R. E., and Price, V. E., courtesy of authors.

only difference between them was that one came from normal animals and the other from animals which had carried a transplanted tumor (Novikoff) in the peritoneum for 7 days. It would appear that nearly all the catalase was concentrated in the first two peaks, and Greenfield and Price succeeded in obtaining crystalline catalase from the eluate of the first peak from the respective preparations of normal liver and of the liver of the tumor-bearing animal; there appeared to be no qualitative difference whatever between these two crystalline enzyme proteins.

Spectrophotometric studies of each of the peaks in Fig. 58 yielded the data in Fig. 59. Thus, the first peak is composed of nearly pure catalase, but there is ten times as much catalase in this peak in normal liver as in the liver of the tumor-bearing animal. There is more non-catalase protein than catalase in each of the other three peaks, and the distribution appears different, both qualitatively and quantitatively, in each of these peaks between the two kinds of livers. There is some possibility that in these latter three peaks the lesser absorption at 405 mμ than at 278 mμ may be due to combination of inhibitor with catalase, as suggested from the experiments of Hargreaves and Deutsch (64). Such an explanation would obviously not hold for the first peak in which, for both the normal liver and for the liver of the tumor-bearing animal, the ratio of the maxima at 278 mμ and 405 mμ is close to unity, which is characteristic of nearly pure

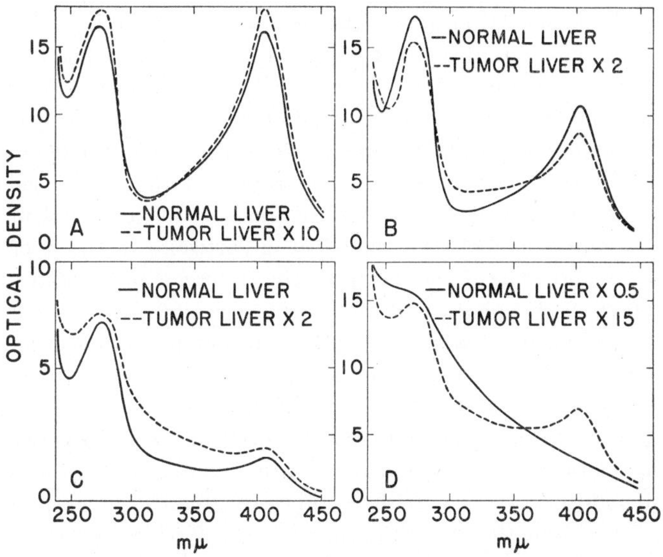

FIG. 59. Spectrograms of the four chromatographic peaks in Fig. 58 obtained from the catalase-protein complexes of the livers of normal and of tumor-bearing rats. From Greenfield, R. E., and Price, V. E., courtesy of the authors.

catalase. The tenfold difference in catalase for this peak can therefore be interpreted only on the basis that there is, as far as this fraction is concerned, an actual decrease in catalase protein in the liver of the tumor-bearing animal. Until the presence of an inhibitor can be excluded from the components of the other three peaks, however, the problem of why the total liver catalase *activity* of the tumor-bearing rat is lower than normal must still remain unsolved.

Rat hepatic catalase is found in the cellular cytoplasm and is nearly equally divided between supernatant and mitochondria (70, 70a). In the early stages of the growth of a distant tumor, the decrease in catalase is chiefly observed in the former cellular fraction, and only after the tumor has reached a critical size does the mitochondrial catalase decrease. These changes are not accompanied by changes in the nitrogen content of these fractions and thus represent apparent changes in the enzyme level.

The hormonal influence on the hepatic catalase level in the normal animal is a factor which must be considered in any tumor effect. Male mice (57) and rats (64) have somewhat higher levels of hepatic catalase than the females of these species, although both sexes are equally affected by the presence of a tumor (cf. Fig. 55). Castration of young adult male mice produces a depression in liver catalase activity, which is restored by injection of testosterone (71); injection of this hormone into female mice elevates their lower normal level to that of the male. Adrenalectomy in rats (72) and in mice (71) lowers the liver catalase activity; cortisone restores the normal level in such adrenalectomized mice but has no effect on normal or castrated mice as far as liver catalase is concerned, whereas in either adrenalectomized or intact rats administration of cortisone produces a further drop in liver catalase activity (55). The rise in the hemoglobin of such cortisone-treated rats is a demonstration of the difference between the effects of the growing tumor and of this sort of hormonal imbalance. The curious difference between the effect of cortisone on the liver catalase levels in rats and mice is remindful of the different effect of testosterone on renal alkaline phosphatase in these two species (cf. 73). A particularly interesting finding by Adams (71) is that, although adrenalectomy of castrated males results in a further fall in liver catalase activity, castration of adrenalectomized males does not. The mean levels in adrenalectomized females and in castrated and adrenalectomized males are practically identical. On the other hand, the activity of the liver catalase in hypophysectomized female rats is two to three times as great as in normal animals (74); to what extent the growth hormone is involved in uncertain. These hormonal effects, however, are not selective as far as liver catalase is concerned, for adrenalectomy causes in rats a decrease in arginase activity (75, 76), and hypophysectomy causes a decrease in bone phosphatase, hepatic D-amino acid oxidase, and renal alkaline phosphatase; no change occurs in renal and hepatic acid phosphatase, renal D-amino acid oxidase, and muscle succinic dehydrogenase; and an increase occurs not only in hepatic catalase but also in hepatic alkaline phosphatase (74).

There appears to be little doubt but that the level of enzymatic activity of all sorts is profoundly affected by the disequilibrium which occurs when hormonal levels are disturbed. Confining attention only to liver catalase, however, the problem arises as to how the tumor effect on the level of this enzyme may be affected by the hormonal status of the animal. Adams has shown (77) that in mice treated with tumor homogenates the adrenal and testicular factors which normally influence hepatic catalase activity are prevented from operating, and this failure appears to be due to the inability of the liver to respond to the hormonal stimuli. Thus, when mice were adrenalectomized and their normal liver catalase levels restored by injection of cortisone, subsequent injection of homogenates of sarcoma 37 produced a sharp fall in the liver catalase level to that found in the untreated adrenalectomized animals, even though cortisone was still being administered. Similarly, castrated male mice with lowered liver catalase were treated with testosterone which restored the catalase level to normal, and, even though testosterone was still being given, the injection of sarcoma 37 tissue produced a drop in the liver catalase to the level of the untreated castrate. Injection of tumor into castrated or adrenalectomized mice untreated by any hormone caused no further lowering of the liver catalase. It is well known that there is a minimum level of catalase activity in the liver which even very rapidly growing tumors do not further depress, and from the data of Adams (77) it appears that this minimum level is that reached by such drastic procedures as castration or adrenalectomy. It would further seem, therefore, that by far the greater part of the liver catalase activity which responds to the presence of a tumor elsewhere in the host is also that part which is normally under adrenal and testicular control (77). The presence of the tumor, or, perhaps more precisely, the toxin which it sends out into the circulation, presumably blocks the influence of the systemic hormonal influences on the liver. In this sense, the toxohormone, to use Nakahara's term, may more properly be called an antihormone, and perhaps its high concentration in tumors serves to render the tumors insensitive to systemic, hormonal influences and thereby contributes to their so-called autonomous nature. This attractive interpretation, however, has been based upon the study of mice, and as shown in the experiments of Begg (55) and of Kochakian (73) hormonal effects may be quite different in different species. Although the end result of tumor growth is a depression in the liver catalase of the host, whether rat or mouse, the mechanisms whereby this result is attained may vary in certain particulars in the two species.

That the supply of metals in the diet, as well as normal hormonal levels, is necessary to maintain the metal-containing enzymes at their usual activities has been clear since the studies of Schultze and Kuiken (78). That there may be an interrelation among all three was shown by Adams (79), who observed that castrated males kept on a milk diet supplemented with iron, copper, and manganese maintained their ordinarily low level of liver catalase, but, when the metals were removed, the level rose, just as it did in females, to that of intact males. This unexpected finding, that a metal deficiency appears to have the same effect as an injection of testosterone, remains to be explained. It may be that testosterone restores the liver catalase in the castrated animals indirectly, perhaps by inhibiting the depressing action of a copper-manganese system (79). An increase in cardiac catalase on a copper-deficient diet has been reported (78). It must be pointed out, however, that the observations of a synthetic response of the liver to form liver catalase in the presence of a metal deficiency hold only for mice and are quite opposite to those noted for rats (78). Rather than being due to a species difference, these opposing results must be based upon some difference in experimental technique or procedure.

The observations described in this section might be considered to have some potential practical clinical value if the presence of the toxic agent derived from a very early tumor could be detected in the host. This has not yet been realized. The properties of the agent or toxohormone are such as to render its isolation fairly straightforward, for its heat stability permits its ready separation from the much greater mass of heat-coagulable proteins present in any tissue studied. Its amazing acid stability, as noted by Greenfield and Meister, could also be of use in this connection. The parabiotic studies of Lucké definitely prove that the toxin is transported via the blood stream, which suggests the use of blood for assay for the presence of the agent. The observation of Hargreaves and Deutsch that tissue *kochsaft* containing the agent can inhibit the activity of crystalline catalase and reduce its absorption at 405 mμ permits the possibility that an *in vitro* assay method for the agent could be developed, obviating the need for the normal animal for bioassay. A possible procedure has been suggested by the experiments of Nakagawa (80), who used a crude method of isolation of the toxic factor from human urine and, after injecting it into normal mice, found distinct decreases in the liver catalase only with samples obtained from the urine of cancer patients; similar observations were made when the gastric juices of patients with gastric cancer were used as the source of the toxin. No evidence was adduced that only catalase of the liver enzymes was affected by injection of the material.

The systemic effects produced by the presence of a tumor are not restricted to mammals, for the liver catalase level of frogs bearing a renal carcinoma is considerably reduced below normal (80a). Intracoelomic injection of a tumor mash results in a reduction of liver catalase within 24 hours, followed by a gradual return toward the normal within 6 days. Young chickens normally have a much lower liver catalase level than do older birds, and although a growing Rous tumor, or injections of Rous tumor tissue, or purified virus has no effect on the liver catalase level of the young birds, injection of homogenized fresh Rous tumor produces a marked lowering of this level in the adult birds (80b).

A rather precise study of the quantitative relationship between the decrease of the liver catalase activity and the increase in the population of tumor cells has been conducted on mice bearing the Ehrlich ascites tumor (81). This tumor grows at a steady exponential rate during the first six days after inoculation, the complete growth curve of the free tumor cells resembling that of a culture of bacteria or other unicellular organisms in a restricted space (cf. 82). During the exponential phase, the time required to double the tumor cell population averages 21.4 hours, and the corresponding percentile reduction of the liver catalase activity, in terms of initial catalase level, is 7.9. Thus in six days, the liver catalase level drops to approximately half of the normal, and it is probable that during this period the inhibitors of liver catalase are elaborated and released at a steady rate by the tumor cells.

Finally, it should be noted that the changes in the enzymatic pattern of the liver of the tumor-bearing animal are in the direction which the liver would take if it were transformed into a hepatoma, i.e., lowered catalase, arginase, D-amino acid oxidase, riboflavin, etc. This alteration in the liver occurs, however, whether the distant tumor is a transplanted hepatoma or some other kind of tumor. What apparently happens is a generalized and systemic "cancerousness" of the organs of the tumor-bearing animal, so that the liver, for example, of such an animal takes on certain neoplastic features. These features may be of relatively small degree compared with those of the hepatoma, but they are, nevertheless, in the direction of the hepatoma. The lowering of the liver catalase is the most striking of the systemic effects evoked in the tumor-bearing animal, but the activity of this enzyme is lowered at the most to about one-twentieth that of the normal liver. In the hepatoma this enzyme has almost disappeared. It may be wondered whether the same influences exerted within the tumor on many enzymatic systems are not operative in part through circulatory channels on susceptible systems in organs at distant sites within the animal.

The search for components which might be altered in the tissues of tumor-bearing animals can with some confidence be narrowed to those components included in category I of Table 68 (Chapter VIII) but not to those included in category II of the same table. Although those components which have been found to be altered in various tissues of the tumor-bearing host are found in category I, it must be pointed out (a) that not *all* components in this category are altered in any one tissue of the cancerous host, and (b) that certain components in this category which are altered in one tissue of the cancerous host are not necessarily altered in other tissues.

Hepatic and Renal D-*Amino Acid Oxidase.* This enzyme, which is most concentrated in liver and kidney, is lowered in these organs in rats bearing growing transplanted tumors (83, 84). The decrease in activity of this enzyme, which, in certain cases, may be as much as to lower the activity to one-third normal, is proportional to the growth rate of the implanted tumor and is reversible on operative extirpation of the tumor (83). When the operation was not completely successful, i.e., when not all the tumor was removed, or when metastases were present, the liver enzymatic activity, which at first reverted nearly to normal, rapidly decreased again with subsequent growth of the residual tumor (83). In order to see whether this effect could be brought about by the presence of rapidly dividing tissue of other origin, the enzymatic activity of liver extracts of burned animals was determined (83). In every case the activity was normal.

D-Amino acid oxidase is a conjugated protein, composed of a protein carrier (apoenzyme) and a prosthetic group (coenzyme) which apparently belongs to the flavins. The coenzyme component of the enzyme is lowered in the liver of tumor-bearing animals (85, 86), i.e., from 29.48 to 21.18 per gram of fresh tissue; apoenzyme is lowered to an even greater extent (84).

The coenzyme component of this enzyme is derived from one of the dietary essentials of the vitamin B group, namely riboflavin. Although the tumor-bearing animal may obtain a sufficient supply of this vitamin, the failure to fully utilize it for intracellular metabolism is noteworthy. Presumably, riboflavin must be phosphorylated before it can be employed in coenzyme capacity, and it may be the partial failure of this process which accounts, to some degree, for the lowered amino acid oxidase activity. The even more striking decrease in the protein carrier (apoenzyme) of the enzyme in the livers of the tumor-bearing animals is yet another indication of the loss of the protein-synthesizing capacity of the liver as reflected in the decrease in serum albumin.

In some instances, certain investigators have failed to note a decrease in the enzymatic activity of the livers of tumor-bearing animals, but in no case did these investigators describe the weights of the tumors. It is necessary, in experiments of this kind, to note the relative weight of tumor to body weight, for, with a low ratio for this relation, a possible effect may be missed. It is unfortunately true that in nearly all investigations of the effect on the livers or other tissues of tumor-bearing animals, marked findings are obtained only when the tumors represent at least 5% of the total body weight, thus limiting clinical application at the present time.

Hepatic and Renal Arginase. This enzyme, which is concerned with the hydrolytic conversion of arginine to urea and ornithine, is relatively slightly depressed in activity in the liver and in the kidneys of tumor-bearing animals (Table 158). The effect on this activity after removal of the tumor has not yet been studied.

Relatively little effect of growing mouse tumors has been noted on hepatic, plasma, and muscle arginase levels (90). Injection of purified

TABLE 158

ARGINASE ACTIVITY OF NORMAL AND OF TUMOR-BEARING ANIMALS

Tissue	Activity	Reference
Normal rat livers	213[1]	(87)
Livers of rats bearing transplanted hepatoma	170[1]	(87)
Normal rat livers	10.0[2]	(88)
Livers of rats bearing transplanted sarcoma	6.1[2]	(88)
Normal mouse livers	4031[3]	(89)
Livers of mice bearing transplanted carcinoma	3068[3]	(89)
Normal mouse kidneys	312[3]	(89)
Kidneys of mice bearing transplanted carcinoma	169[3]	(89)

[1] Data refer to values of ratio of per cent hydrolysis to cube root of total nitrogen concentration in extract used.

[2] In terms of millimeters carbon dioxide measured in unit time manometrically.

[3] In terms of arginase units.

arginase intraperitoneally into tumor-bearing mice produced no effect on the growth of the tumor or on its arginase level (90).

In tuberculous guinea pigs the arginase activity of the livers and kidneys progressively falls (89) so that the effect noted is not unique for cancer. The arginase activity of the livers of pregnant rabbits is, however, normal (87).

The amount of free arginine is about three times as high in tumors and in the muscles of tumorous animals as in the muscles of normal animals, the amount bound in the muscle proteins of the former being correspondingly reduced (91).

Hepatic Riboflavin. The riboflavin content of the livers of rats bearing transplanted hepatomas is lower than normal (Table 159). Although the absolute data in Table 159 do not check very well, both sets of data are consistent in demonstrating that the livers of the cancerous hosts are lower than normal in riboflavin. This phenomenon explains in part the lowered D-amino acid oxidase activity in the livers of cancerous hosts (83, 84). However, xanthine dehydrogenase, which also may be a flavin enzyme, does not alter in such animals. It is likely that changes in the protein component of the amino acid oxidase must also occur in the liver of the cancerous host.

Tissue Esterase and Lipase. The tissues of animals bearing large tumors of various sorts possess abnormally low values for esterase and for lipase activity (92, 93). The larger the tumor or the faster the growth rate of the tumor, the lower are the activities of these enzymes. Certain data are given in Table 160.

The zona fasciculata of the adrenal cortex of male mice contains considerable alkaline phosphatase which is lacking in the adrenals of females (94). Male hosts bearing the transplanted granulosa-cell tumor show the female distribution of this enzyme in their adrenals, indicating an estrogenic effect by the tumor. It is possible, therefore, that the alkaline phosphatase of the male adrenal cortex is maintained at its normal high level by androgen

Tissue Lipoids and Steroids. Comparison of the fatty components in several tissues of hepatoma-bearing rats with the same components in the

TABLE 159

RIBOFLAVIN CONCENTRATION IN LIVERS OF HEPATOMA-BEARING RATS

Tissue	Reference	Riboflavin content, γ/100 g. fresh tissue
Normal liver	(86)	2940
Liver of cancerous animal	(86)	2110
Normal liver	(85)	1328
Liver of cancerous animal	(85)	800

TABLE 160

ESTERASE AND LIPASE ACTIVITY IN TISSUES OF RATS BEARING THE JENSEN SARCOMA

Tissue	Esterase[1] (92)		Lipase[2] (93)	
	Normal	Tumor-bearing	Normal	Tumor-bearing
Liver	56.4	20.6	210	76
Kidney	30.9	20.4	—	—
Brain	—	—	267	95
Lung	22.5	6.2	—	—

[1] In terms of milliliters 0.01 *N* NaOH to neutralize ethyl butyrate hydrolysis by tissue extract containing 0.1 g. moist tissue in 2 hours.

[2] In terms of cubic millimeters CO_2 liberated through extracts equivalent to 2 mg. liver or 100 mg. brain in 1.5 hours with tributyrin as substrate.

same tissues of normal rats revealed that the concentration of certain of these materials in the former was considerably altered from the normal (95, 96) (Table 161).

The adrenal gland in particular shows marked loss of fatty substances in the tumor-bearing animal. These chemical findings are consistent with histological examination with special fat stains of the adrenals of tumor-bearing mice (97) (Fig. 60).

Late symptoms of cancer appear to simulate adrenal insufficiency. The adrenals respond fairly regularly to toxic agents introduced into the host, to infection, to various forms of inflammatory disease and to tissue anoxia. Lipid loss accompanies the adrenal changes. Dalton, and others, have suggested that some of the symptoms of the cachexia characteristic of late neoplastic disease may be the result of acute or chronic adrenal cortical insufficiency (97).

TABLE 161

LIPOID AND STEROID CONCENTRATION IN TISSUES OF NORMAL AND OF HEPATOMA-BEARING RATS[1] (95)

Tissue	Fatty acids		Cholesterol		Cholesterol esters		Phospholipid	
	Normal	Tumor-bearing	Normal	Tumor-bearing	Normal	Tumor-bearing	Normal	Tumor-bearing
Muscle	1.19	0.71	0.046	0.040	0.022	0.009	1.14	1.26
Liver	2.72	1.56	0.224	0.138	0.077	0.049	3.16	2.69
Heart	0.76	0.39	0.066	0.068	0.087	0.048	3.03	2.69
Kidney	2.10	0.89	0.257	0.367	0.052	0.084	3.05	2.24
Lung	1.84	1.26	0.393	0.343	0.063	0.113	2.52	1.94
Brain	2.76	3.00	0.240	0.307	0.050	0.040	4.96	4.70
Spleen	0.98	0.46	0.255	0.221	0.037	0.034	1.81	1.59
Adrenal	6.97	4.74	1.362	0.930	2.412	0.351	6.35	4.76

[1] Data given in terms of per cent of wet weight of tissue.

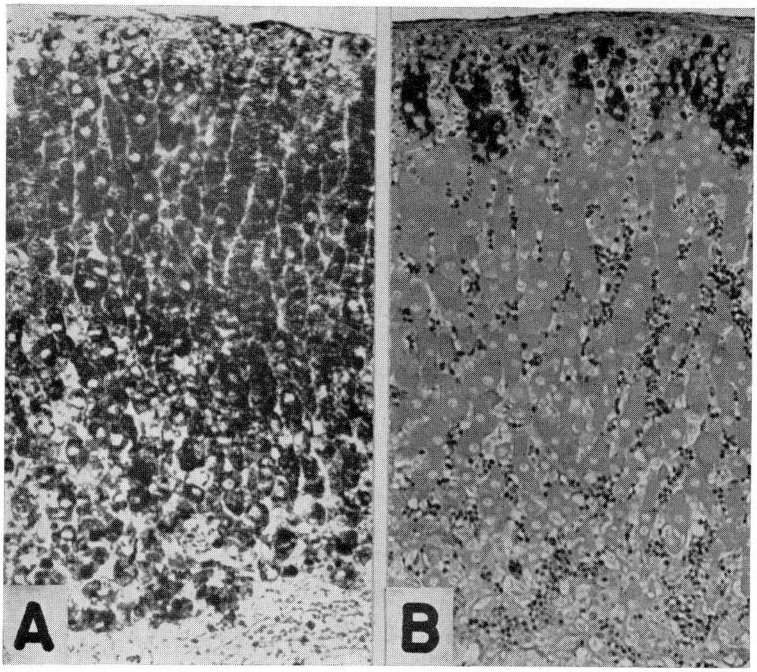

FIG. 60. A, normal lipoid pattern in the adrenal cortex of a 5-month-old strain *C* male mouse; B, lipoid depletion of the cortex of a 5-month-old strain *C* male mouse carrying a transplanted spindle-cell carcinoma of the salivary gland. From Dalton, A. J., and Peters, V. B., *J. Natl. Cancer Inst.* **5**, 99 (1944).

Water Content. Almost invariably, the tissues of tumor-bearing animals contain a slight but definitely higher water content than similar tissues in normal animals (86, 95) (Table 162). The increase may amount to only 1 to 4%, but few exceptions to this finding have been noted. The reason for this phenomenon is not yet apparent. The phenomenon itself is essentially a reflection of some disturbance in osmotic equilibrium between intracellular and extracellular fluid. Studies of salt distribution would be helpful in this respect.

It is interesting to note that hepatomas have a higher content of water than normal liver, and, thus, water content would be a characteristic to be placed in category I of Table 68 (Chapter VIII). The fact that the tissues of tumor-bearing animals are also higher than normal in water content is, therefore, not surprising. A high water content is characteristic of rapidly growing tissues, fetal and regenerating, as well as neoplastic. The tissues of the cancerous host are not growing, but, in their abnormally high water content, they reflect the properties of the cancer.

Copper and Other Metals. The copper content of the livers of cancerous

TABLE 162

TOTAL SOLIDS IN THE LIVERS OF TUMOR-BEARING RATS AND MICE (86)

Tumor borne by animal	Total solids, %
Rat:	
Controls	29.9 ± 1.0
Jensen sarcoma	25.6 ± 1.8
Hepatoma 31	26.5 ± .8
Mouse:	
Controls	30.9 ± 2.1
Lymphosarcoma	22.8 ± 1.5
Intestinal adenocarcinoma	26.1 ± 1.3
Salivary gland tumor	26.2 ± 2.0
Fibrosarcoma	28.4 ± 1.2
Melanoma	27.1 ± 1.3
Sarcoma 37	27.4 ± 1.5
Sarcoma CR-180	27.9 ± .2
Brain tumor	27.9 ± 1.6
Mammary tumor	27.6 ± 1.1
Gastric adenocarcinoma	27.1 ± 1.2
Hepatoma	27.0 ± 1.9
Hemangioendothelioma	27.6 ± 0.7
Squamous cell carcinoma	27.2 ± 1.1

hosts, both animal and human, is raised, often considerably, above the normal level (98–100) (Table 163). Although copper is diminished in the hepatoma as compared with normal liver, it is increased in the liver of tumor-bearing animals.

The copper content of the whole blood of normal rats is 0.43 mg. per 100 ml., that of the whole blood of rats bearing the transplanted Jensen sarcoma is 0.28 mg. per 100 ml. (98). The copper content of the whole blood of normal animals is only slightly higher than that of serum (0.32 mg. %),

TABLE 163

COPPER CONTENT OF LIVERS OF NORMAL AND OF CANCEROUS HOSTS

Source	Copper content, mg./100 g. dry tissue	Reference
Normal rats	2.5	(98)
Rats bearing hepatomas	4.0	(98)
Rats bearing Jensen sarcoma	4.0	(98)
Normal mice	3.1	(98)
Mice bearing hepatomas	5.0	(98)
Mice with mammary carcinoma	3.5	(98)
Normal human beings	1.4–4.5	(100)
Human beings with various forms of cancer[1]	1.8–6.7	(100)

[1] The data cover 146 cases of neoplastic disease.

which implies that the copper is not far from being equally distributed between cells and serum. The copper content of the serum of tumor-bearing rats is slightly lower than normal (0.26 mg. %). The decrease in whole blood of the cancerous host may be due to the accompanying anemias.

In many cases of neoplastic disease accompanied by severe secondary anemia, considerable amounts of iron as well as copper may accumulate in both liver and spleen (100). Even where anemia does not exist, such storage frequently takes place. The iron and copper retention in liver and spleen is especially high in cases with extensive metastasis, and iron may be stored to an even greater extent than copper.

These findings in the presence of severe anemia are somewhat paradoxical for, although depletion of iron and copper leads to anemia with decrease in hemoglobin and hematin enzymes (78), there is present here a considerable storage of iron and copper in the liver. The ability of the cancerous host to utilize these metals must be impaired, and with this impairment must follow the decrease in hemoglobin and liver catalase observed in such a host.

Using radioactive elements injected into mice bearing the transplanted LCS mammary tumor, it was found that after 3 hours most of the metal is located in the cytoplasm of the tissues (101). The presence of the tumor apparently caused a higher uptake of cobalt and copper in liver, and a decrease in kidney; a marked increase of copper in the spleen was also noted (Table 164).

Hepatic Tissue Glycolysis in Leukemia. The $Q_A^{N_2}$ value for normal mouse liver has been estimated to be 0.05 (102) and 0.5 (103); *e.g.*, anaerobic glycolysis is extremely low in this tissue and, indeed, the Pasteur effect turns out to be negative. In mice with leukemia, the livers have a $Q_A^{N_2}$ value of 3.4 (102) or 2.4 (103)—in any event, a very considerable rise above normal. That part of this rise is due to infiltration of malignant lymphocytes is shown by the fact that with increasing proportion of such infiltra-

TABLE 164

CONCENTRATION OF METALS IN TISSUES OF NORMAL AND OF TUMOR-BEARING MICE[1] (101)

	Liver		Kidney		Spleen		Lung	
Metal	Normal	Tumor-bearing	Normal	Tumor-bearing	Normal	Tumor-bearing	Normal	Tumor-bearing
Co^{60}	8.5	15.0	1.4	0.57	0.17	0.17	0.41	0.43
Cu^{64}	29.4	36.1	1.3	1.07	0.15	0.73	0.10	0.30

[1] As per cent of the administered dose recovered, 3 hours after injection.

TABLE 165

CITRIC ACID CONTENT OF RAT TISSUES (105)

Tissue	Animals with Walker 256 tumor	Animals without tumor
Kidney[1]	8.88	6.11
Liver[1]	5.97	4.41
Spleen[1]	8.23	6.81
Plasma[2]	6.29	4.86

[1] Milligrams per 100 g. wet weight.
[2] Milligrams per 100 ml.

tion the $Q_A^{N_2}$ can rise as high as 5.6. On the other hand, a considerable part of this rise must be due to non-visible changes in the liver parenchyma of the leukemic animals for, in the absence or near-absence of any lymphocytic infiltration, the $Q_A^{N_2}$ values averaged 1.8 as against 0.05 for that of the liver of normal animals. There appears, therefore, to be an enhanced glycolysis of the liver cells of leukemic animals.

The glycolytic rates of the lymphocytes in lymph nodes and in liver appear to be of the same order of magnitude, e.g., 8.3 and 9.2.

Citric Acid. Citric acid is present in elevated amounts in various tumors (104) and in the tissues of tumor-bearing animals (105) (Table 165).

Tissue Nucleic Acid. There is an increased rate of incorporation of P^{32} and of formate-C^{14} and glycine-2-C^{14} into the deoxyribonucleic acid of livers and spleens in rats and mice bearing transplanted tumors (106–108). However, this effect is not specific for cancer but occurs also in the tissues of pregnant animals. An increased incorporation of 4-amino-5-imidazolecarboxamide-C^{14} into the liver purines of tumor-bearing mice has also been noted (108a).

Tissue Components of Cancerous Hosts Which Do Not Apparently Alter from Normal. Knowledge of those components of the tissues of tumor-bearing hosts which do not alter from the normal may be as important as knowledge of those components which do alter. The following systems, arranged according to the tissues in which they occur, are apparently not changed from the normal. It is understood that no pathology other than cancer is involved.

Liver: Cytochrome oxidase (66, 67), vitamin A (109), glyoxalase (110), deoxyribonucleodepolymerase (111), acid and alkaline phosphatase (112), xanthine dehydrogenase (111), cystine desulfurase, and phosphorylase (113).

Kidney: Glyoxalase (110), and acid and alkaline phosphatase (112).

Spleen: Cytochrome oxidase (67), glyoxalase (110), deoxyribonucleodepolymerase (36), and acid and alkaline phosphatase (112).

Skeletal muscle: Glyoxalase (110) and acid and alkaline phosphatase (112).

Muscle, liver, kidney, brain, and spleen: Total dehydrogenase as measured by capacity to reduce methylene blue, as well as lactic and malic dehydrogenases (114).

Blood: Catalase (39).

Serum: Acid phosphatase [except in disseminated prostatic carcinoma (115)], and alkaline phosphatase [except in osteogenic sarcoma, disseminated prostatic carcinoma (115), and hepatic carcinoma (115)].

Three suggestions of caution must be expressed in relation to the data given above: (a) for the most part each of the systems described has been studied with only one kind of neoplasm growing in the host, and there is no guarantee that other types of neoplasms would not produce an effect on these systems; (b) for the most part each of the systems has been studied in only one species of animal, and it may be that in other species such systems would be susceptible to the presence of tumors in a distant site; (c) with few exceptions, these negative results (negative in the sense of no changes being observed) have not been properly controlled by making sure that, in the animals studied, known susceptible systems were altered. It is likely that suggestions (a) and (b) are not important, for it is very probable that systemic effects evoked in the tumor-bearing host are common to all kinds of neoplasms and occur in all species. Suggestion (c), on the other hand, involves a decisive step in the consideration of the acceptance of the data, for the validity of the former observation must remain open to doubt unless it can be shown that, simultaneously with the observation of the absence of an effect on a particular system in a given tissue, yet another known system in the same animal (not necessarily in the same tissue) is affected. A host with a small, or very slowly growing tumor, may demonstrate no systemic effects on any tissue component.

It is seemingly possible for the liver of a tumor-bearing animal to have a markedly lowered glycogen content (from a normal level in rats of 0.16 grams percent wet weight, and in mice of 0.37 grams, to 0.11 and 0.20 grams, respectively) in the presence of a nearly normal level of adenylic acid-activated phosphorylase (113). There is no apparent relation between the levels of these components whether in normal tissues or in tumors.

SPECIFIC SYSTEMS IN BLOOD

Hemoglobin Concentration. Anemia is frequently an accompanying feature of neoplastic disease in many kinds of animals. There appears to be a progressive depression in the blood hemoglobin level with neoplastic growth elsewhere in the animal. Even before the growth appears, there may be a marked falling off of the hemoglobin concentration, as shown by Strong and

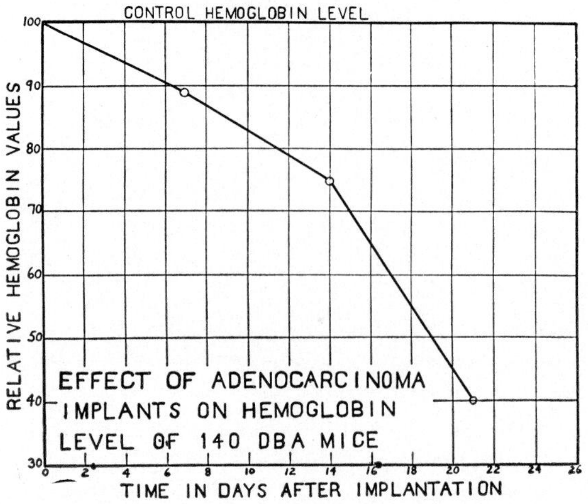

FIG. 61. Effect of growth of mouse mammary tumors on hemoglobin level. From Taylor, A., and Pollack, M. S., *Cancer Research* **2,** 223 (1942).

his coworkers (116, 117). Clear-cut experiments which demonstrate a direct and primary, rather than a secondary, effect of tumors on the hemoglobin level have been presented by Taylor and Pollack (118) (Fig. 61).

In animals either injected with methylcholanthrene or fed 4-dimethylaminoazobenzene there was a progressive drop with time in the hemoglobin level long before tumors appeared in the animals (118). These results, similar to those of Strong's, in which changes in the hemoglobin level occured before the appearance of spontaneous mammary tumors, are suggestive of changes occurring in the animal during precancerous stages. In the cases of the induced tumors, however, it would have made the results surer had non-carcinogenic isomers been employed so as to specifically relate the blood picture observed with a precancerous state. The laboratory findings are outside the limit of experimental error, but the results do not reveal differences from the normal of a sufficiently high order of magnitude as to warrant clinical applications at the present time.

Hemoglobin, like catalase, is an active protein with a hemin prosthetic group. Although the prosthetic group in both kinds of conjugated proteins is the same, the protein moieties are different. Whereas the liver catalase and the erythrocyte hemoglobin are depressed in the tumor-bearing host, the erythrocyte catalase is little depressed, if at all. It may be that the centers of catalse synthesis in animals occur in different sites and are affected to different degrees. As noted above, the effect of the presence of the tumor on the kidney catalase is intermediate between that of the liver and the erythrocyte catalase. The unequal effect of the tumor on catalase and on hemoglobin carried by the erythrocyte would suggest that these components are enfolded by the erythrocyte at different sites.

Although extramedullary hematopoiesis is a rare finding in human pathology, even in cases of widespread cancer, it occurs frequently in the livers and spleens of tumor-bearing mice of certain strains (119). It may be that the myelopoiesis in such animals is connected with the same cancerous mechanisms which result in the lowered blood hemoglobin and liver catalase levels. This suggests a general alteration in porphyrin metabolism in the tumor-bearing host.

Amyloid infiltration of liver and spleen occurs in tumorous mice of certain strains and can be induced in normal mice by injection of a mixture of pentose nucleotides (120), a phenomenon due to the adenylic and guanylic acids contained therein (121). The similarity in the blood picture of tumorous animals and of normal animals treated with nucleotides suggests that the latter may be liberated during the development of tumors (121). In this connection, it is of interest to note that, with increasing size of the tumor, the purine content of the liver of the tumorous host markedly increases (122).

Blood Plasma Proteins. Plasma proteins constitute a part of the labile proteins of the body, and changes in the concentration or ratios of these components may be expected to reflect alterations in the demands of those tissues subjected to various pathologic stresses. A vast literature exists on all phases which are known of the plasma proteins, and yet it is interesting to contemplate that much of these almost countless studies rests upon two analytical procedures, namely, precipitation reactions involving sulfate salts, and relative mobilities in an electric field (electrophoresis). The earliest studies employing salts recognized the existence of some four plasma protein components—fibrinogen, albumin, euglobulin, and pseudoglobulin—in addition to the presence of non-protein nitrogenous components which remained in the final filtrates. The development by Tiselius of electrophoretic procedures showed that the albumin and globulin components obtained by salt fractionation were electrophoretically inhomogeneous, and that there appeared to be at least four globulin fractions (α_1, α_2, β, and γ) in addition to albumin and fibrinogen. The most recent development in plasma fractionation has been that of Cohn, in which methods involving low temperature-alcohol and heavy metal salt precipitations have been employed, and by which at least thirty plasma protein components have been recognized. It is possible that the full number of the plasma components is not yet known. Only a few of them have been studied in diseased states of the host. The subject has been reviewed by several authorities (123–126).

It was early recognized that the plasma proteins in cancer patients are usually lower than normal and that this loss was chiefly at the expense of the albumin fraction. At first believed to be a result of a frequent negative nitrogen balance in the patient, hypoalbuminemia was found to exist even in the presence of an over-all positive nitrogen balance (5, 127). However, a positive nitrogen balance could exist even in the presence of considerable normal tissue catabolism, provided that the tumor was being synthesized at a still faster rate. Since the liver is the major site of albumin synthesis, it may well be that the level of the diminished albumin is a reflection of still another hepatic dysfunction (cf. 128). The levels of α_1-, α_2-, and β-globulins may increase significantly in neoplastic disease, whereas those of γ-globulin show no very consistent change. Fibrinogen may show an increase, but, since this protein also originates in the liver, it is difficult to interpret a loss of albumin and a gain in fibrinogen as due to the same hepatic dysfunction unless some compensatory mechanism comes into operation. Much of the screening studies on the plasma of cancer patients has been performed by Petermann (129, 130), Seibert (131), Mider (132), Winzler (133), Boyland (134), and Chanutin (135). There is good agreement among all these workers in that electrophoretic patterns at pH 8.5 of the plasma proteins in neoplastic disease reveal an abnormal distribution of the proteins which becomes more pronounced with an increase in extent of the cancerous growth. A summary of the study by Mider, Alling, and Morton (132) on 222 individual cancer patients is given in Table 166 and is illustrative of the general findings in this area and at this pH. There is a decrease in total protein, a considerable decrease in albumin, a considerable increase in fibrinogen, and a moderate increase in total globulin. Although Table 166 suggests a slight rise in the γ-globulin component, some cancer patients in terminal stages show a marked decrease of this protein (132). Since the γ-globulin fraction contains a major proportion of the specific antibodies, it does not appear that any considerable rise in such materials occurs as a response to the presence of a spontaneous neoplasm. On the other hand, there may be a definite immune response to transplanted and to virus-induced tumors in experimental animals (cf. Chapter II).

When electrophoretic analyses were conducted at pH values other than 8.5, new electrophoretic components of the plasma made their appearance. Thus, an acid component with an isoelectric point lower than pH 4 was

TABLE 166

ELECTROPHORETIC COMPONENTS IN PLASMA OF NORMAL AND CANCEROUS HUMAN BEINGS[1] (132)

Individuals	Total protein	Albumin	α_1-Globulin	α_2-Globulin	β-Globulin	γ-Globulin	Fibrinogen
Normal	6.83	4.04	0.38	0.66	0.76	0.66	0.31
Cancer	6.60	2.94	0.53	0.90	0.89	0.75	0.58
Advanced cancer	6.55	2.38	0.65	1.05	0.99	0.82	0.82

[1] At pH 8.5; results given as grams per cent.

discovered, which occurred in increased amounts in the plasma of cancer patients (136–138). This component turned out to be a mucoprotein, which was isolated by Winzler from perchloric acid filtrates of plasma by precipitation with phosphotungstic acid (139). At pH 8.5 this mucoprotein migrates with the α_1-globulin component and hence was not previously recognized. It appears to be the major constituent if not identical with the seromucoid of Rimington (140). Polysaccharide appears to be associated with all the globulin fractions (141) (lipids with the β-globulins), and there may be a correlation between the serum polysaccharide levels and the amount of α-globulins in patients with tuberculosis as well as with cancer (131). There is unquestionably a rise in the total polysaccharide content of the plasma of cancer patients (142–144) and of experimental animals bearing tumors (145), but attempts to relate this rise in cancer or other pathologic states to specific serum components, other than Winzler's mucoprotein, are difficult to interpret since chemically isolated fractions are not quite the same as the corresponding electrophoretic components, despite the improved salt precipitation procedures introduced by Milne (146; cf. 126). The data in the literature must therefore be read with this reservation in mind (cf. 142). Nevertheless, comparable fractions isolated from serum by the procedure of Milne indicated a rise in the non-glucosamine polysaccharide in all fractions studied (142) (Table 167) for a number of pathologic conditions. An elevation of polysaccharide associated with the salt-precipitated albumin in pregnancy has been reported (147). Part of the increase in albumin-associated polysaccharide in cancer patients is due to admixture with mucoprotein (142). The suggestion that the mucoprotein is a carbohydrate complex with fairly constant characteristics (133) has received support from the evidence that in all cases of an elevation of this fraction in various forms of clinical neoplasia the ratio of polysaccharide to the protein moiety is appreciably constant (143) (Table 168). In cases of hepatic disease, however, there is a decrease in the protein

TABLE 167

PERCENTILE SERUM POLYSACCHARIDE CONTENT OF SERUM PROTEIN FRACTIONS[1] (142)

Group	Albumin polysaccharide	α-Globulin polysaccharide	β-Globulin polysaccharide	γ-Globulin polysaccharide
Normal adults	0.61	2.93	5.65	2.29
Carcinoma	1.70	4.42	6.31	2.48
Benign tumors	0.88	2.94	5.53	2.53
Arthritis	1.17	4.24	7.18	2.15
Viral infections	0.70	2.81	7.42	2.38
Bacterial infections	0.86	3.37	6.90	2.16

[1] Expressed as ratio of polysaccharide to protein of the particular fraction.

TABLE 168

Serum Mucoprotein in Cancer and Liver Disease (143)

Type	Protein moiety alone[1]	Polysaccharide alone[1]	Ratio of polysaccharide to protein
Normal	60	9.9	0.16
Neoplasia	128.7	23.7	0.17
Hepatic disease[2]	32.6	8.5	0.26

[1] As milligrams per cent. Protein as biuret color. Polysaccharide as galactose-mannose color with tryptophan in H_2SO_4.

[2] Hepatitis and cirrhosis only.

moiety, although the sugar moiety remains constant. A similar situation apparently occurs in multiple myeloma (143). The expected increase in serum mucoprotein in neoplasia may be obscured by the presence of hepatic impairment. So far there is little or no knowledge of the mechanism whereby the glycoproteins of the serum are maintained at their normal level.

The protein-bound carbohydrate appears to consist of nearly equivalent amounts of galactose, mannose, and glucosamine, and thus tests for glucosamine alone in cancer serum also show a proportionate rise above the normal levels (148). The mucoprotein of the serum which is isolated together with the albumin component by chemical methods of fractionation also contains glucosamine in addition to hexose. Whether there is a quantitative change in the sugar or amino sugar components relative to each other when their total amount so markedly increases in many pathological conditions has not been determined. No clear concept as to the origin of the protein-bound carbohydrates is yet available.

Certain types of sugars when heated with tryptophan and acid (fructose) or diphenylamine and acid (deoxy sugars) give characteristic colors. The sera of patients with cancer, rheumatic fever, or tuberculosis when treated with these reagents yield colors frequently more intense than those given by normal sera (141, 149), a phenomenon presumably reflecting the increased carbohydrate content of the former kind of serum, although the exact nature of the substance or substances present which yield these reactions is not known.

Another experimental approach to the characterization of the plasma proteins is based upon polarography, which depends upon the catalytic reduction of hydrogen ion by a cobalt-sulfhydryl complex, and is given only by proteins which contain reactive sulfhydryl groups. Brdicka noted that serum of cancer patients gave lower polarographic values than did normal serum (150), an observation since confirmed by others (151–153). However, it is likely that the subnormal albumin content in the cancer sera might be the major reason for these findings, since the polarographic serum waves are closely proportional to the serum albumin concentration (154). Yet there appears to be some evidence that human serum albumin may consist of at least two components, one containing, and the other lacking, free sulfhydryl groups (155, 156), and Schoenbach and his colleagues (157, 158) showed that, although the sulfhydryl content of patients with cancer and other diseases was markedly reduced below normal levels, this reduction could only be partially accounted for on the basis of reduced albumin content. The possibility of a qualitative change, or change in the ratio of the intermolecular components of serum albumin in pathologic conditions cannot be excluded, although Huggins and his associates (159) found no distinction in the sulfhydryl levels of serum albumin isolated either from normal individuals or from patients with malignant disease. Associated with the possible reactions of the mercaptan groups of serum albumin are methylene blue reduction studies (160, 161), which appear to indicate that by an increased reduction time of this dye when incubated at alkaline pH with cancer sera there may be less available or more slowly released (162) mercaptan groups in the albumin of these sera. Another phenomenon which depends upon reactive groups on the surface of the protein molecule is that of the binding of dyes (163). Huggins has shown that phenol red (159), and Westphal has shown that azorubin (164), are bound per milligram of albumin to a lesser extent in cancer serum than in the serum of normal individuals, although serum albumin isolated from normal and from cancer serum binds phenol red equally well (159). Evidently serum albumin by itself, and serum albumin *in situ*, are not quite the same. Still another phenomenon which appears to be at least partially dependent upon the albumin level in the serum, and probably upon the polysaccharide content and the sulfhydryl groups of this component, is that involved in the thermal coagulation of serum. Glass (165), and Huggins and his colleagues (166), have reported that the serum from cancer patients is frequently less coagulable on heating than is normal serum. Glass determined the coagulation temperature as a measure of coagulability, whereas Huggins first employed the least coagulable concentration as the end point (167) and later used the determination of the amount of iodoacetate sufficient to prevent the serum from coagulation as the end point (168, 169). Again, albumin isolated from normal serum and from the serum of cancer patients possessed the same iodoacetate index (micromoles iodoacetate per gram of protein), although the sera from the two sources showed markedly different indices (167). As in the previous cases, the physical isolation of the albumin from its matrix in the serum may have removed from it those substances responsible for its behavior when combined in the serum.

The proteins of the plasma are readily precipitated by tungstic or phosphotungstic acids, leaving in the filtrate a variety of nitrogenous substances of low molecular weight. When apparently weaker precipitating agents such as trichloroacetic, perchloric, or sulfosalicylic acids are used with plasma, more of the nitrogenous substances remain in the filtrate. Thus, trichloroacetic acid filtrates from normal human plasma contain about 5 mg. % more nitrogen and about 2 mg. % more tyrosine as Folin reagent color than do tungstic acid filtrates (126). These differences are presumably due to low molecular weight proteins, proteoses, or polypeptides which, precipitable from serum only by the stronger precipitating agents, are apparently increased in neoplastic and other diseases. The general designation given this condition is that of polypeptidemia. Only one well-defined component of this spectrum of nitrogenous bodies has so far been recognized, and that is the mucoprotein of Winzler (133), which was isolated from perchloric acid filtrates of serum by precipitation with phosphotungstic acid (cf. 170). This relatively soluble glycoprotein is elevated in the sera of patients with cancer, pneumonia, tuberculosis, rheumatic fever, and other diseases (139).

As a partial result of the decreased albumin in cancer serum, the polarographic properties of the whole serum are generally diminished below normal. On the other hand, as a result of the polypeptidemia of the cancer serum, the polarographic properties of its sulfosalicylic acid filtrates tend to rise above the normal (171). Parallel polarographic studies on whole serum and its filtrate yield a particularly accentuated picture in abnormal states, inasmuch as the results on the former by decreasing below normal, and on the latter by increasing above normal, yield ratios diverging strikingly from the normal (172). A considerable proportion of the rise in the polarographic wave for the serum filtrate is due to the rise in amount of its component mucoprotein (168; cf. 173). Thus, the presence of this interesting glycoprotein in serum can be determined in four ways—by chemical isolation from the filtrate (133), by polarography of the filtrate (133), by its electrophoretic mobility at pH 4.5 (134), and by its contribution to the electrophoretic mobility of α-globulin at pH 8.5 (cf. 137).

The nature of the other components of the polypeptide fraction is unknown. The still smaller components of the tungstic acid filtrates are probably low molecular weight peptides, amino acids, urea, and other small nitrogenous substances. They too, tend to rise in the course of neoplastic disease. Amino nitrogen estimations on such filtrates, using the nitrous acid technique, showed a distinct increase in value in a number of cancerous individuals (174). A more specific approach, using the manometric ninhydrin-CO_2 technique to determine only α-amino acids, also showed an appreciable elevation of amino acids in cancer serum (175). When normal mice were placed on a protein-deficient diet, the mean blood α-carboxyl nitrogen fell from the normal value of 4.8 mg. % to about 2 mg. %; a group of tumor-bearing mice under the same conditions of dietary deprivation showed a decrease from about 8 mg. % to about 5 mg. %. Removal of the tumor results in a drop in the elevated blood amino acid level to the normal. Since individuals with a tumor tend to adopt a lowered voluntary food intake, the rise in serum filtrate amino acid nitrogen, contrary to experience with normal, fasting individuals, is curious. More stringent dietary deprivation apparently results in levels still well above those of normal individuals similarly deprived. These phenomena further serve to emphasize the body-wasting character of cancer and other diseases.

Natural heteroagglutinins for human red cells of groups AB and O exist in the serum of rats. After implantation of malignant tumors of various kinds into rats, there was a rapid drop in the heteroagglutinin titer, followed by a rise to a level still below normal, and finally followed by a progressive loss in the titer until it disappeared completely after 21 days (175a).

The phenomena described so far, inclusive of the electrophoretic and polarographic patterns, the polysaccharide levels, the individual protein levels, and the mercaptan and associated physical reactions, are extremely interesting manifestations of the lability of the equilibrium among the components of the plasma under conditions of disease. Not one of these phenomena is unique for cancer, and nearly all are characteristic of some form of wasting disease. Applied to the individual patient, each may contribute to the knowledge of the clinical status of the patient and with care may be used for prognosis (153). On a more fundamental level, each may contribute its share to a better understanding of the metabolic reactions of the diseased state and, pursued further, may illuminate and lead to the discovery of new phenomena. When these phenomena are approached from the standpoint of differential diagnosis, however, their scientific values seemingly disappear, and their further development is replaced by that oft-repeated melancholy chronicle of profitless controversy. A diagnostic test for cancer is an important goal to strive for, but its application to that most labile of all tissues, the plasma, seems not likely to be successful. Despite the enormous labor expended by both proponents and antagonists of the various diagnostic tests for cancer, no clearly useful purpose can be served by reporting histories so evanescent. A particularly lucid description of the principles and criteria for evaluating such tests, without reference to any particular test, has been written by Dunn and Greenhouse (176). Informative reviews of the various tests may be found in references 126, 177 and 178.

Multiple Myeloma and Bence-Jones Proteins. Multiple myeloma is a tumor of the bone marrow which is characterized frequently by (a) a hyperproteinemia, (b) a very considerable increase in an electrophoretic component of the serum which migrates with the globulin group, and (c) the excretion in the urine of an unusual form of protein to which the designation of Bence-Jones protein has been given (cf. 124, 179). The abnormal globulin can be demonstrated by electrophoretic or salt-fractionation methods (180–185). It is possible that this component of the plasma has its origin in the tumor, for the large, sharp peak that is characteristic of the electrophoretic pattern of the multiple myeloma plasma is also observed in extracts of the tumors of the same subject (186). Control studies on normal marrow and on myelogenous leukemia tissue, as well as on marrow from a patient treated with urethane, failed to reveal the presence of the abnormal globulin (cf. 183).

The normal protein distinctive for myeloma, although found in the plasma family of globulins, is not identical from patient to patient but possesses a variety of electrophoretic mobilities (183) and molecular sizes (187). Studies by Putnam suggest that the MM (multiple myeloma blood plasma) proteins form a family with gradually varying ionic structure which possess a mobility range very close to that of the components of normal γ-globulin (188). When the MM proteins were studied in the isolated condition, their electrophoretic peaks were sharp, indicating a high degree of electrical homogeneity, with mobilities which differed from sample to sample. Thus the serum protein increment in this disease represents an increase in a peculiar species of γ-globulin which might vary from one patient to another. Sedimentation studies revealed two categories of sizes, namely, proteins with a single or a major component with $S = 6.6$, and proteins with a major component of $S = 9.5$ (188). A value of $6.46S$ for the MM protein was reported by Rundles *et al.* (187). The molecular weight for this protein, about 160,000, agreed well with that of normal γ-globulin. The presence of the $9.5S$ component among the MM proteins is more puzzling, although a normal β-globulin with $S = 9$ was reported by Kekwick (189), and a $9S$ subcomponent has been detected in γ_1-globulin (190). The molecular weight of this $9.5S$ component of the MM proteins is about 400,000 (188) and appears to be an occasional but unique feature of multiple myeloma in a few patients. It would appear that multiple myeloma is characterized by the production in nearly each patient of a large amount of a relatively homogeneous protein which is ordinarily present only in small proportion or not at all in the group of normal serum globulins.

Cryoglobulins, those curious serum proteins which precipitate from serum on cooling, occur in several disease states, but somewhat more regularly in cases of multiple myeloma. They may be identical with the MM proteins in cases of this disease, but in other disease states they resemble no known normal component of the serum.

The over-all amino acid composition patterns of the myeloma serum proteins show a striking similarity to that of normal γ-globulin (190a). Such minor variations noted among the myeloma proteins themselves, and between these and γ-globulin, must be evaluated in light of the fact that γ-globulin itself is a designation for a number of proteins.

In many cases of multiple myeloma, the urine contains a group of proteins with the characteristic property of precipitating from solution at 45° to 58° and of redissolving at 100° (Bence-Jones proteins). Almost invariably in cases of Bence-Jones proteinuria there is an accompanying hyperproteinemia, and it seems probable, in the absence of any indication of a renal origin, that the Bence-Jones proteins are carried from their source of origin via the blood to the kidneys. The possibility may also exist that, in the absence of these proteins in the urine, they may still be present in the serum as non-diffusible complexes. The Bence-Jones proteins are generally grossly heterogeneous and vary strikingly from one patient to another (187, 191). Sedimentation values for various preparations range from 2.8 to 4.0, and the proteins differ considerably in isoelectric point (i.e., pH 4.6 to 6.7), electrical or molecular homogeneity, and pH stability (191). The molecular constants of these proteins indicate that they are all smaller than serum albumin, and this fact, together with their apparent molecular symmetry, offers an explanation of their passage from blood stream to urine. It is not improbable that the smaller size of the Bence-Jones proteins may be due to cleavage, perhaps in the kidney, of some larger serum component. The lack of such urinary proteins in the presence of frank multiple myeloma accompanied by marked hyperproteinemia would render such an explanation difficult. Moreover, if the cleavage were naturally enzymatic, it might be expected that the products of the reaction would be much more uniform than they are. The etiology of the Bence-Jones proteins, like that of the large globulin increment in the serum, is still unknown.

Serum Aldolase. Aldolase (zymohexase), the enzyme which splits the six-carbon chain of glucose into two trioses, is found in appreciable amounts in normal rat serum (192). The serum, however, does not have the capacity to ferment glucose completely because the necessary coenzymes and other fermentation systems are absent. In rats carrying the transplanted Jensen sarcoma the aldolase activity of the serum is increased, and the increase is roughly proportional to the ratio of tumor weight to body weight (Fig. 62). This effect is not observed in pregnant rats.

Esterase activity is diminished, but aldolase activity is increased in the serum of tumor-bearing animals. Since it may be assumed that the source of serum esterase is the liver and since the level of this enzyme in the livers of tumor-bearing animals is diminished, the low level of serum esterase in such animals may be interpreted on the basis of an interference by tumor products in the hepatic synthesis of this enzyme. The increase in serum phosphatase in cases of osteogenic sarcoma and of disseminated prostatic carcinoma have been interpreted on the basis of a "leakage" of these phosphatase-rich tissues into the blood stream. Thus, the changes in the serum enzyme pattern, in so far as they relate to esterase and to phosphatase, are not insusceptible to reasonable explanation. On the other hand, the increase in serum aldolase is rather puzzling.

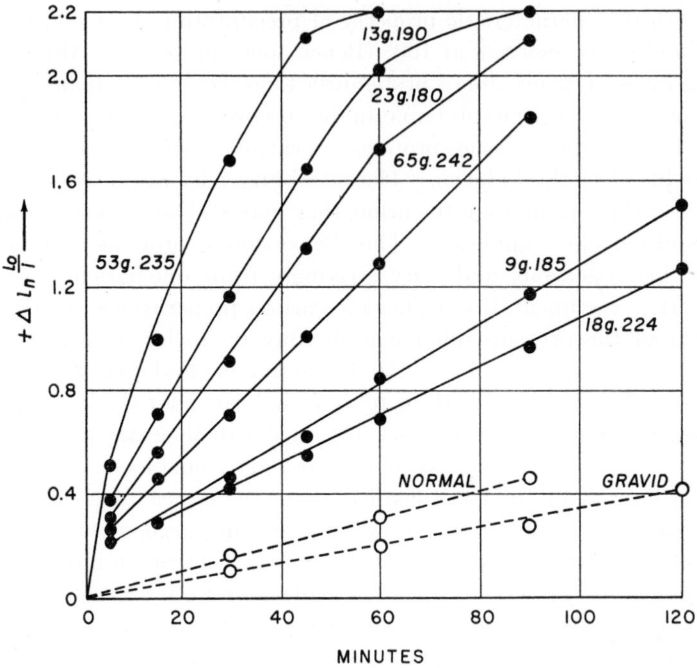

FIG. 62. Plasma aldolase activity (change of light absorption with time) in relation to the ratio of tumor weight to body weight of rats bearing the transplanted Jensen sarcoma. From Warburg, O., and Christian, W., *Biochem. Z.* **314,** 399 (1943).

Warburg and Christian suggested three sources for the increase in serum aldolase in their tumor-bearing animals: (a) the tumor itself, (b) the red blood cells, and (c) the musculature of the animal. There is thus implied that the enzyme "leaks" from one or more of these tissues into the blood stream and the authors indeed calculated that it would require, respectively, 0.17 ml., 0.023 ml., and 0.0014 ml. of red cells, tumor cells, and muscle cells, to raise 1.0 ml. of blood plasma from the normal to the cancerous value. The rise in the serum enzyme must be constantly maintained from whatever source, for a pure preparation of the enzyme injected intravenously into normal animals very rapidly disappears from the circulation. The authors cited believed that the most likely source of the increased serum enzyme is the enzyme-rich musculature. No matter what source is assumed, however, it is indeed curious that, of all the eleven or so fermentation systems involved in glycolysis, only aldolase enters into the blood stream. It may be that this enzyme is a very small molecule and is readily diffusible through cellular membranes. It is otherwise hard to see why, if the tissue, whether muscle, tumor, or erythrocyte, simply undergoes some disintegration under the influence of tumor substances, all the enzymatic systems do not spill into the blood stream. There is here an apparently selective leakage of aldolase. Although, the muscle cell appears to be a plausible source of the serum enzyme increase, it would be of interest to examine the activity of many tissues of the tumor-bearing host other than the serum, in order to observe any possible changes from the normal. It is conceivable that tumor substance in the circulation might stimulate the site of aldolase synthesis (at present unknown) which maintains the normal level in the serum. If this were the case, then only this enzyme, and not the other fermentation enzymes present in this site, would be altered, since the former is the only one altered in cancerous serum. It is conceivable that the systemic studies with tumor fractions, so illuminating in the case of hepatic catalase, might be of value here.

More recent work by Sibley and Lehninger (193) has confirmed the general findings of Warburg and Christian. In rats bearing sarcoma 39 or the Walker 256 tumor, the serum aldolase levels may increase as high as seven times the normal value. Surgical removal of the tumors caused a prompt decline of the serum aldolase to the normal level as did the administration of the chemotherapeutic agent, ethyl carbamate, which retards the growth of these tumors. Cachexia, anemia, infection, and pregnancy were without effect on the serum aldolase level, and the corresponding tissues of normal and of tumor-bearing animals possessed nearly the same level of aldolase activity. This latter observation is indeed of interest for, if the tissues of the tumor-bearing host have the normal amount of enzyme, it seems probable that the only source from which the extra serum aldolase could come from is the tumor. Of 104 cases of human cancer tested, 20% showed increased serum aldolase activity, but there was no connection of these elevations with the clinical status of the patients (193). Twelve out of sixteen patients with advanced prostatic cancer were found to have increased levels of serum aldolase, and, of these twelve, ten responded to hormone therapy by a drop of serum aldolase to the normal range (194). However, there is no correlation between the level of serum aldolase and early prostatic cancer, and patients with untreated hyperthyroidism, diabetes mellitus, or convalescing from hepatitis may have increased values of serum aldolase.

Plasma Prothrombin. A definite plasma prothrombin deficiency has been shown to exist in leukemic rats (195) and in rats with primary hepatomas induced by feeding of 4-dimethylaminoazobenzene (196). The latter findings suggest that an adequate amount of functional liver tissue is necessary for the maintenance of normal levels of prothrombin and that hepatoma tissue itself does not synthesize prothrombin. No increase in prothrombine tissue was noted in animals bearing transplanted tumors. A standard dose (2.5 mg.) of the anticoagulant 3,3-methylenebis-(4-hydroxycoumarin) usually causes a more severe hypoprothrombinemia in rats with primary hepatomas than in normal rats or those bearing tumors elsewhere in the body.

Serum Phosphatase (Monoesterase). Animal tissues contain two separate phosphatases, one with a pH optimum at about 5, the other at about 9. Bone tissue contains an active acid phosphatase and a still more active alkaline phosphatase; prostatic tissue (in man) contains a highly active acid phosphatase and a less active alkaline phosphatase. In cases of osteogenic sarcoma and prostatic carcinoma, these enzymes are increased in activity (per gram of tissue) as compared with the normal tissue of origin.

Serum alkaline phosphatase appears to be in equilibrium with bone phosphatase, for the level of the former enzyme is strongly influenced by any normal or pathological changes associated with the bones. In 1930 Kay (197) pointed out that the plasma phosphatase (at pH 7.6) was considerably elevated in generalized diseases of bone. The rise in plasma phosphatase appears to be a reflection of the tendency of bone formation and thus occurs normally in growing children as well as abnormally in cases of osteogenic sarcoma. Osteolytic diseases, however, such as hyperparathyroidism, also cause a rise in serum alkaline phosphatase, as do both osteoblastic and osteolytic metastases to bone from carcinoma of various tissues (198–202). The activity of serum phosphatase is frequently high in lymphoid diseases long before bone changes become evident, and it has been suggested (203) that the bone changes may occur more frequently than was formerly suspected. It seems clear at the present time than an elevation in the serum alkaline phosphatase activity, in the absence of hepatic obstruction, is evidence for the presence of bone changes in the host brought about by a variety of conditions. This phenomenon leads to difficulty in differential diagnosis. Woodard (204) has studied the levels of phosphatase in various bone diseases and has proposed the following useful table (Table 169) as a guide in such diagnosis.

The highest values reported as a result of most of the neoplastic diseases of bone occur in cases of osteogenic sarcoma of the osteoblastic type (200, 205, 206). Removal of the osteogenic sarcoma at operation is followed by a drop of the plasma phosphatase to the normal level, and recurrence of the tumor is followed by a second rise (200). The effect of the tumor is thus reversible; a typical case is illustrated in Fig. 63. Irradiation of osteogenic sarcoma with X-rays of high frequency results, in some cases, in a temporary inactivation of the tumor accompanied by a temporary drop in the serum phosphatase. With resumption of growth by the tumor the serum alkaline phosphatase rises again.

Metastases to bone from carcinoma of other tissues may be osteolytic or osteoplastic, the former type yielding little or no alkaline phosphatase to the serum, the latter yielding a considerable quantity. Metastases of cancer of the breast are most frequently osteolytic, those from the prostate

TABLE 169

CHEMICAL FINDINGS IN NEOPLASTIC DISEASES OF BONE (204)

Disease	Serum acid phosphatase	Serum alkaline phosphatase	Serum inorganic phosphorus	Total serum calcium
Chondroma, osteochondroma, osteoma, exostosis	—	Normal	Normal	Normal
Solitary bone cyst	—	Normal	Normal	Normal
Giant cell tumor	Normal	Normal or little over	Normal	Normal
Osteogenic sarcoma	Normal	Usually high	Normal	Normal
Endothelioma of bone	—	Normal or little over	Normal	Normal
Reticulum cell sarcoma of bone	—	Normal or little over	Normal	Normal
Rickets	—	High	Normal or low	Normal or low
Inflammatory disease of bone	—	Usually normal	Normal	Normal
Osteolytic metastatic disease	Normal	Normal or moderately raised	Normal or high	Normal or high
Osteoplastic metastatic not from prostate	Normal	High	Normal	Normal
Carcinoma prostate metastatic to bone	High in most cases	High	Normal	Normal
Plasma cell myeloma	Normal	Normal or little over	Normal or high	Normal or high
Osteomalacia	Normal	Moderately high	Normal or low	Usually low
Senile osteoporosis	Normal	Normal	Normal	Normal
Hyperparathyroidism	—	High	Low	High
Osteitis deformans	Normal	High	Normal	Normal

more often osteoplastic. The reason why bone reacts so differently to invasion by various tumors is not apparent at the present time. Prostatic carcinoma, in contrast with mammary carcinoma, is fairly high in alkaline phosphatase activity, and it may be that the former tissue already contains osteoplastic elements (201). Normal kidney is quite high in alkaline phosphatase. Whether the transformation of renal tissue into carcinoma is accompanied by a loss, a retention, or a gain in alkaline phosphatase activity is not known at present. It appears to be true, however, that bone metastases from renal carcinomas are usually osteolytic in character. Only in the case of prostatic carcinoma may the site of the original tumor, from which the bone metastases are derived, be determined, and this is because

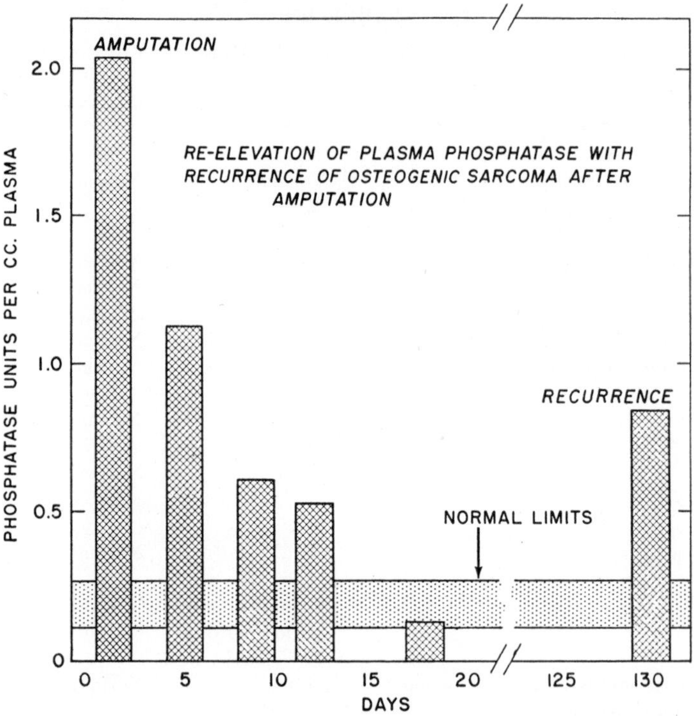

FIG. 63. Course of plasma alkaline phosphatase in case of osteogenic sarcoma after removal of tumor and recurrence. From Franseen, C. C., and McLean, R., *Am. J. Cancer* **24,** 299 (1935).

not only is the serum alkaline phosphatase considerably elevated but so, too, and uniquely, is the serum acid phosphatase.

Significantly correlated with the level of serum alkaline phosphatase in patients with metastatic cancer of the skeleton or liver is the level of serum phosphohexose isomerase, the enzyme which mediates the reversible conversion of glucose-6-phosphate to fructose-6-phosphate (207). Individuals with a high level of one enzyme had a high level of the other, and vice versa. Whether these two enzymes have a common source, or are adventitiously correlated in diseases of this sort, remains for further investigation.

Serum Phosphatase Levels in Prostatic Carcinoma. This topic continues the discussion on the clinical effects of endocrine alterations in the treatment of prostatic carcinoma presented in Chapter VI.

Animal tissues show the presence of at least two phosphatases, each with a widely separated pH optimum. So-called acid phosphatase has a pH optimum at 5 to 6; so-called alkaline phosphatase has a pH optimum at 9 to 10. These enzymes have recently been separated from the mammalian kidney in relatively pure form as homogeneous proteins (208). In 1935, while investigating the source of the acid phosphatase activity of urine, Kutscher and Wolbergs (209) discovered that normal human prostate tissue is extremely rich in acid phosphatase. The activity of the enzyme in adult human prostatic tissue is phenomenally high, far exceeding that of the prostate of any other species except the monkey (210). Cat, rabbit, guinea pig, and rat prostatic tissue contains very small amounts of the enzyme; that of the dog is somewhat greater than these. Acid phosphatase makes its appearance in the human and monkey prostate at puberty. However, injections of testosterone propionate into immature Rhesus monkeys, whose prostates are very low in the enzyme, produce within a short time a precocious rise in the level of acid phosphatase to that characteristic of the adult; injection of estrogen has no such effect. The enzyme is normally excreted in relatively high concentration as part of the prostatic contribution to the seminal fluid, but the precise function of acid phosphatase in the semen is not yet known.

In 1936, Gutman *et al.* made the observation that tumor cells arising from the prostatic epithelium retain the high acid phosphatase activity of the normal prostatic cells of origin, as do also the distant skeletal metastases from the primary tumor (199). The latter observation suggested the possibility that prostatic acid phosphatase might be found in the blood of patients with disseminated prostatic carcinoma. In 1938, the Gutmans (198) and, independently, Barringer and Woodard (211) did in fact observe that a striking increase in the acid phosphatase level occurred in the serum of patients with disseminated—but not non-disseminated—cancer of the prostate. This observation, one of the most original in modern chemical pathology, has since been extended in such a way as to serve not only for diagnostic but also prognostic purposes.

Normal human subjects, both male and female, immature and mature, show a slight acid phosphatase activity in the serum. This serum enzyme is most likely in equilibrium with the acid phosphatase of the various tissues which possess this enzyme in varying degree (cf. Chapter VIII). In terms of arbitrary phosphatase activity units introduced by King and Armstrong (212), the normal level of acid serum phosphatase may be considered to be 3 ± 0.5 (213–215). It should be noted that this figure holds only in the absence of hemolysis, for the erythrocyte has an active acid phosphatase (216). The erythrocyte phosphatase can, however, be distinguished from the serum phosphatase by the greater sensitivity of the latter to fluoride inhibition. In cases of metastasizing carcinoma of the prostate, the normal serum acid phosphatase level is usually, if not invariably, considerably exceeded and there is frequently a parallelism between the height of the enzyme level and the severity of the disease (215, 217). Thus, in quite advanced cases with extensive metastases, the serum acid phosphatase level may go as high as, or higher than, 1000 King-Armstrong units (214).

A fairly accurate diagnosis and prognosis of the disease can be attained, as illustrated in Table 170 taken from a paper by Gutman (217) and including data of Herger and Sauer (218).

A few subjects with diseases other than disseminated prostatic carcinoma are found to have minor increases in serum acid phosphatase levels above the normal, but these rarely exceed 5 to 9 King-Armstrong units (214). These cases include individuals with skeletal metastases secondary to mammary and pulmonary carcinoma. In no event do these exceptions to the general rule yield as consistent a serum alteration as in cases of disseminated prostatic carcinoma, and, indeed, those observed may have been due to individual peculiarities of the patients concerned. Bone contains an acid phosphatase as well as an alkaline phosphatase, and it may be that the activity of the metastases at skeletal sites sometimes releases both enzymes into the circulation. The reason for the small proportion of negative cases, i.e., normal serum acid phosphatase levels in definite and independent diagnoses of metastasizing prostatic cancer, is not known at the present time.

There is also present in serum, as in all body tissues, an alkaline phosphatase with a pH activity optimum at 9 to 10. No data are available for the level of activity of this enzyme in prostatic carcinoma cells, but the activity of skeletal metastases from this tumor is quite high (198). There would be expected, therefore, and there actually is, a considerable elevation in the serum alkaline phosphatase in cases of metastasizing prostatic carcinoma. However, in the case of this enzyme, no possibility of specific diagnosis based upon its level in the serum may be reached because of the large number of unrelated pathological conditions which produce a rise in the level of activity of the enzyme. Among these conditions is osteogenic sarcoma. Nevertheless, it is of interest to observe the fluctuations of this enzyme in various cases of prostatic carcinoma, as presented in Table 171 taken from the work of Emmett and Greene (215).

Hormonal and biochemical techniques merged in the striking experiments of Huggins and Hodges (213). These workers demonstrated that the high serum acid phosphatase level of many cases of disseminated prostatic carcinoma can be reduced promptly and sharply by surgical castration or by injection of estrogens, whereas injection of androgens caused a further increase in the blood level. The serum acid phosphatase level fell rapidly after castration to values approximating the normal. The serum alkaline phosphatase rose postoperatively, then fell to or toward normal. In later reports Huggins and his associates described the remarkable clinical improvement which accompanied these chemical changes (219, 220) (cf. Chapter VI). Little if any change in the serum acid phosphatase level is produced by castration or injection of estrogen if such level is normal before instituting either therapy.

TABLE 170

PERCENTILE DISTRIBUTION OF SERUM ACID PHOSPHATASE VALUES IN CASES OF PROSTATE CARCINOMA WITH AND WITHOUT METASTASES AND IN OTHER CONDITIONS

Diagnosis	Number of cases studied	Percentage of cases with levels of serum acid phosphatase — Units/100 ml. of serum					
Series of Sullivan and the Gutmans (214)		Less than 3	3–4.9	5–9.9	10–100	100–1000	More than 1000
I. Prostate carcinoma	200						
a. Bone metastases by X-ray	130	15	12	25	35	9	4
b. No bone metastases by X-ray	70	89	11				
II. Benign prostatic hypertrophy	75	100					
III. Prostatitis	10	100					
IV. Non-prostatic diseases	570	90	7.5	2.5			
V. Normal	30	100					
Series of Herger and Sauer (218)		Less than 4	4–6	6.1–10	10–100	100–1000	More than 1000
I. Prostate carcinoma	147						
a. Bone metastases demonstrable by X-ray or suspected	47	9	4	30	30	19	2
b. No X-ray or clinical evidence of metastases	100	77	22[1]	1			
II. Control patients	283	92.5	7.5				

[1] Only 8% consistently gave serum acid phosphatase values between 4 and 6 units (King-Armstrong).

TABLE 171

PHOSPHATASE DETERMINATION IN 159 CASES OF CARCINOMA OF THE PROSTATE (215)

King-Armstrong Units	Clinical roentgenologic evidence of metastasis			
	Present		Not present	
	Acid phosphatase	Alkaline phosphatase	Acid phosphatase	Alkaline phosphatase
More than 50	8	24	0	0
20.1–50	8	27	0	1
10.1–20	18	32	1	5
5.1–10	24	30	0	20
3.6–5	24	5	3	4
0–3.5	44	8	29	3
Total	126	126	33	33

CORRELATION OF SERUM ACID AND ALKALINE PHOSPHATASE DETERMINATIONS IN 159 CASES OF CARCINOMA OF THE PROSTATE GLAND

Acid phosphatase	Alkaline phosphatase	Clinical evidence of metastasis	
		Present	Not present
Elevated	Elevated	65	3
Elevated	Normal	17	1
Normal	Elevated	18	3
Normal	Normal	26	26
Total		126	33

Normal values: Acid phosphatase 0–3.5 K.-A units/100 ml.
Alkaline phosphatase 0–10.0 K.-A units/100 ml.

Representative data taken from Huggins and Hodges (213) are given in Fig. 64. Cessation of administration of stilbestrol was followed by a rise in enzyme activity, and subsequent administration was again followed by a return to the normal level. In many cases castration or administration of stilbestrol was followed by clinical improvement.

The serum acid phosphatase level is thus associated with growth of the tumor, and the relation between enzyme and tumor may apparently be mediated by hormonal control. The activity of the prostatic tissue, as reflected by the rise of the serum acid phosphatase, depends in part upon the degree of androgenic hormone activity. This enzyme varies according to the effect of androgen control of the prostatic epithelium.

It will be noted from Fig. 64 that there is little correlation of either symptomatology or course of acid phosphatase level with the course of alkaline phosphatase level. The extra serum acid phosphatase activity may be ascribed to increased osteoblastic activity at the site of skeletal metastases.

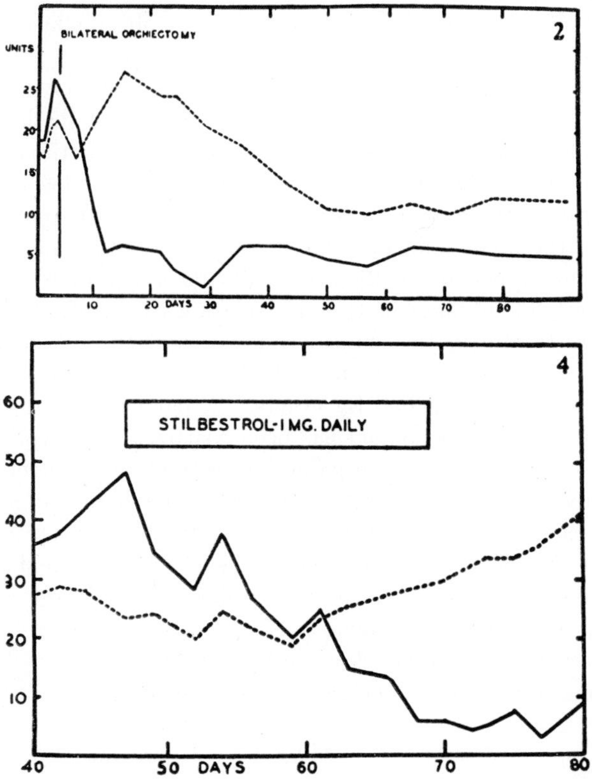

FIG. 64. Effect of castration or of stilbestrol administration in disseminated prostatic carcinoma on acid and alkaline phosphatase of serum. Continuous line acid, dotted line alkaline phosphatase. Ordinate in terms of King-Armstrong phosphatase units (normal level for acid and alkaline phosphatase, 3 and 12 respectively). From Huggins, C., and Hodges, C. V., *Cancer Research* **1,** 293 (1941).

Thus, after castration, the serum acid phosphatase quickly declines and remains low during the effective, comparatively androgen-free period; but the serum alkaline phosphatase usually rises after castration, owing presumably, to osteoplastic healing at the site of skeletal mestastases which may be independently demonstrated by roentgenograms. When the healing ceases ,the serum alkaline phosphatase falls off (214). It would be interesting to observe the course of serum alkaline phosphatase activity in cases of prostatic carcinoma metastatic to tissues other than bone.

If the carcinomatous prostatic epithelium is inhibited by estrogens, it might be expected that it would be activated by androgen injections, and this is indeed the case. A rise in the serum acid phosphatase above the pre-injection level was observed. Bilateral orchiectomy in normal dogs resulted in no change in the level of the serum phosphatases. Attempts to influence the acid phosphatase activity of the prostate glands of both mature and immature rats by injection of various sex hormones were unsuccessful. Further studies in experimental animals of the hormonal control of tumors of the sexual and accessory tissues await the production of such tumors in animals of appropriate strains. It may be, however, that the properties of the human prostate are quite different from those of the prostates of the lower animals. So far, only the human prostate appears to contain such a phenomenally large quantity of acid phosphatase.

The remarkable findings of Huggins relating to the effect of surgical or chemical castration on the clinical response and the concomitant serum phosphatase response in patients with disseminated prostatic carcinoma were confirmed and extended by others. A particularly full and critical report of the techniques applied has been written by Sullivan *et al.* (214). Castration frequently results in palliation of the painful effects of the disease, but recurrences frequently occur after the period of amelioration. Then, too, cases are encountered which are refractory to estrogen administration or to surgical castration, and the level of serum acid phosphatase reflects this resistance. Typical susceptible and resistant cases are illustrated in Table 172 by Gutman (217).

The therapeutic techniques for prostatic carcinoma are still too recent for their long-term effects to be gauged, but a conservative estimate at the

TABLE 172

EFFECT OF CASTRATION ON SERUM ACID AND ALKALINE PHOSPHATASES IN TWO PATIENTS WITH METASTATIC PROSTATE CARCINOMA (217)

	Case T. B.[1]		Case L. B.[2]	
	Acid phosphatase, units/100 ml.	Alkaline phosphatase, Bodansky units/100 ml.	Acid phosphatase, units/100 ml.	Alkaline phosphatase, Bodansky units/100 ml.
Preoperative	80.6	43.3	44.8	12.4
Postoperative				
2 days	68.6	31.6	45.8	9.8
4 days	42.2	31.1	37.0	12.1
1 week	21.1	38.3	35.0	15.1
2 weeks	—	—	39.3	17.3
3 weeks	7.4	52.1	42.5	15.2
4 weeks	—	—	35.7	12.0
8 weeks	3.0	23.7	59.0	10.2
12 weeks	4.1	13.4	393.0	23.6
16 weeks	3.6	8.3	740.0	33.9

[1] T. B. illustrates typical results when the clinical response proves to be very satisfactory.

[2] L. B. is illustrative of a refractory case, with death occurring 6 months after castration.

present time would suggest that at least one out of five patients so treated has survived beyond the ordinary period of expectancy and that most of the remainder have benefited clinically for some space of time. Whatever the final medical judgment may be, the biochemical techniques employed have proved their value.

It may be of interest to consider briefly the source of the rise in the serum phosphatases. Bone tissue and prostatic tissue are quite high, respectively, in alkaline and in acid phosphatase (see preceding chapter). When these tissues become neoplastic the activity of these enzymes (per unit weight of tissue) increases. Such findings are somewhat unusual, for more often the transformation of a normal into a malignant tissue is accompanied by a reduction in the activity of specialized function. The only other clear-cut exception to this more or less general rule is the case of the rat hepatoma which possesses an acid phosphatase activity about double and an alkaline phosphatase activity about 120 times that of the corresponding activity of these enzymes in normal rat liver (112). Yet rats bearing the transplanted phosphatase-rich hepatoma possess a normal serum phosphatase level. The reason lies in the fact that the rat hepatoma is encapsulated and rarely, if ever, metastasizes. Human prostatic carcinoma possesses a phenomenally high acid phosphatase activity, and osteogenic sarcoma an extremely high alkaline phosphatase activity; the contents of very few prostatic or bone tumor cells need leak into the circulation to markedly raise the level of the respective enzymes. In the consideration of the source of the prostatic contribution to the serum acid phosphatase, it has been noted that prostatic acid phosphatase, unlike the erythrocyte enzyme, is inhibited by L-tartrate (221). In patients with advanced prostatic malignancy, most of the rise in the level of the serum acid phosphatase can be inhibited by tartrate, thus indicating the prostatic origin of the increased level of enzyme (222, 223). Palpation of the prostate may or may not result in an abnormal rise in the total serum acid phosphatase (224), but in nearly every case a transitory rise in the prostatic component of this activity has been observed (223). In non-metastatic cancer of the prostate, the total serum acid phosphatase almost always remains within the normal range of activity, but the L-tartrate-inhibited component frequently rises (223). Similarly, in those cases in which the total serum acid phosphatase activity does not appreciably alter in level as a result of hormonal therapy, the "prostatic" component invariably rises with androgen and falls with estrogen administration (223).

The use of serum enzyme levels as an aid to the clinical diagnosis of suspected cancer or to the prognosis of known cancer may thus be limited at the present time to the cases of only a few tumors which possess specific enzymes in very high concentration. Since very few tumors are known at present to be so marked—by far the larger number of tumors being known to have a relatively low and uniform enzymatic activity (see Chapter VIII)—it would appear that the employment of serum enzymatic acids to clinical study, although invaluable in a few specific instances of neoplasia, may not be generally applicable. In other words, before looking into the serum for various kinds of effects, the proper approach is first to examine the tumor itself for the presence of unusual chemical properties. Only in this way can effects specific to the particular tumor be recognized. On the other hand, all tumors may possess certain common properties which produce systemic effects on the host animals, such as the reduction in serum esterase or liver catalase. It is necessary, therefore, to distinguish between the systemic effect evoked in the liver by nearly all tumors, as reflected in the liver catalase activity, and certain of the changes evoked in the enzyme concentration of the serum through obvious leakage from the tumor. The former is a nearly universal, the latter a usually specific, effect. A tumor may apparently exert an effect upon an organ in a distant site without throwing off tumor substance (e.g., alkaline phosphatase from the rat hepatoma) into the blood stream. To infect the circulation with enzymes, some disintegration of tumor cells is apparently necessary. If the mechanism whereby the liver catalase is decreased is due to the giving off by tumors of a toxic substance, this substance may be so small in molecular size as to be readily diffusible through the cell walls even of encapsulated, intact tumors. The intensive study of the mechanism of both universal and specific systemic effects would greatly clarify many of the problems of tumor characteristics.

Serum Alkaline Phosphatase in Neoplastic Involvement of the Liver. In the absence of diseases of the bone, whether primary or through osteoplastic metastatic involvement, the serum alkaline phosphatase level is a good indication of the presence of major disorders of the liver and biliary tract. It may be assumed that the serum enzyme is derived from bone-forming cells and after escaping into the circulating fluids is excreted in the bile. Skeletal disorders which result in osteogenesis thus raise the level of the enzyme in the serum because it is synthesized at a faster rate than it can be excreted. In hepatic disorders of the obstructive type, the increase in the serum enzyme may be explained on the same grounds, only in this case the rise is due not to an abnormally high rate of synthesis but to an abnormally low rate of excretion; i.e., the enzyme is retained.

Gross obstruction of the common bile duct nearly invariably results in a decidedly increased serum alkaline phosphatase activity (115). This obstruction may be due to a number of causes, such as abscess or primary or secondary neoplastic involvement. Primary cancer of the liver is relatively rare in man, but the liver is quite frequently the site for distant metastases in many types of tumors. This secondary involvement cannot be detected in its early stages short of exploration. Gutman *et al.* (115)

noted that, usually before there is any demonstrable liver enlargement, the alkaline serum phosphatase activity of individuals with liver metastases often shows a distinct rise. The same is true in cases of primary carcinoma of the liver, which may be expected since primary as well as secondary neoplastic growths in the liver possess in equal potential measure the capacity for biliary obstruction. Thus, a rise in serum alkaline phosphatase may suggest some degree of neoplastic involvement of the liver, but only when the following possibilities are excluded: (a) diseases of bone, (b) stone in the bile duct, (c) catarrhal jaundice, (d) administration of hepatoxic drugs, and (e) hepatic cirrhosis. Table 173, by Gutman and his collaborators (115), illustrates the distribution of serum alkaline phosphatase values in major disorders of the liver and biliary tract.

The increase in alkaline serum phosphatase activity as a result of liver damage is apparently due to a phosphatase or phosphatases which to a very much greater degree than the normal component are sensitive to cyanide even in the presence of magnesium (225). A similar cyanide-sensitive phosphatase can be obtained by fractionation of the liver proteins.

Serum and Blood Esterase and Lipase. A great many pathological states, including infection, vitamin A deficiency, and general toxemia, as well as neoplasia, result in a marked lowering of the serum and blood esterase and lipase activity (92, 93; 226–230). Nevertheless, in animals otherwise healthy, the change in serum esterase apparently begins at an early stage of tumor growth, decreases progressively with growth of the tumor, and reverts to the normal level with removal of the tumor. Certain data are given in Table 174. As a general rule, the level of tissue esterase anywhere in the body is a sensitive reflection of all kinds of pathological alterations.

The fact that esterase activity is lowered in the sera of tumor-bearing subjects while that of many of the other enzymes mentioned is raised, may be explained on the following grounds. Serum esterase, like many of the serum protein fractions, is synthesized in the liver, and its level is maintained by this organ. The presence of a tumor in a distant site produces liver damage which may include an impairment in the capacity of the liver to synthesize serum esterase. With the exception of the hepatomas, tumors possess very little esterase activity (Chapter VIII), and, therefore, any esterase which the tumor itself could furnish directly to the blood stream would be negligible. The net result is a decrease in the amount of esterase present in the serum. The main difficulty in this explanation is the fact that the liver esterase activity itself is not affected by the presence of a distant tumor. Some recent investigations have shown, however, that it is possible to markedly alter the level of serum esterase without affecting the liver esterase activity (cf. Chapter VIII), and it is possible that the levels of the two enzymes are maintained by separate mechanisms. Collateral evidence in support of the explanation offered comes from the fact that the

TABLE 173

DISTRIBUTION OF SERUM PHOSPHATASE VALUES IN MAJOR DISORDERS OF THE LIVER AND BILIARY TRACT, ANALYSIS OF RESULTS IN 308 ADULTS (INITIAL VALUES ONLY)[1] (115)

Pathologic conditions	Total number of cases	Distribution of cases by phosphatase values				
		Zone of normal values		Zone of indeterminate diagnostic significance		
		<4.0	4.1–9.0	9.1–12.0	12.1–25.0	>25.0
Stone in common bile duct	34	0	5	5	21	3
Noncalculous obstruction of common bile duct	45	0	1	5	25	14
Catarrhal jaundice	69	8	48	8	4	1
Jaundice after hepatotoxic drugs	38	2	18	4	13	1
Hemolytic jaundice	13	13	0	0	0	0
Hepatic cirrhosis (non-biliary)	44	14	20	5	4	1
Neoplastic involvement of liver	47	4	18	5	18	2
Liver abscess	10	0	2	3	3	2
Chronic passive congestion of liver	8	3	5	0	0	0

[1] Normal values = 1–4 Bodansky units.

TABLE 174

BLOOD AND SERUM ESTERASE AND LIPASE ACTIVITY IN TUMOR-BEARING HOSTS[1]

Host	Serum esterase		Blood lipase	
	Normal	Tumor-bearing	Normal	Tumor-bearing
Rats with Jensen sarcoma	18.1[1] (92)	4.4[1] (92)	244[2] (93)	182[2] (93)
Humans with evidence of metastases	10.8[1] (92)	5.7[1] (92)	—	—
Mice with spontaneous mammary carcinoma	11.4[3] (230)	7.6[3] (230)	—	—

[1] In terms of milliliters 0.01 *N* NaOH to neutralize ethyl butyrate hydrolysis in 2 hours.

[2] In terms of cubic millimeters CO_2 liberated in 1.5 hours with tributyrin as substrate.

[3] In terms of milliliters 0.01 *N* alc. KOH to neutralize digest containing 0.1 ml. serum, buffer, and methyl butyrate in 2 hours.

serum protein level is progressively decreased in rats and human beings with growth of tumors.

On the other hand, the increase in the phosphatases and the fermentation enzymes must be due to "leakage" from the tumor directly into the bloodstream. Thus, the effect on the serum esterase level of the presence of a tumor is indirect, that on the phosphatase and aldolase levels in the serum, direct. The former, indirect effect may justly be called a generalized systemic effect because it is evoked by nearly all tumors. The latter, direct effect is specifically related to the tumor concerned.

Serum Proteases, Peptidases, Antiproteases, and Nucleases. The presence of an enzyme in serum which catalytically degrades proteins was described in 1945 by Christensen and MacLeod (231), and the numerous studies of this system which followed have been reviewed by MacFarlane and Biggs (232). There is a curious confusion in the nomenclature of this enzyme, for at various times it has been referred to as plasmin, fibrinolysin, serum protease, and serum tryptase. This confusion is compounded by the following phenomena: (a) the enzyme is associated with a protease inhibitor from which it must first be separated and then be activated by chloroform (cf. 233); (b) natural activators for the enzyme exist in the tissues of the host (234, 235); and (c) there seemingly may be still another proteolytic enzyme which is present in the euglobulin fraction of serum, which, when separated from its inhibitor by dilution, is already active and does not require the chloroform treatment (proteolysin) (236). Casein has been the frequent substrate of choice to measure the activity of these enzymes. The relationship of chloroform-activated plasmin to proteolysin is obscure (cf. 233), and attempts to correlate plasmin activity with that of proteolysin and of the proteolytic inhibitor have been unsuccessful (236). Dillard and Chanutin (236) have noted that proteolysin, which exists at a very low level in the serum of normal persons, is very markedly elevated in the serum of several disease states, including cancer, and drops to its low normal level after surgical removal of the tumor or after successful antibiotic therapy in the case of infectious disease. Some elevation of the chloroform-activated plasmin is present in a proportion of untreated cancer and other cases. The proteolytic inhibitor, which is present in the diluted euglobulin supernatants and which is measured by the capacity to inhibit trypsin activity, is also considerably elevated in nearly all cases of cancer and other diseases (236). Unlike the proteolysin, however, it remains elevated for some time after successful surgery or antibiotic therapy. It is possible that the increases in these particular serum components may be associated with necrotic and inflammatory processes (236). In view of the association of protease and inhibitor, the presence of activators in tissues, and the uncontrolled procedures for such activation by chloroform, etc., the quantitation of the elevations that occur in diseased states is not only difficult to achieve but, for the time being at least, must remain quite tentative in character.

The presence in the serum of powerful inhibitors of trypsin enzymes has been well-established. Trypsin (236–239) and chymotrypsin (240, 241), as well as the serum's own plasmin and, more recently reported, rennin (240, 241), can all be remarkably inhibited by relatively small quantities of serum (cf. 237). Whether a single substance is responsible for the inhibition of these four different proteolytic enzymes, or whether several such inhibitors coexist in serum, is not yet clear, although it would appear that the inhibition of chymotrypsin and of rennin is effected by different substances (242). In cancer and other diseases, the inhibitors for trypsin and chymotrypsin become markedly elevated, to an extent that one group of investigators has calculated that approximately 15 g. of pure chymotrypsin could be completely inhibited by the *excess* of inhibitor present in the serum of the average cancer patient (242). In the serum of normal children the rennin inhibitor is at a very high level, and in maturity the excess of rennin inhibitor over chymotrypsin inhibitor more or less persists (242); in the cancer state the situation is reversed, for the chymotrypsin inhibitor rises to abnormal levels while the level of rennin inhibitor remains more or less normal (242). Successful control of the disease produces a reversal to the normal, relative levels of the two inhibitors (Fig. 65).

Crystalline pepsin and trypsin inhibitors have been prepared from various sources and shown to be highly specific proteins which react to form inert, dissociable complexes with the respective protease. Their teleology, like that of the serum inhibitors, is entirely obscure. Inhibitors for bacterial gelatinases (243), hyaluronidase (244), and catecholase (245) also appear to be present in serum. A shorter induction period for catecholase inhibi-

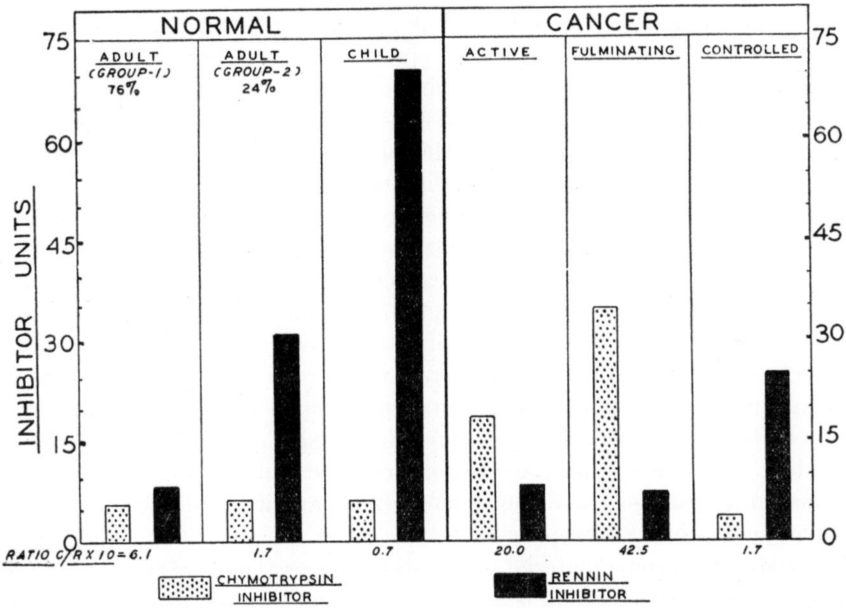

FIG. 65. Enzyme inhibitors in serum. From West, P. M., and Hilliard, J., *Ann Western Med. Surg.* **3,** 227 (1949).

tion in cancer serum, as a possible result of the decreased sulfhydryl titer in such serum, has been reported by Shacter and Shimkin (245). An inhibitor for human serum deoxyribonuclease is present in human leukocytes (246). The purification of the blood plasma trypsin inhibitor has been accomplished by a series of ammonium sulfate fractionations (246a), and the material obtained appears to be quite different from the well-known crystalline pancreatic inhibitor.

Peptidases (247) and dehydropeptidases (248) exist in serum, and their level is increased in cases of hepatic disease and tuberculosis, but not in cancer. A Mg^{++}-activated deoxyribonuclease also exists in human serum (249); its level is not significantly altered in various disease states, including cancer (250). The problem of whether so-called D-peptidases exist in serum must wait until well-characterized substrates, only recently available, are employed; the conflicting data in the literature may be due to the use of substrates whose optical purity is questionable (cf. 251, 252).

The proteases and peptidases are activated by a variety of organic compounds and inorganic ions, and estimations of the level of activity of these enzymes in the absence of optimal concentration of the specific activator may merely reflect the varying amounts of the activator in different pathologic conditions.

Hypervolemia. The presence of transplanted granulosa cell tumors in mice produces an increase in blood volume associated with marked cavernous congestion of certain visceral organs (253–256). Thus, in females, the presence of this tumor results in an increase of 131 % in the ratio of blood to body weight, and in males, an increase of 78 % (225). The pathogenesis of these phenomena is unknown. The increase in plasma volume of tumor-bearing mice is not particularly specific to cancer, for pregnancy may also produce this effect (256), nor is there any definite evidence that the estrogenic secretion of the granulosa cell tumor is responsible (256). The normal parabiotic partner of a mouse bearing the granulosa cell tumor does not show the characteristic hypervolemia (257), which may be due to the possibility that the agent responsible for the hypervolemia is not produced in sufficient concentration to cross over to the normal animal, or else it may be inactivated more efficiently by the normal animal. The chemical alteration by blood of estrone (and possibly related substances) has been demonstrated (258). Yet hypervolemia appears to be a phenomenon peculiar to transplanted estrogen-producing tumors (255), and if it is not known estrogenic agents which are responsible for the effect, the causative agent must be sought for in some material which accompanies them. A very marked oligemia of ovarian tumors is associated with an increase in related blood volumes of livers, kidneys, and lungs of the tumor-bearing mice (255) (Table 175).

The spleens of tumor-bearing mice, on the other hand, have a lower blood volume per weight of the organ, than those of normal mice. All of these organs are enlarged in size over those of normal animals, but, excepting the spleen, the blood volume increase is greater than the increase in organ weight.

Studies of this sort have not been extensively pursued in animals bearing tumors other than the ovarian. Clinical studies on patients with advanced cancer in several forms indicate that the relative plasma volume may increase above normal and that this increase is not due to decreased packed cell volume, blood proteins, or the presence of edema (259).

Urinary Steroids. The isolation of individual steroids from the urine of patients with various forms of neoplasia has been reported by many

TABLE 175

Organ and Ovarian Tumor Blood Volumes (255)

Tissue	Total blood volume as per cent weight of organ				
	Tumor	Liver	Spleen	Kidney	Lung
Normal	—	28.4	34.8	23.9	39.6
Granulosa cell tumor	4.3	35.7	17.9	34.4	43.6
Ovarian carcinoma	1.5	36.0	13.0	31.0	—
Luteoma	3.5	34.0	18.0	30.0	47.0

investigators (260–263). Several of the findings are interesting, but the specificity of such findings to neoplasia is often open to doubt. Frequently the studies have been performed on isolated cases, and the necessary comparisons with other types of neoplastic disease as well as with a wide range of normal subjects have not been at hand.

Thus far, the study of such urinary components has been of most clinical usefulness in neoplastic disease of the adrenals and the gonads. In cases of tumors of the testicle in man, two types of gonadotropic hormones have been noted in the urine, one similar to the chorionic type normally found in the urine of pregnant women, and the other, a hypophyseal gonadotropin similar to that found in human beings who have been castrated or who have passed through the menopause (264). There seems to be a correlation between the amount of the former substance excreted and the extent of the neoplastic disease. In the absence of metastases, orchiectomy is usually followed by a prompt disappearance of the hormones from the urine. If metastases appear subsquently, the hormone levels may again rise and, in some cases, may assist in predicting recurrences before they can be detected clinically. If metastases are present at the time of orchiectomy, the urinary level shows little change. A study of the excretion rate assists in the judgment of the effectiveness of X-ray therapy. Table 176 illustrates how the various neoplasms of the testicle may be diagnosed by examination of the distribution of the urinary hormones.

Adrenal cortical tumor may be differentiated from adrenal hyperplasia by the excessively large amounts of dehydroisoandrosterone excreted in the urine in the former case (265, 266). The precursor of this substance is not known, but the relation of cholesterol to the production of the adrenal hormones (267) suggests the possibility that the large amounts of dehydroisoandrosterone associated with adrenal tumors may be the result of uncontrolled oxidation of cholesterol to this substance by the tumor (266).

Pregnanediol has been found in the urine of women with adrenal tumor and adrenal hyperplasia, suggesting that these diseases of the adrenal cortex result in a relatively large production of progesterone or of deoxycorticosterone, or both.

Neutral ketones, androsterone, etiocholan-3α-ol-17-one, dehydroisoan-

TABLE 176

URINARY HORMONES IN CASES OF TESTICULAR TUMORS (cf. 270)

No. of cases	Diagnosis	Negative	Traces	Hypophyseal hormone	Chorionic hormone	Both hormones
42	Seminoma	13	4	25	0	0
2	Pseudoseminoma	0	0	0	2	0
21	Mixed epithelioma	3	1	0	14	3
10	Polycystic teratoid	4	2	4	0	0

drosterone, and isoandrosterone are present in the urine of normal men and women. When an adrenal tumor is present, there is often a greatly increased excretion of androsterone and etiocholan-3α-ol-17-one, but the

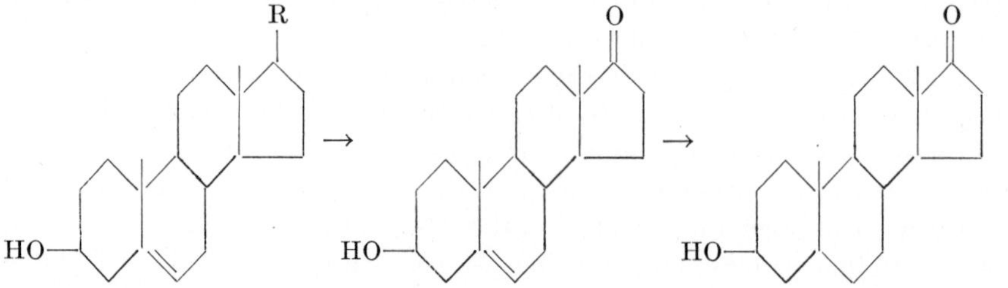

Cholesterol Dehydroisoandrosterone Androsterone

amount of dehydroisoandrosterone is even still greater. When cortical hyperplasia is present, the excretion of steroids is more often within normal limits. The chemical criteria for the differential diagnosis of adrenal cortical tumor and of cortical hyperplasia are not absolute. It seems that

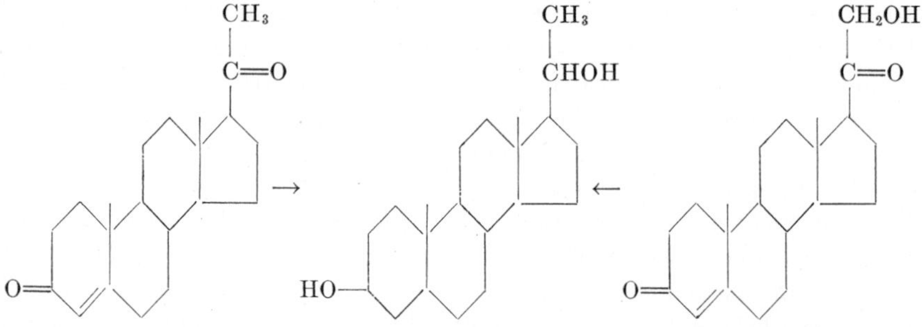

Progesterone Pregnanediol Deoxycorticosterone

most patients having functioning adrenal cortical tumors excrete dehydroisoandrosterone in the urine and that most patients having adrenal cortical hyperplasia excrete pregnane-3α-17,20-triol (266; 268), but exceptions to these rules occur. The adrenal precursor of the pregnanetriol is probably 17-hydroxyprogesterone.

No unusual urinary estrogen excretion appears to occur in cases of women with breast cancer (269).

It must be remembered that the urinary excretion of hormones and other substances represent only the end products of metabolism, and it is not definitely known whether the levels of many of these components are truly representative either of the blood levels or the rates of secretion, destruction, or utilization in the tissues. The determination of the urinary levels of various components, such as the estrogens and 17-ketosteroids, and the estimation of the relative amounts thereof, may demonstrate interesting empirical relationships to various types of neoplastic disease. Whether

TABLE 177

Nitrogenous Constituents in Tumor-Bearing Rats[1] (272)

	Urinary excretion of:				Muscle[2]	
State of animals	Ammonia-N[3]	Urea-N[3]	Creatinine-N[4]	Creatine-N[4]	Total N	Creatine-N
Normal	3.3	84.6	1.41	<0.4	33.1	1.28
Cancerous	3.4	84.5	1.51	1.6–2.6	32.8	1.31

[1] Jensen sarcoma rats, about 17 days after inoculation of the tumor, prior to cachexia.

[2] Milligrams per gram wet weight of tissue.

[3] Per cent of total N excretion per rat per day.

[4] Average excretion as milligrams N per rat per day.

abnormal alterations in levels of these components are characteristic of neoplastic disease in general, or are merely representative of a disturbed metabolism in a cachectic patient, awaits further study.

Urinary Creatine. Tumor-bearing mice (271) and rats (272) appear to excrete considerable quantities of creatine in the urine. The development of the Jensen sarcoma in rats fed a creatine-free diet is accompanied by a steadily increasing creatinuria, which in later stages of growth of the tumor may be eight to twelve times as high as the normal level (272). During this period of growth, while the animals appear to be healthy and free of cachexia, the excretion of ammonia, urea, and creatinine, and the creatine content of the skeletal muscle of the host rats, do not differ from the normal levels (Table 177). These observations suggest that the increased excretion of creatine by the tumorous animals may be related to an increased rate of creatine synthesis (272). The precursors of creatine are glycine, methionine, and arginine. Whether the increase in creatine excretion is unique to cancer may be open to question, since certain conditions of muscular dystrophy are also characterized by this phenomenon (cf. 273, 274), as well as are other abnormalities (275). Although creatinuria may occur during food deprivation, and it is well known that the food intake *ad libitum* of tumorous animals is usually less than normal, this latter factor is not likely to be involved in the creatinuria of the tumorous animals in view of their unchanged excretion of urea, ammonia, and creatinine, and level of muscle creatine. The problem deserves further study.

References

(1) Abels, J. C., Rekers, P. E., Binkley, G. E., Pack, G. T., and Rhoads, C. P., *Ann. Internal Med.* **16,** 221 (1942).

(2) Greenstein, J. P., and Thompson, J. W., *J. Natl. Cancer Inst.* **4,** 63 (1943).

(3) Mider, G. B., *Cancer Research* **11,** 821 (1951).

(4) Fenninger, L. D., and Mider, G. B., *Advances in Cancer Research* **2,** 229 (1954).

(5) Mider, G. B., Tesluk, H., and Morton, J. J., *Acta Unio Intern. contra Cancrum* **6,** 409 (1948).

(6) Mider, G. B., Sherman, C. D., Jr., and Morton, J. J., *Cancer Research* **9,** 222 (1949).
(7) Sherman, C. D., Jr., Morton, J. J., and Mider, G. B., *Cancer Research* **10,** 371 (1950).
(8) Yeakel, E. H., and Tobias, G. L., *Cancer Research* **11,** 830 (1951).
(9) Annau, E., Manginelli, A., and Roth, A., *Cancer Research* **11,** 304 (1951).
(10) Poo, L. J., Lew, W., Lee, D. D., and Addis, T., *J. Nutrition* **19,** 505 (1940).
(11) McEwen, H. D., and Haven, F. L., *Cancer Research* **1,** 148 (1941).
(12) Schlottman, H., and Rubenow, W., *Z. Krebsforsch.* **36,** 120 (1932).
(13) White, F. R., *J. Natl. Cancer Inst.* **5,** 265 (1945).
(14) Green, J. W., Jr., Benditt, E. P., and Humphreys, E. M., *Cancer Research* **10,** 769 (1950).
(14a) Babson, A. L., *Cancer Research* **14,** 89 (1954).
(15) Norberg, E., and Greenberg, D. M., *Cancer* **4,** 383 (1951).
(16) LePage, G. A., Potter, V. R., Busch, H., Heidelberger, C., and Hurlbert, R. B., *Cancer Research* **12,** 153 (1952).
(17) Tyner, E. P., Heidelberger, C., and LePage, G. A., *Cancer Research* **13,** 186 (1953).
(18) Payne, A. H., Kelly, L. S., and White, M. R., *Cancer Research* **12,** 65 (1952).
(19) Levy, H. M., Montanez, G., Murphy, E. A., and Dunn, M. S., *Cancer Research* **13,** 507 (1953).
(20) Begg, R. W., and Dickinson, T. E., *Cancer Research* **11,** 409 (1951).
(21) Stewart, A. G., and Begg, R. W., *Cancer Research* **13,** 556, 560 (1953).
(22) Begg, R. W., *Cancer Research* **11,** 406 (1951).
(23) Savard, K., *Science* **108,** 381 (1948).
(24) Haven, F. L., Bloor, W. R., and Randall, C., *Cancer Research* **9,** 511 (1949).
(25) Begg, R. W., *Cancer Research* **11,** 341 (1951).
(26) Young, N. F., Kensler, C. J., Seki, L., and Homburger, F., *Proc. Soc. Exptl. Biol. Med.* **66,** 322 (1947).
(27) Homburger, F., *Science* **107,** 648 (1948).
(28) Ingle, D. J., *Proc. Soc. Exptl. Biol. Med.* **72,** 604 (1949).
(29) Mider, G. B., *Ann. Rev. Med.* **4,** 187 (1953).
(30) Haven, F. L., Bloor, W. R., and Randall, C., *Cancer Research* **11,** 619 (1951).
(31) Mider, G. B., Fenninger, L. D., Haven, F. L., and Morton, J. J., *Cancer Research* **11,** 731 (1951).
(32) Waterhouse, C., Fenninger, L. D., and Keutmann, E. H., *Cancer* **4,** 500 (1951).
(33) Bateman, J. C., *Arch. Internal Med.* **86,** 355 (1950).
(34) Brahn, B., *Sitzber. kgl. preuss. Akad. Wiss.* **1916,** 478–481.
(35) Greenstein, J. P., Jenrette, W. V., and White, J., *J. Biol. Chem.* **141,** 327 (1941).
(36) Greenstein, J. P., Jenrette, W. V., and White, J., *J. Natl. Cancer Inst.* **2,** 283 (1941).
(37) Greenstein, J. P., and Andervont, H. B., *J. Natl. Cancer Inst.* **2,** 345 (1942).
(38) Greenstein, J. P., *J. Natl. Cancer Inst.* **2,** 525 (1942); **3,** 397 (1943).
(39) Greenstein, J. P., Andervont, H. B., and Thompson, J. W., *J. Natl. Cancer Inst.* **2,** 589 (1942).
(40) Rosenthal, E., *Deut. med. Wochschr.* **38,** 2270 (1912).
(41) Greenstein, J. P., and Andervont, H. B., *J. Natl. Cancer Inst.* **4,** 283 (1943).
(42) Greenstein, J. P., *J. Am. Med. Assoc.* **148,** 697 (1952).
(43) Theorell, H., Beznak, N., Bonnichsen, R., Paul, K-G., and Akeson, A., *Acta Chem. Scand.* **5,** 445 (1951).
(44) Miller, L. L., *J. Biol. Chem.* **172,** 113 (1948).

(45) Feinstein, R. N., Butler, C. L., and Hendley, D. D., *Science* **111,** 149 (1950).
(46) Dounce, A. L., and Shanewise, R. P., *Cancer Research* **10,** 103 (1950).
(47) Beers, R. F., Jr., and Sizer, I. W., *Science* **117,** 710 (1953).
(48) Chance, B., *Acta Chem. Scand.* **1,** 236 (1947).
(49) Appleman, D., Skavinski, E. R., and Stein, A. M., *Cancer Research* **10,** 498 (1950).
(50) Klatt, O. A., and Taylor, A., *Cancer Research* **11,** 764 (1951).
(51) Skavinski, E. R., and Stein, A. M., *Cancer Research* **11,** 768 (1951).
(52) Yeakel, E. H., *Cancer Research* **8,** 392 (1948).
(53) Weil-Malherbe, H., and Schade, R., *Biochem. J.* **43,** 118 (1948).
(54) Appleman, D., Skavinski, E. R., and Stein, A. M., *Cancer Research* **11,** 926 (1951).
(55) Begg, R. W., Dickinson, T. E., and White, A. V., *Can. J. Med. Sci.* **31,** 307 (1953).
(56) Begg R. W., Dickinson, T. E., and Millar, J., *Can. J. Med. Sci.* **31,** 315 (1953).
(57) Adams, D. H., *Brit. J. Cancer* **4,** 183 (1950).
(58) Adams, D. H., *Brit. J. Cancer* **5,** 115 (1951).
(59) Lucké, B., Berwick, M., and Zeckwer, I., *J. Natl. Cancer Inst.* **13,** 681 (1952).
(60) Nakahara, W., and Fukuoka, F., *Japan Med. J.* **1,** 271 (1948).
(61) Nakahara, W., and Fukuoka, F., *Gann* **40,** 45 (1949); **41,** 47 (1950).
(62) Fukuoka, F., and Nakahara, W., *Gann* **42,** 55 (1951); **44,** 1 (1953).
(63) Greenfield, R. E., and Meister, A., *J. Natl. Cancer Inst.* **11,** 997 (1951).
(63a) Korngold, L., and Pressman, D., *Cancer Research,* **14,** 96 (1954).
(64) Hargreaves, A. B., and Deutsch, H. F., *Cancer Research* **12,** 720 (1952).
(65) Deutsch, H. F., and Gustafson, T., *Arkiv. Kemi* **4,** (41), (1952).
(66) Shack, J., *J. Natl. Cancer Inst.* **3,** 389 (1943).
(67) Greenstein, J. P., Werne, J., Eschenbrenner, A. B., and Leuthardt, F. M., *J. Natl. Cancer Inst.* **5,** 55 (1944).
(68) Greenfield, R. E., and Price, V. E., *J. Biol. Chem.* (in press).
(69) Cohn, E. J., Surgenor, D. M., and Hunter, M. J., *in* "Enzymes and Enzyme Systems," p. 105. Harvard University Press, Cambridge, 1951.
(70) Euler, H. von, and Heller, L. *Z. Krebsforsch.* **56,** 393 (1949).
(70a) Ludewig, S., and Chanutin, A., *Arch. Biochem.* **29,** 441 (1950).
(71) Adams, D. H., *Biochem. J.* **50,** 486 (1952).
(72) Begg, R. W., and Reynolds, E. F., *Science* **111,** 721 (1950).
(73) Kochakian, C. D., *Recent Progr. Hormone Research* **1,** 177 (1947).
(74) Gaebler, O. H., and Mathies, J. C., *Endocrinology* **48,** 623 (1951).
(75) Folley, S. J., and Greenbaum, A. L., *Nature* **160,** 364 (1947).
(76) Kochakian, C. D., and Vail, V. N., *Am. J. Physiol.* **150,** 580 (1947).
(77) Adams, D. H., *Brit. J. Cancer* **5,** 409 (1951).
(78) Schultze, M. O., and Kuiken, K. A., *J. Biol. Chem.* **137,** 727 (1941).
(79) Adams, D. H., *Biochem. J.* **54,** 328 (1953).
(80) Nakagawa, S., *Proc. Japan Acad.* **28,** 305 (1952).
(80a) Lucké, B., and Berwick, M., *Proc. Am. Assoc. Cancer Research* (1954).
(80b) Adams, D. H., *Brit. J. Cancer* **7,** 501 (1954).
(81) Lucké, B., and Berwick, M., *J. Natl. Cancer Inst.* **14,** (in press).
(82) Monod, J., *Ann. Rev. Microbiol.* **3,** 371 (1949)
(83) Westphal, U., *Z. physiol. Chem.* **276,** 213 (1943).
(84) Lan, T. H., *Cancer Research* **4,** 37 (1944).
(85) Masayama, T., and Yokoyama, T., *Gann* **33,** 214 (1939).
(86) Robertson, W. van B., and Kahler, H., *J. Natl. Cancer Inst.* **2,** 595 (1942).

(87) Greenstein, J. P., Jenrette, W. V., Mider, G. B., and White, J., *J. Natl. Cancer Inst.* **1,** 687 (1941).
(88) Weil, L., *J. Biol. Chem.* **110,** 201 (1935).
(89) Fujiwara, H., *Z. physiol. Chem.* **185,** 1 (1929).
(90) Greenberg, D. M., and Sassenrath, E. N., *Cancer Research* **13,** 709 (1953).
(91) Klein, G., and Ziese, W., *Z. Krebsforsch.* **37,** 323 (1932).
(92) Green, H. N., and Jenkinson, C. N., *Brit. J. Exptl. Pathol.* **15,** 1 (1934).
(93) Edlbacher, S., and Neber, M., *Z. physiol. Chem.* **233,** 265 (1935).
(94) Li, M-H., and Lu, Y-L., *Chinese J. Physiol.* **17,** 157 (1949).
(95) Aoki, C., *Gann* **32,** 100 (1938).
(96) Jones, H. B., Chaikoff, I. L., and Lawrence, J. N., *J. Biol. Chem.* **128,** 631 (1939).
(97) Dalton, A. J., and Peters, V. B., *J. Natl. Cancer Inst.* **5,** 99 (1944).
(98) Greenstein, J. P., and Thompson, J. W., *J. Natl. Cancer Inst.* **3,** 405 (1943).
(99) Edlbacher, S., and Gerlach, W., *Z. Krebsforsch.* **42,** 272 (1935).
(100) Sandberg, M., Gross, H., and Holly, O. M., *Arch. Pathol.* **33,** 834 (1942).
(101) Rosenfeld, I., and Tobias, C. A., *J. Biol. Chem.* **191,** 339 (1951).
(102) Hall, V. E., *Cancer Research* **4,** 785 (1944).
(103) Burk, D., Sprince, H., Spangler, J. M., Boon, M. C., and Furth, J., *J. Natl. Cancer Inst.* **3,** 249 (1942).
(104) Dickens, F., *Biochem. J.* **35,** 1011 (1941).
(105) Haven, F. L., Randall, C., and Bloor, W. R., *Cancer Research* **9,** 90 (1949).
(106) Kelly, L. S., Payne, A. H., White, M. R., and Jones, H. B., *Cancer Research* **11,** 694 (1951).
(107) Payne, A. H., Kelly, L. S., and White, M. R., *Cancer Research* **12,** 65 (1952).
(108) Payne, A. H., Kelly, L. S., Beach, G., and Jones, H. B., *Cancer Research* **12,** 426 (1952).
(108a) Conzelman, G. M., Jr., Mandel, H. G., and Smith, P. K., *Cancer Research* **14,** 100 (1954).
(109) Abels, J. C., Gorham, S. T., Pack, G. T., and Rhoads, C. P., *Proc. Soc. Exptl. Biol. Med.* **48,** 488 (1941).
(110) Platt, M. E., and Schroeder, E. F., *J. Biol. Chem.* **106,** 179 (1934).
(111) Greenstein, J. P., Edwards, J. E., Andervont, H. B., and White, J., *J. Natl. Cancer Inst.* **3,** 7 (1942).
(112) Greenstein, J. P., *J. Natl. Cancer Inst.* **2,** 511 (1942).
(113) Goranson, E. S., McBride, J., and Weber, G., *Cancer Research* **14,** 227 (1954).
(114) Lenta, M. P., and Riehl, M. A., *Cancer Research* **9,** 47 (1949).
(115) Gutman, A. B., Olson, K. B., Gutman, E. B., and Flood, C. A., *J. Clin. Invest.* **19,** 129 (1940).
(116) Strong, L. C., and Francis, L. D., *Arch. Pathol.* **23,** 202 (1937).
(117) Strong, L. C., and Francis, L. D., *Am. J. Cancer* **38,** 399 (1940).
(118) Taylor, A., and Pollack, M. S., *Cancer Research* **2,** 223 (1942).
(119) Maver, M. E., and Dunn, T. B., *J. Natl. Cancer Inst.* **6,** 49 (1945).
(120) Parsons, L. D., *J. Pathol. Bacteriol.* **57,** 9 (1945).
(121) Barker, G. R., Gulland, J. M., and Parsons, L. D., *Nature* **157** 482 (1946).
(122) Edlbacher, S., and Baumann, W., *Z. Krebsforsch.* **44,** 441 (1936).
(123) Toennies, G., *Cancer Research* **7,** 193 (1947).
(124) Gutman, A. B., *Advances in Protein Chem.* **4,** 155 (1948).
(125) Huggins, C., *Cancer Research* **9,** 321 (1949).
(126) Winzler, R. J., *Advances in Cancer Research* **1,** 503 (1953).
(127) Homburger, F., and Young, N. F., *Blood* **3,** 1460 (1948).
(128) Abels, J. C., Ariel, I., Rekers, P. E., Pack, G. T., and Rhoads, C. P., *Arch. Surg.* **46,** 844 (1943).

(129) Petermann, M. L., and Hogness, K. R., *Cancer* **1,** 100 (1948).
(130) Petermann, M. L., Karnofsky, D. A., and Hogness, K. R., *Cancer* **1,** 109 (1948).
(131) Seibert, F. B., Seibert, M. V., Atno, A. J., and Campbell, H. W., *J. Clin. Invest.* **26,** 90 (1947).
(132) Mider, G. B., Alling, E. L., and Morton, J. J., *Cancer* **3,** 56 (1950).
(133) Winzler, R. J., Devor, A. W., Mehl, J. W., and Smyth, I. M., *J. Clin. Invest.* **27,** 609 (1948).
(134) Boyland, E., Butler, L. O., and Conway, B. E., *Brit. J. Cancer* **5,** 235 (1951).
(135) Dillard, G. H. L., Pearsall, H. R., and Chanutin, A., *Cancer Research* **9,** 661 (1949).
(136) Petermann, M. L., and Hogness, K. R., *Cancer* **1,** 104 (1948).
(137) Mehl, J. W., Golden, F., and Winzler, R. J., *Proc. Soc. Exptl. Biol. Med.* **72,** 110 (1949).
(138) Mehl, J. W., *Texas Repts. Biol. and Med.* **8,** 169 (1950).
(139) Winzler, R. J., and Smyth, I. M., *J. Clin. Invest.* **27,** 617 (1948).
(140) Rimington, C., *Biochem. J.* **34,** 931 (1940).
(141) Seibert, F. B., Pfaff, M. L., and Seibert, M. V., *Arch. Biochem.* **18,** 279 (1948).
(142) Shetlar, M. R., Shetlar, C. L., Richmond, V., and Everett, M. R., *Cancer Research* **10,** 681 (1950).
(143) Greenspan, E. M., Lehman, I., Graff, M. M., and Schoenbach, E. B., *Cancer* **4,** 972 (1951).
(144) Novak, J., and Lustig, B., *J. Mt. Sinai Hosp.* **14,** 534 (1947).
(145) Shetlar, M. R., Erwin, C. P., and Everett, M. R., *Cancer Research* **10,** 445 (1950).
(146) Milne, J., *J. Biol. Chem.* **169,** 595 (1947).
(147) Shetlar, M. R., Kelly, K. H., Foster, J. V., Shetlar, C. L., and Everett, M. R., *Am. J. Obstet. Gynecol.* **59,** 1140 (1950).
(148) Shetlar, M. R., Foster, J. V., Kelly, K. H., Shetlar, C. L., Bryan, R. S., and Everett, M. R., *Cancer Research* **9,** 515 (1949).
(149) Niaza, S., and State, D., *Cancer Research* **8,** 653 (1948).
(150) Brdicka, R., *Nature* **139,** 1020 (1937).
(151) Waldschmidt-Leitz, E., and Mayer, K., *Z. physiol. Chem.* **261,** 1 (1939).
(152) Robinson, A. M., *Brit. J. Cancer* **2,** 360 (1948).
(153) Butler, L. O., *Brit. J. Cancer* **5,** 225 (1951).
(154) Rusch, H. P., Klatt, T., Meloche, V. W., and Dirksen, A. J., *Proc. Soc. Exptl. Biol. Med.* **44,** 362 (1940).
(155) Hughes, W. L., *Cold Spring Harbor Symposia Quant. Biol.* **14,** 79 (1949).
(156) Weissman, N., Schoenbach, E. B., and Armistead, E. B., *J. Biol. Chem.* **187,** 153 (1950).
(157) Schoenbach, E. B., Armistead, E. B., and Weissman, N., *Proc. Soc. Exptl. Biol. Med.* **73,** 44 (1950).
(158) Schoenbach, E. B., Weissman, N., and Armistead, E. B., *J. Clin. Invest.* **30,** 762 (1951).
(159) Huggins, C., Jensen, E. V., Player, M. A., and Hospelhorn, V. O., *Cancer Research* **9,** 753 (1949).
(160) Savignac, R. J., Gant, J. C., and Sizer, I. W., "Research Conference on Cancer," p. 241. American Association for the Advancement of Science, Washington, D. C., 1945.
(161) Black, M. M., *Cancer Research* **7,** 321, 592 (1947).
(162) Black, M. M., *Science* **108,** 540 (1948).
(163) Klotz, I. M., *Cold Spring Harbor Symposia Quant. Biol.* **14,** 97 (1949).
(164) Westphal, U., and Gedigk, P. *Proc. Soc. Exptl. Biol. Med.* **76,** 838 (1951).

(165) Glass, G. B. J., Boyd, L. J., and Dworecki, I. J., *Proc. Soc. Exptl. Biol. Med.* **76,** 10 (1951).
(166) Huggins, C., Cleveland, A. S., and Jensen, E. V., *J. Am. Med. Assoc.* **143,** 11 (1950).
(167) Huggins, C., Miller, G. M., and Jensen, E. V., *Cancer Research* **9,** 177 (1949).
(168) Huggins, C., and Jensen, E. V., *J. Biol. Chem.* **179,** 645 (1949).
(169) Jensen, E. V., Hospelhorn, V. E., Tapley, D. F., and Huggins, C., *J. Biol. Chem.* **185,** 411 (1950).
(170) Mayer, K., *Biochem. Z.* **275,** 16 (1942).
(171) Brdicka, R., *Klin. Wochschr.* **18,** 305 (1939).
(172) Müller, O. H., and Davis, J. S., *Arch. Biochem.* **15,** 39 (1947).
(173) Winzler, R. J., and Burk, D., *J. Natl. Cancer Inst.* **4,** 417 (1944).
(174) Goldfeder, A., *Z. Krebsforsch.* **40,** 394 (1933).
(175) El Mehairy, M. M., *Brit. J. Cancer* **4,** 95 (1950).
(175a) Bogden, A. E., and Aptekman, P. M., *Cancer Research* **13,** 890 (1953).
(176) Dunn, J. E., and Greenhouse, S. W., *U. S. Public Health Service Publs.* No. **9,** (1950).
(177) Stern, K., and Wilheim, R., "The Biochemistry of Malignant Tumors." Chemical Publishing Co., Brooklyn, 1943.
(178) Maver, M. E., *J. Natl. Cancer Inst.* **4,** 571 (1944).
(179) Adams, W. S., Alling, E. L., and Lawrence, J. S., *Am. J. Med.* **6,** 1101 (1949).
(180) Gutman, A. B., Moore, D. H., Gutman, E. B., McClellan, V., and Kabat, E. A., *J. Clin. Invest.* **20,** 765 (1941).
(181) Moore, D. H., Kabat, E. A., and Gutman, A. B., *J. Clin. Invest.* **22,** 67 (1943).
(182) Pearsall, H. R., and Chanutin, A., *Am. J. Med.* **7,** 301 (1949).
(183) Rundles, R. W., Dillon, M. L., and Dillon, E. S., *J. Clin. Invest.* **29,** 1243 (1950).
(184) Perlzweig, W. A., Delrue, G., and Geschickter, C., *J. Am. Med. Assoc.* **90,** 775 (1928).
(185) Mehl, J. W., and Golden, F., *J. Clin. Invest.* **29,** 1214 (1950).
(186) Miller, G. L., Brown, C. E., Miller, E. E., and Eitelman, E. S., *Cancer Research* **12,** 716 (1952).
(187) Rundles, R. W., Cooper, G. R., and Willett, R. W., *J. Clin. Invest.* **30,** 1125 (1951).
(188) Putnam, F. W., and Udin, B., *J. Biol. Chem.* **202,** 727 (1953).
(189) Kekwick, R. A., *Biochem. J.* **34,** 1248 (1940).
(190) Deutsch, H. F., Alberty, R. A., and Gosting, L. J., *J. Biol. Chem.* **165,** 21 (1946).
(190a) Grisolia, F. T., and Cohen, P. P., *Cancer Research* **13,** 351 (1953).
(191) Putnam, F. W., and Stelos, P., *J. Biol. Chem.* **203,** 347 (1953).
(192) Warburg, O., and Christian, W., *Biochem. Z.* **314,** 399 (1943).
(193) Sibley, J. A., and Lehninger, A. L., *J. Natl. Cancer Inst.* **9,** 303 (1949).
(194) Baker, R., and Govan, D., *Cancer Research* **13,** 141 (1953).
(195) Sturm, E., *Cancer Research* **4,** 35 (1944).
(196) Field, J. B., Baumann, C. S., and Link, K. P., *Cancer Research* **4,** 768 (1944).
(197) Kay, H. D., *J. Biol. Chem.* **89,** 249 (1930).
(198) Gutman, A. B., and Gutman, E. B., *J. Clin. Invest.* **17,** 473 (1938).
(199) Gutman, E. B., Sproul, E. E., and Gutman, A. B., *Am. J. Cancer* **28,** 485 (1936).
(200) Franseen, C. C., and McLean, R., *Am. J. Cancer* **24,** 299 (1935).
(201) Gutman, A. B., Gutman, E. B., and Robinson, J. R., *Am. J. Cancer* **38,** 103 (1940).
(202) Albers, D., *Z. ges. exptl. Med.* **104,** 146 (1938).
(203) Woodard, H. Q., and Craver, L. F., *J. Clin. Invest.* **19,** 1 (1940).

(204) Woodard, H. Q., *Arch. Surg.* **47,** 368 (1943).
(205) Cade, S., Maclagen, N. F., and Townsend, R. F., *Lancet* **i,** 1074 (1940).
(206) Woodard, H. Q., *Cancer Research* **2,** 497 (1942).
(207) Bodansky, O., *J. Biol. Chem.* **202,** 829 (1953).
(208) Perlmann, G. E., and Ferry, R. M., *J. Biol. Chem.* **142,** 513 (1942).
(209) Kutscher, W., and Wolbergs, H., *Z. physiol. Chem.* **236,** 237 (1935).
(210) Gutman, A. B., and Gutman, E. B., *Proc. Soc. Exptl. Biol. Med.* **39,** 529 (1938).
(211) Barringer, B. S., and Woodard, H. Q., *Trans. Am. Assoc. Genito-urin. Surgeons* **31,** 363 (1938).
(212) King, E. J., and Armstrong, A. R., *Can. Med. Assoc. J.* **31,** 376 (1934).
(213) Huggins, C., and Hodges, C. V., *Cancer Research* **1,** 293 (1941).
(214) Sullivan, J. R., Gutman, E. B., and Gutman, A. B., *J. Urol.* **48,** 426 (1942).
(215) Emmett, J. L., and Greene, L. F., *J. Am. Med. Assoc.* **127,** 63 (1945).
(216) Gutman, E. B., and Gutman, A. B., *Proc. Exptl. Biol. Med.* **47,** 513 (1941).
(217) Gutman, A. B., *J. Am. Med. Assoc.* **120,** 1112 (1942).
(218) Herger, C. C., and Sauer, H. R., *Cancer Research* **2,** 398 (1942).
(219) Huggins, C., Stevens, R. E., and Hodges, C. V., *Arch. Surg.* **43,** 209 (1941).
(220) Huggins, C., Scott, W. W., and Hodges, C. V., *J. Urol.* **46,** 997 (1941).
(221) Abdul-Fadl, M. A. M., and King, E. J., *Biochem. J.* **45,** 51 (1949).
(222) Fishman, W. H., and Lerner, F., *J. Biol. Chem.* **200,** 89 (1953).
(223) Fishman, W. H., Dart, R. M., Bonner, C. D., Leadbetter, W. F., Lerner, F., and Homburger, F., *J. Clin. Invest.* **32,** 1034 (1953).
(224) Hock, E., and Tessier, R. N., *J. Urol.* **62,** 488 (1949).
(225) Drill, V. A., and Riggs, D. C., *J. Biol. Chem.* **162,** 21 (1946).
(226) Troescher, E. E., and Norris, E. R., *J. Biol. Chem.* **132,** 553 (1940).
(227) Hangleiter, F., and Reuter, S., *Z. ges. exptl. Med.* **107,** 355 (1940).
(228) Homma, J., and Issiki, T., *Gann* **21,** 38 (1927).
(229) Jones, M. S., and Stadie, W. C., *Quart. J. Exptl. Physiol.* **29,** 63 (1939).
(230) Shimkin, M. B., Greenstein, J. P., and Andervont, H. B., *J. Natl. Cancer Inst.* **5,** 29 (1944).
(231) Christensen, L. R., and MacLeod, C. M., *J. Gen. Physiol.* **28,** 363 (1945).
(232) MacFarlane, R. G., and Biggs, R., *Blood* **3,** 1167 (1948).
(233) Ratnoff, O. D., *J. Exptl. Med.* **87,** 199 (1948).
(234) Astrup, T., Crockston, J., and MacIntyre, A., *Acta Physiol. Scand.* **21,** 238 (1950).
(235) Tagnon, H. J., and Palade, G. E., *J. Clin. Invest.* **29,** 317 (1950).
(236) Dillard, G. H. L., and Chanutin, A., *Cancer Research* **9,** 665 (1949).
(237) Clark, D. G. C., Cliffton, E. E., and Newton, B. L., *Proc. Soc. Exptl. Biol. Med.* **69,** 276 (1948).
(238) Waldvogel, M. J., and Schmitt, L. H., *Cancer Research* **10,** 371 (1950).
(239) Ungar, G., and Damgaard, E., *J. Exptl. Med.* **93,** 89 (1951).
(240) West, P. M., and Hilliard, J., *Proc. Soc. Exptl. Biol. Med.* **71,** 169 (1949).
(241) Tauber, H., *Proc. Soc. Exptl. Biol. Med.* **74,** 486 (1950).
(242) West, P. M., and Hilliard, J. *Ann. Western Med. Surg.* **3,** 227 (1949).
(243) Duthie, E. S., and Lorenz, L., *Biochem. J.* **44,** 173 (1949).
(244) Glick, D., *J. Mt. Sinai Hosp.* **17,** 207 (1950).
(245) Shacter, B., and Shimkin, M. B., *J. Natl. Cancer Inst.* **10,** 637 (1949).
(246) Kurnick, N. B., Schwartz, L. I., Pariser, S., and Lee, S. L., *J. Clin. Invest.* **32,** 193 (1953).
(246a) Peanosky, R. J., and Laskowski, M., *J. Biol. Chem.* **204,** 153 (1953).
(247) Fleischer, G. A., and Butt, H. R., *J. Clin. Invest.* **32,** 674 (1953).

(248) Meister, A., and Greenstein, J. P., *J. Natl. Cancer Inst.* **8,** 169 (1948).
(249) Wroblewski, F., and Bodansky, O., *Proc. Soc. Exptl. Biol. Med.* **74,** 443 (1950).
(250) Kurnick, N. B., *Arch. Biochem. and Biophys.* **43,** 97 (1953).
(251) Waldschmidt-Leitz, E., Hatschek, R., and Hausmann, R., *Z. physiol. Chem.* **267,** 79 (1940).
(252) Bayerle, H., and Podloucky, F. H., *Z. Krebsforsch.* **50,** 220 (1940).
(253) Ball, T., and Furth, J., *Cancer Research* **9,** 449 (1949).
(254) Furth, J., and Moshman, J., *Cancer Research* **11,** 543 (1951).
(255) Storey, R. H., Wish, L., and Furth, J., *Cancer Research* **11,** 943 (1951).
(256) Cliffton, E. E., and Wolstenholme, J. T., *Cancer Research* **9,** 331 (1949).
(257) Wolstenholme, J. T., *Cancer Research* **10,** 344 (1950).
(258) Werhessen, N. T., Baker, C. G., and Field, N. S., *J. Biol. Chem.* **184,** 145 (1950).
(259) Kelly, K. H., Bierman, H. R., and Shimkin, M. B., *Cancer Research* **12,** 814 (1952).
(260) Dobriner, K., Rhoads, C. P., Lieberman, S., Hill, B. R., and Fieser, L F *Science* **99,** 494 (1944).
(261) Butler, G. C., and Marrian, G. F., *J. Biol. Chem.* **119,** 565 (1937); **124,** 237 (1938).
(262) Wolfe, J. K., Fieser, L. F., and Friedgood, H. B., *J. Am. Chem. Soc.* **63,** 582 (1941).
(263) Warren, F. L., *Cancer Research* **5,** 49 (1945).
(264) Nathanson, I. T., *New Engl. J. Med.* **230,** 764, 795 (1944).
(265) Crooke, A. C., and Callow, R. K., *Quart. J. Med.* **8,** 233 (1939).
(266) Mason, H. L., and Kepler, E. J., *J. Biol. Chem.* **161,** 235 (1945).
(267) Sayers, G., Sayers, M. A., Fry, E. G., White, A., and Long, C. N. H., *Yale J. Biol. and Med.* **16,** 361 (1944).
(268) Marrian, G. F., and Butler, G. C., *Nature* **142,** 400 (1938).
(269) Ross, M., and Dorfman, R. I., *Cancer Research* **1,** 52 (1941).
(270) Dodds, E. C., *Vitamins and Hormones* **2,** 353 (1944).
(271) Karnofsky, D. A., Nathanson, I. T., and Aub, J. C., *Cancer Research* **4,** 772 (1944).
(272) Bach, S. J., and Maw, G. A., *Biochim. et Biophys. Acta* **11,** 69 (1953).
(273) Morgulis, S., and Spencer, H. C., *J. Nutrition* **12,** 191 (1936).
(274) Melville, R. S., and Hummel, J. P., *J. Biol. Chem.* **191,** 383 (1951).
(275) Zierler, K. L., Folk, B. P., Magladery, J. W., and Lilienthal. J. L., *Bull. Johns Hopkins Hosp.* **85,** 370 (1949).

Chapter X

The Present Status of the Problem

Biochemical approaches to the cancer problem have yielded many basic facts, among them (a) the susceptibility of experimental animals to a wide and unrelated array of carcinogenic agents, (b) the nearly uniform metabolic pattern of tumors of different etiology and histogenesis, (c) the many similar systemic effects induced in the host by the presence of a variety of different kinds of tumors, (d) the successful inhibition of tumor induction in experimental animals by techniques involving underfeeding, and (e) the partial destruction or inhibition of further growth of tumors by the systemic administration of chemicals native or foreign to the host. The contrast between (a) and (b), which appears to be somewhat paradoxical, is of fundamental importance and significance. The control of tumor induction and of tumor growth, as illustrated by (d) and (e), have thus far depended to some extent upon procedures applicable to the control of normal growth.

No matter how or from which tissues tumors arise, they more nearly resemble each other chemically than they do normal tissues or than normal tissues resemble each other. In making this generalization the fact is not overlooked that, in some properties, certain tumors, such as the hepatoma, the osteogenic sarcoma, or the adrenal carcinoma, may resemble to a greater or less extent the normal tissues of origin. These vestiges, however, appear in only a limited number of instances, are often of a low order of magnitude, and are considerably diminished in late-generation transplants. The metabolic pattern of tumors, furthermore, is nearly similar in all species studied. Thus, in tumors in rats, mice, or man, the catalytic systems involved in aerobic oxidations are considerably reduced as compared with normal tissues and, indeed, in each species, are reduced to nearly the same extent. A high rate of glycolysis, an increased water content, and a low activity of cytochrome are among the characteristics of practically all tumors in all species studied. Nearly all rapidly growing tumors in mice and rats produce identical systemic effects in the host animals, as shown by the marked reduction in liver catalase activity. These are but a few features of what appears to be a remarkable chemical uniformity in tumors as a class of tissues and suggests that mechanisms involved in malignant uncontrolled growth are common to all tumors regardless of etiology, histogenesis, or species wherein found.

The possibility must, nevertheless, be envisaged that this uniformity, at our present stage of knowledge, may be something of an oversimplification and that essential differences among tumors, even though in quite minor degree, may in certain instances be of a decisive and crucial nature.

This possibility is emphasized by attempts which have been made on the control of tumors.

The problem of the control of cancer may be divided into two parts as it relates (a) to control of the induction of tumors, and (b) to control of the growth rate of established tumors. If all tumors were induced in an identical manner, it might be expected that one and the same control would be effective for the induction of all of them. This, however, is not the case, as exemplified by the observation that deprivation of cystine in the diet of mice prevents the appearance of mammary but not of pulmonary tumors. If all tumors possessed an identical metabolic pattern, it might be expected that one and the same control would be universally effective on their growth rate. It is, however, a matter of record that sarcomas are more sensitive than carcinomas to the necrotizing action of the bacterial polysaccharides, and that some tumors are more sensitive than others to the effect of X-radiation. It seems probable that cancer in different sites may arise in different ways and that the tumors which develop, although resembling each other chemically in very many respects, also possess important differences. These differences, which must be taken into account when measures of control are considered, are still much less in magnitude than those existing between normal tissues within the same species and certainly much less than those existing between the tissues of different species. In experimental animals, the differences existing among tumors may be reduced through many transplant generations, and this suggests that such differences are originally due (a) to the nature of the normal tissue of origin, and (b) to the mode of evocation of the neoplastic transformation.

In addition to the possibility of small but important differences among various types of tumors, there is considerable evidence that the properties of an individual tumor may alter during the course of its development, and that samples of the tumor transplanted and grown elsewhere in the host will show properties removed from those possessed by the primary neoplastic focus. Thus, the primary rat hepatoma possesses properties at once similar to and different from those of normal liver, and the transplanted rat hepatoma possesses more of those properties different from those of normal liver and more in common with those of other transplanted tumors of different etiology and histogenesis. It would appear that the metastases of a primary tumor more nearly resembled in chemical properties the metastases of other primary tumors than the primary tumors themselves resembled each other. Thus, the further away from the normal tissue of origin a tumor is in the course of its development, the more nearly is it like other tumors. Nevertheless, even among heterologous and homologous tumor transplants some differences must occur.

It is possible to find, therefore, that in attempts to control the growth of two different types of tumor, viz., sarcoma and carcinoma, by means of a particular agent, a partial success may be achieved with one tumor and practical failure with the other tumor. Since chemical analysis may reveal few striking differences between these tumors, it is evident that such analysis has not yet been sufficiently extensive to reveal those differences between them which are responsible for their varying response to the same agent. This, in turn, suggests that the measures of tumor control thus far have involved agents which depend upon those properties of tumors which differ among themselves, or, as in the case of such agents as X-radiation and colchicine, depend as well upon characteristics shared in various measure with those of certain normal tissues (viz., phases of rapid cell division). A successful and practical control of cancer by systemic means must be applied to those mechanisms which are common and not different in all tumors. There is one phenomenon which appears to be universally common to all tumors, and that is the property of increased autonomy, or the capacity for unlimited and uncontrolled growth. The ultimate control of cancer necessitates an understanding of the chemical factors involved in this capacity, factors presumably absent or present to different degrees in normal tissues.

Normal cells form an integrated and interdependent community within the living organism, and their growth is controlled by exogenous and endogenous factors in such a way that they are maintained in a state of dynamic equilibrium with other cell communities. It would, therefore, be expected that alterations in any one, or a number, of such exogenous and endogenous factors might affect the growth and maintenance of any one, or a number, of the normal cell communities. Thus, the level of vitamin A controls the integrity of epithelial structures as well as of certain visual mechanisms, insulin controls to some extent the level of blood sugar, and a hormone in the anterior pituitary controls the growth of the bony skeleton. The readiness with which normal tissues respond to exogenous and endogenous factors indicates the precise nature of the control which, through equable distribution, such factors exert.

Neoplastic cells arise when, in some as yet unknown manner, the normal exercise of control has been disturbed. The agents which induce this disturbance have been described in Chapters III and IV, but the mechanism of their action is not yet understood. The disturbance of control can take a form ranging from slight to complete, or apparently complete, loss of control. Thus, an autonomous potentiality may exist to any degree in a group of neoplastic cells. Furthermore, a given group of neoplastic cells may exhibit early in its growth stages a partially dependent, partially controlled, not completely autonomous phase of development, only to alter subsequently, through some set of circumstances, into an apparently independent, uncontrolled phase of development. These phenomena are long familiar in the clinic where few, if any, examples of a reversal of the above-mentioned sequence in phases, i.e., autonomous back to dependent, have ever been noted.

The induction of tumors is a function of exogenous and endogenous factors, as is, in a dependent phase, the growth and maintenance of an established tumor. It would, therefore, be expected that the proper manipulation of these factors would give rise to conditions in which the appearance of tumors is retarded or prevented, and the growth rate of established tumors is depressed. Under such conditions a prophylactic or systemic therapy is possible, regardless of the cost. Thus it is that severe restriction in caloric intake with hormonal alterations reduces the incidence of spontaneous tumors in mice, and either castration or administration of estrogen produces a regression of prostatic carcinoma. So far as has been observed, the use of the body's own mechanisms of growth and maintenance must be employed in such drastic fashion as to make the treatment as troublesome as the disease, and the efficacy of such treatment is palliative only over a relatively short space of time. Tumors, perhaps not so many of them, eventually appear in diet-depleted animals and grow luxuriantly, and prostatic carcinoma recurs in the majority of cases. Such tumors are no longer amenable generally to the original course of treatment; either they have acquired a growth stimulus from elsewhere in the host or else they have acquired the full or nearly full capacity for autonomous growth, i.e., they grow out of themselves.

The autonomous cancer cell is almost completely independent of body control, and apparently only in its blood supply does it participate to any observable extent in the life of the host. In a sense, the control may be in the opposite direction, for the presence of the proliferating cancer cells produces systemic effects and causes the tissues of the host to break down to supply the needs of the cells for nourishment. Under such circumstances it might be too much to ask of the host that it cooperate in any degree to help control the tumor growing out of it. Only when cell division is inhibited in the host is the tumor likewise affected. Unfortunately, the autonomous cancer is a hardy plant, and so also, to a perhaps lesser extent, are tumors in dependent phases. A systemic therapy, therefore, faces this tremendous obstacle.

We do not yet know how completely autonomous the cancer cell may be, and, even if this cell hangs from the host by but a single thread, all avenues of approach utilizing techniques of systemic control, e.g., nutrition, endocrinology, and chemotherapy, should not go unexplored. But seeing how little we know of the characteristics of the cancer cell, how can such approaches be other than at random? A few things are known about the normal cell, e.g., that it needs vitamin X, is stimulated by hormone Y, and contains component Z. We then apply normal techniques of control to the growth of the neoplasm that arises from this normal cell and generally find that nothing decisive emerges. Perhaps the neoplasm does not need any of these things and draws from itself or from its host the factors necessary for its growth.

More than that, different tumors may draw upon this circumambient source to a different degree, and even the same tumor at successive phases in its growth makes demands different in intensity and perhaps in quality. The data of Foulds and of Mider illustrate this clearly. The tumor does not develop in a vacuum, and in order to establish itself to grow it must continuously cope with the reparative capacities of the host. Only when these latter are finally disposed of does the full malignancy of the tumor emerge. It would hardly be expected that even litter mates in an inbred strain of mice would possess an identical physiological constitution, and the natural history of the same kind of tumor in such litter mates is bound to be somewhat different from one host to another. It has been said that since antitumor drugs act differently on different tumors, even in the same strain of mice, this demonstrates that the various tumors possess different metabolic patterns. Many clinicians, impressed by the frequently bizarre natural history of tumors and their occasional unpredictable response to therapeutic measures, have felt that cancer is a name for a host of possibly quite unrelated diseases. These are hopeless viewpoints, from which no conceivable approach of therapeutic value can emerge. It is easy to understand why, when the same drug damages one tumor and leaves another kind of tumor unaffected, the results are interpreted as being due to a different basis of metabolism in each tumor; but can the same interpretation apply to the distribution of positive and negative responses to the same drug among a group of inbred mice carrying the same tumor? It is not at all inconceivable that the variable results obtained with inbred strains are due to the very use of such pure lines, and that a lesser degree of genetic uniformity, would, paradoxically, lead to less variance in experimental therapy (environmental buffering).

The fact that cancer tissues appear to have a nearly similar chemical pattern offers hope and encouragement in their study. When Bashford and his colleagues introduced the use of mouse tumors in experimental cancer research, they suffered a certain amount of criticism in many quarters because it was felt then (and even now) that whatever was discovered with such material was restricted to the species concerned and inapplicable to other species, including man. On the whole, the use of experimental animals in the study of neoplastic disease has been amply justified from the many analogous biological findings in cancer of several different species and needs no further defense. The recent chemical observations have served to support this point of view.

Since the chemical properties of tumors arising in experimental animals and in human beings appear to be very much alike, it may be assumed that such phenomena as are noted with a species like the mouse may, with some justification and with the necessary modifications, be transferred into human terms. There is some danger in an oversimplification of the picture, for species may be analogous without being identical and the conditions of human existence are not quite the same as those of the mouse. It is evident that cancer tissue forms a new and different type of cellular aggregate, with quantitative characteristics which distinguish it from all other kinds of tissue generally referred to as normal (except for the embryonic), and which is more or less uniform from species to species. Thus, the livers of the mouse and of man possess very nearly the same functions; there are a few obvious differences, as in uric acid metabolism, but on the whole the livers of the two species resemble each other more than they do any other tissue. Similarly, most of the tumors in each species resemble each other more, on the whole, than they do any other known tissue. It is possible to speak of cancer tissue in much the same way as one speaks of hepatic or renal tissue, namely as a tissue with limited and ascertainable properties. Since the properties of tumors are apparently independent of the tissues of origin, such tissues represent a more or less common type—in effect, a lowest common denominator—and this picture suggests that a set of phenomena or an effective therapeutic approach found and directed toward any one tumor would be, to some degree at least, applicable to other tumors. Such an expectation may appear overoptimistic and is certainly not warranted in the case of tumors yet in phases dependent on body systems of control, i.e., little autonomous. Nevertheless, some deduction of this sort springs inevitably from the chemical data so far revealed. If even only partial truth be granted to such an assumption, then the proper chemical study of one type of cancer will illuminate most other types of cancer, and a method of therapy effective on one type of cancer may be equally effective within certain limitations on other types and in other species. The line of demarcation between the normal cell and the malignant cell may be distinct for certain phenomena and quite indistinct for others—both are living entities and invariably contiguous. To destroy the one without affecting the other harmfully demands a more penetrating insight into the machinery of each than has so far been attained.

The Chemical Pattern

Every normal cell in a multicellular organism carries on two functions. One function is to survive and reproduce itself. The other function is to carry out highly specialized activities which, summed up over all the various kinds of cells of the organism, permit the organism to survive and reproduce itself. The former function is common to all cells of the organism, regardless of the nature of the specialized function which they possess.

When the normal cell becomes cancerous, it loses its specialized functions but naturally retains those basic functions which it requires for survival and reproduction. Among these basic functions are those concerned with internal energy cycles geared with normal anabolic and catabolic reactions of carbohydrates and fats. Weinhouse and LePage have well portrayed the nearly equal levels of the individual enzymatic components of those basic mechanisms concerned with the Krebs cycle and with glycolysis in a variety of normal and neoplastic tissues, and it may be accepted that tumors must share with normal tissues to a nearly equal degree those fundamental reactions which are necessary to provide the energy to maintain their existence.

Therefore, the most apparent metabolic change which a normal cell undergoes as it becomes cancerous is the loss of specialized function which once distinguished it in the differentiated organism of which it was a part. The liver cell loses it capacity to produce urea, the gastric mucosa cell loses its capacity to produce pepsin, and these examples can be multiplied by many times. Thus, the cancer cell, stripped cf the distinguishing properties which characterized the normal cell from which it arose, tends to resemble other cancer cells regardless of their histogenesis.

However, the tumor cell has acquired at least one distinguishing function, and that is growth. To this extent it may resemble the characteristics of the embryo, but in its metabolic development it is in direct contrast with that of the embryo. The experimental data show that the primary tumor may yet retain, to some degree, certain of the specialized functions of the normal tissue of origin. With transplantation or metastasis, these specialized functions diminish, and with extensive transplantation, in the case of experimental animals, these specialized functions disappear nearly completely, concomitantly with an increased growth capacity of the tumor. In contrast, the embryo in its early, relatively undifferentiated stages grows very rapidly, and in the later courses of its growth, as it acquires more and more specialized metabolic tissues, its growth rate diminishes. The concept

	↗	Primary tumor cell, less metabolically differentiated	→	Transplanted tumor cell, metabolically undifferentiated
Normal, fully metabolically differentiated cell				
	↖	Late, embryonic cell, more metabolically differentiated	←	Early, embryonic cell, metabolically undifferentiated

of the analogy of the tumor cell with the embryonic is not new. Although the recent chemical data are not inconsistent with such a concept, it must still be regarded as purely speculative. The rapid growth of residual liver tissues following hepatectomy suggests that growth *per se* is not incompatible with the presence of specialized metabolic functions. Whether regenerative growth, on the one hand, is comparable with malignant or embryonic growth, on the other, in which apparently growth and the presence of specialized metabolic function are mutually incompatible, is open to question. Both malignant and embryonic tissue can be grown indefinitely in tissue culture *in vitro*, whereas the growth of adult liver cells under such conditions is difficult if not impossible. The growth stimulus of the former two tissues lies largely within themselves, and perhaps an effective agent which will inhibit the growth of one will also inhibit the growth of the other.

In the course of development of the malignant tissue, certain susceptible tissues elsewhere in the host and at a distance from the tumor demonstrate certain chemical changes in a direction which these particular tissues would take if they became neoplastic. Thus, the presence of a tumor in one site may be reflected in changes in tissues in distant sites which, although not themselves neoplastic by histologic criteria, reveal chemically neoplastic qualities. The host itself is cancerous even in the absence of demonstrable metastases. These systemic changes in the tissues of the tumor-bearing host are produced by all kinds of rapidly growing malignant tumors and yield in this way another demonstration of the essentially similar properties possessed by this class of tissues, as well as of the generalized nature of the disease. The active agent which produces these systemic effects is evidently a material which is elaborated by the growing tumor in apparently excessive amounts and which, since it can pass through the parabiotic union, undoubtedly circulates through the blood stream. The effect of this agent is most notably revealed by its inhibitory action on iron-containing enzyme systems, particularly catalase, and in the tumorous host is present not only in the tumor but in other, apparently normal tissues. Embryonic tissue does not elaborate this agent, and this distinction between malignant and embryonic tissue reveals the clearest metabolic difference in the two tissues so far known. It should be pointed out, however, that very early embryonic tissue has never been studied in this connection. Whatever the nature of the agent may be, and there are very few clues to its chemical properties at this time, it is not completely absent from normal adult tissues but is present in extremely small amounts. Its presence in embryonic tissue might also be revealed were a sufficiently large amount of such material available for chemical fractionation. It would simply appear that cancer tissue in the course of its growth produces abnormally large amounts of this substance (or substances, perhaps), to such an extent that its presence can be revealed in other, presumably normal tissues. The normal animals, inclusive perhaps of embryonic tissue, may produce this agent as one of the mechanisms of enzyme control, but only in relatively minute amounts. The specific effect of this agent, or agents, revealed in the early stages of tumor growth, must be distinguished from those secondary toxic effects elicited both by the tumor in the later stages of its growth and by other wasting diseases. Even so normal a neoplastic process as pregnancy can induce systemic changes in the tissues of the maternal host, as revealed by the turnover rate of nucleic acids in the liver or by increased plasma volume. The increased serum polysaccharide response to several disease states is recognized, and the stress to which the living host is subjected by the intervention of a pathologic process is naturally answered by many forms of apparently unrelated physiological readjustments. Only cancer appears at the moment to markedly influence the catalase level, and that chiefly in the liver, to a lesser extent in kidney, and not at all in the erythrocyte. It cannot be sufficiently emphasized that the study of such a systemic effect possesses validity only (a) when it affects certain but not all metabolic systems, and (b) when it affects an organ completely normal to all appearances both grossly and microscopically. The curious rearrangement, and alteration in physical as well as chemical properties, of the liver proteins of animals bearing a distant tumor during the very early stages of the growth of the tumor reveal the profound systemic effect which the tumor produces in a tissue whose histology shows no abnormality whatever. It is probable that the tumor produces an amount of the effective, circulating agent in proportion to its size and growth rate. Since normal tissues possess a considerable metabolic reserve, the effect of the accumulation of the circulating cancer toxin is not severely felt until the later stages of growth of the tumor when the reparative powers of the host can no longer cope with it. It is important to recognize that this agent is a toxin only in the sense that it is a probably normal material whose rate of production by the tumor has outstripped the host's capacity to handle it. Just as one metabolic characteristic of the tumor is to produce an unusually large amount of lactic acid, another is to produce a relatively large amount of this particular agent, although all tissues can apparently produce both. The excess of lactic acid also enters the blood stream where it is subsequently buffered. The excess of agent is apparently buffered by combination with the synthetic systems for the iron-containing enzymes. The latter obviously results in a more profound dislocation of the components of the affected tissue.

Thus, as the normal cell assumes its malignant character, it retains nearly unaltered those basic systems necessary for its survival, it jettisons its specialized metabolic functions, and in addition it develops two characteristics, namely growth and the production of a circulating toxin, both of which it shares to a degree with normal tissues. Neither is as yet expressible in chemical nomenclature, and neither offers any particular aspect of vulnerability. How the normal cell changes in the first instance to the malignant is relatively unimportant, except as obvious means of prophylaxis in industry and in certain social habits may affect this problem. If the etiologic agents for cancer in man were to be entirely disclosed and methods discovered for their avoidance or neutralization, the problem of cancer control could be transferred to the province of preventive medicine and to the benevolent power of public authority. However, the problem is not so simple, and it is necessary to assume that cancer is a phenomenon coexistent with the living process, that it will be present for some time to come, and that emphasis must be laid on a direct study on the site of malignancy itself. Hypotheses relating the development of the neoplastic cell to a loss of one or more crucial systems or to a gain of some adventitious growth-promoting system may each have some element of truth. They cannot be mutually exclusive, however, for the cancer cell is not a system isolated from the living universe, and the first law of thermodynamics would demand that even in the cancer cell the loss or gain of metabolic reactions must be compensated for by the gain or loss of other reactions, respectively. No matter what mechanisms are suggested, however, the neoplastic transformation ends in a cell with only the two characteristics mentioned above to identify it. Growth is a name given to an over-all biological phenomenon, but a cancer toxin is a chemical approachable by conventional methods of analysis. At the least, this latter characteristic offers an experimental handle whereby further knowledge of an unusual metabolic feature of the cancer cell may be grasped. The question of why the developing cancer cell should discard all its specialized metabolic functions but retain this unusual function in greatly enhanced degree cannot be answered until the possible relation of this enhanced toxin-producing function to the growth property of the tumor is itself understood.

Epilogue

Since the time when the first lines of this monograph were written, the atomic bomb was developed, and the power of scientific discovery, invention, and application was brought vividly to the attention of the world. In the wave of enthusiasm for the miracles of science which ensued, it was inevitable that the healing arts would share in this public attention and encouragement, for the saving grace of the human species has always been its solicitude for and protection of the weak and infirm. Research on cancer appears to be supported by truly staggering sums of money, which is a tribute to the generosity and vision of the American people and of their government. The obligations laid upon the scientific investigator are correspondingly great, but it must be the duty of the administrators of these funds that they are not only dispensed wisely but that the obligations which they entail are imposed lightly. Money *per se* is an uncertain short-cut to scientific discovery. Basic and penetrating discoveries in the field of cancer research, as in other fields of science, are not purchasable nor obtainable by narrow schemes of coercive authority but are secured only under conditions which permit the individual investigator the widest possible freedom within the bounds of scientific and personal discipline and responsibility. The control of cancer is not like the development of the atomic bomb which was an application of discoveries already made but rather is contingent on the discovery of biological and chemical principles inherent in living matter and which for the most part are still unknown.

The solution of the problem of cancer is no simple task, but the solution will be found. More than many others, it is a subject for courage, imaginative insight, integrity, and sustained and dedicated effort.

Irrtum verlässt uns nie, doch ziehet ein höher Bedürfniss immer den strebenden Geist leise zur Wahrheit hinan.

Author Index

Numbers in parentheses are references numbers and are included to assist in locating references when the authors' names are not mentioned in the text. Numbers in italics indicate the page on which the reference is listed at the end of the chapter.

D

E

L

M

N

O

P

T

U

V

W

Y

Z

Subject Index

D

M

N

Q

R

S

U

V